PRINCIPLES OF DRUG ACTION

PRINCIPLES

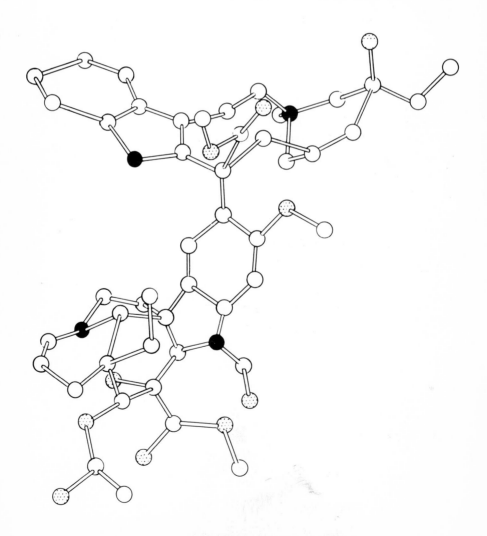

With 476 Illustrations

OF DRUG ACTION

THE BASIS OF PHARMACOLOGY

Avram Goldstein, M.D.
PROFESSOR OF PHARMACOLOGY

Lewis Aronow, Ph.D.
ASSOCIATE PROFESSOR OF PHARMACOLOGY

Sumner M. Kalman, M.D.
PROFESSOR OF PHARMACOLOGY

STANFORD UNIVERSITY SCHOOL OF MEDICINE
PALO ALTO, CALIFORNIA

Hoeber Medical Division

Harper & Row, Publishers, New York, Evanston, and London

Reprinted with corrections 1969

PRINCIPLES OF DRUG ACTION
The Basis of Pharmacology

Copyright © 1968 by Hoeber Medical Division
Harper & Row, Publishers, Incorporated
Printed in the United States of America

Library of Congress catalog card number: 67–25604

*The illustration on the title page and book cover is
a structural drawing of a vincristine methiodide molecule
as it actually appears in the crystal (Fig. 13-2b, p. 756).
(Courtesy of W. N. Lipscomb)*

CONTENTS

v

Pharmacology is the science of drugs, their chemical constitution, their biologic action, and their therapeutic application in man. It includes toxicology, which encompasses the harmful effects of all chemicals, whether they are used medicinally or not. The variety of new uses to which drugs are being put, and the increasing exposure of whole populations to potent chemical agents, have created a wider and more intense interest in pharmacology than has ever existed before. The time is long past when anyone can acquire a complete knowledge about all drugs. But many people in diverse fields of endeavor need a foundation, a conceptual framework, upon which may be built the specific knowledge about drugs that is most germane to their own needs.

In this book we have tried to provide a coherent, rational, and scientifically correct account of the principles underlying every aspect of this science. For physicians, medical students, and others whose aim is to acquire an up-to-date and comprehensive understanding of pharmacology, this book is intended to serve as a basic text, to be supplemented by the systematic textbooks. The fundamental concepts developed here, which ordinarily occupy but a few pages in standard texts, are meant to provide the physician and medical student with the requisite background both for understanding the basis of drug therapy, and for appraising new developments in the field. We hope the book will also be a valuable introduction to pharmacology for all those investigators and students of the natural sciences who, using drugs as research tools, wish to learn the principles of drug action but have no need of a comprehensive catalogue.

Our aim was to expose and elaborate upon the fundamentals of pharmacology in a systematic and rigorous manner. We have tried to re-examine critically those areas in which generalizations seemed to rest upon shaky foundations, and to furnish a new theory or interpretation when it seemed to be called for. The book focuses upon principles and mechanisms rather than upon drugs but a great many drugs are specifically discussed in order to illustrate and exemplify. We have drawn widely upon the published literature for pertinent examples, many of them directly relevant to the use of drugs in man. Research papers and reviews are cited in the footnotes; we have chosen principally those that will serve the student best, without regard to completeness of citation or priority of discovery.

The scope of the book is broad, reflecting the breadth of modern pharmacology. The first chapter deals with mechanisms of drug-receptor interaction and considers the theoretical basis of dose-response relationships. This is followed by three chapters on the fate of drugs in the body—their absorption, distribution, excretion, and metabolism—and the factors that determine the time course of drug action. Chapters 5 through 12 deal with the adverse effects of drugs and the mechanisms responsible. Dose-related toxicity is considered, along with methods for its quantitative estimation and the modes of action of specific antidotes. The pharmacogenetic basis of drug idiosyncrasy is presented as well as the immunochemical basis of drug allergy. Drug resistance in lower species is contrasted with drug tolerance and physical dependence in man and other animals. Special chapters are devoted to effects of drugs upon cell heredity—chemical mutagenesis, carcinogenesis, and teratogenesis—and some consideration is given to the public-health aspects of these phenomena in relation to the widespread exposure of human populations to drugs. The last two chapters discuss the strategy of the discovery and development of new drugs, and the methods employed to assess their potential usefulness in experimental animals and in clinical trials in humans. Guidelines are also presented for the selection of drugs in clinical practice. A concise summary of the principles of prescribing is given in Appendix I.

We have adhered, in general, to the standardized terminology and abbreviations followed by the *Journal of Biological Chemistry*. For the column headings in tables and the labeling of coordinate axes in the illustrations the convention is that units accompanied by a multiplication factor are to be understood as part of an equation: for example, under the heading "Cells $\times$ 10^{-5}" an entry of 3.0 would mean 3.0×10^5 cells, from the equation "Cells $\times$ $10^{-5} = 3.0$." All temperatures are Centigrade, although the symbol C. is omitted. Logarithms to the base 10 are indicated by log, natural logarithms by ln. Nonproprietary drugs names are used, without capitalization; trade names, if used at all, are capitalized, but the superscript symbol ® is not employed. The abbreviations found in this book (unless they are self-explanatory) are listed in Appendix II.

We are indebted to the Literary Executor of the late Sir Ronald A. Fisher, F.R.S., to Dr. Frank Yates, F.R.S., and to Oliver and Boyd Ltd., Edinburgh, for permission to reprint Table IX from their book *Statistical Tables for Biological, Agricultural and Medical Research*.

We are deeply indebted to our teachers, colleagues, and students who helped guide our thinking toward the outlook upon pharmacology that is embodied in this book. We are grateful to Professor Walther Wilbrandt and Dr. William B. Pratt for reading and commenting upon various chapters. We thank Mrs. Ray Jeffery for skillful and efficient typing of the manuscript, and Mrs. John Naughton for careful checking of bibliographic citations and other assistance in preparing the book for publication. It has been a pleasure to work with Paul B. Hoeber and his staff, especially Miss Claire Drullard, Miss Jo Hinkel, and Mrs. Rose Yager. The authors are responsible for any deficiences or errors that remain and would be grateful if readers would call them to our attention. We also welcome readers' suggestions for future editions concerning the inclusion of new material exemplifying principles and mechanisms.

Palo Alto, California

AVRAM GOLDSTEIN
LEWIS ARONOW
SUMNER M. KALMAN

1

MOLECULAR MECHANISMS

OF DRUG ACTION

RECEPTORS

Whatever effects a drug produces in a biologic system must be regarded as ultimate consequences of physicochemical interactions between that drug and functionally important molecules in the living organism. Sometimes a drug may act by combining with a small molecule or ion, as when a gastric antacid neutralizes hydrochloric acid or a chelating agent complexes free Pb^{++} ion in the treatment of lead poisoning. In the great majority of cases, however, drugs are presumed to interact with macromolecular components of tissues. These tissue elements with which drugs combine we call *receptors*.

The concept of receptors has its origin in two quite different lines of experimentation carried out in the early years of the 20th century. Paul Ehrlich (1845–1915) was greatly impressed by the high degree of antibody specificity against the antigenic substances that stimulated their production and imagined a stereospecific lock-and-key fit between them. He postulated specific "side chains" in protoplasm, with unique chemical and steric architecture with which only antibodies of the right shape and chemical composition could combine. Later, in his pioneering work on chemotherapy, when the phenomena under investigation were interactions between synthetic organic chemicals and parasitic protozoa, the same concepts were extended. Again a high degree of specificity was observed. On the one hand, small variations in a drug's chemical structure affected its antiparasitic potency in a dramatic way. On the other hand, several drugs with about the same antiparasitic efficacy might differ greatly in toxicity to the host. To explain these findings Ehrlich assumed that all cells had "side chains" which were essential for their life processes, but that the composition and shapes of these differed in different kinds of cells. Thus, chemotherapeutic drugs could be fashioned to combine specifically with "side chains" of the parasite, yet at the same time fit poorly the "side

1

chains" of host tissues. From sketches in Ehrlich's notebooks it is apparent that he thought of the "side chains" as functional chemical groupings such as sulfhydryl groups ($-SH$), amino groups ($-NH_2$), and so on, embedded in some sort of stereospecific macrostructure. To those hypothetical specific chemical groupings of protoplasm upon which chemotherapeutic drugs were assumed to act Ehrlich gave the name *receptors*.[1]

About the same time, J. N. Langley (1852–1926) was following up Claude Bernard's basic work on the South American arrow poison, curare. Bernard had found that this drug blocked transmission of impulses from motor nerves to skeletal muscles, and had localized the site of the block to the fine nerve terminals embedded in the muscle substance.[2] Langley found, however, that when a motor nerve was cut and allowed to degenerate, it was still possible to stimulate the muscle chemically by application of nicotine to the region where the nerve had formerly terminated. Moreover, curare blocked this action of nicotine. Yet even during curare blockade, either in innervated or denervated muscle, direct electrical stimulation of the muscle fibres elicited a contractile response. These observations could only mean that nicotine and curare both act upon some substance which is neither nerve nor muscle. When nicotine combines with it, this substance somehow triggers the contractile response of muscle. Curare can combine with it, yet not trigger a contractile response, thereby preventing the interaction with nicotine. To this hypothetical specialized material in muscle Langley gave the name *receptive substance*.[3-5]

Ehrlich and Langley were influential in establishing a new tradition in pharmacology. They were guided by the principle that the explanation of drug actions was to be sought not in vague "tonic" effects or poorly defined "poisonous" actions on the whole body, not in a mysterious power to combat "disease," but rather in physicochemical interactions of drugs at definite sites of action. Ehrlich's dogma that drugs cannot act unless they are bound to receptors—"corpora non agunt nisi fixata"—was controversial in his time but seems commonplace to us today. As more and more receptors are identified as specific proteins or nucleic acids, the receptor concept itself is becoming outmoded. At present, however, it still has some value in the analysis of drug effects whose molecular basis is not yet understood. In this book we shall retain the term *receptor* to describe, without

---

[1] P. EHRLICH: Chemotherapeutics: scientific principles, methods and results. *Lancet* 2:445 (1913).

[2] C. BERNARD: *Leçons sur les Effets des Substances Toxiques et Médicamenteuses.* Paris, J. B. Bailliere et Fils, 1857, chapters 16–23.

[3] J. N. LANGLEY: On nerve endings and on special excitable substances in cells. *Proc. Roy. Soc. B78:*170 (1906).

[4] J. N. LANGLEY: On the contraction of muscle, chiefly in relation to the presence of 'receptive' substances. Part IV. The effect of curari and of some other substances on the nicotine response of the sartorius and gastrocnemius muscles of the frog. *J. Physiol. 39:*235 (1909).

[5] W. M. FLETCHER: John Newport Langley. In memoriam. *J. Physiol. 61:*1 (1926).

further specification, a macromolecule with which a drug interacts to produce its characteristic biologic effect.[6-11]

BINDING FORCES IN THE DRUG-RECEPTOR INTERACTION

Bond Types [12]

THE COVALENT BOND

A covalent bond is formed when two atoms share a pair of electrons. This is the familiar strong bond that holds together the atoms of organic molecules, with typical bond energy of about 100 kilocalories per mole. Because of the high binding energy, covalent bonds are essentially irreversible at ordinary temperatures unless a catalytic agent (e.g., an enzyme) intervenes. The covalent binding of drugs to receptors, unlike most drug-receptor interactions, results in stable, long-lasting complexes.

Let us consider drugs that behave as alkylating agents (Table 1-1).[13-15] Such compounds form a reactive cationic intermediate, a carbonium ion, by virtue of the strong electron-attracting power of the group to which the alkyl residue is initially attached.

In the case of nitrogen mustard and similar alkylating agents, it is supposed that the initial step in the formation of carbonium ion is a cyclization to ethyleneimmonium ion, simultaneous with release of a chloride ion, followed by ring scission.

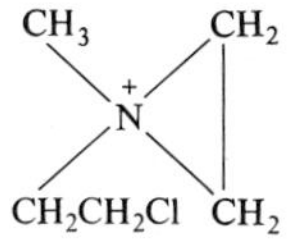

$$CH_3 \diagdown \qquad \diagup CH_2$$
$$N^+$$
$$CH_2CH_2Cl \diagup \qquad \diagdown CH_2$$

The carbonium ion then reacts avidly with an electron donor group such as a carboxylate, phosphate, or sulfhydryl anion. Uncharged atoms of N, S, and O are effective electron donors and therefore also undergo alkylation reactions.

6 A. ALBERT: *Selective Toxicity,* 3rd ed. New York, John Wiley & Sons, 1965.

7 J. A. BAIN and S. E. MAYER: Biochemical mechanisms of drug action. *Annu. Rev. Pharmacol.* 2:37 (1962).

8 E. A. ZELLER and J. R. FOUTS: Enzymes as primary targets of drugs. *Annu. Rev. Pharmacol.* 3:9 (1963).

9 E. J. ARIËNS: *Molecular Pharmacology.* New York, Academic Press, 1964.

10 E. J. ARIËNS and A. M. SIMONIS: A molecular basis for drug action. *J. Pharm. Pharmacol.* 16:137, 289 (1964).

11 R. F. FURCHGOTT: Receptor mechanisms. *Annu. Rev. Pharmacol.* 4:21 (1964).

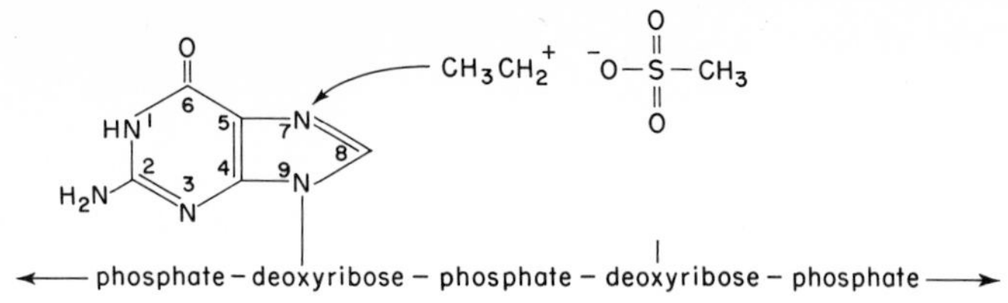

FIG. 1-1. ALKYLATION OF DNA GUANINE BY A MUTAGEN, ETHYL METHANE SULFONATE. *The carbonium ethyl group is shown making an attack on the electron-rich nitrogen atom in position 7. The deoxyribose-phosphate backbone of the DNA strand is also shown, but the base attached to the neighbor deoxyribose has been omitted for clarity.*

Ethyl methane sulfonate (Table 1-1) is a potent mutagen (p. 618) which acts by alkylating the nitrogen atom in position 7 of guanine in the intact deoxyribonucleic acid (DNA) molecule (Fig. 1-1), thereby changing the properties of the genetic material and its behavior at subsequent replications.[16]

A bifunctional alkylating agent is capable of forming two covalent bonds and thereby cross-linking two macromolecules or two parts of the same macromolecule. Such an agent is busulfan (Table 1-1), a drug used in the treatment of myeloid leukemia. This compound is seen to be simply two residues of ethyl methane sulfonate joined "back to back." Some postulated mechanisms of action are illustrated in Fig. 1-2.

Another bifunctional agent used in cancer chemotherapy is mechlorethamine (nitrogen mustard) (Table 1-1). This simple molecule, as might be surmised, reacts rather nonspecifically with a variety of functional groups of proteins and nucleic acids. A bifunctional agent need not necessarily cross-link. For example, a postulated reaction with proteins involves alkylating a glutamic acid carboxyl group with mechlorethamine, the second carbonium ion formed by the alkylating agent reacting with water (Fig. 1-3).

More interesting alkylating agents are those with complex structures, which offer more possibilities for specific interaction at specialized sites. Thus, whereas nitrogen mustard reacts in vivo with water, with all sorts of protein molecules, with ribonucleic acid (RNA), and with DNA, phenoxybenzamine (Table 1-1) is an alkylating agent with a far more

[12] L. PAULING: *The Nature of the Chemical Bond,* 3rd ed. Ithaca, Cornell University Press, 1960.

[13] D. A. KARNOFSKY, Consulting Ed.: Comparative clinical and biological effects of alkylating agents. *Ann. N.Y. Acad. Sci. 68:*657–1266 (1958).

[14] S. S. BROWN: Nitrogen mustards and related alkylating agents. *Advance. Pharmacol. 2:*243 (1963).

[15] P. BROOKES and P. D. LAWLEY: Alkylating agents. *Brit. Med. Bull. 20:*91 (1964).

[16] P. BROOKES and P. D. LAWLEY: Reaction of some mutagenic and carcinogenic compounds with nucleic acids. *J. Cell. Comp. Physiol. 64:* suppl 1, 111 (1964).

TABLE 1-1. Structures and reaction mechanisms of some alkylating agents.

Alkylating agent	Structure	Carbonium ion form	Product of reaction with R^-
Ethyl methane sulfonate	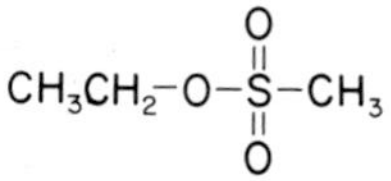 $CH_3CH_2-O-\overset{O}{\underset{O}{\overset{\parallel}{\underset{\parallel}{S}}}}-CH_3$	$CH_3CH_2^+$	CH_3CH_2-R
Busulfan	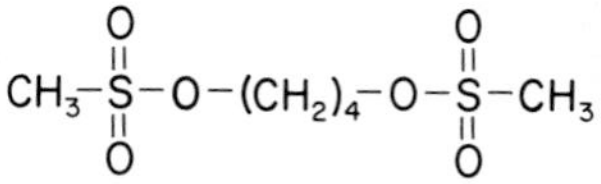 $CH_3-\overset{O}{\underset{O}{\overset{\parallel}{\underset{\parallel}{S}}}}-O-(CH_2)_4-O-\overset{O}{\underset{O}{\overset{\parallel}{\underset{\parallel}{S}}}}-CH_3$	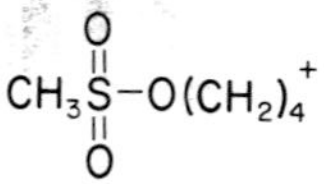 $CH_3-\overset{O}{\underset{O}{\overset{\parallel}{\underset{\parallel}{S}}}}-O(CH_2)_4^+$ $R-(CH_2)_4^+$	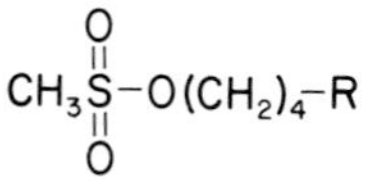 $CH_3-\overset{O}{\underset{O}{\overset{\parallel}{\underset{\parallel}{S}}}}-O(CH_2)_4-R$ $R-(CH_2)_4-R'$
Mechlorethamine (nitrogen mustard)	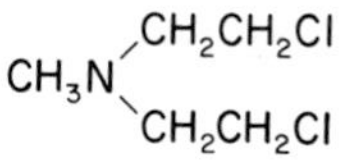 $CH_3N\Big\langle \begin{matrix} CH_2CH_2Cl \\ CH_2CH_2Cl \end{matrix}$	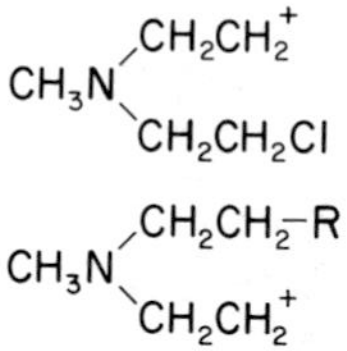 $CH_3N\Big\langle \begin{matrix} CH_2CH_2^+ \\ CH_2CH_2Cl \end{matrix}$ $CH_3N\Big\langle \begin{matrix} CH_2CH_2R \\ CH_2CH_2^+ \end{matrix}$	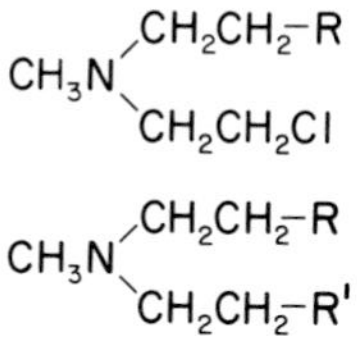 $CH_3N\Big\langle \begin{matrix} CH_2CH_2-R \\ CH_2CH_2Cl \end{matrix}$ $CH_3N\Big\langle \begin{matrix} CH_2CH_2-R \\ CH_2CH_2-R' \end{matrix}$
Phenoxybenzamine	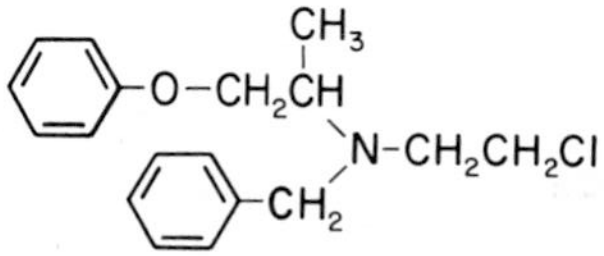	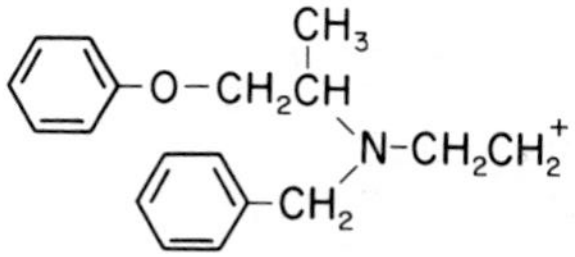	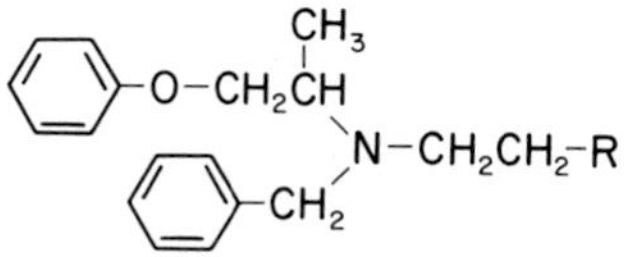

FIG. 1-2. POSTULATED EFFECTS OF BIFUNCTIONAL ALKYLATING AGENTS.

$$x—cys—x—x—x—x—x$$
$$S-CH_2-CH_2-CH_2-CH_2-S$$
$$x—x—x—x—x—cys—x$$
$$x—x—x—x—x—x—x$$
$$x—x—x—x—x—x—x$$

a

Intramolecular cross-linking in protein by alkylation of cysteine (cys) *sulfhydryl groups. Each x represents an unspecified amino acid.*

base—ribose   ribose—base

$$O=P-O-CH_2-CH_2-CH_2-CH_2-O-P=O$$

base—ribose   ribose—base

b

Cross-linking of nucleic acid strands by alkylation of phosphate.

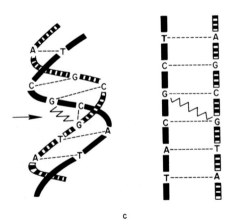

c

Cross-linking of DNA strands by alkylation of diagonally placed guanine residues. The bases of DNA are represented by their initial letters and the alkyl chain by the zigzag *line. A, adenine; T, thymine; G, guanine; C, cytosine. (From Brookes and Lawley, Fig. 4.[15])*

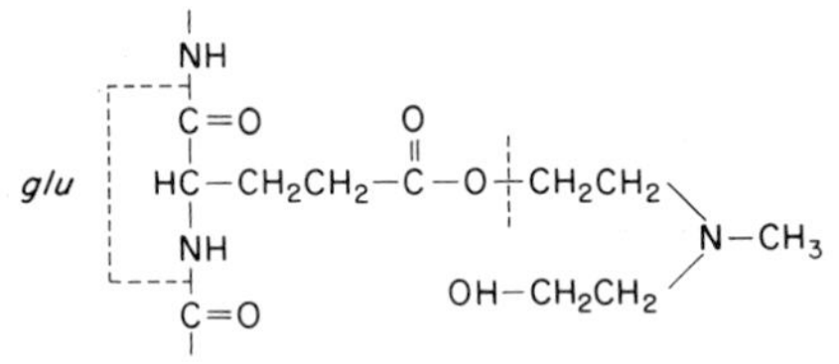

FIG. 1-3. POSTULATED PRODUCT OF ALKYLATION OF A GLUTAMIC ACID (*glu*) RESIDUE BY MECHLORETHAMINE, THE SECOND CARBONIUM ION OF THE ALKYLATING AGENT HAVING REACTED WITH WATER.

specific action. Vascular smooth muscle is innervated by sympathetic nerves, which release norepinephrine at their endings. The norepinephrine combines with specific receptors, which trigger contraction of the smooth muscle. In arterioles this is the mechanism for maintaining the normal degree of resistance to the blood flow. Phenoxybenzamine is remarkable in that it blocks the norepinephrine receptors with a fairly high degree of specificity.[17,18] Thus, during phenoxybenzamine blockade, the smooth muscle can still contract in response to other agents. That the blockade caused by phenoxybenzamine results from an alkylation of the receptors is suggested by its long persistence and practically irreversible character.

An even more unusual example of complexity and specificity in an alkylating agent is presented by the antibiotic mitomycin (Fig. 1-4), which alkylates and cross-links the complementary strands of the DNA duplex, thus preventing their replication. Here, the original compound must first be reduced and undergo a molecular rearrangement in order to become an effective alkylating agent, as shown.[19]

One of the best understood examples of drug-receptor interaction through formation of a covalent bond is the long-lasting inhibition of the cholinesterase enzymes by organic phosphates and carbamates.[20-22] The cholinesterases belong to the class of "serine enzymes," which have a serine residue in the active center that plays an essential role in the catalysis.[23] In alkaline phosphatase, liver aliesterase, and pseudocholinesterase, the

[17] R. F. FURCHGOTT: Dibenamine blockade in strips of rabbit aorta and its use in differentiating receptors. *J. Pharmacol. Exper. Therap. 111:*265 (1954).

[18] S. C. HARVEY and M. NICKERSON: Reactions of dibenamine and some congeners with substances of biological interest in relation to the mechanism of adrenergic blockade. *J. Pharmacol. Exp. Therap. 112:*274 (1954).

[19] V. N. IYER and W. SZYBALSKI: Mitomycins and porfiromycin: chemical mechanism of activation and cross-linking of DNA. *Science 145:*55 (1964).

[20] D. R. DAVIES and A. L. GREEN: The mechanism of hydrolysis by cholinesterase and related enzymes. *Advance. Enzymol. 20:*283 (1958).

[21] I. B. WILSON: Molecular complementarity and antidotes for alkylphosphate poisoning. *Fed. Proc. 18:*752 (1959).

[22] J. E. CASIDA: Esterase inhibitors as pesticides. *Science 146:*1011 (1964).

[23] D. E. KOSHLAND, JR.: Correlation of structure and function in enzyme action. *Science 142:*1533 (1963).

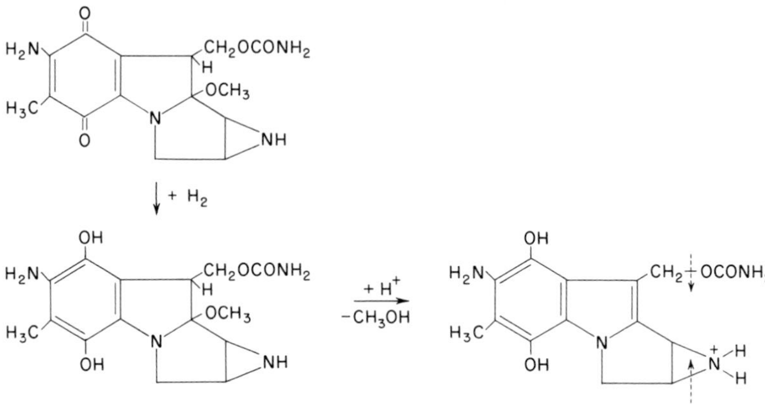

FIG. 1-4. MITOMYCIN C (UPPER LEFT) AND ITS POSTULATED REACTIVE FORM (LOWER RIGHT). *The broken arrows show bonds that are known to be split when the reactive carbonium ions are formed. (From Iyer and Szybalski.[19] By permission of the American Association for the Advancement of Science.)*

amino acid sequence in the active center is *glutamic acid-serine-alanine.* In chymotrypsin, trypsin, and others it is *aspartic acid-serine-glycine.* In phosphoglucomutase it is *alanine-serine-histidine.* These enzymes have completely different substrate specificity requirements, so substrate access to the active center must, in each instance, be governed by specific features of the tertiary protein structure, dependent, in turn, upon differences in primary structure. Yet the actual catalytic steps mediated by these several enzymes are essentially the same. The enzyme carries out a nucleophilic attack upon an acyl carbon or phosphorus atom, resulting in the transient acylation of the enzyme and release of the group formerly acylated. Then the acyl group is transferred to a water hydroxyl ion (peptidases, esterases, phosphatases) or to another acceptor (phosphoglucomutase).

Figure 1-5 illustrates the mechanism of catalysis in the hydrolysis of acetylcholine by a cholinesterase and the mode of action of two inhibitors of the enzyme. Figure 1-5a represents the active center of the enzyme. Substrate specificity is determined by two sites approximately 7 A apart, an anionic site that forms an ionic bond with the cationic N of choline esters, and an esteratic site at which the ester bond is actually split. The initial interaction here is thought to be electron donation (probably from a histidine nitrogen atom) to the electrophilic carbonyl carbon atom. At a subsequent step (Fig. 1-5b) this carbon atom is transferred to a serine hydroxyl group and choline is liberated. The transient acetylated enzyme then reacts with water, yielding acetic acid and regenerating the enzyme.

Diisopropylfluorophosphate (DFP)(Fig. 1-5c) and similar organic phosphates are themselves esters containing a phosphorus atom that is

FIG. 1-5.   SUBSTRATE AND INHIBITOR INTERACTIONS WITH A CHOLINESTERASE.
In b, c, and d, only the reactions with the essential serine (ser) *residue in the
esteratic site are shown.*

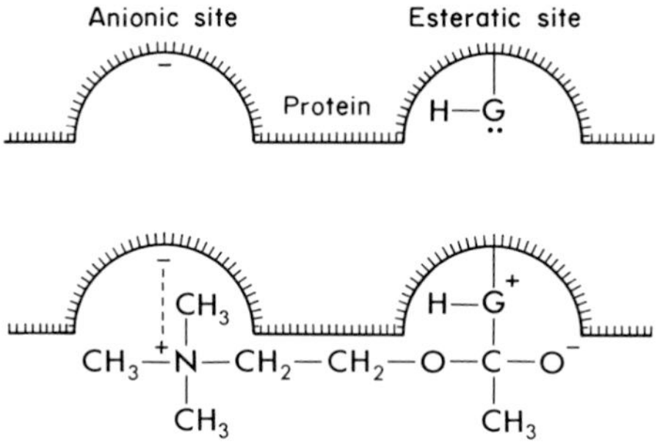

Anionic site   Esteratic site

Protein   H—G

CH$_3$ H—G$^+$

CH$_3$—$^+$N—CH$_2$—CH$_2$—O—C—O$^-$

CH$_3$ CH$_3$

a

Representation of the active center of a cholinesterase (above) *and its
interaction with acetylcholine* (below); G *represents an electron-rich center,
presumably the N atom of a histidine* (his) *imidazole group.* (*From Wilson,
Fig. 1.*[21])

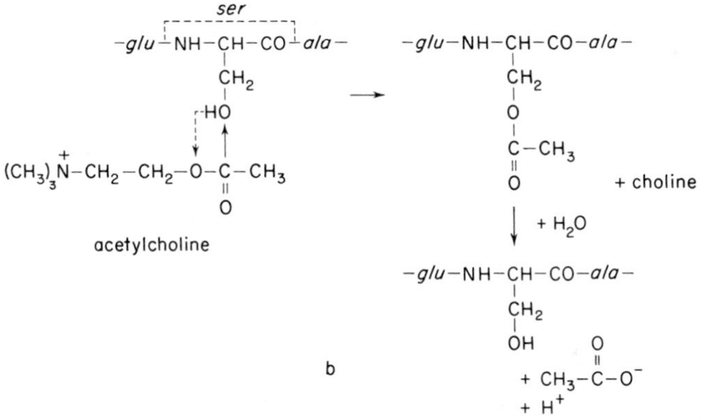

ser
—glu—NH—CH—CO—ala—   —glu—NH—CH—CO—ala—

CH$_2$ CH$_2$

HO   O

(CH$_3$)$_3$N—CH$_2$—CH$_2$—O—C—CH$_3$ C—CH$_3$
                                   ‖
O   O   + choline

acetylcholine   + H$_2$O

—glu—NH—CH—CO—ala—

CH$_2$

b   OH   O
                                 ‖
                          + CH$_3$—C—O$^-$
                          + H$^+$

Hydrolysis of acetylcholine, showing intermediate acetyl enzyme.

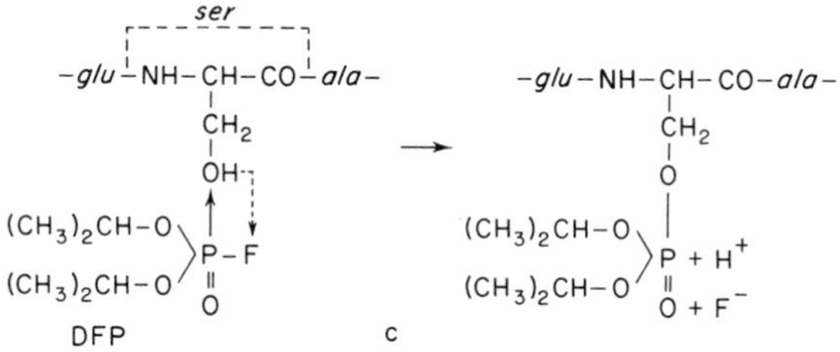

ser
—glu—NH—CH—CO—ala—   —glu—NH—CH—CO—ala—

CH$_2$ CH$_2$

OH   O

(CH$_3$)$_2$CH—O   (CH$_3$)$_2$CH—O
          >P—F   >P + H$^+$
(CH$_3$)$_2$CH—O ‖   (CH$_3$)$_2$CH—O ‖
              O   O + F$^-$
DFP   c

Mechanism of inhibition by DFP.

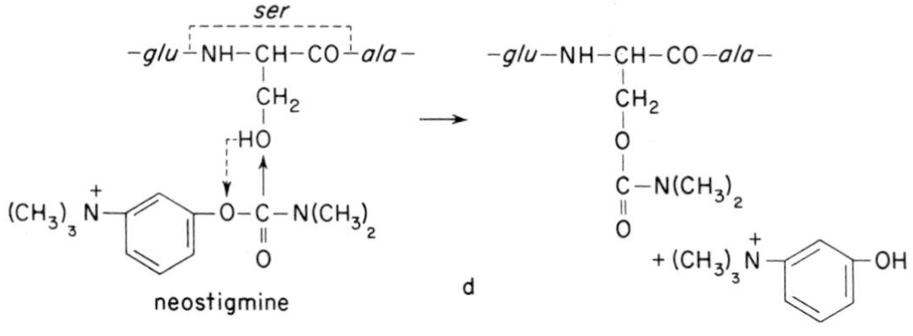

ser
—glu—NH—CH—CO—ala—   —glu—NH—CH—CO—ala—

CH$_2$ CH$_2$

HO   O

(CH$_3$)$_3$N—⟨ ⟩—O—C—N(CH$_3$)$_2$ C—N(CH$_3$)$_2$
              ‖   ‖
              O   O

neostigmine   d   + (CH$_3$)$_3$N$^+$—⟨ ⟩—OH

Mechanism of inhibition by neostigmine.

electron deficient by virtue of the electron-attracting power of the attached halogen. Such a molecule can enter the active sites of all the "serine enzymes" and there participate in a reaction analogous to the normal acylation of enzyme by substrate. The phosphorus atom makes an electrophilic attack on the electron-rich oxygen atom of the serine residue, yielding diisopropylphosphorylserine, and the fluorine anion and a proton are released. Phosphorylated serine residues have been isolated from enzymes treated in this way.[24] The reaction is nonspecific; DFP enters the active sites of all the enzymes, even though each has its own exacting substrate specificity requirements. The phosphorylation is practically irreversible, unlike the normal transient acylation mechanism.

A contrast to the lack of specificity of DFP is provided by the drug neostigmine (Fig. 1-5d). This compound, by virtue of its close structural similarity to a choline ester, inhibits cholinesterases quite specifically. It is now known that the long-lasting component of its inhibitory action is the result of a dimethylcarbamylation of the enzyme center, presumably at the same serine residue with which DFP combines. The molecular architecture of neostigmine restricts its effective access to the active centers of those enzymes whose substrates it resembles, namely, the cholinesterases.

A *coordinate covalent bond* is formed when both electrons of the electron pair that forms the bond between two atoms are donated by the same atom. In biologic systems the donor atom is usually nitrogen, oxygen, or sulfur, since these contain a pair of *s*-orbital electrons, usually unshared when the valence electrons have participated in bond formation. The electronic configuration of these elements is shown in Table 1-2. Consider the electron distribution in the outer orbitals of a typical carbon-bound amino group:

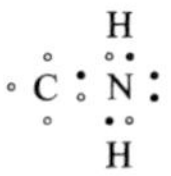

$$\overset{\displaystyle H}{\underset{\displaystyle H}{\,^{\circ}_{\circ}C\,^{\circ}_{\circ}\,^{\bullet}_{\bullet}N\,^{\bullet}_{\bullet}}}$$

The five electrons originally associated with the nitrogen atom are distinguished here from those contributed to the bonds by hydrogen and carbon, but it should be evident that all electrons are actually equivalent. The nitrogen electron octet is complete, and the valence of 3 for nitrogen is satisfied, yet the 2*s* electron pair remains unshared. (The inner, 1*s* orbital, containing two electrons, the helium core, is not shown here.) The simplest example of a coordinate covalent bond is the donation of this unshared electron pair to a proton:

24 H. S. JANSZ, D. BRONS, and M. G. P. J. WARRINGA: Chemical nature of the DFP-binding site of pseudocholinesterase. *Biochim. Biophys. Acta 34:*573 (1959).

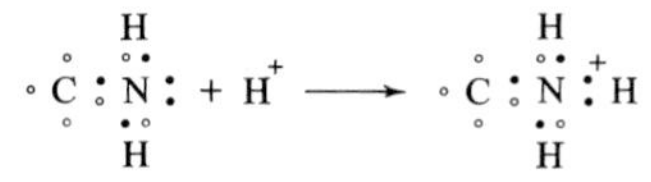

$$\overset{H}{\underset{H}{\circ\, C\, \colon\! \overset{\bullet\bullet}{\underset{\bullet\bullet}{N}}\colon}}\ +\ \overset{+}{H}\ \longrightarrow\ \overset{H}{\underset{H}{\circ\, C\, \colon\! \overset{\bullet\bullet}{\underset{\bullet\bullet}{N}}\colon\! \overset{+}{H}}}$$

Note that the positive charge associated with the proton is retained by the complex since there has been no net gain or loss of electrons. This type of bond formation plays a very important role in the ionization of drugs and in certain classes of drug-receptor interaction. Below we consider the formation of coordination complexes, especially chelate complexes.

Except for the coordination of a hydrogen ion, the atoms that share donated electron pairs in coordination complexes are usually metallic cations. These are the biologically important ions Na^+ and Mg^{++} (atomic numbers 11, 12), K^+ and Ca^{++} (atomic numbers 19, 20), Cu^+ (or Cu^{++}) and Zn^{++} (atomic numbers 29, 30). In addition, the transition elements have a peculiar ability to accept an electron in an unfilled inner orbital without disturbing ionic bonding involving the outer-orbital valence electrons. Transition elements of pharmacologic importance include Mn, Fe, and Co (atomic numbers 25, 26, 27). The basis of the behavior described here is evident in the electronic configurations shown in Table 1-2.

Figure 1-6 depicts the formation of coordinate covalent bonds between four nitrogen atoms and a cupric ion (Cu^{++}), resulting in a stable complex. Cupric ion has nine instead of ten electrons in its $3d$ orbital (cf. Table 1-2) and zero instead of one electron in its $4s$ orbital, the double positive charge reflecting the excess of protons over electrons in the whole ionized atom. The pairs of electrons contributed by the ammonia nitrogen atoms complete a stable octet for copper; but because no electrons have been gained or lost in the reaction, there is no change in net charge.

FIG. 1-6.   COPPER COORDINATION COMPLEXES.

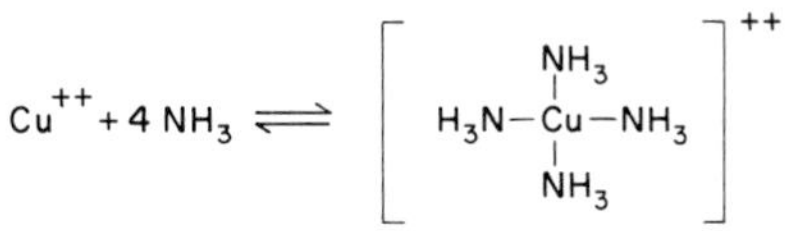

Copper-ammonia coordination complex.

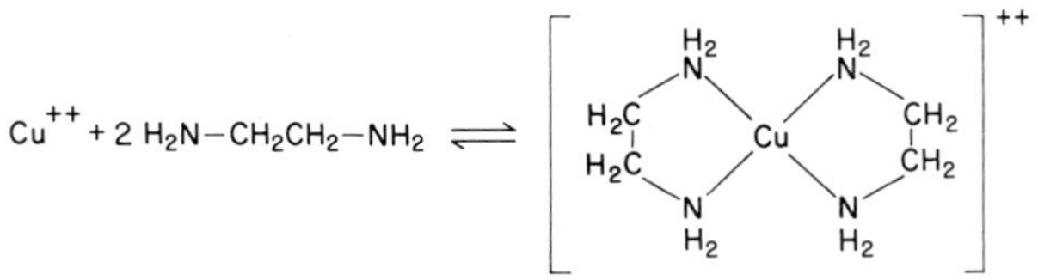

Chelate complex between copper and two molecules of ethylenediamine.

TABLE 1-2   Electron configurations of atoms

Entries in bold-face type represent elements of special pharmacologic interest. (From Pauling,[12] Table 2-4.)

		K	L		M			N				O			P			Q
		1s	2s	2p	3s	3p	3d	4s	4p	4d	4f	5s	5p	5d	6s	6p	6d	7s
H	1	1																
He	2	2																
Li	3	2	1															
Be	4	2	2															
B	5	2	2	1														
C	6	2	2	2														
N	7	2	2	3														
O	8	2	2	4														
F	9	2	2	5														
Ne	10	2	2	6														
Na	11	2	2	6	1													
Mg	12				2													
Al	13				2	1												
Si	14		10		2	2												
P	15		Neon core		2	3												
S	16				2	4												
Cl	17				2	5												
Ar	18				2	6												
K	19	2	2	6	2	6		1										
Ca	20							2										
Sc	21						1	2										
Ti	22						2	2										
V	23						3	2										
Cr	24		18				5	1										
Mn	25		Argon core				5	2										
Fe	26						6	2										
Co	27						7	2										
Ni	28						8	2										
Cu	29	2	2	6	2	6	10	1										
Zn	30							2										
Ga	31							2	1									
Ge	32		28					2	2									
As	33		Copper core					2	3									
Se	34							2	4									
Br	35							2	5									
Kr	36							2	6									
Rb	37	2	2	6	2	6	10	2	6			1						
Sr	38											2						
Y	39									1		2						
Zr	40									2		2						
Cb	41									4		1						
Mo	42		36							5		1						
Ma	43		Krypton core							6		1						
Ru	44									7		1						
Rh	45									8		1						
Pd	46									10								

TABLE 1-2 (continued)

		K	L		M			N				O			P			Q
		1s	2s	2p	3s	3p	3d	4s	4p	4d	4f	5s	5p	5d	6s	6p	6d	7s
Ag	47	2	2	6	2	6	10	2	6	10		1						
Cd	48											2						
In	49											2	1					
Sn	50					46						2	2					
Sb	51					Silver core						2	3					
Te	52											2	4					
I	53											2	5					
Xe	54											2	6					
Cs	55	2	2	6	2	6	10	2	6	10		2	6		1			
Ba	56					54									2			
La	57					Xenon core								1	2			
Ce	58	2	2	6	2	6	10	2	6	10	1	2	6	1	2			
Pr	59										2			1	2			
Nd	60										3			1	2			
Il	61										4			1	2			
Sm	62										5			1	2			
Eu	63										6			1	2			
Gd	64										7			1	2			
Tb	65					46					8		8	1	2			
Ds	66					1s to 4d					9		5s, 5p	1	2			
Ho	67										10			1	2			
Er	68										11			1	2			
Tm	69										12			1	2			
Yb	70										13			1	2			
Lu	71										14			1	2			
Hf	72	2	2	6	2	6	10	2	6	10	14	2	6	2	2			
Ta	73													3	2			
W	74													4	2			
Re	75					68								5	2			
Os	76					Hafnium core								6	2			
Ir	77													9				
Pt	78													9	1			
Au	79	2	2	6	2	6	10	2	6	10	14	2	6	10	1			
Hg	80														2			
Tl	81														2	1		
Pb	82					78									2	2		
Bi	83					Gold core									2	3		
Po	84														2	4		
———	85														2	5		
Rn	86														2	6		
———	87	2	2	6	2	6	10	2	6	10	14	2	6	10	2	6		1
Ra	88																	2
Ac	89																1	2
Th	90					86											2	2
Pa	91					Radon core											3	2
U	92																4	2

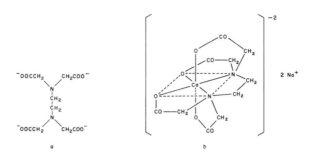

FIG. 1-7. ETHYLENEDIAMINE TETRAACETATE (EDTA) (*a*) AND ITS SALT, CAL-
CIUM DISODIUM EDATATE (*b*). *In* (b) *bonds are shown in* heavy lines, *a plane
of reference is indicated by* broken lines. (*From Martell, p. 9.*[25] *By permission of
J. B. Lippincott.*)

Chelation is the formation of coordination complexes through the
establishment of five- or six-membered rings. Such a complex is shown in
Fig. 1-6b, between the bidentate (i.e., containing "two teeth") chelating
agent ethylenediamine and the cupric ion. The donation of electrons by
four nitrogen atoms is identical to that in the copper-ammonia complex,
but here the metal atom is held very much more tightly, in two five-membered rings. A tetradentate chelating agent of considerable pharmacologic
importance, ethylenediaminetetraacetate (EDTA, edetate, edathamil), is
shown in Fig. 1-7, together with its calcium complex.

Chelate complexes vary greatly in stability (i.e., in the tendency of
the metal to dissociate) depending upon the nature of the chelating agent
and of the metal. Stability is expressed quantitatively by the "stability
constant" K in the mass law equation for the equilibrium relationship between free and complexed reactants, as follows:

$$\text{metal} + \text{chelating agent} \underset{k_2}{\overset{k_1}{\rightleftharpoons}} \text{complex}$$

$$\frac{(\text{complex})}{(\text{metal}) \times (\text{chelating agent})} = \frac{k_1}{k_2} = K$$

For any given chelating agent the magnitude of the stability constants is
determined largely by the atomic structures of the various metals, so that
the rank order of the metals remains roughly the same regardless of which
particular chelating agent may be used. A typical rank order is shown in
Table 1-3, for the complexing of different metals by EDTA. The very wide

[25] A. E. MARTELL: "The Relationship of Chemical Structure to Metal-Binding Action," in *Metal-Binding in Medicine*, ed. by M. J. Seven. Philadelphia, Lippincott, 1960.

TABLE 1-3 **Stabilities of chelate complexes of various metal ions with EDTA.**

(From Martell and Calvin, Appendix I.[26]) By permission of Prentice-Hall.

Metal ion	Log of stability constant of complex
Na^+	1.7
Li^+	2.8
Ba^{++}	7.8
Sr^{++}	8.6
Mg^{++}	8.7
Ca^{++}	10.6
Mn^{++}	13.4
Fe^{++}	14.4
Co^{++}	16.1
Zn^{++}	16.1
Cu^{++}	18.3
Ni^{++}	18.4
Cd^{++}	16.4
Pb^{++}	18.2

range of stabilities, extending over many orders of magnitude, is noteworthy. A metal with a higher stability constant would effectively compete for the chelating agent with a metal of lower stability and, given sufficient time, would displace the less tightly bound metal from complexes already formed.[26]

Naturally occurring chelate complexes are known to play important roles in biologic systems. It may well be that the principal importance of the metals essential for life lies in their ability to form functional chelate complexes. These are evidently well suited to act as bridges to facilitate electron transfer, such as must occur in the catalytic formation or cleavage of any covalent bond. In cytochrome c, for example, as in other heme proteins, an iron atom is chelated, forming four six-membered rings containing the imidazole nitrogen atoms of the porphyrin nucleus. Two additional coordinate covalent bonds hold the complexed iron to imidazole N of histidine residues in the associated protein (Fig. 1-8). Analogous chelate complexes of biologic importance are chlorophyll (a magnesium complex) and vitamin B_{12} (a cobalt complex, Fig. 1-9).

Magnesium and other divalent cations that behave as enzyme activators are thought to function by binding substrate at the active site through chelation. This role is illustrated for the zinc enzyme carboxypep-

[26] A. E. MARTELL and M. CALVIN: *Chemistry of the Metal Chelate Compounds.* Englewood Cliffs, N.J., Prentice-Hall, 1952.

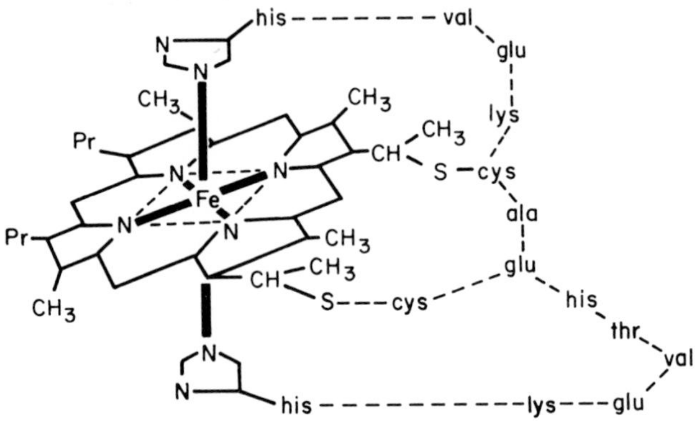

FIG. 1-8. CYTOCHROME C. *The* dashed lines *between the imidazole N atoms define the plane that also contains the Fe atom. Pr denotes propionate residue. (From Eichhorn, Fig. 4.*[27] *By permission of J. B. Lippincott.)*

tidase in Fig. 1-10. The Zn^{++} ion is bound to S^- of the single cysteine residue of the protein, and also by a coordinate covalent bond to N of the amino-terminal asparagine residue. The substrate is probably held to Zn^{++} by coordinate bonds to carbonyl O and peptide N, thus forming a chelate ring. Binding of substrate to electron donor (B) and proton donor (A) groups of the protein is also postulated. The peptide bond could then be weakened by the tendency of the metal ion to draw electrons away from it, so that an acyl enzyme intermediate would be formed, which could then react with OH^- to regenerate $-COOH$. The ionic radius of Zn^{++} plays a key role in determining reaction specificity. Substitution of other metals for zinc not only diminishes or abolishes the usual peptidase action, but may at the same time greatly enhance a completely different catalytic action, such as hydrolysis of ester bonds.[29]

Any discussion of the tight complexing of metals to receptors calls for special consideration of sulfhydryl groups in proteins and coenzymes. Bonds between sulfur and metal ions, which may be ionic, covalent, or of mixed type, are exceptionally strong. This is reflected in the practically irreversible character of such metal sulfides as AgS, HgS, CuS, and PbS. When a metal-sulfur bond is included in a chelate ring, stability is greatly enhanced. Such chelation may involve oxygen or nitrogen in addition to sulfur, but the most stable chelate structures of this type are those in which two sulfur atoms participate in a five- or six-membered mercaptide ring (Fig. 1-11). Thus, mercaptide formation may proceed in several ways, as depicted in Fig. 1-12. Profound biologic consequences ensue because cer-

27 G. L. EICHHORN: "The Role of Metal Ions in Enzyme Systems," in *Metal-Binding in Medicine,* ed. by M. J. Seven. Philadelphia, Lippincott, 1960.

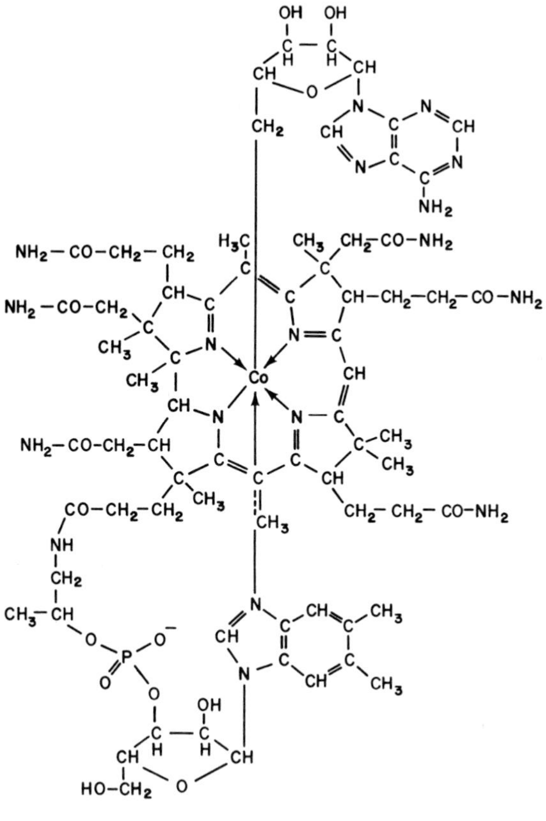

FIG. 1-9.   COENZYME FORM OF VITAMIN B$_{12}$.   (*From Hodgkin, Fig. 1.*[28])

tain enzymes require —SH as part of their active centers, and because —SH groups or specific —S—S— bonds often play key roles in the maintenance of the correct configuration of a protein. Sulfhydryl-combining reagents such as *p*-chloromercuribenzoate (PCMB) have long been employed as enzyme inhibitors, and pharmacologic agents containing a heavy metal atom in an organic molecule are quite common. For example, organic mercurials act as diuretic agents, and organic arsenicals, antimonials, and bismuth compounds have chemotherapeutic efficacy against certain spirochetal and protozoan parasites. Organic silver compounds are effective antibacterial antiseptics. All the heavy metals have

[28] D. C. HODGKIN: Vitamin B$_{12}$ and the porphyrins. *Fed. Proc.* 23:592 (1964).
[29] B. L. VALLEE: Active center of carboxypeptidase A. *Fed. Proc.* 23:8 (1964).

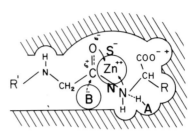

FIG. 1-10. POSTULATED INTERACTION OF A TERMINAL DIPEPTIDE WITH CAR-
BOXYPEPTIDASE.   *The zinc ion is bound to a cysteine sulfur atom and an asparagine nitrogen atom of the enzyme; these groups are shown just above and below
Zn^{++}. B is an electron donor group and A is a proton donor group of the
enzyme. Partial ionic character of the carbonyl oxygen and carbon is indicated
in the usual way. The postulated series of electron shifts, which weaken the
peptide bond as described in the text, are shown by* arrows. (*From Vallee,
Fig. 7.*[29])

toxic effects in man, particularly upon the liver, kidneys, heart, and
brain.[30]

    Chelation is not only important in binding substrates to their en-
zymes and coenzymes to their apoenzymes; it may also be a primary mechanism for the maintenance of subcellular structure in general. This is
suggested by the growing body of data implicating metal ions in the reversible association of particles (e.g., the two ribosomal subunits, whose
functional integrity depends upon an adequate concentration of Mg^{++})
and in the formation of complexes between macromolecules and particles
(e.g., the magnesium-dependent binding of messenger-RNA to ribosomes).
Metallic cations (e.g., Ca^{++}) are evidently involved in the structure and

FIG. 1-11.   TWO FORMS OF A ZINC-CYSTEINE CHELATE (*a* AND *b*) AND THE PROB-
ABLE STRUCTURE OF THE COMPLEX BETWEEN DIHYDROLIPOIC ACID AND ORGANIC
ARSENICAL (*c*).

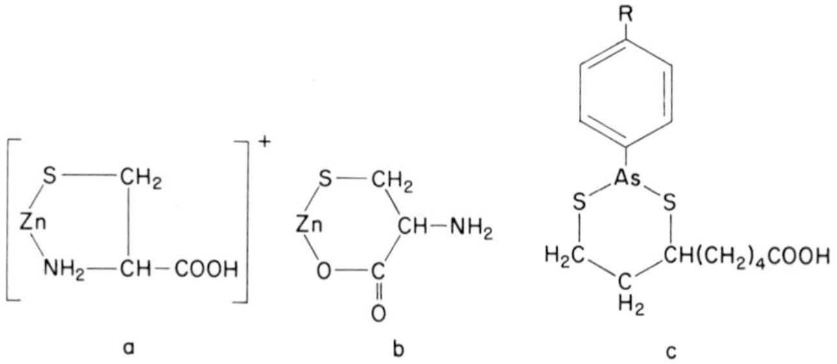

[30] H. PASSOW, A. ROTHSTEIN, and T. W. CLARKSON: The general pharmacology of
the heavy metals. *Pharmacol. Rev.* 13:185 (1961).

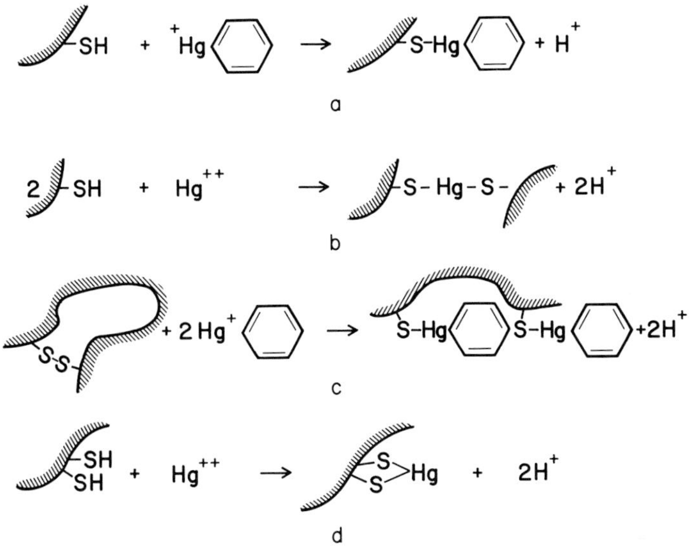

FIG. 1-12.   FOUR DIFFERENT MODES OF MERCAPTIDE FORMATION WITH A PRO-
TEIN (CYSTEINE) SULFHYDRYL GROUP.

function of membranes and in the generation of bioelectric potentials.
Recognition of specific functional roles for metal atoms in biochemical
reactions should open the way to understanding the molecular basis of
many pharmacologic and toxicologic effects caused by metal-containing
and metal-complexing drugs.[31]

THE HYDROGEN BOND[32]

The hydrogen bond arises from the ability of a proton to accept an
electron pair in part from each of two electron donor atoms such as oxygen
or nitrogen, and thus to form a bridge approximately 3 A in length between them. The bond strength is very much less than for a covalent bond
(only about 2 to 5 kilocalories per mole) but the additive effects of several
such bonds can stabilize an interaction significantly. This is best illustrated
by the hydrogen bonding between complementary base pairs in the DNA
helix (Fig. 1-13). Here, the hydrogen bonds not only determine the
specific complementarity of A-T and G-C pairs, but the total of two to
three hydrogen bonds per base pair, multiplied by many hundreds of base
pairs in the long DNA molecule, confers a high degree of stability on the

[31] M. J. SEVEN, ed.: *Metal-Binding in Medicine.* Philadelphia, Lippincott, 1960.
[32] G. C. PIMENTEL and A. L. MC CLELLAN: *The Hydrogen Bond.* San Francisco,
W. H. Freeman, 1960.

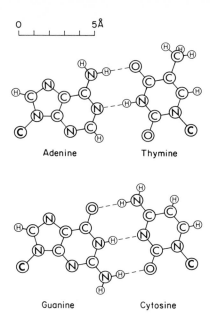

Adenine   Thymine

Guanine   Cytosine

FIG. 1-13. SPECIFIC HYDROGEN BONDING BETWEEN THE COMPLEMENTARY BASE PAIRS OF DNA. *Pairing of adenine and thymine and of guanine and cytosine in the double-helical DNA molecule. Hydrogen bonds are shown as* dotted lines. *The 1' C atom of each deoxyribose residue is also shown.* (*From Stent, Fig. 3-9.*[33] *By permission of W. H. Freeman.*)

whole structure (Fig. 1-14). These bonds can only be broken by thermal agitation at quite high "melting temperatures," usually around 80° or higher (Fig. 1-15). In the process of DNA replication hydrogen bonds must also be broken, but it is thought that only one base pair at a time is separated as the double helix unwinds; the exact mechanism, however, is not yet known.

Hydrogen bonds account for the specificity of those drugs which are incorporated into nucleic acids by a "counterfeit" mechanism, in place of natural bases (p. 102). They also can stabilize complexes between drugs and receptors which would otherwise interact only weakly. Finally, internal hydrogen bonds may greatly affect the physical properties of drug molecules. This is illustrated by the properties of salicylic acid, the ortho isomer of hydroxybenzoic acid (Fig. 1-16). The intramolecular hydrogen bond in this molecule effectively reduces the affinities of both the carboxyl

[33] G. S. STENT: *Molecular Biology of Bacterial Viruses.* San Francisco, W. H. Freeman, 1963.

[33a] M. FEUGHELMAN, R. LANGRIDGE, W. E. SEEDS, A. R. STOKES, H. R. WILSON, C. W. HOOPER, M. H. F. WILKINS, R. K. BARCLAY, and L. D. HAMILTON: Molecular structure of deoxyribose nucleic acid and nucleoprotein. *Nature 175:*834 (1955).

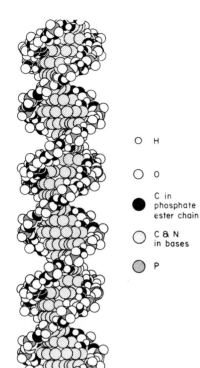

O H

○ O

● C in
phosphate
ester chain

○ C & N
in bases

◉ P

FIG. 1-14. A SEGMENT OF THE DNA DU-
PLEX, HYDROGEN BONDED AT EACH BASE
PAIR. (*From Stent*,[33] *Fig. 3-9, after
Feughelman et al.*[33a], *Fig. 1; by permis-
sion of W. H. Freeman and Macmillan
Journals Ltd.*)

and the phenolic hydroxyl groups for water molecules, and thus drastically
alters the solubility. The para and meta isomers, which cannot possibly
form such an intramolecular hydrogen bond, are soluble to the extent of
about 1 gram per 100 ml water at 20°, whereas salicylic acid is soluble to
less than one fifth this amount.[35]

THE IONIC BOND

The ionic bond results from coulombic forces (electrostatic attraction) between oppositely charged ions. The bond strength is approximately 5 kilocalories per mole and the force of attraction between the ions
diminishes as the square of the distance between them. Proteins and
nucleic acids have many potential anionic and cationic groups, but only a
restricted set of these is actually ionized in the physiological pH range. As
shown in Table 1-4, the anionic groups of proteins are the terminal carboxyl
groups, the carboxyl groups of aspartic acid and glutamic acid, and to

34 J. MARMUR and P. DOTY: Determination of the base composition of deoxyribonucleic acid from its thermal denaturation temperature. *J. Mol. Biol.* 5:109 (1962).
35 N. V. SIDGWICK and R. K. CALLOW: Abnormal benzene derivatives. *J. Chem. Soc.*
125:527 (1924).

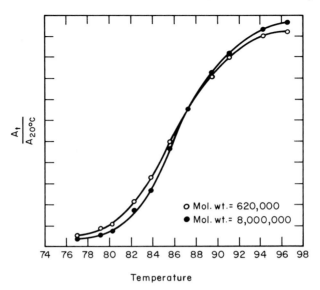

some extent the sulfhydryl groups of cysteine. The anionic groups of nucleic acids are the phosphoryl residues. Cationic groups are derived from lysine, arginine, histidine, amide $-NH_2$ of glutamine and asparagine, and termi-nal amino $-NH_2$ of proteins. Mucopolysaccharides contain anionic sulfate residues, and cationic amino sugars may occur in other macromolecules. In any particular instance the availability of charged groups for interaction will depend upon the composition and tertiary structure of the receptor macromolecule. An ionic group, for example, may be folded into a com-

FIG. 1-16.   ISOMERS OF HYDROXYBENZOIC ACID.

o-hydroxybenzoic acid   *m*-hydroxybenzoic acid   *p*-hydroxybenzoic acid
(salicylic acid)

pletely inaccessible location, or may already be bonded internally to another ionic group of the same protein. In the case of the nucleic acids the phosphoryl groups may serve as ionic links to an associated basic protein (e.g., a histone) and thus be unavailable for interaction.

Drugs may contain potential cationic and anionic groups of all kinds, capable of forming ionic bonds with oppositely charged receptor groups. The influence of pH upon the ionization of drugs is discussed later. Electrostatic attraction may operate between ionized receptor groups and atoms of a drug molecule that are not frankly ionized but have a partial ionic character. The carbonyl group offers a good illustration. Here, the electrons forming the $C=O$ bond are known to be shared unequally. The oxygen atom has a relative excess, the carbon atom a relative deficit.

TABLE 1-4.   Ionizing groups in proteins and nucleic acids

For discussion of pK_a' see pp. 26-30. (Data of Jordan,[36] Cohn and Edsall,[37] and Steinhardt and Beychok, Table II.[38] By permission of Reinhold Publishing Corp. and Academic Press.)

Group	Potential charge	pK'_a
I. *Groups completely or almost completely ionized at pH 7.4*		
α-carboxyl (terminal –COOH)	—	1.8–2.4
β-carboxyl (*asp*)	—	3.7
γ-carboxyl (*glu*)	—	4.3
primary phosphoryl (terminal)	—	0.7–1.0
secondary phosphoryl	—	5.9–6.0
ϵ-ammonium (*lys*)	+	10.5
guanidinium (*arg*)	+	12.5
II. *Groups partially ionized at pH 7.4*		
sulfhydryl (*cys*)	—	8.2
imidazolium N (*his*)	+	6.0
α-ammonium (terminal –NH$_2$)	+	7.5–10.3
amide N (*gln*)	+	9.1
amide N (*asn*)	+	8.8
III. *Groups practically nonionized at pH 7.4*		
phenolic hydroxyl (*tyr*)	—	10.0
aromatic hydroxyl (uracil, thymine, guanine)	—	9.2–9.8
sugar hydroxyl	—	12.3–12.6
aromatic amino (adenine, guanine, cytosine)	+	3.3–4.6

[36] D. O. JORDAN: "The Physical Properties of Nucleic Acids," in *The Nucleic Acids,* ed. by Chargaff, E., and Davidson, J. N. New York, Academic Press, 1955. Vol. I.

[37] E. J. COHN and J. T. EDSALL: *Proteins, Amino Acids and Peptides.* New York, Reinhold, 1943.

[38] J. STEINHARDT and S. BEYCHOK: "Interaction of Proteins With Hydrogen Ions and Other Small Ions and Molecules," in *The Proteins,* 2nd ed., ed. by Neurath, H. New York, Academic Press, 1964.

Thus the bonded pair as a whole is a dipole, either end of which may be attracted to another ion. Interactions are known, for example, in which the carbonyl carbon atom, by virtue of its partial positive charge, combines with an anionic site of an enzyme or other receptor surface. An example has already been shown in Fig. 1-5.

THE DIPOLE-INDUCED DIPOLE BOND

The dipole-induced dipole bond is a very weak interaction between similar atoms. Because of their abundance in organic molecules, carbon atoms are principally involved in bonds of this type between drugs and receptors. The theory of these close-range attractive forces was developed by van der Waals, and further by Heitler and London, whose names are commonly used in describing them. The attractive forces (also known as *electron correlation attraction*[39]) arise from slight distortions induced in the electron clouds surrounding each nucleus as two atoms are brought very close together. Very weak transient atomic dipoles are produced, which then attract each other electrostatically. The bond energy is only about 0.5 kilocalories per mole. The force of attraction is inversely proportional to the 7th power of distance, so a very close approximation of the interacting atoms is much more important here than for ordinary ionic bonds. It might be imagined, because of their weakness and because they decrease so rapidly with slight increase of interatomic distance, that van der Waals forces would be unimportant. On the contrary, there is every reason to believe that they play a major role in determining the specificity of drug-receptor interactions. First of all, when these forces are summed over a large number of interacting atoms, a considerable binding may result albeit the individual bond is weak, as for hydrogen bonding in DNA. Second, the very fact that the binding force is so critically dependent upon interatomic distance provides a physicochemical basis for the high degree of selectivity that may be observed among a series of closely related drugs, a phenomenon ascribed to "goodness of fit." Thus, a drug molecule whose three-dimensional shape (conformation) allows a very close approximation to a receptor surface is said to "fit" that receptor better (and therefore to be more effective there) than a related molecule with slightly different conformation. As a drug molecule approaches the receptor surface, a sharp increase in binding force will be manifested quite abruptly (provided a close-enough approach is possible), as many electron correlation attractions come into play simultaneously. In this situation even a minor degree of misfit could, by impeding the necessary perfect approximation of the complementary molecular surfaces, produce a major disruptive effect upon the overall binding.

[39] L. PAULING: The hydrate microcrystal theory of general anesthesia. *Anesthesia Analg. Curr. Res. 43:*1 (1964).

Drug-Receptor Interaction as Resultant of the Several Bond Types

The binding force that holds a drug in combination with its receptor arises from the concerted operation of numerous bonds of the several types discussed. Once distributive and diffusive processes have brought a drug molecule into the vicinity of a receptor surface, random thermal agitation produces multiple collisions with that surface. The drug is usually in solution, that is to say, surrounded wholly or partly by water molecules. The receptor surface, likewise, by virtue of its polar groups, can be thought of as covered by a sheath of water molecules. The binding of the drug to the receptor must then entail the mutual squeezing out of the intervening water layers. The interaction as a whole is therefore sometimes described as the formation of hydrophobic bonds.

What is the primary attractive force that comes into play as a drug molecule approaches its receptor? Consider the fields of force as one moves outward, away from the receptor surface, into the surrounding aqueous medium. The van der Waals attraction will fall off to a negligible value at a relatively short distance, but the coulombic forces, which diminish only as the square of the distance, will continue to be felt farther from the center of the charge density. Therefore, although usually only one or a few ionic bonds are formed, the earliest attraction that draws an approaching drug molecule toward its receptor is often an electrostatic one.

In order to result in a significant drug action, and in order for specificity to be manifested, the primary interaction has to be reinforced by accessory bonds. Indeed, the energy of thermal agitation at 37° is sufficient to disrupt a single, unreinforced ionic bond. Here, hydrogen bonds, van der Waals attractions, and covalent bonds (if any are to be formed) come into play. A good fit will allow a maximum area of close approximation between the drug and the receptor, bringing appropriate groups on both surfaces into close enough contact (1 to 3 A) for bond formation. Even without formation of a covalent bond, the concerted effects of ionic bonds, hydrogen bonds, and dipole-induced dipole bonds may yield quite stable complexes. One of the fascinating aspects of pharmacology is the seeming paradox that many drugs are obviously unreactive in the chemical sense, yet biologically these same inert molecules may be highly potent, extremely selective, and also bound remarkably tightly to components of living cells. With most drugs, however, the binding to receptors is not so tight as to preclude dissociation entirely. A reversible interaction is established, which obeys the law of mass action. If this were not so, most drugs would have exceedingly long persistence and duration of action in the body.

The Ionization of Drugs

An acid is a proton donor, a base is a proton acceptor. The strength of the bond between proton and base is determined by the electron-attracting or electron-repelling properties of other atoms in the molecule. This bond strength determines the extent of ionization at a given pH, as reflected in the pK_a' (negative logarithm of the acid dissociation constant). Recall that

$$\text{acid} \underset{k_2}{\overset{k_1}{\rightleftharpoons}} \text{base} + H^+.$$

At equilibrium,

$$k_1(\text{acid}) = k_2(\text{base})(H^+)$$

$$(H^+) = \frac{k_1}{k_2} \cdot \frac{(\text{acid})}{(\text{base})} = K_a' \cdot \frac{(\text{acid})}{(\text{base})}$$

whence the Henderson-Hasselbalch equation:

$$pH = -\log(H^+) = pK_a' + \log \frac{(\text{base})}{(\text{acid})},$$

and at 50% ionization, $\log \dfrac{(\text{base})}{(\text{acid})} = 0$, so

$$pK_a = pH.$$

Most drugs contain weak acidic or basic groups (or both), so that their states of ionization, which influence their interactions with receptors, will depend upon the pK_a values of these groups and upon the ambient pH.

The concepts of acid and base should not be confused with those of cation and anion. They are unrelated, except that by virtue of proton dissociation a base necessarily has one less positive charge than its conjugate acid. Figure 1-17 presents a few examples.

The ability of nitrogen to donate an unshared pair of electrons, already discussed in connection with the coordinate covalent bond, plays a central role in the ionization of drugs. Compounds containing trivalent nitrogen are capable of associating with hydrogen ion and thereby acquir-

FIG. 1-17.   SOME EXAMPLES OF ACID-BASE EQUILIBRIA.

Acid		Base			pK_a'
$CH_3\overset{O}{\overset{\|}{C}}-OH$	$\rightleftharpoons$	$CH_3\overset{O}{\overset{\|}{C}}-O^-$	$+$	H^+	4.8
NH_4^+	$\rightleftharpoons$	NH_3	$+$	H^+	9.3
H_2CO_3	$\rightleftharpoons$	HCO_3^-	$+$	H^+	6.5
H_3PO_4	$\rightleftharpoons$	$H_2PO_4^-$	$+$	H^+	2.0
$H_2PO_4^-$	$\rightleftharpoons$	$HPO_4^=$	$+$	H^+	7.1
$HPO_4^=$	$\rightleftharpoons$	$PO_4^\equiv$	$+$	H^+	12.3

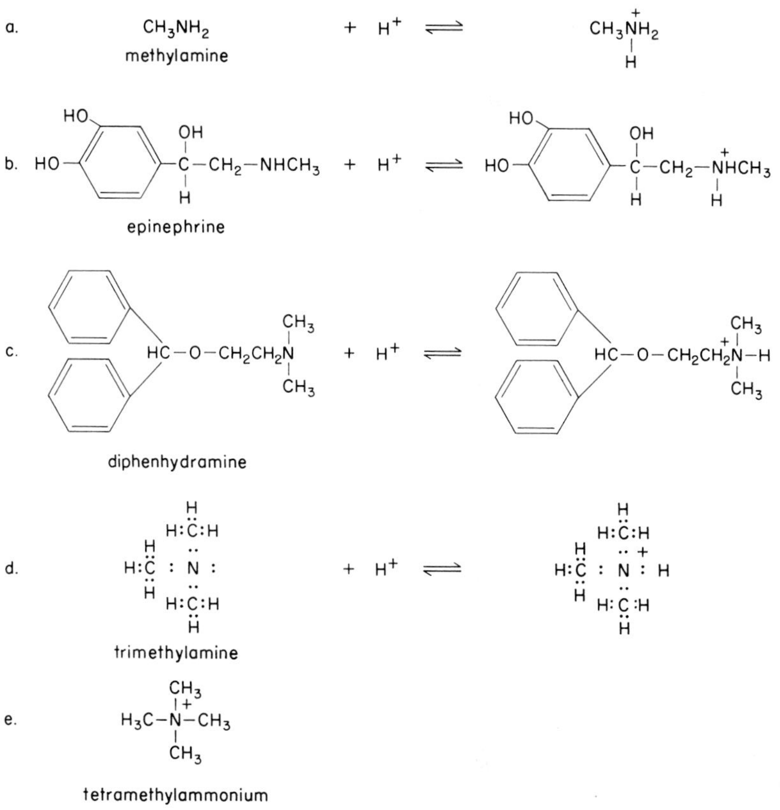

a. CH_3NH_2 + H^+ ⇌ $CH_3\overset{+}{N}H_2$
   methylamine   H

FIG. 1-18. TERTIARY NITROGEN COMPOUNDS AND THEIR IONIZATION (*a-d*), AND A QUATERNARY COMPOUND (*e*).

ing a positive charge. This is shown in Figure 1-18 for three different drugs. Methylamine contains a primary amino group, epinephrine a secondary amino group, and diphenhydramine a tertiary amino group, but all can become cations under acidic conditions. The mechanism, which is the same for all three, is indicated in Fig. 1-18d, using trimethylamine as an example. Since the ability to neutralize a hydrogen ion resembles the behavior of alkalis, drugs of this kind that occur in plant material were called "alkaloids." Alkaloidal drugs, in the free base form, tend to be poorly soluble in water; but if they are treated with acid the acquired positive charge results in a greatly enhanced solubility. Acid salts of these compounds may be crystallized, and these will then dissolve readily in pure water. It should be understood that the particular anion, or cation, with which a drug molecule is associated has no influence upon that drug's biologic action. Just as the properties of Na^+ in solution are the same, whether derived from NaCl or $(Na)_2SO_4$, so the actions of morphine sulfate are not to be distinguished from those of morphine hydrochloride. Rarely, however, certain salts are so insoluble that they may influence the rate of absorption of a compound. The official names of drugs, as given in the United States Pharmacopeia or other compendia, naturally specify particular salts (Table 1-5); but in this book we shall ignore the associated anions or cations.

TABLE 1-5.   Anions and cations associated with drugs

Drugs shown are listed in the United States Pharmacopeia.[40]

ASSOCIATED ANIONS:

Morphine sulfate
Diphenhydramine hydrochloride
Codeine phosphate
Diethylcarbamazine citrate
Chloramphenicol palmitate
Edrophonium chloride
Ergonovine maleate
Ergotamine tartrate
Estradiol benzoate

ASSOCIATED CATIONS:

Sulfadiazine sodium
Potassium penicillin G
Procaine penicillin G

If a nitrogen atom donates its unshared electron pair to an atom other than hydrogen (usually a carbon atom), thus forming a coordinate covalent bond, the nitrogen atom is said to be quaternized (Fig. 1-18e). Drugs containing quaternary nitrogen are not bases (although they are sometimes erroneously called that) but are permanent organic cations, for they cannot lose their positive charge at any pH. In contrast, tertiary nitrogen compounds have a pK_a that is usually near the physiologic pH range. A large fraction of their molecules may be cationic at pH 7.4, but these are in equilibrium with some nonionized free base. This difference between tertiary and quaternary nitrogen compounds has important implications for the passage of drugs across membranes (cf. chapter 2), and it also provides a basis for investigating the role of ionic bonds in drug-receptor interactions, as illustrated below.

The physiologic substrate of the enzyme acetylcholinesterase is the quaternary ester acetylcholine. Neostigmine, an inhibitor of the enzyme, is also a quaternary ester and a structural analogue of the substrate. Another inhibitor is physostigmine, a naturally occurring alkaloid and also

    [40] *The Pharmacopeia of the United States of America,* 16th revision. Easton, Pa., Mack Publishing Co., 1960.

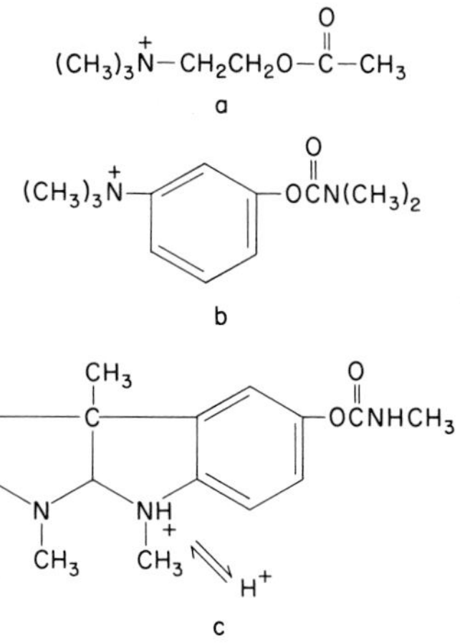

$$(CH_3)_3\overset{+}{N}-CH_2CH_2O-\overset{\overset{O}{\|}}{C}-CH_3$$

a

$$(CH_3)_3\overset{+}{N}-\!\!\!\bigcirc\!\!\!-O\overset{\overset{O}{\|}}{C}N(CH_3)_2$$

b

(Structure c: physostigmine cationic form with CH$_3$, C, N–CH$_3$, NH$^+$–CH$_3$, H$^+$, and –OCNHCH$_3$ groups)

c

FIG. 1-19.   ACETYLCHOLINE   (*a*);   NEOSTIGMINE   (*b*);   AND PHYSOSTIGMINE, CATIONIC FORM (*c*).

a structural analogue of the substrate; its pK'_a is 8.5. These compounds are shown in Fig. 1-19. It is supposed that acetylcholine forms an ionic bond with an anionic site in the active center of the enzyme, and it is also supposed that inhibitors which are structural analogues must interact at the same anionic site.

The broad pH optimum of the enzyme permits studies to be carried out over a wide range of pH values to determine whether the efficacy of an inhibitor depends upon pH. On the hypothesis that a positive charge (as in acetylcholine) is essential for interaction with the enzyme,

FIG. 1-20.   INHIBITION OF CHOLINESTERASE BY NEOSTIGMINE AND PHYSOSTIG-MINE AS A FUNCTION OF pH, AND THE IONIZATION OF PHYSOSTIGMINE. (*Adapted from Wilson and Bergmann, Fig. 1*.[41])

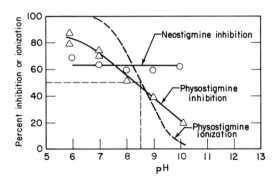

41 I. B. WILSON and F. BERGMANN: Studies on cholinesterase. VII. The active surface of acetylcholine esterase derived from effects of pH on inhibitors. *J. Biol. Chem.* *185:*479 (1950).

one would predict that inhibition by neostigmine (the quaternary inhibitor) should be independent of pH. Inhibition by physostigmine, on the other hand, should be greatest on the acid side of its pK'_a, when practically all molecules are cationic, and should fall toward zero on the alkaline side as bound protons dissociate. The observations illustrated in Fig. 1-20 were in general agreement with these predictions. However, according to the simplest model, the relationship of inhibition to pH should be identical to a pH-ionization curve for a base with $pK'_a = 8.5$. The lack of strict conformity, shown in Fig. 1-20, indicates that complicating factors are present.

STRUCTURE-ACTIVITY RELATIONSHIPS AND THE CONFORMATION OF THE RECEPTOR SURFACE

Methods of Studying Receptors

There are two ways to gain information about a receptor. The first and only really satisfactory approach is to identify and isolate it. Then the investigation can follow established biochemical and physicochemical procedures. Sequence analysis can establish the primary structure of the macromolecules. Techniques like x-ray crystallography, high-resolution electron micrography, spectrophotometry, and analytical ultracentrifugation can yield data from which the secondary and tertiary structures may be deduced.

In the case of proteins, recent years have seen the elucidation of complete primary structures at an ever-increasing rate.[23, 42] Ribonuclease is a good example (Fig. 1-21). Here, x-ray crystallography indicates a com-

FIG. 1-21. BOVINE PANCREATIC RIBONUCLEASE. *Sequence numbers of the amino acids begin at the* NH_2*-terminus. The four* —S—S— *bonds between* cys *residues are shown as* black *regions. (From Stein, Fig. 2.*[43]*)*

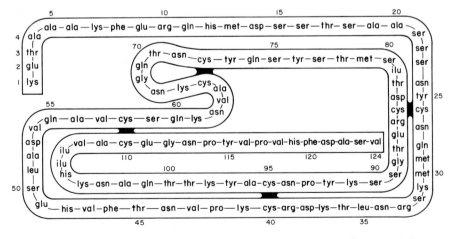

42 H. NEURATH, ed.: *The Proteins,* 2nd ed. New York, Academic Press, 1963.

pact structure with very little helical content. Although a three-dimensional model has not yet been constructed, a number of remarkable features are already evident. The positions of the $-S-S-$ bridges, for example, impose a curious asymmetry upon the entire folded molecule. All the methionine residues are evidently buried inside, whereas most of the basic lysine side chains are exposed on the surface. Residues known to be involved in the catalytic action (and therefore presumed to be in the active center) prove to be far apart on the primary chain. Thus, the two histidine residues at positions 12 and 119, as well as lysine at position 41, are believed to be within about 5 A of each other in the native enzymically active state of the protein.[43]

The power of the new technologic advances and their significance for pharmacology are well illustrated in the recent establishment of a complete three-dimensional structure for hemoglobin, at a resolution of a few angstrom units.[44-46] This molecule is the normal carrier of oxygen, and it can also be regarded as a receptor for the toxic gas carbon monoxide. The scale model (Fig. 1-22) shows how the two α-chains and the two β-chains, folded in an asymmetric pattern, are assembled into a compact structure containing four pockets to accommodate the heme groups and provide for the reversible attachment of four O_2 molecules. Of profound importance here is the discovery that combination with O_2 induces a subtle change in the shape of the whole molecule, so that the heme groups of the two β-chains are brought 7 A closer together.[47] This is a fine example of the wider class of reactions known as *allosteric* (allo = other, steric = shape), which may have quite general significance and which are discussed later in this chapter. For instance, substrates may induce configurational changes in enzymes as part of the normal mechanism of catalysis, and drugs that prevent such changes or induce unfavorable steric alterations may thereby block enzyme action.[48] Allosteric effects in membranes have also been invoked to explain the generation (or blockade) of bioelectric potentials by drugs.

Comparable advances are also taking place in the establishment of complete spatial structures for nucleic acids, which, in some respects at least, appear to be less complicated. The outstanding instance which bears

---

[43] W. H. STEIN: Structure-activity relationships in ribonuclease. *Fed. Proc. 23:*599 (1964).

[44] A. F. CULLIS, H. MUIRHEAD, M. F. PERUTZ, and M. G. ROSSMANN: The structure of haemoglobin. IX. A three-dimensional Fourier synthesis at 5.5 Å resolution: description of the structure. *Proc. Roy. Soc. A265:*161 (1962).

[45] M. F. PERUTZ: *Proteins and Nucleic Acids.* Amsterdam, Elsevier, 1962.

[46] H. MUIRHEAD and M. F. PERUTZ: Structure of haemoglobin. A three-dimensional Fourier synthesis of reduced human haemoglobin at 5.5 Å resolution. *Nature 199:*633 (1963).

[47] M. F. PERUTZ: X-ray analysis of hemoglobin. *Science 140:*863 (1963).

[48] D. E. KOSHLAND, JR.: Conformation changes at the active site during enzyme action. *Fed. Proc. 23:*719 (1964).

FIG. 1-22. TERTIARY STUCTURE OF HEMOGLOBIN.

The complete molecule. α-Chains are shown white, β-chains are black. Heme groups are represented by flat grey disks each carrying an oxygen molecule.

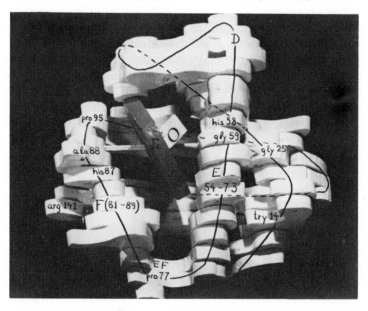

Detail of one α-chain, showing the course of the peptide-bonded backbone and the positions of some amino acids with their sequence numbers, counting from the —NH₂ terminus. (From Cullis et al., Figs. 3 and 10;[44] prints obtained through the courtesy of M. F. Perutz.)

upon drug action is the confirmation, through a multitude of physico-chemical, biochemical, and genetic techniques, of the Watson-Crick double-helical structure for DNA (Fig. 1-14). This key molecule is the receptor upon which several mutagenic and carcinolytic (possibly also carcinogenic) drugs act. It has also been shown to be the receptor for the antibiotics mitomycin C and actinomycin D.[49, 50] The latter drug blocks transcription of DNA into messenger-RNA by specific binding in the lesser groove of the DNA helix, thereby preventing the normal attachment of RNA polymerase. The recent elucidation of the complete primary sequence of a transfer-RNA molecule[51] further opens the way for understanding actions of drugs upon nucleic acid receptors.

As the foregoing examples suggest, we are evidently at the threshold of an era in which it will be possible to explain the actions of many more drugs at the ultimate level. Not only shall we be able to identify which proteins and nucleic acids are responsible for the biologic effects of a drug, we shall also understand exactly how the formation of a set of specific bonds modifies macromolecular function in such a way as to produce the characteristic drug action.

There remains a special class of receptors which appear to be integral parts of the structure of membranes. These receptors, when acted upon by appropriate agonist drugs (i.e., drugs having a positive action, in contradistinction to antagonists, which block an action) or by transmitter substances that occur normally in the body, trigger (perhaps by an allosteric effect) a sudden change in membrane permeability to ions, which is manifested in the development or alteration of bioelectric potentials. Some think that receptors of this type may be impossible, in principle, to be isolated. If separated from the integrated system of which they are a part, they would lose all function, it is argued, and could not even be identified as receptors any longer. Only future research will tell if such pessimism is warranted.[52-55]

The second way of obtaining information about receptors is indirect. It has dominated pharmacologic research in the past. The approach is to draw inferences about a receptor from the biologic end results

49 I. H. GOLDBERG and E. REICH: Actinomycin inhibition of RNA synthesis directed by DNA. *Fed. Proc. 23:*958 (1964).

50 E. REICH: Actinomycin: correlation of structure and function of its complexes with purines and DNA. *Science 143:*684 (1964).

51 R. W. HOLLEY, J. APGAR, G. A. EVERETT, J. T. MADISON, M. MARQUISEE, S. H. MERRILL, J. R. PENSWICK, and A. ZAMIR: Structure of a ribonucleic acid. *Science 147:*1462 (1965).

52 S. EHRENPREIS: Isolation and identification of the acetylcholine receptor protein of electric tissue. *Biochim. Biophys. Acta 44:*561 (1960).

53 D. NACHMANSOHN: Chemical factors controlling nerve activity. *Science 134:* 1962 (1961).

54 H. B. HIGMAN and E. BARTELS: New method for recording electrical characteristics of the monocellular electroplax. *Biochim. Biophys. Acta 57:*77 (1962).

55 S. EHRENPREIS: Acetylcholine and nerve activity. *Nature 201:*887 (1964).

caused by drugs. A powerful tool employed toward this end has been the study of structure-activity relationships (abbreviated SAR).[56-59] A suitable biologic effect of a drug is chosen for study. A prototype drug, which elicits the characteristic effect, is then modified systematically in its molecular structure. Substituents are added or subtracted at various positions and in different steric configurations. A series of such chemically related drugs is known as a congeneric series. By testing the members of a series and observing how biologic potency is affected by each molecular modification, one may ultimately draw conclusions about the precise mode of combination of a drug with its receptor surface. In the following sections we illustrate, with selected examples, the types of information that can be obtained in SAR studies, and the kinds of inference (and their limitations) that can be drawn about the nature of the drug-receptor interaction and the conformation of the receptor surface.

Drug-Protein Interactions as Models of Drug-Receptor Interactions

The specific reversible binding of small organic molecules to a protein in solution can serve as a useful model of drug-receptor interactions.[60] In both the model and the real receptor in the body a specific set of bonds must be formed between the interacting molecules. The outstanding difference is, of course, that in the case of a receptor "something happens" as a consequence of the interaction, whereas in the model system only the binding itself can be observed. Thus, a wide variety of tissue proteins and nucleic acids may be thought of as "silent receptors." They display the same sorts of specific and nonspecific interactions with drugs as do functional receptors, and they also may bind sufficient drug (often far more than the actual receptors) to modify significantly the quantity available for combination with the primary receptors. As an introduction to SAR studies in which biologic responses are related to drug structure, let us consider some typical investigations in which physical binding of small molecules to a pure protein was measured.

The two principal methods that have been employed are spectrophotometry and equilibrium dialysis (or ultrafiltration). The basis of the spectrophotometric procedure is the fact that the absorption spectrum of an organic compound, which depends upon resonance within the mole-

---

56 N. ROBINSON: Molecular size and shape. *J. Pharm. Pharmacol. 12*:129, 193 (1960).

57 B. M. BLOOM and G. D. LAUBACH: The relationship between chemical structure and pharmacological activity. *Annu. Rev. Pharmacol. 2*:67 (1962).

58 J. M. VAN ROSSUM: The relation between chemical structure and biological activity. *J. Pharm. Pharmacol. 15*:285 (1963).

59 F. N. FASTIER: Modern concepts in relationship between structure and biological activity. *Annu. Rev. Pharmacol. 4*:51 (1964).

60 A. GOLDSTEIN: The interactions of drugs and plasma proteins. *Pharmacol. Rev. 1*:102 (1949).

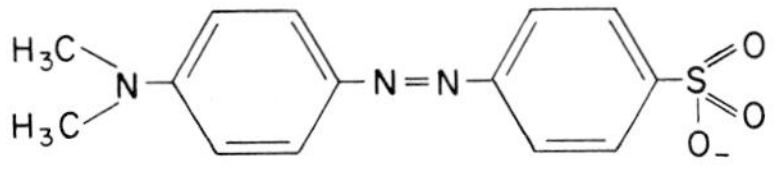

FIG. 1-23.   STRUCTURE OF METHYL ORANGE.

cule, may be altered in characteristic ways when the molecule interacts with another.

Investigations that illustrate the method and its applications were carried out with an anionic azo dye, methyl orange (Fig. 1-23).[61] The compound consists of a diazobenzene nucleus carrying a dimethylamino group and a sulfonate ion. When this dye was mixed with a solution of bovine serum albumin, at pH values from 5.7 to 9.2, a small spectral shift to shorter wavelength was induced (Fig. 1-24, upper line). This shift, similar to that observed in nonaqueous solvents, was attributed to the formation of ionic bonds between the sulfonate group and cationic groups of the protein, a result tantamount to suppressing the ionization of the dye.

With human serum albumin (Fig. 1-24, lower line) similar effects were seen at acid pH, but in the more alkaline solutions a dramatic change occurred. The peak absorbance was greatly enhanced, and the position of

FIG. 1-24.   SPECTRAL SHIFTS INDUCED BY COMBINATION OF METHYL ORANGE WITH BOVINE AND HUMAN PLASMA ALBUMIN.   Solid curves, *dye alone;* broken curves, *dye in the presence of albumin. The four panels represent different pH values, from left to right, as shown at top. (From Klotz et al., Fig. 11.[61] By permission of the American Chemical Society.)*

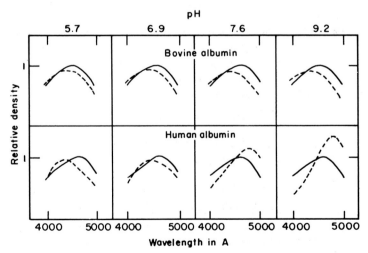

[61] I. M. KLOTZ, R. K. BURKHARD, and J. M. URQUHART: Structural specificities in the interactions of some organic ions with serum albumin. *J. Amer. Chem. Soc.* 74:202 (1952).

the peak was shifted to a longer wavelength. Clearly, an interaction of a qualitatively different kind occurred under these conditions. The new binding proved to be interesting in two ways. First, as already illustrated, it only occurred with human albumin, not with bovine albumin, and moreover only under conditions known to favor a configurational change (perhaps unfolding) of the protein. Second, as will be described shortly, the new binding depended critically upon certain features of molecular architecture in the methyl orange molecule, whereas the interaction with bovine albumin was rather nonspecific.

In equilibrium dialysis the protein and drug solutions are placed on opposite sides of a dialysis bag and the whole assembly is shaken at a constant temperature (commonly near $0°$) until equilibrium is achieved. Since only the small drug molecule is freely diffusible, the difference between the drug concentration in the compartment containing protein (bound drug plus free drug) and that in the compartment containing free drug alone gives the concentration of bound drug. The relationship between the moles of drug bound per mole of protein and the free drug concentration in equilibrium with bound drug is clearly a measure of affinity. The tighter the binding, the more drug will be bound at a given free drug concentration. If the simplifying assumption is made that all groups on a protein that are capable of binding a given drug have the same affinity for that drug, then the law of mass action leads to a straightforward descriptive equation:

$$(R) + (X) \rightleftharpoons (RX)$$

$$\frac{(R)\,(X)}{(RX)} = K$$

where (X) is the concentration of free drug at equilibrium; (R) the concentration of free binding sites; and (RX) the concentration of occupied binding sites. If n is the number of binding sites per protein molecule, and P the molar concentration of protein in the system, then nP, the total concentration of binding sites, is equal to $(RX) + (R)$, and

$$nP(X) - (RX)\,(X) = K(RX)$$

$$[K + (X)]\,(RX) = nP(X).$$

Now let r be moles of drug bound per mole of total protein; then

$$r = (RX)/P = n(X)/[K + (X)].$$

If a series of determinations is carried out, with constant protein and varying drug concentrations, then a plot of r against (X) will have the familiar form of an adsorption isotherm, as shown in Fig. 1-25a. Here, r approaches a saturation value n, the number of binding sites per molecule. If r is plotted against $\log (X)$, a symmetrical sigmoid curve will be obtained, as shown in Fig. 1-25b. This form of plot is easy to interpret at a

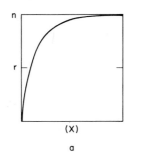 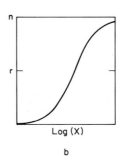

FIG. 1-25.   TWO WAYS OF PLOTTING THE ADSORPTION ISOTHERMS FOR DRUG-PROTEIN INTERACTION.   *In* (a) *and* (b), r *is the moles drug bound per mole protein;* n, *the number of binding sites per molecule protein;* X, *drug concentration.* (*From Goldstein, Figs. 1 and 6.*[60])

glance. The value of n can be estimated from the approach to a maximum value. The position of the curve on the horizontal axis corresponds to the affinity, and the value of log (X) at half-saturation is log K. For the case $n = 1$, this curve is analogous to a plot of fraction ionized against pH, from the Henderson-Hasselbalch equation. For multiple binding sites $(n > 1)$ with different affinities for the drug, the curve could assume a rather complex shape.

The results of equilibrium dialysis with methyl orange and human albumin are shown in Fig. 1-26, upper curve. One mole of dye was bound

FIG. 1-26.   COMPARISON OF AFFINITY OF HUMAN ALBUMIN FOR METHYL ORANGE (**X**) AND BUTYL ORANGE (*Black Circle*). (*From Klotz et al., Fig. 5.*[61] *By permission of the American Chemical Society.*)

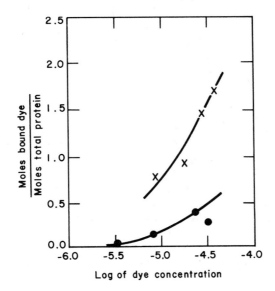

per mole of protein at about $10^{-5}M$ free dye concentration, but the data were not extended sufficiently to permit any estimate of n. The effects of altering the dimethylamine group were studied by obtaining comparable data for modified molecules containing diethyl, dipropyl, and dibutyl instead of dimethyl on the amine nitrogen. There was a progressive loss of binding affinity, illustrated in Fig. 1-26, lower curve, for the dibutyl derivative (butyl orange). This finding was remarkable inasmuch as nonspecific binding to protein surfaces almost invariably increases with increasing length of alkyl substituents, by virtue of the hydrophobic properties of polymethylene chains. Apparently, therefore, the site on albumin that interacted with the amine nitrogen could be regarded as embedded in a cavity that would accommodate only very short alkyl chains.

Altering the nature of the anionic residue produced only small effects; thus, the sulfonate (methyl orange) and carboxylate (methyl red) were bound somewhat more strongly than the phosphonate or arsonate. Changing the position of the anionic group, on the other hand, produced major effects regardless of the nature of the group. This is shown clearly in the spectra reproduced in Fig. 1-27. Both for methyl orange (upper parts) and methyl red (lower parts), although the meta-substituted compounds were bound about as well as the para-substituted ones the interaction no longer occurred when the anionic group was placed ortho to the azo link. To test whether an ortho substituent disrupted the binding by steric interference with an interaction involving the diazo group, a derivative of methyl orange was tested in which methyl groups had been introduced ortho to both azo nitrogen atoms. This compound was bound as

FIG. 1-27.   EFFECTS OF HUMAN ALBUMIN ON THE SPECTRA OF TWO AZO DYES. *Solid curves, dyes alone; broken curves, dyes in the presence of albumin. (From Klotz et al., Fig. 3.[61] By permission of the American Chemical Society.)*

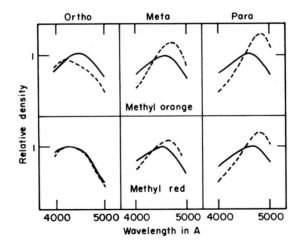

strongly as methyl orange itself. It was inferred, therefore, that the anionic group itself must interact, presumably with a particular cationic side chain of the albumin. The position effects indicated that another point on the dye molecule must also be involved in the interaction, presumably the dimethylamine (as suggested previously by the effects of substitution on this group), and that the distance between the two receptor groups must correspond to that between dimethylamine nitrogen and a meta or para anionic substituent, about 12 A.

Further investigations revealed that iodination of the albumin, which specifically altered 13 of the 18 tyrosine residues in the protein, markedly reduced the extent of the binding (Fig. 1-28). Implication of tyrosine in the binding strongly suggested that hydrogen bonding plays a role, since the phenolic −OH of that amino acid readily donates hydrogen to form a bond with amine nitrogen. The picture that emerged from these experiments was, therefore, of several specific binding sites on the albumin surface, at each of which a tyrosine residue is very nearly 12 A distant from a cationic group (e.g., an ε-amino group of lysine).

FIG. 1-28.   COMPARISON OF AFFINITIES FOR METHYL ORANGE OF HUMAN ALBUMIN AND OF IODINATED HUMAN ALBUMINS.   (*From Klotz et al., Fig. 8.*[61] *By permission of the American Chemical Society.*)

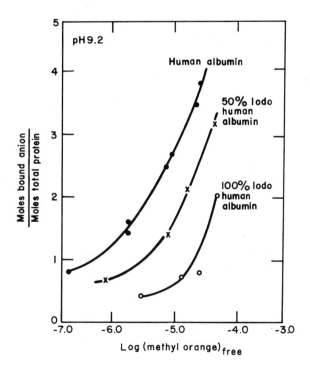

Interesting findings bearing upon specificity emerged from equilibrium dialysis experiments with bovine albumin.[62] With phenylacetate the value of n was found to be 25 moles per mole of protein. With phenoxyacetate n was only 7, but the affinity was 17 times greater. Thus, what seemed a very small modification (introducing an oxygen atom between the ring and the anionic group) abolished the binding to 18 sites previously available, but resulted in much tighter binding to the other seven. Similar effects were observed with nitrophenols, in which only the position of the nitro group was varied. The meta and para compounds reacted with about 22 sites per molecule, but with the ortho compound n was only 6. In this case the ortho substituent actually prevented interaction at the other 16 sites, since 2,4-dinitrophenol (which has both ortho and para substituents) was still only bound at six sites.

Acetylcholine and Congeners

Acetylcholine (AcCh) is a neurotransmitter which is released from cholinergic neurons at many locations in the body. It acts upon receptors in skeletal muscle end-plates, in smooth muscles, in cells of secretory glands, in ganglion cells of the autonomic nervous system, and probably in certain nerve cells of the central nervous system. In addition, AcCh receptors are found in smooth muscles that have no cholinergic innervation, for example, most arteriolar smooth muscles.

A convenient tissue upon which the biologic action of AcCh and its congeners can be assayed is the clam heart.[63] This organ beats spontaneously when it is suspended in a bath of sea water, and the frequency and amplitude of the contractions can be recorded, as illustrated in Fig. 1-29. A drug to be tested is diluted serially in sea water. A small volume of the most dilute solution is added to the bath. If no effect is observed, a larger volume may be added, and then progressively more concentrated solutions are tried until an action is obtained. Between doses the tissue bath is flushed with sea water to remove the drug. The concentration required to produce any given effect may be estimated by interpolating between doses or by more accurate biostatistical procedures.[64] In order to make results obtained with different clam hearts comparable, it is customary to use as criterion the concentration of drug that elicits 50 per cent of the maximal effect obtainable; this is referred to as the ED50 (ED = "effective dose").

The characteristic action of AcCh and related compounds on the clam heart is to reduce the amplitude of contraction, as illustrated in Fig. 1-30. A major advantage of the clam heart is that it does not hydrolyze

---

62 J. D. TERESI and J. M. LUCK: The combination of organic anions with serum albumin. VI. Quantitative studies by equilibrium dialysis. *J. Biol. Chem. 174:*653 (1948).

63 J. H. WELSH and R. TAUB: The action of choline and related compounds on the heart of *Venus Mercenaria. Biol. Bull. 95:*346 (1948).

64 A. GOLDSTEIN: *Biostatistics: An Introductory Text.* New York, Macmillan, 1964.

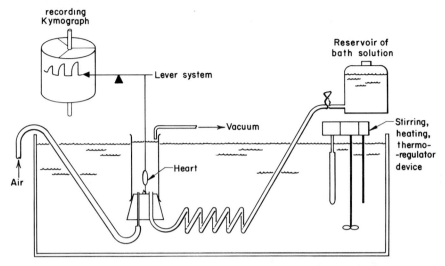

FIG. 1-29.   APPARATUS FOR RECORDING EFFECTS OF DRUGS ON ISOLATED CLAM HEART OR OTHER MUSCLE TISSUE.   *Agonists, antagonists, or extracts containing unknown substances may be added directly to tissue bath and removed by flushing with several volumes of solution from the reservoir. Bath solution is aerated by a constant stream of air or oxygen.*

choline esters rapidly. Consequently, differences in potency within this series of drugs can be detected readily, uncomplicated by differences in rates of degradation.

The chemical formula of AcCh is shown in Table 1-6 (compound 1). The salient features are: (*1*) a quaternary nitrogen atom bearing a positive charge and surrounded by three methyl groups; (*2*) a two-carbon methylene chain; (*3*) an oxygen atom in the main axis of the molecule; (*4*)

FIG. 1-30.   CHARACTERISTIC EFFECT OF ACETYLCHOLINE UPON SPONTANEOUSLY BEATING CLAM HEART.   *Record on kymograph drum is depicted. Contractions cause upward deflection. Addition of AcCh, and removal of AcCh by washing, are shown by* arrows. (*After Welsh and Taub, Fig. 1.*[65])

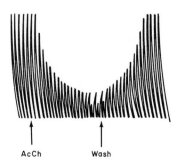

[65.]J. H. WELSH and R. TAUB: Structure-activity relationships of acetylcholine and quaternary ammonium ions. *J. Pharmacol. Exp. Therap.* 99:334 (1950).

TABLE 1-6.   SAR data for AcCh and some congeners

The trimethylammonium group remains unmodified through-out this series. (Data of Welsh and Taub.[65, 66] By permission of Williams & Wilkins.)

Compound	Relative potency (AcCh = 1000)
1. $CH_3-\overset{\overset{\displaystyle CH_3}{\overset{\displaystyle +\mid}{}}}{\underset{\underset{\displaystyle CH_3}{\mid}}{N}}-CH_2-CH_2-O-\overset{\overset{\displaystyle O}{\overset{\displaystyle \parallel}{}}}{C}-CH_3$ (AcCh)	1000
2. $-CH_2-CH_2-CH_2-\overset{\overset{\displaystyle O}{\parallel}}{C}-CH_3$	83
3. $-CH_2-CH_2-O-CH_2-CH_3$	15
4. $-CH_2-CH_2-CH_2-CH_2-CH_3$	14
5. $-CH_2-CH_2-\overset{\overset{\displaystyle O}{\parallel}}{C}-CH_2-CH_3$	6.2
6. $-CH_2-\overset{\overset{\displaystyle O}{\parallel}}{C}-CH_2-CH_2-CH_3$	1.6
7. $-CH_3$	0.05
8. $-CH_2-CH_3$	0.07
9. $-CH_2-CH_2-CH_3$	3.0
10. $-CH_2-CH_2-CH_2-CH_3$	4.3
11. $-CH_2-CH_2-CH_2-CH_2-CH_3$	21.5[a]
12. $-CH_2-CH_2-CH_2-CH_2-CH_2-CH_3$	2.9
13. $-CH_2-CH_2-CH_2-CH_2-CH_2-CH_2-CH_3$	0.05

[a] The difference between this value and that for the identical compound 4 results from the determinations being carried out on different occasions.

66 J. H. WELSH and R. TAUB: The significance of the carbonyl group and ether oxygen in the reaction of acetylcholine with receptor substance. *J. Pharmacol. Exp. Therap.* *103:*62 (1951).

a carbonyl oxygen atom about 7 A from the cationic charge; and (5) a two-carbon acyl residue. The relative importance of some of these features was explored by systematic testing of congeners on the clam heart, with the results shown in Table 1-6.

When the oxygen atom in the ester bond was replaced by a methylene group, so that this portion of the molecule became an aliphatic ketone (compound 2), potency dropped to about 8 per cent. When, on the other hand, the carbonyl oxygen atom alone was eliminated, leaving an ether oxygen atom in the main chain (compound 3), potency was reduced to 1.5 per cent. If, however, the ether oxygen in compound 3 was replaced by carbon (compound 4), there was no further change in potency. Thus, the full biologic effect of AcCh on this system requires the ester structure, but the carbonyl group itself plays a significant role. Compounds 5 and 6 show that the exact position of the carbonyl group, 7 A from the cationic nitrogen atom, is very important.

In another series of molecular modifications the length of the alkyl chain was varied, all oxygen atoms having been eliminated. Compounds 7 to 13 show clearly that a five-carbon chain is optimal. Choline does not differ in potency from compound 8, from which it differs only by an alcoholic $-OH$. Finally, changes in the alkyl groups attached to the nitrogen atom were tried. Starting with AcCh, one methyl group at a time was removed. The results (not shown in Table 1-6) were clear-cut. The analogous dimethylamine, which still retained a positive charge by accepting a proton, was nearly as potent as AcCh itself. The monomethylamine, however, showed a striking loss of potency, although it was still cationic; and the unsubstituted primary amine was practically inert. In the other direction, when one of the AcCh methyl groups was replaced by ethyl, there was little loss of activity. When a second group was changed to ethyl, activity was reduced drastically. When more than two groups were so replaced, an excitatory rather than inhibitory effect on the clam heart was produced. The uncharged carbon analogue of AcCh, dimethyl-

$$CH_3-\overset{\overset{\displaystyle CH_3}{|}}{\underset{\underset{\displaystyle CH_3}{|}}{C}}-CH_2-CH_2-O-\overset{\overset{\displaystyle O}{\|}}{C}-CH_3,$$

butyl acetate, was wholly inert.

These findings, referred to a three-dimensional molecular model of AcCh (Fig. 1-31a), permit one to draw certain conclusions about the nature of the receptor site in the clam heart (Fig. 1-31b). The requirement for a cationic group at one end of the drug molecule indicates the presence of a complementary anionic group on the receptor surface. The steric model reveals that the nitrogen atom, bearing its substituent methyl groups, is free to rotate with relation to the carbon chain. The changes in activity on methyl removal and ethyl substitution on the cationic "head" therefore suggest that the anionic site on the receptor is embedded in a cavity that

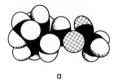

a

Scale model of acetycholine. Oxygen atoms are indicated by cross-hatching. (From Waser, Fig. 2.[67])

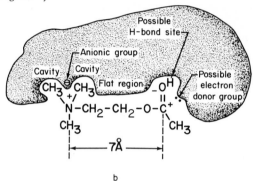

b

Hypothetical complex of acetylcholine with its receptor. Partial ionic character of the carbonyl group is shown by symbols for positive and negative charges.

FIG. 1-31. ACETYCHOLINE AND ITS POSTULATED INTERACTION WITH A RECEPTOR.

will just accommodate two methyl groups. Since one of the three symmetrically disposed methyls must necessarily point away from the receptor surface, and since free rotation makes all three methyls equivalent, removing one or changing it to ethyl has little effect. We assume that the two essential methyl groups help to stabilize the AcCh-receptor complex through van der Waals forces, and that any larger substituent, not fitting properly into the cavity, seriously distorts the goodness of fit of the rest of the molecule to its complementary site. It is likely that the carbon atoms of the main chain lie in close approximation to a flat portion of the receptor surface, contributing further van der Waals attractions to the overall binding. The carbonyl oxygen atom might well participate in hydrogen bond formation with an appropriate receptor group (e.g., the −NH of a peptide bond), thus further stabilizing the interaction. Although wholly inferential, such a picture offers a consistent and reasonable explanation of the SAR data.[68]

The Polymethylene Bis-Methonium Series

Good examples of acetylcholine antagonist drugs are the polymethylene bis-methonium compounds, which block certain classes of

    [67] P. G. WASER: Chemistry and pharmacology of muscarine, muscarone, and some related compounds. *Pharmacol. Rev. 13:*465 (1961).
    [68] P. G. WASER: The cholinergic receptor. *J. Pharm. Pharmacol. 12:*577 (1960).

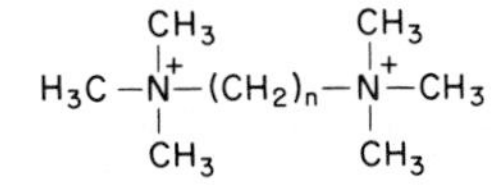

$$H_3C - \underset{\underset{\overset{|}{CH_3}}{|}}{\overset{\overset{CH_3}{|}}{N^+}} - (CH_2)_n - \underset{\underset{\overset{|}{CH_3}}{|}}{\overset{\overset{CH_3}{|}}{N^+}} - CH_3$$

FIG. 1-32. GENERAL FORMULA OF THE POLYMETHYLENE BIS-METHONIUM COMPOUNDS.

AcCh receptors. The prototype structure is shown in Fig. 1-32. These molecules are perfectly symmetrical, containing two cationic groups separated by a simple aliphatic chain. The only molecular variable to be considered here is *n,* the number of carbon atoms in the polymethylene chain or, in other words, the distance between the two positively charged nitrogen atoms.

Two distinct biologic effects of importance are produced by compounds in this series: *ganglionic blockade* and *neuromuscular blockade.* We shall examine SAR data for both kinds of action in a single species, the cat.[69, 70] The assay system for ganglionic blockade employs the nictitating membrane, or "second eyelid." This structure is composed largely of smooth muscle, innervated by postganglionic sympathetic nerve fibers originating in the superior cervical ganglion (Fig. 1-33). The ganglion cells whose axons carry impulses out to the nictitating membrane receive impulses from preganglionic sympathetic nerve fibers, which emerge in the ventral roots of

FIG. 1-33. INNERVATION OF THE NICTITATING MEMBRANE (*a*) AND OF SKELETAL MUSCLE (*b*).

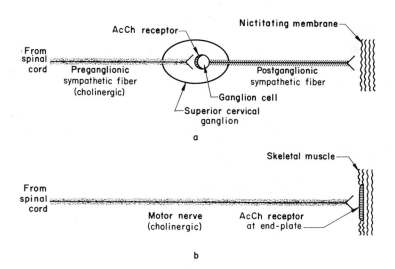

69 W. D. M. PATON and E. J. ZAIMIS: The pharmacological actions of polymethylene bis-trimethylammonium salts. *Brit. J. Pharmacol.* 4:381 (1949).
70 W. D. M. PATON and E. J. ZAIMIS: The methonium compounds. *Pharmacol. Rev.* 4:219 (1952).

the spinal cord. These preganglionic fibers are cholinergic (i.e., they liberate AcCh) and the ganglion cells upon which they impinge are called "cholino-ceptive" (i.e., they contain AcCh receptors). In the assay system the nictitating membrane is attached to a lever or strain gauge for recording its contractions. A continuous train of electrical stimuli to the preganglionic fibers results in a corresponding train of impulses along the postganglionic fibers, and the nictitating membrane responds with a sustained contraction. If, during stimulation, synaptic transmission from the preganglionic termi-nals to the ganglion cells is blocked, then no impulses will arrive at the nictitating membrane, which will therefore relax. If this happens, a simple way to confirm that the blockade is at the ganglion rather than at a more peripheral site is to stimulate the postganglionic fiber electrically and elicit a normal response of the nictitating membrane. In the assay a drug to be tested is injected intravenously at appropriate dosage to produce a certain degree of blockade (Fig. 1-34). The relative potencies of various drugs may then be expressed in terms of the ratios of the respective doses that produce the same degree of blockade.

The assay system for skeletal neuromuscular blockade employs any convenient muscle (e.g., tibialis anterior) and the appropriate motor nerve (e.g., sciatic). Motor nerves are cholinergic and skeletal muscle contains specialized cholinoceptive structures (end-plates) where the nerve fibers terminate. In the assay the motor nerve is stimulated at regular intervals by single shocks large enough to elicit maximal contractions from the muscle. These muscle contractions are recorded. A drug-induced blockade of transmission between nerve ending and muscle end-plate manifests itself as a decline in amplitude and ultimate disappearance of the muscle twitches (Fig. 1-35). During such neuromuscular blockade direct electrical stimu-lation of the muscle fibers will confirm that their intrinsic capacity for contraction is unimpaired (arrow 2 in Fig. 1-35). The procedure for de-termining relative drug potencies is like that described for the cat nictitating membrane preparation.

FIG. 1-34. TYPICAL EFFECTS OF GANGLIONIC BLOCKING AGENTS ON THE NICTI-TATING MEMBRANE OF THE CAT. *Sustained contraction of nictitating membrane excited by stimulation of cervical sympathetic; hexamethonium* (C6) *and penta-methonium* (C5) *given intravenously at* arrows. (*From Paton and Zaimis, Fig. 10.*[69] *By permission of the* British Medical Journal.)

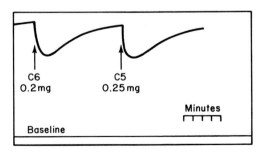

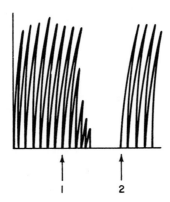

FIG. 1-35. TYPICAL EFFECT OF A NEUROMUSCULAR BLOCKING AGENT ON CAT NERVE-MUSCLE PREPARATION IN SITU. *Tension recording from tibialis muscle stimulated by nerve shock every 10 seconds; at* arrow 1, *decamethonium (0.1 mg.) injected intravenously; at* arrow 2, *muscle was stimulated directly. (From Paton and Zaimis, Fig. 2.*[69] *By permission of the* British Medical Journal.)

Eight different compounds were tested in both assay systems, with the results shown in Fig. 1-36. Two distinct optima were found, one at $n = 5$ to 6 for ganglionic blockade, another at $n = 10$ for neuromuscular blockade. It is apparent, therefore, that even though the ganglionic and muscle end-plate receptors both are stimulated by local release of acetylcholine from nerve endings, these receptors cannot be identical. One way

FIG. 1-36. SAR DATA FOR GANGLIONIC AND NEUROMUSCULAR BLOCK BY POLY-METHYLENE BIS-METHONIUM COMPOUNDS. n *is number of* $-CH_2-$ *groups between cationic groups; relative potency has logarithmic scale. (From Paton and Zaimis, Fig. 17.*[69] *By permission of the* British Medical Journal.)

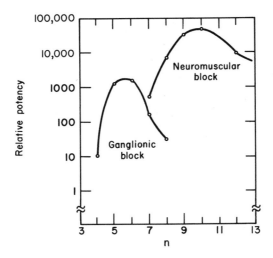

to interpret the data is shown in Fig. 1-37. We assume there is in both receptors (as we did in the case of the clam heart) a configuration complementary to that of acetylcholine. That the presence of a second cationic group confers blocking potency leads us to deduce the presence of a second anionic site on the receptor surface, lying outside the acetylcholine-combining region. Both anionic sites are presumed to be embedded in cavities capable of accommodating two methyl groups (the third methyl group is then oriented away from the surface). The essential difference between the ganglionic and muscle end-plate receptors is presumed to be in the distance between these anionic sites. As Fig. 1-37 demonstrates, the ganglionic site would interact strongly with pentamethonium, the C5 compound shown at (b), or with hexamethonium (C6, not shown); these drugs would then act as ganglionic blockers by preventing the receptor from responding to acetylcholine (a). The C10 compound, decamethonium (c), is too long to fit the ganglionic receptor but would act as a neuromuscular blocker by preventing the combination of acetylcholine (e) with muscle end-plate receptor. Finally, succinylcholine (d), a neuromuscular blocking agent of practical importance is shown; it is obviously well endowed for specific interaction with the muscle end-plate receptor.[71]

Figure 1-38 presents evidence for similarities and differences among receptors in the same tissue of various species.[69] The doses required to produce the same degree of neuromuscular blockade in cat, rabbit, mouse, and rat are shown as a function of the length of the polymethylene chain. Here, the lower the dose, the more potent the compound. (To accommodate a very wide range of potencies, the doses are shown on a logarithmic scale.) The muscle end-plate receptors of all four species appear to contain anionic sites at the same separation (n = 10), but the binding affinities vary greatly. It has also been shown that various skeletal muscles of a single animal may have different affinities for the same neuromuscular blocking agent.[72] These observations are understandable if the receptors are proteins, since so many cases of species and tissue differences in enzymes and other proteins are already known. Isozymes, for example, are demonstrably different forms of enzyme protein, which may be present in varying ratios in different tissues, but which have the same catalytic function. We can speculate on the possibility that genetically determined abnormalities of receptor structure could result in defective function (as in myasthenia gravis) or in unusual sensitivity to a drug.[73, 74]

71 D. GROB: Neuromuscular pharmacology. *Annu. Rev. Pharmacol. 1:*239 (1961).

72 D. B. TAYLOR, R. D. PRIOR, and J. A. BEVAN: The relative sensitivities of diaphragm and other muscles of the guinea pig to neuromuscular blocking agents. *J. Pharmacol. Exp. Therap. 143:*187 (1964).

73 D. GROB and R. J. JOHNS: "Further Studies on the Mechanism of the Defect in Neuromuscular Transmission in Myasthenia Gravis, With Particular Reference to the Acetylcholine-Insensitive Block," in *Myasthenia Gravis,* Proceedings 2nd International Symposium, ed. by Viets, H. R. Springfield, Ill., Charles C Thomas, 1961.

74 G. H. GLASER: Pharmacological considerations in the treatment of myasthenia gravis. *Advance. Pharmacol. 2:*113 (1963).

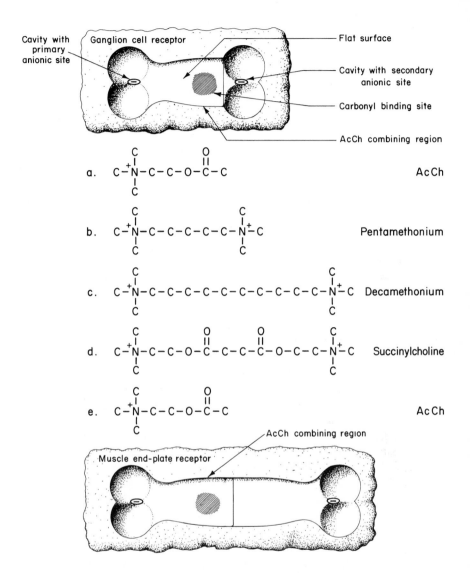

FIG. 1-37. HYPOTHETICAL ACETYLCHOLINE RECEPTORS. *Schematic visualizations of receptors in ganglion cell* (above) *and in muscle end-plate* (below), *deduced from SAR data. The structures of AcCh and several blocking agents are shown, with their various chemical groupings aligned to the receptor regions with which they are assumed to interact. A similar AcCh-combining region is shown on both receptors. Pentamethonium shows greatest selectivity for the ganglion cell receptor, decamethonium and succinylcholine for the end-plate receptor.*

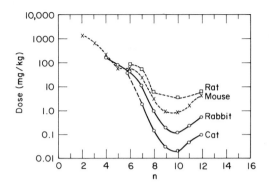

FIG. 1-38.   SAR DATA FOR NEUROMUSCULAR BLOCKADE BY POLYMETHYLENE
BIS-METHONIUM COMPOUNDS IN SEVERAL SPECIES.   *Doses plotted (logarithmic
scale) are those which reduce control amplitude by one-half in each case.* (n
has the same meaning as in Fig. 1-36). (*From Paton and Zaimis, Fig. 7.*[69] *By
permission of the* British Medical Journal.)

The Morphinelike Analgesics

We have seen how systematic variation in the structure of a drug
molecule leads to alterations in potency for some specified biologic effect,
and how certain inferences can be drawn about the nature of the receptor
surface with which the drug must interact. Thus far we have considered
only symmetric molecules or those in which free rotation about bonds
would permit functional groups to assume various positions in space. We
now turn our attention to stereoisomers, the study of whose biologic effects
has led to what is known as *conformation analysis*. Here, inferences are
drawn about the three-dimensional structure of the receptor surface.

In the case of geometric isomers (e.g., *cis-trans* configurations) it
is obvious why one of a pair should show preferential biologic activity. In
Fig. 1-39, for example, if functional groups A and B both have to interact
with complementary groups on the receptor, only the *cis* isomer will have
biologic activity. In the case of optical isomers, all interatomic distances
are identical in the two enantiomorphs, which are mirror images of each
other, but a receptor surface can nevertheless distinguish the two forms.
As is the case in many stereospecific enzyme reactions, it is only necessary
to suppose that the drug-receptor interaction involves at least three of the
groups (or three regions) attached to the asymmetric carbon atom, as illustrated in Fig. 1-40. If the complementary interacting regions C′, D′, and
B′ were arranged as shown on the left, the optical isomer depicted on the
right could not interact properly.

SAR studies with a series of narcotic analgesic compounds provide
a wealth of material for deducing properties of the receptor that mediates

a

Cis isomer

b

Trans isomer

FIG. 1-39. GEOMETRIC ISOMERISM. *The rectangle represents a receptor surface. (From Beckett, Fig. 2.[75])*

their pain-relieving properties.[75-77] The methods are quite simple. Constant heating is applied to a rat's tail, so that in about 10 seconds a tail "flick" is observed. After injection of an analgesic agent into the rat, the tail flick is delayed and may even be abolished. The extent of delay is dose related, so the potencies of various compounds may be compared. For example, the relative doses of different drugs may be found that prolong the tail-flick time to the same extent. It is known that narcotic analgesics act upon pain pathways in the central nervous system and that all the congeners investigated enter the brain and spinal cord readily. However, we have no idea how the analgesic effect is brought about, nor, in particular, what bio-

FIG. 1-40. A PAIR OF OPTICAL ENANTIOMORPHS, SHOWING THE DIFFERENT PATTERNS OF PROJECTION OF THREE FUNCTIONAL GROUPS ONTO A RECEPTOR SURFACE. *(From Beckett, Fig. 1.[75])*

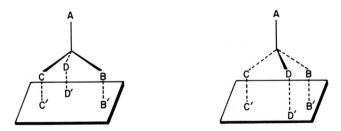

[75] A. H. BECKETT: Stereochemical factors in biological activity. *Fortschr. Arzneimittelforsch. 1:*455 (1959).

[76] A. H. BECKETT and A. F. CASY: Synthetic analgesics: stereochemical considerations. *J. Pharm. Pharmacol. 6:*986 (1954).

[77] R. B. BARLOW: "Steric Aspects of Drug Action," in *Steric Aspects of the Chemistry and Biochemistry of Natural Products* (Biochemical Society Symposia #19), ed. by Grant, J. K. and Klyne, W. Cambridge, Cambridge University Press, 1960, p. 46.

chemical events might be implicated. It must be remembered, therefore, that the receptor, whose structural features are inferred from the SAR studies to be described, is entirely hypothetical.

Figure 1-41a depicts the morphine molecule in its usual flat representation. This compound was long regarded as a substituted phenanthrene derivative, as indeed it is; but eventually it was realized that although the phenanthrene nucleus could be modified or even eliminated without loss of analgesic activity, the piperidine ring was essential. The nitrogen atom of this ring is about 80 per cent cationic at physiologic pH ($pK_a' = 7.9$), so it is supposed that one important element of the drug-receptor interaction may be an ionic bond to an anionic site on the receptor surface. The narcotic (morphine-like) analgesics are best thought of as N-methylpiperidine compounds with bulky ring substituents.

The two enantiomorphs of morphine are shown in Figs. 1-41b and c. There is a center of optical asymmetry at carbon atom 13 in the morphine molecule, and only one of the optical enantiomorphs, D($-$)-morphine, has analgesic activity.[78] It is inferred from the spatial representations that the receptor surface must accommodate the protruding $-CH_2-CH_2-$ between carbon atom 13 and the nitrogen atom in such a way that the nitrogen atom (bearing a proton) may form the necessary ionic bond. This leads to the conclusion that a groove of some kind serves this purpose, thereby allowing a large part of the planar aromatic and adjacent rings to come into flat contact with the receptor surface, probably stabilized there by van der Waals forces. The phenolic $-OH$ at carbon atom 3 and the alcoholic $-OH$ at carbon atom 6 are dispensable, as is also the $-O-$ bridge; a synthetic congener, levorphanol (Fig. 1-41d), lacks the last two of these groups but retains analgesic potency. Figure 1-42 depicts some likely features of the receptor that would account for the SAR data. It is obvious, for example, that the L($+$) isomers of morphine and its congeners would not fit; and, indeed, these are devoid of analgesic properties.

A synthetic analgesic, meperidine, provides an interesting test of the proposed receptor surface. Figure 1-43a shows the ordinary flat representation of this compound, which seems to have little in common with the morphine structure. However, when the spatial configuration is shown correctly (Fig. 1-43c), the D($-$) isomer fits all the surface features of the proposed receptor. Here again, the L($+$) optical enantiomorph is found to be inactive biologically.

Finally, we examine another synthetic analgesic, methadone (Fig. 1-43b). Here it is even more astonishing that the compound should behave like morphine, because it seems to be merely an aliphatic chain bearing two benzene rings and a terminal dimethylamine group. Yet molecular models reveal not only that it is possible to arrange the atoms so that they simulate the morphine configuration, but that steric factors

---

[78] L and D relate configuration to that of L-glyceraldehyde or D-glyceraldehyde; ($-$) and ($+$) signify optical levo- and dextrorotation, respectively.

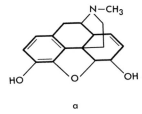

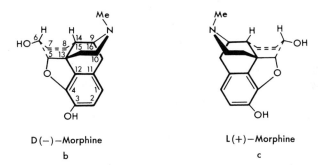

FIG. 1-41. MORPHINE AND LEVORPHANOL. *The planar structure of morphine is shown at* (a); *the phenanthrene nucleus is in the plane of the paper, the piperidine ring is in a plane almost perpendicular to it. The two enantiomorphs of morphine are shown at* (b) *and* (c). *The surface of* D(−)-*morphine that would combine with the receptor is shown facing the reader. The configuration of* D(−)-*levorphanol, a synthetic morphinelike compound, is shown at* (d). Me *denotes methyl group.* (From Beckett, Fig. 17.[75])

Receptor surface

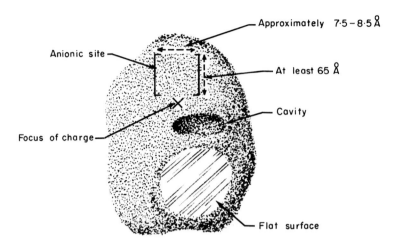

FIG. 1-42.   HYPOTHETICAL   RECEPTOR   SURFACE   FOR   NARCOTIC   ANALGESICS.
(*From Beckett, Fig. 17.*[75])

force such a configuration upon the compound. Thus, as depicted in Fig.
1-43d, a pseudopiperidine ring is formed, which protrudes outward from
the plane of the aromatic rings. Indeed, the benzene rings themselves are
not free to rotate about carbon atom 4 of the aliphatic chain (as might
have been thought on the basis of the flat structural representation), but
are restricted to a conformation like that of the corresponding rings in the
phenanthrene nucleus of morphine (cf. Fig. 1-41). Again, of the two
optical isomers, only D($-$)-methadone, which fits the postulated receptor,
is analgesic.

　　Certain minor modifications of the D($-$)-methadone molecule
emphasize further the principle of "goodness of fit" in drug-receptor interactions. If the $-CH_3$ attached to the carbon atom adjacent to the nitrogen
atom is removed, analgesic potency decreases but the compound is still an
effective analgesic. If, instead, a second $-CH_3$ is attached to the same
carbon atom, analgesic potency is abolished. Evidently, the groove on the
receptor surface will accept $-CH_2-CH-$ as well as (or somewhat better

$$\underset{\displaystyle CH_3}{|}$$

than) $-CH_2CH_2-$, as would be expected from the fact that the additional
methyl group is free to orient outward from the groove. The difficulty with

$$\overset{\displaystyle CH_3}{\underset{\displaystyle CH_3}{|}}$$

the structure $-CH_2-CH-$ is presumably that the groove cannot accom-

$$\underset{\displaystyle CH_3}{|}$$

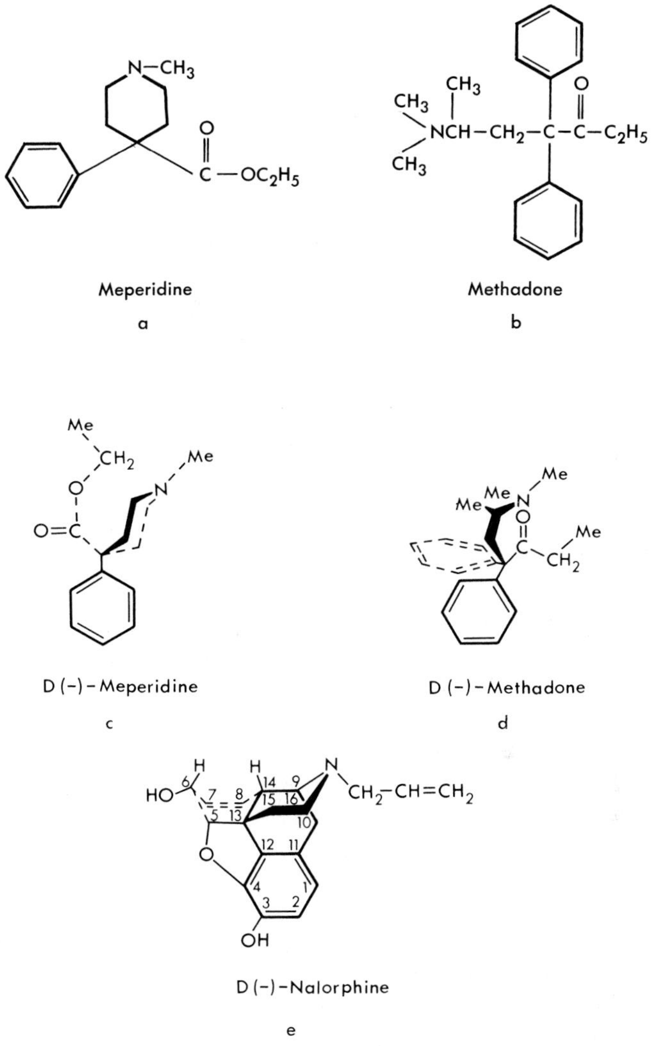

Meperidine

a

Methadone

b

D (-)-Meperidine

c

D (-)-Methadone

d

D (-)-Nalorphine

e

FIG. 1-43. MEPERIDINE, METHADONE, AND NALORPHINE. *The usual representation of the structure of meperidine is at* upper left, *the actual conformation
of* D(−)-*meperidine is shown just* below. *The methadone structure, as usually
drawn, is at* upper right, *the actual conformation of* D(−)-*methadone is shown
just* below. *The conformation of* D(−)-*nalorphine is at* bottom; *the full structure of the allyl group, which replaces the N-methyl group of morphine, is
shown.* Me *denotes methyl group.* (*From Beckett[75] and Beckett and Casy.[76]*)

modate the additional width at all, or that one methyl group will necessarily project downward; in either case the entire molecule will be prevented from achieving the necessary perfect fit to the receptor surface.

Finally, one very minor change in the morphine molecule produces a compound that is a specific antagonist of analgesia (and other central effects) produced by any of the narcotic analgesics. This compound is nalorphine (Fig. 1-43e), in which N-allyl has been substituted for N-methyl. Only the D(−) isomer is effective as an antagonist; it is inferred that nalorphine acts by combination with the same receptor, apparently displacing morphine or its congeners.

Congeners of the Adrenal Glucocorticoid Hormones

Another illustration of conformational specificity is found in the steroid hormones of the adrenal cortex, known as glucocorticoids. The prototype structure, that of cortisol (hydrocortisone), an important adrenal hormone in man, is shown in Fig. 1-44. In contrast to the morphinelike analgesics, here the active molecules contain no ionizing groups; therefore their interactions with the receptors must depend wholly upon conformational fit, with electron correlation (van der Waals) attractions probably playing the major role in stabilizing the hydrophobic binding.

At physiologic levels in the body these compounds promote the conversion of amino acids to carbohydrate—the glucocorticoid effect. When administered at high dosage they also suppress inflammatory reactions in tissues. The anti-inflammatory effect is not well understood, but it seems to parallel the glucocorticoid action in a large series of compounds of widely differing potencies. The effects upon salt retention (the so-called mineralocorticoid action) are quite independent; although cortisol itself has moderate activity of this kind, other steroids vary widely in the ratio of glucocorticoid to mineralocorticoid activity.

FIG. 1-44.   CORTISOL (HYDROCORTISONE, 17-HYDROXYCORTICOSTERONE). *As drawn here, the α surface is away from the reader, α-substituents are indicated by* dotted lines; *the β surface faces the reader, β-substituents are shown by* solid lines.

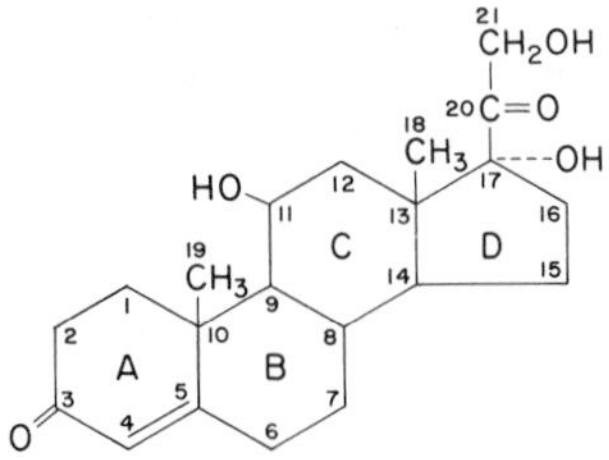

We shall now consider SAR data for glucocorticoid effects only, for a limited set of compounds closely related to cortisol.[79] For investigating the influence of structural modifications the liver glycogen deposition test is employed. An alcoholic solution of the steroid to be tested is injected into fasting mice. Some time later (usually 7 to 12 hours) liver glycogen determinations are performed. Criterion of effect is the increase of liver glycogen content per gram of body weight. Although tests differ in detail, a reference compound is usually employed so that relative potencies may be estimated. Thus, in the following discussion the potency of congeners is always related to that of cortisol.

In order to appreciate the implications of some of the data one must recall that the steroid nucleus is a fairly planar structure (Fig. 1-44). There is a lower edge, defined by carbon atoms 3–8, 14, and 15, and an upper edge, defined by carbon atoms 2, 1, 10, 9, 11–13, and 17. In addition, there is an α surface, away from the reader (i.e., on the back side of the page), and a β surface, facing the reader. As usual, α-substituents are shown by a broken line, β-substituents by a solid line. The substituent groups in cortisol are a ketonic oxygen at C-3, β-methyl groups at C-18 and C-19, a β-hydroxyl at C-11, and a β-glycollyl side chain as well as an α-hydroxyl at C-17. Besides, the bond between C-4 and C-5 is unsaturated. The question is, which of these features of the molecular structure are essential to the glucocorticoid effect, and what may be deduced about the surface of the receptor that mediates this effect.

As for the structural features already present in cortisol, the SAR findings may be summarized as follows. At C-11, activity was abolished if the β-hydroxyl was removed or blocked by acetylation or shifted to the α configuration, or even if an α-methyl was introduced without deleting the β-hydroxyl. Also, the β-hydroxyl could be oxidized to ketonic oxygen without loss of activity; but this is not conclusive because body enzymes reduce it to hydroxyl again. Thus, 11-β-hydroxyl is essential to activity and is evidently an important point of interaction with the receptor surface.

Specific quantitative data about the β-methyl at C-18 are lacking, but β-methyl at C-19 could not be removed without loss of activity. The β configuration of the side chain at C-17 was found to confer much greater potency than the α configuration. As to the side chain itself, reduction of C-20 to an alcohol led to drastic loss of potency. At C-21, oxidation to an aldehyde had no effect; but as was true of oxidation at C-11, the conclusion is uncertain because the aldehyde was probably converted back to an alcohol in the body. Replacement of the alcoholic hydroxyl at C-21 by halogens, in the order of increasing atomic radius, led to interesting results. With fluorine the potency was enhanced fivefold, but the larger chlorine or bromine abolished activity. Thus, unlike the situation at C-11, the hydroxyl

79 I. E. BUSH: Chemical and biological factors in the activity of adrenocortical steroids. *Pharmacol. Rev. 14*:317 (1962).

at C-21 as such is not essential, but excessive bulk is not tolerated. The adverse effect of bulk at C-21 was confirmed by esterifying the hydroxyl with glycine; the resulting compound was inert.

Little specific information is available about the α-hydroxyl at C-17, except that when it was replaced by an acetonide bridge between C-16 and C-17, activity was enhanced some fivefold, indicating that the alcoholic hydroxyl as such is not required.

The double bond between C-4 and C-5 was found to be absolutely essential; hydrogenation here abolished activity. Moreover, a second double bond, between C-1 and C-2, enhanced activity fivefold. On the other hand, when ring A contained three double bonds, all biologic activity disappeared. Interpretation is ambiguous, however, since making the ring aromatic alters the planar structure and at the same time changes $\diagdown \text{C}=\text{O}$ at C-3 to $\diagup$

$\diagdown\!\!\diagup \text{C}-\text{OH}.$

Now we turn our attention to substituents that can be added to the cortisol molecule. At C-2 we find a situation much like that at C-21; a small addition (α-methyl) enhanced activity almost tenfold, whereas a more bulky group (α-ethyl) abolished it. At C-9 a complete series of α-halogen additions have been studied; fluorine enhanced activity some tenfold, chlorine enhanced to a lesser degree, while the bulkier bromine and iodine diminished potency. Likewise, $-\text{OH}$ and $-\text{OCH}_3$ practically abolished activity. Addition of fluorine at C-12 in the α configuration increased activity tenfold, much as did the same substitution at C-9. It seems, therefore, that the α surface in this region of the molecule plays a rather critical role in attaining a good fit to the receptor.

Substitutions at C-16 produced no dramatic effects. An α-methyl group enhanced potency fourfold, whereas a β-methyl reduced potency by about one-half. An α-hydroxyl here, unlike α-methyl, reduced potency somewhat. Quantitative data on the addition of substituent groups along the lower edge of the molecule are not available, except that methyl at C-4 abolishes activity.

It should be recognized how difficult a task it has been, from the chemical point of view, to synthesize and prove the structures of so many steroid congeners. Yet a really thorough systematic survey, which could reveal the relative importance of every structural feature of the molecule, would require a far larger number of compounds. Two important limitations should also be noted. First, as long as assays are carried out in a whole animal, it is always possible that the effect of a molecular alteration is primarily to modify the metabolism or elimination of a drug, or its access to a site of action. Consequently, any inferences about a receptor surface must be tentative. Second, a substituent may act primarily to change the electron density at an adjacent atom, so the finding that alterations at a given location influence biologic activity does not necessarily implicate that location in the interaction with receptor.

Despite the qualified nature of the evidence, it seems possible, nevertheless, to draw some limited conclusions from the SAR data cited here. Substituents of the cortisol molecule that are essential to its gluco-corticoid activity are arrayed along the upper edge (Fig. 1-44) in the β configuration, and the hydroxyl group at C-11 seems to play a key role in the drug-receptor interaction. As a first approximation, then, we might imagine that the β surface of the molecule has to lie flat against a comple-mentary receptor surface. If this were the case, however, the α surface would face away from the receptor, and α-substituents should be without effect. The fact is, as we have seen, that α-substituents may either enhance activity greatly or abolish it altogether. We are forced to the conclusion, therefore, that the receptor must be something like a pocket into which the cortisol molecule can fit. Presumably, the upper edge of the steroid is ori-ented toward the bottom of the pocket, where interacting groups and recesses are spatially arranged to accommodate the essential substituents. The α and β surfaces of the hormone would each be in contact with one side of the pocket, so that substituents of both kinds would influence (for better or worse) the fit of the whole molecule to the receptor.[80]

Congeners of the Pituitary Polypeptide Hormones

The polypeptide hormones oxytocin and vasopressin afford a further illustrative example of how critically biologic action may depend upon precise configuration of a drug molecule.[81] Both hormones, products of the posterior pituitary gland, consist of nine amino acid residues of the usual L-configuration (Fig. 1-45). A disulfide bridge between the cysteine residues at positions 1 and 6 creates a hexapeptide ring, and residues 7,

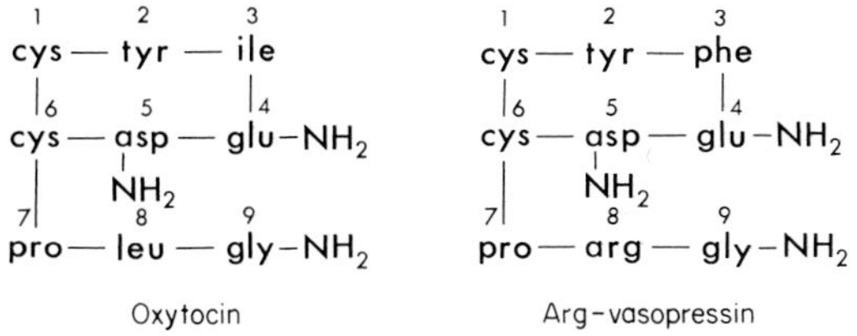

FIG. 1-45. TWO POLYPEPTIDE HORMONES OF THE POSTERIOR PITUITARY. *Asp--NH₂ and glu-NH₂ represent asparagine* (asn) *and glutamine* (gln), *respec-tively; gly-NH₂ is glycine amide.*

[80] Recent findings with other planar compounds suggest the possibility that steroids may interact with DNA by fitting into pockets formed by adjacent base pair layers (intercalation): L. S. LERMAN: The structure of the DNA-acridine complex. *Proc. Nat. Acad. Sci. U.S.A. 49*:94 (1963).

[81] R. A. BOISSONNAS, ST. GUTTMANN, B. BERDE, and H. KONZETT: Relationships between the chemical structures and the biological properties of the posterior pituitary hor-mones and their synthetic analogues. *Experientia 17*:377 (1961).

8, and 9 form a "tail," as shown. Oxytocin and vasopressin differ in two ways. In oxytocin residue 3 in the ring is isoleucine, whereas in vasopressin it is phenylalanine. Residue 8, in the tail, is leucine in oxytocin and arginine in most mammalian vasopressins (lysine in the pig and hippopotamus).

Oxytocin characteristically causes contraction of uterine smooth muscle, an important function of the hormone at parturition. The primary action of vasopressin is antidiuretic; it acts on cells of the renal tubules, in a way not fully understood, to cause increased water reabsorption from the tubular lumen. Another action of vasopressin, from which its name is derived, is to cause contraction of arteriolar smooth muscle and thereby increase blood pressure in experimental animals (but not in man). These typical effects can be assayed quite easily. To assay oxytocic activity, for example, one horn of a rat uterus may be suspended in a tissue bath of appropriate aerated medium, and attached to a lever or strain gauge so that the magnitude of uterine contractions can be measured. Dilutions of a test compound and of oxytocin may then be compared by ascertaining the concentrations of each that are required in the tissue bath to cause equal and moderate contraction of the muscle (e.g., 50 per cent of maximal). Vasopressin-like activity may be assayed by the blood pressure increase in the rat or cat after intravenous injection, or by the antidiuretic effect in the rat. When oxytocin was compared with arginine-vasopressin in two such assay systems, the results shown on the first and third lines of Table 1-7 were obtained. Oxytocin had a strongly selective effect upon uterine smooth muscle. Arginine-vasopressin, conversely, showed high potency on rat blood pressure but relatively little effect on the uterus.

Since oxytocin and vasopressin differ with respect to two amino acids, one in the ring and one in the tail, the question arises what relative role is played by each. Here nature has performed a crucial experiment for us. In the lower vertebrates a hormone is found, arginine-oxytocin (vasotocin), in which the oxytocin ring has arginine instead of leucine at

TABLE 1-7.   Comparison of polypeptide hormones and congeners in two assay systems

Figures represent relative potency in international units per mg. (Data of Boissonnas et al.[81])

	Oxytocin-like activity on rat uterus	Vasopressin-like activity on rat blood pressure
Oxytocin	450	5
Arg-oxytocin (vasotocin)[a]	75	125
Arg-vasopressin	20	400
Leu-vasopressin (oxypressin)[b]	20	3

[a] *Arg* replaces *Leu* in position 8 of tail, oxytocin ring intact.
[b] *Leu* replaces *Arg* in position 8 of tail, vasopressin ring intact.

position 8 in the tail. Table 1-7 shows that this single substitution in the tail somewhat reduces the oxytocic potency, but the main effect is a dramatic enhancement of vasopressin-like activity. The converse experiment has been performed by means of a synthetic analogue containing the vasopressin ring but leucine instead of arginine in the tail. Table 1-7 shows that this compound, leucine-vasopressin (oxypressin), is as ineffective an oxytocic agent as vasopressin itself, but the vasopressin-like activity has been almost abolished. Thus, the bioassay data for both modified hormones lead to the same generalization. Oxytocin-like activity is reduced if the tail is modified, and even more so if the ring is modified. Vasopressin-like activity, on the other hand, cannot survive the substitution of a neutral leucine for a basic amino acid (arginine or lysine) in the tail, but is not greatly reduced by substitution at position 3 in the ring.

The most thorough and systematic investigations have been carried out on the oxytocin series. Any shortening of the tripeptide tail causes a drastic reduction in both kinds of biologic activity, even if a terminal amide is retained. Within the ring nearly any substitution of one amino acid for another leads to considerable loss of potency, even when the substitution is a reciprocal one (e.g., an interchange of tyrosine and phenylalanine in positions 2 and 3 of the vasopressin ring) so that the amino acid composition remains exactly the same. The importance of the phenolic hydroxyl of tyrosine in position 2 is also indicated by the effect of O-methylation of this residue; oxytocic and vasopressin-like activities both disappear and some antagonism to vasopressin is manifested. Other instances of antagonism to one or the other hormone effect have been noted as results of small substitutions in the ring or the tail peptides.

It is instructive to note how seemingly trivial an alteration may have major effects. In oxytocin, the substitution of leucine for isoleucine at ring position 3 entails no more than shifting a side-chain methyl group to an adjacent carbon atom, yet the oxytocic potency falls to 1/10, and the pressor potency decreases even more. When valine is substituted at this position, the loss of oxytocic activity is not so great, but there is a disproportionate decrease of pressor potency. This kind of unequal influence of a substituent upon two different biologic effects may have great practical value, despite the fact that both potencies are diminished. A larger dose will still elicit the desired oxytocic action, but at that effective dosage the undesirable pressor side effects will be reduced. From a practical point of view, therefore, valine-oxytocin represents a more selectively oxytocic drug than the natural hormone. In the same way, in the vasopressin series, greater selectivity of antidiuretic action relative to pressor side effects may be obtained through appropriate molecular modifications.

The hexapeptide ring of oxytocin contain 20 members. Removal of the $-NH_2$ group from the cysteine residue at position 1 yielded a crystalline compound, deamino-oxytocin (Fig. 1-46), which was about as potent

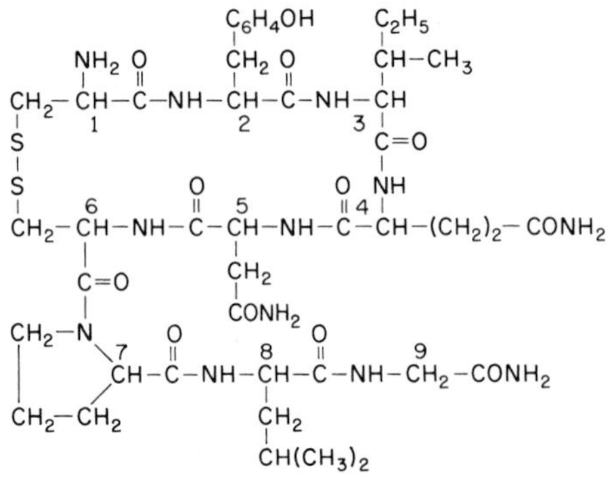

$$
\begin{array}{c}
\qquad\qquad\quad C_6H_4OH \qquad C_2H_5 \\
\qquad NH_2\ O \qquad CH_2\ O \qquad CH{-}CH_3 \\
CH_2{-}CH{-}C{-}NH{-}CH{-}C{-}NH{-}CH \\
\ \ |\qquad\quad 1\qquad\qquad 2\qquad\qquad 3\ |\ \\
\ \ S\qquad\qquad\qquad\qquad\qquad\qquad C{=}O \\
\ \ |\qquad\qquad\qquad\qquad\qquad\qquad\quad | \\
\ \ S\qquad\qquad\qquad O\qquad\qquad O\ \ NH \\
\ \ |\qquad\quad 6\qquad\quad \|\ \ 5\qquad\ \|\ 4\ | \\
CH_2{-}CH{-}NH{-}C{-}CH{-}NH{-}C{-}CH{-}(CH_2)_2{-}CONH_2 \\
\qquad\qquad |\qquad\qquad\quad | \\
\qquad\qquad C{=}O\qquad\qquad CH_2 \\
\qquad\qquad |\qquad\qquad\quad | \\
\qquad\ CH_2{-}N\qquad\qquad CONH_2 \\
\qquad\quad |\qquad\ \ \backslash 7\quad O\qquad\ \ 8\quad O \\
\qquad\quad |\qquad\qquad CH{-}C{-}NH{-}CH{-}C{-}NH{-}CH_2{-}CONH_2 \\
\qquad\ CH_2{-}CH_2\qquad\qquad |\qquad\qquad\qquad 9 \\
\qquad\qquad\qquad\qquad\qquad CH_2 \\
\qquad\qquad\qquad\qquad\qquad CH(CH_3)_2
\end{array}
$$

FIG. 1-46.   DEAMINO-OXYTOCIN.   *(From Jarvis and du Vigneaud, Fig. 1.*[82] *By permission of the American Association for the Advancement of Science.)*

as oxytocin itself.[82] An analogue, containing an additional $-CH_2-$ at position 1 (i.e., a 21-membered ring) was practically inactive, and the corresponding compound with a $-CH_2-$ removed at position 1 (i.e., a 19-membered ring) was less than 1/20 as potent as deamino-oxytocin. These observations make it plain that the 20-membered ring is necessary for biologic activity in this series, an intriguing finding in view of the presence of a 20-membered ring in the apparently unrelated pancreatic hormone insulin. Finally, a $-CH_2-$ was removed from position 1 and added at position 6, yielding a 20-membered ring that differed from deamino-oxytocin in only one detail: the $-S-S-$ group was shifted about 1.5 A away from the tail. The oxytocic potency of this compound was as low as though it contained a 19-membered ring. Thus, the position of the $-S-S-$ group relative to the rest of the molecule is critical.

    In summary, SAR studies with these posterior pituitary hormones permit some crude deductions to be drawn about the nature of the complementary receptor surfaces with which the hormones must interact. The cyclic polypeptide structure with its 20-membered ring is essential. This provides a fairly rigid framework from which the amino acid side chains and the tripeptide tail project (Fig. 1-47). Because of the identical L-configuration of the nine amino acids, all the side chains can form a complex "molded" contour on the same surface, which can then match the complementary surface of the correct receptor. Evidently, receptor surfaces in uterine muscle, arteriolar muscle, and renal tubule epithelium have in common certain features such as a shape and area suited to accommodate a ring-and-tail structure of this size, and also a critically situated site for attachment to, or reaction with, the disulfide bridge. In addition, each kind of receptor must have differentiating features that specify optimal distances between essential functional groups on the interacting hormone. Antago-

    [82] D. JARVIS and V. DU VIGNEAUD: Crystalline deamino-oxytocin. *Science 143:*545 (1964).

FIG. 1-47.   MOLECULAR MODELS SHOWING POSSIBLE CONFORMATIONS OF OXY-
TOCIN.   Top, *An extended form.* Bottom, *A possible compact configuration.*
The two S *atoms are clearly indicated. Black atoms are* C; *dark grey,* O; *light*
grey, N; *white,* H. *The group marked* a *is the tyrosine hydroxyl at position 2;*
b *marks the methyl group attached to the β-carbon of isoleucine at position 3,*
whose critical role is discussed in the text; c *marks the β-methylene group of*
leucine at position 8 in the "tail." (Compare with Fig. 1-45.)

nistic effects of structural analogues are probably best interpreted as resulting from reasonably good fit, without those key interactions between
functional groups on the hormone and on the receptor surface that must
"trigger" the characteristic biologic response.

Cycloserine and the Inhibition of Bacterial Cell Wall Synthesis

Interference with cell wall synthesis is a common mode of action of
antibacterial drugs. Penicillin acts in this way and causes the accumulation of complexes containing UDP and oligopeptide fragments linked to

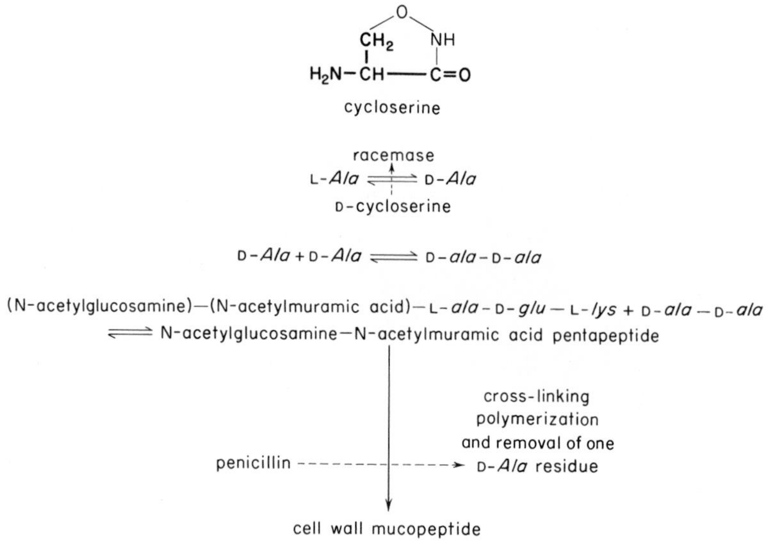

$$
\begin{array}{c}
\text{O} \\
\diagup \quad \diagdown \\
\overset{|}{\text{CH}_2} \qquad \text{NH} \\
| \qquad\qquad | \\
\text{H}_2\text{N}-\text{CH}\!-\!\!-\!\!-\text{C}=\text{O}
\end{array}
$$

cycloserine

$$
\begin{array}{c}
\text{racemase} \\
\text{L-}Ala \rightleftharpoons \text{D-}Ala \\
\text{D-cycloserine}
\end{array}
$$

$$\text{D-}Ala + \text{D-}Ala \rightleftharpoons \text{D-}ala\text{-D-}ala$$

(N-acetylglucosamine)—(N-acetylmuramic acid)—L-*ala*-D-*glu*—L-*lys* + D-*ala*—D-*ala*
$$\rightleftharpoons \text{N-acetylglucosamine—N-acetylmuramic acid pentapeptide}$$

```
                                     |
                                     |        cross-linking
                                     |        polymerization
                                     |        and removal of one
            penicillin - - - - - - - - - - - ->   D-Ala residue
                                     |
                                     ↓
                          cell wall mucopeptide
```

FIG. 1-48.   CYCLOSERINE AND ITS INHIBITION OF BACTERIAL ALANINE RACEMASE. *The structure of cycloserine is shown at* top; *atoms shown in* bold type *are analogous to those in* ala. *The alanine racemase reaction, which is inhibited by cycloserine, is shown. The subsequent steps in the biosynthetic chain, whereby* D-ala *is utilized for bacterial cell wall synthesis, are also presented.* (Broken arrows *indicate inhibitory effects.*) (*From Wise and Park,*[89] *and Roze and Strominger.*[90])

acetylglucosamine, which can be identified with known constituents of the bacterial cell wall. Evidently, penicillin blocks a cross-linking polymerization reaction that yields the completed cell wall mucopolypeptide (Fig. 1-48).[83] Several other drugs interfere at other stages in this biosynthetic pathway. One of these, cycloserine, provides us with a remarkable illustration of steric specificity in drug action.

Cycloserine (Fig. 1-48) is the amide of serine, closed on itself by dehydrogenation to form a five-membered ring. It obviously resembles not only serine, but also the very similar amino acid alanine. Cycloserine inhibits the enzyme alanine racemase, which catalyzes the transformation of L-alanine to D-alanine. D-Alanine, in turn, is an essential constituent of the cell wall peptide. In the presence of cycloserine, therefore, D-alanine is depleted, the partial peptide (lacking its terminal D-*ala*—D-*ala* fragment) accumulates, new cell wall synthesis cannot proceed, and cell death results.

In this antibacterial action only D-cycloserine is effective, not its enantiomorph. Studies with purified alanine racemase[84] showed that K_i (the

83 E. M. WISE, JR. and J. T. PARK: Penicillin: its basic site of action as an inhibitor of a peptide cross-linking reaction in cell wall mucopeptide synthesis. *Proc. Nat. Acad. Sci. U.S.A. 54:*75 (1965).

enzyme-inhibitor dissociation constant) for D-cycloserine was about $5 \times 10^{-5}M$, whereas L-cycloserine was wholly without effect even at concentrations greater than $1 \times 10^{-2}M$. This difference seems surprising. A racemase obviously has to interact with both stereoisomers of its substrate; thus with alanine racemase, the values for the enzyme-substrate dissociation constants were approximately $5 \times 10^{-3}M$ for both L-alanine and D-alanine. How, then, can an enzyme that fails to distinguish between the L- and D-forms of its amino acid substrate nevertheless make such a sharp distinction between the L- and D-forms of a structural analogue inhibitor? The answer is that the open-chain structure of an amino acid permits free rotation about several bonds and consequently there is a high degree of flexibility in the conformation as a whole. Although D-alanine and L-alanine obviously could not occupy identical three-dimensional spaces, they can both look remarkably similar on one surface (e.g., the surface that has to interact with an enzyme). The rigid internal ring of cycloserine abolishes, in large

FIG. 1-49. STERIC CONFIGURATIONS OF ALANINE AND CYCLOSERINE. Bottom row, *alanine;* top row, *cycloserine. The alanine structure is viewed with its —COOH grouping at front right, —NH₂ at left. In* L*-alanine* (left) *the methyl group projects upward; in* D*-alanine* (right) *it projects downward to rear and is hidden. The a-carbon atom is seen between the carbonyl O and amino N, and its H atom projects upward. The corresponding cycloserine structures are viewed at the same angle.* D*-cycloserine* (right) *assumes the same configuration as* L*- and* D*-alanine; the ring is in the viewing plane, and the ring O atom is hidden in the rear. The rigid ring structure prevents* L*-cycloserine* (left) *from assuming a similar configuration. With the carbonyl O and the ring in the same plane, the amino group is forced upward into a different plane, as shown. (After Roze and Stromininger.[84])*

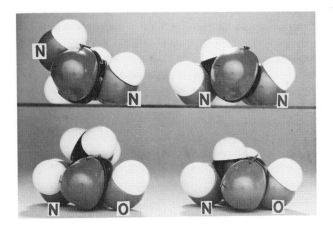

[84] U. ROZE and J. L. STROMINGER: Alanine racemase from *Staphylococcus aureus:* conformation of its substrates and its inhibitor D-cycloserine. *Mol. Pharmacol.* 2:92 (1966).

measure, this conformational flexibility, so that the two stereoisomers cannot be forced onto the same surface.

Three-dimensional models are almost a necessity for visualizing this kind of restriction in shape. Figure 1-49 shows all four compounds. We know that D-cycloserine is the active form; so we start with the assumption that it fits the enzyme surface well. As a matter of fact, the dissociation constants given above indicate that the enzyme surface offers a substantially better fit to D-cycloserine than to either of the substrates, inasmuch as the affinity was about 100 times greater. Let D-cycloserine be placed (as in the figure at upper right) on a plane surface with its free amino group, carbonyl group, and ring −NH− from left to right. Then, as shown in the bottom row of the figure, both D-alanine and L-alanine can assume the corresponding configuration, with carboxyl −OH in the place of the homologous ring −NH− of cycloserine. L-Cycloserine (upper left) cannot be forced into the same configuration. When two of the three groups are in the plane, the third one projects upward, as shown by the free amino group in the figure. The specificity of the enzyme-inhibitory action of D-cycloserine is thus apparently accounted for. Of course, an alanine racemase can be imagined, which would have a different surface configuration, so that L-cycloserine would be the effective inhibitor. Both forms of alanine would still be able to "fit," but D-cycloserine would not. No such enzyme has yet been found.

Antibacterial Sulfonamides

In the series of antibacterial sulfonamides biologic potency is modified by substituents which do not themselves seem to partake in the combination with receptor, but rather influence the ionic character of another group on the molecule. Figure 1-50 shows the structure of *p*-aminobenzoic acid (PAB), an essential growth factor or biosynthetic intermediate in many bacteria. This compound is normally condensed enzymically with a glutamylpteridine compound to form folic acid, the precursor of a coenzyme essential in the biosynthetic utilization of single-carbon units. Figure 1-50 also shows the nonionized and ionized forms of a prototype sulfonamide. In view of the close structural similarity of the sulfonamides to PAB, it is not surprising that these compounds also can combine with the condensing enzyme, thereby competitively inhibiting the normal entry of PAB into folic acid. The ultimate consequence is a folic acid deficiency manifested as a reversible inhibition of bacterial growth.

The simplest member of the sulfonamide series is sulfanilamide, in which both hydrogen atoms on the amide nitrogen are unsubstituted. The other sulfonamides carry substituents; a few out of the hundreds that have been synthesized and tested are shown in Table 1-8. Just as a free *p*-amino group is essential for substrate activity in PAB, so in a sulfonamide drug a free *p*-amino group is essential for antibacterial action. In contrast, there

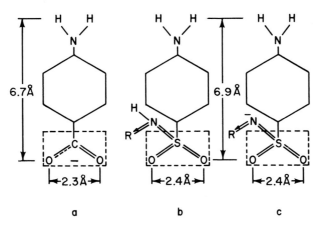

FIG. 1-50. *p*-AMINOBENZOATE (PAB) AND SULFONAMIDE STRUCTURES. a, *PAB ionized form; b, sulfonamide, nonionized form; c, sulfonamide, ionized form. All three rings are aromatic. Although negative charge resulting from loss of proton is shown associated with sulfonamide N atom, strict localization of the charge is not implied. (From Bell and Roblin, Fig. 2.*[85] *By permission of the American Chemical Society.)*

are almost no limitations to the possible substituents on the amide nitrogen compatible with antibacterial efficacy. It may be deduced that whereas the *p*-amino group combines with the enzyme surface, the amide nitrogen with its substituent probably does not.

What then is the role of substituents? A plausible explanation is suggested by the relationship between the $-SO_2-$ group in the sulfonamides and the $-CO_2^-$ group of PAB. The latter is completely ionized at neutral pH, and there is independent evidence that a negative charge here promotes combination with the enzyme. Thus it may be inferred that sulfonamides should become more potent with increasing electron density in the $-SO_2-$ region, and this property should be influenced by electron-attracting substituents on the amide nitrogen. Any tendency to draw electrons away from the N$-$H bond will be reflected in an increased ease of proton dissociation which can be measured by the pK_a' value of each compound. That various R substituents are capable of altering pK_a profoundly is seen in Table 1-8. Sulfanilamide itself is a very weak acid, i.e., its proton its tightly bound; but electrophilic substituents in the other compounds increase the acid strength to varying degrees.

In order to explore the relationship between pK_a and antibacterial potency, a great many sulfonamides were tested.[85] Cultures of *Escherichia*

[85] P. H. BELL and R. O. ROBLIN, JR.: Studies in chemotherapy. VII. A theory of the relation of structure to activity of sulfanilamide type compounds. *J. Amer. Chem. Soc. 64:* 2905 (1942).

TABLE 1-8.   Some sulfonamides with different acid strengths

(Data of Bell and Roblin.[85] By permission of American Chemical Society.)

Compound	R (cf. Fig. 1—50)	pK'_a
Sulfanilamide	—H	10.43
Sulfapyridine	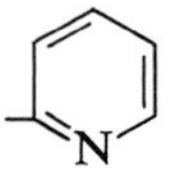	8.43
Sulfathiazole	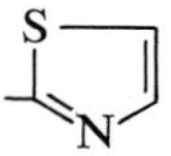	7.12
Sulfadiazine	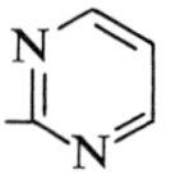	6.48
Sulfacetamide	$\overset{\text{O}}{\overset{\|}{\text{—C—CH}_3}}$	5.38

coli were maintained in buffered medium at pH 7. By means of a dilution series the minimum molar concentration of each sulfonamide required to inhibit growth was estimated, and the pK_a was also determined for each compound. The observations are presented in Fig. 1-51. Here, for greater clarity, the graph shows reciprocals of bacteriostatic concentrations as indices of potency (since lower effective concentration means greater potency), and in order to span several orders of magnitude in potency a logarithmic scale is used. Beginning at the extreme right with the weakest acids, and moving toward the left, antibacterial potency is seen to increase as acid strength increases. Since the tests were performed at pH 7, this portion of the curve shows that an increasing degree of ionization favors antibacterial activity. Thus, under the experimental conditions, a compound with a pK'_a of 11 would be practically nonionized, whereas one with a pK'_a of 6 would be 91 per cent ionized.

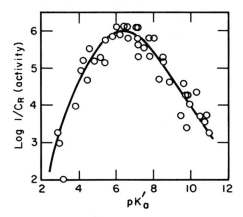

FIG. 1-51. RELATIONSHIP OF ANTIBACTERIAL POTENCY TO ACID STRENGTH IN THE SULFONAMIDE SERIES. *The logarithm of the reciprocal of the bacteriostatic concentration is the measure of potency. Each point represents a different sulfonamide. One discrepant point has been eliminated for justifiable reasons. All the testing was done at pH 7. (From Bell and Roblin, Fig. 1.*[85] *By permission of the American Chemical Society.)*

The findings, thus far, are consistent with the conclusion that the anionic form of a sulfonamide is the active form. One would predict, however, that all compounds with $pK'_a < 6$ should be maximally active, since all these would be nearly completely ionized at pH 7. Some special explanation is therefore required to account for the decreasing potency of the more acidic sulfonamides. One such explanation focuses more closely upon the charge distribution in the sulfone group itself. As the substituent R is made more electrophilic, so that the amide proton dissociates (as described above), the sulfone group shares in the electronegative character of the resulting anionic amide. Beyond a certain point, however, when complete ionization has already been attained, a still more strongly electrophilic substituent will begin to draw electrons away from the sulfone group. The altered charge distribution, with diminished electron density in the $-SO_2-$ region, will cause a diminution in antibacterial potency.[86]

[86] For interesting recent attempts to rationalize SAR observations in terms of measurable molecular parameters, see C. HANSCH and T. FUJITA: $\rho\text{-}\sigma\text{-}\pi$ Analysis. A method for the correlation of biological activity and chemical structure. *J. Amer. Chem. Soc.* 86: 1616 (1964). C. HANSCH, A. R. STEWARD, and J. IWASA: The correlation of localization rates of benzeneboronic acids in brain and tumor tissue with substituent constants. *Mol. Pharmacol.* 1:87 (1965). The use of Hammett functions in biologic systems is also described in O. R. HANSEN: Hammett series with biological activity. *Acta Chem. Scand.* 16:1593 (1962). An interesting application of molecular orbital theory to SAR data may be found in W. B. NEELEY: The use of molecular orbital calculations as an aid to correlate the structure and activity of cholinesterase inhibitors. *Mol. Pharmacol.* 1:137 (1965).

CONSEQUENCES OF DRUG-RECEPTOR INTERACTIONS: ANALYSIS OF THE GRADED DOSE-RESPONSE RELATIONSHIP

Application of the Law of Mass Action

Biologic responses to drugs are, as a rule, *graded*. They can be measured on a continuous scale, and there is a systematic relationship between the dose (or effective concentration) of a drug and the magnitude (or intensity) of the response it elicits. Application of the law of mass action to the dose-response relationship was largely the contribution of A. J. Clark (1885–1941).[87, 88] An observed biologic effect was assumed to be a reflection of the combination of drug molecules with receptors, much as the rate of appearance of products in an enzyme reaction reflects the degree of combination of substrate molecules with enzyme-active centers. The magnitude of a response was postulated to be directly proportional to the occupancy of receptors by drug molecules, with a maximal response corresponding to occupancy of all the receptors. Then equations could be derived from simple mass law principles, describing the dependence of effect upon dose.

Let a drug, X, combine with a receptor site, R, to yield a complex, *RX*, producing a biologic response of magnitude Δ proportional to the amount (or concentration) of *RX*, so that

$$R + X \underset{k_2}{\overset{k_1}{\rightleftharpoons}} RX$$

$$\Delta = k_3 \, (RX).$$

Then at equilibrium,

$$\frac{(R) \, (X)}{(RX)} = \frac{k_2}{k_1} = K_X,$$

where K_X is the dissociation constant of the complex. Then if (R_T) is the total receptor concentration, and since $(R_T) = (R) + (RX)$,

$$\frac{(R_T - RX) \, (X)}{(RX)} = K_X$$

and, rearranged,

$$\frac{(RX)}{(R_T)} = \frac{(X)}{K_X + (X)} .$$

[87] A. J. CLARK: The Mode of Action of Drugs on Cells. London, E. Arnold Co., 1933.

[88] A. J. CLARK: "General Pharmacology," in *Handbuch der Experimentellen Pharmakologie,* vol. IV, ed. by Heffter, A. Berlin, Springer, 1937.

Now let Δ_{max} be the maximal response of which the system is capable, obtained when all receptors are occupied; so

$$\Delta_{max} = k_3 \, (R_T).$$

Then,

$$\frac{\Delta}{\Delta_{max}} = \frac{(RX)}{(R_T)}$$

and therefore

$$\Delta = \frac{\Delta_{max} \, (X)}{K_X + (X)}. \tag{1}$$

This is the familiar hyperbolic function in which $\Delta = 0$ when $(X) = 0$, and Δ approaches Δ_{max} when (X) becomes very large. When half-maximal response is obtained,

$$\frac{\Delta}{\Delta_{max}} = \frac{(X)}{K_X + (X)} = \frac{1}{2},$$

so the concentration of (X) required for half-maximal response is equal to K_X.

   The derivation of equation (1) is identical to that of the classical Michaelis-Menten equation, which gives the velocity v of an enzyme reaction as a function of the substrate concentration (S), the enzyme-substrate dissociation constant K_m, and the maximum velocity V_{max}:

$$v = \frac{V_{max} \, (S)}{K_m + (S)}.$$

Here the proportionality $v = k_3 \, (ES)$ refers to the breakdown of a steady-state intermediate, whereas the analogous proportionality $\Delta = k_3 \, (RX)$ is assumed without reference to any particular underlying mechanism. The equations developed here are quite generally applicable; they subsume enzyme-substrate and enzyme-inhibitor interactions as special cases.

   Three critical assumptions, which underlie the derivation or usual application of equation (1), may be formulated explicitly, as follows:

   1. *Response is proportional to receptor occupancy.* This will be referred to as the "occupancy assumption." In the case of enzyme-substrate and enzyme-inhibitor interactions, since the observed response is determined directly by the concentration of enzyme-bound substrate or inhibitor, the assumption is soundly based. With respect to drug effects in general, however, we are as yet unable to accept or reject the assumption on experimental or theoretical grounds. In a later section we shall discuss alternatives to the "occupancy assumption."

   2. *One drug molecule combines with one receptor site.* This is the simplest reaction mechanism, from which equation (1) (and also the

Michaelis-Menten treatment) is derived. We shall consider later some molecular combining ratios other than unity.

3. *A negligible fraction of total drug is combined,* so that in equation (1) the term (X), which refers to uncombined drug, may be replaced by (X_T), the total drug concentration. A system in which this assumption is true is said to operate in zone A.[89] In experiments where binding is actually measured, as in equilibrium dialysis, uncombined drug is determined and equation (1) (equivalent to the equations on p. 139) can be used rigorously. However, when a biologic response is the criterion of effect, only *total* drug added to the system is known. It is then usual to assume zone A behavior, as we shall do in the following section (and as is customary in mathematical treatments of enzyme reactions based on the Michaelis-Menten approach). Later, however, we shall examine the consequences when a system does not operate in zone A.

The Double-Reciprocal Plot

If equation (1) is inverted, the equation of a straight line is obtained:

$$\frac{1}{\Delta} = \frac{K_X}{\Delta_{max}} \cdot \frac{1}{(X)} + \frac{1}{\Delta_{max}} \tag{2}$$

with slope K_X/Δ_{max} and intercept $1/\Delta_{max}$ when reciprocal response magnitudes $1/\Delta$ are plotted against reciprocal doses $1/(X)$—actually $1/(X_T)$, as explained above in connection with the *zone A* assumption.

This procedure is known as a double-reciprocal (or Lineweaver-Burk) plot (Fig. 1-52).[90] Increasing drug concentrations are to the left, so the y-axis is at $1/(X) = 0$, corresponding to infinite drug concentration, where all receptors are occupied. The y-intercept gives $1/\Delta_{max}$. Since the slope, given by Equation (2), is K_X/Δ_{max}, K_X could be obtained by estimating the slope; but an easier way is simply to extend the line downward and to the left, as shown. The x-intercept will then be $-1/K_X$. The reason is evident from the geometry of Fig. 1-52. If the y-intercept is doubled and a horizontal is drawn from this point to intersect the experimental line, then a perpendicular cuts the x-axis at $1/K_X$, since $(X) = K_X$ at $\Delta_{max}/2$; whence the x-intercept of the experimental line must be at an equal distance to the left of the origin.

The double-reciprocal plot has been applied widely to the analysis of antagonisms and particularly to enzyme inhibitions.[91] An antagonist Z is said to be *noncompetitive* if it inactivates the receptor so that the effective

89 O. H. STRAUS and A. GOLDSTEIN: Zone behavior of enzymes. *J. Gen. Physiol.* 26:559 (1943).

90 J. L. WEBB: Enzyme and Metabolic Inhibitors, vol. I. New York, Academic Press, 1963.

91 This method of plotting data may introduce serious distortions, as discussed thoroughly in J. E. DOWD and D. S. RIGGS: A comparison of estimates of Michaelis-Menten kinetic constants from various linear transformations. *J. Biol. Chem.* 240:863 (1965).

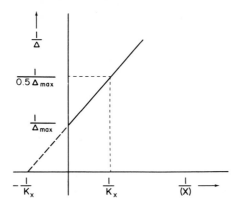

FIG. 1-52. THE DOUBLE-RECIPROCAL PLOT. *Symbols are defined in text. Intercept on y-axis gives reciprocal of Δ_{max}; that on x-axis gives negative reciprocal of K_X.*

complex with agonist X cannot be formed, regardless of the concentration of X. Z might combine with R at the same site where X ordinarily combines, but so firmly that it cannot be displaced. Alternatively, Z could combine at a different site, in such a manner as to prevent a configurational change in R that is essential to its proper combination with X, or that is requisite to producing the characteristic biologic response. Yet again, Z might itself induce a configurational change in R that abolishes the reactivity of the site where X should interact. In noncompetitive antagonism the effects upon receptors may be reversible or irreversible; the essential point is that the agonist has no influence upon the degree of antagonism or its reversibility.

If the dose-response range is first explored with an agonist alone and then in the presence of a fixed dose (or concentration) of a noncompetitive antagonist, the system will behave as though the total number of available receptor sites had been reduced. Nevertheless, whatever receptors remain should display unchanged affinity for X. In the double-reciprocal plot (Fig. 1-53a), since Δ_{max} is reduced proportionately to the decrease in free receptors, the y-intercept will increase. On the other hand, the x-intercept ($-1/K_X$) will remain unchanged.

An antagonist is said to be *competitive* if it combines reversibly with the same receptor sites as the agonist. In the most straightforward mechanism, Z occupies the same sites as X, but without triggering those special events that cause the biologic response. In the case of enzyme inhibition this may simply mean that the Z molecule, although it combines with enzyme, is incapable of undergoing catalytic transformation, or that it is acted upon very slowly compared with the normal substrate. In the case of a receptor that normally undergoes a change in shape by virtue of combination with X, the Z molecule may occupy the site without producing the essential configurational change. The effect of the competition, in any

FIG. 1-53. ANALYSIS OF ANTAGONISMS BY DOUBLE-RECIPROCAL PLOTS.

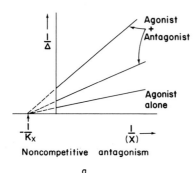

Noncompetitive antagonism

a

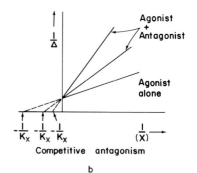

Competitive antagonism

b

Noncompetitive antagonism. The lower line *represents data obtained with agonist alone, the* upper lines *are data for agonist in the presence of two different concentrations of antagonist.* Δ_{max} *is changed by each antagonist concentration, but* K_X *remains apparently the same.*

Competitive antagonism. Δ_{max} *is unchanged in the presence of antagonist, but each antagonist concentration yields an apparently different value of* K_X.

case, is a reduction of the apparent affinity of X for R in the presence of Z, as predicted by the law of mass action. In competitive antagonism Δ_{max} is not altered, since a high enough ratio of X to Z should force complete occupancy of receptors by X despite the presence of Z. In the double-reciprocal plot, therefore (Fig. 1-53b), the y-intercept remains unchanged, but the affinity ($-1/K_X$, x-intercept) is reduced. It should be realized that any molecular mechanism that leads to this experimental result will be interpreted as competitive antagonism. For example, if the combination of Z with R induced a conformational change that altered the binding energy of RX, the antagonism would be classified as competitive, even if Z and X combined with R independently at different sites.

Abbreviated derivations follow for equations that apply to double-reciprocal plots of noncompetitive and competitive antagonisms.[90]

For reversible noncompetitive antagonism, where antagonist Z forms a complex RZ with dissociation constant K_Z,

$$\frac{(R)\ (Z)}{(RZ)} = K_Z.$$

Following the same steps as in the derivation of equation (1), and then substituting, gives

$$\frac{1}{\Delta'} = \left(1 + \frac{Z}{K_Z}\right)\left(\frac{K_X}{\Delta_{max}}\right)\left(\frac{1}{X}\right) + \left(1 + \frac{Z}{K_Z}\right)\left(\frac{1}{\Delta_{max}}\right)$$

where Δ' is the response magnitude in the presence of a fixed concentration (Z) of antagonist. Thus both the slope and the y-intercept of equation (2) are increased by the same factor $\left(1 + \dfrac{Z}{K_Z}\right)$, and since (Z) is known, K_Z can be found.

For competitive antagonism, uncombined receptors (R) must be in simultaneous equilibrium with (RX) and (RZ). Solution of the simultaneous equations yields

$$\frac{1}{\Delta'} = \left(1 + \frac{Z}{K_Z}\right)\left(\frac{K_X}{\Delta_{\max}}\right)\left(\frac{1}{X}\right) + \frac{1}{\Delta_{\max}} \cdot$$

Compared with equation (2), the y-intercept is unchanged, but the slope is increased by the factor $\left(1 + \dfrac{Z}{K_Z}\right)$. In effect, the apparent dissociation constant K_X is increased by this same factor, so that the x-intercept now yields a new apparent value $-1/K_X$, which is the original $-1/K_X$ times the factor $\left(\dfrac{K_Z}{K_Z + Z}\right)$. Again here, as with noncompetitive antagonism, since (Z) is known, K_Z can be found.

FIG. 1-54. DOUBLE-RECIPROCAL PLOT FOR ANALYSIS OF ENZYME INHIBITION. *Effect of chlorpromazine on N-demethylation of ethylmorphine by a microsomal system. Chlorpromazine concentrations are shown on the* two upper curves; *the* lower curve was obtained in the absence of chlorpromazine; V *is reaction velocity,* (S) *is substrate concentration. The parameters computed from the intercepts (x-intercept not actually shown) are given at* lower right. (*From Rubin et al., Fig. 2.*[92])

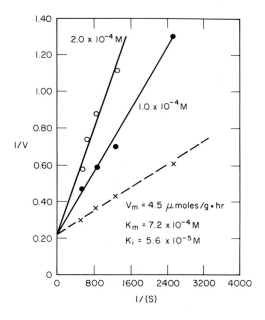

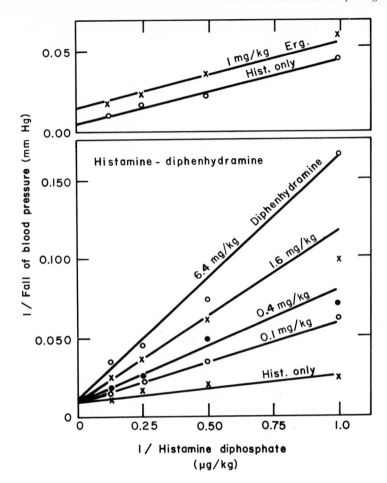

FIG. 1-55. DOUBLE-RECIPROCAL PLOT FOR ANALYSIS OF BIOLOGIC RESPONSE. *Blood pressure fall caused by histamine in the dog was measured. In* upper section, *antagonism by ergotamine was studied; in* lower section, *antagonism by an antihistaminic drug, diphenhydramine, at several concentrations (doses per kg). (From Chen and Russell, Fig. 4.[94])*

A good example of the use of a double-reciprocal plot to establish the mechanism of an inhibitory effect is shown in Fig. 1-54. The N-demethylation of a morphine analogue by a microsomal drug-metaboliz-ing system was studied.[92] The rate of formation of formaldehyde, the ultimate product of the reaction, was measured at various substrate concen-trations. The results shown as a broken line were obtained, whence the intercept and slope yielded $V_{max} = 4.5$ μmoles per gram per hour and

[92] A. RUBIN, T. R. TEPHLY, and G. J. MANNERING: Kinetics of drug metabolism by hepatic microsomes. *Biochem. Pharmacol. 13:*1007 (1964).

$K_m = 7.2 \times 10^{-4}$ M.[93] The experiment was repeated in the presence of chlorpromazine at two different concentrations. Clearly, chlorpromazine inhibits the reaction competitively; its K_i was found to be 5.6×10^{-5} M, i.e., its affinity for the enzyme was more than 12 times greater than that of the morphine analogue.

Figure 1-55 illustrates the application of a double-reciprocal plot to biologic responses in which the nature of the receptors is unknown.[94] If histamine is injected into the blood stream, there is a prompt fall in blood pressure, and this effect can be antagonized by pretreatment with antihistaminic drugs. In the experiments depicted, it could be concluded that diphenhydramine acts as a competitive antagonist of histamine, whereas the antagonism caused by ergotamine is noncompetitive.

The Log Dose-Response Curve

In pharmacology it is conventional to show the relationship between dose and response more directly than on a double-reciprocal plot. In Fig. 1-56, two methods of graphical presentation are compared. The dose of a glucocorticoid drug was varied, as in the SAR studies described earlier, and the amount of glycogen deposited in the liver was measured. In both cases the dependent variable (amount of glycogen) is plotted on an arithmetic scale of ordinates. On the left the values of the independent variable (dose) are also plotted on an arithmetic scale on the x-axis, but on the right these same data are plotted on a logarithmic scale. The curves, which are fairly typical, indicate that from a practical standpoint the logarithmic dosage scale is preferable. Line segments rather than hyperbolic curves are obtained, which are much easier to deal with in statistical analysis. Moreover, drugs that produce the same effect by the same mechanism but differ in potency yield parallel line segments, and this is very convenient. For example, in Fig. 1-56b the constant horizontal separation of the lines is a measure of the potency ratio for the two drugs, since the difference (log dose A − log dose B) is the same as log (dose A/dose B), where the doses are those required to produce an equal response. Another practical advantage of the logarithmic dosage scale is that a wide range of doses can be presented readily in a single graph. Thus, quite apart from any theoretical considerations, there are sufficient reasons for plotting dose-response relationships on semilogarithmic coordinates, and it has become customary to do so.

Obviously, the line segments of Fig. 1-56b could not extend indefinitely to both extremes of the log dose scale. There must be some

---

[93] Here the symbols are those customarily used in enzymology, v for the reaction velocity (instead of Δ), V_{max} instead of Δ_{max}, (S) for substrate concentration (instead of (X)), K_m for Michaelis constant (instead of K_x), and K_i for enzyme-inhibitor dissociation constant (instead of K_z).

[94] G. CHEN and D. RUSSELL: A quantitative study of blood pressure response to cardiovascular drugs and their antagonists. *J. Pharmacol. Exp. Therap.* **99:**401 (1950).

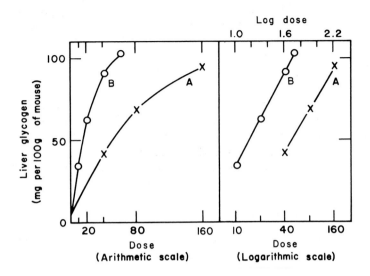

FIG. 1-56.   LINEAR AND SEMILOGARITHMIC DOSE-RESPONSE CURVES.   *Effects of two steroids, 11-dehydrocorticosterone* (A) *and cortisone* (B), *on liver glycogen in mice.* (*From Gaddum, Fig. 85[95] adapted from Venning, Fig. 2.[95a]*)

dose which is so low that no perceptible response is obtained, and there must also be doses so high that the capacity of the biologic system to respond is exceeded. In the case of the glucocorticoids, there would be a maximum possible increment in the amount of liver glycogen. Thus we might predict, a priori, some kind of sigmoid curve, approaching zero response at very low doses and a maximum response at very high doses. This prediction is borne out experimentally. A typical log dose-response (LDR) curve extending over a wide dose range is shown in Fig. 1-57. Here, several concentrations of histamine were added to a tissue bath in which a section of guinea pig ileum was suspended, and the amplitude of the resulting contractions was measured. The curve is seen to be sigmoid, and to approach zero and a maximum asymptotically. It is symmetrical about the point at which 50 per cent of the maximum response is obtained, and its maximum slope and point of inflection occur at this midpoint. Line segments, such as those in Fig. 1-56b, are derived from the central nearly linear portions of sigmoid LDR curves. The lower the ED50 (p. 351) the more potent the drug. The ED50 for histamine in Fig. 1-57 is approximately 0.6 μg.

    [95] J. H. GADDUM: *Pharmacology,* 5th ed. London, Oxford University Press, 1959.
    [95a] E. H. VENNING, V. E. KAZMIN, and J. C. BELL: Biological assay of adrenal corticoids. *Endocrinol. 38:*79 (1946).

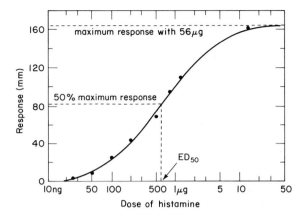

FIG. 1-57. LDR CURVE FOR HISTAMINE ACTING ON GUINEA PIG ILEUM IN A
TISSUE BATH. *Response magnitude (read directly from a kymograph tracing)
is proportional to actual contraction of the ileum. Histamine dose added to
constant-volume tissue bath is shown on a logarithmic scale. (Adapted from
Paton, Fig. 4.[96])*

The position of a LDR curve on the x-axis reflects the affinity of the
drug for its receptor. Since by convention the scale of dosage increases
from left to right, it follows that for a series of congeneric drugs interacting
with the same receptor a set of parallel LDR curves is expected. The curve
for the most potent drug will be at the left, curves for drugs with poorer
affinities for the receptor will lie further to the right. An example is shown
in Fig. 1-58. Here, the response measured was contraction of the isolated
cat spleen strip upon exposure to epinephrine or norepinephrine in a tissue
bath. The actual record of responses is shown on the upper line, the corresponding LDR curves below. The apparent affinity of epinephrine for
the receptor that mediates the contractile response is seen to be about twice
that of norepinephrine. Just as the parallelism of these two curves is regarded as consistent with an identical mechanism of action (i.e., interaction
with the same receptor site), so in general would a lack of parallelism
create the strong presumption that two drugs produce the same end effect
by different mechanisms. Further evidence that the two drugs combine at
the same receptor is the fact that the same maximum contraction was
obtained.

The analysis of antagonisms in the framework of the LDR curve is
straightforward.[98,99] In the presence of a competitive antagonist, the curve

96 W. D. M. PATON: A theory of drug action based on the rate of drug-receptor
combination. *Proc. Roy. Soc. B154:*21 (1961).

97 R. K. BICKERTON: The responses of isolated strips of cat spleen to sympathomimetic drugs and their antagonists. *J. Pharmacol. Exp. Therap. 142:*99 (1963).

98 Symposium on drug antagonism. *Pharmacol. Rev. 9:*211–268 (1957).

99 O. ARUNLAKSHANA and H. O. SCHILD: Some quantitative uses of drug antagonists.
*Brit. J. Pharmacol. 14:*48 (1959).

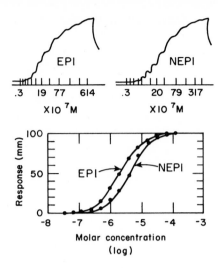

FIG. 1-58.   LDR CURVES FOR EPINEPHRINE (EPI) AND NOREPINEPHRINE (NEPI)
ACTION ON ISOLATED CAT SPLEEN.   Upper portion: *Actual concentration activity recordings for the two catecholamines obtained in a single spleen strip.*
Lower portion: *Semilogarithmic plot of the data in upper panel. (From Bickerton, Fig. 1.[97])*

for an agonist will be shifted to the right, but neither the slope nor the
maximum response would be expected to change. The antagonist simply
alters the effective affinity of agonist drug for receptor. Figure 1-59a gives
a typical example. In the same system as described above, using the spleen

FIG. 1-59.   LDR CURVES IN ANALYSIS OF ANTAGONISMS.   *Isolated cat spleen, as
in Fig. 1-58, stimulated by norepinephrine (NEPI) at various molar concentrations, as indicated. In* (a) *and* (b) *the curve farthest to left is the control, the
others were obtained in the presence of two antagonist concentrations. (From
Bickerton, Fig. 3.[97])*

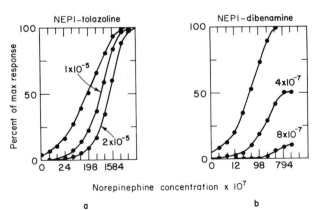

strip, contractions were elicited by norepinephrine as before, and also in the presence of two different concentrations of an antagonist, tolazoline. The parallelism of the curves is not perfect, but the interpretation is obvious; tolazoline occupies the receptor site competitively but cannot itself trigger a contractile response. If sufficient norepinephrine is present, the tolazoline blockade can be overcome completely.

The effect of a noncompetitive antagonist upon the LDR curve will be quite different. The agonist curve will again be shifted to the right, but the slope will be reduced and the maximum response will diminish, in relation to the degree of noncompetitive blockade established. This is nicely illustrated in the same biologic system (Fig. 1-59b) by the effects of two concentrations of dibenamine, an alkylating agent, upon the contractile response to norepinephrine.

Now we shall examine to what extent actual LDR curves can be described by equations based on the law of mass action. Let f be the fraction of maximal response obtained at a given dose, as follows:

$$f = \frac{\Delta}{\Delta_{max}} = \frac{(RX)}{(R_T)}.$$

Substituting from Equation (1), and rearranging yields

$$f = \frac{(X)}{K_X + (X)}$$

$$(X) = K_X \left(\frac{f}{1-f} \right).$$

By substituting $(X_T) - (RX)$ for (X) and $f(R_T)$ for (RX), we obtain

$$(X_T) = K_X \left(\frac{f}{1-f} \right) + f(R_T) \qquad (3)$$

Total drug = Free drug + Bound drug

Equation (3) is broadly applicable to dose-response relationships in which the "occupancy assumption" applies, and in which the molar combining ratio of drug to receptor is unity (our first and second assumptions); it does not presuppose any particular fraction of total drug bound to receptors (our third assumption). If in equation (3) the term $f(R_T)$, representing bound drug, is very much smaller than K_X ($f/(1-f)$), representing free drug, it may be ignored. For any moderate values of f this simplification can be made if (R_T) is small compared with K_X (e.g., R_T/K_X less than 1/10). We will then have the *zone A* approximation, in which practically all drug molecules are free even at receptor saturation, so that

$$(X_T) \cong (X) = K_X \left(\frac{f}{1-f} \right). \qquad (3A)$$

At the other extreme, if R_T is very much larger than K_X, then the expression $K_X \left(f/(1 - f) \right)$, representing free drug, becomes negligible for any moderate values of f. We will then have the *zone C* approximation, in which practically no drug molecules are free, as follows:

$$(X_T) \cong f(R_T) \qquad\qquad (3C)$$

Here, because the drug-receptor dissociation constant is so small, or the receptor concentration is so large, the binding is essentially stoichiometric ("pseudo-irreversible") even though the interaction is technically a reversible one. A truly irreversible drug-receptor combination would give the same equation and corresponding LDR curve.

Behavior intermediate between these two extremes, which has to be described by the full form of equation (3), is known as *zone B* behavior. The validity of simplifying equation (3), in the cases of *zone A* and *zone C*, it should be noted, depends entirely upon the ratio R_T/K_X, i.e., upon the concentration of receptors expressed in units of the drug-receptor dissociation constant.

For the same reason equation (3) can be written more usefully in the following way:

$$\frac{(X_T)}{K_X} = \frac{f}{1 - f} + f \left\{ \frac{(R_T)}{K_X} \right\}$$

The three forms of this equation are plotted as LDR curves in Fig. 1-60. Here the x-axis shows log dose, each dose being expressed in units of the drug-receptor dissociation constant. Thus f is plotted against log (X_T/K_X).

The LDR curve for *zone A* in this graph will be recognized as the familiar symmetrical sigmoid, which inflects at $f = 0.5$. Indeed, the zone-A

FIG. 1-60. THEORETICAL LDR CURVES FOR THE THREE ZONES OF BEHAVIOR. *Ordinal values f are fractions of maximal response or fractional occupancy of receptors. Abscissal values are logarithms of drug concentration (dose) normalized by expressing in units of the drug-receptor dissociation constant. In* zone A *practically all the drug is free. In* zone C *practically all the drug is combined with receptor sites. In* zone B *neither free nor combined drug can be neglected; only a single representative curve is shown. (Adapted from Straus and Goldstein, Fig. 2.[89] By permission of Cambridge University Press.)*

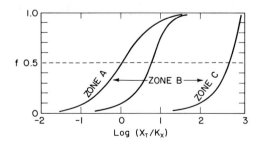

LDR curve is identical to the graphic representation of the Henderson-Hasselbalch equation, and for the following reason. We may rewrite equation (3A):

$$\log (X) = \log K_X + \log \left(\frac{f}{1-f} \right)$$

which is completely equivalent to

$$\log (\mathrm{H}^+) = \log K_a' + \log \left(\frac{\text{acid}}{\text{base}} \right)$$

$$= \log K_a' + \log \left(\frac{\beta}{1 - \beta} \right)$$

where β is the nonionized fraction. Inversion yields the description of the customary plot of fraction ionized as a function of pH.

Zone-A LDR curves for a congeneric drug series (like ionization-pH curves for a set of weak acids) are parallel sigmoids (Fig. 1-61) with invariant slopes at their midpoints. The position of each curve on the x-axis is determined by its K_X. The midpoint slope is found by differentiating the logarithmic form of equation (3A) (see above), as follows:

$$d \ln (X) = d \ln \left(\frac{f}{1-f} \right) = \frac{df}{f(1-f)}$$

$$\frac{df}{d \log (X)} = 2.303 \, f(1-f)$$

FIG. 1-61. ZONE-A LDR CURVES FOR TWO CONGENERIC DRUGS WITH DIFFERENT AFFINITIES FOR RECEPTOR, OR pH-IONIZATION CURVES FOR TWO WEAK ACIDS WITH DIFFERENT $\mathrm{p}K'_a$. *Perpendiculars dropped from the intersections indicated by arrows will give ED50 (equal to K_X under zone A conditions) or $\mathrm{p}K'_a$, respectively.*

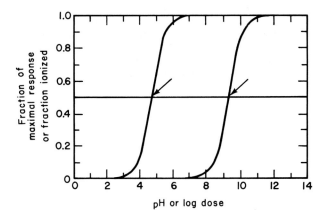

Fraction of maximal response or fraction ionized

pH or log dose

and, at the midpoint, when $f = 0.5$,

$$\frac{df}{d \log (X)^\cdot} = 0.576.$$

For zone C the theoretical curve is described by the logarithmic form of equation (3C):

$$\log f = \log (X_T/R_T)$$

in which the molecular ratio of drug to receptors determines the fractional response. The LDR curve (Fig. 1-60) is no longer sigmoid, and differentiation yields a midpoint slope of 1.15, just double that of the zone A curve. LDR curves for zone B are in all respects transitional between zone A and zone C; one such curve is depicted in Fig. 1-60.

Figure 1-62 presents typical experimental data on enzyme-substrate and enzyme-inhibitor interactions plotted as LDR curves. The slopes of both curves at their midpoints are almost exactly 0.576, the theoretical zone A value.

In all the foregoing we have assumed that one molecule of drug combines with one receptor site, and there are good reasons to believe

FIG. 1-62.   TYPICAL ENZYME-SUBSTRATE AND ENZYME-INHIBITOR INTERACTIONS PLOTTED AS LDR CURVES.   *Both curves depict experiments with plasma cholinesterase. Fraction of maximal velocity or fractional inhibition is plotted against logarithm of substrate or inhibitor concentration. (a) Acetylcholine as substrate; (b) physostigmine as inhibitor. Velocity measured in the presence of a saturating concentration of substrate. (Adapted from Goldstein, Fig. 1,[100] and Straus and Goldstein, Fig. 4.[89] By permission of Cambridge University Press.)*

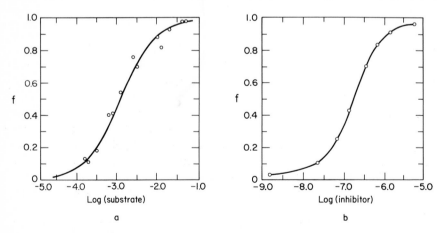

100 A. GOLDSTEIN: The mechanism of enzyme-inhibitor-substrate reactions. *J. Gen. Physiol.* 27:529 (1944).

that this is usually the case. But other combining ratios are not out of the question. A cross-linking alkylating agent would give the reaction

$$X + 2R \rightleftharpoons XR_2$$

with drug/receptor combining ratio 1/2. Also, two substrate molecules may sometimes occupy an enzyme active center in such a way that the functional 1/1 combination is prevented ("excess substrate inhibition"), and there may be other ways in which two drug molecules could occupy one receptor site, according to the following reaction scheme:

$$2X + R \rightleftharpoons X_2R$$

with drug/receptor combining ratio 2/1. Equations for the corresponding LDR curves will not be derived, but some conclusions may be stated briefly. In zone A the midpoint slope is $0.576n$, where n is the drug/receptor combining ratio; so for ratios 1/2, 1/1, 2/1 the respective slopes are 0.288, 0.576, 1.15, respectively. In zone C the slope is 1.15 for all values of n.

A systematic change in the shape and symmetry of the curves is evident as one passes from zone A to zone C (Fig. 1-60), but in a real biologic test system the precision of observations at near-maximum responses would not usually be good enough to distinguish between a curve that flattens at the top (zones A and B) and one that abruptly reaches maximum response (zone C). Midpoint slopes, on the other hand, can often be measured quite accurately. Evidently, any slope between 0.288 and 1.15 is compatible with mass law theory, assuming that response is proportional to receptor occupancy and that the drug/ receptor combining ratio may be 1/2, 1/1, or 2/1. If the combining ratio 1/2 can be excluded, then the slope is restricted to the range 0.576 to 1.15. Finally, if one drug molecule combines with one receptor site, and if a negligible fraction of total drug is combined with receptors, then the slope should have the value 0.576.

In an unusually large number of cases, involving drugs of many kinds acting upon diverse biologic systems, LDR curves are found to have midpoint slopes that do not differ significantly from 0.576. This is true, for example, not only in the AcCh-cholinesterase and physostigmine-cholinesterase interactions (Fig. 1-62), where the receptor is well defined, but also in the actions of histamine upon guinea pig ileum (Fig. 1-57) and of norepinephrine and epinephrine upon cat spleen (Fig. 1-58). In the absence of any other reason why a particular slope should be favored, the recurrence of values close to 0.576 suggests strongly that the mass law interpretation of the LDR curve (including the "occupancy assumption") is generally correct, even in cases where the receptors have not been characterized.

A variety of ingenious alternatives to the "occupancy assumption" can be imagined. One modification of the assumption demands serious consideration because it has a sound theoretical basis and is evidently applicable to some known examples of enzyme inhibition. If the receptors with which a drug combines do not have a rate-limiting role in the overall reaction sequence leading to the characteristic biologic response, then no drug effect at all will occur until a certain *fractional occupancy threshold* has been exceeded. Consider a sequence of metabolic conversions in which the biologic response produced by a drug X is proportional to the reduction in the steady-state concentration of a product M brought about by drug inhibition of one enzyme, E_3, in the pathway as follows:

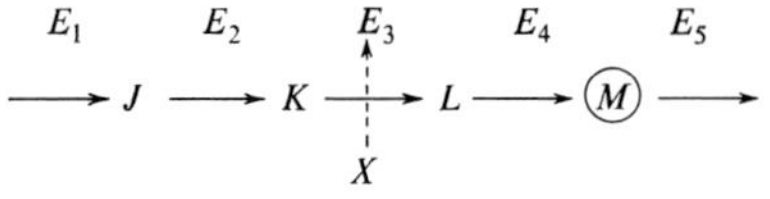

$$\begin{array}{ccccccccc}
E_1 & & E_2 & & E_3 & & E_4 & & E_5 \\
\longrightarrow & J & \longrightarrow & K & \vdots & L & \longrightarrow & \textcircled{M} & \longrightarrow \\
& & & & X & & & &
\end{array}$$

If X inhibits the enzyme E_3, and if E_3 is rate limiting for the production of M, then we should expect the "occupancy assumption" to be valid, since the fractional inhibition of E_3 will reduce the rate of production of M proportionately. If, on the other hand, E_3 is present in excess, then some degree of inhibition may occur without significant effect upon M. But with increasing inhibition a point will finally be reached when E_3 becomes rate limiting, and then further reduction in its activity will cause the onset of drug effect. The general result is to steepen the LDR curve.

For drug/receptor molecular combining ratio 1/1, if f_0 be the *fractional occupancy threshold* below which no drug effect occurs, and if (as before) the maximal drug effect ($f = 1.0$) occurs at receptor saturation, then in zone A

$$(X_T) = K_X \left\{ \frac{f + [f_0/(1 - f_0)]}{1 - f} \right\} \tag{4A}$$

and in zone C

$$(X_T) = (R_T) \{f + (1 - f) f_0\}. \tag{4C}$$

These modified equations describe LDR curves with interesting new properties. Figure 1-63 is an illustration for $f_0 = 0.5$. The curve representing fractional occupancy $(RX)/(R_T)$ is no longer identical to that representing fractional response f; the latter is displaced to the right and it will rise more steeply the greater the value of f_0.

In zone A the midpoint slope cannot exceed 1.15, twice the slope of the usual zone A curve. In zone C, however, the greater the value of f_0, the steeper the slope, without limit. For example, in Fig. 1-63 with fractional occupancy threshold 0.5, the LDR slope at $f = 0.5$ is 0.863 in zone A and 3.45 in zone C. For a very large excess of receptors (e.g., $f_0 = 0.9$) the LDR curve in zone C could be so steep as to mimic an all-or-none type of response.

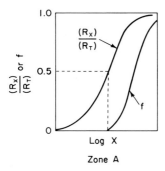 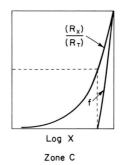

FIG. 1-63. THEORETICAL LDR CURVES FOR FRACTIONAL OCCUPANCY THRESHOLD 0.5. *It is assumed that no biologic response occurs until one-half the receptors are occupied* $(f_0 = (RX)/(R_T) = 0.5)$. *As usual, f represents the fraction of maximal response, but it is no longer identical to fractional occupancy of receptors,* $(RX)/(R_T)$. *Total drug concentration* (X_T) *is plotted logarithmically along the abscissal axis.* Broken lines *define* f_0; *up to half-saturation of the receptors there is no biologic response* $(f = 0)$.

An interesting consequence of the displacement of biologic response curves to the right of receptor occupancy curves is that the experimentally determined LDR will now underestimate the true affinity of drug for receptor, i.e., the ED50 will be a larger number than K_X.

A concrete example of the influence of excess receptors is found in the properties of carbonic anhydrase inhibitors.[101] These drugs cause diuresis by blocking hydrogen ion secretion in the kidney tubules.

$$\overset{\text{C.A.}}{CO_2 + H_2O \rightleftharpoons H_2CO_3 \rightleftharpoons H^+ + HCO_3^-}$$
$$\underset{X}{}$$

$$\downarrow \underset{\text{urine}}{- - - - - - - -} \overset{\text{cell}}{}$$

The enzyme carbonic anhydrase (C.A.) catalyzes the hydration of CO_2, which is a slow process in the absence of the enzyme. Thus, the availability of sufficient H^+ to maintain a normal rate of acidification of the tubular urine requires the presence of C.A. As expected, if C.A. is sufficiently inhibited, the urine becomes more alkaline. Since HCO_3^- in the glomerular filtrate is no longer neutralized as completely, the effect of a

[101] T. H. MAREN: The relation between enzyme inhibition and physiological response in the carbonic anhydrase system. *J. Pharmacol. Exp. Therap. 139*:140 (1963).

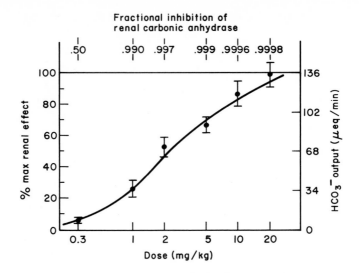

FIG. 1-64.   FRACTIONAL OCCUPANCY THRESHOLD WITH A CARBONIC ANHYDRASE
INHIBITOR.   *Acetazolamide was given intravenously to dogs (7 to 13 animals at
each dose), and urine HCO_3^- output was measured for a 30-minute period.
Points and vertical bars are means and their standard errors. Untreated dogs
excreted only 4 μeq of HCO_3^- per minute. Fractional inhibitions of renal
carbonic anhydrase were estimated from determinations of renal acetazolamide
content at each dose level and the known enzyme-inhibitory properties of this
drug. (From Maren, Fig. 3.*[101]*)*

C.A. inhibitor can be estimated by measuring the urinary HCO_3^-. Figure
1-64 shows a LDR curve for one such drug, acetazolamide, in comparison
with the computed fractional inhibition of the enzyme at each drug dose.
Clearly, C.A. is present in excess initially. As in the theoretical illustration
(Fig. 1-63) about one-half of the enzyme activity has to be abolished
before any biologic response is seen (f_0 approximately 0.5). Similarly, 99.7
per cent of the enzyme activity has to be abolished in order to achieve half
of the maximum possible effect.

Anomalous Antagonisms and Their Interpretation

It has been recognized for many years that certain drug antagonists
behave in a way that is not readily explained by simple mass law theory.
These anomalous cases occur chiefly in systems where the receptor is an unidentified membrane component and the biologic response is a muscle
contraction.

The "atropine anomaly" is typical.[102] Acetylcholine reduces the
amplitude of contraction of the frog heart; the LDR curve is shown in Fig.
1-65, curve a. The vertical axis here has been modified so that the curves

[102] A. J. CLARK: The antagonism of acetyl choline by atropine. *J. Physiol.* *61:*547
(1926).

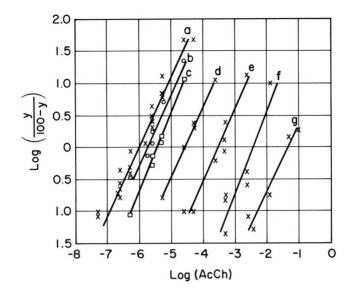

FIG. 1-65. ANTAGONISM BY ATROPINE OF ACTION PRODUCED BY ACch ON
ISOLATED FROG HEART. *Abscissal scale is log molar concentration of AcCh in
the tissue bath. On ordinal scale, y is per cent reduction of amplitude of spontaneous contractions by AcCh, and log of y/(100 − y) is plotted. Curves show
results with the following molar concentrations of atropine:* (a) *none;* (b)
10^{-8}; (c) 10^{-7}; (d) 10^{-6}; (e) 10^{-5}; (f) 10^{-4}; (g) 10^{-3}. (From Clark,
Fig. 1.[102])

are linear rather than sigmoid. If the heart, in a tissue bath, is treated with
a small dose of atropine and then retested with AcCh, the entire LDR
curve is shifted slightly to the right (curve b). Increasing doses of atropine
shift the curve progressively further to the right (curves c–g). The set of
curves is essentially parallel. Each tenfold increment in atropine concentration makes it necessary to increase the AcCh dosage about tenfold to obtain
the same response as before. At all atropine concentrations the same maximal response can be elicited, provided the AcCh concentration is made
high enough.

These effects of atropine on the AcCh LDR curve seem to fit the
classical description of competitive antagonism. According to mass law
theory and the "occupancy assumption," when maximal response is obtained in the presence of atropine the receptors should be fully occupied by
AcCh molecules and the atropine molecules should have been displaced.
Therefore, if the contents of the tissue bath are removed while a high concentration of AcCh is present, then replaced several times by solution containing the same high AcCh concentration, and finally replaced by fresh
solution without AcCh or atropine, the heart should have regained its
original sensitivity to AcCh. In fact, however, the decreased sensitivity
produced by atropine persists. With repeated washings, the atropine effect

does diminish very slowly and eventually disappears, but the rate of wash-out is the same whether or not AcCh is in the wash solutions. Thus, the antagonism, which is apparently competitive, is at the same time practically irreversible and is also unaffected by the presence of agonist!

A similar anomaly is observed with the alkylating agents related to dibenamine, which are thought, on grounds of chemical reactivity, to combine irreversibly with receptors.[103] A strip of guinea pig ileum was exposed to histamine at various concentrations and the amplitudes of the isotonic contractions were measured. The control LDR curve shown in Fig. 1-66 was obtained. Now the tissue was exposed to a dibenamine-like drug for five minutes. The sensitivity of the tissue to histamine was markedly reduced by this treatment, and the effect was practically irreversible; repeated washing failed to remove the blockade. Higher concentrations of histamine, however, overcame the antagonism, as shown, except at the highest antagonist concentration. Again, as in the atropine anomaly, neither by eliciting maximal responses nor by repeated washing could the original sensitivity of the tissue be restored. If the data are plotted according to the double-reciprocal method, both dibenamine and atropine fulfill the criteria for competitive antagonists, despite their irreversibility. Figure 1-67 presents a diagrammatic, mechanical analogue description of how the tissue

FIG. 1-66.   LDR CURVES FOR ACTION OF HISTAMINE UPON GUINEA PIG ILEUM, SHOWING EFFECTS OF AN ANTAGONIST RELATED TO DIBENAMINE.   *Curve at far left is control, concentrations of antagonist are shown on other curves. (From Nickerson, Fig. 1.[103])*

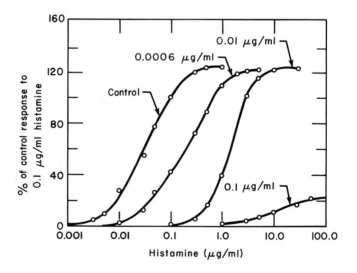

[103] M. NICKERSON: Receptor occupancy and tissue response. *Nature 178*:697(1956).

FIG. 1-67.   ANOMALOUS ANTAGONISMS: MECHANICAL ANALOGY OF FINDINGS. *A spring-loaded lever is pictured. The effect of antagonist is to make lever less sensitive to agonist.*

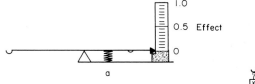

The resting state of the muscle.

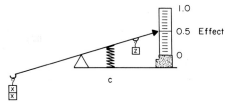

In the presence of Z two units of X are required to elicit same response as before.

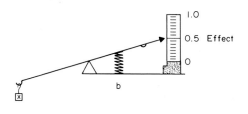

50 Per cent of maximal response produced by one unit of agonist X.

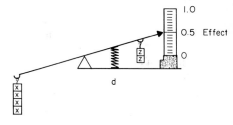

With twice the amount of antagonist, four units of X now produce same response as before.

sensitivity to agonist is altered by antagonist in cases of anomalous antagonism.

The new concept of allosteric interaction[104] offers a possible explanation. It has long been recognized that an inhibitor could destroy the function of an enzyme by combining elsewhere than at the substrate site. For example, a heavy metal could form mercaptides and thereby alter the configurational state of an enzyme in such a manner as to destroy essential functional relationships at the active center. It had been assumed that inhibition of this kind would have to be noncompetitive. However, recent observations indicate that substrate and inhibitor may combine at different sites, yet nevertheless mutually influence each other's affinity for the enzyme through induced configurational (allosteric) changes in the enzyme protein. Figure 1-68 suggests some possibilities. Here, ABC represents a flexible active site, which assumes a catalytically active form under the influence of a substrate molecule. An inhibitor of an entirely different shape, combining at a different site, could impede the substrate-induced configurational change. In the model case shown here, the inhibition could appear to be competitive, if the affinity of substrate or inhibitor for their

104 J. MONOD, J. P. CHANGEUX, and F. JACOB: Allosteric proteins and cellular control systems. *J. Mol. Biol.* 6:306 (1963).

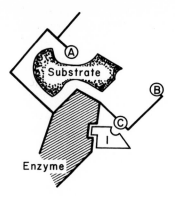

FIG. 1-68.   CONFORMATION CHANGE AT AN ENZYME ACTIVE SITE.   *A flexible active site is depicted, in which groups* A *and* B *must both be in contact with substrate for catalytic action to occur. An inhibitor* I *attracts group* C *and thus prevents proper alignment of* B. *If this changes the affinity of substrate for enzyme, competitive inhibition will be observed. From Koshland, Fig. 9.*[48])

respective sites were each diminished by combination of the other with its site.

A case of allosteric inhibition that has been studied extensively is the "feedback" inhibition of aspartyl transcarbamylase (ATCase) by cytidine triphosphate (CTP), an end-product of the pyrimidine biosynthetic pathway in which ATCase participates.[105,106] The step catalyzed by this enzyme is the coupling of carbamyl phosphate to aspartate at the beginning of the reaction sequence:

carbamyl   aspartate   carbamyl aspartate
phosphate

cytidine triphosphate (CTP)

(6 steps)

105 J. C. GERHART and A. B. PARDEE: The enzymology of control by feedback inhibition. *J. Biol. Chem. 237*:891 (1962).

106 J. C. GERHART and A. B. PARDEE: Aspartate transcarbamylase, an enzyme designed for feedback inhibition. *Fed. Proc. 23*:727 (1964).

That CTP inhibits by combining at a different site from the substrates has been shown in treatments such as heat, urea, or Hg++, which abolish the affinity of enzyme for CTP without affecting its activity toward aspartate or carbamyl phosphate. Moreover, the enzyme, which is a hexameric aggregate, can be separated physically into two subunits, a dimer that interacts with substrates but not with CTP and a tetramer that interacts with CTP alone. Despite this clear evidence for physically distinct substrate and inhibitor sites, an apparently competitive LDR curve was obtained when reaction velocity was measured in the presence of CTP (Fig. 1-69). Thus, all reaction velocities up to the control V_{max} could be obtained in the presence of CTP by increasing the substrate concentration sufficiently.

> Note that the scale of abscissas in Fig. 1-69 is not logarithmic but linear. On a linear plot, however (cf. Fig. 1-25), the enzyme-substrate saturation curve should be hyperbolic. The sigmoidal nature of the curve observed here is typical of what is seen when there are cooperative effects, i.e., when the combination of a molecule of substrate enhances the affinity of the enzyme for the next molecule of substrate. The example best studied is the oxygen-hemoglobin saturation curve, where the effect depends upon the substrate-induced interaction of the four subunits. For ATCase it is thought that the substrate induces a change in the state of aggregation of the enzyme from an inactive to an active state. CTP, in turn, modifies the enzyme conformation so that the affinity for aspartate is decreased.

FIG. 1-69. REVERSAL OF CTP INHIBITION OF ATC-ASE BY ASPARTATE. *Reaction mixture contained an excess of carbamyl phosphate; aspartate was varied as indicated. Note that abscissal scale is linear, not logarithmic, so normal Michaelis-Menten kinetics should give a rectangular hyperbola. The sigmoid curve is characteristic of reactions showing cooperative effects of subunits. (From Gerhart and Pardee, Fig. 3.[106])*

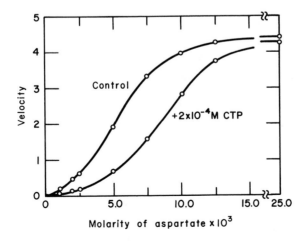

Allosteric transitions can also be imagined, whereby one drug would *enhance* the affinity between the receptor and another drug. Examples of such potentiation without change in maximal response are known; see, for example, Fig. 25, section IIB, of ref. 9.

By analogy to the CTP-ATCase interaction, atropine might possibly combine tightly at a special site on the receptor, thereby inducing a configurational change at the AcCh site. The consequence would be a decreased affinity for AcCh, but higher AcCh concentrations would still produce complete receptor occupancy and maximal response, as observed experimentally, despite the continued firm attachment of atropine. No evidence has yet been adduced to support such a hypothesis, but it has the attraction of accounting for anomalous antagonisms within the framework of mass law theory, and without discarding the assumption of proportionality between response and receptor occupancy.[107]

Other Ways of Interpreting the Log Dose-Response Relationship

EFFICACY (INTRINSIC ACTIVITY) AND SPARE RECEPTORS

According to the mass law interpretation, as developed above, the magnitude of a response is determined by the number of receptors occupied. Agonist drugs are supposed to differ in affinity for the receptor, so that different doses are required to achieve the same degree of receptor occupancy, and hence the same response. A molecule of any agonist occupying a given receptor site is assumed to make the same quantal contribution to the overall response as a molecule of any other agonist.

However, instances are known in which various agonists that apparently act on the same receptor site produce maximal responses of different magnitudes, an observation not readily accounted for by the theory. Attempts have therefore been made[10,108] to modify receptor theory, by endowing every drug with two independent properties concerned with its receptor combination: affinity (as discussed already) and a new property, "efficacy," or "intrinsic activity." Affinity describes the tendency of the drug to form a stable complex with receptor. "Efficacy" describes the biologic effectiveness of the drug-receptor complex. The two properties are considered to be unrelated, much in the same way as are affinities and turnover rates in a series of substrates of a given enzyme. Here, for example, an agonist and an antagonist could have the same affinity for a receptor site, but the former would have a high, the latter a low "efficacy." Since the biologic effect of a drug at a given dose would be determined both by the

107 A recent explicit formulation of a theory based upon drug-induced configurational changes is found in B. BELLEAU: A molecular theory of drug action based on induced conformational perturbations of receptors. *J. Med. Chem.* 7:776 (1964).

108 R. P. STEPHENSON: A modification of receptor theory. *Brit. J. Pharmacol. 11:* 379 (1956).

extent of receptor occupancy (determined by affinity) and by the "efficacy," it follows that according to this theory equal biologic responses need not imply equal degrees of receptor occupancy, and maximal responses may vary from drug to drug.

Casting aside the "occupancy assumption" in this way obviously broadens the applicability of receptor theory, so that it will now "explain" instances of variable maximal response. However, introducing a new ad hoc assumption to improve the adaptability of a theory often weakens rather than strengthens it, and the present instance is no exception. A prominent and consistent feature of the LDR relationship for most series of congeners is the identity of maximal response within the series. This is in accord with the "occupancy assumption" but very difficult to explain if "efficacy" varies from drug to drug. Moreover, the concept of "efficacy" offers no real clarification of the molecular events triggered by the combination of agonist drug with receptor.

One version of this theory[108] stresses the supposition that a maximal response may be obtained when only a fraction of the available receptors are occupied by an agonist, whence it follows that "spare receptors" are abundant under normal circumstances. Anomalous antagonisms are then accounted for as follows. The antagonist combines irreversibly with that small fraction of receptors ordinarily available to agonist, thereby preventing the usual responses to low agonist doses. At higher doses, however, agonist molecules may occupy "spare receptors" with which no antagonist had combined, and thus elicit maximal responses despite the continued presence of antagonist in the system. This suggestion lacks any plausible molecular basis and also seems to require a hierarchy of receptors with graded affinities for agonist and antagonist. This is so because the receptors that combine with agonist at low doses and cause the full range of biologic response must be precisely those which are blocked by low doses of antagonist. The "spare receptors" which then combine with agonist at higher dose, so that the antagonism is overcome, must have been unreactive with agonist or antagonist at the previous doses.

THEORY BASED ON THE RATE OF DRUG-RECEPTOR COMBINATION (RATE THEORY)[96,109,110]

The central concept here is that "instead of attributing excitation to the occupation of receptors by drug molecules, it is attributed to the *process* of occupation, each association between a drug molecule and a receptor

109 W. D. M. PATON: The principles of drug action. *Proc. Roy. Soc. Med.* 53:815 (1960).

110 W. D. M. PATON and D. R. WAUD: A quantitative investigation of the relationship between rate of access of a drug to a receptor and the rate of onset or offset of action. *Arch. Exp. Pathol. Pharmakol.* 248:124 (1964).

providing one quantum of 'excitation.' "[111] The magnitude of a response is proportional to the *rate* at which drug molecules associate with receptor sites. This rate depends upon the concentration of free drug, the concentration of free receptor sites, and k_1, the rate constant for association of drug molecules with receptors. Thus, the "occupancy assumption" is abandoned, and the principle of intrinsic activity is adopted; however, "efficacy" is no longer an ad hoc constant but is defined by the rate constant k_1, which may differ from drug to drug. According to this theory, the distinction between an agonist and an antagonist is determined solely by the value of k_2, the rate constant for dissociation. If k_2 is large, then the rate of dissociation of the drug-receptor complex will be high, making free receptor sites available at a high rate for new effective collisions with drug molecules. Thus, drugs with high k_2 are agonists. In contrast, if k_2 is small, the drug-receptor complex, once formed, will be stable, the rate of dissociation will be low, free receptors will become available for new association events only infrequently, and consequently there will be little or no excitation. Therefore, drugs with low k_2 will display only weak agonist action or none at all. The persistent occupancy of receptor sites by such a drug will reduce the number of sites available for combination with an agonist, so that the drug will behave as an antagonist. Both for agonists and for antagonists the potency is, of course, determined by the equilibrium dissociation constant k_2/k_1, which as usual describes the affinity of drug for receptor.

According to this theory, two rate constants determine a number of different aspects of drug action, and the theory predicts certain relationships between these. Some striking examples of agreement between prediction and observation have indeed been found. It is important to note, however, that values for k_1 and k_2 are deduced from the biologic effects, in terms of the theory itself, since no way has yet been found to measure these constants independently. Under these conditions internal consistency of the data is less impressive than if these constants could have been predicted a priori from physicochemical data.

Rate theory offers a possible explanation of why some drugs are agonists, some partial agonists, and some antagonists, depending upon the value of k_2. It has been suggested that excitation (agonist action) may actually depend upon an ion displacement mechanism wherein the magnitude of response is determined by the rate of displacement of ions (e.g., K^+) from receptor sites in a membrane. Concrete supporting evidence for some such molecular hypothesis would greatly strengthen the case for rate theory, by providing a plausible basis for the crucial thesis that the *process* of occupation of receptor sites provides the excitatory stimulus.

The theory is said to explain why antagonists tend to be bulkier than agonists, since there is alleged to be greater chance for nonspecific binding of bulky molecules than of small molecules at receptor sites. It is

[111] Page 23 in Paton, ref. 96.

also claimed that the theory explains why antagonists that are very potent have a slow onset of action, since the more potent they are, the lower the dose (or concentration) at which they must be used, and consequently the slower will they equilibrate. Both of these arguments apply with equal force to the mass law theory based upon the "occupancy assumption"; the latter argument, in particular, has long been recognized with respect to enzyme inhibitors.[112]

Rate theory offers a provocative explanation for the finding that some antagonists stimulate first and then block as the stimulation fades. A good example is nicotine, which initially excites the autonomic ganglion cell, then blocks it so that it no longer responds to various agonists, including nicotine itself. According to rate theory, the stimulation is a consequence of the initial associations between drug molecules and receptors, which proceed at a high rate (much as is assumed for agonists) because at the outset all receptors sites are vacant. However, this kind of initial stimulatory behavior, which is predicted by the theory, is not observed with all antagonists.

Rate theory accounts for a phenomenon known as "fade," in which an agonist causes an immediate peak response that fades off to a lower plateau at equilibrium. The theory predicts such behavior for all agonists, since the initial rate of combination is bound to be higher than the eventual rate at the steady state. However, numerous instances are known in which "fade" cannot be observed at all.

Anomalous antagonisms of the kind discussed earlier in connection with atropine (p. 88) are said to be accounted for by rate theory. The effect of a tightly bound antagonist occupying some receptor sites is to reduce the number of sites with which agonist molecules can combine. This will reduce the total number of association events per minute, but raising the dose of agonist may increase the rate of its association with the remaining free receptors sufficiently to restore the full response. This may be plausible, but how is the overcoming of a complete blockade to be explained? If complete blockade is interpreted to mean that all receptor sites are occupied by antagonist molecules, then no free receptors remain, and the explanation fails. The explanation, therefore, must really presuppose the notion of "spare receptors," which as already pointed out falls short of explaining anomalous antagonisms satisfactorily.

Rate theory has been used to predict successfully the slopes of LDR curves, which are found to depend upon the same two rate constants. It is interesting to note, however, that the two uncomplicated LDR curves presented in the original description of rate theory[113] fit nearly perfectly

112 A. GOLDSTEIN: A relationship between the rate of attaining equilibrium and the velocity constant of the reverse reaction in certain enzyme-inhibitor systems. *Experientia* 8:442 (1952).
113 Histamine and AcCh acting on guinea pig ileum, Figs. 4 and 5 in Paton, ref. 96. The histamine curve is also reproduced here as Fig. 1-57.

the theoretical mass law curve based upon the "occupancy assumption," with slope 0.576 as predicted for zone A with molecular combining ratio 1/1. One prominent feature of LDR curves that cannot be accounted for at all by rate theory is the common observation that for a given biologic effect, every agonist in a series of congeners yields the same maximal response, regardless of its potency. Explanations have to be sought outside the framework of the theory, in terms of hypothetical limitations in the response capacity of the contractile tissue. The same inadequacy of theory was discussed in connection with the concept of "efficacy."

Finally, whether or not rate theory proves to be valid for drug effects in contractile tissues, it is clearly inapplicable to the considerable class of drug-receptor interactions in which the occupancy assumption is known to be valid because the drug is a substrate or inhibitor of an enzyme, and also to a growing number of cases involving a functional macromolecule other than an enzyme (e.g., drugs acting upon nucleic acids).

STATISTICAL DISTRIBUTION OF RECEPTOR SENSITIVITIES[114]

Another way of looking at the typical LDR curve takes no account of molecular events or mechanisms. It is supposed that a receptor can exist in either of two states, dormant or activated. Every activated receptor is assumed to contribute, in the case of an agonist drug, an equal increment to the overall response (in the case of an antagonist, an equal decrement). Each receptor has its own threshold drug concentration at which activation occurs, so that the whole population of receptors in a tissue displays a range of drug sensitivities. The distribution of these sensitivities is postulated to be log normal, i.e., if the frequency in various sensitivity classes is plotted against log dose (or concentration), a Gaussian curve will be obtained whose breadth reflects the variance of the individual receptor sensitivities. When plotted instead as a cumulative frequency distribution, a typical LDR curve will result (Fig. 1-70) whose slope now reflects the variance of receptor sensitivities. It is possible that receptors exist which are complex enough to form a heterogeneous population with respect to drug sensitivity. It is also possible that variable diffusion of drug molecules to receptor sites at different locations in the tissues might result in a range of apparent sensitivities. No such instances, however, have actually been demonstrated. On the other hand, in those numerous cases in which receptors have been identified as macromolecules, this theory is inapplicable, because macromolecules of a specified kind are identical and therefore have identical affinities for a given drug. Moreover, the observed tendency for LDR slopes in diverse systems to cluster near the single value 0.576 accords well with the mass law interpretation but finds no plausible explanation in terms of a statistical distribution of receptor sensitivities.

114 J. H. GADDUM: Theories of drug antagonism. Symposium on drug antagonism. *Pharmacol. Rev.* 9:211 (1957).

FIG. 1-70.   STATISTICAL DISTRIBUTION OF RECEPTOR SENSITIVITIES.

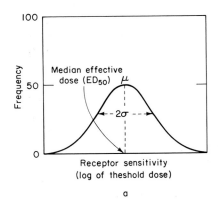

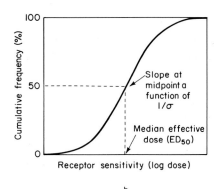

a

b

Log-normal distribution of sensitivities of individual receptors. The median effective dose is identical to the mean μ, and the breadth of the curve between the points of inflection is equal to twice the standard deviation.

Cumulative frequency distribution of (a). The transformation results in a symmetrical sigmoid reminiscent of a typical LDR curve, whose slope is inversely proportional to the heterogeneity of postulated receptor sensitivities. (The symbol ED_{50}, as shown here, is an alternative way of writing ED50.)

DRUG ACTIONS THAT ARE NOT MEDIATED DIRECTLY BY RECEPTORS

The earlier sections of this chapter concerned specific interactions between drugs and receptors, leading directly to a characteristic biologic response. We now consider three mechanisms of drug action that do not depend upon any drug-receptor complex, or in which a receptor is only remotely involved.

1. *Biologic effect is a nonspecific consequence of physical or chemical properties of a drug.* The osmotic diuretics, such as urea or mannitol, provide a good example of this mechanism. The compound, once taken into the body, is filtered at the glomeruli and thus increases the osmolarity of the tubular urine. Water must therefore be reabsorbed against a higher osmotic gradient than otherwise, so reabsorption is slower and a diuretic effect is observed. In the same category are the osmotic cathartics, such as magnesium sulfate. Neither Mg^{++} nor $SO_4^=$ traverses the intestinal

wall readily, so that an osmotic equivalent of water is necessarily retained within the lumen of the gut. The same principle underlies the action of intravenously administered plasma substitutes (e.g., polyvinyl pyrrolidone) or blood plasma itself. In acute blood loss or other situations where it is essential to restore and maintain the blood volume, these osmotically active macromolecules remain within the vascular system together with their osmotic equivalent of water.

Certain drugs owe their actions entirely to their acidic or basic properties. The antacids, for example, comprise various inorganic and organic bases and ion exchange resins which can be administered by mouth for the purpose of neutralizing excessive acidity in the stomach. Ammonium chloride, used to acidify the urine, contributes a hydrogen ion to the body fluids when NH_4^+ is metabolized to the neutral end-product urea. Some common organic acids that function as antiseptics in the urinary tract and as topical spermicides in the vaginal canal are thought to act primarily as acidifying agents.

Several kinds of nonspecific destructive agent are used in disinfection and antisepsis, as well as in contraception. Detergents destroy the integrity of lipoprotein membranes and also cause the dissociation of nucleoprotein complexes (e.g., ribosomes) whose integrity depends upon ionic bonds. Halogens, peroxides, and other oxidizing agents bring about a widespread destruction of organic matter. Denaturants belonging to numerous chemical classes destroy the integrity and functional capacity of cell membranes, subcellular particles, and proteins.

Perhaps the most interesting drugs in this category are the volatile general anesthetics. These are remarkable for their lack of any obvious molecular feature in common. Substances as unrelated as diethyl ether, cyclopropane, nitrous oxide, and even xenon produce very similar effects on the brain. It has long been recognized that the usual drug-receptor models would not accommodate these drugs. An observed positive correlation between oil/water partition coefficient and anesthetic potency led to the concept that volatile anesthetics dissolve in lipoprotein membranes of neuronal tissues and thereby somehow alter physiologic function.[115,116] It is true that, at least approximately, equimolar concentrations of the volatile anesthetics in the lipids of brain tissues would produce equal degrees of anesthesia. However, equally good correlations are also found between anesthetic potency and other physicochemical properties.[117] Most

115 H. H. MEYER: Zur Theorie der Alkoholnarkose: Erste Mittheilung. Welche Eigenschaft der Anästhetica bedingt ihre narkotische Wirkung? *Arch. Exp. Pathol. Pharmakol. 42:*109 (1899).

116 E. OVERTON: Beiträge zur allgemeinen Muskel- und Nervenphysiologie. *Arch. ges. Physiol. 92:*115 (1902).

117 J. FERGUSON: The use of chemical potentials as indices of toxicity. *Proc. Roy. Soc. B127:*387 (1939).

recently the ability of the volatile anesthetics to stabilize water clathrates has been made the basis of a theory of anesthesia,[39, 118] the validity of which, however, has been questioned.[119]

2. *Biologic effect is a consequence of direct chemical interaction between drug and a small molecule or ion.* The best examples of this mechanism are found among the therapeutically useful chelating agents, the principles of whose actions were outlined earlier. Calcium disodium edetate is a therapeutically useful salt of EDTA (Fig. 1-7.), a specific antidote in lead poisoning. The drug removes free Pb^{++} from blood and tissues and renders it inert by complexing it very tightly. Eventually the soluble lead chelate is excreted from the body. Of course, Pb^{++} could be complexed even more efficiently by administering the tetrasodium salt of EDTA rather than the calcium disodium chelate. However, the Ca^{++} concentration of body fluids would then be seriously depleted because calcium would replace sodium in the chelate. Even in lead poisoning, the atom ratio Pb/Ca is extremely low. Thus, Pb^{++} would be chelated far more efficiently than Ca^{++}, as indicated by the relative stability constants (Table 1-3), but the total amount of calcium complexed would be much greater than the amount of lead complexed. By supplying the chelating agent as a calcium complex, we ensure that none of the essential body calcium will be removed, yet Pb^{++} will effectively displace Ca^{++} from EDTA in accordance with its 10^7-fold greater affinity.[26]

Another therapeutic use of a chelating agent is the employment of penicillamine (β, β-dimethylcysteine, Fig. 1-71) to remove copper from body tissues in the hereditary disorder of copper metabolism known as hepatolenticular degeneration, or Wilson's disease.[120] Here there appears to be defective synthesis of the copper-binding protein ceruloplasmin, resulting in progressive accumulation of free copper in the liver and brain. The damage to these organs may be prevented, and to some extent reversed, by repeated administration of the chelating agent. The complexed and solubilized copper is excreted in large amounts in the urine.

FIG. 1-71. PENICILLAMINE (a) AND ITS COPPER CHELATE (b).

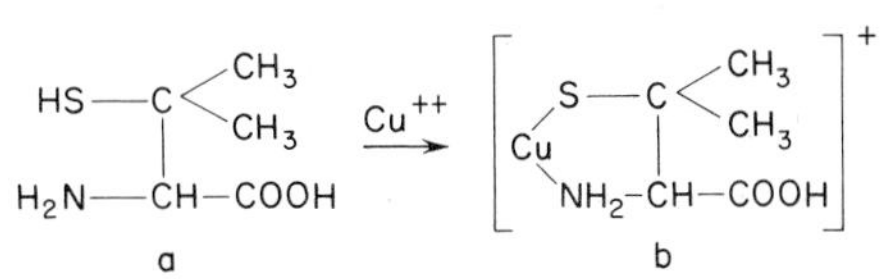

118 R. M. FEATHERSTONE and C. A. MUEHLBAECHER: The current role of inert gases in the search for anesthesia mechanisms. *Pharmacol. Rev. 15*:97 (1963).

119 K. W. MILLER, W. D. M. PATON, and E. B. SMITH: Site of action of general anaesthetics. *Nature 206*:574 (1965).

120 I. H. SCHEINBERG and I. STERNLIEB: Copper metabolism. *Pharmacol. Rev. 12*: 355 (1960).

The principle of mercaptide formation is applied in the use of dimercaprol (British anti-lewisite, BAL).[31,121] This drug is a simple glycerol derivative containing two vicinal sulfhydryl groups capable of forming a very stable mercaptide ring, as already described (p. 16).

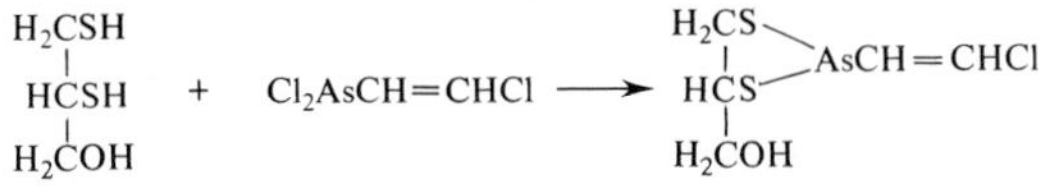

$$
\begin{array}{c}
H_2CSH \\
| \\
HCSH \\
| \\
H_2COH
\end{array}
\quad + \quad Cl_2AsCH=CHCl \quad \longrightarrow \quad
\begin{array}{c}
H_2CS \\
| \quad\searrow AsCH=CHCl \\
HCS \quad\nearrow \\
| \\
H_2COH
\end{array}
$$

dimercaprol   lewisite   mercaptide complex

By virtue of its free hydroxyl group, dimercaprol remains soluble even after it has chelated a metal atom. Thus, various heavy metals (arsenic, mercury, gold, antimony, bismuth), whether present as free ions or in organic complexes (such as lewisite), may be removed from the tissues and body fluids, rendered nontoxic by combination with dimercaprol, and then excreted in the urine.

3. *Biologic effect is a consequence of the incorporation of a drug instead of a normal metabolite.* A "counterfeit incorporation" mechanism, wherein a drug replaces a normal metabolite in the synthesis of an important cellular constituent, certainly requires the activity of enzymes. The effect of the drug, however, is not attributable directly to interaction with an enzyme. Rather, the drug participates as a substrate; the reaction product rather than the drug produces the characteristic biologic response.[122]

A case of "counterfeit incorporation" that has been studied intensively is that of the thymine analogue 5-bromouracil (BU).[123] The van der Waals radii of Br and $-CH_3$ are very nearly the same (Table 1-9), so BU resembles thymine quite closely. BU enters all the preliminary reactions that ordinarily lead to the synthesis of thymidine triphosphate; bromode-

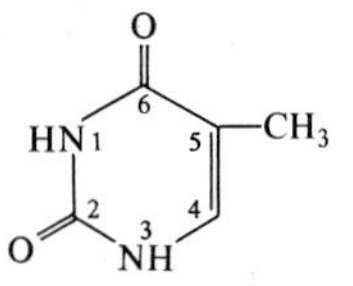

thymine 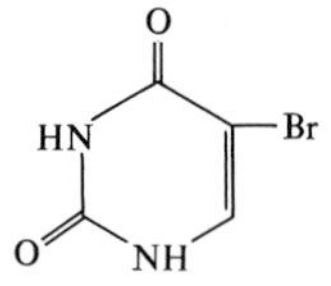   5-bromouracil

121 R. A. PETERS, L. A. STOCKEN, and R. H. S. THOMPSON: British Anti-Lewisite. *Nature 156:*616 (1945).

122 R. M. HOCHSTER and J. H. QUASTEL, eds.: *Metabolic Inhibitors,* Vol. I. New York, Academic Press, 1963.

123 R. W. BROCKMAN and E. P. ANDERSON: "Pyrimidine Analogues," in *Metabolic Inhibitors,* vol. I, ed. by Hochster, R. M., and Quastel, J. H. New York, Academic Press, 1963.

TABLE 1-9.   Atomic radii (van der Waals) of halogens and related groups

(Data from *Handbook of Chemistry and Physics,* 45th edition. Cleveland, Ohio, Chemical Rubber Co., 1964–65, p. D-90.)

Atom or group	Radius (A)
H	1.20
F	1.35
Cl	1.80
Br	1.95
CH_3	2.00
I	2.15

oxyuridine triphosphate then enters the DNA polymerase reaction, pairing opposite adenine. Depending upon the ratio of BU to thymine in the cellular environment, DNA can be synthesized in which up to 40 per cent of the thymine is replaced by BU, without significant adverse effect. Under these conditions, cell populations grow and divide normally; it is obvious, therefore, that practically all the incorporated BU molecules function as though they were thymine, both at replication and at transcription. Because of the increased density of BU (compared with thymine), BU-substituted DNA has proved useful in experiments requiring density labeling of one DNA strand. BU-containing DNA, despite its generally normal function, shows an increased mutation rate, presumably because of a heightened probability that BU will pair anomalously with guanine instead of with adenine (p. 636). Other abnormalities resulting from the presence of BU and other base analogues in DNA are increased sensitivity to x-irradiation, increased frequency of chromosome breakage, and mitotic abnormalities in mammalian cells.[124] These effects are discussed at greater length in chapter 10.

5-Fluorouracil (FU) presents an interesting contrast.[123] This compound is not incorporated into DNA at all, but acts readily as a counterfeit of uracil, consistent with the small van der Waals radius of the fluorine atom.

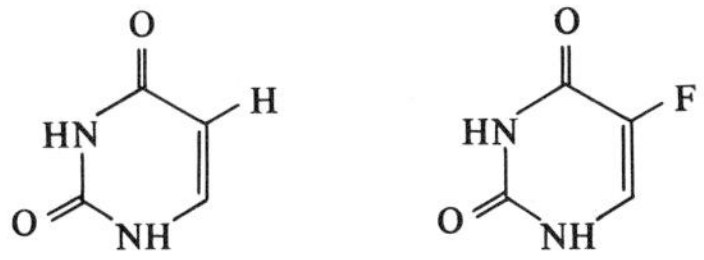

uracil   5-fluorouracil

124 Y. MARUYAMA, G. SILINI, and H. S. KAPLAN: Studies of the LSA ascites lymphoma of C57B1 mice. II. Radiosensitization *in vivo* with 5-bromodeoxycytidine and combined 5-fluorodeoxyuridine and 5-bromodeoxycytidine. *Int. J. Radiat. Biol.* 7:453 (1963).

FU has two primary effects. It is handled metabolically like uracil, forming a riboside and riboside phosphates. The monophosphate strongly inhibits the enzyme thymidine synthetase (which normally converts deoxyuridine monophosphate to thymidine monophosphate), thereby blocking the de novo synthesis of thymine. At the same time, FU is converted to the nucleoside triphosphate and then incorporated into messenger-RNA in place of uracil. "Miscoding" may result through misreading of codons containing FU during the assembly of polypeptide chains, so that incorrect amino acids are inserted. Phenotypically altered proteins are thus formed, which may be nonfunctional, partly functional, or even fully functional, depending upon the particular protein and the nature and position of each amino acid substitution.

An amino acid analogue may be incorporated into a protein in place of a natural amino acid, provided it can serve as substrate for an amino acid-activating enzyme. Once attached to a transfer-RNA molecule, its addition to a growing polypeptide chain appears to be inevitable, since it has been shown that informational specificity during the stepwise assembly of the polypeptide resides only in the m-RNA codon, the transfer-RNA itself, and some features of the ribosomal binding site. Thus, for example, if the analogue ethionine is activated and combined with the specific methionine transfer-RNA, it will then be treated exactly as though it were methionine at the subsequent steps.[125]

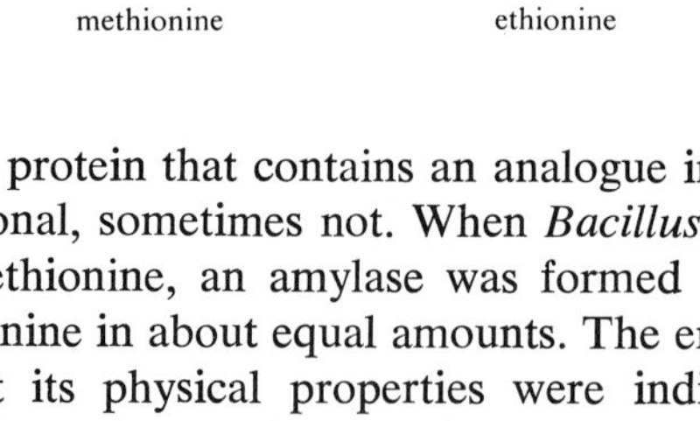

$$
\begin{array}{cc}
 & CH_3 \\
 & | \\
CH_3 & CH_2 \\
| & | \\
S & S \\
| & | \\
CH_2 & CH_2 \\
| & | \\
CH_2 & CH_2 \\
| & | \\
H_2N-CH-COOH & H_2N-CH-COOH \\
\text{methionine} & \text{ethionine}
\end{array}
$$

Sometimes a protein that contains an analogue in place of a natural amino acid is functional, sometimes not. When *Bacillus subtilis* was grown in the presence of ethionine, an amylase was formed that contained this analogue and methionine in about equal amounts. The enzyme not only had normal activity, but its physical properties were indistinguishable from those of the normal amylase. When *Escherichia coli* was grown in the presence of *p*-fluorophenylalanine, the induced enzyme β-galactosidase contained the analogue in place of phenylalanine but nevertheless displayed

[125] F. CHAPEVILLE, F. LIPMANN, G. VON EHRENSTEIN, B. WEISBLUM, W. J. RAY, and J. BENZER: On the role of soluble ribonucleic acid in coding for amino acids. *Proc. Nat. Acad. Sci. U.S.A.* 48:1086 (1962).

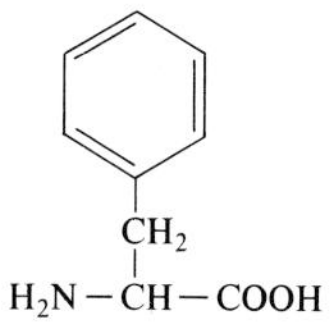

phenylalanine 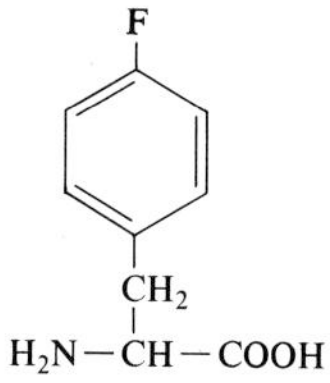   *p*-fluorophenylalanine

normal activity. In the same organism, under the same conditions, however, activities of several constitutive enzymes were absent.[126] In *Bacillus cereus* grown in *p*-fluorophenylalanine, the induced enzyme penicillinase contained the analogue and had impaired activity as well as altered (but still identifiable) immunologic properties.[127]

[126] W. SHIVE and C. G. SKINNER: "Amino Acid Analogues," in *Metabolic Inhibitors,* vol. I, ed. by Hochster, R. M., and Quastel, J. H. New York, Academic Press, 1963.

[127] M. H. RICHMOND: Immunological properties of exopenicillinase synthesized by *Bacillus cereus* 569/H in the presence of amino acid analogues. *Biochem. J. 77:*112 (1960).

2

THE ABSORPTION,

DISTRIBUTION, AND

ELIMINATION OF DRUGS

INTRODUCTION

In the first chapter we considered in some detail the interactions between drugs and their receptors at the sites of drug action. We now turn our attention to the factors that determine the access of a drug to its site of action. Most drugs are distributed throughout the body in the water phase of the blood plasma. In order to act, therefore, unless it acts topically at the site of application, a drug must first enter the blood. It will then reach the tissues of each organ at a rate determined by the blood flow through that organ and by the rapidity of passage of the drug molecules across the capillary bed and into the cells of that particular organ.

Within the blood plasma a variable proportion of the total drug molecules may be bound to proteins and thus not be freely diffusible out of the plasma. As a general rule the amount of any drug in the tissues where it acts is but a very small part of the total drug in the body. Most of the drug remains in the various fluid compartments in solution, or is localized by adsorptive or partition processes in subcellular particles, at macromolecular surfaces, or in fat depots. Even within the target cells themselves, cellular fractionation studies and radioautography usually reveal that most drug molecules are associated with structures having nothing to do with the specific drug effect.

Finally, even if no cell components other than the specific receptors were capable of binding drug molecules, we should nevertheless expect to find only a small fraction of the drug associated with these receptors. The reason is that approximately 80 per cent of the cell mass is water and only a very small fraction of the cell dry weight is likely to be represented by the specific receptors. Moreover, the receptors are macro-molecules of high molecular weight, each bearing only one or a few specific drug-binding sites. Thus, even at complete receptor occupancy, and even with fairly high drug-receptor affinity, provided the drug interacts reversibly, most of the drug molecules will be in the ambient water phase in equilibrium with those bound to the receptor. This general view of drug distribution is represented schematically in Fig. 2-1.

A drug enters the circulation by being injected there directly (intravascular route) or by absorption from depots where it has been placed. The commonest such depot is the gastrointestinal tract, the drug having been taken by mouth or, rarely, administered by rectum. The other common routes of administration are subcutaneous and intramuscular. Several less usual routes are also employed, for example, through the skin (percutaneous) and by inhalation. Drugs are sometimes applied for their local effects, and then the aim is to *minimize* absorption into the circulation; an example is the injection of a local anesthetic agent subcutaneously or into the spinal canal.

A drug is eliminated from the circulation by metabolism, excretion, and accumulation in tissues. The rate of each of these processes that contribute to termination of the drug action is determined by the chemical and physical properties of the drug and its interaction with the specialized tissues responsible for the elimination reactions. The kidney plays the major role in drug excretion. However, other excretory routes may be of prime importance for one or another drug. An example is excretion into

FIG. 2-1.   THE FATE OF A DRUG IN THE BODY.   Broken lines *represent membranes. Numbers at bottom are percentages of body weight represented by each fluid compartment in the adult male. X is free drug;* PX, *drug-protein complex in plasma;* P′X, *complex of drug with nonspecific binding sites in tissues;* Y, *a metabolic product of* X; *and* RX, *drug-receptor complex.*

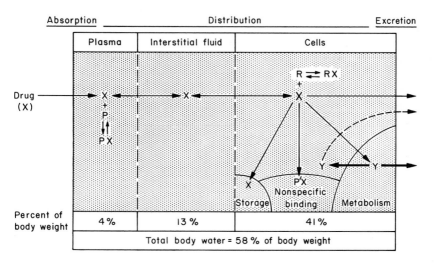

the gastrointestinal tract, directly from the blood or by way of the bile. The sweat may be significant for excretion of some drugs. Volatile agents are eliminated at the lungs. The liver is of chief importance in drug metabolism, but drugs are also degraded in other tissues. Often, metabolic alteration of structure is a prerequisite to renal excretion (see p. 206). Accumulation at any site must obviously remove drug molecules from every other site. Thus, lipid-soluble drugs may be localized in the large depots of neutral fat that comprise a significant fraction of the body weight. It is not unusual, long after administration of such a drug, to find practically all the drug molecules in the body stored in this way.

It follows from this superficial review that the time course of drug action, determined by the effective concentration of drug at receptor sites, depends in a complex way upon the relative rates of all the processes cited. In this chapter we shall first examine the various routes by which drugs may be administered, and the important characteristics of each route. Then the factors influencing the distribution of drugs into the tissues will be considered, with special attention to the passage of drugs into the central nervous system and across the placenta into the fetus. Finally, routes of drug elimination will be analyzed. The principles and pathways of drug metabolism will be deferred to the next chapter. In chapter 4 we shall consider the combined effects of absorption, distribution, and elimination upon the time course of drug action.

DRUG ABSORPTION: ROUTES OF ADMINISTRATION

The possible routes of drug entry into the body may be divided into two classes—*enteral* and *parenteral*. In enteral administration the drug is placed directly in the gastrointestinal tract by placing it under the tongue (*sublingual*), by swallowing it (*oral, p.o., per os*), or by rectal administration. In parenteral administration the gastrointestinal tract is bypassed. There are many parenteral routes. The commonest are subcutaneous (*s.c.*), intramuscular (*i.m.*), and intravascular; but drugs may also be applied to the skin or injected intradermally, for local effect or to be absorbed percutaneously; they may be inhaled for direct action on the bronchial tree or to be absorbed into blood at the alveoli; they may be injected into or near the spinal canal; they may be introduced intravaginally. We shall discuss the principal routes of administration, their peculiar advantages and disadvantages, and the various determinants of the rate of onset and the duration of drug action.

Intravascular Administration

The common method of introducing a drug directly into the blood stream is to inject it intravenously (*i.v.*), usually into the antecubital vein. The obvious advantage of this route is that the drug is placed in the circulation with minimum delay, a matter of great importance when speed is essential. Another advantage is controllability. The injection can be made slowly, and it can be stopped instantaneously if untoward effects should develop. Large quantities of fluid can be introduced over a long time by means of a constant infusion apparatus, and thus the rate of drug administration can be held constant for indefinite periods. Sometimes it is important that the drug concentration in plasma be held within fairly narrow limits, or that it not fall below some desired minimum; in such instances the establishment and maintenance of a plasma plateau by means of continuous infusion (p. 295) necessitates use of the intravenous route. The intravenous route is also suited for substances that cannot be absorbed well from tissue depots or the gastrointestinal tract, or that would be destroyed before appreciable absorption could occur (e.g., whole blood, blood plasma and plasma substitutes, and protein hormones). Finally, drugs that would be intolerably painful in the subcutaneous or muscle tissues by virtue of their irritant properties may often be injected slowly into a vein without any difficulty; an example is nitrogen mustard (p. 3), used in cancer chemotherapy.

The intravenous route has drawbacks. A drug once injected into a vein cannot be recalled, whereas a stomach pump or emetic can remove material from the stomach, and various procedures can delay absorption from a subcutaneous depot. Too rapid an injection rate may evoke catastrophic effects in the circulatory and respiratory systems. Blood pressure may fall to dangerous levels, cardiac irregularities or arrest may ensue, respiration may become shallow and irregular.

These effects, in their speed of onset and in their manifestations, do not resemble anaphylactoid reactions (cf. chapter 7). They may be seen even with simple salt solutions or other pharmacologically inert substances if these are injected rapidly enough. Probably the precipitating factor is a transient wave of concentrated solute suddenly reaching the myocardium and the chemoreceptors in the aortic arch and carotid sinus. The possible magnitude of solute concentration to which these tissues may be exposed can be calculated readily. Let x be the total dose (in grams) of a drug to be injected intravenously in order to achieve a therapeutic concentration throughout the body water at eventual equilibrium. In a 70-kg man with about 42 liters of body water, this eventual concentration (ignoring elimination processes) will be $(x/42)$ mg/ml. Now suppose the injection is made into a vein in a period of 1 second. The blood returning to the heart in one second is 1/60 of the cardiac output (6 liters/min), or about 100 ml. Since all the injected drug will pass through the lungs, reach the heart, and be expelled into the aorta, we shall have $(x/100)$ g/ml, or $10x$ mg/ml, for a period of 1 second in these tissues. This is a 400-fold higher concentration than the therapeutic level that will be reached eventually, at equilibrium. Even if we assume that the concentration is tolerable if the total amount of drug is dissolved in the whole volume of circulating plasma, calculation still indicates a transient 30-fold excess over this concentration after a 1-second injection.

Safety, therefore, demands that all intravenous injections be performed slowly, preferably over a period not much less than that required for a complete circulation of the blood, i.e., 1 minute. Quite apart from the need to avoid high transient drug concentrations, one wishes to be able, if necessary, to discontinue the administration if anything untoward happens; and many seconds may be required for adverse reactions to develop. The circulation time, for example, between the antecubital vein and the brain is roughly 10 to 15 seconds. If sudden loss of consciousness or convulsions were to occur 15 seconds after the start of a drug injection, the difference between having emptied the syringe and having it still three-quarters full could be very significant for the patient's welfare. The same argument applies to the consequences of accidentally injecting a wrong solution, whether a wrong drug or the right drug at a wrong concentration.

Anaphylactoid reactions, caused by administration of a drug to a sensitized individual (cf. chapter 7), may be especially severe after intravenous injection, probably because of the sudden massive antigen-antibody reaction. When the drug is given by other routes, its access to antibody molecules is necessarily slower; moreover, its further absorption can be retarded or prevented at the first sign of a serious allergic reaction.

Embolism is another possible complication of the intravenous route. Particulate matter may be introduced if a drug intended for intravenous use precipitates for some reason, or if a particulate suspension intended for intramuscular or subcutaneous use is inadvertently given into a vein. Hemolysis or agglutination of erythrocytes may be caused by injection of hypotonic or hypertonic solutions, or by more specific mechanisms. Some drugs damage the vascular wall and lead to local venous thrombosis, especially after prolonged infusions.

Infection by bacterial contaminants was commonplace until the development of aseptic technique, and the infectious hepatitis virus was sometimes spread from person to person by syringes and needles until disposable sets came into use. Self-administration of drugs, particularly by narcotic addicts, remains a cause of infection because asepsis is usually ignored. Intravenous injection of drugs was long complicated by the development of fever due to pyrogens in water, especially when large volumes were infused. The pyrogenic substances (bacterial lipopolysaccharides) are heat stable but can be removed by special procedures; thus, solutions for injection are now prepared in pyrogen-free water. Finally, excessive amounts of fluid (e.g., salt solutions given intravenously) may lead to elevated blood pressure and cardiovascular failure, especially when renal function is deficient.

The intra-arterial route is used rarely, principally for the injection of substances used diagnostically. A typical example is the injection of a radiopaque compound into the carotid artery to visualize the circulation of the brain roentgenographically. Certain specialized techniques in cancer chemotherapy call for regional infusions of drugs by an arterial route.

Intramuscular Administration

Drugs injected into skeletal muscle (usually in the deltoid or gluteal regions) are generally absorbed rapidly. Blood flow through the muscles at rest is about 0.02 to 0.07 ml/min per gram of tissue, and this flow rate may increase many times during exercise as additional vascular channels open. Quite large amounts of solution can be introduced intramuscularly, and there is usually less pain and local irritation than is encountered by the subcutaneous route. Ordinary aqueous solutions of drugs are usually absorbed from an intramuscular site within 10 to 30 minutes, but faster or slower absorption is possible, depending upon the vascularity of the site, the ionization and lipid solubility of the drug, the volume of the injection, the osmolality of the solution, and probably other variables. Small molecules are absorbed directly into the capillaries from an intramuscular site, whereas larger molecules (e.g., proteins) gain access to the circulation by way of the lymphatic channels.

Drugs that are insoluble at tissue pH, or that are in an oily vehicle, form a depot in the muscle tissue, from which absorption proceeds very slowly. Because frequently repeated injections are inconvenient to patients and physicians alike, much ingenuity has been expended in developing *depot preparations* of various drugs for intramuscular use. For example, the procaine salt of penicillin is injected as a microcrystalline suspension that dissolves and enters the blood stream over a period of a few days. The kinetics of absorption from depots and some of the advantages and disadvantages of depot preparations are discussed fully later.

Subcutaneous Administration

Absorption of drugs from the subcutaneous tissues is influenced by the same factors that determine the rate of absorption from intramuscular sites. Blood flow is said to be poorer than in muscle, so the absorption rate is often stated to be slower. Actually, there seems to be no simple way to measure blood flow in a subcutaneous area. Some drugs, at least, are known to be absorbed as rapidly from subcutaneous tissues as from muscle. Figure 2-2 illustrates this for an anionic dye administered (as the sodium salt) by either route to dogs. The rates of absorption, reflected by increases in plasma level, were essentially the same by both routes. The generalization that intramuscular injection affords faster rates of absorption than subcutaneous injection needs critical re-examination.

Certain drugs produce severe pain when injected subcutaneously; local necrosis and sterile abscesses may also occur. Some agents have to be administered intravenously because no solution concentrated enough to be useful can be given subcutaneously or intramuscularly.

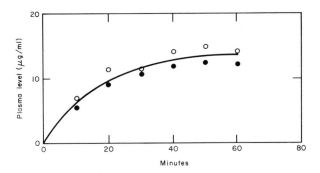

FIG. 2-2.   ABSORPTION OF AN ANIONIC DYE FROM SUBCUTANEOUS AND INTRA-
MUSCULAR SITES IN THE DOG.   *Phenolsulfonphthalein (PSP) was given as the
sodium salt at a dose of 20 mg/kg, and plasma levels were measured periodically.* Solid circles *represent intramuscular injection;* open circles, *subcutaneous
injection. Each point is the mean plasma level in five dogs. (A. Goldstein, unpublished data.)*

The rate of absorption from a subcutaneous depot may be retarded
by immobilization of the limb, local cooling to cause vasoconstriction, and
application of a tourniquet proximal to the injection site to block the superficial venous drainage and lymphatic flow. These techniques, customarily
applied to slow down venom absorption in snake bites, are also of value in
the emergency treatment of adverse drug reactions after subcutaneous or
intramuscular administration. Epinephrine, in minute amounts, may be
incorporated with a subcutaneous injection in order to constrict the local
vasculature and thereby retard absorption. This is of special value when
the injected drug is meant to act locally at the injection site rather than
systemically. The best example is the inclusion of epinephrine in preparations of local anesthetic agents to prolong their action on sensory nerve
fibers passing through the subcutaneous tissues. Drugs may affect the rate
of their own absorption if they alter the blood supply or capillary permeability locally. Methacholine, for example, causes vascular dilation as
part of its cholinergic action; consequently it enters the blood stream so
rapidly from a subcutaneous site that it causes systemic effects as early as
1½ minutes after injection.

A prime determinant of the absorption rate from a subcutaneous
depot is the total surface area over which the absorption can occur. Although the subcutaneous tissues are somewhat loose, and moderate amounts
of fluid can be administered, the normal connective tissue prevents indefinite lateral spread of the injected solution. These barriers may be overcome with the aid of hyaluronidase, an enzyme that breaks down mucopolysaccharides of the connective tissue matrix; the resulting spread of injected solution leads to a much faster absorption rate. This technique is

sometimes used for administering large fluid volumes to infants, in whom continuous intravenous infusions present special difficulties.

An effective way of achieving slow absorption for a long time is to incorporate a drug into a compressed pellet that can be implanted under the skin. The drug must be relatively insoluble and the pellet must resist disintegration by the subcutaneous fluid environment. These conditions have been achieved with certain steroid hormones.[1] Pellets of testosterone, of a cylindrical shape, about 5 mm in diameter, 5 mm thick, and weighing 100 mg, were implanted subcutaneously into human subjects. Upon removal at different intervals for individual subjects, the pellets were weighed carefully and the weight loss thus determined. Figure 2-3 shows that the absorption rate was nearly constant at about 1 per cent per day for two months and then diminished gradually, with absorption essentially complete at five to six months. For spherical pellets the ratio of surface area to volume increases with decreasing diameter. Thus, when drugs are prepared as spheres of known diameter the rate of absorption can be predicted; the larger the spheres the slower the rate of absorption of a given amount of drug. This principle has been used in the design of long-acting insulin preparations; the so-called Lente insulins are small zinc insulin crystals (about 30μ), of uniform size to provide a reproducible rate of absorption.

The ideal shape of a subcutaneous pellet for achieving a constant rate of absorption would be a flat disc. Absorption should occur almost

FIG. 2-3. RATE OF ABSORPTION OF TESTOSTERONE PELLETS IN HUMAN SUBJECTS. *Pellets weighed 100 mg and were cylindrical (diameter 2.5 mm, thickness 4.6 mm). Implantation sites were subcutaneous. Each point represents a pellet in a single subject. Pellets were weighed initially and again after removal. The curve is a theoretical one calculated from an arbitrary rate constant of absorption and the assumption that absorption rate is proportional to surface area throughout the dissolution process. (From Bishop and Folley.[1])*

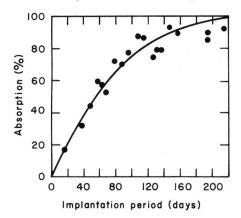

[1] P. M. F. BISHOP and S. J. FOLLEY: Implantation of testosterone in cast pellets. *Lancet 1:*434 (1944).

exclusively from the two opposite surfaces, since the area of the edge is negligibly small by comparison. Moreover, the exposed area for absorption would hardly change at all as the disc becomes thinner, so that the absorption rate should be nearly constant until practically all the drug is absorbed. Studies in rats have verified the correctness of these predictions.

Absorption of Drugs through the Skin

The skin efficiently retards the diffusion and evaporation of water except at the sweat glands; the outer, horny layer, densely packed with keratin, is probably responsible. Beneath the horny layer, and separating it from the underlying granular layer of epithelial cells, is the so-called *barrier area,* a clear dense region quite different from the horny layer both in microsocopic appearance and in chemical properties. Permeability studies show that if all the horny layer is stripped away but the barrier area is left intact, little change in permeability occurs although water loss increases. But removal of the barrier area leads to an abrupt increase in permeability for all kinds of molecules, large and small, lipid-soluble and water-soluble. Thus the underlying dermis, which consists of loosely arranged connective tissue and capillaries, is freely permeable. Only a few systematic studies on skin permeability have yet been carried out, but from these it appears that the intact epidermis behaves qualitatively like cellular membranes in general. Drugs penetrate at rates determined largely by their lipid/water partition coefficients (p. 153), water-soluble ions and molecules (except for the very smallest) being practically excluded.[2] Even highly lipid-soluble substances penetrate skin slowly in comparison with their rates of penetration of other, thinner, cellular membranes.

Toxic effects are often produced by the accidental absorption through the skin of highly lipid-soluble substances used for various industrial purposes. General experience leads people to suppose that the skin is a reliable protection against the environment, so little thought is given to the possibility of poisoning by this route. Carbon tetrachloride and other organic solvents penetrate the body in this way and can cause serious toxic effects. Organic phosphate (DFP, parathion, malathion) and nicotine insecticides have caused deaths in agricultural workers as a result of percutaneous absorption. Chlorovinylarsine dichloride (lewisite), a mustard gas, is readily absorbed through the intact skin.

Drugs may be applied to the skin for local effect, especially on the superficial layers of the epidermis. They may be incorporated into vehicles (creams, ointments) that will adhere to the skin and permit the drug to diffuse out, or baths containing the drug may be employed. However, if

---

[2] R. D. GRIESEMER: "Protection Against the Transfer of Matter Through the Skin," in *The Human Integument, Normal and Abnormal,* ed. by S. Rothman. Washington, D.C., Publication No. 54 of the American Association for the Advancement of Science, 1959, p. 25.

the drug is water soluble, and if the pathologic condition is in the deeper layers of the epidermis, or in the dermis, systemic administration of the drug is necessary. Thus, antibacterial and antifungal agents are often much more effective in skin infections when given by mouth or by injection than when applied to the skin surface.

Recent studies[3] have suggested the possibility of using pharmacologically inactive solvents to facilitate the penetration of drugs through the skin. Dimethyl sulfoxide (CH_3SOCH_3, DMSO) is a liquid, miscible with water and with many organic solvents, that has been tried as a vehicle for certain drugs. When applied to the human skin it causes erythema, dehydration, and defatting, as would any organic solvent. In aqueous solution, however, up to 20 per cent DMSO produced no adverse effects. Three drugs with DMSO as vehicle were studied in human subjects: a quaternary anticholinergic agent, hexopyrronium bromide; a sympathomimetic amine, naphazoline; and a steroid, fluocinolone. Absorption from the volar surface of the forearm was measured, and also local effects deep in the skin were observed (inhibition of sweating, vasoconstriction, pilomotion). DMSO promoted the absorption of hexopyrronium and of naphazoline, but there was less effect on the steroid, perhaps because it was absorbed so well anyway. Local effects were increased in proportion to the increased absorption.

DMSO has very low toxicity in laboratory animals, but untoward effects were observed during clinical trials in humans. It is too early to say, therefore, whether this compound or a related one will have any practical importance for dermatologic therapy, or for expanding the usefulness of the percutaneous route for drugs with systemic actions.

Electrical gradients have been used to drive drugs into the skin in the method known as *iontophoresis*. An ionized drug in solution is placed in an absorbent material on the skin in contact with an electrode. By applying a galvanic current to this electrode and to another placed elsewhere on the body surface, the drug ions are made to migrate through the epidermis. Studies with iodine 131 have shown that this method is quite efficient, at least for introducing very small amounts of drugs into the skin and general circulation.[4] The reproducibility, however, between subjects and even between different skin areas in the same subject leaves much to be desired. The general utility of the method is obviously rather limited.

Inhalation of Drugs

Drugs may be inhaled as gases and enter the circulation by diffusing across the alveolar membranes. This is the mode of administration of the volatile anesthetics. These drugs all have relatively high lipid/water

3 R. B. STOUGHTON and W. FRITSCH: Influence of dimethylsulfoxide (DMSO) on human percutaneous absorption. *Arch. Dermatol.* 90:512 (1964).

4 R. GHYS: La résorption cutanée de l'iode radioactif introduit par iontophorèse chez l'homme. *Strahlentherapie 105:*457 (1958).

partition coefficients, and inasmuch as their atomic or molecular radii are quite small and the alveolar membrane is quite permeable, they all equilibrate practically instantaneously with blood in the alveolar capillaries. The interesting differences among these agents in the kinetics of their equilibration in whole body water and in the rates of onset and offset of their anesthetic effects depend primarily upon their aqueous solubilities (blood/air partition coefficients). This will be discussed fully elsewhere (p. 323).

Drugs may also be inhaled as *aerosols*,[5] and many toxic substances enter the body in this way. Aerosols are liquid or solid particles so small that they remain suspended in air for a long time instead of sedimenting rapidly under the force of gravity. Table 2-1 gives sedimentation rate as a function of particle diameter, computed from Stokes' law for the viscous drag on a moving sphere.

Stokes' law:

$$f = 6\pi nrv,$$

where f is force in dynes; n is viscosity of air at 20° and atmospheric pressure and is equal to 1.9×10^{-4} g sec^{-1}cm^{-1}; r is radius of sphere in cm; and v is constant velocity of movement when force f is balanced by the viscous drag.

For a sphere moving under the force of gravity, $f = $ mass $\times g$, where $g = 980$ cm sec^{-2};

and assuming unit density,

$$f = \frac{4}{3} \pi r^3 g.$$

TABLE 2-1.   **Rate of gravitational sedimentation in quiet air as a function of particle size**

Sedimentation rates are computed from Stokes' law as described in the text.

Particle diameter (μ)	Sedimentation rate (cm/sec)
100	28.7
50	7.17
25	1.79
10	0.287
5	0.072
1	0.0029

[5] T. F. HATCH and P. GROSS: *Pulmonary Deposition and Retention of Inhaled Aerosols.* New York, Academic Press, 1964.

When the viscous drag opposes the force of gravity so that the rate of fall is constant,

$$6\pi n r v = \frac{4}{3} \pi r^3 g$$

$$v = \frac{D^2 g}{18n} \text{ (where } D \text{ is diameter of sphere in cm)}$$

$$v = 2.87 \times 10^5 D^2.$$

Particles below about 10μ in diameter are of interest for the present discussion. Examples are bacteria and viruses, smoke, industrial fumes, dust laden with fission products from nuclear explosions, pollens, insecticide dusts or sprays, and inhalant sprays used in the therapy of pulmonary disease.

Impaction is the term used to describe the deposition of aerosol particles in the respiratory tract. The degree of impaction is determined by the rates of sedimentation, diffusion, and inertial precipitation. In considering the rate of movement of substances within the respiratory tract, diffusion may be ignored, except for very small particles. Inertial precipitation arises from the tendency of a particle moving in a stream of air to continue in its original direction when the air current changes direction, and thus to impact upon some tissue. This occurs, for example, at bronchial branch points.

The extent of impaction in different parts of the respiratory tract may be computed for particles of various sizes, and such computations have been confirmed by some experimental data. In the nasal passages large particles ($> 10\mu$) are almost completely removed; particles 5μ in diameter are removed to an extent of about one-half; and particles 2μ in diameter, to an extent of about one-fifth. Below 1μ, nasal impaction is negligible. Table 2-2 gives theoretical results for particle sizes between 0.2 and 20μ, at two extreme values of the tidal air. The following conclusions may be drawn: (*1*) The larger the particle the greater its tendency to impact and be retained in the upper respiratory tract. (*2*) At high tidal volumes and the same respiratory rate, the airstream velocity is greater, and so particles of all sizes tend to be driven deeper into the pulmonary tree before impacting. (*3*) As particles become smaller, their retention is primarily limited to the most peripheral parts of the pulmonary tree, beyond the terminal bronchioles, but the total retention is substantially less than for larger particles. (*4*) When particles become extremely small (0.2μ), the total retention begins to increase again, probably because diffusion becomes a significant factor in the translocation of particles from the lumen to the walls of the bronchioles and alveoli.

A mucous blanket, propelled cephalad by ciliary movements, covers the upper respiratory tract down to the terminal bronchioles, and impacted

TABLE 2-2.   **Per cent retention of inhaled aerosol particles in various regions of the respiratory tract**

The figures in the columns are per cent retention; the column headings are particle sizes in μ. A 4-sec respiratory cycle is assumed. (From Hatch and Gross,[5] Table 3-4.)

	Per cent retention									
	450 cm³ Tidal air					1500 cm³ Tidal air				
	20	6	2	0.6	0.2	20	6	2	0.6	0.2
Mouth	15	0	0	0	0	18	1	0	0	0
Pharynx	8	0	0	0	0	10	1	0	0	0
Trachea	10	1	0	0	0	19	3	0	0	0
Pulmonary bronchi	12	2	0	0	0	20	5	1	0	0
Secondary bronchi	19	4	1	0	0	21	12	2	0	0
Tertiary bronchi	17	9	2	0	0	9	20	5	0	0
Quarternary bronchi	6	7	2	1	1	1	10	3	1	1
Terminal bronchioles	6	19	6	4	6	1	9	3	2	4
Respiratory bronchioles	0	11	5	3	4	0	3	2	2	4
Alveolar ducts	0	25	25	8	11	0	13	26	10	13
Alveolar sacs	0	5	0	0	0	0	18	17	6	7
Totals	93	83	41	16	22	99	95	59	21	29

aerosol particles are cleared by this mechanism. Particles that deposit in the alveolar sacs must first be transported up to the mucous layer, presumably in a fluid film covering the epithelium, but the exact mechanism is not known. Particles in the alveoli are also ingested by phagocytic cells. The efficiency of clearance of solid particles from the lungs is remarkable. For example, not more than a minute fraction of all the mineral dust inhaled during a lifetime is retained in the lungs. However, a small decrease in the clearance capacity of the lungs could cause a marked increase in the amount of retained particulate matter; this may be a factor leading to the development of pneumoconiosis in miners exposed to silica dusts.

Particle size strongly influences the rate at which material is absorbed through the alveolar epithelium, probably because of the greatly increased surface area for solubilization as particle diameter becomes smaller. For example, particles of uranium dioxide larger than 3μ had no toxic effect whatsoever when introduced into the trachea in rats, but the same relatively insoluble material caused kidney damage when smaller particles were employed.[5a]

[5a] H. P. DYGERT, C. W. LA BELLE, S. LASKIN, U. C. POZZANI, E. ROBERTS, J. J. ROTHER-MEL, A. ROTHSTEIN, C. J. SPIEGL, G. F. SPRAGUE, JR., and H. E. STOKINGER: "Toxicity Following Inhalation," chapter 10 in *Pharmacology and Toxicology of Uranium Compounds,* ed. by C. Voegtlin and H. C. Hodge, New York, McGraw-Hill, 1949.

Drugs in aerosol form can elicit very rapid responses when inhaled. Histamine or pilocarpine administered in this way to dogs or guinea pigs can cause bronchiolar constriction and fatal asphyxia within 1 minute. An aerosol containing atropine can reverse within a minute the bronchospasm caused by a carbachol aerosol.

Particles larger than 2μ in diameter probably do not reach the alveolar sacs, as shown in Table 2-2. Some commercially available nebulizers apparently produce particles 1 to 3.5μ in diameter, so most of the deposition will occur in the larger bronchial passages. But for most effective therapy the smallest bronchi and alveolar ducts should be reached by the drug, so particles smaller than 1μ in diameter are desirable. A technique that promotes deposition of particles is for the subject to hold his breath after inhalation, to maximize the effective time for particle diffusion. Another technique is to add hygroscopic substances to the aerosol; the droplets then become larger as they traverse the moist respiratory tract, and the rate of impaction due to sedimentation is increased.

With aerosols of small particle size the amount of drug reaching the alveoli may be large; and since the rate of absorption into the blood stream is much more rapid at the alveolar sacs than elsewhere in the pulmonary tree, the systemic absorption of the drug may be appreciable. Hence care must be exercised in giving drugs such as the sympathomimetic bronchodilators by aerosol to avoid side effects on the cardiovascular system. Isoproterenol, for example, in a 0.5 per cent aerosol, is an effective bronchodilator, but a 1 per cent aerosol is apt to cause undesirable cardio-accelerator and hypotensive actions after only a few inhalations. On the other hand, the efficient absorption at the alveoli can be turned to advantage when systemic effects are desired. Among the substances that have been administered by aerosol for their systemic actions are penicillin, digitalis glycosides, diuretics, and tranquilizers.

Therapy by inhalation has not been exploited very widely. In general, this route should be used whenever rapid relief is needed intermittently from acute exacerbations of a chronic illness, and especially if self-administration of a drug is desirable. Thus, aerosols of epinephrine or aminophylline are commonly employed for acute asthmatic attacks, and antibiotics are sometimes incorporated for the treatment of complicating bronchopulmonary infections. For a person allergic to bee venom the inhalation of epinephrine from a nebulizer may avert an anaphylactic episode.

Administration of Drugs by the Enteral Route

Drugs are given most commonly by mouth. This is certainly the most convenient route, and it is the only one of practical importance for self-administration. Absorption, in general, takes place along the whole length of the gastrointestinal tract, but the chemical properties of each drug determine whether it will be absorbed in the strongly acid stomach or in the nearly neutral intestine. Gastric absorption is favored by an empty stomach, in which the drug, in undiluted gastric juice, will have good access to the mucosal wall. Drug absorption is impeded by food, both because access to the gastrointestinal wall is impeded and, for those drugs absorbed in the intestine, because food delays gastric emptying. Only when a drug would be irritating to the gastric mucosa is it rational to administer it with or after a meal. However, the antibiotic griseofulvin is an example of a substance with poor water solubility, the absorption of which is aided by a fatty meal.[6] The large surface area of the intestinal villi, the presence of bile, and the rich blood supply all favor intestinal absorption.

Drugs are occasionally administered by rectum, but most are not as well absorbed here as from the upper intestine. Aminophylline, used in suppository form for the management of asthma, is one of the few drugs routinely given in this way. Inert vehicles employed for suppository preparations include cocoa butter, glycerinated gelatin, and polyethylene glycol. Because the rectal mucosa is irritated by anisotonic solutions, fluids administered by this route should always be isotonic with plasma (e.g., 0.9 per cent NaCl).

The principles governing the absorption of drugs from the gastrointestinal lumen are the same as for the passage of drugs across biologic membranes elsewhere (p. 145). Low degree of ionization, high lipid/water partition coefficient of the nonionized form, and small atomic or molecular radius of water-soluble substances all favor rapid absorption. Water passes readily in both directions across the wall of the gastrointestinal lumen. Sodium ion is probably transported actively from lumen into blood. Magnesium ion is very poorly absorbed and therefore acts as a cathartic, retaining an osmotic equivalent of water as it passes down the intestinal tract. Ionic iron is absorbed as an amino acid complex, at a rate usually determined by the body's need for iron. Glucose and amino acids are transported across the intestinal wall by specific carrier systems. Some compounds of high molecular weight (polysaccharides, neutral fats) cannot be absorbed *until* they are degraded enzymically. Other substances are not absorbed *because* they are destroyed by gastrointestinal enzymes; insulin, epinephrine, histamine are examples. Substances that form insoluble precipitates in the gastrointestinal lumen or that are not soluble either in water or in lipid obviously cannot be absorbed.

ABSORPTION OF WEAK ACIDS AND BASES

The gastric juice is very acid (about pH 1), whereas the intestinal contents are nearly neutral (actually very slightly acid). The pH difference between plasma (pH 7.4) and the lumen of the gastrointestinal tract plays a major role in determining whether a drug that is a weak electrolyte will

---

[6] R. G. CROUNSE: Human pharmacology of griseofulvin: the effect of fat intake on gastrointestinal absorption. *J. Invest. Dermatol. 37:*529 (1961).

be absorbed into plasma, or whether it will be excreted from plasma into the stomach or intestine. We may assume, for practical purposes, that the mucosal lining of the gastrointestinal tract is impermeable to the ionized form of a weak acid or base (p. 156), but that the nonionized form equilibrates freely. The rate of equilibration of the nonionized molecule is directly related to its lipid solubility. If there is a pH difference across the membrane, then the fraction ionized may be considerably greater on one side than on the other. At equilibrium, the concentration of the *nonionized* moiety will be the same on both sides, but there will be more *total* drug on the side where the degree of ionization is greater. This mechanism is known as *ion trapping*. The energy for sustaining the unequal chemical potential of the acid or base in question is derived from whatever mechanism maintains the pH difference; in the stomach this mechanism is the energy-dependent active secretion of hydrogen ions against a concentration gradient.

Consider how a weak electrolyte distributes across the gastric mucosa between plasma (pH 7.4) and gastric fluid (pH 1.0). In each compartment the Henderson-Hasselbalch equation gives the ratio of the concentrations (base)/(acid)[6a]:

$$pH = pK_a + \log \frac{(base)}{(acid)},$$

$$\log \frac{(base)}{(acid)} = pH - pK_a,$$

$$\frac{(base)}{(acid)} = antilog\ (pH - pK_a).$$

For a weak acid with $pK_a = 3$, $pH - pK_a = 4.4$ in plasma and -2 in stomach. Thus, in plasma at equilibrium, log [(base)/(acid)] = 4.4, and (base)/(acid) = 25000. In stomach, log [(base)/(acid)] = −2, and (base)/(acid) = 0.01. Now for a weak acid it is the acid moiety that is nonionized and is in free equilibrium in both compartments:

Plasma pH 7.4		Stomach pH 1.0
$H^+ + A^- \rightleftharpoons HA \rightleftharpoons$	$\rightleftharpoons HA \rightleftharpoons H^+ + A^-$	
25,000 $\rightleftharpoons$ 1 $\rightleftharpoons$	$\rightleftharpoons$ 1 $\rightleftharpoons$ 0.01	
Total drug (i.e., base + acid):		
25,001	1.01	
or:		
24,800	1	

6a In the following discussion, for the sake of simplicity, the term pK_a will be used in place of the more rigorously correct pK_a'.

For a weak base with the same pK_a, the fraction (base)/(acid) in each compartment will, of course, be exactly the same as above. The difference is that now the nonionized form, which has to be equated on both sides, is the base:

	Plasma	Stomach
$\dfrac{\text{(base)}}{\text{(acid)}}$	$\dfrac{25{,}000}{1}$ ⇌	$\dfrac{0.01}{1}$

Rewriting these fractions to equate the numerators, we obtain

	Plasma	Stomach
	$\dfrac{1}{4 \times 10^{-5}}$ ⇌	$\dfrac{1}{100}$

	Plasma	Stomach
Total drug concentration ratio	1	101

The conclusions are obvious. Weak acids are absorbed readily from the stomach. Weak bases are not absorbed well; indeed, they would tend to accumulate within the stomach at the expense of drug in the blood stream. Naturally, in the more alkaline intestine, bases would be absorbed better, acids more poorly.

A simple general equation to describe the concentration ratios of a drug on both sides of a membrane at equilibrium, as determined by the ion trapping mechanism, may be derived as follows:[7]

Let the two sides be at pH_I and pH_{II}. Then

$$pH = pK_a + \log \frac{\text{(base)}}{\text{(acid)}},$$

$$\log \frac{\text{(base)}}{\text{(acid)}} = pH - pK_a$$

$$\frac{\text{(base)}}{\text{(acid)}} = 10^{(pH - pK_a)}$$

and R, the ratio of total drug concentration on side I to that on side II, is given by

$$R = \frac{\text{(acid}_I) + \text{(base}_I)}{\text{(acid}_{II}) + \text{(base}_{II})} .$$

Substituting base $=$ acid$\cdot 10^{(pH - pK_a)}$, we obtain

$$R = \frac{\text{(acid}_I) \, [1 + 10^{(pH_I - pK_a)}]}{\text{(acid}_{II}) \, [1 + 10^{(pH_{II} - pK_a)}]} .$$

[7] M. H. JACOBS: Some aspects of cell permeability to weak electrolytes. *Cold Spring Harbor Symp. Quant. Biol.* 8:30 (1940).

For acids,
$$(\text{acid}_\text{I}) = (\text{acid}_\text{II}), \text{ so that}$$

$$R = \frac{1 + 10^{(\text{pH}_\text{I} - \text{pK}_\text{a})}}{1 + 10^{(\text{pH}_\text{II} - \text{pK}_\text{a})}}$$

$$R = \frac{1 + \text{antilog } (\text{pH}_\text{I} - \text{pK}_\text{a})}{1 + \text{antilog } (\text{pH}_\text{II} - \text{pK}_\text{a})}.$$

For bases,

$$(\text{acid}) = \frac{(\text{base})}{10^{(\text{pH} - \text{pK}_\text{a})}} = (\text{base}) \cdot 10^{(\text{pK}_\text{a} - \text{pH})}$$

$$R = \frac{(\text{base}_\text{I}) \, [1 + 10^{(\text{pK}_\text{a} - \text{pH}_\text{I})}]}{(\text{base}_\text{II}) \, [1 + 10^{(\text{pK}_\text{a} - \text{pH}_\text{II})}]};$$

and since $(\text{base}_\text{I}) = (\text{base}_\text{II})$,

$$R = \frac{1 + 10^{(\text{pK}_\text{a} - \text{pH}_\text{I})}}{1 + 10^{(\text{pK}_\text{a} - \text{pH}_\text{II})}}$$

$$R = \frac{1 + \text{antilog } (\text{pK}_\text{a} - \text{pH}_\text{I})}{1 + \text{antilog } (\text{pK}_\text{a} - \text{pH}_\text{II})}.$$

It should be realized that although the principles outlined here are correct, the system is dynamic, not static. Drug molecules that are absorbed across the gastric or intestinal mucosa are removed constantly by blood flow; thus, simple reversible equilibrium across the membrane does not occur until the drug is distributed throughout the body.

Absorption from the stomach, as determined by direct measurements, conforms, in general, to the principles outlined above. Organic acids are absorbed well since they are all almost completely nonionized at the gastric pH; indeed, many of these substances are absorbed faster than ethyl alcohol, which had long been considered one of the few compounds that were absorbed well from the stomach. Strong acids whose pK_a values lie below 1, which are ionized even in the acid contents of the stomach, are not absorbed well. Weak bases are absorbed only negligibly, but their absorption can be increased, as expected, by raising the pH of the gastric fluid. All this is shown in Table 2-3, the results of experiments in which drugs were placed in the ligated stomachs of rats and the residual amounts determined after 1 hour. Especially interesting is the effect of changing the stomach pH by addition of sodium bicarbonate. Acids like salicylic and nitrosalicylic acids, with pK_a's well on the acid side of neutrality, were absorbed much more poorly when the gastric acidity had been neutralized, for they were then almost completely ionized. Very weak acids like thiopental and phenol were but little affected by the same pH change, since even at pH 8 they remained almost wholly nonionized.

TABLE 2-3.   Absorption of organic acids and organic bases from the rat stomach

The per cent absorbed in 1 hour is expressed as mean ± range, followed by the number of experiments in parentheses. (After Schanker et al.,[8] Tables I and II.)

	pK_a	Per cent absorbed in 1 hour	
		0.1M HCl	NaHCO$_3$, pH 8
Acid			
5-Sulfosalicylic	(strong)	0 ± 0 (2)	0 ± 0 (2)
Phenolsulfonphthalein	(strong)	2 ± 2 (3)	2 ± 1 (2)
5-Nitrosalicylic	2.3	52 ± 3 (2)	16 ± 2 (2)
Salicylic	3.0	61 ± 7 (4)	13 ± 1 (2)
Acetylsalicylic	3.5	35 ± 4 (3)	—
Benzoic	4.2	55 ± 3 (2)	—
Thiopental	7.6	46 ± 3 (2)	34 ± 2 (2)
p-Hydroxypropiophenone	7.8	55 ± 3 (2)	—
Barbital	7.8	4 ± 3 (4)	—
Secobarbital	7.9	30 ± 2 (2)	—
Phenol	9.9	40 ± 5 (3)	40 ± 5 (3)
Base			
Acetanilid	0.3	36 ± 3 (2)	—
Caffeine	0.8	24 ± 3 (2)	—
Antipyrine	1.4	14 ± 3 (4)	—
m-Nitroaniline	2.5	17 ± 0 (2)	—
Aniline	4.6	6 ± 4 (3)	56 ± 3 (2)
Aminopyrine	5.0	2 ± 2 (3)	—
p-Toluidine	5.3	0 ± 0 (2)	47 ± 4 (2)
α-Acetylmethadol	8.3	0 ± 0 (4)	—
Quinine	8.4	0 ± 0 (2)	18 ± 2 (2)
Dextrorphan, levorphanol	9.2	0 ± 2 (8)	16 ± 1 (2)
Ephedrine	9.6	3 ± 3 (2)	—
Tolazoline	10.3	7 ± 2 (4)	—
Mecamylamine	11.2	0 ± 0 (2)	—
Darstine	(cation)	0 ± 0 (2)	—
Procaine amide ethobromide	(cation)	0 ± 0 (2)	5 ± 1 (2)
Tetraethylammonium	(cation)	0 ± 1 (2)	—

The three barbituric acid derivatives studied (Table 2-3, thiopental, barbital, secobarbital) are interesting because, although they have about the same pK_a, the extent of their gastric absorption differed considerably. This is related to the difference in lipid/water partition coefficients of their nonionized forms. Measurements in a number of organic solvents have revealed that thiopental has the highest partition coefficient, secobarbital a considerably smaller one, barbital the smallest of all.

[8] L. S. SCHANKER, P. A. SHORE, B. B. BRODIE, and C. A. M. HOGBEN: Absorption of drugs from the stomach. I. The rat. *J. Pharmacol. Exp Therap. 120:*528 (1957).

As for bases, only the weakest were absorbed to any appreciable extent (Table 2-3) at normal gastric pH, but their absorption could be increased substantially by neutralizing the stomach contents. The quaternary cations, however, were not absorbed at either pH.

The accumulation of weak bases in the stomach by ion trapping mimics a secretory process; if the drug is administered systemically it accumulates in the stomach. Dogs were given various drugs intravenously by continuous infusion to maintain a constant drug level in the plasma, and the gastric contents were sampled by means of an indwelling catheter. The results, representing concentrations after 30 to 60 minutes, are shown in Table 2-4. Both acids and bases behaved according to expectation. The stronger bases ($pK_a > 5$) accumulated in stomach contents to many times their plasma concentrations; the weak bases appeared in about equal concentrations in gastric juice and in plasma. Among the acids only the weakest appeared in detectable amounts in the stomach. It may be won-

TABLE 2-4.   Gastric secretion of drugs in the dog

Measurements were made 30 to 60 minutes after initiation of continuous intravenous drug infusion. (From Shore et al.,[9] Tables 1 and 3.)

	pK_a	Plasma protein binding (%)	Plasma conc. (total) (mg/ liter)	Gastric juice conc. (mg/ liter)	Gastric / Plasma conc. ratio	Ratio corrected for plasma binding	Theor. ratio
Bases							
Acetanilid	0.3	0	126	126	1.0	1.0	1.0
Theophylline	0.7	15	81	118	1.5	1.3	1.5
Antipyrine	1.4	0	230	938	4.1	4.2	4.2
Aniline	5.0	25	8.5	358	42		10^4
Aminopyrine	5.0	15	24	1010	42		10^4
Quinine	8.4	75	4.7	189	40		10^6
Levorphanol	9.2	50	0.2	8.3	42		10^6
Tolazoline	10.3	23	13.2	135	10		10^6
Acids							
Salicylic	3.0	75	338	0	0	0	10^{-4}
Probenecid	3.4	75	14	0	0	0	10^{-4}
Phenylbutazone	4.4	90	195	0	0	0	10^{-3}
p-Hydroxypropiophenone	7.8	75	5.5	0.62	0.11	0.5	0.6
Thiopental	7.6	75	20	2.0	0.10	0.5	0.6
Barbital	7.8	0	254	152	0.6	0.6	0.6

[9] P. A. SHORE, B. B. BRODIE, and C. A. M. HOGBEN: The gastric secretion of drugs: a pH partition hypothesis. *J. Pharmacol. Exp. Therap.* 119:361 (1957).

dered why the strong bases, which are completely ionized in gastric juice, and whose theoretical concentration ratios (gastric juice/plasma) are very large, should nevertheless have attained only about 40-fold excess over plasma. Direct measurements of arterial and venous blood showed that essentially all the blood flowing through the gastric mucosa was cleared of these drugs; obviously, no more drug could enter the gastric juice in a given time than was brought there by the circulation. Another limitation comes into play when the base pK_a exceeds 7.4; now, a major fraction of the circulating base is cationic and a decreasing fraction is nonionized, so that the effective concentration gradient for diffusion across the stomach wall is reduced.

Absorption from the intestine has been studied by perfusing drug solutions slowly through rat intestine in situ and by varying the pH as desired. The principles that emerge from such studies are the same as those for stomach; the difference is that the intestinal pH is normally near neutrality. Some data are presented in Table 2-5. As the pH was increased, the bases were absorbed better, the acids more poorly. Detailed studies with a great many drugs in unbuffered solutions revealed that in the normal intestine, acids with $pK_a > 3.0$ and bases with $pK_a < 7.8$ are very well absorbed; outside these limits the absorption of acids and bases, respec-

TABLE 2-5.   **In situ intestinal absorption of drugs from solutions of various pH values in the rat**

The per cent absorbed is expressed as mean ± range; figures in parentheses indicate number of animals. (From Hogben et al.,[10] Table 1.)

		Per cent absorbed			
		pH of intestinal solution			
	pK_a	3.6–4.3	4.7–5.0	7.2–7.1	8.0–7.8
Bases					
Aniline	4.6	40 ± 7 (9)	48 ± 5 (5)	58 ± 5 (4)	61 ± 8 (10)
Aminopyrine	5.0	21 ± 1 (2)	35 ± 1 (2)	48 ± 2 (2)	52 ± 2 (2)
p-Toluidine	5.3	30 ± 3 (3)	42 ± 3 (2)	65 ± 4 (3)	64 ± 4 (2)
Quinine	8.4	9 ± 3 (3)	11 ± 2 (2)	41 ± 1 (2)	54 ± 5 (4)
Acids					
5-Nitrosalicylic	2.3	40 ± 0 (2)	27 ± 2 (2)	<2 (2)	<2 (2)
Salicylic	3.0	64 ± 4 (4)	35 ± 4 (2)	30 ± 4 (2)	10 ± 3 (6)
Acetylsalicylic	3.5	41 ± 3 (2)	27 ± 1 (2)	—	—
Benzoic	4.2	62 ± 4 (2)	36 ± 3 (4)	35 ± 4 (3)	5 ± 1 (2)
p-Hydroxypropiophenone	7.8	61 ± 5 (3)	52 ± 2 (2)	67 ± 6 (5)	60 ± 5 (2)

[10] C. A. M. HOGBEN, D. J. TOCCO, B. B. BRODIE, and L. S. SCHANKER: On the mechanism of intestinal absorption of drugs. *J. Pharmacol. Exp. Therap. 125*:275 (1959)

tively, fell off rapidly. This behavior leads to the conclusion that the "virtual pH" in the microenvironment of the absorbing surface in the gut is about 5.3; this is somewhat more acidic than is usually considered to be the pH in the intestinal lumen.

SUSTAINED-RELEASE PREPARATIONS

Some drugs intended for oral administration are manufactured in such a way that they are released slowly into the intestinal lumen. This special form of depot preparation is known as a *sustained-release medication*. Often the drug is applied in soluble form to the outside layer of a tablet that contains an insoluble core (of such materials as synthetic polymers or waxes). More of the same drug trapped inside the core will dissolve as intestinal fluid gains access through pores in the matrix. This arrangement provides an initial dose in the outer coating, followed by delayed release from the core.

Several variables have been shown to affect the rate of release of drugs from sustained-release preparations in vitro; for example, the size of the tablet and concentration of drug determine the surface area for solution and the actual rate at which drug will dissolve. The pore size of the inert matrix and its resistance to sloughing, the presence of water-soluble substances in the matrix, and the intrinsic solubility of the drug in an aqueous medium also affect the rate of release.[11] Obviously the rate of movement of the preparation through the gastrointestinal tract can also affect the amount absorbed.[12] If the intestinal contents move too rapidly, a portion of the drug may be wasted in the feces.

Carried out in a standardized manner, in vitro tests are essential for evaluation and control of sustained-release preparations.[13] But actual measurements of drug blood levels in animals and man are even more pertinent. A typical evaluation is shown in Fig. 2-4. A piperazine derivative was fed to six fasted dogs. The drug was given in ordinary solution or incorporated into a plastic matrix for sustained release (in twice the dose). Notable are the different shapes of the two plasma level curves. If twice as much drug had been given in solution, to match the dose in the sustained-release preparation, the peak plasma level would obviously have been higher than at the lower dose, but the shape of the curve would not be much altered (cf. p. 320). The effect of the sustained-release form was to delay both the rise and the fall of the plasma level, thereby smoothing the undesirable fluctuations.

11 J. LAZARUS, M. PAGLIERY, and L. LACHMAN: Factors influencing the release of a drug from a prolonged-action matrix. *J. Pharm. Sci. 53*:798 (1964).

12 T. M. FEINBLATT and E. A. FERGUSON, JR.: Timed-disintegration capsules. An *in vivo* roentgenographic study. *New Engl. J. Med. 254*:940 (1956).

13 *The Pharmacopeia of the United States of America,* 17th revision. Easton, Pa., Mack Publishing Co., 1965, p. 920.

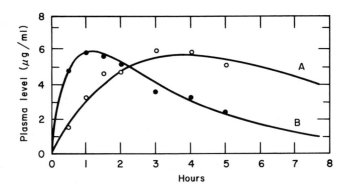

FIG. 2-4.   KINETICS OF PLASMA DRUG LEVELS AFTER ADMINISTRATION OF A
SUSTAINED-RELEASE PREPARATION IN DOGS.   *A piperazine derivative was given
by mouth to six dogs. Data are the average plasma concentrations.* A, *sustained-
release preparation, 79 mg/kg;* B, *aqueous solution, 39.5 mg/kg. (From Wiegand and Taylor, Fig. 2.*[14])

   In contrast, a trial with quinidine in human patients with cardiac
arrhythmias (Fig. 2-5) revealed very little difference between ordinary
quinidine sulfate and the same drug covered by an enteric coating designed
to prevent it from dissolving until it reached the intestine. Inasmuch as
quinidine, a weak base, would be absorbed negligibly from the stomach
anyway, it would seem that an enteric coating could hardly have been
expected to alter the rate of absorption of this drug.
   Variability in drug absorption from sustained-release preparations
may be very great. A well-conducted trial compared a sustained-release
with a conventional dosage form of ferrous sulfate in 12 patients.[16] To
estimate absorption the preparations were labeled with radioactive iron.
Each subject had a two-day trial of each regimen: standard preparation
three times daily, sustained-release preparation once daily. All the tests
were arranged in a random order. Nine patients absorbed much more (1.5
to 10 times more) of the conventional dosage form than of the sustained-
release form. Two patients absorbed more of the sustained-release preparation. One patient absorbed less than 2 per cent of the total dose of either
preparation. Most important, the variation between subjects was much
greater with the sustained-release preparation than with the conventional
form.
   A clear danger of sustained-release preparations is that a larger
dose than usual is administered at one time, it being assumed that the
sustained release will yield a continuous slow rate of absorption. If the
actual rate of release should be unexpectedly high, potentially toxic levels
may result; if unexpectedly low, therapeutically inadequate levels may

   14 R. G. WIEGAND and J. D. TAYLOR: Kinetics of plasma drug levels after sustained
release dosage. *Biochem. Pharmacol. 3:*256 (1960).

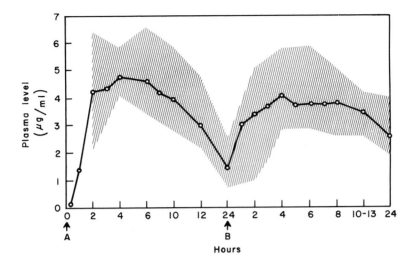

FIG. 2-5. KINETICS OF PLASMA DRUG LEVELS IN HUMANS AFTER A SUSTAINED-RELEASE PREPARATION OF QUINIDINE. *A single dose of ordinary USP quinidine sulfate (0.8 g) was given by mouth to seven subjects (at A). The following day (at B) an enteric-coated preparation (0.9 g) was administered. Solid line denotes average plasma levels; shaded area shows ranges observed. (From Richardson et al., Fig. 1.[15])*

result. Either outcome might endanger the patient. Furthermore, sustained-release preparations are invariably more expensive than ordinary dosage forms. So the choice of such preparations ought to be justified by some real need. Certainly the oral ingestion of a drug three or four times daily presents no hardship to the patient; the substitution of a single daily dose of a sustained-release preparation would not be warranted unless some advantage other than convenience had been demonstrated. Some drugs only need to be administered once daily in their ordinary dosage forms (e.g., reserpine, digitalis glycosides); with these there is no possible justification for sustained-release preparations. Current federal regulations[17] require that all sustained-release preparations be regarded as new drugs; thus their safety and efficacy must be demonstrated before they may be introduced into clinical use.

15 D. W. RICHARDSON, M. E. ZEE, and E. M. WYSO: Maintenance quinidine therapy. Value of enteric-coated quinidine tablets. *Amer. J. Cardiol.* 5:417 (1960).

16 P. CROSLAND-TAYLOR, D. H. KEELING, and B. M. CROMIE: A trial of slow-release tablets of ferrous sulphate. *Curr. Therap. Res.* 7:244 (1965).

17 U.S. Department of Health, Education and Welfare; Food and Drug Administration: Code of Federal Regulations, Title 21, Part 1, p. 64, para. 3.512. Washington, D.C., January, 1965.

DRUG DISTRIBUTION

Apparent Volumes of Distribution

The body water may be regarded as partitioned into several compartments that are functionally distinct. These are the vascular fluid, the extracellular (interstitial) fluid, and the intracellular fluid. In a normal lean 70-kg man, the whole body water comprises about 58 per cent of the body weight, or about 41 liters. The extracellular water is about one-third of the total, around 17 per cent of the body weight, or approximately 12 liters. Included in this is the volume of circulating plasma water, about 4 per cent of body weight, or 3 liters. The whole blood volume, including the intracellular water of the erythrocytes, is about twice the plasma volume, or about 6 liters. These data were summarized in Fig. 2-1. The volumes of the various compartments differ slightly between adult males and females. In obese people a larger fraction of the body weight is fat, so the fluid compartments all represent smaller percentages of the body weight. In infants the body water is a higher percentage of the body weight (as much as 77 per cent), in part because the bony tissues are incompletely calcified and hence contribute less to body weight than in the adult.

The *apparent volume of distribution* (V_d) of a drug is the fluid volume in which it seems to be dissolved. The determination of V_d is simple in principle.[18] A known amount of a drug is injected intravascularly, and after sufficient time for it to distribute, a sample of blood is taken and the drug's concentration in plasma water is determined. Suppose the drug were distributed ideally, without any metabolic degradation, without being eliminated from the body, and without any binding or sequestration. The situation would then be analogous to finding the volume of fluid in a flask by adding a known amount of dye, mixing, and then determining the resulting concentration.

Let x be the amount of dye added, and c the resulting concentration; then $c = x/V_d$, or $V_d = x/c$.

A high molecular-weight dye, Evans Blue, is almost wholly confined to the circulating plasma, and therefore can be used in just this way to determine the total plasma volume (and the blood volume, if the hematocrit is also known). Several minutes are needed for complete mixing of the dye with the circulating plasma. During this time the plasma concentration falls to a plateau, which then remains unchanged, whence V_d is found (Fig. 2-6). A significant fraction of the circulating blood is in tissues where the blood flow is slow. The initial very fast mixing (about 1 minute) distributes

    [18] S. CHIEN and M. I. GREGERSEN: "Determination of Body Fluid Volumes," chapter 1 in *Physical Techniques in Biological Research,* vol. IV, ed. by W. L. Nastuk. New York, Academic Press, 1962.

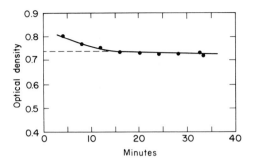

FIG. 2-6. USE OF THE DYE EVANS BLUE TO DETERMINE PLASMA VOLUME. *At time zero, 2 μg/kg of the dye was given intravenously. Samples of venous blood were drawn periodically and the dye concentration in plasma was determined in the spectrophotometer. The data plotted are the actual spectrophotometer readings of each sample. (From Gibson and Evans, Fig. 1.[19])*

the dye into the volume of blood that perfuses kidney, brain, liver, lungs, and the active musculature. Over the next several minutes this solution will be diluted by the entry of dye-free blood from the more slowly perfused tissues (fat depots, skin, etc.). If 100 μg of Evans Blue were injected, the plateau concentration would be about 33 μg/liter, and $V_d = 100/33 = 3$ liters.

Many different substances distribute approximately into the extra-cellular fluid volume. Chloride and sodium ions, for example, are primarily extracellular, but a small fraction is always found within cell water; consequently V_d's determined with isotopes of these ions (^{24}Na is often used) tend to be a little higher than the true volume of extracellular space. Stable or radioactive bromide salts, thiocyanate, radioactive iodide, sucrose, and inulin have been used to estimate the extracellular fluid, and each V_d differs slightly from another. Actually, the ratio of extracellular fluid volume to tissue water differs from tissue to tissue, and so does the capillary permeability, so the differences in V_d probably reflect real differences in distribution. In general, with these substances, the initial very rapid fall of the plasma level due to intravascular mixing blends into a further decline, reflecting distribution into the interstitial fluid. Thus a lower plateau is reached than with Evans Blue. If 100 mg of bromide ion were injected (as NaBr), the ultimate plateau reached before significant excretion could occur would be about 8 mg/liter, whence $V_c = 100/8 = 12$ liters, the approximate volume of the extracellular fluid.

Finally, the volume of the total body water may be estimated by tracer water (D_2O or ^3H_2O) or any substance with high lipid/water par-

19 J. G. GIBSON, 2ND, and W. A. EVANS, JR.: Clinical studies of the blood volume. I. Clinical application of a method employing the azo dye "Evans Blue" and the spectrophotometer. *J. Clin. Invest. 16:*301 (1937).

tition coefficient, since all these cross cell membranes readily (p. 153). Here, an hour or more may be required for all the body tissues to come to equilibrium, and various fractions of the body water may be observed to equilibrate at different rates. Figure 2-7 shows a typical curve for the distribution of tritiated water after intravenous injection in a human subject. Sampling of the mixed venous blood showed that a plateau was reached in about 1 hour.

In Fig. 2-8 a similar experiment with heavy water is shown. Here, 80 ml of D_2O was injected intravenously and samples of blood from the femoral artery were analyzed for their deuterium content by means of a falling-drop density determination. The standard deviation of this determination is surprisingly small, about four parts per thousand; the final estimates of body water are accurate to ± 0.2 liters. The upper curve represents the raw data, D_2O concentration (on a logarithmic scale) plotted against time. Equilibrium was attained in about an hour, at a plateau level of about 0.16 vol%, or 1.6 g/liter; thus $V_d = 80/1.6 = 50$ liters, representing 61 per cent of the body weight in this subject who weighed 82 kg.

Especially interesting in this experiment was the analysis of the arterial concentration curve into two log-linear kinetic components. The procedure is as follows: The net rate of movement of D_2O out of the blood stream should be proportional to the difference, at any moment,

FIG. 2-7.   USE OF TRITIATED WATER TO DETERMINE TOTAL BODY WATER.   *In a patient ^3H_2O was injected intravenously at time zero. Plasma samples were obtained periodically and their radioactivity determined. Note that scale of ordinates is logarithmic. (Adapted from Prentice et al., Fig. 1[20]; two completely aberrant points were deleted.)*

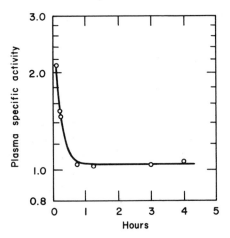

[20] T. C. PRENTICE, W. SIRI, N. I. BERLIN, G. M. HYDE, R. J. PARSONS, E. E. JOINER, and J. H. LAWRENCE: Studies of total body water with tritium. *J. Clin. Invest.* **31**:412 (1952).

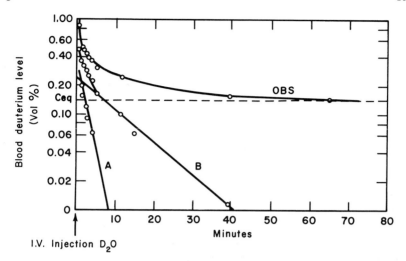

FIG. 2-8.   DISTRIBUTION OF DEUTERIUM OXIDE INTO TOTAL BODY WATER. D_2O, *80 ml, was given intravenously to a human subject weighing 82 kg. Samples were taken from the femoral artery. Note logarithmic scale of ordinates.* Upper curve (*OBS*): *raw observations; lower curves* (A *and* B): *analysis into kinetic components, as described in the text.* C_{eq} *denotes the equilibrium concentration eventually attained. (Adapted from Schloerb et al., Fig. 8.[21])*

between the arterial concentration and the eventual concentration to be attained at equilibrium. The first step was, therefore, to subtract the equilibrium concentration (C_{eq}) from each point. This yielded the middle curve B. This curve seems to be composed of at least two processes going on at different rates. The final part is log linear, so it was assumed that whatever process it represented had gone on from the start. An extrapolation was therefore made back to time zero. Now the extrapolated part of curve B was subtracted from the actual early points on curve B, yielding another straight line (A) with a much steeper slope. In other words, the observed course of decline of the arterial plasma level could be accounted for by two simultaneous exponential decay curves with different time constants.

The process represented by curve A, with half-time 1.2 minutes, presumably represents the passage of D_2O out of the circulation at the capillaries. We may ask what the volume of distribution of D_2O was before this fast process started, i.e., just after the intravenous injection. To estimate this, we must move line A up to tangency with the real curve OBS, keeping its slope unchanged, and then extrapolate back to time zero. This gives a D_2O concentration of 0.9 vol%, whence $V_d = 80/9.0 = 9$

[21] P. R. SCHLOERB, B. J. FRIIS-HANSEN, I. S. EDELMAN, A. K. SOLOMON, and F. D. MOORE: The measurement of total body water in the human subject by deuterium oxide dilution. *J. Clin. Invest. 29:*1296 (1950).

liters, a value somewhat larger than the estimated volume of circulating blood (8 per cent of 82 kg $= 6.6$ liters).

The process represented by curve B, with half-time about 10 minutes, could represent the passage of D_2O across cell membranes throughout the body. Moving curve B up to tangency with OBS and extrapolating back gives an estimate of V_d at the completion of process A, i.e., the volume out of which the heavy water was distributing at the rate represented by curve B. The extrapolated value is 0.5 vol%, and $V_d = 80/5.0 = 16$ liters, a reasonable volume for the extracellular fluid. We have already determined the final volume of distribution, 50 liters, or 61 per cent of the body weight, corresponding to the total body water.

Despite the alluring simplicity of calculations like the above, they can be very misleading. The processes going on at such different rates, for example, could have nothing to do with fluid compartments but might represent the equilibration of two groups of tissues with very different vascularity. Frequently the volume of distribution of a drug is determined experimentally and (as in this example) is found to correspond reasonably well with the actual volume of some fluid compartment. Thus, any drug with V_d approximately 12 liters might be supposed to enter extracellular fluid but not to penetrate cells. Two factors may operate frequently to invalidate such direct and simple interpretations. On the one hand, if (as is commonly done) the total plasma drug concentration is determined rather than that in plasma water, then a high degree of protein binding will make the observed concentration unduly high, and the estimate of V_d will therefore be falsely low. If a substantial fraction of the drug is bound to plasma proteins in the concentration range studied, this error can be very large. For example, in the hypothetical case just proposed, where $V_d = 12$ liters, if the original dose were 100 mg, then the observed plasma concentration was about 8 $\mu g/ml$. If the drug is 70 per cent bound at this total concentration, then the true equilibrium concentration in plasma water is only 2.4 $\mu g/ml$ and the true volume of distribution is 42 liters, a volume greatly in excess of the extracellular fluid and close to that of the total body water. On the other hand, binding or sequestration of drug at an extravascular site can withdraw so much from the circulation that V_d will appear to be very large. A drug that is stored in fat depots (e.g., cyclopropane, thiopental) may have an apparent volume of distribution very much greater than the entire fluid volume of the body.

A practical problem in estimating V_d is the fact that drugs do not often display ideal behavior. They are metabolized, excreted, or sequestered, so that no real distribution plateau is ever attained. The plasma concentration falls rapidly at first, more slowly later, and then the concentration continues to fall. What is needed is an estimate of what the plasma concentration would have been in the absence of the process responsible for the continuous decline. This estimate is obtained by extrapolating the eventual stable rate of decline back to the time of injection. Naturally, this has to be done on a semilogarithmic plot, it being assumed that the various phases of drug disappearance from plasma are all first order. An illustration is presented in Fig. 2-9. Antipyrine (1 g) was injected intravenously in four human subjects. Inasmuch as the investigators were not interested in the kinetics of approach to equilibrium but only in estimating V_d, the first venous blood samples were drawn after an hour had elapsed. The rates of plasma level decline were nearly identical in the four subjects, corresponding to the rate of metabolism of antipyrine. The extrapolated values, 28 to 41 μg/ml, yielded values for V_d from 25 to 36 liters. These volumes are rather low for total body water, but direct determinations of antipyrine in dog tissues (Table 2-6) showed that the drug does equilibrate (or nearly so) with cell water. In the subjects represented in Fig. 2-9, D_2O gave slightly higher values of V_d. The D_2O estimates are usually somewhat too high because water in the gastrointestinal tract (usually not considered part of the body water) equilibrates with the heavy water; and more important, because deuterium exchanges with hydrogen in many compounds in the body tissues, so that part of the deuterium removed from the plasma

FIG. 2-9. DISTRIBUTION OF ANTIPYRINE INTO TOTAL BODY WATER. *Antipyrine (1 g) was injected intravenously in four human subjects. Plasma levels are shown. The rapid fall of plasma level during the first hour (phase of distribution) was not measured. The slopes represent metabolism and excretion. (From Soberman et al., Fig. 1.[22])*

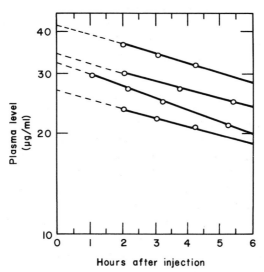

[22] R. SOBERMAN, B. B. BRODIE, B. B. LEVY, J. AXELROD, V. HOLLANDER, and J. M. STEELE: The use of antipyrine in the measurement of total body water in man. *J. Biol. Chem. 179:*31 (1949).

TABLE 2-6.   **Distribution of antipyrine in dog tissues**

Antipyrine (1.5 g) was given intravenously; tissues
were obtained for analysis 1.5 hours later. The dog
weighed 13 kg (From Brodie and Axelrod,[23] Table 2.)

Tissue	Antipyrine in tissue water (μg/ml)	Tissue water antipyrine / Plasma water antipyrine
Plasma	148	1.0
Whole blood	147	1.0
CSF	122	0.82
Brain	141	0.95
Muscle	145	0.98
Heart	145	0.98
Lung	135	0.91
Kidney	154	1.04
Liver	145	0.98
Spleen	149	1.00

is no longer in the form of water at all. The antipyrine estimates, on the
other hand, are usually low because an appreciable fraction of the plasma
antipyrine is bound to plasma protein; how this affects the estimate of V_d
was explained earlier.

The Binding of Drugs to Plasma Proteins

The interactions between drugs and proteins were discussed in
chapter 1 from the standpoint of the molecular mechanisms responsible.
Here we shall consider how interactions with plasma proteins influence the
distribution of drugs in the body and their access to sites of action, of
metabolism, and of excretion.

Several kinds of plasma protein interact with small molecules (Fig.
2-10). The metal-binding globulins transferrin and ceruloplasmin interact
strongly and specifically with iron and copper, respectively, and are essential to the transport of these ions in the body. The α- and β-lipoproteins
account in large measure for the binding of lipid-soluble molecules, including those of physiologic importance, such as vitamin A and other carot-
enoids, vitamin D, cholesterol, and the steroid hormones. The antibody
γ-globulins interact very specifically with antigens but negligibly with
most drugs.

By far the most important contribution to drug binding is made by
albumin, the principal protein of plasma (50 per cent of the total). It has

[23] B. B. BRODIE and J. AXELROD: The fate of antipyrine in man. *J. Pharmacol. Exp.
Therap. 98:*97 (1950).

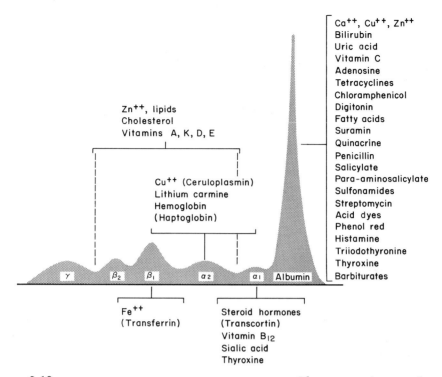

Zn++, lipids
Cholesterol
Vitamins A, K, D, E

Cu++ (Ceruloplasmin)
Lithium carmine
Hemoglobin
(Haptoglobin)

Ca++, Cu++, Zn++
Bilirubin
Uric acid
Vitamin C
Adenosine
Tetracyclines
Chloramphenicol
Digitonin
Fatty acids
Suramin
Quinacrine
Penicillin
Salicylate
Para-aminosalicylate
Sulfonamides
Streptomycin
Acid dyes
Phenol red
Histamine
Triiodothyronine
Thyroxine
Barbiturates

γ   β₂   β₁   α₂   α₁   Albumin

Fe++
(Transferrin)

Steroid hormones
(Transcortin)
Vitamin B₁₂
Sialic acid
Thyroxine

FIG. 2-10. INTERACTIONS WITH PLASMA PROTEINS. *Plasma proteins are depicted according to their relative amounts (y-axis) and electrophoretic mobilities (x-axis). Some representative interactions are listed. (Adapted from Putnam, Fig. 6.[24])*

been crystallized and well characterized; and because it reacts with a wide variety of drugs, it is used frequently in model investigations of drug binding. Its molecular weight is about 69,000 and at its isoelectric point (pH 5) it carries about 100 each of negative and positive charges (Table 2-7). At plasma pH (7.4) it has a net negative charge, but nevertheless it can interact with anions as well as with cations. Every positively or negatively charged group could be considered a binding site for the predominant counterion species; thus, Na^+ interacts at the anionic groups, Cl^- at the cationic groups. These purely coulombic interactions are very weak. The number of binding sites for drug molecules per albumin molecule is usually much smaller than the total number of charged groups (sometimes only one or two), the affinity at these few sites is very much greater than that for the common counterions, and the binding depends strongly upon the

24 F. W. PUTNAM: "Structure and Function of the Plasma Proteins," chapter 14 in *The Proteins*, vol. III, 2nd ed., ed. by H. Neurath. New York, Academic Press, 1965.

TABLE 2-7.   **Potential binding sites for charged molecules or ions in bovine serum albumin**

(Analytical data from Tanford et al.[25] By permission of the American Chemical Society.)

Amino acid	Group	No. of residues per molecule
Aspartic and glutamic	$-COO^-$	101
Tyrosine	$-O^-$	18
Cysteine	$-S^-$	0.7
Terminal	$-COO^-$	1
Histidine	$-NH^+-$	17
Lysine	$-NH_3^+$	57
Arginine	$=NH_2^+$	22
Terminal	$-NH_3^+$	1

molecular structure of the drug. Some of the methodologic aspects of studies on binding specificity were discussed elsewhere (p. 34 ff.).

The reversible binding of drugs by proteins requires, as a rule, that the native configuration (tertiary structure) of the protein be intact. This has important practical consequences for the assay of bound and free drug. Most routine procedures for determination of drug concentrations in plasma or other body fluids begin with a deproteinization step. This step is invariably a precipitation (e.g., with phosphotungstic or trichloroacetic acid), followed by removal of protein by filtration or centrifugation. In such procedures the analytical data will represent *total* drug concentrations because the protein-bound drug is released into the supernatant solution or filtrate. Most bioassay procedures, on the other hand, will be sensitive only to *free* (unbound) drug if whole plasma is used for the assay. Dilution of the plasma, however, favors dissociation because it reduces the concentration of free drug in equilibrium with the protein-bound moiety; therefore, the degree of binding will usually be underestimated if a dilution step precedes the assay. At infinite dilution all reversible complexes would be completely dissociated.

If a drug is able to combine with a certain number of sites, *n*, on each protein molecule, and if all these sites have the same affinity for the drug, and if there are no cooperative effects on affinity (i.e., the binding of a drug molecule to one site does not influence the affinity for the next site), then simple mass law expressions describe the relationship between binding and the concentration of free drug at equilibrium. The total number of binding sites is *nP*, where *P* is the total protein concentration; so, exactly

25 C. TANFORD, S. A. SWANSON, and W. S. SHORE: Hydrogen ion equilibria of bovine serum albumin. *J. Amer. Chem. Soc.* 77:6414 (1955).

26 A. GOLDSTEIN: The interactions of drugs and plasma proteins. *Pharmacol. Rev.* 1:102 (1949).

as in the expression for receptor binding (p. 71), we have

$$\frac{(PX)}{nP} = \frac{(X)}{K + (X)},$$

where (X) is the concentration of free drug, (PX) is the concentration of drug-protein complex, and K is the dissociation constant. Let r be the ratio $(PX)/P$, i.e., the moles of drug bound per mole of protein. Then

$$r = \frac{n(X)}{K + (X)},$$

and a plot of r against (X) (Fig. 2-11a) yields a typical hyperbolic curve, identical to an adsorption isotherm. The same equation, in the familiar form of a log dose-response curve, is plotted in Fig. 2-11b. The saturation of available sites (in this example, when $r = 10$) is evident.

The problem that concerns us in this chapter is not how many drug molecules can be bound to a molecule of plasma protein, but rather what *fraction* of the total drug molecules in the plasma is bound. We should like to know how the bound fraction β varies with drug concentration, protein concentration, maximum number of binding sites, and affinity constant. By definition,

$$\beta = \frac{(PX)}{(PX) + (X)} = \frac{1}{1 + \dfrac{(X)}{(PX)}}.$$

FIG. 2-11. RELATIONSHIP BETWEEN DRUG CONCENTRATION (X) AND MOLES BOUND PER MOLE OF PROTEIN (r), FOR A DRUG INTERACTING WITH PLASMA ALBUMIN.

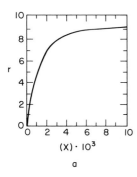

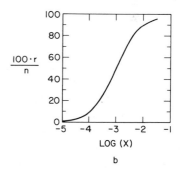

a

b

Plotted in the manner of an adsorption isotherm.

Plotted in the manner of a log dose-response (cf. p. 77). Assumed albumin concentration, 10^{-4}M; drug-albumin dissociation constant, 10^{-3}M; ten binding sites per molecule albumin (n = 10) assumed to be available with the same affinity for drug. (From Goldstein, Figs. 1 and 6.[26])

But from the previous equation

$$\frac{(X)}{(PX)} = \frac{K + (X)}{nP},$$

so that

$$\beta = \frac{1}{1 + \dfrac{K}{nP} + \dfrac{(X)}{nP}}.$$

This equation tells us that for a given protein concentration, and a given number of binding sites per protein molecule, if the binding affinity is very high (K very low) and the drug concentration is very low, practically all the drug present will be bound (β approaches unity). As common sense suggests, if the total number of binding sites is reduced, a greater fraction of total drug tends to become free. An exact quantitative analysis, shown in Fig. 2-12, illustrates some important principles. Here, the horizontal scale is $\log(X)/nP$, and the individual curves are for chosen values of K/nP.

    In plasma, P is fixed, and both n and K are determined by the particular drug whose distribution is under consideration; thus, nP is invariant and the whole expression K/nP is invariant. The horizontal scale becomes a measure of the logarithm of the free drug concentration. For a given drug, one particular curve (for one value of K/nP) will be relevant. We see that all drugs at high enough concentration saturate the binding sites. At still

FIG. 2-12.   EFFECT OF DRUG CONCENTRATION UPON THE FRACTIONAL BINDING OF A DRUG TO PLASMA PROTEINS.   *Axis of ordinates: fraction bound (β); axis of abscissas: relative scale of log concentration for a fixed protein concentration. See text for explanation. (From Goldstein, Fig. 7.[26])*

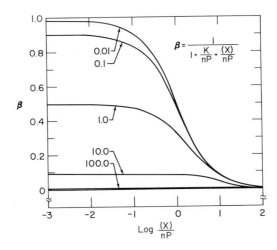

higher concentration the additional drug is all free, so that the fraction bound decreases toward zero. At high concentrations the maximum amount of drug is bound to the plasma proteins, but this maximum amount represents only a small fraction of total drug. As the drug concentration is progressively reduced (e.g., by elimination mechanisms in the body) the fraction bound tends to increase; but the extent of the increase may be negligibly small, for some drugs have too low an affinity to be bound significantly even at very low concentrations. In those cases where the fraction bound does increase at low drug concentration, a maximum fraction bound is always approached. If the affinity is high enough or the concentration of binding sites is high enough, or both, then this maximum fractional binding may approach unity, i.e., practically all the drug is bound. But it need not do so, and many drugs are only partially bound even under the most favorable conditions.

It follows that reports about the fractional binding of drugs in plasma (usually expressed as "per cent of drug bound to plasma protein") are meaningless unless qualified by a statement of the free drug concentration at the equilibrium actually measured. Interactions should be measured at therapeutic drug concentrations if conclusions relating to these concentrations are to be drawn; investigations carried out at higher concentrations may provide greater convenience or accuracy in the assay procedures, but the degree of fractional binding may be underestimated seriously.

The effects of protein binding upon drug distribution can be deduced readily from the same principles.[27] At equilibrium the concentration in the extravascular water will be the same as the unbound concentration in plasma water, i.e., usually lower than the total plasma level. The difference in total drug concentration between plasma and cerebrospinal fluid in patients led to the initial observation of reversible drug-protein interaction.[28] Several sulfonamide drugs were found to reach levels in cerebrospinal fluid that were always below that in plasma, sometimes as low as one-quarter the plasma concentration. Yet the sulfonamides were very effective in bacterial meningitis, so the low concentrations were obviously adequate. It was found that the concentrations in cerebrospinal fluid were the same as in plasma water; these, indeed, were the true bacteriostatic concentrations.

Only free drug is available for glomerular filtration; therefore the persistence of a drug that is excreted in this way can be influenced by the fractional binding. Moreover, the rate of disappearance from the body tends to be self-limiting, at least through the range in which fractional bind-

---

[27] B. K. MARTIN: Potential effect of the plasma proteins on drug distribution. *Nature 207*:274 (1965).

[28] B. D. DAVIS: The binding of sulfonamide drugs by plasma proteins. A factor in determining the distribution of drugs in the body. *J. Clin. Invest. 22*:753 (1943).

ing increases with falling drug concentration; the lower the concentration, the smaller the fraction subject to filtration at the glomeruli.

On the other hand, active processes like secretion at the renal tubules, or carrier-mediated transport across other cell membranes, are not restricted to free drug. The reversibility of the drug-protein interaction is so rapid that free drug molecules withdrawn from the water phase by one of these active processes are replaced instantly by more free drug derived by dissociation of the bound complex. Penicillin and *p*-aminohippuric acid (PAH) are examples; even at concentrations where they are bound as much as 90 per cent to plasma protein they are cleared almost completely from the blood by renal secretory mechanisms during a single passage through the kidney.

The rate of transfer of drug molecules from the blood stream into the tissues, by diffusion across capillary membranes, depends upon the concentration gradient of free drug. Thus, protein binding can slow the disappearance of drug from the circulation and also provide a reservoir of bound drug, which will replenish (by dissociation) some of the drug that is lost by metabolism and excretion. A striking example is suramin, a polycyclic sulfonated compound used in the prophylaxis of trypanosomiasis. Some of this drug is bound very tightly to plasma protein,[29] and it is apparently not metabolized in the body. Effective plasma levels persist for weeks after a single intravenous injection. Another example of retention by the plasma proteins is the dye Evans Blue, mentioned earlier. It is useful in estimating the plasma volume only because the high fractional binding to plasma proteins minimizes the escape of dye at the capillaries. Another example is trypan blue, a similar dye, which fails to enter brain or cerebrospinal fluid after injection into the circulation; this observation was made many years ago and led to false conclusions about an absolute "blood-brain barrier" (p. 163). A principal reason for the nearly complete exclusion of trypan blue from the central nervous system appears to be its high fractional binding to plasma proteins.

A most remarkable example of tight binding to plasma albumin is presented by an iodinated contrast medium, 3-hydroxy-2,4,6-triiodo-α-ethylhydrocinnamic acid (Fig. 2-13). This compound was used some years

FIG. 2-13.   3-HYDROXY-2,4,6-TRIIODO-α-ETHYLHYDROCINNAMIC ACID.

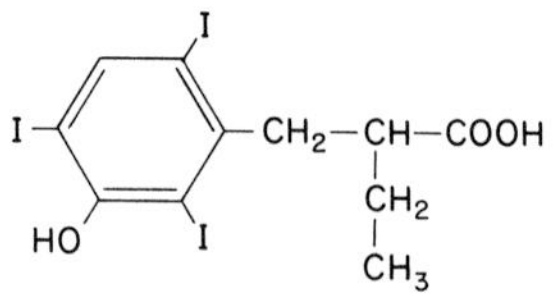

[29] H. OTT and C. SEEGER: Untersuchungen zur Frage der Germaninbindung an die Serumproteine. *Z. Gesamte Exp. Med. 125:*455 (1955).

ago for the purpose of visualizing the gallbladder with x-rays. The determination of serum protein-bound iodine (PBI) is a valuable procedure in the assessment of thyroid function. When the PBI procedure was attempted in patients who had received the iodinated contrast medium, absurdly high PBI values were obtained. This led to the discovery that a metabolic derivative of the iodinated contrast medium was retained in the plasma for years; determinations in patients at various intervals after they received the drug yielded an estimate of about 2.5 years for the half-life of the complex with plasma albumin (Fig. 2-14).

Differences in the drug-binding capacity of plasma proteins are found between species. Such differences have also been noted occasionally among people (e.g., in the extent of digitoxin binding) and in a few instances a genetic basis has been demonstrated (cf. chapter 6). People vary greatly in the dosage of many drugs that is required to produce a therapeutic action. Possibly a part of this variability might be accounted for by differences in protein binding.

Competition between different drugs for the same binding sites on plasma proteins may have remarkable consequences. In premature infants the conjugating system responsible for coupling bilirubin with glucuronic acid (cf. p. 274) is deficient. Normally, the rapid excretion of the water-soluble bilirubin glucuronide accounts for most of the elimination of bilirubin, whereas bilirubin itself is very slowly excreted. Thus, the meta-

FIG. 2-14. PLASMA PROTEIN-BOUND IODINE CONCENTRATIONS AFTER ADMINISTRATION OF AN IODINATED CONTRAST MEDIUM (3-HYDROXY-2,4,6-TRIIODO-α-ETHYLHYDROCINNAMIC ACID). *Data are shown for 15 patients who presumably received the same standard dose. Iodine levels are shown as a function of time after administration of the contrast medium. (From Astwood, Fig. 5.[30])*

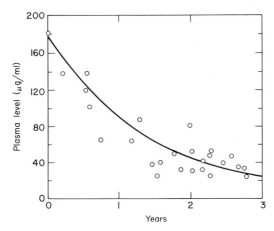

[30] E. B. ASTWOOD: Occurrence in the sera of certain patients of large amounts of a newly isolated iodine compound. *Trans. Ass. Amer. Physicians* 70:183 (1957).

bolic deficiency leads to a prolonged and elevated bilirubin level. The situation is made worse by the high rate of bilirubin formation during the first few days after birth, attributable to the destruction of excess erythrocytes present in the fetus. A large fraction of the bilirubin in the body is bound by plasma proteins and thereby prevented from entering the tissues. Sulfonamide drugs and vitamin K, which are also bound extensively to plasma proteins, interact at the same sites as do the bilirubin molecules. When these drugs are administered, the competition for binding sites leads to considerable displacement of bilirubin, and the free bilirubin passes into the tissues. The entry of bilirubin into brain causes a grave disturbance known as kernicterus, which is often fatal. The effect was discovered by accident in a clinical trial of the comparative efficacy of tetracycline and of a penicillin-sulfonamide mixture in the management of premature infants.[31] The sulfonamide mixture led to significantly higher mortality, and kernicterus was found frequently at autopsy.

An elegant experimental illustration of the same phenomenon is shown in Fig. 2-15. Here, a strain of rats was used that lack glucuronyl transferase and therefore have a high level of unconjugated protein-bound bilirubin. After sulfonamide administration, a rising plasma sulfonamide level was associated with a falling plasma bilirubin concentration, as displaced bilirubin diffused out into a much larger volume of distribution in the tissues. As the sulfonamide was eliminated, the plasma bilirubin be-

FIG. 2-15.   DISPLACEMENT OF BILIRUBIN FROM PLASMA PROTEIN BINDING SITES BY A SULFONAMIDE.   *Sulfisoxazole was administered to rats of the Gunn strain at time zero. These rats are unable to conjugate bilirubin because they lack the glucuronyl transferase. (Data of Johnson et al., from Nyhan, Fig. 6.[32] By permission of C. V. Mosby.)*

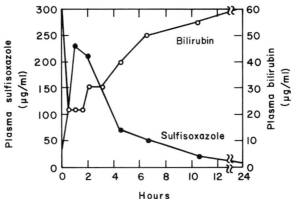

31 W. A. SILVERMAN, D. H. ANDERSEN, W. A. BLANC, and D. N. CROZIER: A difference in mortality rate and incidence of kernicterus among premature infants allotted to two prophylactic antibacterial regimens. *Pediatrics 18:*614 (1956).

32 W. L. NYHAN: Toxicity of drugs in the neonatal period. *J. Pediat. 59:*1 (1961).

came bound again to protein. This reduced the free bilirubin concentration in plasma, creating a diffusion gradient for re-entry of bilirubin from the tissues, and finally the initial plasma bilirubin level was restored.

Passage of Drugs across Biologic Membranes

BLOOD CAPILLARIES

Drug molecules are distributed throughout the body by means of the circulation of blood. The cardiac output (about 6 liters per minute) is equivalent to the whole volume of the vascular system. Thus, within a minute or so after a drug enters the blood stream it is largely diluted into the total blood volume as a result of turbulent mixing and of unequal flow rates through the various vascular beds. This initial phase of dilution is best observed with a drug that passes only slowly, or not at all, out of the blood stream. With such a drug the volume of distribution in the first few minutes should approach 6 liters if the drug permeates erythrocytes freely, or about 3 liters (the approximate plasma volume) otherwise. If a drug can leave the capillaries readily, its concentration may fall so fast that the initial phase of dilution is obscured, and a much larger volume of distribution is then approached (p. 130).

The rate of entry of a drug into the various tissues of the body obviously depends upon the relative rates of blood flow through the respective capillary beds and the permeability of the capillaries for the particular drug molecules. Blood flow varies within wide limits, from the brain, which is most richly supplied, to cartilage, tendons, joints, and depots of neutral fat, which are poorly vascularized. Blood flowing through the kidneys is ultrafiltered at the capillaries of the renal glomeruli, and most of the ultrafiltrate is reabsorbed by the renal tubules. Drug molecules, to the extent to which they are free in the plasma, and filterable, will also appear in the glomerular filtrate, whence they may be reabsorbed or excreted in the urine. A small fraction of the cardiac output gives rise, at the choroid plexus of the brain, to cerebrospinal fluid; and this protein-free solution, circulating over the tissues of the central nervous system, may contain some of the drug. The aqueous humor too may contain filterable drug derived from the blood. The bile may serve as a route for passage of drug out of the circulation into the intestinal tract, and drug molecules also pass directly from the blood across the gastrointestinal mucosa. At all the capillaries some ultrafiltration occurs, driven by high hydrostatic pressure at the arterial end; and there is some reabsorption of interstitial fluid at the venous end, driven primarily by the colloid osmotic pressure of plasma. Depending upon their molecular size and other properties, drug molecules may move with this bulk flow of solvent. Some of the drug in the interstitial fluid will remain in lymph and return to the circulation by way of the lymphatic channels. Since drug molecules that pass out of the circulation have first to traverse the capillary walls, we shall consider what is known about capillary permeability.

The functional anatomy of capillaries has been studied by direct microscopic observation of living tissue, but quantitative data about permeability have been obtained chiefly by perfusion of isolated regions such as the cat hindlimb.[33-35] Blood was perfused through the femoral artery, and the rate of disappearance of various solutes was studied. One method was to measure the "osmotic transient," i.e., the change in osmotic pressure as the solute passed into the interstitial fluid. This was accomplished by suspending the limb in a delicate balance and opposing the osmotic movement of fluid by adjustments of the hydrostatic venous and arterial pressures so as to maintain isogravimetric (constant weight) conditions. This procedure sufficed to measure a wide range of transfer rates with half-times from a few minutes to more than an hour. Another method was to measure directly the arteriovenous concentration difference; this method would be useful for transfer rates not much slower than the flow rates employed.

Lipid-soluble molecules like urethane, paraldehyde, or triacetin left the blood almost instantaneously in its passage through the tissue, and so did the gases of physiologic or pharmacologic interest (oxygen, carbon dioxide, nitrogen, and the anesthetic gases). For all the substances in this class, the most important determinant of the rate of transcapillary movement was the lipid/water partition coefficient. The *partition coefficient* is the ratio of concentration in lipid phase to concentration in aqueous phase when a substance is allowed to come to equilibrium in a two-phase system. The conditions of measurement (e.g., temperature, pH) must be specified. Glycerol derivatives, for example, passed through capillary walls at rates that varied with their lipid/water partition coefficients, but in the opposite order to what would be expected from their aqueous diffusion coefficients. In the glycerol series increasing molecular size is achieved by increasing the length of hydrophobic substituents, so that partition coefficients and aqueous diffusion coefficients tend to vary inversely. The rapid rates of movement of all lipid-soluble compounds indicated that practically the entire capillary endothelial surface must be available for their diffusion.

For water-soluble molecules of various sizes, the results were quite different, as indicated in Table 2-8. Here, the smaller the molecule the more rapidly did it pass out of the capillary. Even the smallest molecules (including water itself) behaved as though only a very small fraction of the capillary wall (about 0.2 per cent) was available for their filtration or

[33] J. R. PAPPENHEIMER: Passage of molecules through capillary walls. *Physiol. Rev.* *33*:387 (1953).

[34] E. M. RENKIN: Transport of large molecules across capillary walls. *The Physiologist 7*:13 (1964).

[35] J. R. PAPPENHEIMER, E. M. RENKIN, and L. M. BORRERO: Filtration, diffusion and molecular sieving through peripheral capillary membranes: a contribution to the pore theory of capillary permeability. *Amer. J. Physiol. 167*:13 (1951).

TABLE 2-8. **Permeability of muscle capillaries to water-soluble molecules**

Data for radius of equivalent sphere are calculated from viscosity or diffusion measurements, taking into account the degree of hydration. The diffusion coefficient across the capillary is the rate of movement for unit molar concentration difference as given by the Fick equation, $dM/dt = (C_1 - C_2)P$. (Data from Pappenheimer[33] and Renkin.[34])

| | Molecular weight | Radius of equivalent sphere (A) | Diffusion coefficient | |
			In water, D (cm^2/sec) $\times$ 10^5	Across capillary, P (cm^3/sec·100 g)
Water	18		3.20	3.7
Urea	60	1.6	1.95	1.83
Glucose	180	3.6	0.91	0.64
Sucrose	342	4.4	0.74	0.35
Raffinose	594	5.6	0.56	0.24
Inulin	5,500	15.2	0.21	0.036
Myoglobin	17,000	19	0.15	0.005
Hemoglobin	68,000	31	0.094	0.001
Serum albumin	69,000		0.085	<0.001

diffusion. Moreover, the impediments to free diffusion (i.e., discrepancies between theoretical diffusion coefficients and transcapillary diffusion coefficients) were greater as molecular size increased. It appeared that a system of pores about 30 A in radius must be present to account for the restricted diffusion as molecular radii approached 30 A (corresponding to a molecular weight of approximately 60,000), and for the sharp cutoff above this. Curiously, however, no pores have thus far been observed in electron micrographs of mammalian capillaries, although the resolving power of the electron microscope is much better than the postulated pore size.

The relatively small water-soluble molecules traverse the capillary membrane (whether through pores or otherwise) largely by diffusion in aqueous medium; their rates of movement are nearly independent of the perfusion pressure but are directly proportional to the concentration gradient across the capillary. Molecules the size of proteins penetrate only very slowly, and their rate of movement is strongly dependent upon the pressure difference between the arterial and venous ends of the capillary. Since the actual passage of large molecules across the capillary is so slow, the methods described above cannot be employed. Instead, studies were carried out by labeling proteins or polysaccharides in the perfusion inflow, then analyzing the lymph drainage from the perfused limb. Contrary to earlier concepts that considered interstitial fluid as an ultrafiltrate of blood, the protein content of lymph was found to be nearly one-half that of blood plasma. This lymph protein undoubtedly originated in the blood and crossed the capillary wall. There is still doubt about the precise mechanism whereby macromolecules traverse the capillary endothelium, albeit very slowly. Pinocytosis (the engulfing of fluid by cell processes) has been suggested as a possible mechanism, and computations based upon microscopic study of the formation and movement of pinocytotic vesicles indicate that the known rates of transcapillary passage of macromolecules could be accounted for by this mechanism.

It follows from all the above that the rate at which a drug leaves the blood stream will depend upon its lipid solubility, its molecular weight, and its physical state of aggregation. If it is bound to macromolecules, then its rate of transcapillary passage will be determined by that of the protein or other substance to which it is bound. Capillaries differ widely in their permeability characteristics; those of the glomeruli, for example, are very much more permeable to molecules of all sizes than are those of the muscles (hindlimb). The sinusoidal capillaries of the liver appear to lack any endothelial wall and therefore permit the passage of large molecules quite readily. Thus, capillaries in the various organ systems display wide variation in their permeability to drugs. Nevertheless, all the capillaries except those of the brain permit drugs to pass with relative ease compared with cell membranes, and thus all drugs of small or intermediate molecular size that are free in the circulation gain access readily to the interstitial fluid. In brain, on the other hand, a special histologic feature (investment of the capillaries by a cellular sheath, p. 162) drastically reduces the permeability to water-soluble molecules of all sizes.

The capillaries are not rigid tubes with invariant properties. They too are subject to the actions of drugs as well as to effects of tissue metabolites and hormones. Capillary permeability can be enhanced by such agents as histamine and estrogens, and by decreased tissue pH associated with lactic acid production. Humoral agents like norepinephrine affect the passage of substances across capillaries by constricting arterioles, thus reducing capillary blood flow and hydrostatic pressure in the capillary lumen.

CELL MEMBRANES

Membrane Structure.[36-39]   Some drugs (e.g., calcium salts, vasopressin) are thought to act by altering the physical state of the cell surface and thereby affecting the permeability of the membrane, while other drugs

[36] H. DAVSON and J. F. DANIELLI: *The Permeability of Natural Membranes,* 2nd ed. Cambridge, Cambridge University Press, 1952.

[37] L. S. SCHANKER: Passage of drugs across body membranes. *Pharmacol. Rev.* 14:501 (1962).

[38] A. M. SHANES, ed.: *Biophysics of Physiological and Pharmacological Actions.* Washington, D.C., Publication No. 69 of the American Association for the Advancement of Science, 1961.

[39] E. OVERTON: Beiträge zur allgemeinen Muskel-und Nervenphysiologie. *Arch. ges. Physiol.* 92:115 (1902), esp. p. 264.

act upon enzymes that are thought to be located at cell surfaces. But most drugs have to penetrate cell membranes in order to gain access to receptors in the cell interior. What is known of the structure and properties of such membranes that determine their permeability to drugs?

The generalized picture that has emerged from chemical, physiologic, and electron micrograph studies is represented in Fig. 2-16. The characteristic feature appears to be a bimolecular layer of lipid molecules coated by a protein layer on each surface. The long axis of each lipid molecule is perpendicular to the cell surface. All the hydrophobic portions are in proximity to each other, and the hydrophilic ends are combined with charged groups of the protein components at the inner and outer cell surfaces. The electron microscope shows that the thickness of the cell membrane is approximately 100 A. Some kinds of cell membrane show an asymmetry, consistent with the presence of an added thickness of proteinaceous material at the inside surface, as shown diagrammatically in Fig. 2-16.

Studies with synthetic films of lipid and protein suggest that the layer of protein closely applied to the lipid is in an unfolded state. The additional inner layer of protein appears to be folded into an ordered tertiary configuration; this fits well with biochemical studies that implicate enzymes in transport processes (p. 159).

Older models of the cell membrane included pores, whose presence was inferred from rates of penetration of water-soluble substances. As

FIG. 2-16.   SCHEMATIC DIAGRAM OF MOLECULAR ARCHITECTURE OF CELL MEMBRANE.   *The lipid double-layer is shown coated with a layer of unfolded proteins at the outer and inner surfaces. Proteins in folded configurations, capable of performing enzyme functions, are shown at the inner surface. (After F. S. Sjöstrand, p. 188.[40])*

Outer surface

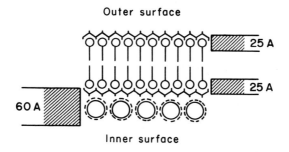

25 A

25 A

60 A

Inner surface

[40] F. S. SJÖSTRAND: "Electron Microscopy of Myelin and of Nerve Cells and Tissue," in *Modern Scientific Aspects of Neurology*, ed. by J. N. Cumings. London, Edward Arnold Ltd., 1960, p. 188 ff.

with capillary membranes, however, electron micrographs have failed to reveal any pores.

Membranes of different cells vary considerably in structural detail and in function. For example, liver and pancreas cells, because they produce proteins for use elsewhere in the body, require a mechanism for secreting macromolecules. This seems to be accomplished by packaging the proteins in vesicles that become confluent with the cell membrane; the contents are thus extruded and enter the extracellular spaces or gland ducts. Cells differ also in the sensitivity of their membranes to hormones. For example, the cells of the distal and collecting tubules of the kidney respond to vasopressin by a great increase in permeability to water, whereas proximal tubules do not seem to be affected.

Microelectrode techniques have established the presence of a potential difference across cell membranes, generally around 60 to 90 millivolts (mV). The inside of the cell is negative with respect to the outside. The Gibbs-Donnan equilibrium predicts an unequal distribution of other ions when any ion is prevented from equilibrating across the membrane. The resulting concentration gradients produce a potential difference whose magnitude is given by the Nernst equation.[41]

> Suppose C^+ and A^- diffusible, and X^- nondiffusible. Then, to satisfy the gross requirements of electrical neutrality (total cation charges = total anion charges), $(C^+)_i = (A^-)_i + (X^-)$ inside, and $(C^+)_o = (A^-)_o$ outside. Now if A^- could equilibrate at equal concentrations on both sides of the membrane, we would evidently have $(C^+)_i > (C^+)_o$, whereas if C^+ attained equality on both sides we would have $(A^-)_o > (A^-)_i$. There is a tendency, therefore, for C^+ to move from the inside to the outside of the cell membrane, and for A^- to move from the outside to the inside, both ion movements creating a slight excess of negative charge inside. These net movements will stop when the ionic concentration gradients are balanced by the electrical potential gradient.

Analysis of the ion concentrations in intracellular and interstitial fluids of mammalian muscle cells (Table 2-9) reveals that whereas K^+ and Cl^- are in equilibrium with the membrane potential, Na^+ is not. The observed excess of external over internal Na^+ concentration would be in equilibrium with a membrane potential of $+65$ mV, in contrast to the actual -90 mV. Thus, the membrane behaves as though it is largely impermeable to Na^+, but freely permeable to the other small ions. The great excesses of internal over external K^+ and of external over internal Cl^- are seen as the expected consequence of the Na^+ impermeability, as predicted by the Gibbs-

41 J. W. WOODBURY: "The Cell Membrane: Ionic and Potential Gradients and Active Transport," in *Medical Physiology and Biophysics,* ed. by T. C. Ruch and J. F. Fulton. Philadelphia, W. B. Saunders Co., 1960. 18th edition.

TABLE 2-9. Approximate steady state ion concentrations and potentials in mammalian muscle cells and interstitial fluid

Vertical line represents membrane. (From Woodbury,[41] Table 1.)

Interstitial fluid		Intracellular fluid		$\dfrac{[\text{Ion}]_o}{[\text{Ion}]_i}$	E^a (mV)
	$[\text{Ion}]_o$ (μM per cm^3)		$[\text{Ion}]_i$ (μM per cm^3)		
Cations		Cations			
Na+	145	Na+	12	12.1	65
K+	4	K+	155	1/39	−95
H+	3.8×10^{-5}	H+	13×10^{-5}	1/3.4	−32
pH	7.43	pH	6.9		
others	5				
Anions		Anions			
Cl−	120	Cl−	3.8[b]	31.6	−90
HCO$_3$−	27	HCO$_3$−	8	3.4	−32
others	7	A−	155		
Potential	0		−90 mV	31.6[b]	−90

[a] Electrochemical potential for each ion ratio, computed from Nernst equation.
[b] Calculated from membrane potential using the Nernst equation.

Donnan equilibrium. Studies with radioactive Na+, however, revealed that this ion does indeed cross the membrane, at a sufficient rate so that equal concentrations would soon be established inside and outside the cell, unless Na+ were being extruded continually. The conclusion generally accepted today is that a "sodium pump" operates to exclude Na+ from the cell interior. This, of course, is tantamount to making the membrane selectively impermeable to Na+.

The entry of drugs into cells depends upon many of the same mechanisms already considered for transcapillary movement. Very small water-soluble molecules and ions (e.g., K+, Cl−) evidently diffuse through aqueous channels of some kind. Lipid-soluble molecules of any size diffuse freely through the cell membranes. Water-soluble molecules and ions of moderate size, including the ionic forms of most drugs, cannot enter cells readily except by special transport mechanisms. Finally, since proteins do gain access to cell interiors, it may be that pinocytosis plays some role here.

Figure 2-17 depicts the cell membrane as a barrier to the passage of drug molecules. An analogy is made to chemical reactions, which may proceed (*a*) spontaneously "downhill," (*b*) "downhill," but only after first surmounting an energy barrier, or (*c*) "uphill" to a higher energy level through utilization of energy from a coupled energy-yielding system. Here, mechanism (*a*) corresponds to the diffusion of drug molecules through aqueous channels in a membrane (if the molecules are small enough) or through the substance of the membrane, in accordance with Fick's law,

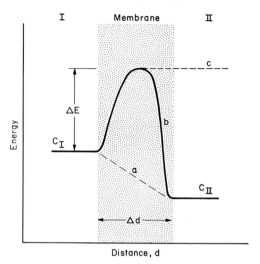

FIG. 2-17. RELATION BETWEEN ENERGY LEVELS OF A SUBSTANCE BEFORE, DURING, AND AFTER PENETRATION THROUGH A BARRIER SUCH AS A CELL MEMBRANE OR CAPILLARY WALL. *Here, C_I represents concentration at surface I; C_{II}, concentration at surface II. Thickness of membrane is Δd. Simple downhill diffusion is represented by broken line* a. *Downhill diffusion after overcoming an energy barrier, ΔE, is represented by solid curve* b. *Uphill transport, as in a "pump" mechanism, is indicated by uphill portion of curve* b, *then by broken line* c.

down a chemical potential gradient. Mechanism (*b*) is illustrated by the example of a drug that is too large to pass through any pores that may be present, and is also practically insoluble in the membrane, but can form a lipid-soluble complex at the membrane surface. The complex then moves by diffusion within the membrane, down a gradient with respect to *its* chemical potential, to the other wall, where free drug can be released. Finally, mechanism (*c*) is represented by an active concentrating or secreting mechanism, in which a coupled system furnishes energy for driving ("pumping") the drug to a region of higher concentration, also, presumably, by means of a carrier complex intermediate.

Transfer Processes.   Diffusion. Rates of diffusion of substances across biologic membranes can be measured in many ways. The most reliable method is to sample the solutions on both sides of the membrane at intervals, and thus determine the concentrations of a substance as it diffuses into the cell from the medium. More than 30 years ago an elegant series of experiments was performed on the penetration of nonelectrolytes into the large cells of the marine plant *Chara ceratophylla.* The findings turned out to be generally relevant to penetration of other kinds of cells by nonelectrolytes.

The entrance rates conformed to the diffusion equation of Fick, i.e., they were proportional to the concentration gradients. However, a distinctive diffusion coefficient had to be assigned to each substance because the membrane (as in the case of capillaries, p. 147) offered different degrees of resistance to the passage of each substance. There was no polarity; diffusion rates were the same for influx and efflux of a given substance.

There was a good correlation between partition coefficients (olive oil/water) and penetrating ability. This is shown in Fig. 2-18, where molecular size is indicated by the size of the symbol used for each compound. Except for very small or very large molecules, there was a fairly direct proportionality between the rate of penetration (permeability constant) and the partition coefficient. Molecules below about 15 A radius penetrated faster than their partition coefficients would lead one to predict. Very large molecules with high partition coefficients were retarded somewhat.

The influence of partition coefficient upon the diffusion of drugs into cell membranes has an important bearing upon certain biologic actions. Various nonelectrolytes of wholly unrelated structures produce general anesthesia (formerly called "narcosis") when they are present in

FIG. 2-18. RELATIONSHIP BETWEEN OIL/WATER PARTITION COEFFICIENT AND CELL MEMBRANE PERMEABILITY. Abscissas: *partition coefficient, olive oil/water;* ordinates: *permeability rate constant in* Chara ceratophylla. *Each* circle *represents a single compound;* radius of circle *symbolizes the molecular radius, in angstroms, as indicated. (From Collander and Bärlund.*[42]*)*

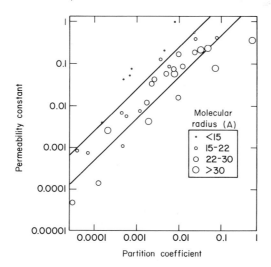

[42] R. COLLANDER and H. BÄRLUND: Permeabilitätsstudien an Chara ceratophylla. II. Die Permeabilität für Nichtelektrolyte. *Acta Bot. Fenn. 11:*1 (1933).

sufficient concentration in the central nervous system. Ether (diethyl ether), cyclopropane, nitrous oxide, the primary alcohols, carbon disulfide, and chloroform are examples. The diversity of molecular structure among these drugs has always been puzzling. A systematic relationship is found, however, between anesthetic potency and oil/water partition coefficient. One of the earliest examples studied is summarized in Table 2-10, showing the concentration of four alcohols required in the aqueous medium in order to produce equivalent degrees of anesthesia in tadpoles immersed in that medium. As the length of the hydrophobic chain increases, so does the oil/water partition coefficient, and also the anesthetic potency, the required aqueous concentration becoming lower and lower. Thus, the effective concentration in a lipid biophase would be the same for a wide variety of compounds. This has led to the concept that a certain amount of an anesthetic drug, physically dissolved in the membranes of nerve cells, suffices to alter the functional properties of those membranes. The excitability of nerve cells arises from the ability of their membranes to become depolarized quite suddenly by the inrush of Na^+ ions. Possibly the dissolved molecules of anesthetic prevent this reversible permeability change.

The argument that simple solution of anesthetic molecules in cell membranes causes anesthesia loses force when, in a homologous series of compounds, other parameters than partition coefficients are examined. All these vary coordinately, as illustrated in Fig. 2-19 for the primary alcohols. Here, antibacterial potency is correlated with oil/water partition coefficient. But with increasing length of the carbon chain, antibacterial potency is seen also to be correlated with decreasing water solubility, increasing effect on aqueous surface tension, and decreasing vapor pressure.

TABLE 2-10.   **Anesthesia produced by primary alcohols in tadpoles**

(Data of Overton[43] and Meyer and Hemmi.[44])

Alcohol	Anesthetic conc. in aqueous medium (M)	Partition coefficient (cottonseed oil/water)
CH_3OH	0.57	0.00966
C_2H_5OH	0.29	0.0357
C_3H_7OH	0.11	0.156
iso-C_4H_9OH	0.045	0.588

[43] E. OVERTON: *Studien über die Narkose zugleich ein Beitrag zur allgemeinen Pharmakologie.* Jena, Gustav Fischer, 1901, p. 101.

[44] K. H. MEYER and H. HEMMI: Beiträge zur Theorie der Narkose. III. *Biochem. Z.* 277:39 (1935) esp. p. 45.

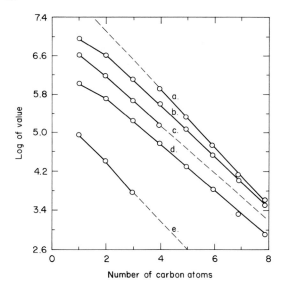

FIG. 2-19. PROPERTIES OF NORMAL PRIMARY ALCOHOLS. a, *Solubility (moles × 10⁻⁶/liter)*; b, *toxic concentration for typhoid bacillus (moles × 10⁻⁶/liter)*; c, *concentration reducing surface tension of water to 50 dynes/cm (moles × 10⁻⁶/liter)*; d, *vapor pressure at 25° (mm Hg × 10⁴)*; e, *partition coefficient between cotton seed oil and water (×10³)*. *(From Ferguson, Fig. 1.*[45])

Even when unrelated compounds are compared with respect to some physical property, good correlation with biologic potency may be found. Table 2-11 illustrates such a correlation for volatile anesthetic agents in mice. The partial pressure of each agent was determined that would produce a given depth of anesthesia at equilibrium. These partial pressures varied over a 20-fold range. But the chemical activities, estimated as ratios of anesthetic partial pressure (p_t) to saturation pressure (p_s), varied over a very much smaller range.

The correspondence between a particular physical property and anesthetic potency obviously cannot be assigned a cause-and-effect relationship if other physical properties vary in closely correlated fashion.[46] Thus, the fact that high oil/water partition coefficient is associated with high anesthetic potency does not necessarily mean that the anesthetic acts in the lipid phase of cell membranes. The very same hydrophobic groupings that make a molecule "prefer" the lipid to the water phase would also give it a high affinity for the surface of a protein or other macromolecule in preference to the ambient aqueous solution. Moreover, some anesthetics do not fit the lipid solubility theory at all. For example, L-arabinochloralose

[45] J. FERGUSON: The use of chemical potentials as indices of toxicity. *Proc. Roy. Soc. B127:*387 (1939).

TABLE 2-11.   **Concentrations of gases and vapors producing the same degree of anesthesia in mice at 37°.**

Thermodynamic activity is expressed as the ratio of the partial pressure p_t of the agent to its saturation vapor pressure p_s. (Data of Ferguson,[45] Table V.)

	Saturation pressure at 37° (p_s) (mm Hg)	Anesthetic conc. (% by volume)	Activity (p_t/p_s)
Nitrous oxide	59,300	100	0.01
Acetylene	51,700	65	0.01
Methyl ether	6,100	12	0.02
Methyl chloride	5,900	14	0.01
Ethylene oxide	1,900	5.8	0.02
Ethyl chloride	1,780	5.0	0.02
Diethyl ether	830	3.4	0.03
Methylal	630	2.8	0.03
Ethyl bromide	725	1.9	0.02
Dimethylacetal	288	1.9	0.05
Diethylformal	110	1.0	0.07
Dichlorethylene	450	0.95	0.02
Carbon disulfide	560	1.1	0.02
Chloroform	324	0.5	0.01

is twice as potent as its D isomer, yet the partition coefficients of optical isomers are identical. Recent experiments to test the clathrate theory of anesthesia (p. 100) have revealed other discrepancies between partition coefficients and anesthetic potency.[47]

For weak acids and bases the ionized and nonionized forms have completely different lipid/water partition coefficients. The ionized groupings (usually $-COO^-$ or $-NR_2H^+$, see p. 25) interact strongly with water dipoles and consequently penetrate only poorly or not at all into the lipoidal cell membranes. Thus, drugs that are partially ionized at body pH enter cells at rates that are strongly pH dependent. For all practical purposes the diffusion rate can usually be ascribed to the concentration gradient for the nonionized form alone.

Figure 2-20 shows this typical pH dependence for an acridine dye with a pK$_a$ of 9.65. Here, the rate of entry into cultured human conjunctival cells was measured by a quantitative fluorescence technique. At pH 8.5 about 8 per cent of the dye is in the nonionized form, the remainder having a proton associated to a nitrogen atom in the acridine ring. At the more acidic pH values, an ever smaller fraction is nonionized. The pene-

    [46] T. C. BUTLER: Theories of general anesthesia. *Pharmacol Rev.* 2:121 (1950).
    [47] A. CHERKIN and J. F. CATCHPOOL: Temperature dependence of anesthesia in goldfish. *Science 144*:1460 (1964).

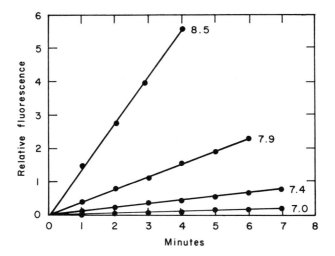

FIG. 2-20. EFFECT OF pH ON ENTRY OF AN ACRIDINE DYE INTO CULTURED HUMAN CONJUNCTIVAL CELLS. *Intracellular dye concentration was measured by a fluorometric technique. The dye, proflavin, has* $pK_a = 9.65$. *The pH value of the surrounding medium is given on each curve. (After Robbins, Fig. 5.[48] By permission of the Rockefeller University Press.)*

tration rates are seen to vary as though only the nonionized form crossed the cell membrane.

Figure 2-21 illustrates the same principle for benzoic acid. The concentration required to inhibit cell division by 50 per cent in fertilized sand dollar eggs was ascertained at various values of pH in the medium. The graph shows these 50 per cent inhibitory concentrations as a function of pH. Although diffusion rate is not measured directly here, the result is similar. Increasing concentrations of the ionized form are required to achieve the same end-point, but always the same concentration of the nonionized benzoic acid. Here, of course, in contrast to the acridine dye, increasing pH causes a greater degree of ionization.

The same phenomena occur in the whole animal and profoundly influence the distribution of drug between plasma and interstitial fluid on the one hand, and intracellular water on the other. Figure 2-22 shows experiments in which phenobarbital, a weak acid, was administered to dogs. When the plasma pH was lowered by CO_2 inhalation, there was a drop in the plasma drug level. This could be attributed to the fact that a greater fraction of the total phenobarbital in the blood assumed the nonionized acid form. The plasma concentration of undissociated diffusible phenobarbital was thus increased, and a larger amount of the drug moved across

48 E. ROBBINS: The rate of proflavin passage into single living cells with application to permeability studies. *J. Gen. Physiol.* 43:853 (1960).

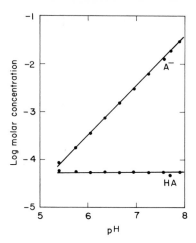

FIG. 2-21.   EFFECT OF pH ON THE INHIBITION OF CELL DIVISION IN FERTILIZED
SAND DOLLAR EGGS BY BENZOIC ACID.   *Fertilized eggs of* Echinarachnius parma
*were allowed to develop in sea water solutions of different pH values. At each
pH the effective concentration of benzoic acid for 50 per cent inhibition was
determined, and the concentrations of the benzoate ion* (A⁻) *and the undissociated benzoic acid* (HA) *were computed from the Henderson-Hasselbalch
equation.* (*Data of Smith, Table 5.*[49])

the cell membranes and into cells, where the pH remains relatively stable.
Plasma alkalosis produced the opposite shift. These shifts occurred in all
the tissues studied, including brain, where the depth of anesthesia paralleled the tissue concentrations. In other words, administration of acid

FIG. 2-22.   EFFECTS OF ACIDOSIS AND ALKALOSIS ON PHENOBARBITAL PLASMA
LEVELS IN DOGS.   *Phenobarbital concentrations are designated by circles, blood
pH values by triangles.* (*From Waddell and Butler, Figs. 2 and 3.*[50])

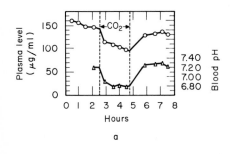

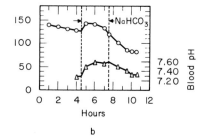

a   b

Acidosis induced by CO₂ inhalation   *Alkalosis induced by NaHCO₃*

[49] H. W. SMITH: The action of acids on cell division with reference to permeability
to anions. *Amer. J. Physiol.* 72:347 (1925).

[50] W. J. WADDELL and T. C. BUTLER: The distribution and excretion of phenobarbital. *J. Clin. Invest.* 36:1217 (1957).

deepened the anesthesia, while alkalosis lightened it. To promote just such a shift of drug out of the tissues (and also for a similar effect at the kidneys, see p. 383), alkalosis is induced therapeutically in the treatment of barbiturate poisoning.

Membrane transport.[51,52] Substances that are insoluble in the cell membrane may nevertheless pass into the cell interior by forming a complex with a "carrier." The process is represented schematically in Fig. 2-23. The carrier complex XC is assumed to be freely diffusible in the membrane. Since XC is formed at surface I and cleaved at surface II, its concentration gradient will run down from I to II, but that of free carrier will run down in the opposite direction. Thus, diffusion can provide the means for cycling (or shuttling) the carrier across the membrane. If the concentration of X remains lower at II than at I (as when it is metabolized inside a cell), then the transport is "downhill" and requires no net expenditure of energy by the cell. Glucose in erythrocytes is a good example; because it moves down a concentration gradient into the cells, the process has been described as "facilitated diffusion," but the high degree of substrate specificity makes it evident that some kind of carrier is involved. A system of acceptor-donor macromolecules, in fixed positions across the membrane, and operating in the manner of a bucket brigade, could possibly serve as the carrier mechanism, but a diffusible carrier is easier to imagine.

If the concentration of X is higher at II, the transport is "uphill"; chemical energy must then be expended to drive the unidirectional transport, for otherwise the same system would operate to move X in the opposite direction, from II to I. Transport requiring energy is also called

FIG. 2-23.   SCHEMATIC REPRESENTATION OF A CARRIER TRANSPORT SYSTEM. X *is a drug insoluble in the substance of the membrane;* C *is a carrier molecule, freely diffusible in the membrane; and* XC *is a drug-carrier complex.*

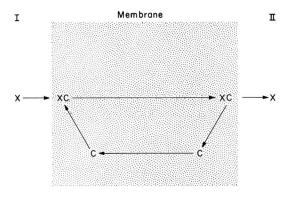

[51] W. WILBRANDT and T. ROSENBERG: The concept of carrier transport and its corollaries in pharmacology. *Pharmacol. Rev. 13*:109 (1961).

[52] J. H. QUASTEL: Molecular transport at cell membranes. *Proc. Roy. Soc. B163*:169 (1965).

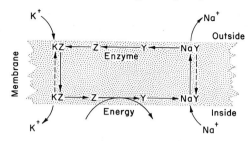

FIG. 2-24. HYPOTHETICAL SCHEME OF A NA$^+$-K$^+$ · EXCHANGE PUMP. *Substances Z and Y are assumed to be confined to the membrane. Z has a high affinity for K$^+$; Y, a high affinity for Na$^+$. Z and Y move through the membrane only when in combination with an ion. (From Woodbury, Fig. 6.*[41]*)*

"active transport" because of the active coupling of energy-yielding reactions needed to drive the transport; work is done by the cell at the expense of energy derived from metabolism. The "sodium pump" is a good example, illustrated schematically in Fig. 2-24. Here, the carrier is assumed to be activated by enzymes at the inside surfaces. The activated form *Y* has a high affinity for Na$^+$, the deactivated form *Z* carries K$^+$; thus a one-for-one exchange is mediated. Other examples of active transport are the secretion of H$^+$ into the stomach and into the renal tubular urine, the accumulation of iodide ions in the thyroid gland, the reabsorption of glucose and amino acids in the kidney, and the secretion of numerous organic anions and cations by the proximal renal tubules.

A number of drugs appear to be moved across cell membranes by transport systems. Examples are the renal tubular secretion of penicillin, phenol red, and tetraethylammonium ion; the secretion of penicillin or sulfobromophthalein (BSP) into the bile; and the transport of some drugs from cerebrospinal fluid into blood (p. 163). Membrane transport systems display a high degree of steric specificity. They can be blocked by drugs that interfere with energy production. They are subject to competitive inhibition by compounds that bear a close structural relationship to the normal transport substrates. For these reasons it is supposed that proteins are somehow involved; enzymes are obviously required for activation of a carrier in an uphill transport. In bacteria active transport is mediated by "permeases" that have enzymic functions, are inducible, and cannot be formed if protein synthesis is blocked.

Passage of Drugs into the Central Nervous System

THE CAPILLARIES AND THE CEREBROSPINAL FLUID

The brain constitutes only 2 per cent of the body weight, yet receives about 16 per cent of the cardiac output. It is the most richly supplied with blood of all the body tissues. The average blood flow is about 0.5

ml per gram per minute, compared with approximately 0.05 in resting muscle. One might expect, therefore, that drugs would equilibrate very rapidly between blood and brain. And indeed some do, but many substances enter brain tissue only very slowly, and some practically not at all.

A drug may gain access to the tissues of the central nervous system by two distinct routes: the capillary circulation and the cerebrospinal fluid (CSF). The internal carotid and vertebral arteries come together at the base of the brain to form the circle of Willis, from which major vessels issue to supply each side of the brain, including the choroid plexuses of the lateral and third ventricles where the CSF is formed. Blood flow rates to various parts of the brain have been estimated by measuring the rate of transfer of radioactive krypton (^{79}Kr) from blood to tissues. Table 2-12 reveals wide differences. For example, cerebral white matter has a much lower blood supply than several parts of the cortex. This corresponds to the observed density of capillaries, about 300 per mm^2 cross section in the cerebral white matter, as compared with about 1000 in cortex. Radioautographic studies (p. 166) showed that drugs penetrate into cortex more readily than into white matter, probably because of the greater delivery rate of drug to the tissues. The lateral nuclei of the hypothalamus receive a particularly rich blood supply, and here again drugs enter quite rapidly. Certain specialized areas are also found to be penetrated unusually well by dyes and other substances, but whether because of a rich blood supply or exceptionally permeable capillaries, or both, is not clear. These include the area postrema in the roof of the fourth ventricle (containing the chemoreceptor trigger zone for emesis, an important site of drug action), the pineal body, and the posterior lobe of the hypophysis.

TABLE 2-12. **Blood flow in representative areas of the brain of the unanesthetized cat**

(From Kety,[53] Table 2.)

	Mean blood flow (ml/g per min)		Mean blood flow (ml/g per min)
Inferior colliculus	1.80	Caudate	1.10
Sensorimotor cortex	1.38	Thalamus	1.03
Auditory cortex	1.30	Association cortex	0.88
Visual cortex	1.25	Cerebellar nuclei	0.87
Medial geniculate	1.22	Cerebellar white matter	0.24
Lateral geniculate	1.21	Cerebral white matter	0.23
Superior colliculus	1.15	Spinal cord white matter	0.14

[53] S. S. KETY: "The Cerebral Circulation," vol. III, section I, Neurophysiology, chapter 71, in *Handbook of Physiology,* ed. by J. Field, H. W. Magoun, and V. E. Hall. Washington, D.C., American Physiological Society, 1960.

It has already been stated that some capillaries in the body (e.g., those of the glomeruli and liver) are more permeable than those of muscle. In the brain, however, the capillaries are much less permeable to a variety of water-soluble substances. The outstanding structural feature underlying the decreased permeability of capillaries in the central nervous system is the close application of the glial connective tissue cells (astrocytes) to the basement membrane of the capillary endothelium. Electron micrographs indicate that this glial sheath is about 85 per cent complete (Fig. 2-25). Beneath this sheath the basement membrane is homogeneous, relatively dense, and about 300 to 500 A thick. The endothelium appears to be a continuous sheet of cells without visible pores. A drug leaving the capillaries in the central nervous system has therefore to traverse not only the capillary endothelium itself but also the membranes of glial cells in order to gain access to the interstitial fluid. Estimates of the volume of this fluid are as low as 5 to 15 per cent of the brain volume. Its composition differs strikingly from that of interstitial fluid elsewhere by the nearly complete absence of protein; there are also some differences in the ionic composition.

FIG. 2-25.   ELECTRON MICROGRAPH OF THE VASCULAR BED OF RAT CEREBRAL CORTEX. *Longitudinally sectioned capillary showing its sheath of astrocytic processes and a nearby astrocyte. The cellular sheath, a unique feature of brain capillaries, impedes the passage of water-soluble drugs and accounts for the "blood-brain barrier." (From Maynard et al., Plate I.[54])*

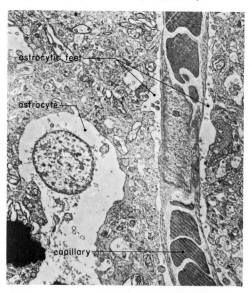

[54] E. A. MAYNARD, R. L. SCHULTZ, and D. C. PEASE: Electron microscopy of the vascular bed of rat cerebral cortex. *Amer. J. Anat. 100:*409 (1957).

One would predict from their investment by a cellular sheath that the permeability characteristics of brain capillaries should be rather like those of cell membranes elsewhere in the body, and not like the permeability characteristics of the usual, porous capillary structure. This is, in general, true. Ionized or nonionized water-soluble substances may be practically excluded, unless they are quite small, but lipid-soluble compounds enter the brain easily and rapidly. Misconceptions about an absolute "blood-brain barrier" arose from early studies showing the failure of certain dyes to enter the brain after their intravenous administration. These observations failed to take into account the strong binding of dyes to plasma proteins, reducing the concentration of free dye available for diffusion; they failed to consider the degree of ionization, a major determinant of diffusion into brain; and they failed to control the possible decolorizing of dyes by metabolic processes in brain tissue. Results obtained by modern techniques, described below, indicate that the "blood-brain barrier" really represents a quantitative rather than a qualitative difference in capillary permeability, as compared with other tissues.

The CSF is formed at the choroid plexus by unknown mechanisms that are thought to involve, at least in part, active transport. It flows through the ventriculocisternal system, bathes the surfaces of the brain and spinal cord, and then flows into the venous blood sinuses through a system of large channels and valves in the arachnoid villi.[55] In man its rate of formation is about 0.3 ml per minute and its total volume about 200 ml, so the rate of turnover is approximately 10 per cent per hour. Drugs may enter CSF by way of the choroid plexus or by diffusion directly across the capillaries into the interstitial fluid. Drugs may leave the CSF by bulk flow into the venous sinuses, by diffusion back into the capillaries, by absorption at the choroid plexus, or by diffusion into the neuronal cells. One consequence for drug equilibration is that brain cells, brain interstitial fluid, and CSF may come to equilibrium with plasma water at quite different rates. It is even possible for a drug entering CSF to be "washed out" continually by the bulk flow, so that no true equilibrium between its concentrations in plasma water and in CSF is ever achieved. This can occur if there is a sufficiently high preferential rate of water entry into the ventriculocisternal system compared with the rate of drug entry.

Let us begin with no drug in CSF, and abruptly establish a constant plasma level of drug. Then the net rate of entry of drug into CSF is given by $P(c_p - c_c)$, where P is a rate constant with the dimensions of clearance (ml of plasma water cleared of drug per minute), determined by the permeability for the drug; c_c is the drug concentration in CSF; and c_p is the drug concentration in plasma water. The rate of exit of drug from CSF is given by Fc_c, where F is the bulk flow rate. Then

55 K. WELCH and V. FRIEDMAN: The cerebrospinal fluid valves. *Brain* 83:454 (1960).

$$\frac{dc_c}{dt} = \frac{1}{V} [P(c_p - c_c) - Fc_c],$$

where V is the volume of CSF. This equation can be integrated to give the exponential approach of c_c to its steady-state level. The steady state itself is found directly by setting $dc_c/dt = 0$, whence

$$\frac{c_c}{c_p} = \frac{P}{(P + F)} = \frac{1}{\left(1 + \dfrac{F}{P}\right)}.$$

Evidently, the ratio of drug concentration in CSF to that in plasma water approaches unity (true equilibrium) as the rate of bulk flow becomes small relative to the "clearance" of drug from blood into brain; but the steady-state ratio can become indefinitely low at the other extreme.

In addition to its almost complete lack of protein, CSF differs from plasma water by having lower concentrations of K^+, Ca^{++}, and phosphate, and a higher concentration of Cl^-. The glucose level is lower, but this is not necessarily remarkable in view of the rapid metabolic utilization of glucose in CSF. The pH of CSF is about 0.1 unit more acid than plasma.[56] Interpretation of these differences in ionic concentrations requires a knowledge of the electrochemical potential difference. Fragmentary data suggest that CSF may be about 10 mV positive with respect to plasma; this would be sufficient to explain the cation and anion inequalities (by the Gibbs-Donnan equilibrium), provided Na^+ were actively secreted into CSF. Other evidence also points to a "sodium pump" in the choroid plexus, intimately associated with the mechanism of formation of CSF. Moreover, the choroid plexus has been demonstrated to be a site of active transport of iodide and thiocyanate, and also of phenol red, penicillin, and other organic acids from CSF into blood. This mechanism accounts for the fact that the normal CSF concentration of iodide is very low compared with that in plasma water.[57]

The most systematic studies of the functional permeability of membranes separating blood from CSF were carried out in goats.[58] The ventriculocisternal system was perfused with a solution approximating the normal composition of CSF, under controlled pressure and flow rate. The perfusate entered the lateral ventricle and was collected at the cisterna magna. The difference between the concentration of a substance added to

[56] H. DAVSON: "Intracranial and Intraocular Fluids," vol III, section I, Neurophysiology, chapter 72 in *Handbook of Physiology,* ed. by J. Field, H. W. Magoun, and V. E. Hall. Washington, D.C., American Physiological Society, 1960.

[57] K. WELCH: Active transport of iodide by choroid plexus of the rabbit in vitro. *Amer. J. Physiol. 202:*757 (1962).

[58] S. R. HEISEY, D. HELD, and J. R. PAPPENHEIMER: Bulk flow and diffusion in the cerebrospinal fluid system of the goat. *Amer. J. Physiol. 203:*775 (1962).

the perfusion fluid and its effluent concentration could be ascribed to loss by bulk flow into the venous system and to diffusion across the ependymal lining into the capillary system. The clearance of inulin was found to be proportional to the CSF hydrostatic pressure, falling to zero when the pressure was reduced slightly below that in the venous sinuses. It was concluded that inulin was cleared only by bulk flow; this was entirely consistent with the previous finding that inulin and dextran (a very much larger polymer) were cleared at the same rate. Thus, the normal rate of bulk flow (i.e., rate of formation of CSF) could be estimated from the rate of disappearance of inulin at normal CSF pressure.

Knowing the rate of bulk flow, and the conditions for abolishing it entirely, made it possible to estimate the diffusional components of clearance of various molecules. For water, measured by means of tritiated water, the diffusional component predominated, even at high rates of bulk flow (i.e., at high hydrostatic pressures). As molecular size of various solutes was increased, the diffusion rate became restricted. As compared with muscle capillaries (p. 147) where the observations on restricted diffusion were consistent with a system of pores with radius about 30 A, here it was concluded that the equivalent pore radius was no larger than about 8 A. Thus, inulin (15 A) was completely excluded, whereas sucrose (4.4 A) diffused across, but more slowly than predicted from its diffusion coefficient in free solution. Even molecules as small as fructose and creatinine showed some restriction in their diffusion. The general picture was that of a porous membrane with aqueous channels very much smaller than those in muscle capillary endothelium.

Differences in the rates of penetration into various parts of the brain have been revealed by the injection of radioactive substances. Figure 2-26 shows the course of entry of ^{14}C-urea after intravenous injection in the rat. Six hours were required for equilibration of cerebellar cortex; entry into CSF and cerebellar white matter was probably slower and perhaps less complete; the uncertainty arises from the fact that the blood level was constantly falling. Possibly CSF and cerebellar white matter came to near-equilibrium with blood at 8 hours, but even at 12 hours their levels appear to be lower. Other studies also indicate that the heavy myelinization of white matter significantly impedes the entry of drugs. For example, in newborn kittens, where myelinization is still incomplete, ^{14}C-urea achieved equal penetration into cerebral white and grey matter within 1 hour, but the same experiment in an adult cat revealed a marked impediment to penetration of the white matter. This may possibly be relevant to the problem of kernicterus in infants (p. 376). In addition to the explanations advanced earlier, it may be that incomplete myelinization permits bilirubin to penetrate brain cells in abnormally large quantities.

Autoradiograms have furnished visual evidence about the routes of entry of drugs into brain and of differences in drug distribution and

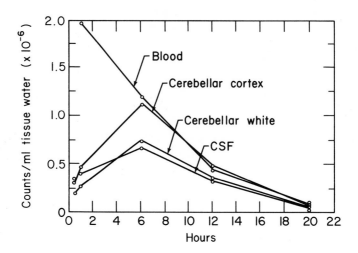

FIG. 2-26.   PENETRATION OF ^{14}C-UREA INTO CERTAIN PARTS OF RAT BRAIN. (*From Roth and Barlow, Fig. 7.[59] By permission of the American Association for the Advancement of Science.*)

binding among the various brain areas. When such studies were performed in the cat with lipid-soluble substances like thiopental, which penetrate into brain extremely fast, the observed pattern of labeling corresponded to the relative vascularity of the different areas. Thus, at 1 minute the label appeared in cortex, geniculate bodies, and inferior colliculi; and in 30 minutes the entire brain became uniformly labeled. At no time was there any preferential labeling of the ventricular system.

In contrast to such a pattern is that seen in Fig. 2-27, where ^{35}S-acetazolamide was injected intravenously in cats. The earliest labeling observed, at 1 hour, clearly outlines the ependymal lining of the ventricles and the surrounding tissue, suggesting that this drug first gains access to the CSF. The choroid plexus was found to be a primary site of entry of acetazolamide into CSF. Much later, at 4 hours, the drug has evidently entered areas of the brain remote from the ventricular borders. Finally, at 8 hours, especially high concentrations are observed (presumably bound) in the caudate nucleus, hypothalamus, and hippocampus, whereas drug concentrations in other areas have declined. The binding of a drug to a discrete area of the brain, as in this instance, may not be uncommon. For example, the anticonvulsant diphenylhydantoin reaches a total concentration in brain ten times that in plasma water, persisting more than 24 hours after a single injection. If the concentration in whole brain is so high, then accumulation in the regions of brain with greatest affinity for the drug must be very intense indeed.

59 L. J. ROTH and C. F. BARLOW: Drugs in the brain. *Science 134:*22 (1961).

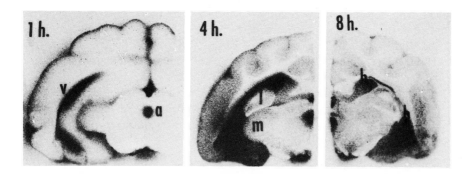

FIG. 2-27. AUTORADIOGRAMS OF CAT BRAIN AFTER INTRAVENOUS INJECTION OF ^{35}S-ACETAZOLAMIDE. *Transverse sections from cats sacrificed at 1, 4, and 8 hours after injection.* V *is lateral ventricle;* h *is hippocampus. (From Roth et al., Fig. 1.*[60]*)*

In these studies, the entry of a drug into brain initially by secretion at the choroid plexus and then across the ependymal linings of the ventricles raises the question how the subsequent passage of drug into brain structures is mediated. Does a slow diffusion out of the capillaries throughout the brain finally become manifest, as in the autoradiogram in Fig. 2-28 at 4 hours? Or does the drug continue to enter brain tissue primarily across the ventricular walls? Intraventricular injections of bromphenol blue in cats showed that intense staining occurred that penetrated deep into the brain, even to the outer surfaces.[61] Moreover, this penetration did not occur if the intraventricular injection was made after death. There appears, therefore, to be a transfer of substances across the ependymal borders of the ventricles, perhaps (it is thought) mediated by metabolically active glial cells. Such an indirect route of entry into brain cells may explain why the central actions of some drugs may be slower in onset and last much longer than the peripheral actions.

FACTORS THAT DETERMINE RATES OF DRUG PENETRATION INTO BRAIN AND CSF

The very wide range of penetration rates observed for substances passing from the blood stream into the brain and CSF seemed to defy rational explanation and led to the convenient but rather mysterious concept of a "blood-brain barrier." Evidence amassed in recent years[62, 66, 67]

[60] L. J. ROTH, J. C. SCHOOLAR, and C. F. BARLOW: Sulfur-35 labeled acetazolamide in cat brain. *J. Pharmacol. Exp. Therap. 125:*128 (1959).

[61] W. FELDBERG: *A Pharmacological Approach to the Brain, from Its Inner and Outer Surface.* Baltimore, Williams and Wilkins Co., 1963.

[62] D. P. RALL and C. G. ZUBROD: Mechanisms of drug absorption and excretion: Passage of drugs in and out of the central nervous system. *Annu. Rev. Pharmacol. 2:*109 (1962).

has provided the basis for understanding how the physical properties of each drug determine how readily it will cross the membranes that separate the cerebral blood supply from the brain cells or CSF. In order to obtain valid data in this field one must, of course, be able to measure drug concentrations in blood, CSF, and brain at short time intervals and accurately. The method of determination has to be specific, distinguishing the drug from any of its metabolic products. Otherwise, one might measure drug plus metabolite in plasma and drug alone in brain or CSF, and thus arrive at completely false relative concentrations. In addition, the following criteria have to be satisfied:

1. *Protein Binding.* Since only free drug molecules pass across the membranes under study, the drug concentrations should ideally be measured in the water phase of all tissues. Determination of drug concentration in whole brain (the common procedure) presupposes that a negligible fraction is bound, but instances are known in which binding to cellular sites is considerable. Certainly the degree of binding to plasma proteins must be ascertained; because the rate of diffusion across a membrane is proportional to the *free* drug concentration, the measured rates will be determined by this concentration, and not by the total drug concentration in plasma. At equilibrium, the concentration in CSF will be equal to the free drug concentration in plasma (i.e., in plasma water). CSF contains practically no protein, so corrections do not have to be made for free drug concentrations in this fluid. Since the fraction of drug that is bound to protein depends upon the drug concentration (p. 140), the relevant information is the fraction bound at the concentration actually studied in the experiment. If the plasma drug level falls during an experiment, the fraction bound may increase, and it is therefore best to maintain a constant plasma level throughout the whole experimental period. Obviously, binding to plasma protein should be measured at normal plasma pH and, if possible, at normal body temperature.

2. *Ionization.* For drugs that are weak electrolytes the pK_a must be known so that the degree of ionization at pH 7.4 can be computed from the Henderson-Hasselbalch equation. In all instances studied thus far, the permeability of membranes to the nonionized form of a weak electrolyte is so much greater than to the ionic form that for all practical purposes the latter may be considered not to penetrate at all. This major influence of ionization is illustrated by a study[63] in which sulfonamides were injected intraperitoneally into rats. One hour later the animals were decapitated and the concentrations of drug compared in brain and in whole blood. Despite the fact that no corrections were made for protein binding or binding to brain tissue, there was a clear-cut result. For 12 different sulfonamides

63 P. D. GOLDSWORTHY, R. B. AIRD, and R. A. BECKER: The blood-brain barrier—the effect of acidic dissociation constant on the permeation of certain sulfonamides into the brain. *J. Cell Comp. Physiol. 44:519* (1954).

with pK$_a$'s in the range of 2.9 to 7.8, the brain/blood ratio at 1 hour was approximately 0.1, and actually may have been zero since blood trapped in the brain was included in the brain drug analyses. With pK$_a$ greater than 7.8 there was a systematic increase in the brain/blood ratio, to nearly unity at pK$_a$ 10.4. Inasmuch as the plasma pH is 7.4, and sulfonamides dissociate as acids, those compounds whose pK$_a$ values lay below 7.4 would be largely ionized as anions at plasma pH. Sulfonamides with pK$_a$ values much above 7.4 would be almost completely nonionized at plasma pH. Thus, the results are tantamount to saying that the sulfonamide anion did not penetrate into brain at all, even in an hour, whereas the nonionized sulfonamide moieties all equilibrated with brain water in that time. Ideally, the pH should be measured, not only in plasma but in all the compartments under study, since relatively small pH differences on the two sides of a membrane may appreciably influence the distribution ratio through an ion-trapping effect (p. 121).

3. *Partition Coefficient.* The lipid solubility of a drug plays a major role in determining the rate at which it penetrates into brain and CSF. Lipid solubility is estimated by determining the partition coefficient between an organic solvent and water. Because the only meaningful measurement here is that for the nonionized form of the drug, the determination of partition coefficient should be performed with a strongly acid aqueous phase when the drug is an acid and a strongly alkaline aqueous phase when the drug is a base. If (as frequently done) partition coefficients are measured at pH 7.4, relationships between drugs may be obscured by simultaneous changes in the degree of ionization and in the partition coefficient of the nonionized form. Unfortunately, there is no way to decide which organic solvent most resembles cell membranes. In general, when compounds are ranked according to their partition coefficients in one solvent, there is approximate correspondence to the rank order in a different solvent, although minor discrepancies do occur. The best empirical correlations with rates of passage across biologic membranes are apparently obtained with nonpolar solvents like *n*-heptane or benzene. The absolute values of the partition coefficients have not proved useful; it is the rank order in a series of compounds that one tries to relate to the rates of penetration into brain or CSF.

Figure 2-28 presents the results of a series of experiments in which rates of drug entry into CSF were measured in dogs. The plasma drug levels were held constant by means of a continuous intravenous infusion. The data are plotted on logarithmic ordinates as the difference between the plasma level and the CSF level, divided by the plasma level at each sampling. As plasma levels the free drug concentrations in plasma water were used. A penetration process that was truly exponential (as expected from the Fick equation) would yield a family of straight lines with slopes representing the penetration rate constant for each drug. Conformity to the expectation is obvious in Fig. 2-28.

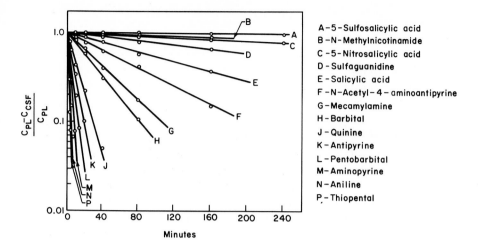

A – 5 – Sulfosalicylic acid
B – N – Methylnicotinamide
C – 5 – Nitrosalicylic acid
D – Sulfaguanidine
E – Salicylic acid
F – N – Acetyl – 4 – aminoantipyrine
G – Mecamylamine
H – Barbital
J – Quinine
K – Antipyrine
L – Pentobarbital
M – Aminopyrine
N – Aniline
P – Thiopental

FIG. 2-28.   KINETICS OF ENTRY OF VARIOUS DRUGS INTO CSF. C_{PL} *is concentration of drug in plasma water,* C_{CSF} *is concentration in cerebrospinal fluid. The drug level in plasma was held constant. Note that the ordinal scale is logarithmic. (From Brodie et al., Fig. 1.[64])*

According to Fick's law, the rate of diffusion is proportional to the concentration gradient. Thus, the rate at which the concentration *difference* $c_p - c_c$ decreases is proportional to that difference. The symbols have the same meaning as before (p. 163):

$$\frac{d(c_p - c_c)}{dt} = -P(c_p - c_c).$$

If the drug level in plasma water is held constant, as by a continuous infusion, we may divide both sides of the equation by c_p, as follows:

$$\frac{d\left(\dfrac{c_p - c_c}{c_p}\right)}{\left(\dfrac{c_p - c_c}{c_p}\right)} = -Pdt;$$

and integrating, we obtain

$$\ln\left(\frac{c_p - c_c}{c_p}\right) = -Pt.$$

The constant of integration is zero, since when $t = 0$, $c_c = 0$, and $\ln[(c_p - c_c)/c_p] = 0$.

[64] B. B. BRODIE, H. KURZ, and L. S. SCHANKER: The importance of dissociation constant and lipid-solubility in influencing the passage of drugs into the cerebrospinal fluid. *J. Pharmacol. Exp. Therap.* 130:20 (1960).

It follows that semilogarithmic plots of $\left(\dfrac{(c_p - c_c)}{c_p}\right)$ against time should yield a family of straight lines whose negative slopes are the penetration (permeability) rate constants. The dimensions of P are min^{-1}, and the half-times to equilibrium are given by $t_{1/2} = 0.693/P$.

From experiments of this kind the penetration rate constants for many drugs have been obtained. Table 2-13 presents such data for some of the drugs included in Fig. 2-28, and for others. The tabulation includes all three parameters that should influence the rate of drug penetration, if that process is purely a physical diffusion of nonionized drug through a lipid barrier: the fraction bound to plasma protein, the nonionized fraction, and the n-heptane/water partition coefficient of the nonionized moiety. In column (f) an "effective partition coefficient" has been computed by multiplying together the fraction not ionized and the partition coefficient. The observed values of P, the penetration rate constant, were obtained by considering only that fraction of drug in the plasma which is not bound to protein; the actual data showing fraction bound are given in column (b). The fairly good semiquantitative agreement between the rank orders in columns (f) and (g) is noteworthy. Possibly a still better correlation would be found if the partition coefficients were determined with an organic solvent that resembled the functional characteristics of cell membranes more closely than does n-heptane.

Some prototype data in Table 2-13 may be examined profitably. Compounds like thiopental and aniline penetrate into CSF very quickly because they are largely nonionic at plasma pH and have very high partition coefficients. Pentobarbital, although it is even less ionized than thiopental, has a very much lower partition coefficient, and therefore penetrates more slowly. Barbital, although its nonionized fraction is about the same as that of thiopental, and although it is much less bound to plasma protein, has so low a partition coefficient that its penetration is very slow. Sulfaguanidine is the extreme example of a compound whose very poor lipid solubility retards its penetration into CSF. Salicyclic acid is largely bound to plasma protein, and the free fraction is nearly all ionized; it would hardly penetrate at a measurable rate were it not for the fact that the partition coefficient of its nonionic form is so high. Similar considerations apply to mecamylamine. Its nonionized form has a much higher partition coefficient than any other compound listed, so on these grounds alone it would be expected to penetrate extremely fast. However, it is a basic compound with pK_a well above the physiologic range, so that a negligibly small fraction is nonionic at pH 7.4. The diffusion gradient for the lipid-soluble form of the drug is therefore extremely small compared with the total drug concentration present in plasma. The unfavorable

TABLE 2-13. Correlation of physical properties of weak electrolyte drugs with their rates of penetration into cerebrospinal fluid

The penetration rates into CSF were determined in dogs as in Fig. 2–28. Data for plasma protein binding may not always have been obtained at the same concentrations used in the in vivo experiments on penetration rate. The entries in column (f) are obtained by multiplying the nonionized fraction (d) by n-heptane/water partition coefficient (e). The letters (A) and (B) after drug names indicate *acid* and *base*, respectively. (Data from Brodie et al.,[64] Tables 1 and 2 and text, and from Hogben et al.,[10] Table 3.)

(a) Drug	(b) Fraction bound to plasma protein at pH 7.4	(c) pK_a	(d) Fraction nonionized at pH 7.4	(e) Partition coefficient n-heptane/water of nonionized form	(f) "Effective partition coefficient" (d) × (e) $(\times 10^3)$	(g) Penetration rate constant P (min^{-1})	(h) Penetration half-time (min)
Thiopental (A)	0.75	7.6	0.613	3.3	2000.	0.50	1.4
Aniline (B)	0.15	4.6	0.998	1.1	1100.	0.40	1.7
Aminopyrine (B)	0.20	5.0	0.996	0.21	210.	0.25	2.8
Pentobarbital (A)	0.40	8.1	0.834	0.05	42.	0.17	4.0
Antipyrine (B)	0.08	1.4	>0.999	0.005	5.0	0.12	5.8
Barbital (A)	<0.02	7.5	0.557	0.002	1.1	0.026	27.
Mecamylamine (B)	0.20	11.2	0.016	>400.	>4.8	0.021	32.
N-Acetyl-4-aminoantipyrine (B)	<0.03	0.5	>0.999	0.001	1.0	0.012	56.
Salicylic acid (A)	0.40	3.0	0.004	0.12	0.48	0.006	115.
Sulfaguanidine (A)	0.06	>10.0	>0.998	<0.001	<1.0	0.003	231.

ionization effectively cancels out the highly favorable partition coefficient, to yield a moderately low rate constant of penetration.

Figure 2-29a shows a typical result for the passage of a poorly lipid-soluble drug into CSF, brain, and liver. The more rapid passage into the cells and interstitial fluid of liver than into brain or CSF is obvious. For drugs that enter brain and CSF still more slowly, the difference between the rates of eliquilibration of central nervous tissues and other organs becomes more marked, as shown for N-acetyl-4-aminoantipyrine in Fig. 2-29b. Conversely, highly lipid-soluble drugs that enter brain very rapidly equilibrate with that organ even faster than with others, primarily because of the greater relative blood supply of brain.

The extraordinary sluggishness with which a water-soluble ion may pass from blood into brain (or vice versa) is illustrated in Table 2-14. ^{32}P-Orthophosphate was administered to rabbits, intravenously or directly into the cisterna magna at 1/20 the intravenous dose. Animals were sacrificed at various intervals, and the tissues were analyzed for radioactivity. No meaningful comparison could be made between the various parts of the brain because so many factors other than membrane permeability to orthophosphate must have influenced the outcome. The uptake of the isotope, for example, depends strongly upon the metabolic turnover of phosphate and the pool sizes, which differ from one tissue to another. Moreover, although one would like to know about the distribution of orthophosphate, the observed radioactivity probably represented numerous

FIG. 2-29. KINETICS OF ENTRY OF BARBITAL AND N-ACETYL-4-AMINOANTIPY-RINE INTO CSF, BRAIN, AND LIVER. (*From Mayer et al., Figs. 3 and 4.*[65])

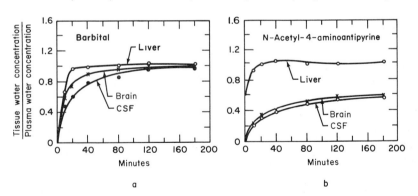

[65] S. MAYER, R. P. MAICKEL, and B. B. BRODIE: Kinetics of penetration of drugs and other foreign compounds into cerebrospinal fluid and brain. *J. Pharmacol. Exp. Therap. 127:*205 (1959).

[66] D. P. RALL, J. R. STABENAU, and C. G. ZUBROD: Distribution of drugs between blood and cerebrospinal fluid: general methodology and effect of pH gradients. *J. Pharmacol. Exp. Therap. 125:*185 (1959).

[67] B. B. BRODIE: "Physico-Chemical Factors in Drug Absorption," page 16 in *Absorption and Distribution of Drugs,* ed. by T. B. Binns and C. Dodds. Baltimore, Williams and Wilkins, 1964.

TABLE 2-14. **Distribution of ^{32}P-orthophosphate in the central nervous system after intravenous and intracisternal administration**

Figures represent cpm per milligram tissue, except where otherwise stated. (From Bakay,[68] p. 423.)

	[32]P given intravenously	[32]P given intracisternally		
Amount of ^{32}P, μc/kg body wt.	20	1	1	1
Duration of experiment	24 hr	10 min	30 min	60 min
Frontal lobes				
Cortex	2.0	6.0	11.0	36.0–100.0
White matter	1.0	4.0	4.0	32.0
Cerebral hemispheres				
Cortex of convexity	2.5	30.0	9.0–22.0–39.0	8.0–13.0
Basal cortex	3.5	38.0	80.0	260.0
Central substance	1.3	2.0–4.0	25.0	195.0
Lateral and third ventricles				
(Choroid plexus and walls)	4.5–9.0	95.0	90.0	88.0
Aqueduct	6.4	122.0	95.0	430.0
Mesencephalon				
Surface	2.5	199.0	200.0	43.0
Depth	2.0	15.0	38.0	63.0
Pons	2.0	88.0	100.0	124.0
Fourth ventricle				
(Choroid plexus and walls)	9.4	199.0	172.0	185.0
Cerebellum				
Cortex	4.0	30.0	52.0	42.0
White matter	1.5	12.0	28.0	40.0
Medulla	4.4	137.0	126.0	80.0
Spinal cord (thoracic)	3.0	1.0	3.0	6.0
Pituitary gland	85.0	12.0	33.0	69.0

forms of incorporated ^{32}P, such as nucleic acids and phospholipids. Nevertheless it is valid to compare the two routes of administration, tissue by tissue. The striking feature thus revealed is that for most parts of the central nervous system the entry of phosphate within 10 minutes after intracisternal injection far exceeded that in 24 hours after intravenous injection. In the pituitary gland, however, as already noted, the vascular route was much more effective than elsewhere.

PHARMACOLOGIC CONSEQUENCES OF THE DIVERSE RATES OF ENTRY
OF DIFFERENT DRUGS INTO THE CENTRAL NERVOUS SYSTEM

The most obvious consequence of the very slow rate of entry of water-soluble and ionized drugs into the brain and spinal cord is that systemic administration of such substances may be useless if the intended

---

[68] L. BAKAY: Studies on the blood-brain barrier with radioactive phosphorus. *Arch. Neurol. Psychiatr. 66:419 (1951).*

site of action is the central nervous system. Penicillin, for example, is a water-soluble cyclic peptide bearing a carboxyl group that is completely ionized at plasma pH. On the basis of its structure alone one would expect it to enter brain and CSF very slowly. In addition, this drug is actively removed from CSF at the choroid plexus. Thus the drug, despite its general efficacy as a systemic antibacterial and spirocheticidal agent, cannot be relied upon in infections of the central nervous system like meningitis or syphilis. In meningeal infections the restrictions to passage of drugs into the CSF are often lessened as a result of the inflamed abnormal state of the membranes, but this cannot be counted upon.

The converse proposition is also true. Drugs that act upon the central nervous system after systemic administration must obviously have a suitable combination of those properties that confer ready penetration, namely, low ionization at plasma pH, low binding to plasma protein, and fairly high lipid/water partition coefficient. These correlations of physicochemical properties with entry into brain can be taken advantage of. Atropine, for example, is a tertiary amine that penetrates brain readily and has significant pharmacologic actions there; its quaternized derivative, atropine methyl sulfate, is effectively excluded from the central nervous system, yet it produces the same anticholinergic effects in the periphery as does atropine. Neostigmine, a quaternary ammonium cholinesterase inhibitor (p. 29), acts only peripherally; in contrast, the very lipid-soluble organic phosphate insecticides and nerve gases penetrate into the brain, causing convulsions and central respiratory depression as well as the usual array of intensified acetylcholine actions in the peripheral autonomic and neuromuscular systems. Norepinephrine is practically unable to enter brain when administered intravenously in tolerated doses; but a precursor, dopamine, lacking the alcoholic −OH group, and more lipid soluble in consequence, passes readily into brain tissue, where it is converted to norepinephrine.

Some drugs are virtually excluded from the central nervous system when they are administered systemically but have striking actions when injected directly into the CSF.[61] Often, these central effects are unlike any peripheral effects produced by the same drugs, and sometimes they are quite opposite. Penicillin, practically devoid of any toxicity by the usual routes of administration (except in allergically sensitized individuals), causes convulsions if brought into direct contact with spinal cord or brain. Intravenous epinephrine has cardiovascular and hyperglycemic actions and it also produces arousal; injected into a lateral ventricle, on the other hand, it brings about a sleep-like state. Tubocurarine has been studied thoroughly. In the periphery this drug causes paralysis through neuromuscular blockade. When injected into a lateral ventricle in the cat, it initiated a symptom complex that strikingly resembled an epileptic seizure in man: tremor, myoclonic contractions, loud calling, and generalized convulsions associated with spiking activity in the electroencephalogram. These effects did not occur when the drug was injected into the cisterna magna, whence the

CSF flows into the subarachnoid space, indicating that the drug acts on deep structures, not surface ones bathed by subarachnoid fluid. Moreover, the discharge was most pronounced on the side of the injection, suggesting a local action on areas in the vicinity of the lateral ventricles. Other experiments localized this effect of tubocurarine to the hippocampus. Acetylcholine, which certainly cannot enter brain from the capillaries (both because it is a quaternary ammonium cation, and because it is hydrolyzed so rapidly by plasma and tissue cholinesterases), caused a curious catatonic stupor when injected intraventricularly in cats. Cholinesterase inhibitors evoked the same symptom complex when administered by the same route.

An interesting consequence of the relationship between ionization and penetration into brain is the effect of acidosis or alkalosis upon the distribution of drugs between brain and plasma. The general effect, insofar as it applies to all body tissues, has already been discussed (p. 157). Here, the practical importance is that toxic amounts of such central nervous depressants as the barbiturates can be removed from the brain by establishing a pH gradient, as illustrated earlier in Fig. 2-22. If the plasma is made temporarily more alkaline than the CSF (as by sodium bicarbonate infusion), the fraction of ionized barbiturate in plasma increases and the nonionized fraction decreases. A concentration gradient is thus established for the diffusible (nonionized) form of the drug, and a net movement ensues from brain to plasma. Were the drug not excreted or metabolized, this shift would eventually be reversed, as the CSF itself became more alkaline, or the plasma alkalosis was compensated. A second and important effect of the alkalosis, however, is to promote renal excretion of the drug, since ionized compounds are reabsorbed very poorly from the tubular urine (p. 201). As the urine becomes alkaline as well as the blood, an enhanced urinary output results from the ion-trapping effect. Obviously, for all drugs whose range of ionization is near pH 7.4, alkalosis will favor the removal of acidic ones from the central nervous system and passage of basic ones into the central nervous system; acidosis will have the opposite effects.

A dramatic result of the rapid penetration of lipid-soluble substances into the brain is the quick onset of anesthesia caused by gases such as cyclopropane and nitrous oxide, which diffuse very readily through lipid membranes. A less apparent instance of high lipid solubility affecting the onset and duration of drug action is the behavior of thiopental as an intravenous anesthetic agen. Thiopental is unique among the commonly used barbiturates in its very high partition coefficient and extremely rapid passage into the brain. Its oxygen homolog, pentobarbital, has a lower partition coefficient and therefore enters brain somewhat more slowly (Table 2-13). The structures and physical constants for these two drugs are given in Table 2-15. A single intravenous injection of thiopental can produce an almost instantaneous state of anesthesia that lasts for only about 5 minutes, followed by rapid and complete recovery. If the single dose is made very

TABLE 2-15. **Comparison of structures and properties of thiopental and pentobarbital**

	Thiopental	Pentobarbital
Structure	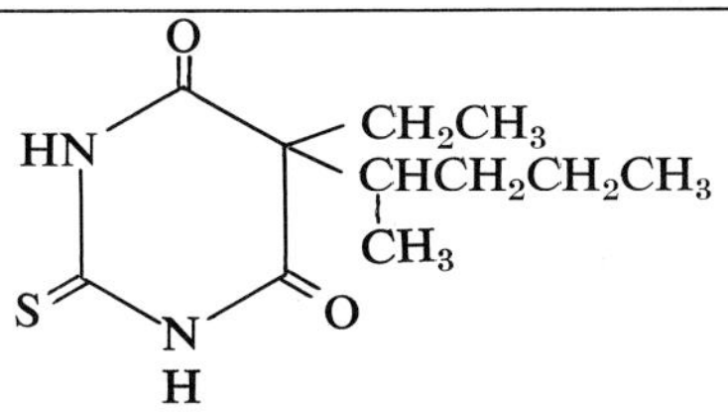	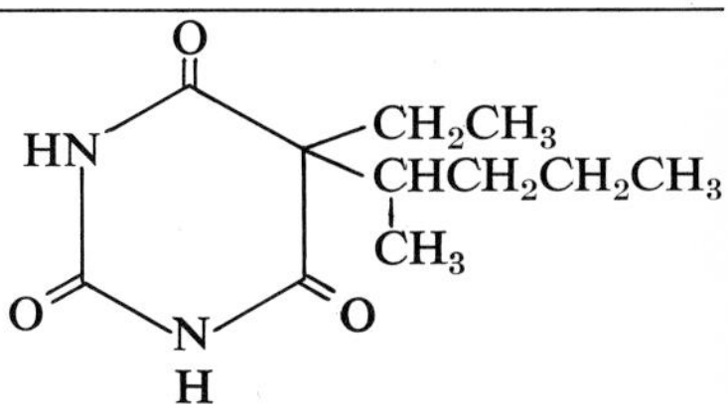
pK$_a$	7.6	8.1
Fraction nonionized at pH 7.4	0.61	0.83
Partition coefficient of nonionized form (heptane/water)	3.3	0.05

much larger, the anesthesia will be too deep and respiratory arrest will occur. With pentobarbital, a single intravenous dose produces, with a gradual onset over a period of several minutes, a state of anesthesia that lasts for an hour or more. Reducing the dose only leads to a lighter anesthesia. No dose can be found that will mimic the ultrashort duration of action of thiopental.

At first the ultrashort duration of thiopental action was ascribed to a rapid rate of metabolism, since the drug disappeared eventually from the blood without being accounted for in the urine. Then it was found that thiopental becomes localized in the fat depots, so that after several hours practically all of a single dose is found there. This manifestation of the drug's high lipid/water partition coefficient was then made responsible for its ultrashort duration of action. This is incorrect. The blood supply to the fat depots is entirely insufficient to transfer more than a small fraction of the total body thiopental there within the 5-minute period that concerns us. What data are available show clearly that the rate of entry of thiopental into fat is relatively slow, extending over a period of hours. What, then, is the real explanation of thiopental's ultrashort duration of action?

Experiments were performed with rats administered thiopental or pentobarbital intravenously, and decapitated at 30 seconds and periodically thereafter. The results, shown in Fig. 2-30, were quite clear. Thiopental entered the brain extremely rapidly, while the blood level was still very high, shortly after the injection. Then, as the blood level fell rapidly as a result of the distribution of thiopental into all the tissues, the drug moved rapidly out of the brain to maintain equilibrium. The time course

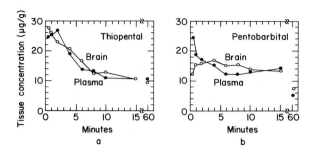

FIG. 2-30.   PLASMA AND BRAIN CONCENTRATIONS OF THIOPENTAL (*a*) AND PENTO-
BARBITAL (*b*) AFTER INTRAVENOUS INJECTION IN RATS.   *The dose for both
drugs was 15 mg/kg. Each point represents the mean value for four male rats.
(From Goldstein and Aronow, Fig. 1.[69])*

of this inflow and outflow of thiopental corresponded with the course of
onset and offset of anesthesia. In contrast, because pentobarbital equilibrated with brain relatively slowly, the rapid fall in the plasma level was
already complete by the time equilibrium was attained; for, during the few
minutes the brain concentration was rising, the plasma level was falling
fast. Finally, after equilibration, the rates of fall of the brain concentration
and of the plasma concentration were determined by the rate of metabolism
and excretion of pentobarbital. Again, the time course of the changes in
brain concentration coincided with the slow onset and prolonged duration
of anesthesia. Ultimately, of course, thiopental becomes highly localized in
fat depots, but this has no influence upon the duration of anesthesia after
a single small dose. If multiple doses of thiopental are administered, however, or a continuous infusion of the drug is given, then equilibrium may
be attained between an anesthetic concentration in the brain and the same
concentration throughout the body fluids. Under these conditions thiopental
has an extremely long duration of action, and the drug effect is terminated
primarily by its sequestration in fat depots, its subsequent very low rate of
metabolism, and consequent gradual lowering of the concentration in all
the body tissues, including the brain. The ultrashort duration of action of
thiopental, therefore, is a consequence of its high lipid solubility, but only
because this confers upon it the ability to enter and leave brain tissue very
rapidly.

Finally, the rate of onset of barbital anesthesia presents an illustrative contrast. Although the rate of penetration of thiopental was

[69] A. GOLDSTEIN and L. ARONOW: The durations of action of thiopental and
pentobarbital. *J. Pharmacol. Exp. Therap.* 128:1 (1960).

shown to be much faster than that of pentobarbital, the latter enters brain considerably faster than many other drugs. Table 2-13 indicates that barbital has an extremely unfavorable partition coefficient, and that it penetrates very much more slowly than either thiopental or pentobarbital. This is reflected very well in its slow onset of action, which renders the drug useless as an anesthetic or hypnotic agent in man; even after intravenous administration of an anesthetic dose to experimental animals, many minutes elapse before any effects are seen.

Passage of Drugs across the Placenta

STRUCTURE AND FUNCTION OF THE PLACENTA

The mature placenta contains a network of maternal blood sinuses into which protrude villi carrying the fetal capillaries (Fig. 2-31). These villi are covered with a trophoblastic layer beneath which is a layer of mesenchymal tissue and, finally, the capillary endothelium. There is also a close apposition of the fetal amnion to the chorionic membrane of the uterine wall. Isolated human amniotic membrane has been shown to be

FIG. 2-31. SCHEME OF PLACENTAL CIRCULATION. (*From Gray, Fig. 45.*[70])

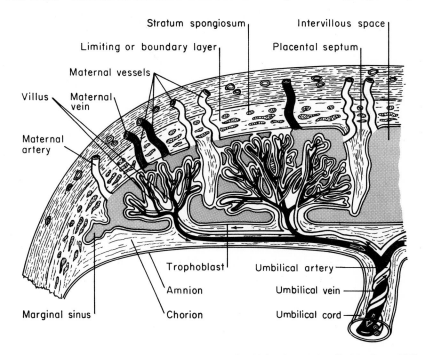

[70] H. GRAY: *Anatomy of the Human Body,* 28th ed., ed. by C. M. Goss. Philadelphia, Lea and Febiger, 1966, Fig. 2-51, p. 40.

permeable to such diverse substances as Na^+, Cl^-, I^-, creatinine, quinine, Fe^{++}, and serum albumin. In the early stages of gestation the passage of substances directly into the amniotic sac may be significant, but later the amniotic fluid is only in contact with the fetal epidermis. The exchange of foodstuffs, oxygen and carbon dioxide, and drugs must occur primarily across the placenta, from the maternal arterial supply by way of the intervillous spaces into the fetal capillaries in the villi, and thus into umbilical venous blood.

The membranes separating fetal capillary blood from maternal blood in the intervillous spaces resemble cell membranes elsewhere in their general permeability behavior. Lipid-soluble substances diffuse across readily, water-soluble substances less well the greater their molecular radii, and large organic ions very poorly or not at all. Very few detailed and systematic quantitative measurements have been made at various times throughout gestation. It is known that the tissue layers interposed between the fetal capillaries and maternal blood become progressively thinner, from about 25μ early in pregnancy to only 2μ at term. Permeability to sodium ions has been found to increase greatly over the same period of time, and it is likely that comparable permeability changes to other substances also occur.

The mature placenta is far more than a semipermeable membrane.[71] It contains energy-coupled specific transport systems for amino acids; L-histidine, for example (but not D-histidine) is transported from maternal the fetal capillaries and maternal blood become progressively thinner, mechanism not unlike that found in human erythrocytes. $^{131}I^-$ is transferred much more rapidly from mother to fetus than in the reverse direction. ^{32}P-Orthophosphate accumulates in placenta to many times its concentration in maternal blood, presumably serving as a reservoir to supply the large requirements for fetal growth. Monoamine oxidase, cholinesterase, and other enzymes are present in placenta; these may play a role in protecting the fetus against substances for which fetal tissues have not yet developed metabolic pathways (cf. p. 274). Throughout pregnancy the placenta synthesizes gonadotropins, estrogens, and progesterone.

TRANSPLACENTAL PASSAGE OF VARIOUS DRUGS[72-74]

Study of the transplacental passage of drugs has been hampered by a number of special circumstances. Kinetic data are difficult to obtain

---

71 A. A. PLENTL, ed.: Symposium on the placenta. *Amer. J. Obstet. Gynecol.* 84:1535–1798 (1962).

72 K. W. CROSS, ed.: Symposium on foetal and neonatal physiology. *Brit. Med. Bull.* 17:79–174 (1961).

73 Symposium: maternal and fetal physiology in the perinatal period. *Anesthesiology* 26:377–549 (1965).

74 F. MOYA and V. THORNDIKE: Passage of drugs across the placenta. *Amer. J. Obstet. Gynecol.* 84:1778 (1962).

because the fetal concentration can usually only be measured once—at the moment the fetus is delivered or (in an experimental situation) removed surgically. No methods have been developed yet for cannulating the fetal circulation in utero in small animals in a nondestructive way so that measurements could be made over a long time. Ideally, one would wish to establish a constant plasma level in the maternal arterial blood and then perform serial determinations of concentrations in the fetal blood. Some techniques have been developed for doing this in large animals (lamb, goat),[75] but data for a variety of drugs are not yet at hand.

The typical study in the human entails the administration of drug to the mother just prior to delivery, then determination of drug concentrations in maternal and cord blood at the moment of delivery. Thus, information about rates of equilibration has to be pieced together from a great many separate experiments. A good example is shown in Fig. 2-32. Here, the equilibration of two sulfonamide drugs between maternal and cord blood was studied. The same dose was given to all the mothers intra-

FIG. 2-32. MATERNAL-FETAL EQUILIBRATION OF TWO SULFONAMIDES IN THE HUMAN. *Sulfonamide, 5 g, was given to mothers intravenously as the sodium salt, at zero time. Maternal and cord blood was drawn for analysis at delivery. Each point represents one subject mother and infant. Data are for unconjugated drug. (Data from Speert, Tables II and IV.[76] By permission of C. V. Mosby.)*

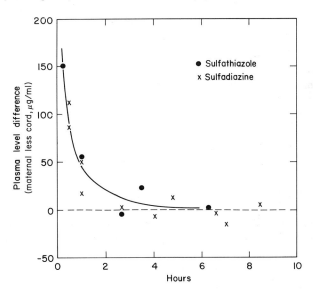

[75] A. M. RUDOLPH and M. A. HEYMANN: The circulation of the fetus in utero. Methods for studying distribution of blood flow, cardiac output, and organ flow. *Circulation Res.* 21:163 (1967).

[76] H. SPEERT: Placental transmission of sulfathiazole and sulfadiazine and its significance for fetal chemotherapy. *Amer. J. Obstet. Gynecol.* 45:200 (1943).

venously. Whenever delivery occurred, the maternal and cord blood samples were taken simultaneously. Thus, each point on the curve represents one mother and her infant. Despite the scatter it is apparent that these sulfonamides require about 2 hours to reach complete equilibrum.

Figure 2-33 provides a good contrast with a drug that appears in cord blood quite rapidly after intravenous injection in the mother; but the scatter is so bad that it is really difficult to say where the curves should lie, or to define the rate of equilibration with satisfactory precision.

A critical comment is in order about the practice of sampling cord blood without distinguishing between umbilical venous and umbilical arterial blood, and then supposing that the concentration found represents that in the fetal tissues. When the fetus has come into complete equilibrium with maternal blood this will be true, but at all earlier times it will be false. At the outset only the umbilical vein carries any drug at all, and the umbilical artery is essentially drug free. If the drug under study is one that crosses the placenta readily, mixed cord blood may therefore be expected to show concentrations approaching half the maternal level very quickly indeed, and before the concentration in fetal tissues is appreciable. The

FIG. 2-33.   MATERNAL-FETAL EQUILIBRATION OF SECOBARBITAL IN THE HUMAN. *Each point represents one subject. Newborn blood specimens were cord blood samples. (From Root et al., Fig. 1.[77] by permission of C. V. Mosby.)*

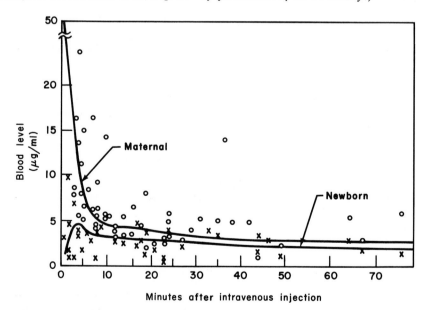

Minutes after intravenous injection

[77] B. ROOT, E. EICHNER, and I. SUNSHINE: Blood secobarbital levels and their clinical correlation in mothers and newborn infants. *Amer. J. Obstet. Gynecol. 81:*948 (1961).

reason is that if initially the umbilical venous blood contained drug at the maternal concentration, and the umbilical arterial concentration was zero, and the sample contained an equal mixture of both, then the measured concentration would be one-half that in maternal blood. If the sample is taken from the cut end of the cord with placenta still in situ, it is likely to be pure umbilical venous blood, at the placental drug concentration, regardless of the amount of drug in the fetus. In general, at any time during the equilibration process, the highest levels will be found in cord venous blood, the next highest in fetal arterial blood (including cord arterial blood), and the lowest in the fetal tissues as a whole, especially those tissues with a poor blood supply.

The necessity of distinguishing between a drug and its metabolite is shown in Table 2-16. Here, sulfanilamide was administered to rabbits near term and the fetal and maternal blood samples were obtained several hours later. The total sulfanilamide concentrations give the impression that equilibrium has not yet been established, but the concentrations of unconjugated sulfanilamide are seen to be about the same in maternal and fetal blood. The experiment did not reveal why the conjugated (acetylated) product was in excess in maternal blood. It might have crossed the placenta more slowly than the parent drug because of its more polar structure; thus free sulfanilamide (the therapeutically active drug) would have attained equilibrium earlier than the acetylated derivative. If a metabolic transformation proceeds rapidly in the mother but not in the fetus, and if the

TABLE 2-16. **Maternal-fetal equilibration of sulfanilamide and acetylsulfanilamide in rabbits**

Sulfanilamide was administered to rabbits near term in a single oral dose and the fetal and maternal blood sampled about 3.5 to 5.5 hours later. Total sulfanilamide includes unchanged drug and the acetylated derivative. Figures represent mg/100 ml plasma. (From Lee et al.,[78] Table I.)

Rabbit no.	Total sulfanilamide		Unconjugated sulfanilamide	
	Maternal	Fetal	Maternal	Fetal
1	26.5	18.1	15.7	14.6
2	24.7	16.7	13.7	12.1
3	21.0	12.5	2.6	2.7
4	29.2	—	9.8	6.2
5	35.2	10.3	6.3	6.4
6	11.5	7.3	4.4	3.1
7	22.0	20.0	20.3	16.9

[78] H. M. LEE, R. C. ANDERSON, and K. K. CHEN: Passage of sulfanilamide from mother to fetus. *Proc. Soc Exp. Biol. Med. 38:*366 (1938).

metabolic product crosses the placenta very slowly, the product might not equilibrate until after all of the parent drug has been metabolized.

An important measurement, without which transplacental transfer rates cannot be assessed meaningfully, is the degree of binding to plasma proteins. Obviously, only free drug is able to cross membranes, and only the free drug concentration need be the same on both sides of a membrane at equilibruim. The free drug may be measured directly (as by analyzing an ultrafiltrate); or the total (free plus bound) concentration may be measured and a correction then applied for the fraction bound, as determined independently (cf. p. 139). The extent of binding to plasma proteins is generally assumed to be the same in maternal and fetal blood, inasmuch as the protein composition of plasma appears to be the same, at least in the mature fetus. The binding of a substantial fraction of a drug to maternal plasma proteins will reduce the concentration gradient of free drug molecules and thereby diminish the rate of their passage across the placenta. It may be argued that only free drug matters anyway, since that is the pharmacologically active form. But every unit of free drug transferred to the fetus will itself undergo binding in the same proportions as in maternal blood. The fetal plasma proteins act as a sink for the drug molecules after they cross the placenta; therefore a relatively large amount of drug may have to be transferred, at a relatively low concentration gradient, in order to establish maternal-fetal equilibrum. Thus, protein binding can considerably retard the passage of drugs across the placenta.

Substances that are very lipid soluble (e.g., the anesthetic gases) diffuse across the placental membranes so rapidly that their overall rates of equilibration are probably limited only by the placental blood flow. Inasmuch as dissociation of the complexes between drugs and plasma proteins is practically instantaneous, equilibration rate would not be affected significantly by protein binding in this group of substances. For drugs transferred at moderate rates or slowly, however, diffusion is rate limiting, and protein binding can play a role.

Consider two drugs, X and Y, both therapeutically effective at the same *free* concentrations $(X),(Y)$. X is 90 per cent bound to plasma protein (so its total concentration is $10(X)$); Y is not bound at all. Since the volume of maternal body water is so much greater than that of the fetus, we may assume, roughly, that after equilibration the maternal plasma level remains unchanged. The net transfer of Y will be (Y) times the volume of fetal body water, and initially this will take place at a concentration gradient $(Y) - 0 = (Y)$. As for X, at equilibrium the fetus will contain (X) times the volume of fetal body water; in addition, there will be a bound component, $9(X)$ times the fetal plasma volume. The initial concentration gradient is $(X) - 0 = (X)$, so that relative to the total amount that has to be transferred the transfer rate will be much lower than it was for Y.

This dependence of the rate of equilibration of free drug upon plasma protein binding is probably unique for transplacental transfer; elsewhere (e.g., brain, renal glomeruli), the fluid on the other side of the membrane contains very little protein, so the sink effect is not operative.

Studies on fetal drug levels at various times during gestation are obviously out of the question in the human, with a few exceptions. Occasionally, data have been obtained at the time of delivery of a nonviable deformed fetus (e.g., an anencephalic monster) or a fetus killed by a drug taken suicidally by the mother. And rarely, advantage has been taken of a therapeutic abortion, usually in the first trimester, to gain information about passage of a drug into the early embryo. Under such conditions it was shown[79] that caffeine, which distributes freely into all the body water, also equilibrated with the fetal tissues when it was administered to women at the seventh or eighth week of gestation.

Despite the difficulties cited above, considerable qualitative and semiquantitative information has been obtained in human and animal studies about which drugs cross readily into the fetal circulation and which do not.[80, 81] Among drugs that enter the fetus at all, two extreme equilibration rates are indicated in Table 2-17. Tubocurarine, a quaternary ammonium compound that is excluded completely from the brain, had barely reached a detectable level in fetal blood at 9 minutes. Thiopental, in contrast, which equilibrates with brain as fast as the blood delivers it,

TABLE 2-17. **Maternal-fetal equilibration of tubocurarine and thiopental in humans**

Thiopental, 125 mg, was given as single rapid intravenous injection. Tubocurarine was given intravenously over a 1-minute period, usually a total dose of 30 to 36 mg. Blood values are μg/ml plasma. (Data of Cohen,[81] Tables 5 and 6.)

Time after drug administration (min)	Tubocurarine		Thiopental	
	Maternal	Fetal	Maternal	Fetal
5	3	0	8.5	5.5
5	2.4	0		
6	3.2	0	8.0	3.5
9	1.1	0.1	4.8	2.5
10			1.9	1.1
11	2.1	0.1	2.0	1.2
12			3.0	2.0

79 A. GOLDSTEIN and R. WARREN: Passage of caffeine into human gonadal and fetal tissue. *Biochem. Pharmacol. 11:*166 (1962).

80 C. A. VILLEE: Placental transfer of drugs. *Ann. N.Y. Acad. Sci. 123:*237 (1965).

81 E. N. COHEN: Thiopental-curare-nitrous oxide anesthesia for cesarean section, 1950–1960. *Anesthesia Analg. 41:*122 (1962).

had attained about half-equilibration with fetal blood at 9 minutes, and had reached a considerable concentration earlier than 5 minutes. The wide range of transplacental transfer rates is reminiscent of the kinetics of equilibration between blood and brain (or CSF). The principles, indeed, are the same, except that the placental membranes are obviously more permeable to water-soluble molecules and ions than are the brain capillaries. Moreover, as discussed in detail below (p. 189), the fastest equilibration possible between maternal and fetal blood is a great deal slower than that between blood and brain, primarily because the blood flow to the placenta limits the rate of delivery of drug to the fetal circulation.

Of the agents (besides thiopental) that would be expected to equilibrate at the maximum rate, trichloroethylene attained equal concentration in fetal and maternal blood within 16 minutes; other anesthetics (ether, cyclopropane, halothane) equilibrated in about the same time. Data showing unequal distribution of nitrous oxide even after 30 minutes are difficult to accept at face value in view of the universal finding that this gas equilibrates rapidly and completely in other tissues, including brain. Oxygen and carbon dioxide, the lipid-soluble respiratory gases, also pass rapidly across the placenta.

Narcotic analgesics have been found near equilibrium values in fetal blood plasma after several hours, but rates of transfer are not available. Some effects of morphine (e.g., depressed respiration, pinpoint pupils) have been observed in newborn infants of mothers given morphine during labor; and the occurrence of withdrawal symptoms in infants born of addicted mothers makes it plain that morphine and heroin have free access to the fetus during gestation. The tranquilizers of the phenothiazine and reserpine classes evidently cross the placenta, as judged by typical drug effects observed in newborn infants.

Steroids, as might be expected, cross the placenta readily (e.g., cholesterol, progesterone, estradiol, estriol), but the more water-soluble glucuronides of these compounds penetrate at much reduced rates. Antibiotics, including penicillin, chloramphenicol, tetracyclines, streptomycin, and erythromycin all appear in fetal blood, but rather slowly and at very different rates. Penicillin equilibrates in about 10 hours, streptomycin in about 18 hours. The tetracyclines crossed the placenta extremely slowly and never reached equal concentrations, in fetal and maternal blood, but this might have been explained by the fact that the conjugated form of the drug (formed only in the mother's liver) could not pass the placental barrier. After erythromycin had been given in adequate dosage to a mother over a 16-hour period, barely detectable amounts were found at the end of this period in cord blood at delivery.

Teratogenic agents of diverse chemical structure obviously cross the placenta, at least during the first six months of fetal life; numerous studies have implicated a direct action of such drugs on the tissues undergoing embryogenesis (p. 711). Of especial concern is the ease with which hazardous products of nuclear fission (e.g., ^{137}Cs, ^{45}Ca, ^{90}Sr, ^{131}I) cross the placental membranes and localize in vulnerable fetal tissues. Not only viruses (e.g., the teratogenic rubella virus) but cellular pathogens (e.g., spirochetes) may cross the placenta and infect the fetus.

Antibody globulins pass from the mother's circulation into that of the fetus, although slowly; but evidently some selective mechanism operates inasmuch as albumins, with lower molecular weights, penetrate the placental barrier much more slowly. More remarkable is the passage of erythrocytes in both directions across the placenta, even in late pregnancy. This used to be attributed to gross breaks in the placental continuity, but electron micrographs offer no support to such an explanation.

It is an obvious clinical fact that a mother deeply anesthetized with a barbiturate can give birth to a fairly alert infant who scores well on the Apgar test, a crude but rapid and exceedingly useful scoring system for evaluating several vital indices immediately after birth. Unfortunately, follow-up has often been haphazard, so that no reliable data are to be found on the longer-lasting and delayed effects of maternal medication on the infant. If adequate records were available, a relationship might even be sought between the extent of drug use at delivery and the overall neonatal mortality. It is clear that infants of mothers who were delivered under deep anesthesia often show depression over the next 24 hours compared with those delivered without benefit of drugs or with short-acting volatile anesthetics. "Although the youngster at birth cries vigorously and, it is true, has an arterial plasma level of thiopental lower than the mother, there is still enough drug within the child for 12 and possibly 24 hours to make this newborn infant much more drowsy than the other child. We feel that the observations at birth and at delivery do not tell the entire story. . . . Although you can arouse the child, the newborn can readily go back into drowsiness and practically not move for several hours."[82] A concrete example is illustrated in Fig. 2-34. The unmedicated infant, although born with a respiratory acidosis caused by CO_2 accumulation, rapidly eliminated the excess CO_2 by vigorous respiration, and the plasma pH rose to a normal level within the first hour. In the infant of the medicated mother this did not occur. With many drugs the difficulty imposed upon the infant by the unwanted drug effect is compounded by the absence of drug-metabolizing enzymes and by poor renal function in the neonatal period.

That a wakeful infant should be born of an anesthetized mother is not surprising when one considers what is known and can be calculated (p. 189) about the rates of equilibration of maternal and fetal tissues with respect to an anesthetic drug. What is confusing and difficult to interpret are findings indicating that fetal and maternal blood have the same concentration of a barbiturate (or other anesthetic agent) at the time of de-

---

[82] P. LEIF: in Villee, ref. 80, discussion, p. 243.

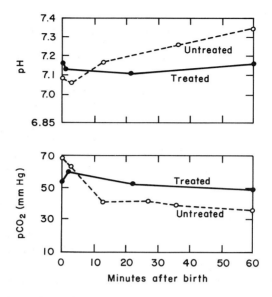

FIG. 2-34.   EFFECT OF DEPRESSANT DRUGS ON RECOVERY FROM BIRTH ASPHYXIA. *Comparison of an infant delivered without sedation or anesthesia* (dotted line) *with one whose mother was given 200 mg barbiturate and 100 mg meperidine 3 hours before delivery. Blood pH* (above) *and partial pressure of carbon dioxide* (p_{co_2}) (below) *are shown. (From James, Fig. 7.[83] By permission of J. B. Lippincott.)*

livery, and yet the mother is anesthetized, the fetus awake. Everything we know indicates that infants should be *more* depressed than adults at a given barbiturate concentration, and should be in still further trouble because of their immature liver microsomal drug-metabolizing system (p. 274). As shown in the next section, data indicating complete equilibration of secobarbital in 3 to 5 minutes, of pentobarbital in 1 minute, of thiopental in 3 minutes, and even of barbital (usually the slowest to penetrate cell membranes) in 4 minutes must be discounted.[77, 84-86] The most likely source of error would be that the analyses were done principally on umbilical venous blood carrying a drug concentration nearly the same as the placenta but greatly in excess of that in fetal brain and body water.

    [83] L. S. JAMES: The effect of pain relief for labor and delivery on the fetus and newborn. *Anesthesiology 21:*405 (1960).

    [84] J. FEALY: Placental transmission of pentobarbital sodium. *Obstet. Gynecol. 11:*342 (1958).

    [85] F. B. MC KECHNIE and J. G. CONVERSE: Placental transmission of thiopental. *Amer. J. Obstet. Gynecol. 70:*639 (1955).

    [86] C. E. FLOWERS: The placental transmission of barbiturates and thiobarbiturates and their pharmacological action on the mother and the infant. *Amer. J. Obstet. Gynecol. 78:*730 (1959).

THEORY OF MATERNAL-FETAL EQUILIBRATION RATES

The kinetics of equilibration of the fetal tissues with drugs in the maternal circulation depend upon the rates of delivery of drug to the placenta and of its removal and circulation on the fetal side, and upon the rate of permeation at each membranous interface in the system. We shall compute *maximum* rates by assuming instantaneous equilibration at every membrane, as might nearly be true of such agents as thiopental or the anesthetic gases. We shall assume at the outset that a constant drug concentration is maintained in the maternal plasma water. Later we shall postulate various rates of decline of the maternal drug level.

The plan of the fetal circulation is presented in Figs. 2-35 and 2-36. Blood from the placental villi, which are bathed in the intervillous maternal blood, enters the fetus by way of the umbilical vein, is mixed with the venous return from the lower body of the fetus, and enters the inferior vena cava through the ductus venosus. Most of this blood, instead of entering the right heart (as it will do after birth), passes directly through the foramen ovale in the atrial septum and into the left heart. The left cardiac output supplies the fetal brain and upper extremity; a part of this blood

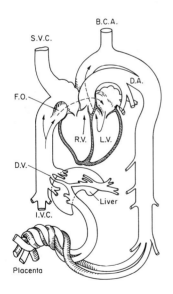

FIG. 2-35. PLAN OF THE FETAL CIRCU-LATION. I.V.C., *Inferior vena cava;* R.V., *right ventricle;* D.V., *ductus venosus;* D.A., *ductus arteriosus;* S.V.C., *superior vena cava;* L.V., *left ventricle;* F.O., *foramen ovale;* B.C.A., *brachiocephalic artery (in man the common carotid artery). (Adapted from Dawes, Fig. 1.*[87] *By permission of the British Council and the Long Island Biological Association.)*

[87] G. S. DAWES: Changes in the circulation at birth. *Brit. Med. Bull. 17:*148 (1961).

[88] C. B. MARTIN, JR.: Uterine blood flow and placental circulation. *Anesthesiology 26:*447 (1965).

[89] D. E. REID: *A Textbook of Obstetrics.* Philadelphia, W. B. Saunders Co., 1962.

[90] I. S. EDELMAN, H. B. HALEY, P. R. SCHLOERB, D. B. SHELDON, J. B. FRIIS-HANSEN, G. STOLL, and F. D. MOORE: Further observations on total body water. I. Normal values throughout the life span. *Surg. Gynecol. Obstet. 95:*1 (1952).

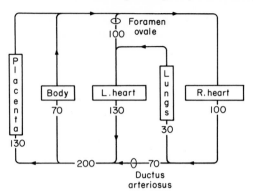

FIG. 2-36.   SCHEMATIC VIEW OF FETAL LAMB CIRCULATION.   *This shows that both sides of the fetal lamb heart work in parallel. Approximate data for blood flow (ml/kg per minute) are shown in each portion of the circuit. (From Dawes, Fig. 3.*[87]*)*

passes into the aorta to supply the remaining fetal tissues, and a part returns to the placenta via the umbilical artery. Blood returning from the head in the superior vena cava enters the right heart. Some passes through the inactive lungs and back to the left atrium, but most bypasses the pulmonary circulation through the ductus arteriosus and enters the aorta directly. The unusual feature of this circulation is, as shown schematically in Fig. 2-36, that both sides of the heart work in parallel rather than in series.

Using the best estimates available for the blood flows and blood volumes in the human,[87-90] we derived expressions for the changes to be expected in each compartment at successive 1-second intervals. These expressions were then evaluated by an iterative process on a digital computer to obtain the time course of drug transfer. The following diagram is a schematic representation of the placental and fetal circulations.

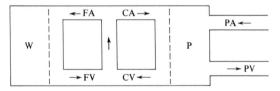

The symbols in the diagram and in the calculations below have the following meanings:

PA = drug concentration in maternal arterial blood to the placenta; flow = 8.33 ml/sec.

P = drug concentration in placental intervillous blood; volume = 250 ml.

PV = drug concentration in maternal venous blood draining the placenta, assumed to be equilibrated with P.

CA = drug concentration in umbilical artery; flow = 8.33 ml/sec = 57 per cent of fetal cardiac output.

CV = drug concentration in umbilical vein, assumed to be equilibrated with P.

FA = drug concentration in fetal arterial blood; flow = 6.28 ml/sec = 43 per cent of fetal cardiac output.

FV = drug concentration in fetal venous return other than umbilical vein, assumed to be equilibrated with W.

W = drug concentration in fetal body water; volume = 77 per cent of 3.5 kg fetal weight = 2700 ml.

t = time in seconds.

k = rate constant (sec^{-1}) for decline in maternal arterial drug level, so that

$$PA_t = PA_{t-1} - k \cdot PA_{t-1}.$$

For our purposes we may consider 1 second to be an infinitesimally small Δt. We shall solve for concentration increments in successive 1-second periods and sum these to obtain the desired time courses.

In P, the net increment in total drug in 1 second is the input less the output, $8.33(PA - PV) + 8.33(CA - CV)$. Since $PV = CV = P$, and the volume of dilution is 250 ml,

$$P_t = P_{t-1} + \frac{8.33(PA + FA - 2P_{t-1})}{250}.$$

Since FA and CA are derived from the mixing of CV and FV in proportion to their respective flows, and since $FV = W$,

$$FA = \frac{(8.33P_t + 6.28W)}{(8.33 + 6.28)}.$$

Finally, the increment in W is given by $\dfrac{6.28(FA - FV)}{2700}$, so that

$$W_t = W_{t-1} + \frac{6.28(FA - W_{t-1})}{2700}.$$

When $t = 0$, $PA = 1$, and all other concentrations are zero. The above equations were evaluated on a high speed digital computer for all values of t until attainment of 95 per cent equilibration, when $W_t = 0.95PA_t$. Solutions were obtained for selected values of k. Flow rates and volumes were taken from references 87–89, fetal body water from reference 90. Uncertainty about the precise volume of the intervillous space has little effect; all time courses computed for 125 ml intervillous blood are identical to those for 250 ml except within the first minute.

The results of these calculations are graphically represented in Fig. 2-37. The curves show the course of equilibration of the cord venous blood (in equilibrium with placental intervillous blood), of the fetal ar-

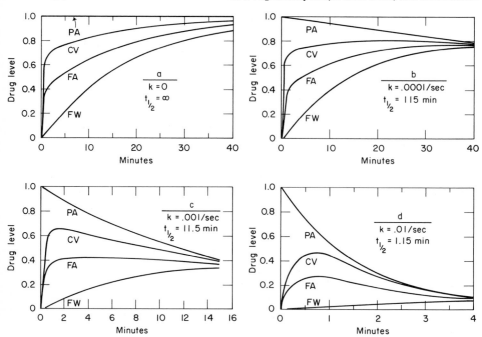

FIG. 2-37. KINETICS OF EQUILIBRATION OF MATERNAL AND FETAL TISSUES. *Theoretical curves, computed as described in the text. Four time courses are shown* (a, b, c, *and* d), *representing four different elimination rate constants* (k) *and the corresponding biologic half-lives* ($t_{1/2}$) *in maternal plasma. In each case are shown the drug levels in maternal* (*placental*) *arterial blood* (PA), *cord venous blood* (CV), *fetal arterial blood* (FA), *and fetal body water* (FW). *Note change in time scale in c and d. All drug levels are expressed as fractions of the initial maternal arterial level. Absorption and distribution in the maternal circulating blood are assumed to be instantaneous.*

terial blood (such as would bathe the fetal brain), and of the fetal tissue water in general. All the assumptions on which the calculations were based would lead to an overestimate of the speed of equilibration. For example, no permeability barrier was assumed to be present in the placenta; so substances whose rates of transfer are diffusion limited may equilibrate very much more slowly than shown. Also, the entire tissue water in the fetus has been supposed to equilibrate as a homogeneous mass, with the whole of the blood traversing the nonplacental circuit, while, in fact, the poorly perfused components of the fetal tissue mass will come to equilibrium more slowly. With these qualifications we may examine the theoretical course of drug transfer.

Consider first what happens if the maternal arterial drug concentration remains constant (Fig. 2-37a). Half-equilibration of the fetal tissues (shown by the curve FW) requires at least 13 minutes; 90 per cent equilibration would take nearly an hour. Throughout the equilibration process, but especially in the first few minutes, cord venous blood contains a much higher concentration than fetal arterial blood; and the drug concentration in fetal tissue water lags well behind that in the fetal arteries. If an infant were delivered a few minutes after establishment of a constant maternal drug level, the cord venous blood would only poorly reflect the fetal drug concentration; even mixed cord blood would give a very false impression. Moreover, as long as the drug concentration in fetal arterial blood exceeds that in fetal tissue water, interruption of the cord at delivery would lead to a rapid redistribution of drug within the fetus; drug would leave organs having a rich blood supply (like the brain), which have equilibrated rapidly, and enter those of greater mass and poorer blood supply, which are still far from equilibrium. It is obvious, then, why anesthetic drugs can affect the mother and not the fetus in many common circumstances.

If the maternal blood level is falling rather than constant, then fetal equilibration is speeded; but the more rapid the disappearance of drug from maternal blood, the lower will be the actual drug level attained in the fetus at equilibrium. Figures 2-37b, c, and d show this effect quite clearly (note change of time scale in c and d). Figure 2-37c could nearly represent the administration of thiopental to a mother at delivery. During the course of the intravenous injection the arterial blood (to brain and to placenta) carries a high enough drug concentration to anesthetize the mother. Immediately after the injection is completed, thiopental leaves the circulation, equilibrating rapidly with the maternal body water, with a half-time probably not too different from the 11.5 minutes represented in the diagram. Suppose the infant is delivered 5 to 10 minutes later. The figure shows that although the mother's brain is still exposed to more than one-half the original anesthetic concentration, the fetal brain was never (and never will be) exposed to an anesthetic drug level. Moreover, the fetal tissue water, still lagging far behind, will accept thiopental from the fetal brain as soon as the cord is cut; very shortly, then, the thiopental concentration in the fetal brain will have been reduced to the lower level.

Although not shown in Fig. 2-37, it is true that when the maternal drug concentration is falling rapidly, the fetal levels may eventually exceed those in the maternal blood. This overshoot simply reflects the sluggishness of the fetal equilibration mechanisms; it is followed, of course, by a reverse flow of drug from fetus to mother. This effect is small and of no practical consequence, but occasional experiments have confirmed that it may indeed occur.

In summary, it may be concluded that the fastest equilibration possible between fetal tissues and a *constant maternal blood level* of a drug requires at least 40 minutes. This makes it understandable that drugs whose passage across the placental membranes is impeded by their size, water-solubility, ionization, or protein binding should require hours for equilibration; many such examples have been presented. Equilibration with a *falling maternal blood level* is, of course, faster; but if the initial drug concentration in the mother was at an appropriate therapeutic level, then the fetus is not likely ever to experience an effective blood level, since the equilibrium concentration will be considerably lower. More systematic kinetic studies in animal fetuses in utero are badly needed, as well as more critical quantitative data and long-term follow-up in humans.

DRUG ELIMINATION: THE MAJOR ROUTES

Metabolism, storage, and excretion are the three mechanisms whereby drugs are ultimately removed from their sites of action. Drug metabolism will be considered in detail in another chapter. Deposition and storage of drugs in fat depots, in the reticuloendothelial system, and in bone play significant roles in the removal of lipid-soluble agents, colloidal substances, and heavy metals, respectively; examples of each process are dealt with elsewhere. Excretion at the kidneys, biliary system, intestine, and sometimes the lungs accounts for most drug elimination, and renal excretion is by far the most important of these routes.

Renal Excretion of Drugs

The kidney is admirably suited to the task of drug elimination. About 130 ml of plasma water is filtered each minute (190 liters per day) through the glomerular membranes. Of this volume only about 1.5 liters are excreted as urine, the remainder is reabsorbed in the renal tubules. A drug will be filtered if its molecular size is not excessively large; since even some plasma albumin appears in the filtrate, most drugs, being smaller, will encounter no difficulty. The glomerular capillaries contain large pores readily visible in electron micrographs, and filtration constants derived experimentally reveal the glomerulus to be far more permeable to solutes than are the capillaries of muscle (cf. p. 147). Only free drug in plasma water (not drug that is bound to plasma proteins) can be filtered. The principles governing passage back from the glomerular filtrate across the tubular epithelium into the blood (reabsorption) are the familiar ones that relate to any trans-membrane passage. Drugs with high lipid/water partition coefficients will be reabsorbed readily; polar compounds and ions will be unable to diffuse back and therefore will be excreted, unless reabsorbed by a carrier transport system.

The kidney receives a very large blood supply (25 per cent of the cardiac output) through wide, short renal arteries that permit blood to enter the tissue with but little drop in hydrostatic pressure. The afferent arterioles bring blood to the glomeruli for filtration; the efferent arterioles carry about four-fifths of the same blood (one-fifth having been filtered) to the tubules, and thence to the venous collecting system. The epithelial cells of the proximal tubules are rich in mitochondria and are supplied with a "brush border" of very large area lining the tubular lumen. These epithelial cells carry on active energy-dependent reabsorption. About 80 per cent of the NaCl and water are isosmotically reabsorbed here, and so are glucose and amino acids. The proximal tubule is also the site of active secretion of various metabolites and drugs from plasma into the tubular urine. Further down the nephron, especially in the loop of Henle, attenuated squamous epithelium is seen. Still further along, the distal tubular cells again resemble those of the proximal tubule, with many mitochondria and a large luminal surface; acidification of the urine occurs here. The distal tubules and collecting ducts are sites of water reabsorption, subject to control by the pituitary hormone vasopressin (p. 59).

The renal excretory mechanisms (glomerular filtration, renal reabsorption, renal secretion, or any combination thereof) have the net effect, under most conditions, of removing a constant fraction of the drug presented to the kidneys by the renal arterial blood. A simplified nomenclature has grown up, describing the quantitative aspects of the excretory process in terms of a hypothetical "clearance" of a certain volume of plasma each minute. Let c be the concentration of a drug in the plasma water, U its concentration in urine, V_u the volume of urine, and t the time of urine collection in minutes. Then UV_u/t is the *amount* of drug excreted per minute, and obviously UV_u/tc is the volume of plasma in which this amount of drug was contained. We may imagine, then, that such a volume of plasma water was actually "cleared" of its drug per minute, and so we speak of the term UV_u/tc as the *clearance* of a drug; its units are ml/min.[91]

The polymeric carbohydrate inulin (in the dog, also creatinine) is not bound appreciably to plasma proteins; it is filtered at the glomeruli and neither reabsorbed nor secreted at the tubules. Its clearance is therefore a measure of the glomerular filtration rate, about 130 ml/min in man. The clearance of glucose under normal conditions is zero, since it is completely reabsorbed in the tubules. If there were a substance so vigorously secreted by the tubules that the renal arterial plasma was completely cleared in a single passage through the kidney, that substance would serve as a measure of the renal plasma flow. *p*-Aminohippurate (PAH) and penicillin approach this ideal; their clearance is about 650 ml/min. Since the plasma volume is about one-half the blood volume, the renal blood flow through both kidneys, as estimated from the PAH clearance, would be about 1300 ml/min, or 25 per cent of the cardiac output. Of course, drugs that are actively secreted are also filtered. However, since secretion is so

---

[91] The symbol P is often used to denote the plasma drug concentration in clearance calculations; for consistency in this book we use c for drug concentrations in plasma. Clearance is usually stated to be UV/P rather than UV_u/tc, UV being defined as the urinary excretion *per minute*.

much more effective than filtration, it is customary to say that a certain drug is "excreted by tubular secretion" even though it is understood that a certain fraction (the *filtration fraction,* about one-fifth) is removed from the blood by filtration before that blood is even presented to the tubules.

The clearance tells us the amount of a drug that is excreted into the urine per minute, as follows:

$$dx/dt = clearance \times c = (\text{ml/min}) \times (\text{mg/ml}) = \text{mg/min}.$$

But it tells us nothing about the extent to which the plasma drug concentration is decreased by the renal excretory process. For this we have to know the apparent volume of distribution V_d. Clearly, for a given renal clearance, the greater the volume of distribution the more total drug will have to be eliminated from the body, and the more slowly will the plasma drug level fall.

The relationship between renal clearance and the overall elimination rate, for various values of V_d, is of general interest. Let k_e be the rate constant of elimination, defined by the first-order equation $dc/dt = k_e c$. The units of k_e are reciprocal time (e.g., min^{-1}). Then

$$k_e = \frac{clearance}{V_d} ;$$

and since the half-time of an exponential process is given by $0.693/k$ (p. 283), the elimination half-time for a drug excreted by the kidneys will be

$$t_{1/2} = 0.693 \, \frac{V_d}{clearance} .$$

The general relationships between clearance, rate constant of elimination, and elimination half-time are shown in Table 2-18 for several possible volumes of distribution. The fastest possible elimination half-time would be for a drug that was wholly contained in the plasma water and was cleared by tubular secretion; half the amount of the drug would be eliminated in 3 minutes. More usual values would lie between 13 and 44 minutes, depending upon the degree to which the drug had entered into body cells. The corresponding range of half-times for a drug cleared by glomerular filtration alone is seen to be 64 to 219 minutes, i.e., 1 to 4 hours. There is no upper limit on elimination half-times, since renal clearances may be as low as zero, and apparent volumes of distribution can exceed the body water volume if extensive tissue binding occurs. The first line of the table represents an arbitrarily selected illustration of partial reabsorption; a clearance of 30 ml/min is assumed, but any clearance between zero (complete reabsorption) and 650 ml/min is possible.

The dependence of the elimination rate constant upon the volume of distribution is illustrated nicely by a study on the adrenergic blocking

TABLE 2-18. **Relationships between clearance, rate constant of elimination, and elimination half-time**

Entries are values for k_e, the rate constant of elimination (units = $\min^{-1}$); parenthetic entries are corresponding values of the elimination half-time. The clearance given under "partial reabsorption" is arbitrary; any clearance between zero (complete reabsorption) and 650 ml/min is possible.

Clearance	Drug distributed in:		
	Plasma water (3000 ml)	Extracellular fluid (12000 ml)	Body water (41000 ml)
Partial reabsorption e.g., 30 ml/min	1.00×10^{-2} (69 min)	2.50×10^{-3} (277 min)	7.32×10^{-4} (947 min)
Glomerular filtration 130 ml/min	4.33×10^{-2} (16 min)	1.08×10^{-2} (64 min)	3.17×10^{-3} (219 min)
Tubular secretion 650 ml/min	2.17×10^{-1} (3 min)	5.42×10^{-2} (13 min)	1.59×10^{-2} (44 min)

agent, tolazoline, a tertiary amine, in the dog.[92] This drug was shown in renal clearance studies to be secreted actively by the renal tubules, at a rate practically identical to that of PAH, which is cleared completely from the plasma passing through the kidney. The very high pK_a of tolazoline means that, at body pH, it is almost entirely present as the ionized moiety, and it is therefore possible that it is confined to the extracellular space, that is, to about 18 per cent of the body weight. We can see from Table 2-18 that a drug with these properties should be eliminated with a half-life of about 13 minutes. The experiment depicted in Fig. 2-38, on the contrary, shows a measured half-life of nearly 2 hours. The discrepancy is accounted for by the fact (which can also be ascertained from Fig. 2-38) that the apparent V_d was enormously greater than the extracellular fluid; indeed, since the dose was 13 mg/kg and the extrapolated concentration was 6 mg/liter, the apparent volume of distribution was about *twice* the body weight. Evidently, tissue penetration and binding has accounted for a major fraction of the administered drug. Direct analyses of various tissues showed this to be true: the concentrations in liver, spleen, and kidney, for example, were more than three times the plasma concentration. The high lipid-solubility of the nonionized moiety, even though it is present in small amount, obviously favors entry into cells. A similar situation is involved in the penetration of mecamylamine in the brain (p. 172). The large volume of distribution accounts very well for the surprisingly long half-life.

92 B. B. BRODIE, L. ARONOW, and J. AXELROD: The fate of benzazoline (Priscoline) in dog and man and a method for its estimation in biological material. *J. Pharmacol. Exp. Therap.* 106:200 (1952).

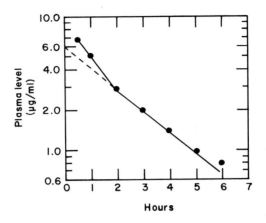

FIG. 2-38.   PLASMA LEVELS OF TOLAZOLINE AFTER INTRAVENOUS ADMINISTRA-
TION.   *The drug was given as a single injection (13 mg/kg) to a dog, and
plasma levels were measured periodically. (From Brodie et al., Fig. 1.[92])*

The availability of a drug for glomerular filtration is strictly dependent upon its concentration in plasma water. Meaningful clearance
values can therefore not be obtained unless the degree of protein binding
is determined at the relevant drug concentrations. For drugs cleared by
tubular secretion, however, it makes no difference what fraction is bound
to plasma protein, provided the binding is reversible. All the drug, bound
as well as free, becomes available for active secretion. Then, as free drug
is removed by the tubular cells, bound drug dissociates very rapidly to
maintain the equilibrium with plasma water.

The tubular secretory process handles organic anions and cations
by separate transport mechanisms. Figure 2-39 shows the structures of
some compounds that are secreted by the tubules. The group of anions has
been studied most thoroughly. The process is energy dependent and is
blocked by metabolic inhibitors. The secretory transport capacity can be
saturated at high concentrations of the anions, so each substance has its
characteristic maximum secretion rate, called "tubular maximum" (T_m).
The anionic group is often a carboxyl group, but sulfones (like phenol red
or chlorothiazide) carrying partial negative charges are transported equally
well. The various anionic compounds compete with one another for secretion, and this can be put to practical use. Thus, probenecid will block the
otherwise rapid renal secretion of penicillin and thereby prolong its duration of action in the body. Evidently, the same (or a similar) mechanism
mediates the tubular reabsorption of the uric acid anion, for this is also
blocked by probenecid; the uricosuric action finds some therapeutic use
in gout, since uric acid excretion is thereby promoted. The normal function of the anion secretion system is apparently to eliminate from the

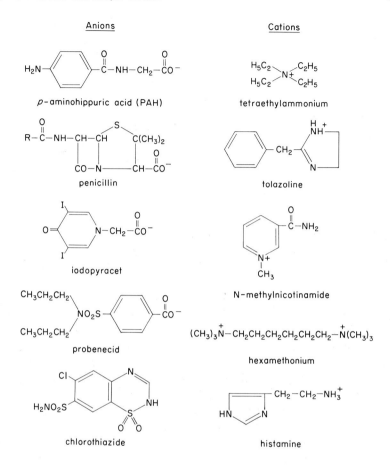

FIG. 2-39. SOME ORGANIC COMPOUNDS THAT ARE SECRETED BY RENAL TUBULES.

body metabolites that have been conjugated with glycine, with sulfate, or with glucuronic acid.

Organic cations are secreted by a different pathway, also energy dependent and stereospecific. The organic cations compete with each other but not with anions. Their secretion is blocked by metabolic inhibitors, but only at inhibitor concentrations much higher than needed to interfere with anion secretion. Tetraethylammonium secretion, for example, is not interfered with by malonate at a concentration that blocks PAH secretion almost completely. On the other hand, organic mercurials (e.g., mersalyl) inhibit secretion of tetraethylammonium much more effectively than they block PAH secretion. Both of these transport-secretion systems evidently depend upon high-energy phosphate compounds, for they are equally sensitive to the "uncoupling" agent 2,4-dinitrophenol. In addition, complete, or nearly complete, clearance of these drugs means passage into the tubular lumen against a concentration gradient. Thus, renal elimination of the organic anions and cations fulfills the criteria outlined earlier (p. 159) for an active transport process.

In newborn infants, especially premature infants, the renal tubular secretory mechanisms are incompletely developed and inefficient.[93-94a] This is shown in the experimental data summarized in Table 2-19. The elimination half-time for inulin (glomerular filtration) is about three times longer in the infant, suggesting some partial impermeability of the glomerular membrane, or more likely a smaller renal blood flow relative to the body water volume. Even more striking is the deficiency in PAH excretion (tubular secretion); here, the elimination half-time is nearly four times longer than in the adult.[94b]

The effects of such immaturity of a major renal excretory pathway will depend upon the circumstances of drug administration. Suppose a drug that is excreted by tubular secretion is given to a premature infant intravenously, or by another route with fast absorption. If the dosage is appropriate, then the usual initial drug level will be established; the only

TABLE 2-19.   Comparison of newborn and adult renal clearances

Computations are for a drug distributed in the whole body water, but any other V_d would give the same relative values. (Data for average infant from West et al.[94a] By permission of Charles C Thomas and Cambridge University Press.)

	Average infant	Average adult
Body weight (kg)	3.5	70
Body water		
(%)	77	58
(liters)	2.7	41
Inulin clearance		
(ml · min^{-1})	approx. 3	130
k (min^{-1})	3/2700 = 0.0011	130/41000 = 0.0032
$t_{1/2}$ (min)	630	220
PAH clearance		
(ml · min^{-1})	approx. 12	650
k (min^{-1})	12/2800 = 0.0043	650/41000 = 0.016
$t_{1/2}$ (min)	160	43

93 H. L. BARNETT: Kidney function in young infants. *Pediatrics 5*:171 (1950).

94 R. F. A. DEAN and R. A. MC CANCE: Inulin, diodone, creatinine and urea clearances in newborn infants. *J. Physiol. 106:*431 (1947).

94a J. R. WEST, H. W. SMITH, and H. CHASIS: Glomerular filtration rate, effective renal blood flow, and maximal tubular excretory capacity in infancy. *J. Pediat. 32:*10 (1948).

94b Confusion is introduced by the common practice of "correcting" clearance values on the basis of surface area. From the standpoint of drug elimination the relevant measure is the actual clearance, relative to the volume of distribution.

effect of the renal secretory deficiency will be to make the slope of the elimination curve less steep than in the adult. This in itself might be beneficial, inasmuch as the duration of action of the single dose is extended. Difficulties ensue, however, with repeated dosage, for the residual drug level just before each successive dose will be higher than would have been expected in the adult. Succeeding doses may therefore build up the drug concentration to excessive levels. The likelihood of cumulation to toxic levels (cf. p. 309) will be greatly increased if the drug is one that is usually given by a slow-absorption route. Here, the customary magnitude and spacing of the doses takes into account both the absorption rate and the elimination rate. If the usual dosage schedule is employed, but the elimination rate is substantially diminished, cumulative buildup to potentially toxic levels will be inevitable. Although several of the recently discovered drug toxicity syndromes in infants have been attributed to defective drug metabolism (cf. p. 274), it is not unlikely that inefficient renal secretory mechanisms are also involved.

The acidity of the urine is maintained within fairly strict limits, usually pH 4.5 to 8.0. The acidification of urine, which takes place in the distal tubules and collecting ducts, may have a profound effect upon the rate of drug excretion. Since the nonionized form of a weak acid or base tends to diffuse readily from the tubular urine back across the tubule cells, it should be obvious that acidification will increase the reabsorption (and thus diminish the excretion) of weak acids whose pK_a is in the neutral range, and promote the excretion of weak bases with pK_a in the same range. What is not so obvious is that the same effects will occur even when the ionization ranges are several pH units away. This seems surprising. Salicylic acid, for example, with $pK_a = 3$, is more than 99.9 per cent ionized at pH 7.4 and still 99 per cent ionized at pH 5.0. One might suppose, therefore, that acidification of the distal tubular urine to pH 5.0 could have only negligible effect. On the contrary, the rate of reabsorption is greatly enhanced, as shown in the following illustration (cf. p. 122).

At pH 7.4, the ratio of base (ionized) to conjugate acid (non-ionized) is calculated from

$$7.4 = 3.0 + \log \frac{(A^-)}{(HA)},$$

$$\frac{(A^-)}{(HA)} = \frac{25000}{1} = \frac{1000}{0.04}.$$

At pH 5.0,

$$5.0 = 3.0 + \log \frac{(A^-)}{(HA)},$$

$$\frac{(A^-)}{(HA)} = \frac{100}{1} = \frac{990}{10}.$$

	Plasma	Urine
	pH 7.4	pH 7.4
Proximal tubule	$\dfrac{1000}{0.04}$	$\dfrac{1000}{0.04}$
		$\rightleftharpoons$
	pH 7.4	pH 5.0
Distal tubule	$\dfrac{1000}{0.04}$	$\dfrac{990}{10}$
		$\leftarrow$

With respect to the diffusible, nonionized form, acidification of the urine creates a very large diffusion gradient from urine to plasma. Consequently, the excretion of salicylate (or other weak acid) is promoted in an alkaline urine, retarded in acid urine. The opposite relationship holds for weak bases. These effects of urine pH have significant practical applications. For example, the elimination of barbiturates may be hastened by administering bicarbonate to alkalinize the urine (cf. p. 383).

Extracorporeal Dialysis

The "artificial kidney" is an apparatus designed to substitute for the kidney in cases of severe but temporary renal shutdown. Overdosage with drugs may lead to just this situation. Collapse of the blood pressure and consequent renal failure are common results of poisoning with barbiturates, tranquilizers, narcotic analgesics, and other drugs. Rapid reduction of the high plasma drug level may be achieved by means of extracorporeal dialysis with an "artificial kidney." It is also used in the treatment of uremia, where high levels of nitrogenous waste products accumulate in the blood. The patient's blood is made to flow across cellophane membranes permeable to water and to solutes of low molecular weight. The membranes are bathed on the other side by an aqueous solution of the same ionic composition as plasma water. Thus, by simple diffusion an artificial process resembling glomerular filtration is established. Frequent changes of the dialysate bath hasten the elimination of drug from the plasma. The capacity of the apparatus depends upon the surface area of the membranes, the hydrostatic pressure difference across the membranes, the pore size, and the particular solute being removed. Substances that ordinarily are largely reabsorbed by back-diffusion may be eliminated very effectively in the "artificial kidney." Thus, a urea clearance of 140 ml/min can be achieved, about twice the normal value in man. Barbiturates, salicylates, and bromides are all effectively cleared. Figure 2-40 shows a typical result for salicylate elimination.

Because "artificial kidneys" are available only at the larger hospitals it is well to bear in mind that a similar dialysis can be carried out by means of peritoneal lavage (p. 381). This technique consists of washing out the peritoneal cavity with isotonic solutions in order to remove metabo-

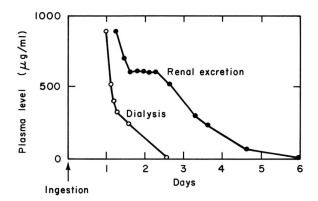

FIG. 2-40. REMOVAL OF ACETYLSALICYLIC ACID BY EXTRACORPOREAL DIALYSIS. *Data from two patients are shown, in one of whom extracorporeal dialysis was employed. (Adapted from Schreiner et al., Fig. 2.[95])*

lites or drugs. It is a relatively simple procedure although less efficient than extracorporeal dialysis.

Biliary Excretion of Drugs

A drug may be excreted by the liver cells into the bile and thus pass into the intestine. If the properties of such a drug happen to be favorable for intestinal absorption (cf. p. 120), a cycle may result (*enterohepatic cycle*) in which bilary secretion and intestinal reabsorption continue until metabolic degradation or urinary excretion eventually eliminate the drug from the body. The main importance of the biliary route of excretion is for the elimination of certain organic anions and cations that cannot be reabsorbed from the intestine because they are ionized at the intestinal pH. Among the organic acids displaying this behavior are sulfobromophthalein (Bromsulphalein, BSP), phenol red, fluorescein, penicillin, and the bile acids.

A number of findings point to a specific carrier-mediated active transport process. First, these compounds are secreted into bile against a high concentration gradient; bile/blood concentration ratios often exceed 50/1. Second, if the drug concentration in plasma is raised progressively, a limiting rate of drug secretion is reached, which cannot be exceeded (transport maximum) (Fig. 2-41). Third, various organic anions compete, so that one depresses the biliary excretion of another; presumably all compounds in the group are handled by the same carrier.

The rate of removal of substances in this group has long been used as a practical test of liver function. Usually the sulfonate dye BSP is used.

[95] G. E. SCHREINER, L. B. BERMAN, J. GRIFFIN, and J. FEYS: Specific therapy for salicylism. *New Engl. J. Med.* 253:213 (1955).

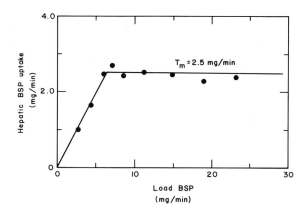

FIG. 2-41.   SATURATION OF THE BILIARY EXCRETORY SYSTEM FOR SULFOBROMO-
PHTHALEIN.   *Sodium sulfobromophthalein (Bromsulphalein, BSP) was infused
intravenously in a 26-kg dog. Plasma levels and hepatic uptake of dye were
measured, and hepatic blood flow was also determined. Hepatic uptake is shown
as function of varying rates of BSP presentation to liver. Transport maximum at
about 2.5 mg/ min is evident. (From Combes et al., Fig. 3.*[96])

In the normal subject after an intravenous dose of 5 mg/kg, 90 to 100 per
cent of the dye is removed from the blood within 30 minutes. The maximum rate of removal of such a dye may be depressed in liver damage, and
return to normal as other aspects of liver function recover. As with renal
tubular secretion, protein-bound drug is fully available for biliary secretion
by virtue of its rapid dissociation; BSP itself is very largely bound to
plasma proteins under the conditions of the liver function test.

There is a distinct, specific mechanism for the biliary excretion of
organic cations. Procaine amide ethobromide, a quaternary derivative of
procaine amide, is a good example. The secretion of this drug is competitively depressed by other quaternary ammonium compounds (mepiperpheni-
dol, benzomethamine, oxyphenonium, N^1-methylnicotinamide), and these
drugs are themselves secreted into the bile. Tubocurarine is also secreted
by this mechanism, but not all quaternary ammonium derivatives are.
Neither the small tetraethylammonium ion nor the large decamethonium
ion are secreted, nor do they affect the secretion of other organic cations.
Similar systems for the excretion of cations operate in the renal tubules
(p. 198) and in the choroid plexus.

A major component of bile is the bile acid anion taurocholate. The
bile pigments are also anions and presumably are handled by the specific
secretory pathway for anions. The alkaloids strychnine and quinine appear
in bile as conjugates of the bile acids, although their major excretory path-

96 B. COMBES, H. O. WHEELER, A. W. CHILDS, and S. E. BRADLEY: The mechanisms
of bromsulfalein removal from the blood. *Trans. Ass. Amer. Physicians* 69:276 (1956).

way is the kidney. The steroid hormones are partially excreted in the bile, but are largely reabsorbed in the intestine. A great many drugs are excreted to a small extent in the bile, for example, digitoxin (in rabbit, rat, and dog but not in man), and mercuhydrin, an organic mercurial diuretic. Penicillin, streptomycin, and the tetracyclines are found in very high concentrations in bile.

3

DRUG METABOLISM

INTRODUCTION

Most drugs undergo metabolic transformation in the body. The main site of drug metabolism is the liver, but other tissues may also participate. The biochemical reactions that have to be considered under the heading of drug metabolism are numerous and diverse. A feature characteristic of nearly all of them is that the metabolic products are more polar than the parent drugs. This has an important consequence for renal and biliary excretion, and it may also have evolutionary significance. Substances with high lipid/water partition coefficients, which pass easily across membranes, also diffuse back readily from the tubular urine through the renal tubular cells into the plasma, and such substances therefore tend to have a very low renal clearance and a long persistence in the body. If such a drug is metabolized to a more polar compound, one with a much lower partition coefficient, its tubular reabsorption will be reduced greatly. Moreover, as we have seen in chapter 2, the specific secretory mechanisms for anions and cations in the proximal renal tubules and in the parenchymal liver cells operate upon highly polar substances. Oxidation of a methyl group to carboxyl, for example, could make a drug suitable for the renal or biliary secretory pathway; that single metabolic alteration could reduce the biologic half-life of the drug from many hours to a few minutes. Conjugation of a relatively nonpolar drug with sulfate anion could have a similar effect. The evolutionary implication is that drug metabolizing systems have developed as adaptations to terrestrial life. Fish and other marine organisms commonly lack some of the major drug-metabolizing systems found in mammals, but they can excrete lipid-soluble exogenous and endogenous compounds directly into the surrounding water across the gill membranes.[1]

Decreased lipid solubility of a drug metabolite does not necessarily mean increased water solubility. The antibacterial sulfonamides, for ex-

---

[1] B. B. BRODIE and R. P. MAICKEL: "Comparative biochemistry of drug metabolism," in *Metabolic Factors Controlling Duration of Drug Action*, Proceedings of First International Pharmacological Meeting, vol. 6, ed. by B. B. Brodie and E. G. Erdös. New York, Macmillan Co., 1962, p. 299.

ample, are metabolized to more polar, less lipid-soluble acetyl derivatives, but some of these are less water soluble than their parent compounds. Sulfathiazole, for example, is transformed to acetylsulfathiazole, which is much less soluble in water than sulfathiazole itself:[2]

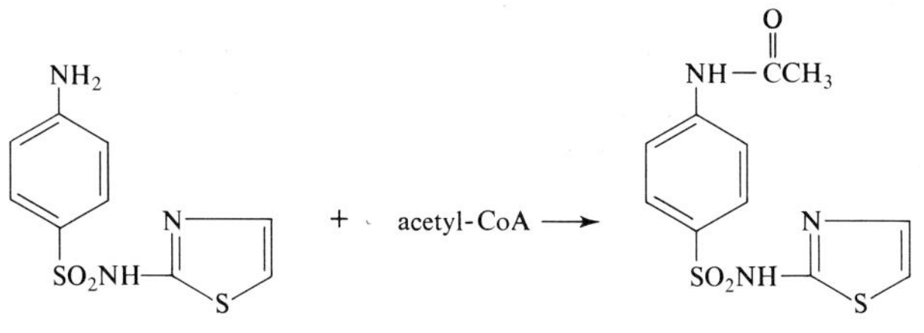

sulfathiazole   acetylsulfathiazole

At pH 5.5 the water solubility of sulfathiazole is $960\mu g/ml$, that of the acetylated derivative only $60\mu g/ml$. The reduced water solubility of acetylsulfathiazole led to such serious toxicity from precipitation in the renal tubules that sulfathiazole was abandoned in favor of sulfonamides with more favorable properties.

Since many of the reactions in drug metabolism are reversible, it can happen that a polar drug yields a less polar product. An example is the deacetylation of acetanilid to aniline, to be discussed shortly. Another example is the reduction of the hypnotic drug chloral hydrate to the pharmacologically active trichloroethanol, with the participation of the reduced form of nicotinamide adenine dinucleotide (NADH):

chloral hydrate   trichloroethanol

Usually, however, the same enzyme (alcohol dehydrogenase) would mediate the oxidation of an alcohol to a more polar aldehyde, passing electrons to NAD^+, the reverse of the reaction shown here.[3, 4]

Although the duration of drug action tends to be shortened by metabolic transformation, as described above, it is not correct to think of drug metabolism as "detoxication." Very frequently, the metabolic product

---

[2] In this chapter, for the sake of simplicity, weak electrolytes will be represented in their nonionized forms, even though they may actually be substantially ionized at physiologic pH. Pathways of metabolism will be indicated, in general, by showing substrates and products (sometimes intermediates, also, when they are known). Diagrams presented here should not be regarded as exact chemical equations; often the detailed reaction mechanisms are unknown, so that precise stoichiometry would be mere speculation.

[3] P. J. FRIEDMAN and J. R. COOPER: The role of alcohol dehydrogenase in the metabolism of chloral hydrate. *J. Pharmacol. Exp. Therap. 129:*373 (1960).

[4] F. J. MACKAY and J. R. COOPER: A study on the hypnotic activity of chloral hydrate. *J. Pharmacol. Exp. Therap. 135:*271 (1962).

to which a drug is converted may have greater biologic activity than the drug itself. Indeed, the desirable pharmacologic actions of some drugs are wholly attributable to their metabolites, the drugs themselves being inert; and likewise the toxic side effects of some drugs may be due in whole or in part to metabolic products.

Some typical and atypical features of drug metabolism are illustrated in Fig. 3-1. Acetophenetidin (phenacetin) and acetanilid are mild analgesic and antipyretic agents that have been in clinical use for over half a century. Studies within recent years have revealed that both compounds are transformed in the body to a more polar metabolite, *p*-hydroxyacetanilid (acetaminophen).[5, 6] As shown in the figure, acetanilid undergoes hydroxylation at the para position on the benzene ring, whereas acetophenetidin undergoes O-dealkylation.

The major metabolite, acetaminophen, is an antipyretic analgesic in its own right. Thus, the observed effects of acetanilid and acetophenetidin could be accounted for by their conversion to acetaminophen. Indeed, it was even possible that the two older, established drugs were inert. This has been tested by inhibiting the metabolism of acetophenetidin by means of SKF 525A (p. 249). The results indicated that the unmetabolized acetophenetidin did have antipyretic activity.[6a]

The further metabolism of acetaminophen entails typical conjugation reactions, yielding a sulfate ester and a glucuronide, both highly polar compounds. The conjugates appear in the urine and are pharmacologically inert. Figure 3-2 shows the time course of the disappearance of acetanilid from the plasma after administration of a single dose to a human subject, and the sequential buildup and decay of plasma concentrations of the two principal metabolites.

Both drugs are also metabolized to a minor extent by deacetylation of the amino group, yielding aniline derivatives, which may then be further transformed to aminophenols (that are eventually conjugated) or to phenylhydroxylamine.

The well-known toxic effect of acetanilid upon the blood affords an excellent illustration of how the main pharmacologic action of a drug and its apparent toxicity may inhere in different chemical entities, the one a metabolic product of the other. After ordinary doses of acetanilid a small amount of methemoglobinemia is often seen, and after large doses of the drug there may be extensive methemoglobin formation and destruc-

5 B. B. BRODIE and J. AXELROD: The fate of acetanilide in man. *J. Pharmacol. Exp. Therap. 94*:29 (1948).

6 B. B. BRODIE and J. AXELROD: The fate of acetophenetidin (phenacetin) in man and methods for the estimation of acetophenetidin and its metabolites in biological material. *J. Pharmacol. Exp. Therap. 97*:58 (1949).

6a A. H. CONNEY, M. SANSUR, F. SOROKO, R. KOSTER, and J. J. BURNS: Enzyme induction and inhibition in studies on the pharmacological actions of acetophenetidin. *J. Pharmacol. Exp. Therap. 151*:133 (1966).

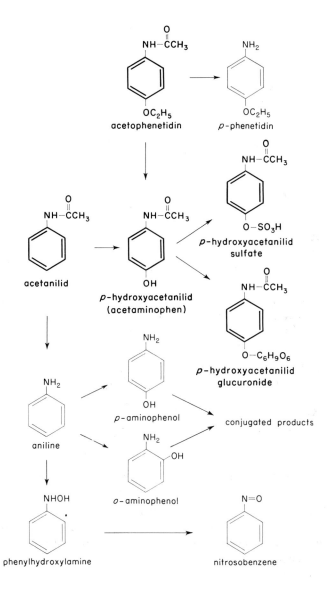

FIG. 3-1. METABOLISM OF ACETANILID AND ACETOPHENETIDIN. *Major pathway is shown in* boldface type.

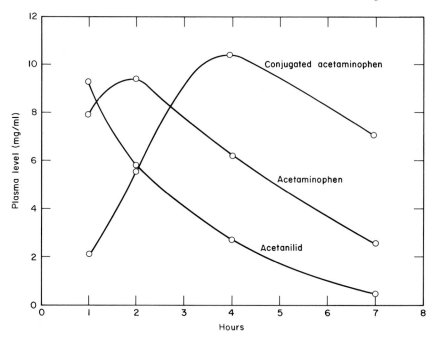

FIG. 3-2.   PLASMA CONCENTRATIONS OF METABOLITES AFTER ORAL ADMINISTRA-
TION OF ACETANILID TO A HUMAN SUBJECT.   *A 1-gram dose was given by mouth
at zero time. (Data of Brodie and Axelrod, Table III, subject F.[5])*

tion of erythrocytes. It has become evident that this toxic action is not
caused by acetanilid itself or by acetaminophen, but by aniline produced
metabolically in the body. Even here, however, the toxic effect is indirect;
aniline itself does not produce methemoglobin in vitro, but its metabolites,
phenylhydroxylamine and nitrosobenzene (Fig. 3-1), can do so.[7]

METHODS OF STUDYING DRUG METABOLISM

The principal aim in studies of drug metabolism is to identify the
pathways by which drugs are transformed in the body, and to ascertain
quantitatively the importance of each pathway and intermediate. Since a
metabolite generally differs from its precursor by only a single chemical
grouping, a typical pathway consists of a series of compounds very closely
related chemically and therefore difficult to assay individually. Occasionally,
a metabolic conversion can be followed directly in biologic material by

---

[7] M. KIESE: Relationship of drug metabolism to methemoglobin formation. *Ann.
N. Y. Acad. Sci. 123:*141 (1965).

virtue of some unique property of the drug or metabolite. Ring scission may abolish an absorption peak in the visible or ultraviolet spectrum; or removal of an amino group may abolish reactivity in a color reaction such as the ninhydrin reaction. Usually, however, some adroit chemical manipulations are necessary before quantitative determinations can be attempted. The most useful procedures for separation of metabolites have exploited differences in their polarizabilities and charges, which determine their hydrophilic properties. These characteristics usually increase progressively through a metabolic sequence.

Separation of Metabolites

Solvent extraction is the simplest of the procedures. If the compound to be separated is a lipid-soluble base, it can be extracted from an alkaline aqueous solution into an organic solvent, because in alkali its ionization (which would make it water soluble) is suppressed. Also, a lipid-soluble acid can be extracted from acid solution into an organic solvent.

What is an appropriate organic solvent? Solvents can be arranged according to their dielectric constants; for example, heptane-benzene-chloroform-isobutanol is a series with increasing polarizability. Heptane is a pure hydrocarbon that will extract none but the most lipid-soluble, nonpolar substances. Isobutanol, on the other hand, although not as polar as water, will nevertheless extract many polar compounds that would not be extracted into heptane. Since compounds that are extractable from an aqueous phase by a nonpolar solvent are also extractable by the more polar ones, the analyst usually chooses the least polar solvent that will extract the compound he is interested in. In this way he increases the specificity of the method, and he will also be less likely to extract extraneous substances that might interfere with the subsequent assay procedure.

Assume that drug A is metabolized to B, which in turn is conjugated, forming a product C, and that the usual order applies—B more polar than A, and C more polar than B. Suppose further that the method of assay cannot distinguish between these three compounds, so that we have to depend entirely upon a separation based on differences in partition coefficient to determine how much of each is present. First, we assay for A in a heptane extract prepared under conditions known to extract A, and only A, essentially completely. Then we might extract another sample with chloroform, under conditions that will extract A and B both, and determine A + B; subtracting the known amount of A gives the amount of B. Finally, another sample could be hydrolyzed under conditions known to release the conjugated group. Extraction with chloroform would then yield A + B + C, and by difference, C. It is noteworthy that in this procedure the solvent extractions based upon partition coefficients are sufficiently selective so that a nonspecific reaction can be used for the quantitative determinations.

The pathways illustrated in Fig. 3-1 were worked out in much this way. The problem was to estimate the amounts of acetanilid, *p*-hydroxyacetanilid, conjugated *p*-hydroxyacetanilid, and aniline when all of these were present in blood, tissue, or urine. Aniline alone is extracted into benzene from an alkaline solution; it can be returned to an aqueous phase merely by shaking the benzene solution with $0.1N$ HCl. Aniline is determined in the acid solution by reacting it with nitrous acid to form a diazonium salt, which then couples readily with an amine (N-(1-naphthyl)-ethylenediamine), forming an azo dye.[8]

Acetanilid is not extracted into benzene, but can be extracted from an alkaline solution into the more polar solvent ethylene dichloride together with any aniline that may be present. After re-extraction into acid, heating will hydrolyze the N-acetyl bond, and the resulting aniline (that originally present plus that produced by hydrolysis) can be assayed as before. The other compounds can be assayed by similar manipulations.

Partition coefficients may be used for identification as well as for separation. How do we known that what we assay and call "aniline" in biologic material is really aniline? One could actually isolate and crystallize the substance, determine its melting point, infrared spectrum, and so on, but such procedures are very costly in time and effort, especially if the quantities are small. Presumptive evidence of identity is behavior identical to that of an authentic standard in various tests. For example, the substance isolated from biologic material could be compared with authentic aniline by measuring its benzene/water partition coefficient at different pH values (Table 3-1).

Countercurrent distribution[9] is a powerful application of the general principle of differential migration, in this case liquid-liquid differential migration. It is capable of separating compounds whose partition coefficients differ only slightly. Repeated stepwise solvent extractions are performed mechanically in such a way that the aqueous and organic phases "flow" in opposite directions. The larger the number of extractions, the more sharply do the individual compounds peak, each according to its own partition coefficient. Figure 3-3 presents a typical example of the use of countercurrent distribution in a study on drug metabolism. In this experiment, a dog was given ephedrine, and urine was collected for 24 hours, concentrated, and extracted with chloroform. The chloroform extract contained a considerable amount of a basic material, which gave a methyl

---

[8] The widely-used Bratton-Marshall reaction, applicable to many aromatic amines: A. C. BRATTON and E. K. MARSHALL, JR.: A new coupling component for sulfanilamide determination. *J. Biol. Chem. 128*:537 (1939).

[9] L. C. CRAIG: Countercurrent distribution. *Methods in Medical Research, 5*:3 (1952).

TABLE 3-1. **Distribution of aniline and "apparent aniline" between benzene and water at various pH values**

The "apparent aniline" was obtained by benzene extraction of urine from a subject who had ingested acetanilid. The material was returned to acid aqueous solution, then samples of this solution, and of an authentic solution of aniline, were adjusted to various pH values and shaken with 5 volumes of benzene. The fraction extracted into benzene at each pH is shown. (Data of Brodie and Axelrod,[6] Table I.)

pH	Fraction extracted into benzene	
	Authentic aniline	"Apparent aniline"
3.2	0.39	0.38
4.3	0.81	0.83
7.0	0.98	0.98

orange reaction.[11] The extract was subjected to countercurrent distribution in a solvent system of chloroform and pH 8.7 aqueous buffer. Under these conditions, pure ephedrine distributes about equally in the aqueous and organic phases, so it would be expected to peak in a central position. The

FIG. 3-3. SEPARATION OF EPHEDRINE FROM A METABOLITE BY COUNTERCURRENT DISTRIBUTION. *Two dogs received 50 mg/kg of ephedrine. Urine was subjected to countercurrent distribution. The two phases were 0.2M borate buffer, pH 8.7, and chloroform, in equal volumes. Optical density refers to intensity of methyl orange color obtained from contents of each tube, as described in text. (From Axelrod, Fig. 1.[10])*

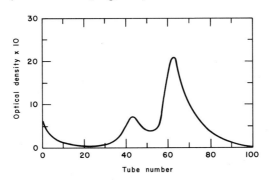

[10] J. AXELROD: Studies on sympathomimetic amines. I. The biotransformation and physiological disposition of l-ephedrine and l-norephedrine. *J. Pharmacol. Exp. Therap.* 109:62 (1953).

[11] This is a nonspecific reaction given by many organic-soluble amines which form a salt ("heliotrope") with the acidic dye methyl orange. The complex is soluble in organic solvents, whereas methyl orange itself is not. Thus, the amount of organic-soluble base present can be titrated as the molar equivalent of the methyl orange that is made soluble in an organic solvent.

smaller of the two peaks (tubes 40 to 50) was identified as unaltered ephedrine. The major product was collected from tubes 58 to 72, crystallized, and identified as the N-demethylated product of ephedrine, norephedrine.

Paper chromatography is an application of liquid-liquid differential migration in which an organic solvent front moves over a hydrated paper. Solutes are partitioned continuously between the phases, and thus the rate of migration is positively correlated with the organic solvent/water partition coefficient. A typical application to drug metabolism is shown in Fig. 3-4. A dog was given pentobarbital labeled with ^{14}C. The urine was concentrated, and a sample was chromatographed on filter paper. The dried chromatogram was placed against a sheet of photographic film, and after sufficient exposure the film was developed. Dark areas result from ^{14}C disintegrations. Evidently, at least nine metabolic products of pentobarbital were separated in this system. Paper chromatography is very convenient, but it is not suitable for handling large quantities. The procedure is most useful for establishing a presumptive identification. If "apparent" and authentic compounds behave identically in different solvent systems, they may be presumed to be identical.

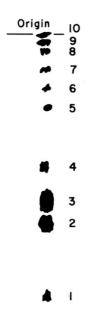

FIG. 3-4. SEPARATION OF METABOLITES OF ^{14}C-PENTOBARBITAL BY PAPER CHROMATOGRAPHY AND RADIOAUTOGRAPHY. *The urine of a dog given pentobarbital-2-^{14}C was chromatographed in a butanol-ammonia system. Component 1 is unaltered pentobarbital. Nine metabolites, all more polar (and therefore moving less rapidly), are shown in the radioautogram. (From Titus and Weiss, Fig. 2.^{12})*

12 E. TITUS and H. WEISS: The use of biologically prepared radioactive indicators in metabolic studies: metabolism of pentobarbital. *J. Biol. Chem. 214:*807 (1955).

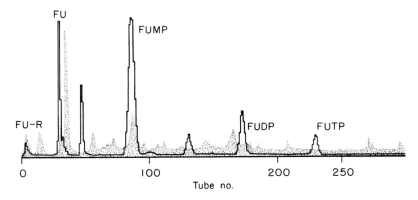

FIG. 3-5. SEPARATION OF METABOLITES OF FLUOROURACIL-2-^{14}C ON AN ANION EXCHANGE RESIN. *Labeled 5-fluorouracil was incubated with Ehrlich ascites cells. After 90 minutes the cells were harvested, and acid-soluble components were placed on an anion exchange (Dowex-1) column, then progressively eluted with increasing concentrations of formate.* Stippled pattern *represents optical density at 260 mμ (i.e., purines and pyrimidines and their derivatives)*; solid lines *represent radioactivity (i.e., substances derived from the fluorouracil).* FU, *Fluorouracil;* FU-R, *fluorouracil riboside;* FUMP, *fluorouridylic acid;* FUDP, *fluorouridine diphosphate;* FUTP, *fluorouridine triphosphate. (From Chaudhuri et al., Chart 8.[13] By permission of the American Chemical Society.)*

Methods of separation based on electric charge include paper and gel electrophoresis and ion exchange chromatography. In *electrophoresis* the mixture to be separated is placed on a paper strip or a gel saturated with buffer at an appropriate pH. A voltage is applied and each compound then migrates toward anode or cathode at a rate proportional to its charge. *Ion exchange chromatography* employs resins carrying fixed anionic (carboxyl or sulfate) or cationic (amine or quaternary ammonium) groups. The resin is usually packed into a column and the material to be resolved is applied at the top. Compounds that carry an opposite charge will be retained on the column. To elute, the pH can be changed so as to suppress the ionization of the adsorbed compound or of the resin. Alternatively, an ion of the same charge may be used to displace the adsorbed compound competitively; for example, to separate cations on an anionic ("cation exchange") resin, elution might be accomplished with increasing concentrations of Na^+ or K^+ as salts, or H^+ as mineral acid. As the concentration of eluting cations increased (either stepwise or by a continuous gradient), more weakly charged cations would be displaced first, more strongly charged ones later, and an elution pattern could be obtained with the aid of a fraction collector. Figure 3-5 is an example of a chromato-

[13] N. K. CHAUDHURI, B. J. MONTAG, and C. HEIDELBERGER: Studies on fluorinated pyrimidines. III. The metabolism of 5-fluorouracil-2-C[14] and 5-fluoroorotic-2-C[14] acid *in vivo. Cancer Res. 18:*318 (1958).

graphic separation on an anion exchange resin. The pyrimidine analogue 5-fluorouracil was incubated with Ehrlich ascites cells. Metabolic products were separated by applying an extract to the column and eluting with increasing concentrations of formate ion. First to emerge were the least acidic products—the pyrimidine bases and nucleosides. Next, in order, were the nucleoside mono-, di-, and triphosphates. This procedure resolved at least 19 different utlraviolet-absorbing compounds, and six major metabolites derived from the radioactive fluorouracil. Methods based upon ion exchange columns are obviously useful for identification and quantitative assay of metabolites (as in this example) because of their high resolving power. They are also suitable for preparative procedures because columns can be adapted to handling large amounts of material.

Quantitative Estimation of Metabolites

After metabolites have been separated, the procedures used most often for quantitative estimation are spectrophotometry, fluorometry, and the measurement of radioactivity. Biologic assay may also be employed (cf. p. 746), especially when quantities are too small for chemical detection.

Spectrophotometry depends upon measuring the absorption of light at a specified wavelength, usually the absorption maximum for the compound in question, and relating the optical density to the concentration. Sometimes a drug or its metabolite is intensely colored or has a very strong absorption peak in the ultraviolet range, so that it can be assayed directly in urine, plasma, or tissue extracts. Often a direct determination of optical density can be carried out after the removal of interfering substances of biologic origin by means of solvent extraction or other separative procedures. Sometimes the compound of interest has to be treated first with a reagent in order to form a light-absorbing product, which can then be measured.

Fluorometry has proved especially useful in studies of drug metabolism because slight metabolic alterations can produce major changes in the fluorescence spectrum, the activation spectrum, or both. The method depends upon the ability of certain molecules to absorb light at one wavelength and re-emit the energy as light at another (longer) wavelength. It is inherently more sensitive than spectrophotometry because, in measuring light emitted from a sample, the sensitivity is limited only by the capabilities of the photomultiplier devices, and the "blank" is practically dark. In spectrophotometry, the assay depends upon accurate measurement of the fraction of incident light that is absorbed; at low concentration of absorbing material, this measurement of a small difference becomes increasingly imprecise. Use of the double-monochromator spectrophotofluorometer permits a high degree of specificity in the fluorometric assay; compounds not activated at the chosen activating wavelength or that do not emit at the chosen fluorescence wavelength are simply "not seen" in the assay.

An illustration of the fluorometric method is the determination of the naturally occurring amine serotonin[14] (Fig. 3-6). Here, as little as $0.2\mu g$ of the amine per gram of brain tissue may be assayed successfully. To obtain an activation spectrum (upper half of figure), one first finds a wavelength at which most of the absorbed light is re-emitted; for serotonin, 550 mμ. Then recording the intensity of light emission at this fixed wavelength, the wavelength of the irradiating light is systematically varied. The resulting spectrum shows a sharp optimum for excitation at 295 mμ.[15] If this incident wavelength is now held constant, and the emitted light is measured at various wavelengths at a right angle to the incident beam, a characteristic fluorescence spectrum is obtained. There is a small peak at 330 mμ and a larger one at 550 mμ. The peak at 295 mμ in the fluorescence spectrum is merely activating light scattered from dust particles.

Radioactivity is used extensively to study drug metabolism. A radioactive isotope, often ^{14}C or ^{3}H, is introduced into a drug molecule by chemical or biologic synthesis. Plant alkaloids and glycosides, for example, have been prepared by growing the plants in an atmosphere con-

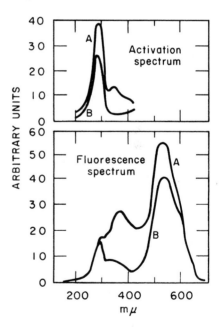

FIG. 3-6. ACTIVATION AND FLUO-RESCENCE SPECTRA OF AN UN-KNOWN SUBSTANCE IN BRAIN AND OF AUTHENTIC 5-HYDROXYTRYPTA-MINE (SEROTONIN). *In both halves of the figure, A is a brain extract and B is authentic serotonin. (From Bogdanski et al., Fig. 1.[14])*

[14] D. F. BOGDANSKI, A. PLETSCHER, B. B. BRODIE, and S. UDENFRIEND: Identification and assay of serotonin in brain. *J. Pharmacol. Exp. Therap.* 117:82 (1956).

[15] This may depend on the particular instrument and light source used. It may well be, for example, that the light source was much brighter at 295 mμ than at other wavelengths. Further details may be found in the monograph by S. Udenfriend, *Fluorescence Assay in Biology and Medicine.* New York, Academic Press, 1962.

taining $^{14}CO_2$; and a radioactive antibiotic, actinomycin D, has been synthesized by growing the actinomycete fungus in ^3H-methionine, a precursor of the antibiotic.[16] It might be thought that methods employing radioactivity should be highly specific, since only the drug and its metabolites (but no naturally occurring compound) will be radioactive. To the extent, however, that the drug is transformed to compounds that can enter normal metabolic pathways, the specificity is lost. Thus, ^{14}C in a methyl group of a drug that undergoes demethylation may enter the single-carbon pool and become incorporated into compounds wholly unrelated to the drug or its metabolites. Usually the whole gamut of separation procedures is carried out, as described above, and radioactivity counting (or radio-autography, as in Fig. 3-4) is used for the quantitative estimations. These are not only obtained more simply and accurately by counting than by chemical determinations, but there is also a very important increase in the sensitivity of the assays, especially when starting materials of high specific radioactivity are available.

CHEMICAL PATHWAYS OF DRUG METABOLISM

Drugs undergo four types of reaction in the body. These are oxidative, reductive, hydrolytic, and synthetic (conjugation) reactions. The oxidative reactions include aliphatic oxidation, aromatic hydroxylation, N-dealkylation, O-dealkylation, S-demethylation, deamination, sulfoxide formation, desulfuration, N-oxidation, and N-hydroxylation. The detailed pathways and mechanisms will be presented later. First we shall consider the properties and characteristics of the microsomal drug-metabolizing system that catalyzes the oxidative transformations.

The Liver Microsomal Drug-Metabolizing System

The oxidative metabolism of many drugs and also of steroid hormones is mediated by enzymes located in the microsomal fraction of mammalian liver. In this context, "microsome" refers to a fragment of the cell's endoplasmic reticulum obtained in the following way. Liver cells are homogenized and the homogenate is centrifuged at 9000 to 12,000 $\times$ g for 30 minutes. Then the supernatant solution is centrifuged at 105,000 $\times$ g for 1 hour, and the sediment (microsome fraction) is collected. An early study on enzyme distribution in subcellular fractions of rabbit liver is shown in Table 3-2. The reaction studied was the oxidative deamination of amphetamine by rabbit liver. The data show that the activity present in the crude homogenate could be obtained in a reconstituted system consisting of a mixture of microsomes and supernatant solution, and of $NADP^+$,

16 E. KATZ, A. B. MAUGER, and H. WEISSBACH: Biosynthesis of highly labeled actin-omycins. *Mol. Pharmacol. 1:*107 (1965).

TABLE 3-2. **Intracellular distribution of the capacity to deaminate amphetamine**

Fractions were prepared from rabbit liver by differential centrifugation, then incubated at 37° for 2 hours with L-amphetamine, $NADP^+$, nicotinamide, Mg^{++}, and oxygen. (From Axelrod,[17] Table II.)

Cell fraction	L-Amphetamine metabolized (μmoles)
Whole homogenate	0.27
Nuclei	0.06
Mitochondria	0.00
Microsomes	0.03
Soluble supernatant	0.00
Nuclei and soluble supernatant	0.08
Mitochondria and soluble supernatant	0.02
Microsomes and soluble supernatant	0.20

Mg^{++}, nicotinamide, and oxygen. The supernatant solution furnished the enzymes necessary to reduce $NADP^+$ to NADPH; the nicotinamide served to stabilize the pyridine coenzymes. Although not shown in the table, it was found that NADPH itself could supplant the supernatant fraction. An apparently identical system was discovered to mediate the side chain oxidation of hexobarbital,[18] and it soon became evident that a number of drugs undergoing different sorts of oxidative reactions could all be metabolized by the liver microsomal system.

The requirement for both NADPH and oxygen is unusual. One could imagine, on the contrary, that the oxidized coenzyme $NADP^+$ might serve as a hydrogen acceptor, oxidizing the drug substrate and passing the electrons along to oxygen, perhaps through the cytochrome system. Further evidence about the characteristics of the NADPH-microsomal system was obtained in a study of the in vitro oxidative demethylation of monomethyl-4-aminoantipyrine (MMAP). The products of this reaction are 4-aminoantipyrine and formaldehyde (p. 226). Table 3-3 shows that in the absence of any added drug, washed microsomes had an active NADPH oxidase system. This system was not inhibited by cyanide. However, it could be stimulated by the addition of cytochrome c, and the stimulation was blocked by cyanide. Obviously, the original NADPH oxidation does not proceed by way of a cytochrome c pathway (which would be cyanide

[17] J. AXELROD: The enzymatic deamination of amphetamine (Benzedrine). *J. Biol. Chem. 214:*753 (1955).

[18] J. R. COOPER and B. B. BRODIE: The enzymatic metabolism of hexobarbital (Evipal). *J. Pharmacol. Exp. Therap. 114:*409 (1955).

TABLE 3-3.   **Oxidation of NADPH by liver microsomes**

The rates of oxidation are given as decrements (in a 5-min period) in light absorption at 340 mμ, the NADPH peak, which disappears upon oxidation. All reaction mixtures contained microsomes and NADPH. (Data of Gillette et al.,[19] Table I.)

Additions to incubation mixture	Rate of NADPH oxidization (Δ OD$_{340}$)
None	0.219
CN^- ($10^{-3}M$)	0.207
Cytochrome c ($2 \times 10^{-5}M$)	0.470
Cytochrome c ($2 \times 10^{-5}M$) + CN^- ($10^{-3}M$)	0.240
Drug substrate, MMAP ($2 \times 10^{-3}M$)	0.223

sensitive) but by a different enzyme system, a NADPH oxidase. Finally, the table shows that addition of the drug MMAP did not enhance the rate of NADPH oxidation.

Attention was turned next from NADPH oxidation to the demethylation of MMAP in a microsomal system capable of generating NADPH. Table 3-4 shows that cyanide did not inhibit the demethylation reaction; but cytochrome c did, and this inhibition was prevented by cyanide. The explanation is that the cytochrome c diverts the electrons removed in NADPH oxidation to a cytochrome c system and away from the NADPH oxidase system. Cyanide, inactivating cytochrome oxidase, prevents this diversion, so NADPH is oxidized by the direct pathway, as before. Evidently, operation of the NADPH oxidase system is coupled

TABLE 3-4.   **Dealkylation of monomethyl-4-aminoantipyrine (MMAP) by liver microsomes**

The incubation mixture contained drug substrate (MMAP), microsomes, Mg^{++}, $NADP^+$ and a NADPH-generating system. (Data of Gillette et al.,[19] Table III.)

Additions to incubation mixture	4-Aminoantipyrine formed (μmoles)
None	1.15
CN^- ($10^{-3}M$)	1.00
Cytochrome c ($2 \times 10^{-5}M$)	0.53
Cytochrome c ($2 \times 10^{-5}M$) + CN^- ($10^{-3}M$)	0.93
Methylene blue ($5 \times 10^{-5}M$)	0.0
Menadione ($5 \times 10^{-5}M$)	0.0

[19] J. R. GILLETTE, B. B. BRODIE, and B. N. LA DU: The oxidation of drugs by liver microsomes: on the role of TPNH and oxygen. *J. Pharmacol. Exp. Therap.* **119**:532 (1957).

somehow to the oxidative dealkylation of MMAP. The striking inhibition of dealkylation by menadione or methylene blue has much the same basis as the cytochrome c effect, for these compounds accept electrons directly from reduced pyridine nucleotides, thereby diverting NADPH from the oxidase pathway.

Clearly, cytochrome c, not normally found in microsomes, is not part of the electron flow pathway in the microsomal oxidation of NADPH. The initial electron acceptor, which oxidizes NADPH to NADP+, is a flavoprotein, probably cytochrome c reductase.[20] Recent studies[21] have partially elucidated the nature of the electron transport chain involved in drug oxidations mediated by the microsomal system. An unusual cytochrome termed "P-450" plays a key role. In the reduced form this heme protein is capable of binding carbon monoxide to yield a pigment with a characteristic absorption peak at 450 mμ. It has also been called "CO-binding pigment" and "reticulochrome" (because of its occurrence in the endoplasmic reticulum). It seems to be the final oxygen-activating enzyme, reducing one oxygen atom to water, and simultaneously introducing an oxygen atom into a drug substrate. Consonant with this interpretation is the finding that carbon monoxide inhibits microsomal drug hydroxylation.[22] It has been suggested that a non-heme, iron-containing protein intervenes in the electron transport chain between the flavoprotein and P-450, but this is not yet firmly established. There is also doubt about whether the P-450 cytochrome is alternately oxidized and reduced (i.e., whether it transports electrons) or whether the reduced form alone carries oxygen, after the manner of hemoglobin. Figure 3-7 summarizes one view of the relationship between NADPH oxidation and drug oxidation. The reactions may be summarized as follows:

1. $\text{NADPH} + O_2 \xrightarrow[\text{system}]{\text{NADPH oxidase}} \text{NADP}^+ + \text{"active oxygen"} + H_2O.$

2. Drug substrate + "active oxygen" $\longrightarrow$ oxidized drug.

The "active oxygen," produced in the reaction of reduced P-450 cytochrome with molecular oxygen, is thought[24, 25] to be a hydroxylating intermediate of some kind, possibly a peroxide.

---

[20] This explains the ability of cytochrome c to inhibit drug oxidations, by drawing electrons away from the drug-metabolizing system and into the usual cytochrome oxidase pathway.

[21] Symposium: Electron transport systems in microsomes. Articles by: P. Siekevitz; P. Strittmatter; H. Kamin, B. S. S. Masters, Q. H. Gibson and C. H. Williams, Jr.; H. S. Mason, J. C. North and M. Vanneste; T. Omura, R. Sato, D. Y. Cooper, O. Rosenthal and R. W. Estabrook; L. Ernster and S. Orrenius. *Fed. Proc. 24:*1153–1199 (1965).

[22] S. ORRENIUS, G. DALLNER, and L. ERNSTER: Inhibition of the TPNH-linked lipid peroxidation of liver microsomes by drugs undergoing oxidative demethylation. *Biochem. Biophys. Res. Commun. 14:*329 (1964).

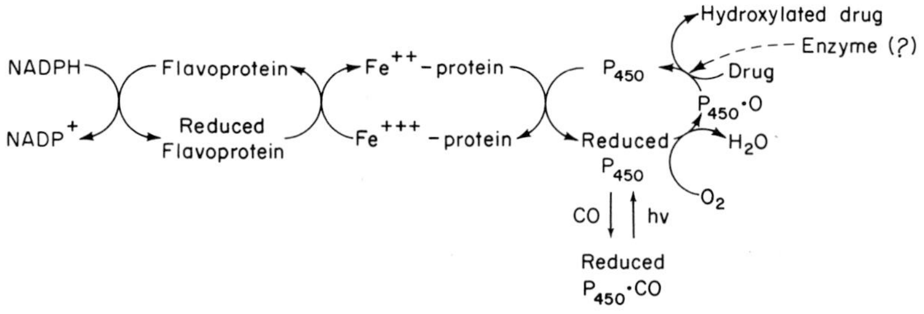

FIG. 3-7. ELECTRON FLOW PATHWAY IN THE COUPLED MICROSOMAL NADPH OXIDASE-DRUG OXIDATION SYSTEM. *"Fe-protein" is a non-heme, iron-containing protein, and P_{450} is a cytochrome oxidase. In the reduced form, it combines with carbon monoxide in a photoreversible reaction. Photon is indicated by* hv. *The carbon monoxide-bound pigment absorbs light at 450 mμ. (From Omura et al., Fig. 15.[23])*

In the second step of the coupled reaction, the combination of drug substrate with "active oxygen," it is still not clear whether or not an enzyme mediates the transfer from P-450 to drug. Several alternatives can be postulated. The P-450 protein itself could interact nonspecifically with all drug substrates and transfer an oxygen atom directly. Or there might be a transferase enzyme for each class of reactions (e.g., aliphatic oxidation, N-dealkylation, etc.), which would interact nonspecifically with all substrates that undergo that particular kind of reaction. Finally, there might be specific transferase enzymes for each kind of compound and each type of oxidative reaction. The available evidence is somewhat ambiguous.

N-Dealkylation of ethylmorphine was found to be inhibited competitively by other drugs with diverse structures that are substrates themselves (e.g., hexobarbital, chlorpromazine, zoxazolamine, phenylbutazone, acetanilid).[26] Mutual inhibitions between unrelated drugs undergoing different kinds of oxidative reaction were also demonstrated; thus, ethylmorphine inhibited the sulfur oxidation of chlorpromazine, and chlorpromazine inhibited the N-dealkylation of ethylmorphine. But drugs like barbital and acetazolamide, which are not metabolized, did not act as inhibitors. Often, the substrate dissocation constant for a given drug as substrate was found to be the same as the K_i (inhibitor dissocation constant) for the

[23] T. OMURA, R. SATO, D. Y. COOPER, O. ROSENTHAL, and R. W. ESTABROOK: Function of cytochrome P-450 of microsomes. *Fed. Proc. 24:*1181 (1965).

[24] B. B. BRODIE, J. R. GILLETTE, and B. N. LA DU: Enzymatic metabolism of drugs and other foreign compounds. *Annu. Rev. Biochem. 27:*427 (1958).

[25] J. R. GILLETTE: "Metabolism of drugs and other foreign compounds by enzymatic mechanisms." *Progress in Drug Research. 6:*11 (1963).

[26] A. RUBIN, T. R. TEPHLY, and G. J. MANNERING: Kinetics of drug metabolism by hepatic microsomes. *Biochem. Pharmacol. 13:*1007 (1964).

same drug acting as inhibitor of the metabolism of a different drug. These findings, and the apparently competitive kinetics that have been observed, imply that several unrelated drugs compete for some component of the system. A possible interpretation is that they all interact with P-450 or with a single oxygen transfer enzyme; but the competitive effect could equally well involve passage through microsomal membranes, or utilization of a limited supply of NADPH.

Other kinds of experiment have suggested a plurality of enzymes. Pretreatment with certain drugs (e.g., 3,4-benzpyrene or phenobarbital) greatly enhances the capacity of the liver to metabolize other drugs (cf. p. 259).[27] 3,4-Benzpyrene stimulates the oxidation of zoxazolamine and acetanilid, yet has little effect on the hydroxylation of chlorzoxazone, the oxidation of hexobarbital, or the demethylation of several N-methyl derivatives of the morphine congeners. That some reactions can be stimulated independently of others would seem to indicate that different enzymes are involved.

An inhibitor of drug oxidations, SKF 525A (p. 249), was found to block the O-dealkylation of codeine to morphine in vitro, but had very little effect on the O-dealkylation of *p*-ethoxyacetanilid to acetanilid.[28] Similarly, it blocked the N-demethylation of morphine congeners but not the N-demethylation of the amino azo dye 3-methyl-4-monomethylaminoazobenzene.[29] Similar differential inhibition has been observed with a variety of alkyl amines.[30] Thus, there appears to be more than one enzyme involved in N-dealkylation, as well as in O-dealkylation. Other experiments indicated that S-demethylation was catalyzed by yet a different enzyme from that involved in N- or O-demethylation.[31]

Although it has not yet proved possible to solubilize the enzyme system located in the liver microsomal fraction,[32, 33] it is now known that the enzyme activity is associated with the so-called smooth-surfaced endoplasmic reticulum.[34] The rough-surfaced variety, studded with ribosomes, can be separated from the less dense, smooth-surfaced microsomes by means of sucrose density gradient centrifugation. NADPH oxidase and drug-oxidizing activities are both much higher in the smooth-surfaced microsomes than in the denser fraction.

[27] A. H. CONNEY, J. R. GILLETTE, J. K. INSCOE, E. R. TRAMS, and H. S. POSNER: Induced synthesis of liver microsomal enzymes which metabolize foreign compounds. *Science 130:*1478 (1959).

[28] J. AXELROD: The enzymic cleavage of aromatic ethers. *Biochem. J. 63:*634 (1956).

[29] A. E. TAKEMORI and G. J. MANNERING: Metabolic N- and O-demethylation of morphine and morphinan-type analgesics. *J. Pharmacol. Exp. Therap. 123:*171 (1958).

[30] L. E. GAUDETTE and B. B. BRODIE: Relationship between the lipid solubility of drugs and their oxidation by liver microsomes. *Biochem. Pharmacol. 2:*89 (1959).

[31] J. F. HENDERSON and P. MAZEL: Studies of the induction of microsomal S-, N- and O-demethylases. *Biochem. Pharmacol. 13:*1471 (1964).

It seems clear that future progress in this area will require further isolation and purification of enzymes capable of mediating single steps in the reaction sequences. Kinetic analyses of the enzyme reactions need to be carried out, if possible, without such complications as a microsomal membrane barrier to drug penetration.

Now we shall examine typical examples of the oxidative transformations catalyzed by the liver microsomal enzyme system.

Side chain (aliphatic) oxidation. The principal metabolites of pentobarbital in dog and man are alcoholic derivatives, formed by side chain oxidation:

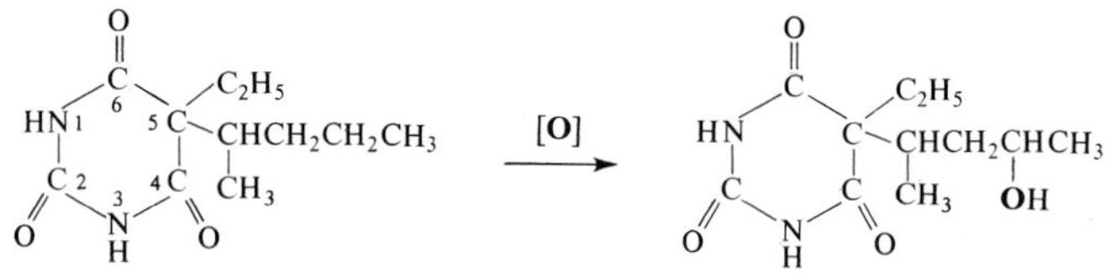

pentobarbital [O] → 5-ethyl-5-(3′-hydroxy-1′-methylbutyl) barbituric acid

Of several minor metabolites, the only one whose structure is known is a carboxylic acid derivative of the following structure:

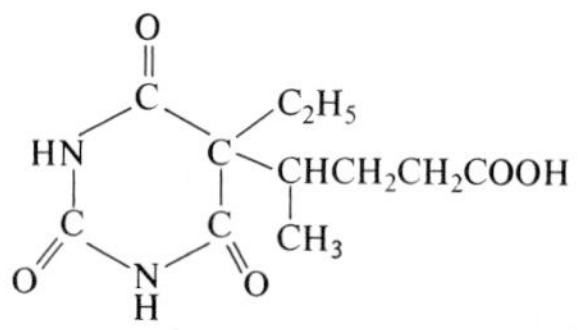

5-ethyl-5-(3′-carboxy-1′-methylpropyl) barbituric acid

However, it has been shown that in aliphatic oxidations the products of the microsomal system are alcohols. Further oxidation to aldehydes and carboxylic acids requires the soluble enzymes alcohol dehydrogenase and aldehyde dehydrogenase (p. 232).[35]

[32] Y. IMAI and R. SATO: Solubilization of aromatic hydroxylase system of liver microsomes and requirement of lipid-like factor. *Biochim. Biophys. Acta* 42:164 (1960).

[33] K. KRISCH: Discussion, p. 25, in *Metabolic Factors Controlling Duration of Drug Action*, Proceedings of First International Pharmacological Meeting, vol. 6, ed. by B. B. Brodie and E. G. Erdös. New York, Macmillan Co., 1962.

[34] J. R. FOUTS: The metabolism of drugs by subfractions of hepatic microsomes. *Biochem. Biophys. Res. Commun.* 6:373 (1961).

[35] J. R. GILLETTE: Side chain oxidation of alkyl substituted ring compounds. I. Enzymatic oxidation of *p*-nitrotoluene. *J. Biol. Chem.* 234:139 (1959).

Side chain oxidation of a slightly different kind is seen with the N_1-methylated barbiturate, hexobarbital.[36] This compound, which has a cyclohexenyl ring attached to position 5, is oxidized to a keto derivative:

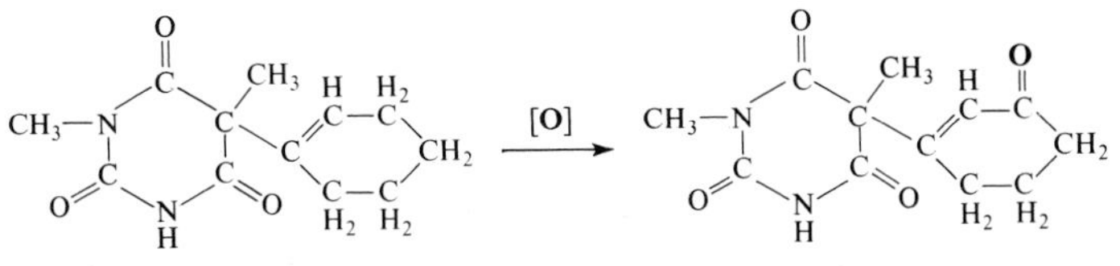

hexobarbital (Evipal)   5-(3'-oxocyclohexen-1'-yl)-1,
                                         5-dimethylbarbituric acid
                                         (Keto-Evipal I)

This was the only metabolite found in an in vitro system consisting of rabbit microsomes, NADPH, and oxygen.[18] In the dog, several additional metabolites are formed, including the N_1-demethylated compound (Norevipal) and its keto analogue (Keto-Norevipal).[37] In addition, a compound very similar to Keto-Evipal I has been reported to occur in dog urine, but with the keto group in a different position:

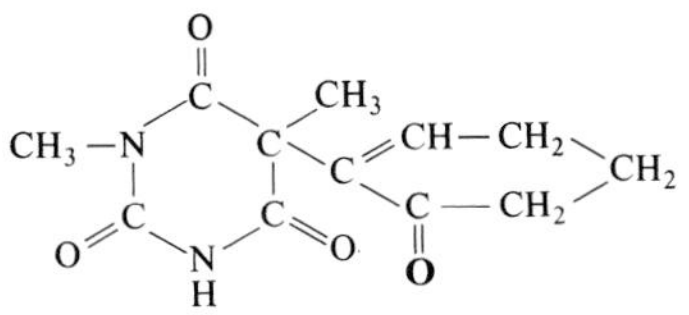

Keto-Evipal II

Aromatic hydroxylation. The conversion of acetanilid to *p*-hydroxyacetanilid illustrates this reaction:

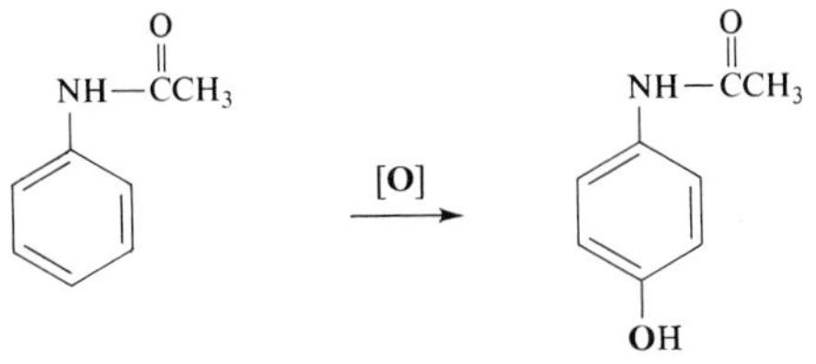

acetanilid   *p*-hydroxyacetanilid

---

36 M. T. BUSH, T. C. BUTLER, and H. L. DICKISON: The metabolic fate of 5-(1-cyclohexen-1-yl)-1,5-dimethyl barbituric acid (hexobarbital, "Evipal") and of 5-(1-cyclohexen-1-yl)-5-methyl barbituric acid ("Norevipal"). *J. Pharmacol. Exper. Therap. 108:*104 (1953).
37 The prefix "nor" comes from the German "N ohne Radikal", describing a derivative in which a nitrogen atom has been dealkylated.

Steroid hormones like testosterone and estradiol-17β are also hydroxylated by a liver microsomal system requiring NADPH,[38] probably the same system that oxidizes drugs. Hydroxylations of non-lipid-soluble metabolic intermediates (e.g., phenylalanine, tyrosine) are carried out by entirely different enzyme systems.

N-Dealkylation. N-Methyl, N-ethyl, and N-alkyl groups in general can be removed oxidatively and converted to aldehydes (formaldehyde, acetaldehyde, etc.). The reactions are clearly different from the usual single carbon transfers in intermediary metabolism, which involve either S-adenosylmethionine or a folic acid derivative. The conversion of aminopyrine to monomethyl-4-aminoantipyrine, and its further conversion to 4-aminoantipyrine, illustrate the reaction sequence:

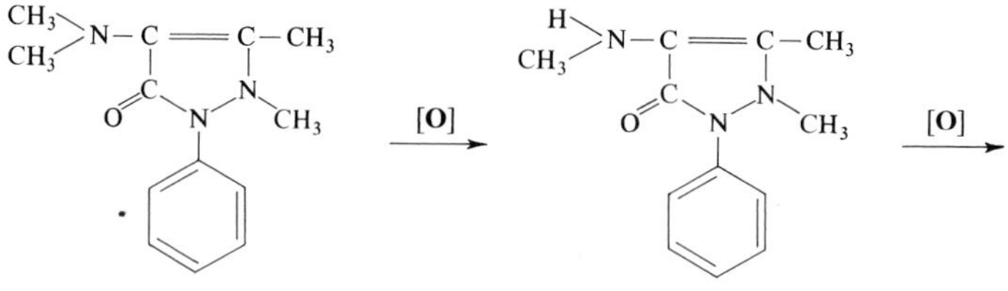

aminopyrine   monomethyl 4-aminoantipyrine

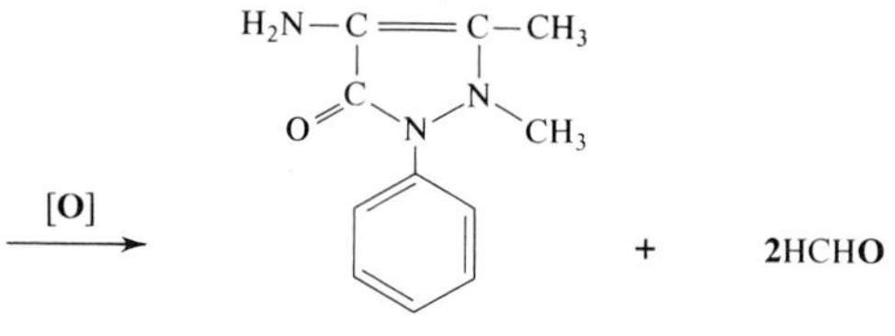

4-aminoantipyrine

Another example is the demethylation of morphine to normorphine (cf. p. 608).

O-Dealkylation. Aromatic ethers are cleaved, as in the following two reactions:

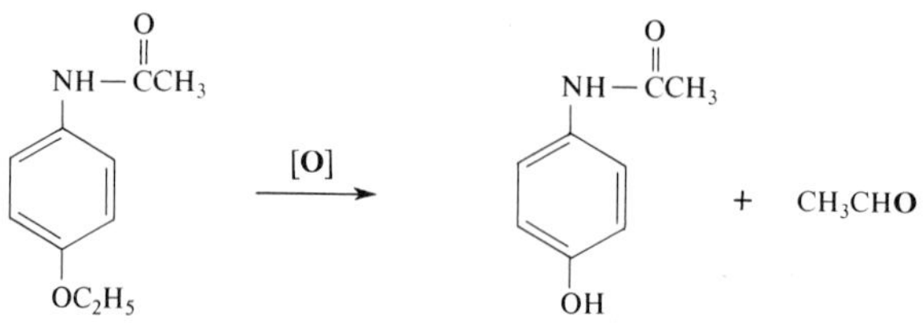

acetophenetidin   *p*-hydroxyacetanilid

[38] R. KUNTZMAN, M. JACOBSON, K. SCHNEIDMAN, and A. H. CONNEY: Similarities between oxidative drug-metabolizing enzymes and steroid hydroxylases in liver microsomes. *J. Pharmacol. Exp. Therap.* 146:280 (1964).

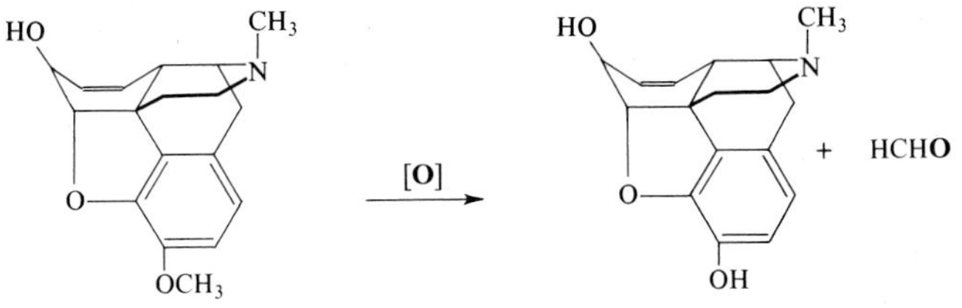

codeine (methylmorphine)   morphine

S-Demethylation. An oxidative reaction similar to N- or O-demethylation occurs with certain methyl thioethers:

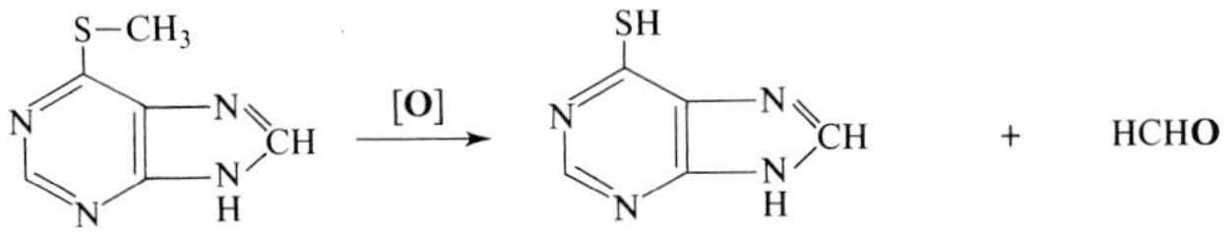

6-methylthiopurine   6-mercaptopurine

Oxidative deamination. The metabolism of amphetamine to phenylacetone by rabbit liver is an example of this type of oxidation:

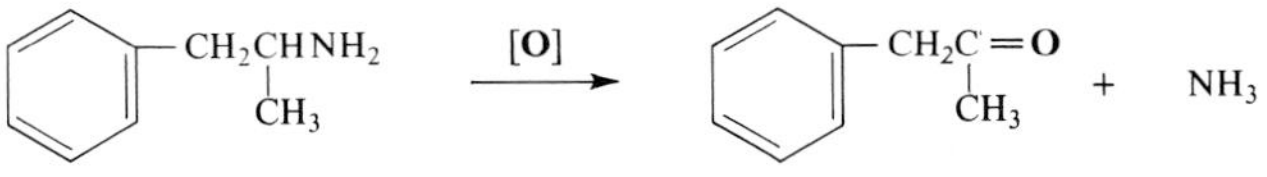

amphetamine   phenylacetone

In the dog and rat, however, amphetamine undergoes *p*-hydroxylation of the benzene ring rather than deamination.

Sulfoxide formation. Thioethers in general are oxidized to sulfoxides, as below:[39]

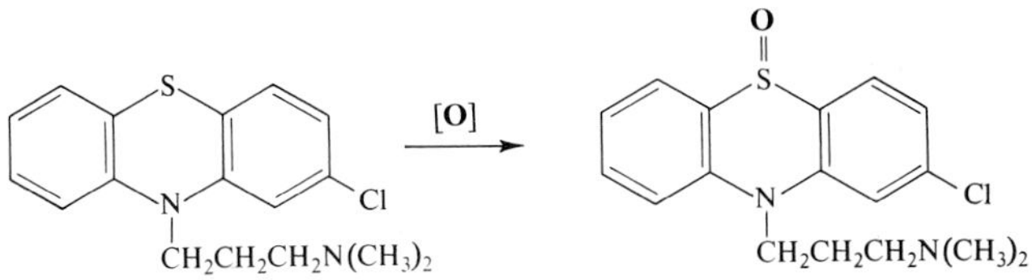

chlorpromazine   chlorpromazine sulfoxide

---

[39] N. P. SALZMAN and B. B. BRODIE: Physiological disposition and fate of chlorpromazine and a method for its estimation in biological material. *J. Pharmacol. Exp. Therap.* *118*:46 (1956).

Another example of sulfoxide formation was discovered in the course of a search for better agents to promote uric acid excretion in gout. Phenylbutazone, a drug with antirheumatic, antipyretic, analgesic, and sodium-retaining activity, also blocks the renal tubular reabsorption of uric acid. An alcoholic metabolite that arises by side chain oxidation of phenylbutazone was found to have little antirheumatic effect but still retained the uricosuric action:

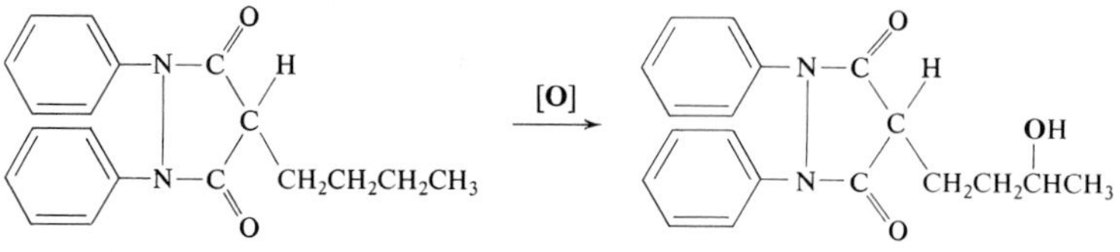

phenylbutazone   phenylbutazone alcohol

Manipulations of the side chain of phenylbutazone alcohol led to the discovery that sulfur-containing derivatives had marked uricosuric action. One of these, the 4-phenylthioethyl analogue of phenylbutazone, was found to be metabolized by sulfoxide formation, to yield an even more potent uricosuric drug, sulfinpyrazone:[40]

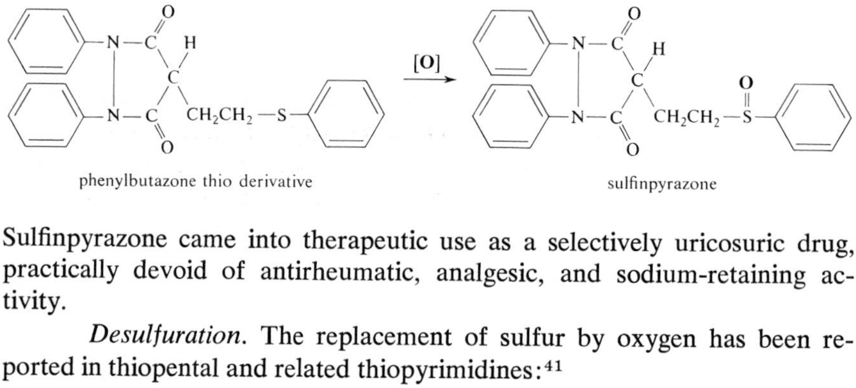

phenylbutazone thio derivative   sulfinpyrazone

Sulfinpyrazone came into therapeutic use as a selectively uricosuric drug, practically devoid of antirheumatic, analgesic, and sodium-retaining activity.

Desulfuration. The replacement of sulfur by oxygen has been reported in thiopental and related thiopyrimidines:[41]

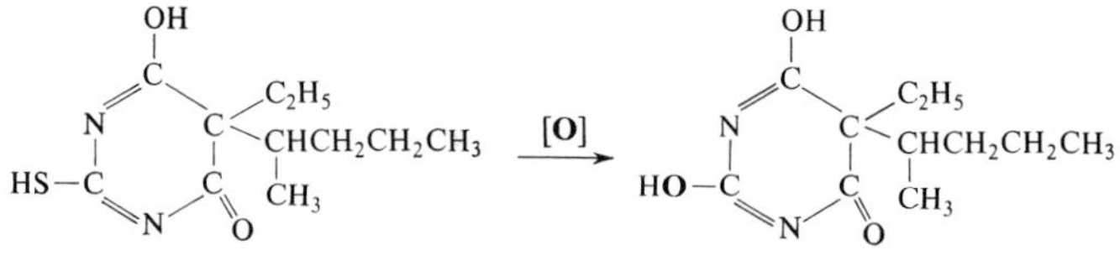

thiopental   pentobarbital (enol form)

[40] J. J. BURNS, T. F. YU, A. RITTERBAND, J. M. PEREL, A. B. GUTMAN, and B. B. BRODIE: A potent new uricosuric agent, the sulfoxide metabolite of the phenylbutazone analogue, G-25671. *J. Pharmacol. Exp. Therap. 119:*418 (1957).

[41] E. SPECTOR and F. E. SHIDEMAN: Metabolism of thiopyrimidine derivatives: thiamylal, thiopental and thiouracil. *Biochem. Pharmacol. 2:*182 (1959).

Another example of this reaction is the conversion of parathion to its oxygen analogue, paraoxon.[42, 43] Parathion is used as an insecticide, but it is biologically inert; it depends for its effectiveness upon oxidative desulfuration in the insect, and for its toxicity to mammals upon oxidative desulfuration in the liver:

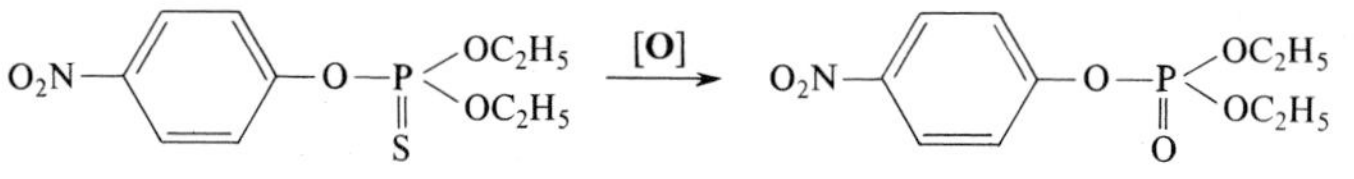

parathion   paraoxon

This reaction is reported to require NADH rather than NADPH, but otherwise it resembles the usual drug oxidations; the system is found in the microsomes, requires oxygen, and is stimulated by Mg^{++}. The requirement for NADH is so unusual that it is deserving of more intensive investigation.

N-Oxidation and N-hydroxylation. N-Oxidation is exemplified by the oxidative conversion of trimethylamine to its N-oxide:[44]

$$(CH_3)_3N \xrightarrow{[O]} (CH_3)_3N = O$$

trimethylamine   trimethylamine N-oxide

When the carcinogenic compound 2-acetylaminofluorene is administered to rabbits or other animal species in which it produces cancer, a N-hydroxy metabolite is found in the urine. There is good evidence showing that this oxidation product, rather than the parent compound, is the actual carcinogen:[45]

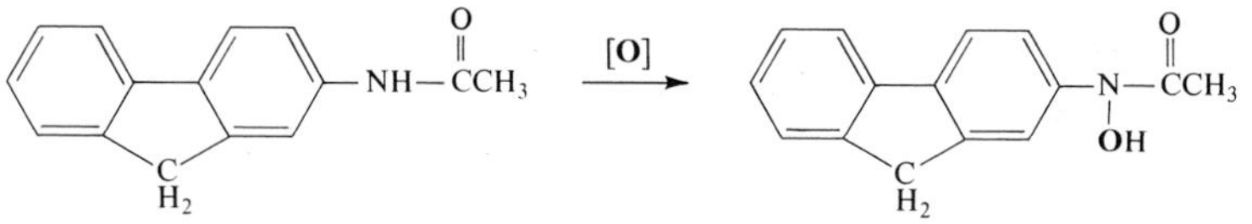

2-acetylaminofluorene   N-hydroxy derivative of
2-acetylaminofluorene

[42] A. N. DAVISON: The conversion of Schradan (OMPA) and Parathion into inhibitors of cholinesterase by mammalian liver. *Biochem. J. 61:*203 (1955).

[43] A. N. DAVISON: Conversion of Schradan and parathion by an enzyme system of rat liver. *Nature 174:*1056 (1954).

[44] J. R. BAKER and S. CHAYKIN: The biosynthesis of trimethylamine-N-oxide. *J. Biol. Chem. 237:*1309 (1962).

[45] J. W. CRAMER, J. A. MILLER, and E. C. MILLER: *N*-Hydroxylation: a new metabolic reaction observed in the rat with the carcinogen 2-acetylaminofluorene. *J. Biol. Chem. 235:*885 (1960).

Formation of the N-hydroxy derivative of aniline, phenylhydroxylamine (p. 209), is another example of N-hydroxylation by the liver microsome system.[46,47] It is possible, as discussed below, that N-hydroxylation is the first step in other oxidative reactions involving the amino group (e.g., deamination, N-dealkylation).[48]

Microsomal enzyme systems requiring NADPH and molecular oxygen have been implicated not only in drug oxidations, but also in the hydroxylation of steroids.[49,50] In steroid hydroxylation,[51] acetanilid hydroxylation,[52] and trimethylamine oxidation,[44] studies with ^{18}O have shown that the oxygen introduced into the substrate molecule is derived from air, not from OH^- of water. In the oxidation of trimethylamine, the overall stoichiometry was shown to be:

$$(CH_3)_3N + NADPH + H^+ + O_2 \longrightarrow (CH_3)_3N{=}O + NADP^+ + H_2O$$

It follows, then, that the oxidase enzyme P-450 (p. 221) belongs to the class of "mixed function oxidases,"[51] in which one atom of a molecule of O_2 is incorporated into a substrate, and the other is simultaneously reduced, appearing in water. The general mechanism of this type of reaction is:

$$AH + O{=}O + 2e \longrightarrow AOH + [O^=]$$

$$[O^=] + 2H^+ \longrightarrow H_2O$$

The nature of the actual hydroxylating intermediate, undoubtedly an oxygenated form of reduced P-450, remains controversial. A positively charged hydroxyl ion (OH^+), hydrogen peroxide (H_2O_2), and various free radicals have all been proposed.[25] For our purposes, the protein P-450 may be considered an oxygen transferase, and many of the oxidative reactions discussed above may be written as hydroxylation reactions. The subsequent steps (e.g., conversion of alcohols to aldehydes, and aldehydes to acids) may be catalyzed by other enzymes (e.g., alcohol or aldehyde dehydrogenases) or may proceed nonenzymically.

[46] M. KIESE and H. UEHLEKE: Der Ort der N-Oxydation des Anilins im höheren Tier. *Arch. exper. Pathol. Pharmakol. 242:*117 (1961).

[47] M. KIESE and H. UEHLEKE: Zwei Wege der Entmethylierung von N-Methylanilin durch Mikrosomen aus Rattenlebern. *Naturwissenschaften 48:*379 (1961).

[48] M. S. FISH, C. C. SWEELEY, N. M. JOHNSON, E. P. LAWRENCE, and E. C. HORNING: Chemical and enzymic rearrangements of N,N-dimethyl amino acid oxides. *Biochim. Biophys. Acta 21:*196 (1956).

[49] R. KUNTZMAN, M. JACOBSON, K. SCHNEIDMAN, and A. H. CONNEY: Similarities between oxidative drug-metabolizing enzymes and steroid hydroxylases in liver microsomes. *J. Pharmacol. Exp. Therap. 146:*280 (1964).

[50] R. KUNTZMAN, D. LAWRENCE, and A. H. CONNEY: Michaelis constants for the hydroxylation of steroid hormones and drugs by rat liver microsomes. *Mol. Pharmacol. 1:*163 (1965).

[51] H. S. MASON: Mechanisms of oxygen metabolism. *Advance. Enzymol. 19:*79 (1957).

[52] H. S. POSNER, C. MITOMA, S. ROTHBERG, and S. UDENFRIEND: Enzymic hydroxylation of aromatic compounds. III. Studies on the mechanism of microsomal hydroxylation. *Arch. Biochem. Biophys. 94:*280 (1961).

The initial hydroxylation reactions can be written as follows:

$$R-CH_3 \xrightarrow{[P_{450}\ \mathbf{O}]} R-CH_2\mathbf{OH}$$

ALIPHATIC OXIDATION

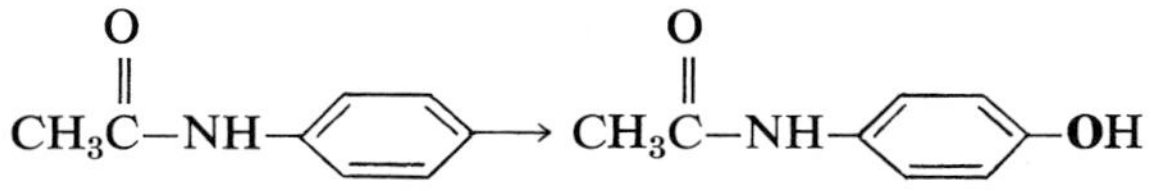

AROMATIC HYDROXYLATION

$$R-NH-CH_3 \longrightarrow [R-NH-CH_2\mathbf{OH}] \longrightarrow R-NH_2 + HC\mathbf{HO}$$

N-DEALKYLATION

$$R-O-CH_3 \longrightarrow [R-O-CH_2\mathbf{OH}] \longrightarrow R-\mathbf{OH} + HC\mathbf{HO}$$

O-DEALKYLATION

$$R-S-CH_3 \longrightarrow [R-S-CH_2\mathbf{OH}] \longrightarrow R-SH + HC\mathbf{HO}$$

S-DEMETHYLATION

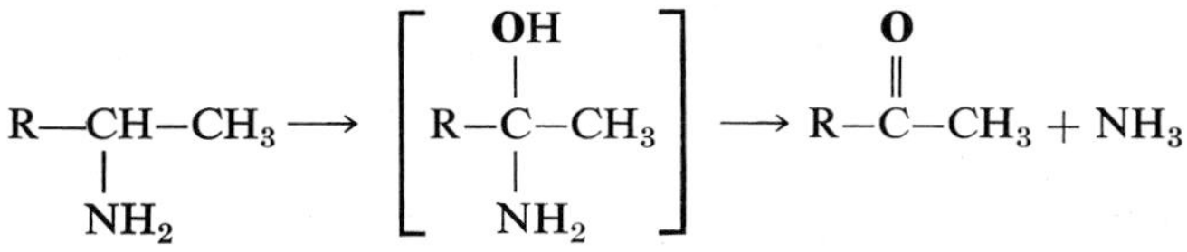

OXIDATIVE DEAMINATION

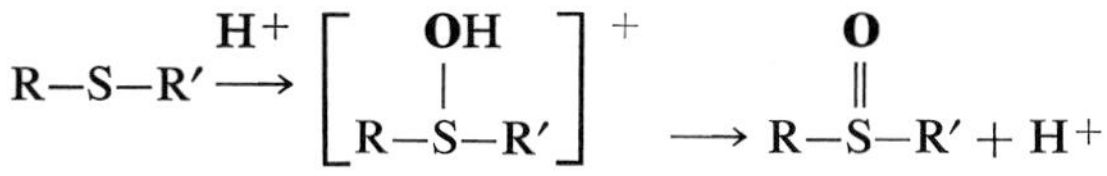

SULFOXIDE FORMATION

$$(CH_3)_3N \xrightarrow{H+} [(CH_3)_3N-\mathbf{OH}]^+ \longrightarrow (CH_3)_3N = \mathbf{O} + H^+$$

N-OXIDATION

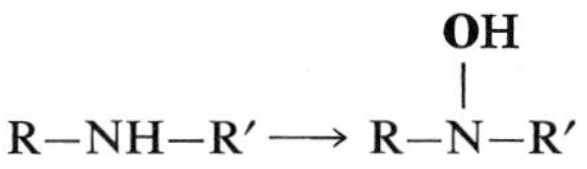

N-HYDROXYLATION

In the oxidative desulfuration reactions, the oxygen atom replaces a sulfur atom, and the latter appears as sulfate, but the mechanism remains obscure.

Drug Oxidations that are not Mediated by the Liver Microsomal System

Aromatization of cyclohexane derivatives. A good example is the formation of benzoic acid from hexahydrobenzoic acid by a mitochondrial enzyme system in guinea pig and rabbit liver. Mitochondria from rat liver are less active, and those from cat, mouse, dog, monkey, and man are completely inactive.

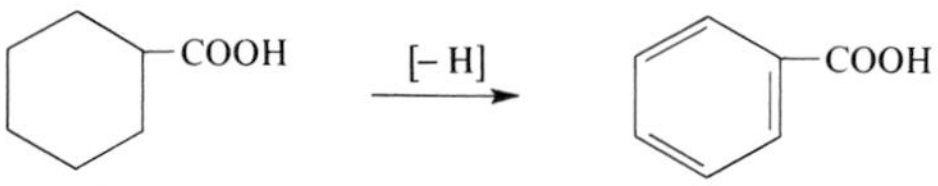

hexahydrobenzoic acid   benzoic acid

The system requires magnesium ions, coenzyme A, ATP or an ATP-generating system, and oxygen.[53] The first step appears to be the formation of hexahydrobenzoyl-CoA, which is then dehydrogenated to the aromatic product. Glycine stimulates the reaction, probably by reacting with the benzoic acid to form hippuric acid.

Alcohol and aldehyde oxidation. Alcohol dehydrogenase and aldehyde dehydrogenase are rather nonspecific enzymes found in the soluble fraction of liver, which catalyze several important oxidative transformations. The substrates include some compounds normally found in the body, for example, the alcohol vitamin A and the aldehyde retinene. Ethyl alcohol and its metabolite, acetaldehyde, are oxidized by this pair of enzymes, as are a variety of other exogenous alcohols and aldehydes, for example, p-nitrobenzyl alcohol and its aldehyde:[35]

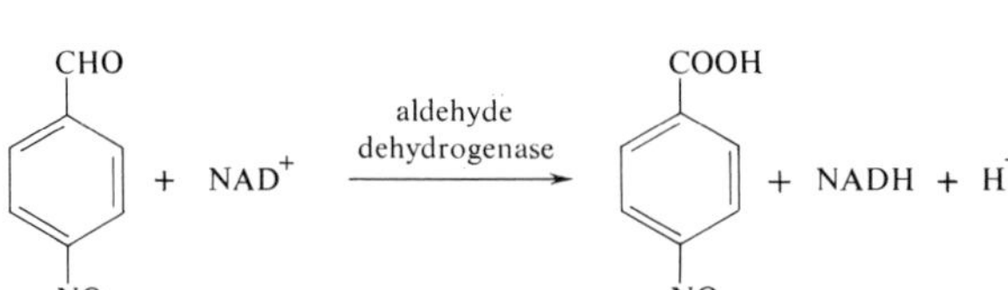

p-nitrobenzyl alcohol p-nitrobenzaldehyde

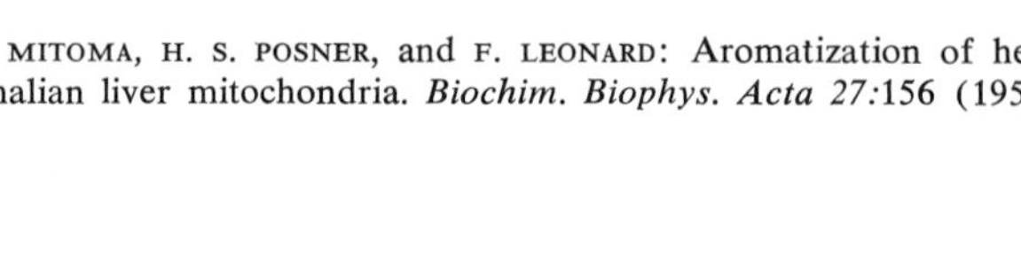

p-nitrobenzaldehyde p-nitrobenzoic acid

[53] C. MITOMA, H. S. POSNER, and F. LEONARD: Aromatization of hexahydrobenzoic acid by mammalian liver mitochondria. *Biochim. Biophys. Acta* 27:156 (1958).

The oxidation of chloral hydrate to trichloroacetic acid also occurs,[54] although the major metabolic pathway for this drug is reduction to trichloroethanol. The enzyme responsible appears to be different from ordinary liver aldehyde dehydrogenase, although it is also found in the soluble fraction of liver and requires NAD^+:

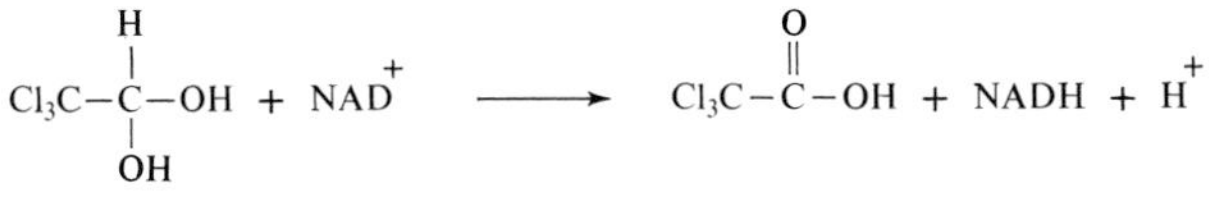

$$\underset{\text{chloral hydrate}}{Cl_3C-\overset{\overset{\displaystyle H}{|}}{\underset{\underset{\displaystyle OH}{|}}{C}}-OH} + NAD^+ \longrightarrow \underset{\text{trichloroacetic acid}}{Cl_3C-\overset{\overset{\displaystyle O}{||}}{C}-OH} + NADH + H^+$$

Purine oxidation. Several purine derivatives (e.g., 6-mercaptopurine, theophylline, caffeine) are known to undergo oxidation in vivo,[55] and it seems likely that xanthine oxidase (which normally interacts with hypoxanthine and xanthine) could participate in some of these reactions. The metabolism of the methylated xanthines is complex;[56] theophylline is largely oxidized to methyl- and dimethyluric acid, while theobromine is demethylated to 3- and 7-methylxanthines, as shown in Fig. 3-8. Caffeine (1,3,7-trimethylxanthine) is metabolized both by demethylation and by oxidation; thus, 1,3-dimethyluric acid, 1-methyluric acid, 1,7-dimethylxanthine, 1-methylxanthine, and 7-methylxanthine all appear in the urine. While some monomethylxanthines are substrates for the enzyme xanthine oxidase, it seems well established[57] that the dimethylxanthines and caffeine are not oxidized by this enzyme.

Monoamine oxidase (MAO)[58] *and diamine oxidase (DAO).*[59] These two similar enzymes oxidatively deaminate several naturally occurring amines as well as a number of drugs. The reaction products are aryl or alkyl aldehydes, which are usually oxidized further by other enzymes to the corresponding carboxylic acids. MAO is a mitochondrial enzyme found especially in liver, kidney, intestine, and nervous tissue. Its substrates include phenylethylamine, tyramine, catecholamines (dopamine, norepinephrine, epinephrine), and tryptophan derivatives (tryptamine, serotonin):

54 J. R. COOPER and P. J. FRIEDMAN: The enzymic oxidation of chloral hydrate to trichloroacetic acid. *Biochem. Pharmacol. 1:*76 (1958).

55 G. B. ELION, S. CALLAHAN, R. W. RUNDLES, and G. H. HITCHINGS: Relationship between metabolic fates and antitumor activities of thiopurines. *Cancer Res. 23:*1207 (1963).

56 H. H. CORNISH and A. A. CHRISTMAN: A study of the metabolism of theobromine, theophylline and caffeine in man. *J. Biol. Chem. 228:*315 (1957).

57 V. H. BOOTH: The specificity of xanthine oxidase. *Biochem. J. 32:*494 (1938).

58 H. BLASCHKO: "Amine Oxidase," *The Enzymes,* 2nd ed., vol. 8, ed. by P. D. Boyer, H. Lardy, and K. Myrbäck. New York, Academic Press, 1963, pp. 337–351.

59 E. A. ZELLER: "Diamine Oxidases," *The Enzymes,* 2nd ed., vol. 8, ed. by P. D. Boyer, H. Lardy, and K. Myrbäck. New York, Academic Press, 1963, pp. 313–335.

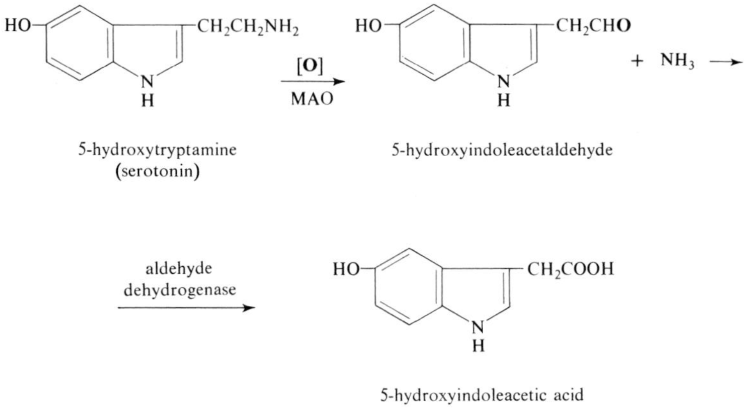

5-hydroxytryptamine
(serotonin)

5-hydroxyindoleacetaldehyde

5-hydroxyindoleacetic acid

Other simple amines, both aryl and alkyl, are attacked by MAO, a relatively nonspecific enzyme, but not all amines are good substrates. Amphetamine, for example, and any other phenylethylamine derivative carrying a methyl group on the α carbon atom, are not oxidized well.

DAO also converts amines to aldehydes in the presence of oxygen. Its substrate specificity overlaps that of MAO. Good substrates include histamine and polymethylene diamines, $H_2N-(CH_2)_n-NH_2$. In the latter series, the most rapid oxidation is seen at $n = 4$ (putrescine) and $n = 5$ (cadaverine). The enzyme is found in bacteria and higher plants, and in the soluble cell fractions of liver, intestine, and placenta.

Dehalogenation. Certain halogenated insecticides and other compounds in industrial use can undergo dehalogenation in the animal body; and since halogenation usually leads to more toxic compounds, dehalogenation often is a true detoxication mechanism. The reactions include displacement by a hydroxyl group, splitting out of hydrogen halide (dehydrohalogenation) and displacement by an acetylcysteine residue (mercapturic acid formation, p. 242). The metabolism of the insecticide DDT (chlorophenothane) in DDT-resistant houseflies[60] illustrates dehydrohalogenation to the nontoxic derivative DDE:

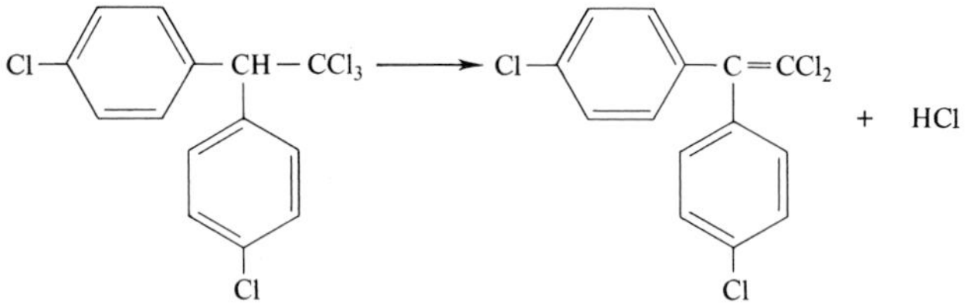

DDT
(chlorophenothane)

DDE
(dichlorodiphenyldichloroethylene)

60 J. STERNBURG, C. W. KEARNS, and H. MOORFIELD: DDT-dehydrochlorinase, an enzyme found in DDT-resistant flies. *Agr. Food Chem.* 2:1125 (1954).

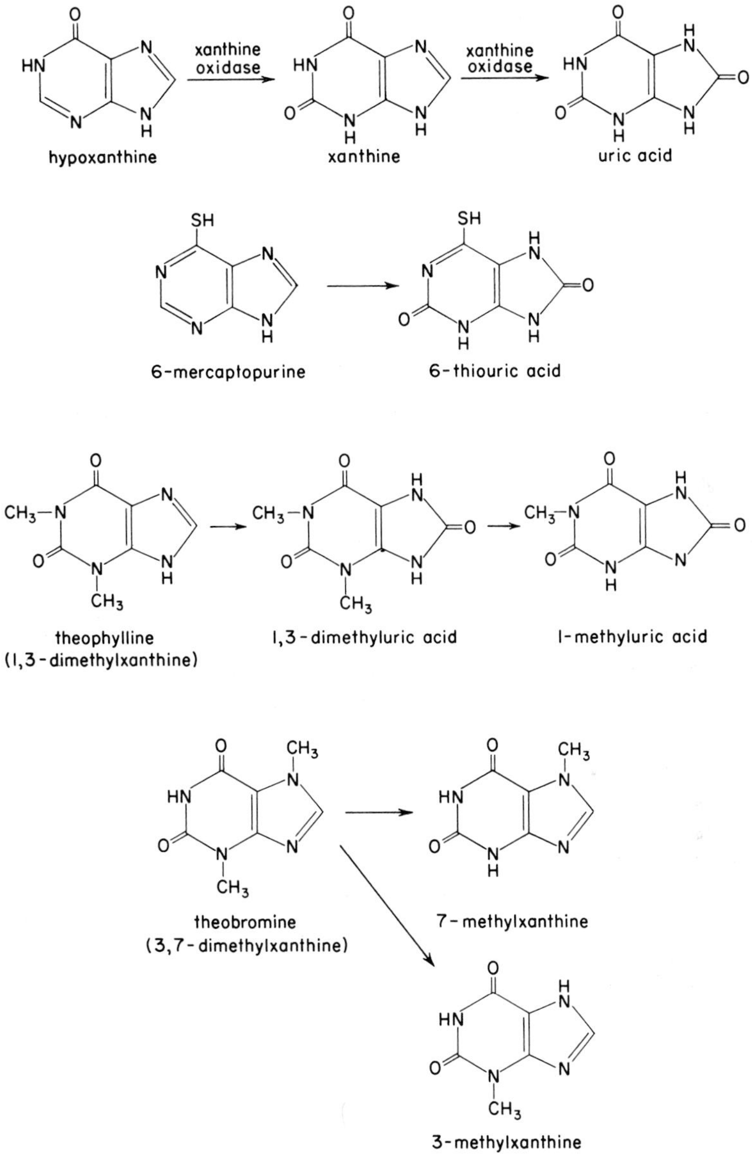

FIG. 3-8. PATHWAYS OF PURINE METABOLISM. (*Adapted from Cornish and Christman.*[56])

TABLE 3-5.   DDT-dehydrochlorinase activity in homogenates of different strains of DDT-resistant and DDT-sensitive flies

The reaction mixture consisted of 2 ml of homogenized flies (equivalent to 12 flies), 0.003M glutathione, 200μg DDT in 50μl alcohol, and 1 ml of 0.137M phosphate buffer, pH 7.4. The reactions were run under a nitrogen atmosphere at 37°, and the amount of DDE formed was measured. Strain D was formerly resistant but had reverted back to nearly normal sensitivity. The actual strain designations have been deleted here; they may be found in the original publication. (Data of Sternburg et al.,[60] Table 6.)

Strain	Median lethal dose (μg DDT)	DDT converted to DDE in 4 hr (μg)
A	0.25	0
B	0.3	0
C	1.5	8
D	1.85	12
E	25.0	24
F	50.0	46
G	75.0	63

The enzyme system requires glutathione. Table 3-5 shows that resistant flies (strains EFG) have this enzyme, but sensitive flies (strains ABC) do not; its presence enables the insect to destroy the insecticide and thus to be immune to its action. More sensitive methods of assay reveal a small amount of enzyme activity even in sensitive flies.[60a] In higher animals, the final product appearing in the urine after DDT ingestion is dichlorodiphenyl-acetic acid, presumably a metabolic product of DDE.

Reduction

Azo and nitro reduction. Azo reduction is illustrated by an important historical example. The era of specific antibacterial chemotherapy began with the introduction of Prontosil, an azo dye, for the treatment of streptococcal and pneumococcal infections. Subsequently it was discovered[61] that the active drug was not Prontosil itself but a metabolite, sulfanilamide (*p*-aminobenzenesulfonamide):

60a H. LIPKE and C. W. KEARNS: DDT dehydrochlorinase. I. Isolation, chemical properties, and spectrophotometric assay. *J. Biol. Chem. 234:*2123 (1959).

61 J. ET MME. TRÉFOUËL, F. NITTI, and D. BOVET: Activité du p-aminophényl-sulfamide sur les infections streptococciques expérimentales de la souris et du lapin. *Compt. Rend. 120:*756 (1935).

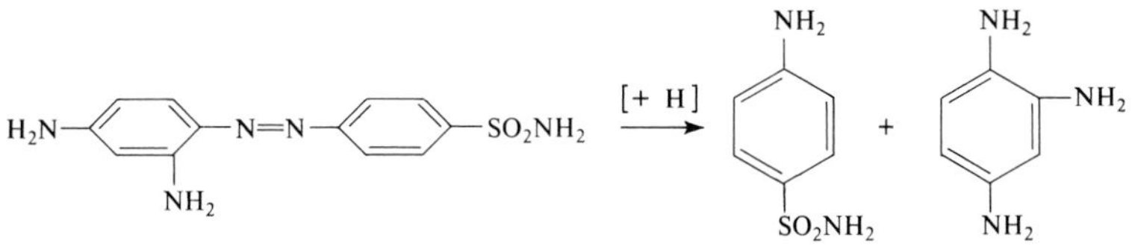

prontosil   sulfanilamide

Nitro reduction is also illustrated well by an antibacterial agent, the antibiotic chloramphenicol, which is transformed in part to an amine by bacterial and mammalian nitro reductase systems:[62]

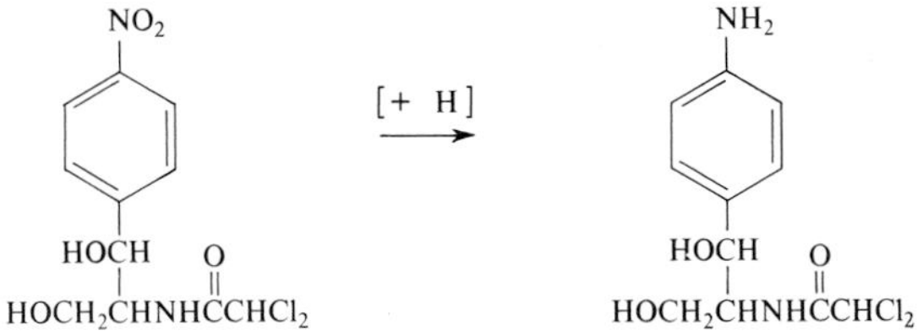

chloramphenicol   chloramphenicol reduction product

Azo and nitro reductions occur in rabbit and rat liver homogenates. At first the activity was thought to be present in the soluble cell fraction as well as in the microsomes. Later reports[34] indicated that the activity of the "soluble" supernatant fraction was actually in a class of light microsomes that sedimented unusually slowly. In contrast to the microsomal drug-oxidizing system, which is confined to the liver, these reductases are found in other tissues too. Although some differences have been noted between the azo and nitro reductase systems, they have many features in common. Both involve anaerobic reactions, require NADPH, and are stimulated by flavins (flavin mononucleotide, flavin adenine dinucleotide, or riboflavin); thus, both these enzymes may well be flavoproteins.[62]

Alcohol dehydrogenase functions as a reductase when it catalyzes the conversion of chloral hydrate to trichloroethanol (p. 207).

Hydrolysis

Drug metabolism by hydrolysis is restricted to esters and amides. The enzymes (esterases and amidases) are found in blood plasma and other tissues, including the liver, usually in the soluble fraction of the cells. Enzymes prepared from different tissues or different species can have widely differing substrate specificities. The hydrolysis of the local anesthetic procaine by plasma cholinesterase is illustrative:

---

62 J. R. FOUTS and B. B. BRODIE: The enzymatic reduction of chloramphenicol, *p*-nitrobenzoic acid and other aromatic nitro compounds in mammals. *J. Pharmacol. Exp. Therap. 119:*197 (1957).

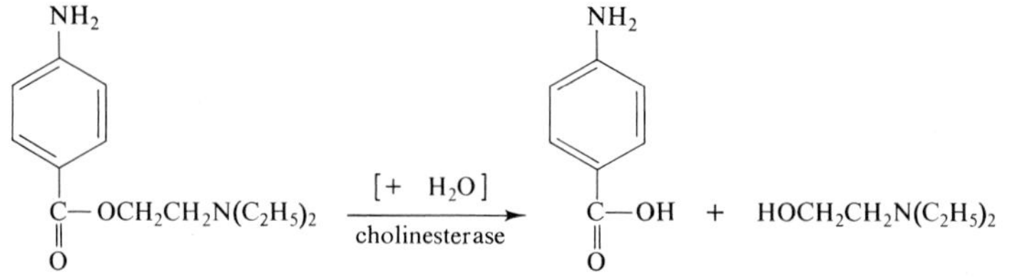

procaine   *p*-aminobenzoic acid   diethylaminoethanol

When the amide bond ($-\overset{\overset{\textstyle O}{\|}}{C}-NH-$) is hydrolyzed, an acid and an amine are formed instead of an acid and an alcohol (as in the hydrolysis of an ester). Procaine amide, the amide analogue of procaine, is hydrolyzed in the tissues much more slowly than procaine, and not at all in plasma.

Not all esters undergo hydrolysis in the body. Atropine, for example, is hydrolyzed to an insignificant extent in mouse and man,[63, 64] but very rapidly by certain rabbits (cf. p. 466).

Synthetic (Conjugation) Reactions

Several kinds of small molecules normally present in the body can react with drugs or with drug metabolites. Glucuronic acid combines with phenols, alcohols, aromatic amines, and carboxylic acids to form the corresponding glucuronides. Addition of ribose and phosphate converts purine and pyrimidine analogues to nucleosides and nucleotides. Amines and carboxylic acids can be acylated. Other examples are the synthesis of mercapturic acids and of sulfuric acid esters, transsulfurations, and methylations.

Synthesis of glucuronides. The soluble fraction of liver contains enzymes that catalyze the synthesis of uridine diphosphate-glucuronic acid (UDPGA):

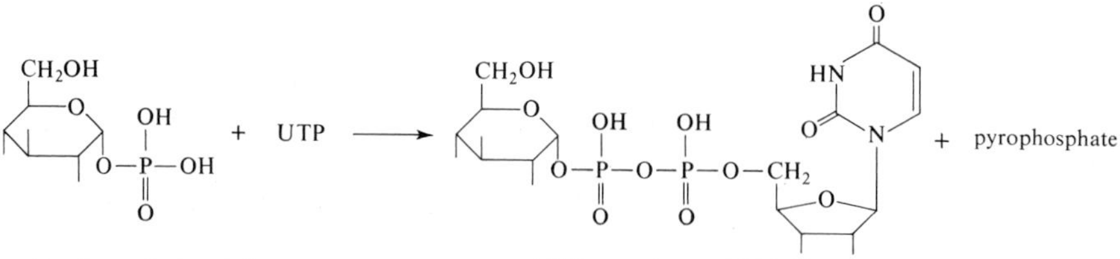

α-D-glucose 1-phosphate   UDP-α-D-glucose (UDPG)

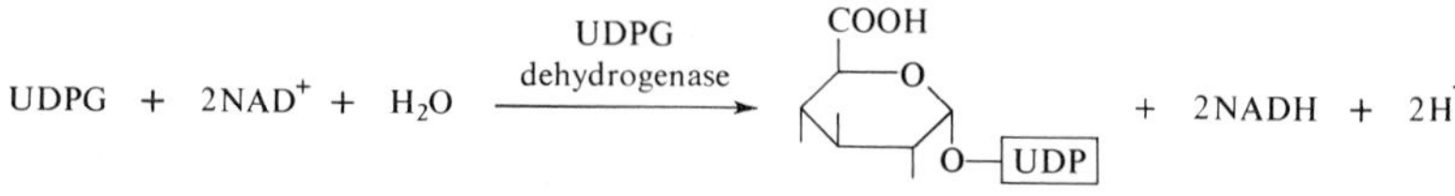

UDP-α-D-glucuronic acid (UDPGA)

UDPGA serves as a donor of glucuronic acid to various acceptors. Enzymes mediating this process are called *transferases*. They are found in the microsomes of liver and other tissues.[65] As shown above, UDPGA has the α configuration at the glucuronic acid-phosphate link; the compound is not affected by the enzyme β-glucuronidase. However, the glucuronides that are formed invariably have the β configuration. Thus, the transfer reaction must proceed by a "backside attack" (Walden inversion).

The hydroxyl group in phenols and aliphatic alcohols is conjugated with glucuronic acid to form a hemiacetal glucuronide. Compounds of this type are often called "ether glucuronides":

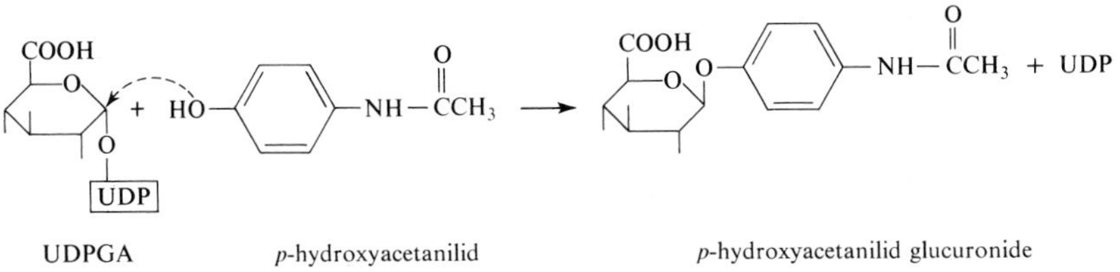

UDPGA   *p*-hydroxyacetanilid   *p*-hydroxyacetanilid glucuronide

Carboxylic acids are conjugated through the carboxyl group to form ester glucuronides:

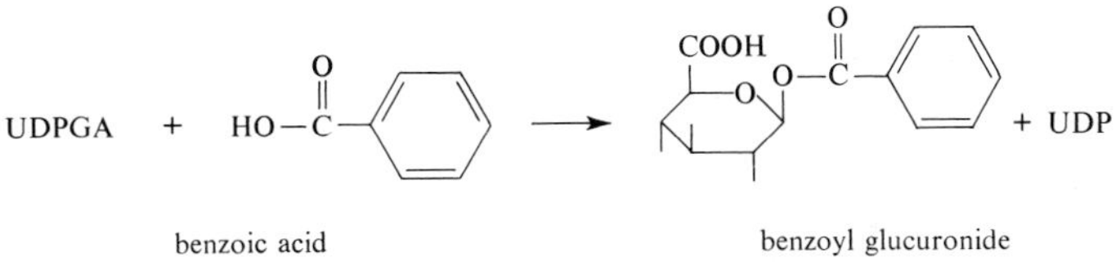

benzoic acid   benzoyl glucuronide

In all these reactions, there is a nucleophilic attack by the electron-rich atom (oxygen, nitrogen, or sulfur) on carbon atom 1 of the glucuronic acid in UDPGA.[68] Glucuronides of naturally occurring compounds (e.g., steroid alcohols, thyroxine, bilirubin) appear to be formed by the same pathways as glucuronides of foreign compounds.

A glucuronyl transferase has been solubilized and partially purified from rabbit liver microsomes.[68a] The enzyme, which required no cofactors other than UDPGA, was active in forming ethereal and ester glucuronides but completely lacked the ability to form N-glucuronides. This indicates

63 J. D. GABOUREL and R. E. GOSSELIN: The mechanism of atropine detoxication in mice and rats. *Arch. Int. Pharmacodyn. 115:*416 (1958).

64 R. E. GOSSELIN, J. D. GABOUREL, and J. H. WILLS: The fate of atropine in man. *Clin. Pharmacol. Therap. 1:*597 (1960).

65 G. J. DUTTON: Uridine diphosphate glucuronic acid as glucuronyl donor in the synthesis of 'ester,' aliphatic and steroid glucuronides. *Biochem. J. 64:*693 (1956).

66 J. AXELROD, J. K. INSCOE, and G. M. TOMKINS: Enzymatic synthesis of *N*-glucosyluronic acid conjugates. *J. Biol. Chem. 232:*835 (1958).

that a different enzyme is responsible for amine glucuronide formation. A similar result has been obtained in studies with the Gunn rat (p. 266), a strain that is genetically incapable of forming bilirubin glucuronide or other ester or ether glucuronides. These animals are able to form aniline glucuronide in normal amounts.[68b]

Aromatic amines[66] and even occasionally a sulfhydryl group[67] can be conjugated. The nitrogen and sulfur glucuronides are acid labile, in contrast to the oxygen-linked glucuronides.

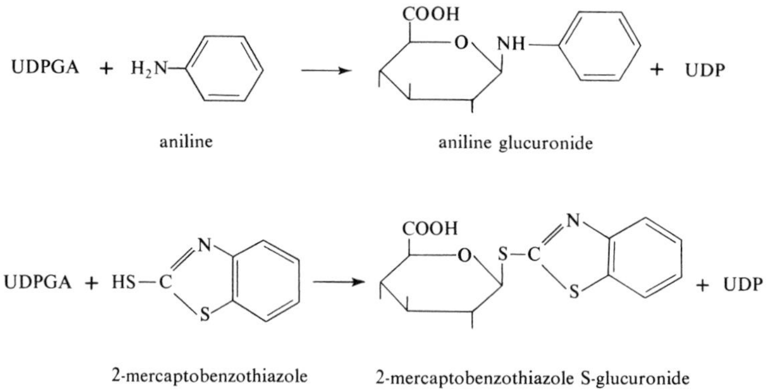

UDPGA + H$_2$N—⟨⟩ → (structure) + UDP

aniline   aniline glucuronide

UDPGA + HS—C(structure) → (structure) + UDP

2-mercaptobenzothiazole   2-mercaptobenzothiazole S-glucuronide

Synthesis of ribosides and riboside phosphates. Certain carbohydrates other than glucuronic acid can participate in synthetic reactions with foreign compounds. Ribonucleosides and ribonucleotides are formed with analogues of purines and pyrimidines, undoubtedly by the same enzyme systems (in the soluble fraction of the cell) responsible for synthesizing nucleosides and nucleotides of the naturally occurring purines and pyrimidines. Many analogues of these compounds, of interest as anticancer agents, have been studied; and in almost every instance, the biologically active compounds are the phosphorylated ribonucleoside derivatives.[69] This type of reaction is exemplified by conversion of 6-mercaptopurine to a ribonucleotide[70] by reaction with PRPP, catalyzed by a nucleotide pyrophosphorylase:

---

[67] J. W. CLAPP: A new metabolic pathway for a sulfonamide group. *J. Biol. Chem.* 223:207 (1956).

[68] J. AXELROD, J. K. INSCOE, and G. M. TOMKINS: Enzymatic synthesis of N-glucuronic acid conjugates. *Nature* 179:538 (1957).

[68a] K. J. ISSELBACHER, M. F. CHRABAS, and R. C. QUINN: The solubilization and partial purification of a glucuronyl transferase from rabbit liver microsomes. *J. Biol. Chem.* 237:3033 (1962).

[68b] I. M. ARIAS: Ethereal and N-linked glucuronide formation by normal and Gunn rats *in vitro* and *in vivo*. *Biochem. Biophys. Res. Commun.* 6:81 (1961).

[69] J. A. MONTGOMERY: On the chemotherapy of cancer. *Progress in Drug Research* 8:431 (1965).

[70] L. N. LUKENS and K. A. HERRINGTON: Enzymic formation of 6-mercaptopurine ribotide. *Biochim. Biophys. Acta* 24:432 (1957).

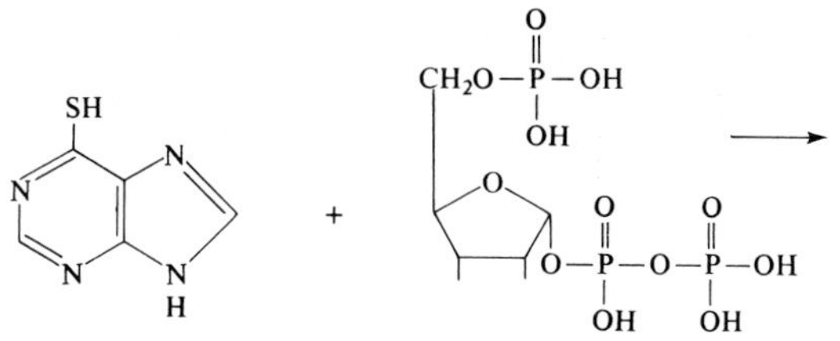

6-mercaptopurine

5-phosphoribosyl
1-pyrophosphate (PRPP)

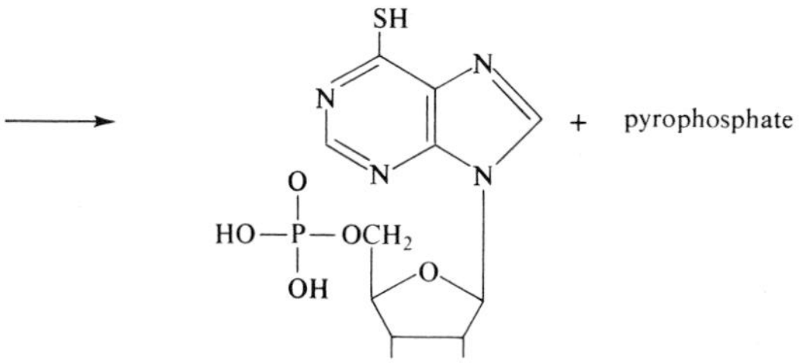

+ pyrophosphate

6-mercaptopurine nucleoside
monophosphate

Alternatively, purines, pyrimidines, and their analogues may react with α-D-ribose 1-phosphate; the phosphate group is split out and a ribonucleoside results. This type of reaction is catalyzed by a nucleoside phosphorylase.

Acylation reactions. Coenzyme A (for "coenzyme of acetylation") (CoA) was discovered in the course of investigations into the acetylation of sulfanilamide.[71] It is now known that a number of acids other than acetic acid can also form CoA derivatives. CoA, through its free sulfhydryl group, reacts with an activated form of a carboxylic acid to form the acyl-CoA derivative. The acyl group is then transferred to a suitable acceptor, such as an aromatic amine. The responsible enzymes are located in the soluble fraction of the liver.

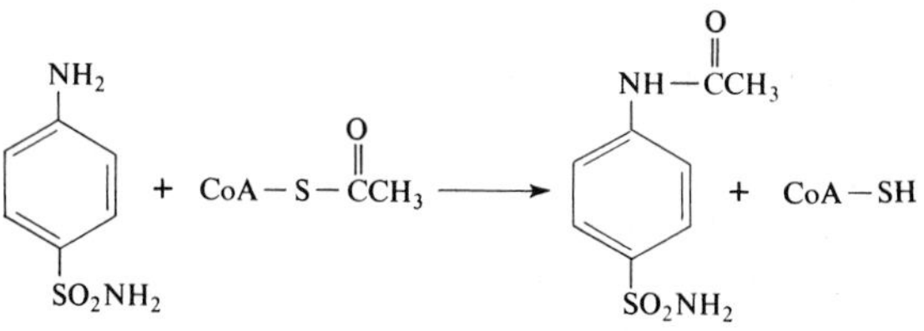

sulfanilamide   acetyl-CoA N_4-acetylsulfanilamide

[71] F. LIPMANN: Acetylation of sulfanilamide by liver homogenates and extracts. *J. Biol. Chem. 160:*173 (1945).

Here, a foreign amine is conjugated with the naturally occurring acetic acid. The converse also occurs, a foreign carboxylic acid forming a CoA derivative, which is then conjugated with a naturally occurring amine, such as glycine, ornithine (in birds and reptiles), or glutamine (in man and chimpanzee).

benzoyl-CoA   glycine   hippuric acid

Mercapturic acid formation. A few aromatic hydrocarbons, halo-genated aromatic hydrocarbons, and halogenated nitrobenzenes are ex-creted in the urine as conjugates with an acetylated cysteine residue. The likely reaction mechanism is shown in Fig. 3-9, for naphthalene as sub-strate. It is thought that an activated substrate first reacts with peptide-bound cysteine (probably an activated form of glutathione). A supernatant fraction of rat liver homogenate has been found to activate glutathione (the enzyme has been called a "glutathiokinase"); the conjugation then pro-ceeds in the microsome fraction in the presence of NADPH and oxygen.[73] The resulting glutathione conjugate is hydrolyzed to form an arylcysteine intermediate, and the cysteine amino group is then acetylated to form the final mercapturic acid. Most of the intermediates shown in Fig. 3-9 have been isolated from rat bile after naphthalene administration.[72] It is thought that a hydroxylation reaction or epoxide formation may be the first step in activation of substrates of this type,[74] especially since the hydroxy deriva-tives (1- and 2-naphthols) appear in the bile. All the 2-hydroxynaphthyl intermediates undergo spontaneous dehydration at acid pH, yielding the corresponding mercapturic acids. The hydroxy compounds are therefore sometimes called "premercapturic acids"; the mercapturic acids themselves (including the end-product shown) probably arise by decomposition of these precursors in acid urine.[75] It is not known which (if any) physiologic substrates are ordinarily metabolized by this pathway.

[72] E. BOYLAND, G. S. RAMSAY, and P. SIMS: Metabolism of polycyclic compounds. 18. The secretion of metabolites of naphthalene, 1:2-dihydronaphthalene and 1:2-epoxy-1:2:3:4-tetrahydronaphthalene in rat bile. *Biochem. J.* 78:376 (1961).

[73] J. BOOTH, E. BOYLAND, T. SATO, and P. SIMS: Metabolism of polycyclic com-pounds. 17. The reaction of 1:2-dihydronaphthalene and 1:2-epoxy-1:2:3:4-tetrahydronaph-thalene with glutathione catalysed by tissue preparations. *Biochem. J.* 77:182 (1960).

[74] E. BOYLAND: "Mercapturic Acid Conjugation," in *Metabolic Factors Controlling Duration of Drug Action,* Proceedings of First International Pharmacological Meeting, vol. 6, ed. by B. B. Brodie and E. G. Erdös. New York, Macmillan Co., 1962, p. 65.

[75] E. BOYLAND and P. SIMS: Metabolism of polycyclic compounds. 12. An acid-labile precursor of 1-naphthylmercapturic acid and naphthol: an *N*-acetyl-*S*-(1:2-dihydro-hydroxynaphthyl)-L-cysteine. *Biochem. J.* 68:440 (1958).

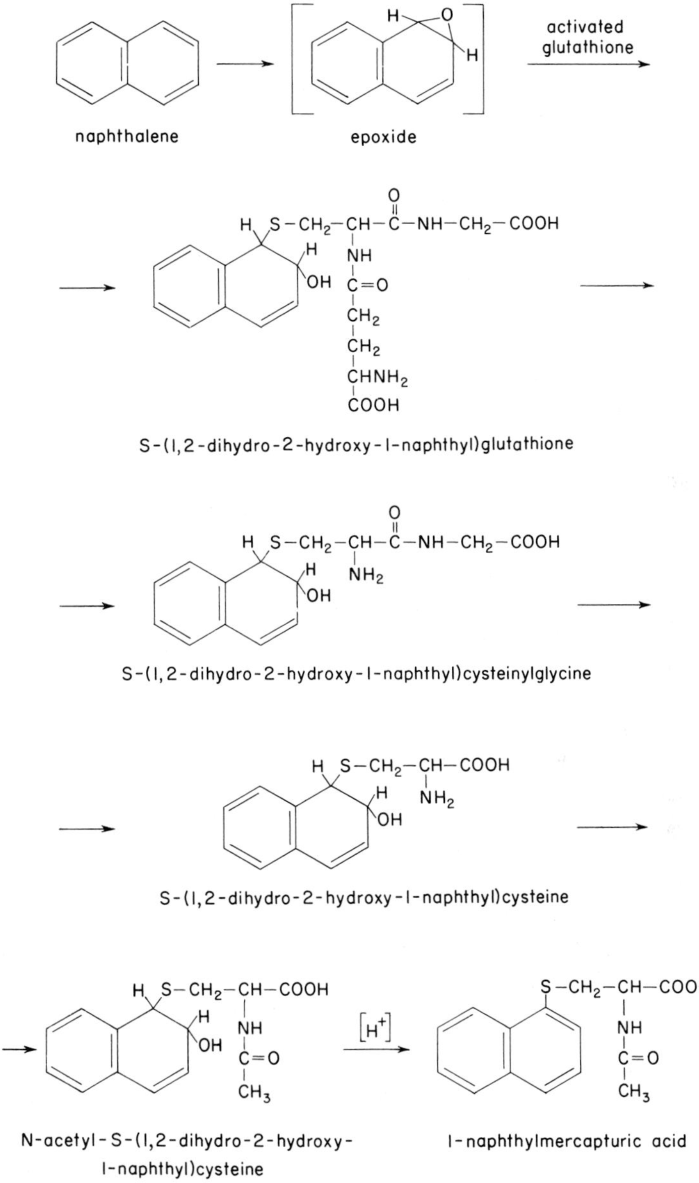

naphthalene → **epoxide** → activated glutathione →

S-(1,2-dihydro-2-hydroxy-1-naphthyl)glutathione

S-(1,2-dihydro-2-hydroxy-1-naphthyl)cysteinylglycine

S-(1,2-dihydro-2-hydroxy-1-naphthyl)cysteine

N-acetyl-S-(1,2-dihydro-2-hydroxy-1-naphthyl)cysteine

[H⁺] → 1-naphthylmercapturic acid

FIG. 3-9.   MERCAPTURIC ACID FORMATION.   (*Adapted from Boyland et al.*[72])

A curious reaction sequence involving mercapturic acid formation leads to the apparent reduction of certain sulfonamides. This unusual pathway is illustrated by the fate of a carbonic anhydrase inhibitor, 2-benzothiazolesulfonamide.[67] In most sulfonamides, which do not undergo this type of reaction, the sulfonamide group is attached to an aromatic ring, but here the sulfonamide sulfur atom is bound to a heterocyclic ring:

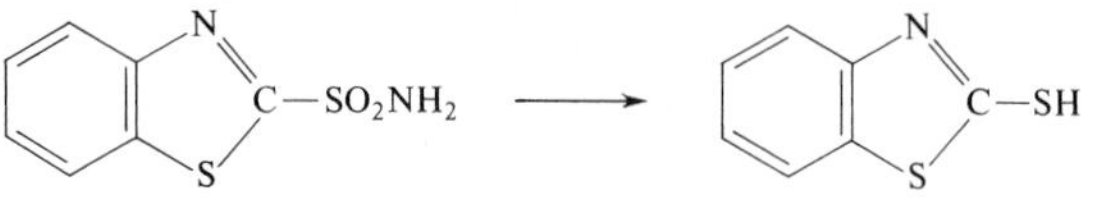

2-benzothiazolesulfonamide   2-mercaptobenzothiazole

Further investigation led to the remarkable finding that the sulfur in the —SH group of the product was not derived from the sulfur of the sulfonamide group, but was contributed by glutathione. The pathway is shown in Fig. 3-10.

FIG. 3-10. PATHWAY FOR THE METABOLISM OF 2-BENZOTHIAZOLESULFONA- MIDE. *These transformations occur in the rat, rabbit, and dog. Conversion of the glutathione derivative to the cysteine derivative probably involves more than one step. (From Colucci and Buyske, Fig. 2.[76])*

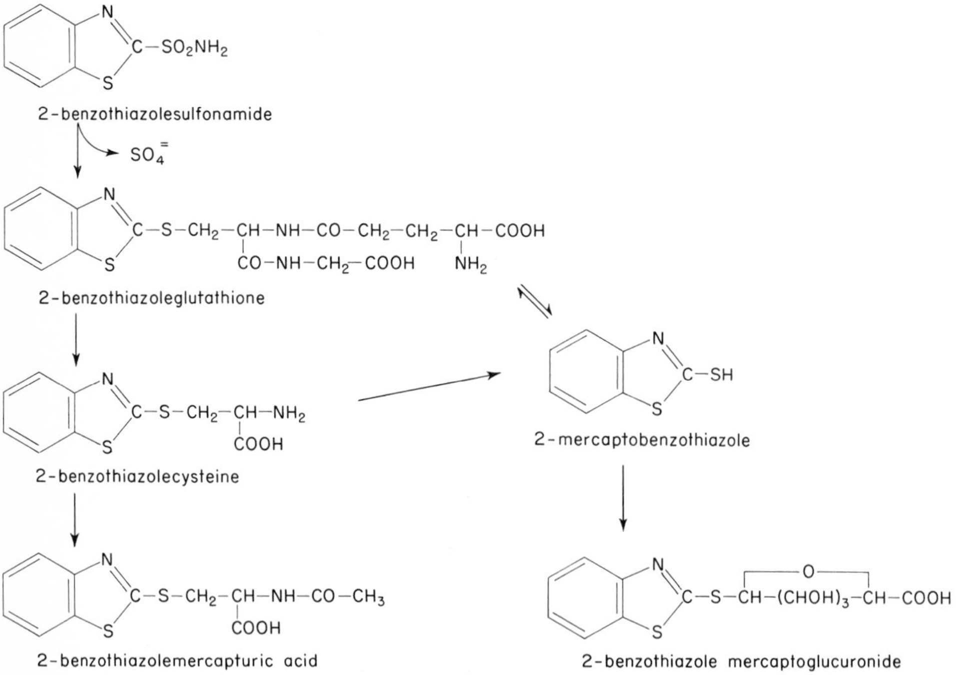

2-benzothiazolesulfonamide

$SO_4^=$

2-benzothiazoleglutathione

2-benzothiazolecysteine

2-mercaptobenzothiazole

2-benzothiazolemercapturic acid

2-benzothiazole mercaptoglucuronide

[76] D. F. COLUCCI and D. A. BUYSKE: The biotransformation of a sulfonamide to a mercaptan and to mercapturic acid and glucuronide conjugates. *Biochem. Pharmacol.* 14:457 (1965).

Synthesis of sulfuric acid esters. These compounds, often called "ethereal sulfates," are formed by the reaction of aromatic and aliphatic hydroxyl groups, and of certain amino groups, with an activated form of sulfate. The enzymes responsible for sulfate activation, and for the transfer of sulfate to the acceptor, are found in the soluble fraction of the liver.[77] The system is normally concerned with the synthesis of sulfated polysaccharides like chondroitin sulfate and heparin. The initiating reaction is the formation of adenosine 5'-phosphosulfate (APS) from the sulfate ion and adenosine triphosphate (ATP), followed by a further reaction with ATP to form 3'-phosphoadenosine 5'-phosphosulfate (PAPS). The sulfate group is then transferred to a phenolic acceptor (e.g., *p*-hydroxyacetanilid) in the presence of an appropriate transfer (sulfokinase) enzyme:

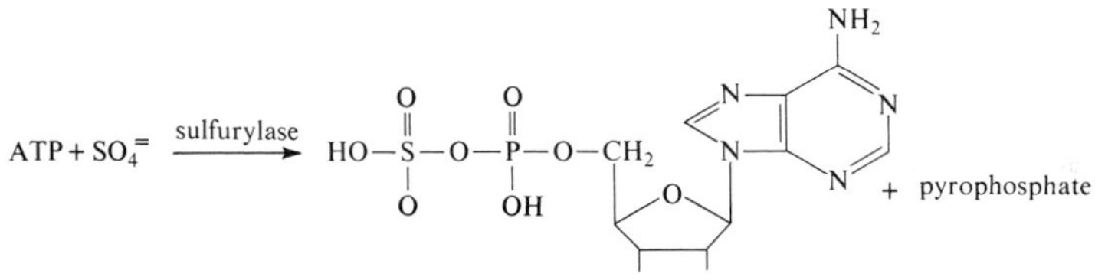

adenosine 5'-phosphosulfate (APS)

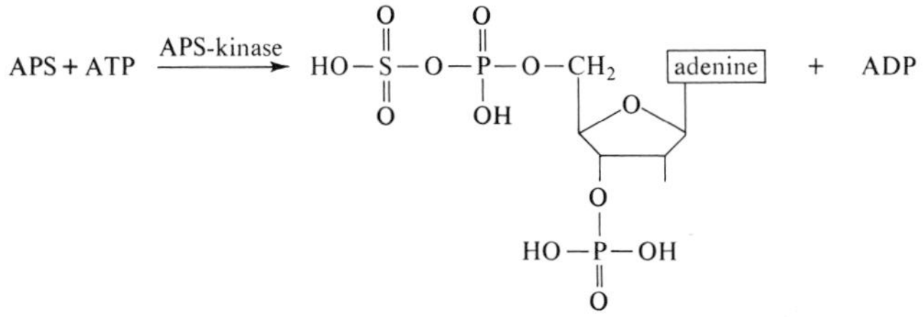

3'-phosphoadenosine 5'-phosphosulfate (PAPS)

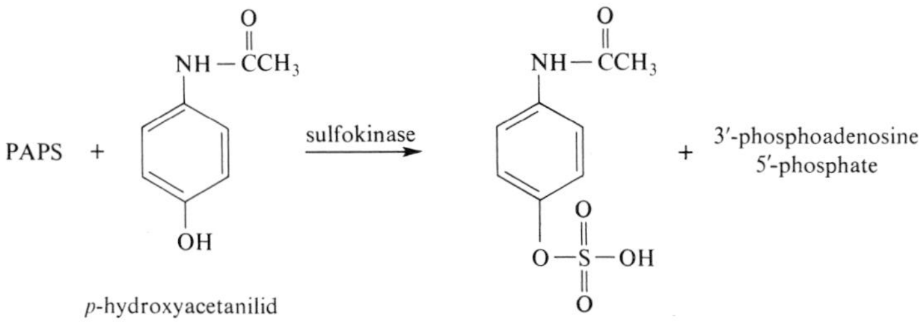

p-hydroxyacetanilid   *p*-hydroxyacetanilid sulfate

There are a number of different sulfokinases specific for different acceptor molecules. In liver, for example, simple phenols, phenolic steroids, alco-

77 P. W. ROBBINS and F. LIPMANN: Isolation and identification of active sulfate. *J. Biol. Chem.* 229:837 (1957).

holic steroids, chloramphenicol, and aromatic amines are all handled by different enzymes.[78]

N-, O-, and S-Methylation. Methylations proceed by a pathway in which S-adenosylmethionine serves as methyl donor. An enzyme, catechol O-methyltransferase, is found in the soluble supernatant fraction of rat liver and other tissues, which can catalyze the transfer of a methyl group to a phenolic −OH of epinephrine, norepinephrine, and other catechol derivatives (e.g., dihydroxyphenylethylamine, dihydroxybenzoic acid).[79]

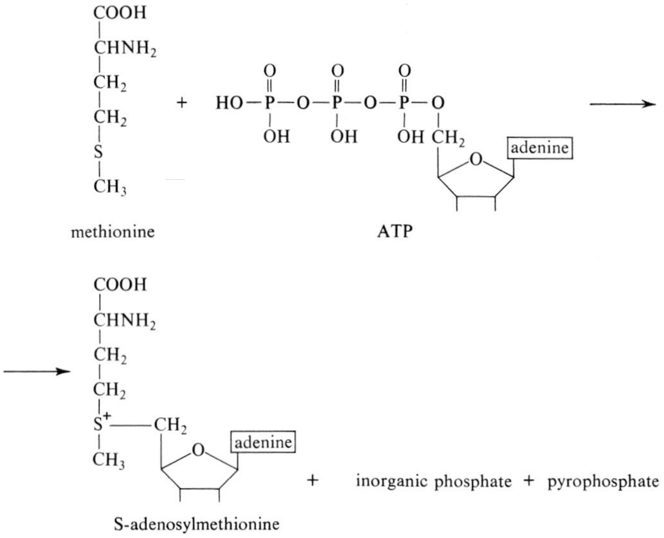

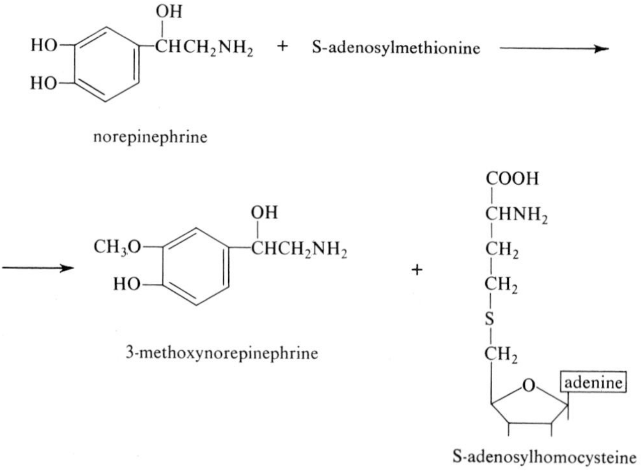

[78] Y. NOSE and F. LIPMANN: Separation of steroid sulfokinases. *J. Biol. Chem.* 233:1348 (1958).

[79] J. AXELROD and R. TOMCHICK: Enzymatic O-methylation of epinephrine and other catechols. *J. Biol. Chem.* 233:702 (1958).

Methylation occurs in the meta position. The reaction is dependent upon magnesium ions; S-adenosylmethionine is required, but ATP and methionine can substitute, in which case S-adenosylmethionine is formed in the presence of rat liver supernatant fraction.

Catechol O-methyltransferase activity is found in many species, and in several tissues besides liver. This enzyme is thought to be involved in the physiologic inactivation of the adrenergic neurotransmitter norepinephrine, as well as of other catechol amines, whether of endogenous or exogenous origin.

A different enzyme catalyzes the O-methylation of N-acetyl-serotonin, to form the pineal hormone melatonin. This enzyme is found only in the pineal gland. It utilizes S-adenosylmethionine, but unlike the catechol O-methyltransferase, it does not require Mg^{++}. It is known as hydroxyindole O-methyltransferase, since it can methylate various hydroxy-indole compounds such as serotonin, bufotenine, and 5-hydroxyindole-acetic acid; however, the best substrate is N-acetylserotonin.[80]

N-Methylation of numerous amines has been reported. A highly specific enzyme methylates histamine.[81] Another enzyme methylates phenyl-ethanolamine derivatives, and is responsible for the conversion of nore-pinephrine to epinephrine:[82]

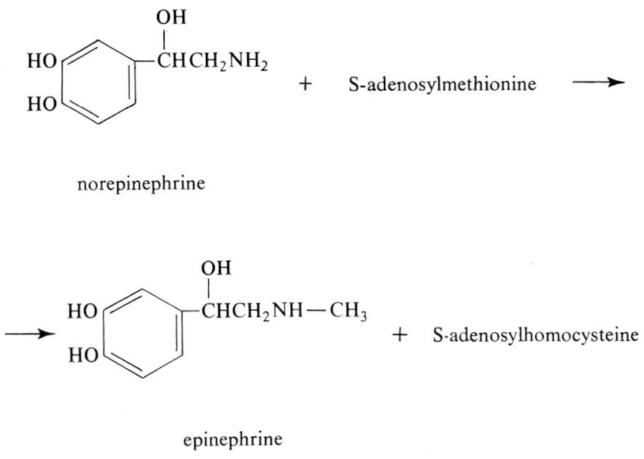

norepinephrine

epinephrine

The reaction occurs in the soluble fraction of adrenal medulla and other tissues. Pyridines and related compounds (nicotine, nicotinamide, quinoline) can be methylated to a minor extent by a similar pathway:

80 J. AXELROD and H. WEISSBACH: Purification and properties of hydroxyindole-*O*-methyl transferase. *J. Biol. Chem. 236:*211 (1961).

81 D. D. BROWN, R. TOMCHICK, and J. AXELROD: The distribution and properties of a histamine-methylating enzyme. *J. Biol. Chem. 234:*2948 (1959).

82 N. KIRSHNER and MC C. GOODALL: The formation of adrenaline from nonadrena-line. *Biochim. Biophys. Acta 24:*658 (1957).

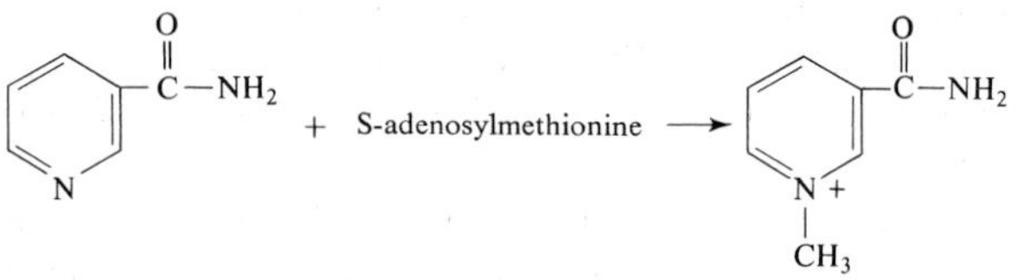

$$\text{nicotinamide} + \text{S-adenosylmethionine} \longrightarrow \text{N'-methylnicotinamide}$$

nicotinamide   N'-methylnicotinamide

Only a few methylated sulfur-containing compounds have been identified in the urine after injection of sulfhydryl compounds,[83] but an in vitro system has been described[84] that methylates such −SH compounds as dimercaprol (BAL), mercaptoethanol, O-methylmercaptoethanol, and hydrogen sulfide. The enzyme has been found in rat liver, kidney, and lung microsomes, and also requires S-adenosylmethionine.

$$\text{HS}-\text{CH}_2\text{CH}_2\text{OH} \xrightarrow{\text{S-adenosylmethionine}} \text{CH}_3-\text{S}-\text{CH}_2\text{CH}_2\text{OH}$$
$$\text{mercaptoethanol} \qquad\qquad \text{S-methylmercaptoethanol}$$

Although a wide range of exogenous sulfhydryl compounds are methylated by this microsomal enzyme system, no sulfhydryl compound of physiologic importance (homocysteine, cysteine, glutathione) will serve as substrate. Apparently, only lipid-soluble substrates have access to the microsomal system. Just how the highly polar, water-soluble S-adenosylmethionine participates in the reaction is not yet understood.

Transsulfuration and the metabolism of cyanide. Cyanide is metabolized in the body by a mitochondrial sulfurtransferase (formerly called "rhodanese"), which has now been crystallized.[85, 86] The enzyme catalyzes the following reaction:

$$\text{CN}^- + \text{S}_2\text{O}_3^= \longrightarrow \text{CNS}^- + \text{SO}_3^=$$
$$\text{cyanide} \quad \text{thiosulfate} \qquad \text{thiocyanate} \quad \text{sulfate}$$

The thiosulfate-cyanide sulfurtransferase is found in liver, kidney, and other tissues, but blood has very little. Small amounts of cyanide are normally ingested in some foods, so the enzyme may possibly have a physiologic protective role in inactivating cyanide.

Another sulfurtransferase in liver, kidney, and blood cells utilizes β-mercaptopyruvic acid as sulfur donor rather than thiosulfate:

[83] E. J. SARCIONE and J. E. SOKAL: Detoxication of thiouracil by *S*-methylation. *J. Biol. Chem. 231:*605 (1958).

[84] J. BREMER and D. M. GREENBERG: Enzymic methylation of foreign sulfhydryl compounds. *Biochim. Biophys. Acta 46:*217 (1961).

[85] B. H. SÖRBO: On the properties of rhodanese: Partial purification, inhibitors and intracellular distribution. *Acta Chem. Scand. 5:*724 (1951).

[86] B. H. SÖRBO: Crystalline rhodanese. I. Purification and physiochemical examination. *Acta Chem. Scand. 7:*1129 (1953).

$$CN^- + HS-CH_2-\overset{\overset{\displaystyle O}{\|}}{C}-COOH \longrightarrow CNS^- + CH_3-\overset{\overset{\displaystyle O}{\|}}{C}-COOH$$
$$\qquad\qquad \beta\text{-mercaptopyruvic acid} \qquad\qquad\qquad \text{pyruvic acid}$$

This enzyme is present in the soluble fraction rather than in the mitochondria, and exhibits a high degree of substrate specificity for mercaptopyruvic acid; however, several compounds besides cyanide can serve as sulfur acceptors. For example, the enzyme can generate thiosulfate from sulfate:

$$HS-CH_2-\overset{\overset{\displaystyle O}{\|}}{C}-COOH + SO_3^= \longrightarrow S_2O_3^= + CH_3-\overset{\overset{\displaystyle O}{\|}}{C}-COOH$$

The thiosulfate can then serve as sulfur donor for thiocyanate sulfurtransferase in cyanide detoxication.

Both enzymes could be involved in the inactivation of cyanide. In cyanide poisoning, cyanide becomes bound to iron atoms in the cytochromes, destroying the electron transport capacity. The immediate removal of this cyanide, in the treatment of cyanide poisoning, is achieved (as described fully on p. 399) by promoting its binding to methemoglobin. The subsequent conversion of cyanide to the nontoxic thiocyanate is promoted by furnishing thiosulfate (or mercaptopyruvate) as substrates for the above reactions.

INHIBITION OF DRUG METABOLISM

SKF 525A

A number of agents can inhibit oxidative drug metabolism; the most widely investigated of these is β-diethylaminoethyl diphenylpropylacetate, more usually known by its commercial code number SKF 525A.[87]

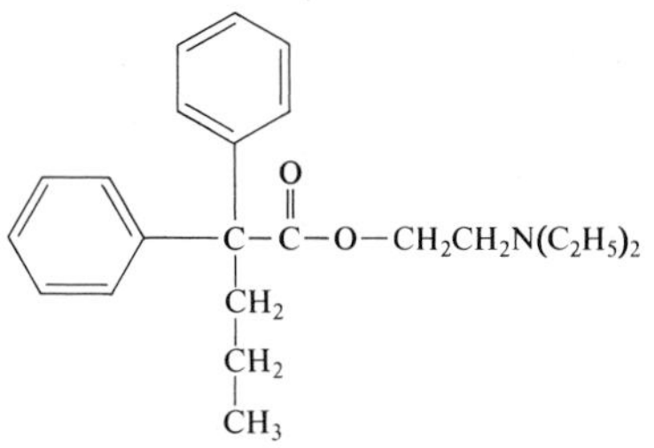

SKF 525A

[87] K. J. NETTER: "Drugs as Inhibitors of Drug Metabolism," in *Metabolic Factors Controlling Duration of Drug Action,* Proceedings of First International Pharmacological Meeting, vol. 6, ed. by B. B. Brodie and E. G. Erdös. New York, Macmillan Co., 1962, p. 213.

TABLE 3-6.   **Effect of SKF 525A on metabolism of hexobarbital in rats**

Adult male rats received hexobarbital (100 mg/kg) intraperitoneally.
The animals were given SKF 525A (15 mg/kg) intraperitoneally 40
minutes before hexobarbital injection. Beginning 1 hour after barbiturate administration, blood samples were taken at 20-minute intervals
for hexobarbital analysis. The design was a cross-over; each rat served
as control once and was given SKF 525A once, one week apart.
(From Axelrod et al.,[88] Table 1.)

Animal no.	Duration of hexobarbital action (to return of righting reflex) (min)		Hexobarbital half-life (min)		Hexobarbital plasma level on awakening (μg/ml)	
	Control	SKF 525A	Control	SKF 525A	Control	SKF 525A
1	21	89	24	69	48	38
2	27	90	24	60	42	34
3	34	86	32	71	40	41
4	23	68	23	49	27	33
5	28	68	27	50	46	38
Means	27	80	26	60	41	37

The selective action of this compound upon the microsomal drug-oxidizing
system was discovered in the course of routine studies of its pharmacologic
properties. The drug had little effect of its own, but when administered
prior to the hypnotic agent hexobarbital, it caused a dramatic prolongation
of the hypnotic action (Table 3-6). In the same experiments blood levels
of the barbiturate were measured, so the biologic half-life of hexobarbital
could be estimated from the die-away curves (p. 287). The data in the
table show that SKF 525A prolonged the duration of action and the biologic half-life of hexobarbital by similar amounts. The intrinsic sensitivity
of the animals to hexobarbital was not altered, as can be seen from the fact
that the hexobarbital plasma levels at the moment of awakening were about
the same in both groups. Moreover, when animals that had received hexobarbital alone were given SKF 525A at the moment of awakening, they did
not go back to sleep, as they ought to have done if SKF 525A had made
them more sensitive to the barbiturate.

An experiment on the rate of hexobarbital metabolism in rat liver
slices is shown in Fig. 3-11. Pretreating the rats with SKF 525A markedly
reduced the ability of their livers to metabolize the barbiturate. Direct addition of SKF 525A (or its hydrolysis product, 2,2-diphenylpropylacetic
acid) to liver slices also reduced the capacity to metabolize hexobarbital.

88 J. AXELROD, J. REICHENTHAL, and B. B. BRODIE: Mechanism of the potentiating
action of β-diethylaminoethyl diphenylpropylacetate. *J. Pharmacol. Exp. Therap.* 112:49
(1954).

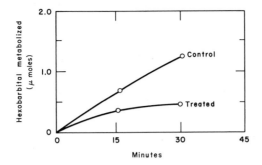

FIG. 3-11. EFFECT OF SKF 525A ON HEXOBARBITAL METABOLISM IN LIVER SLICES. *Treated rats received SKF 525A (25 mg) before sacrifice. Liver slices were incubated with Krebs-Ringer phosphate buffer and 2μmoles of hexobarbital. Samples were removed at 15 and 30 minutes for hexobarbital analysis. (From Cooper et al., Fig. 1.[89])*

It was soon discovered that SKF 525A impaired the metabolism of other drugs, too. Figure 3-12 shows the effect on N-demethylation of aminopyrine in the intact dog. In this experiment, aminopyrine was given intraperitoneally, and plasma levels of aminopyrine and its demethylated

FIG. 3-12. EFFECT OF SKF 525A ON N-DEMETHYLATION OF AMINOPYRINE. *A dog was given aminopyrine intraperitoneally. Plasma levels of aminopyrine and its demethylated product, 4-aminoantipyrine, were measured. One week later the dog received SKF 525A 40 minutes prior to aminopyrine, and experiment was repeated. (From Axelrod et al., Fig. 1.[88] By permission of the* British Medical Journal.)

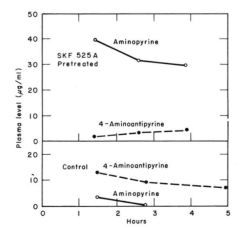

product, 4-aminoantipyrine, were determined. In the normal dog, the demethylation was so rapid that plasma levels of aminopyrine were barely detectable at 1.5 hours, whereas the concentration of 4-aminoantipyrine was considerable. After SKF 525A, very little demethylation occurred, as shown by the high aminopyrine and low aminoantipyrine levels.

The mechanism of the inhibition by SKF 525A was studied by varying the concentration of a substrate, *p*-nitroanisole (*p*-nitromethoxy-benzene) in a microsomal in vitro system in which the rate of O-demethylation was measured in the presence and absence of the inhibitor. The kinetic analysis (Fig. 3-13) revealed a noncompetitive type of inhibition (cf. p. 72).

SKF 525A was found to inhibit many of the microsomal oxidative reactions. Both in vivo and in vitro it blocked not only side chain oxidation and O-dealkylation, but also N-dealkylation, deamination, aromatic hy-

FIG. 3-13. DOUBLE-RECIPROCAL PLOT SHOWING MECHANISM OF INHIBITION BY SKF 525A. *Each point represents value obtained from microsomes of pooled livers of four male rats. Velocities (v) are moles/liter per minute, substrate concentrations (S) are moles/liter. The reaction measured was the demethylation of p-nitroanisole;* $K_m = 2.3 \times 10^{-4}$, $K_i = 0.7 \times 10^{-4}$. *(From Netter and Seidel, Fig. 1.[90])*

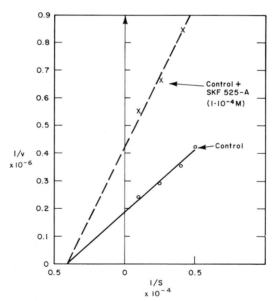

[89] J. R. COOPER, J. AXELROD, and B. B. BRODIE: Inhibitory effects of β-diethylamino-ethyl diphenylpropylacetate on a variety of drug metabolic pathways *in vitro. J. Pharmacol. Exp. Therap. 112:*55 (1954).

[90] K. J. NETTER and G. SEIDEL: An adaptively stimulated O-demethylating system in rat liver microsomes and its kinetic properties. *J. Pharmacol. Exp. Therap. 146:*61 (1964).

droxylation, and sulfoxide formation. It seemed probable that the compound inhibited some common preliminary step involved in these diverse reactions, and the NADPH oxidase system seemed a likely site of action. Surprisingly, however, NADPH oxidase activity of liver microsome preparations in vitro was unaffected by SKF 525A, even while drug metabolism was inhibited in the same preparations.

The inhibitory effect of SKF 525A is not restricted to oxidative pathways. Azo and nitro reduction, which occur in microsomes and which require NADPH but not oxygen, are also inhibited.[62] Glucuronide formation, a microsomal transfer reaction which does not require NADPH, is also affected. On the other hand, various enzymes involved in the microsomal oxidative reactions have different sensitivities to SKF 525A, and some are not inhibited at all (e.g., demethylation of methylaniline, hydroxylation of 3,4-benzpyrene). The mechanism of inhibition by SKF 525A remains obscure. Possibly the compound will prove to act upon the lipoidal membrane of the microsome, thereby impeding the access of substrates to enzymes.

Disulfiram

Another important inhibitor of drug metabolism is disulfiram (tetraethylthiuram disulfide, Antabuse):

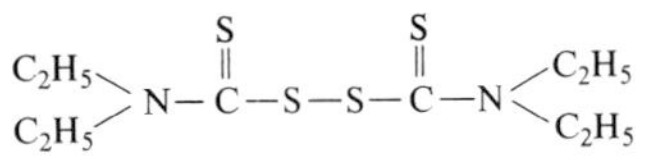

$$C_2H_5\!\!\diagdown \atop C_2H_5\!\!\diagup N - \overset{\overset{\textstyle S}{\|}}{C} - S - S - \overset{\overset{\textstyle S}{\|}}{C} - N \diagup^{C_2H_5}_{\diagdown C_2H_5}$$

disulfiram

This compound has practically no pharmacologic effects of its own. If, after its administration, however, ethyl alcohol is ingested, a violently unpleasant syndrome develops, including flushing, dyspnea, nausea, vomiting, and hypotension. These remarkable effects are specific for alcohol, and they occur even a day or two after disulfiram is taken. The drug was introduced for the treatment of chronic alcoholism. The alcoholic takes disulfiram regularly; thus, his resolve to abstain from alcohol is reinforced by the knowledge of how ill he will inevitably become if he drinks. If he succumbs to temptation nevertheless, serious toxicity may ensue. The hypotension may be severe enough to produce shock, and myocardial damage has been reported. These potentionally dangerous effects limit the use of disulfiram to selected patients under strict medical supervision, who are also usually receiving psychotherapy.

Disulfiram inhibits aldehyde dehydrogenase, apparently by competing with NAD^+.[91] This enzyme normally oxidizes acetaldehyde to acetic

---

91 W. D. GRAHAM: *In vitro* inhibition of liver aldehyde dehydrogenase by tetraethylthiuramdisulphide. *J. Pharm. Pharmacol. 3:*160 (1951).

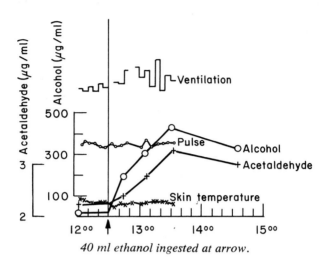

40 ml ethanol ingested at arrow.

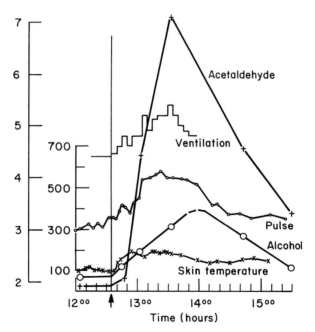

Repeated after ingestion of disulfiram (1.5 g).

92 J. HALD and E. JACOBSEN: The formation of acetaldehyde in the organism after ingestion of Antabuse (tetraethylthiuramdisulphide) and alcohol. *Acta Pharmacol. Toxicol.* 4:305 (1948).

acid in the pathway ethanol → acetaldehyde → acetic acid. Blood levels of ethanol are the same in controls and in disulfiram-treated subjects after ingestion of ethanol, but blood acetaldehyde levels are much higher in the treated group. This accumulation of acetaldehyde and the consequent physiologic disturbances are shown for a single human subject in Fig. 3-14. The upper part of the figure shows the results of ingesting a moderate dose of ethanol. The blood alcohol concentration rose to about $400\mu g/ml$ in an hour, and the acetaldehyde level to a little over $3\mu g/ml$. The pulse, ventilation, and skin temperature remained nearly normal. On another occasion, the same dose of ethanol was given after ingestion of disulfiram (lower part of figure). The ethanol blood level curve is almost indistinguishable from the control, but the acetaldehyde concentration rose to more than twice its control level, to $7\mu g/ml$. Simultaneously, the respiratory minute volume increased, the pulse accelerated, and the skin temperature became higher.

Results like this suggested that the abnormal effects of ethyl alcohol in individuals treated with disulfiram might be due entirely to the excessive acetaldehyde levels. This surmise was confirmed when it was found that

FIG. 3-15. EFFECT OF DISULFIRAM ON RELATIONSHIP BETWEEN BLOOD ALCOHOL AND ACETALDEHYDE CONCENTRATIONS IN RABBITS. *Groups of rabbits were given ethanol after pretreatment with disulfiram, others were given same dose of alcohol without pretreatment. At 1 hour and again at 2 hours, blood ethanol and acetaldehyde levels were determined. Each point represents a single animal, solid circles at 1 hour, open circles at 2 hours. (From Hald et al., Fig. 3.[93])*

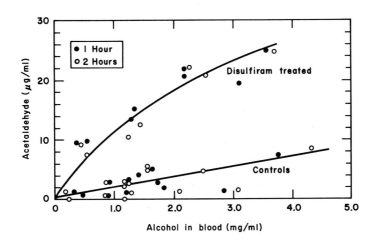

93 J. HALD, E. JACOBSEN, and V. LARSEN: Formation of acetaldehyde in the organism in relation to dosage of Antabuse (tetraethylthiuramdisulphide) and to alcohol concentration in blood. *Acta Pharmacol. Toxicol. 5:*179 (1949).

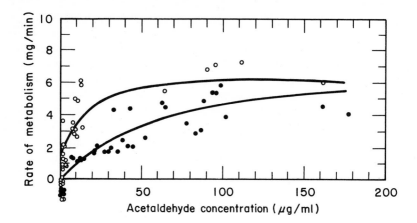

FIG. 3-16.   EFFECT OF DISULFIRAM UPON RATE OF ACETALDEHYDE METABOLISM.
Acetaldehyde was perfused through the livers of untreated rabbits (open circles)
and rabbits pretreated with disulfiram (solid circles). *Six treated and six untreated rabbits were used. Acetaldehyde concentration was measured in the
perfused blood, and rate of metabolism was simultaneously determined.* (*From
Hald et al., Fig. 1.[94]*)

the whole toxic syndrome could be reproduced in human volunteers by
the intravenous infusion of acetaldehyde, in the absence of disulfiram or
ethanol. The symptoms had their onset at blood acetaldehyde levels greater
than 2 to $4\mu g/ml$, as in Fig. 3-14.

Figure 3-15 shows, in rabbits, how the relationship between blood
ethanol concentration and blood acetaldehyde concentration is changed
by disulfiram. At any given concentration of ethanol, the corresponding
acetaldehyde level was increased severalfold by disulfiram.

Acetaldehyde itself can be metabolized just as rapidly by disulfiram-
treated livers as by normal livers, provided a high enough concentration of
acetaldehyde is present. At low concentrations of acetaldehyde, however,
the rate of metabolism is greatly depressed (Fig. 3-16). The finding of a
normal rate of metabolism of ethanol, a normal rate of metabolism of
acetaldehyde, but a higher steady-state level of acetaldehyde can all be explained on the basis of a competitive inhibition of aldehyde dehydrogenase:

$$CH_3CH_2OH \xrightleftharpoons[\text{dehydrogenase}]{\text{alcohol}} CH_3CHO \xrightarrow[\text{dehydrogenase}]{\text{aldehyde}} CH_3COOH$$

ethanol   acetaldehyde   acetic acid

[94] J. HALD, E. JACOBSEN, and V. LARSEN: The rate of acetaldehyde metabolism in
isolated livers and hind limbs of rabbits treated with Antabuse (tetraethylthiuramdisulphide).
Acta Pharmacol. Toxicol. 5:298 (1949).

The equilibrium of the alcohol dehydrogenase reaction lies far to the left, but the oxidation of ethanol proceeds nevertheless, because the acetaldehyde is continuously removed by the irreversible reaction mediated by aldehyde dehydrogenase. Now, if the aldehyde dehydrogenase is inhibited competitively by disulfiram, acetaldehyde accumulates. With increasing acetaldehyde concentration, the enzyme becomes more fully saturated, the inhibitor is displaced, and the reaction velocity increases. Eventually, a new steady state is reached, at which acetaldehyde is metabolized as fast as before. When this happens, the rate of ethanol metabolism will also be normal. The only difference is a much higher acetaldehyde level.

Monoamine Oxidase Inhibitors

Research on synthetic antibacterial agents led to the introduction of iproniazid, a hydrazide, for the chemotherapy of tuberculosis:

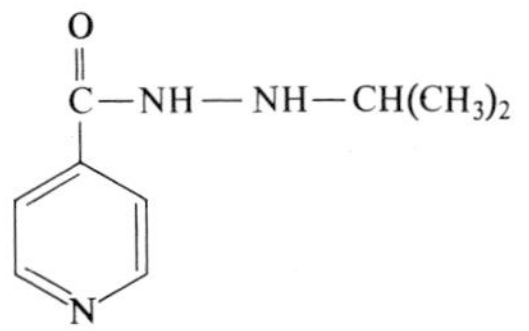

iproniazid

Unexpectedly, mood-elevating effects (euphoria) and other stimulatory actions on the central nervous system were seen. Iproniazid and related compounds were found to be MAO inhibitors. Since amines (e.g., norepinephrine, serotonin) are normally present in the brain, it was thought that inhibition of their metabolism might underlie the psychopharmacologic actions of these drugs. Related hydrazides were introduced for the treatment of severe depressions, for example, phenelzine and isocarboxazid:

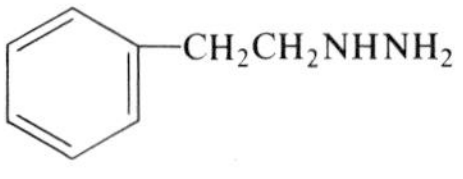

phenelzine 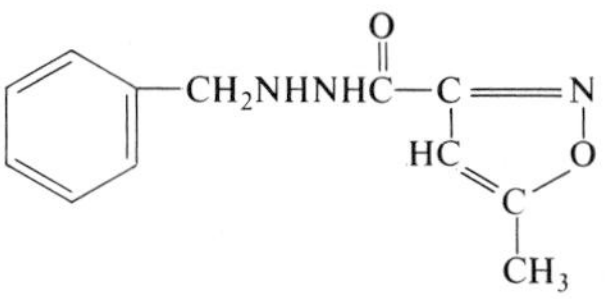   isocarboxazid

Several nonhydrazide inhibitors of MAO have also been developed, such as tranylcypromine and pargyline:

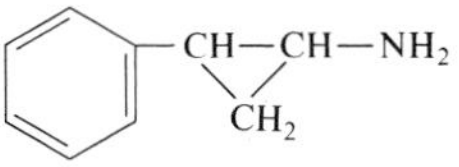

tranylcypromine 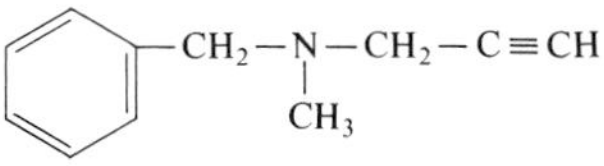   pargyline

All these MAO inhibitors act in vitro as well as in vivo. The administration of iproniazid (5×10^{-5} moles/kg) to rats resulted in complete inhibition of their liver mitochondrial MAO for 24 hours, and normal activity did not return for five days.[95] In vitro, the onset of the inhibition by iproniazid ($5 \times 10^{-5}M$) takes about 10 minutes. Tyramine, a substrate, can protect the enzyme and delay the development of inhibition; but once inhibition develops, it is practically irreversible.

The MAO inhibitors have complex pharmacologic actions, which are not thoroughly understood. They certainly cause elevations in the nor-epinephrine and serotonin levels in the central nervous system; but exactly how this action is related to their mood-elevating action is uncertain. They also may produce a variety of toxic effects, including hypotension, liver damage and jaundice, nausea, vomiting, constipation, dry mouth, and psychic disturbances (delusions, hallucinations). The hypotensive effect has been explored for possible therapeutic application.

The MAO inhibitors have little or no potentiating action upon the cardiovascular effects of the natural catecholamines, presumably because O-methylation and tissue uptake rather than oxidative deamination are primarily responsible for terminating their peripheral actions. However, MAO inhibitors do potentiate the cardiovascular effects of simple phenyl-ethylamines like tyramine. For example, patients receiving tranylcypromine, who also took drugs of the phenylethylamine class, showed exaggerated hypertensive effects, including fatal cerebral hemorrhages.[96-98] Even foods can become dangerous in the presence of MAO inhibitors. A remarkable incident of cheese toxicity[99, 100] that came to light a few years ago highlights the unexpected dangers that may be associated with any new drug. Some cheeses (Camembert, Brie, Stilton, New York Cheddar) are rich in tyramine. Ordinarily harmless because it is oxidized so rapidly by MAO, tyramine was markedly toxic in patients who had received tranylcypromine. Hypertensive crises occurred, and in a few instances, fatal cerebral hemorrhage. Consequently, tranylcypromine was removed from the market by the Food and Drug Administration, but eventually was admitted to use again provided appropriate warnings were included on the label and in the promotional literature.

[95] E. A. ZELLER, J. BARSKY, and E. R. BERMAN: Amine oxidases. XI. Inhibition of monoamine oxidase by 1-isonicotinyl-2-isopropylhydrazine. *J. Biol. Chem.* 214:267 (1955).

[96] L. I. GOLDBERG: Monoamine oxidase inhibitors. Adverse reactions and possible mechanisms. *J. Amer. Med. Ass.* 190:456 (1964).

[97] A. MASON: Fatal reaction associated with tranylcypromine and methylampheta-mine. *Lancet* 1:1073 (1962).

[98] There is no doubt that the toxicity of amphetamine is greatly increased by MAO inhibitors, but the reason is not entirely clear, inasmuch as amphetamine does not serve as a substrate for MAO.

[99] A. M. ASATOOR, A. J. LEVI, and M. O. MILNE: Tranylcypromine and cheese. *Lancet* 2:733 (1963).

[100] B. BLACKWELL: Tranylcypromine. *Lancet* 2:414 (1963).

STIMULATION AND DEPRESSION OF DRUG METABOLISM

A number of drugs cause an increase in the activity of the liver microsomal drug-metabolizing enzymes of treated animals.[101] Among these drugs, phenobarbital, the carcinogenic hydrocarbon 3,4-benzpyrene, and the steroid hormones have been studied most thoroughly. Typically, the activities toward different substrates are differentially stimulated; thus, phenobarbital and 3,4-benzpyrene each have their own typical spectrum of stimulation. Figure 3-17 shows the characteristic response to benzpyrene in rats. The animals were treated with benzpyrene at two different doses, and then the benzpyrene hydroxylase activity of their livers was tested in vitro at intervals for six days. At the higher dose a sevenfold stimulation was seen, with a half-time of about 6 hours. At six days (144 hours), the stimulation caused by both doses had subsided. Similar results were obtained with another carcinogen, 3-methylcholanthrene. Activity toward azo dyes (reduction and demethylation) was also stimulated by these hydrocarbons.

Stimulation of drug metabolism may produce a state of apparent drug tolerance. For example, rabbits pretreated with pentobarbital for three

FIG. 3-17. STIMULATION OF BENZPYRENE-METABOLIZING ACTIVITY OF RAT LIVER BY ADMINISTRATION OF BENZPYRENE. *Weanling rats were given a single intraperitoneal injection of benzpyrene at the doses indicated. Animals were sacrificed periodically, and benzpyrene-metabolizing activity of liver samples was measured for a 12-minute period. Each point is the average from two rats. (From Conney et al., Fig. 1.[102])*

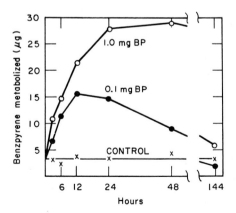

101 A. H. CONNEY and J. J. BURNS: Factors influencing drug metabolism. *Advance. Pharmacol.* 1:31 (1962).

102 A. H. CONNEY, E. C. MILLER, and J. A. MILLER: Substrate-induced synthesis and other properties of benzpyrene hydroxylase in rat liver. *J. Biol. Chem.* 228:753 (1957).

days slept a much shorter time after an intravenous test dose than did controls (Table 3-7). Inasmuch as the blood concentrations of pentobarbital were about the same in both groups at the moment of awakening, all the effect is accounted for by an increased rate of metabolism; there was no significant change in the animals' sensitivities to given drug concentrations.

An abundance of evidence indicates that the stimulation of activity of microsomal enzymes involves new protein synthesis. The stimulating agents are without effect in vitro; animals have to be pretreated, and a period of time has to elapse that corresponds to known rates of protein synthesis. Phenobarbital, which stimulates a great many enzyme activities, produces a detectable increase in the amount of microsomal protein per gram of liver; but 3-methylcholanthrene, which stimulates fewer enzymes, does not. Electron micrographs show[104] that after phenobarbital treatment there is an increase in the amount of smooth endoplasmic reticulum in liver cells, and it will be recalled that the microsomal drug-metabolizing enzymes are associated with this structure. It has also been found that the kinetic properties (substrate affinities, etc.) of the various drug-metabolizing enzymes after phenobarbital stimulation are indistinguishable from those of control enzymes.[90] The amino acid antimetabolite, ethionine, blocks the stimulatory response to phenobarbital; and methionine, which is known to reverse the ethionine blockade of protein synthesis, also pre-

TABLE 3-7.   Effect of pentobarbital pretreatment on duration of pentobarbital action

Rabbits were pretreated with three daily doses of pentobarbital (60 mg/kg) subcutaneously, then given a single challenging dose of 30 mg/kg intravenously. Sleeping times and pentobarbital levels in plasma were measured. (Data of Remmer,[103] Table I.)

Pretreatment	Sleeping time (min)	Plasma level of pentobarbital on awakening (mg/ml)	Pentobarbital half-life in plasma (min)
None	67 ± 4	9.9 ± 1.4	79 ± 3
Pentobarbital	30 ± 7	7.9 ± 0.6	26 ± 2

103 H. REMMER: "Drugs as Activators of Drug Enzymes," in *Metabolic Factors Controlling Duration of Drug Action,* Proceedings of First International Pharmacological Meeting, vol. 6, ed. by B. B. Brodie and E. G. Erdös. New York, Macmillan Co., 1962, p. 235.

104 H. REMMER and H.-J. MERKER: Enzyminduktion und Vermehrung von endoplasmatischem Reticulum in der Leberzelle während der Behandlung mit Phenobarbital (Luminal). *Klin. Wochensch. 41:*276 (1963).

vents the ethionine effect here.[105] Puromycin and actinomycin block protein synthesis more directly than ethionine; puromycin blocks at the ribosome level (translation), actinomycin at the DNA-dependent RNA polymerase reaction (transcription). Both these agents prevent the stimulation of benzpyrene hydroxylase activity in rat liver (Fig. 3-18).

It has been reported that nuclear RNA synthesis is enhanced in the livers of rats treated with 3-methylcholanthrene, and it has been demonstrated that the newly formed RNA is active in promoting protein synthesis in a cell-free *Escherichia coli* system that is dependent upon messenger-RNA for amino acid incorporation into polypeptides.[107, 108]

FIG. 3-18.   ANTAGONISM OF THE STIMULATORY EFFECT OF METHYLCHOLAN-THRENE ON BENZPYRENE HYDROXYLASE BY ACTINOMYCIN AND PUROMYCIN.   C, *Control rats;* M, *methylcholanthrene-injected rats;* A, *actinomycin administered repeatedly throughout the experiment, beginning 2 hours before methylcholanthrene injection;* P, *puromycin, administered on about the same schedule as actinomycin. Rats were killed at 10 hours and livers were assayed in vitro for ability to hydroxylate benzpyrene. Standard errors are shown by the* vertical lines with cross bars. (*Data of Gelboin and Blackburn, chart 2.*[106])

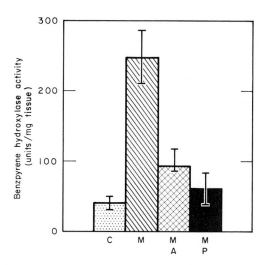

[105] A. H. CONNEY, C. DAVISON, R. GASTEL, and J. J. BURNS: Adaptive increases in drug-metabolizing enzymes induced by phenobarbital and other drugs. *J. Pharmacol. Exp. Therap. 130:*1 (1960).

[106] H. V. GELBOIN and N. R. BLACKBURN: The stimulatory effect of 3-methylcholanthrene on benzpyrene hydroxylase activity in several rat tissues: inhibition by actinomycin D and puromycin. *Cancer Res. 24:*356 (1964).

[107] L. A. LOEB and H. V. GELBOIN: Stimulation of amino-acid incorporation by nuclear ribonucleic acid from normal and methylcholanthrene-treated rats. *Nature 199:* 809 (1963).

[108] L. A. LOEB and H. V. GELBOIN: Methylcholanthrene-induced changes in rat liver nuclear RNA. *Proc. Nat. Acad. Sci. U.S.A. 52:*1219 (1964).

It has become clear[109] that the stimulation produced by phenobarbital is quite specific for the essential components of the microsomal
drug-oxidizing system, namely, the NADPH-cytochrome c reductase and
the CO-binding pigment P-450 (cf. p. 221). Figure 3-19 shows a remarkable parallelism in the time course of stimulation of demethylating activity
in rat liver with repeated injections of phenobarbital, and the increase in
the amounts of these two components. There was also a slight increase in
total microsomal protein in liver, but no change whatsoever in a number
of unrelated enzymes.

There has been a great deal of confusion about just what is proved
by the fact that stimulation of an enzyme activity requires concomitant
protein synthesis. The initial, unstimulated level of microsomal enzyme activity has to be regarded as a steady state, determined by balanced rates of
synthesis and degradation. The stimulation represents a change in this
steady state, but it could be brought about equally well by an increased rate
of synthesis or a decreased rate of degradation, or both. Some instances of
"enzyme induction" (for example, the stimulation of tryptophan pyrrolase
activity by tryptophan) can be attributed to the stabilization of enzyme by
its substrate; stimulation of the same enzyme activity by steroids is appar-

FIG. 3-19.   EFFECT OF PHENOBARBITAL ON ACTIVITIES OF VARIOUS MICROSOMAL
ENZYMES IN THE RAT.   *Rats were injected intraperitoneally with phenobarbital
(100 mg/kg) once daily as shown by* arrows. *Various enzyme activities of liver
were measured.* a, *Demethylation of aminopyrine;* b, *amount of the CO-binding
pigment (P-450);* c, *NADPH-cytochrome c reductase;* d, *amount of liver microsomal protein;* e, *inosine diphosphatase;* f, *NADH-cytochrome c reductase;* g,
amount of cytochrome b_5; h, *glucose-6-phosphatase;* i, *ATPase. Protein content
is per gram liver, other data are calculated per mg of protein.* (*From Orrenius
and Ernster, Fig. 1.*[109])

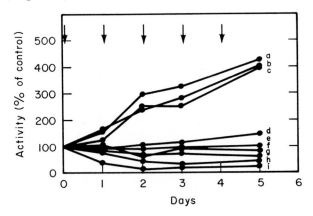

[109] S. ORRENIUS and L. ERNSTER: Phenobarbital-induced synthesis of the oxidative
demethylating enzymes of rat liver microsomes. *Biochem. Biophys. Res. Commun. 16:*60
(1964).

ently a true induction.[110] Suppose the drug-induced enhancement of an enzyme activity is prevented by treatments (ethionine, puromycin) that block protein synthesis. It may be concluded that the drug-induced stimulation did not represent direct activation of an already-formed enzyme. But no conclusion can be drawn as to whether the drug caused an increased rate of enzyme synthesis or a decreased rate of enzyme degradation; no matter which of these two mechanisms is responsible for the shift of a steady state, continued protein synthesis would be required for its manifestation. Judicious use of actinomycin may yield more decisive information about mechanism. This drug should block stimulation that depends upon the synthesis of new messenger-RNA. Provided that existing messenger-RNA continues to function, actinomycin ought not to block stimulation due to enzyme stabilization.

Although alternatives are not ruled out completely, it seems likely that the stimulatory agents act directly on the liver to induce new enzyme synthesis. Pituitary and adrenal hormones are known to increase rates of protein synthesis in various tissues, so the possibility had to be entertained that the drug-induced stimulation was mediated indirectly by a hormonal mechanism. This was ruled out by showing that the stimulatory effects can be obtained in both adrenalectomized and hypophysectomized animals.

Depression of the microsomal drug-metabolizing system can also be produced, chiefly by procedures that have a deleterious effect on liver function. This may account for the clinical impression that drugs are liable to have enhanced or prolonged effects in patients with liver abnormalities. Starvation has prominent effects. Table 3-8 gives the results of an experiment in which mice were starved for 36 hours and then tested for their response to a standard dose of hexobarbital. The livers of these animals were homogenized, and microsomal enzyme activities were determined. All the mice were classified into groups according to how long they had slept. The animals that slept the longest oxidized hexobarbital and certain other drugs more slowly than controls; however, nitro and azo reductions were unaffected or increased. Besides starvation and parenchymal liver damage, other conditions that impair microsomal drug-metabolizing activity are obstructive jaundice, liver tumors, and alloxan diabetes.

If the drug-metabolizing system is depressed, excessive responses or prolonged responses may occur to ordinary doses of drugs. On the other hand, should a suitable maintenance dose be instituted under these abnormal conditions, it might prove inadequate later on when the rate of drug metabolism increases to normal. Or conversely, a patient using barbiturate sedatives regularly is likely to have an unusually high activity of the drug-metabolizing enzymes, as discussed already; if another drug is

[110] R. T. SCHIMKE, E. W. SWEENEY, and C. M. BERLIN: An analysis of the kinetics of rat liver tryptophan pyrrolase induction: The significance of both enzyme synthesis and degradation. *Biochem. Biophys. Res. Commun. 15:*214 (1964).

TABLE 3-8.   Effects of starvation on drug metabolism by mouse liver microsomes

> Mice were starved for 36 hours, then given hexobarbital (80 mg/kg) intraperitoneally. Normal animals usually slept less than 10 minutes, but sleeping time varied greatly in starved mice. Twelve hours later (48 hours starvation) the mice were sacrificed and the liver microsomes were tested for their drug-metabolizing ability. Figures represent drug metabolized in a fixed incubation time. (From Dixon et al.,[111] Table I.)

Substrate	Drug metabolized (μmoles/g liver)		
	Normal mice	Starved mice	
	Sleeping time 5–15 min	Sleeping time 20–40 min	Sleeping time > 80 min
Hexobarbital (aliphatic oxidation)	4.46	2.79	0.77
Chlorpromazine (sulfur oxidation)	2.80	1.98	1.19
Aminopyrine (N-dealkylation)	1.48	1.11	0.46
Acetanilid (aromatic hydroxylation)	2.03	2.22	0.93
p-Nitrobenzoic acid (nitro reduction)	8.22	17.03	8.43
Neoprontosil (azo reduction)	15.55	17.65	12.59

given simultaneously, at customary dosages, it may prove wholly ineffective. If an appropriately higher dosage of the second drug is established for this patient, the drug levels may become excessive later on, should the barbiturate be discontinued. Figure 3-20 illustrates effects of this sort in a human subject. The patient was on a maintenance dosage of 75 mg daily of the anticoagulant drug bishydroxycoumarin. Plasma levels of the drug were followed, as well as prothrombin time, a measure of the drug effect in delaying blood clotting. During periods of regular phenobarbital administration the plasma level of bisydroxycoumarin fell, and the therapeutic action of the drug was significantly diminished. This illustration points up dramatically how drugs may interact. It has not been established, however, that increased metabolism of bishydroxycoumarin is responsible.

For drugs whose effectiveness or toxicity is enhanced by a metabolic transformation, other drugs that stimulate the rate of metabolism will cause an increase in potency and toxicity. This has been demonstrated experimentally with the organic thiophosphate insecticide guthion (dimethoxybenzotriazine dithiophosphoric acid ester). This compound depends for its activity as a cholinesterase inhibitor upon its oxidative desulfuration at a

111 R. L. DIXON, R. W. SHULTICE, and J. R. FOUTS: Factors affecting drug metabolism by liver microsomes. IV. Starvation. *Proc. Soc. Exp. Biol. Med.* *103*:333 (1960)

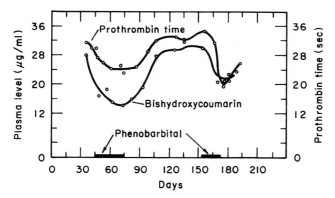

FIG. 3-20. EFFECT OF PHENOBARBITAL ON PLASMA LEVELS OF BISHYDROXY-COUMARIN. *A human subject was treated with bishydroxycoumarin (75 mg daily). Drug plasma levels and prothrombin times were determined periodically. Phenobarbital was administered (65 mg once daily) during periods indicated by heavy marks on abscissal axis. (From Cucinell et al., Fig. 3.*[112] *By permission of C. V. Mosby.)*

microsomal site (cf. p. 228). Pretreatment of rats with benzpyrene or methylcholanthrene substantially increased the rate of that conversion; consequently, a given dose of guthion caused greater inhibition of brain and salivary gland cholinesterase. The median lethal dose of guthion was lowered by about half (i.e., the toxicity was doubled) in pretreated animals.[113] The same investigation revealed that pretreating the animals with SKF525A, the inhibitor of the drug-metabolizing microsomal system, resulted in a lower toxicity of guthion.

These findings dictate great caution in multiple drug therapy of any kind.[114] And since many commercial drug preparations include more than a single drug, real problems may be encountered frequently. Amphetamine, for example, is sometimes used for diet control because it depresses the appetite. Some proprietary appetite control formulations include a barbiturate in the same capsule with amphetamine, supposedly to counteract excessive central excitation. The barbiturate may also be expected to stimulate drug metabolism and thus enhance the destruction of the amphetamine. So perhaps the same end result could have been achieved with a lower dose of amphetamine and no barbiturate at all! Another problem of consequence, but not yet sufficiently investigated, is the possible influence of

112 S. A. CUCINELL, A. H. CONNEY, M. SANSUR, and J. J. BURNS: Drug interactions in man. I. Lowering effect of phenobarbital on plasma levels of bishydroxycoumarin (Dicumarol) and diphenylhydantoin (Dilantin). *Clin. Pharmacol. Therap.* 6:420 (1965).

113 S. D. MURPHY and K. P. DU BOIS: The influence of various factors on the enzymatic conversion of organic thiophosphates to anticholinesterase agents. *J. Pharmacol. Exp. Therap.* 124:194 (1958).

114 J. J. BURNS, S. A. CUCINELL, R. KOSTER, and A. H. CONNEY: Application of drug metabolism to drug toxicity studies. *Ann. N.Y. Acad. Sci.* 123:273 (1965).

drugs upon the metabolism of endogenous steroid hormones. There is real cause for concern about this because these physiologically important substances are evidently metabolized by the microsomal drug-oxidizing system.

On the other hand, it may prove possible to exploit the stimulatory effect of phenobarbital on drug metabolism for a therapeutic purpose. For example, genetic disorders of glucuronide formation occur in man, much as in the Gunn rat mentioned previously; afflicted individuals, because of their impaired ability to conjugate bilirubin, have elevated bilirubin blood levels and appear jaundiced. Administration of nonsedative doses of phenobarbital on a chronic basis may be able to enhance the low glucuronide transferase levels and thus alleviate the hyperbilirubinemia and jaundice.[115]

SPECIES DIFFERENCES AND GENETIC VARIATION IN DRUG METABOLISM

Investigations into the phylogenetic aspects of drug metabolism[1] suggest that drug-metabolizing systems may have developed in response to the special needs of terrestrial life. In fish, lipid-soluble compounds can pass readily across the gills into the aquatic environment; and fish (with some exceptions) lack oxidative drug-metabolizing enzymes, neither can they form glucuronides or sulfuric acid esters. Aquatic amphibia are also unable to oxidize foreign compounds, but they can form glucuronides and sulfuric acid esters. Reptiles, birds, and mammals have the necessary enzymic machinery for increasing the polarity of lipid-soluble compounds and thus achieving their more rapid excretion (cf. p. 194). Insects have enzymes with analogous function but different in many ways from those of the vertebrates.

Azo and nitro reductase enzymes have a somewhat different distribution through the phylogenetic series than the microsomal oxidative enzymes. They (like the oxidative enzymes) are present in land-dwelling reptiles, birds, and mammals. Unlike the oxidative enzymes, they are also found in teleost fish. Amphibia and elasmobranch fishes have the azo reductase activity alone.[116]

Among the mammals there are wide differences in drug metabolism by different species, but no rationale for these differences is apparent. Rates of metabolism may differ, even when the pathways are the same, and different species may also have entirely different metabolic pathways for dealing with the same drug. An example of variation in metabolic rate is afforded by a study of a bromocyclohexenyl derivative of barbituric acid. This com-

[115] S. J. YAFFE, G. LEVY, T. MATSUZAWA, and T. BALIAH: Enhancement of glucuronide-conjugating capacity in a hyperbilirubinemic infant due to apparent enzyme induction by phenobarbital. *New Eng. J. Med.* 275:1461 (1966).

[116] R. H. ADAMSON, R. L. DIXON, F. L. FRANCIS, and D. P. RALL: Comparative biochemistry of drug metabolism by azo and nitro reductase. *Proc. Nat. Acad. Sci. U.S.A.* 54:1386 (1965).

TABLE 3-9. **Species differences in metabolism of hexobarbital**

Dose of barbiturate 100 mg/kg (50 mg/kg in dogs). Figures in parentheses refer to number of animals in each species. Data are given ± standard deviation. The half-life in man is a crude estimate. (Data of Quinn et al.,[118] Table 2.)

	Sleeping time (min)	Hexobarbital half-life (min)	Enzyme Activity (μg/g·hr)
Mice (12)	12 ± 8	19 ± 7	598 ± 184
Rabbits (9)	49 ± 12	60 ± 11	196 ± 28
Rats (10)	90 ± 15	140 ± 54	134 ± 51
Dogs (8)	315 ± 105	260 ± 20	36 ± 30
Man	—	360 (approx.)	—

pound was originally synthesized in an attempt to obtain a barbiturate that would be rapidly metabolized in man. Testing was carried out in dogs, with very promising results, but it turned out that in man the compound was metabolized very slowly (Fig. 3-21). This experiment illustrates a major pitfall in the use of animal screening programs for drug development. The compound selected on the basis of animal screening turned out to be useless

FIG. 3-21. METABOLISM OF A BARBITURATE DERIVATIVE IN DOG AND MAN. *5-Allyl-5-(2-bromo-2-cyclohexenyl)-2-barbituric acid (15 mg/kg) was administered intravenously at time zero. Plasma concentrations were measured periodically, as shown, and plotted on a logarithmic scale. (From Burns, Fig. 4.[117])*

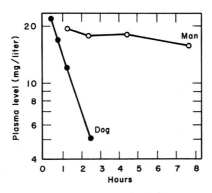

[117] J. J. BURNS: "Species differences and individual variations in drug metabolism," in *Metabolic Factors Controlling Duration of Drug Action,* Proceedings of First International Pharmacological Meeting, vol. 6, ed. by B. B. Brodie and E. G. Erdös. New York, Macmillan Co., 1962, p. 277.

[118] G. P. QUINN, J. AXELROD, and B. B. BRODIE: Species, strain and sex differences in metabolism of hexobarbitone, amidopyrine, antipyrine, and aniline. *Biochem. Pharmacol. 1:*152 (1958).

in man. One wonders how many compounds have been discarded because of results in the dog, which would have been satisfactory in the human. The antirheumatic agent phenylbutazone presents another example. Its biologic half-life is only 3 hours in the rabbit, and less than 6 hours in the rat, guinea pig, and dog, yet in man its half-life is three days.

The metabolism of hexobarbital was shown to be responsible for species differences in its duration of action (Table 3-9). Determinations of plasma levels at various times following intravenous administration of the compound permitted estimation of the biologic half-life in each species. There was a direct relationship between duration of action (sleeping time) and biologic half-life. In addition, the in vitro activity of microsomes prepared from livers of these animals correlated well with the drug metabolism rate in vivo. Thus, mice, with the shortest sleeping time and shortest barbiturate half-life, had the highest liver microsomal enzyme activity. Presumably these species all metabolized hexobarbital by aliphatic side chain oxidation, although direct proof of this is lacking.

The sympathomimetic amine L-ephedrine can be metabolized by N-demethylation, aromatic hydroxylation, and conjugation:

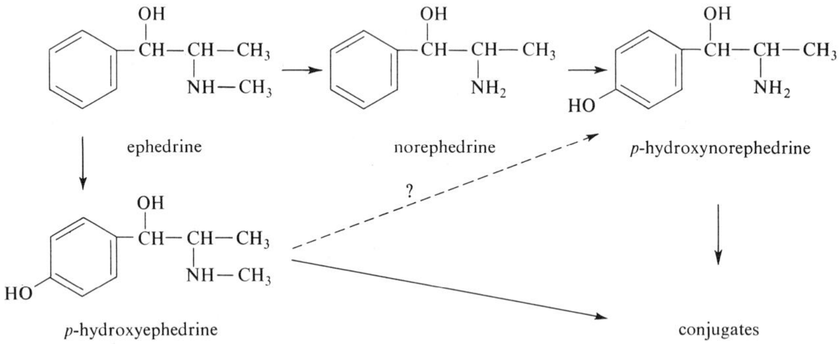

Table 3-10 shows that, in the dog, most of an administered dose of ephedrine appeared in the urine as norephedrine, a potent sympathomimetic agent in its own right. When norephedrine itself was given to dogs, 72 per cent of it was excreted unchanged. Thus, in the dog, the major route of metabolism is by N-demethylation. The guinea pig resembled the dog in this respect, but the rat excreted ephedrine largely unchanged and as hydroxylated derivatives. The rabbit, on the other hand, degraded these compounds still further, since none of the metabolites appeared in significant quantity in rabbit urine after ephedrine administration. When p-hydroxyephedrine was given, about 65 per cent of it was excreted in the urine; but when norephedrine was given, only 3 per cent of it was excreted. These results suggest that ephedrine is demethylated in the rabbit to norephedrine, which is then further metabolized to products not yet

TABLE 3-10.   Fate of ephedrine in several species

Each animal received L-ephedrine (50 mg/kg) intraperitoneally. Urine was collected over a period of 24 hours. Figures in parentheses refer to number of animals in each species. (Data of Axelrod,[119] Table IV.)

	Per cent of administered dose accounted for as:		
	Ephedrine (%)	Norephedrine (%)	Total hydroxyephedrine and hydroxynorephedrine (%)
Dog (5)	6.5	57.8	1.5
Guinea pig (3)	2.0	38.5	0.9
Rat (4)	32.0	7.5	12.8
Rabbit (4)	0.1	1.8	1.9

identified. The further metabolism does not, apparently, involve hydroxylation of the benzene ring, for in that case, the hydroxylated derivatives would have appeared in the urine. Available data for the metabolism of ephedrine in man suggest that in this species the drug is excreted almost entirely unchanged.[120]

Ethylbiscoumacetate, an anticoagulant drug, is metabolized rapidly (about 20 per cent per hour) in both man and rabbit. Man metabolizes it by ring hydroxylation, the rabbit by hydrolysis of the ester group to form an inactive free acid. The dog, on the other hand, metabolizes the compound more slowly, about 3 per cent per hour.[121] In a screening program seeking a short-acting coumarin derivative, ethylbiscoumacetate would have been discarded on the basis of studies in dogs; but it would have been chosen on the basis of its behavior in the rabbit.

There are some indications that in cats glucuronide conjugation is relatively less important than in other species. For example, when the carcinogen N-2-fluorenylacetamide was administered to cats, only 3 per cent of the dose was excreted as glucuronides, whereas guinea pigs eliminated 60 to 80 per cent in this form.[122]

The problems posed by species variation for the development and screening of new drugs are considerable. Obviously, potentially dangerous

119 J. AXELROD: Studies on sympathomimetic amines. I. The biotransformation and physiological disposition of *l*-ephedrine and *l*-norephedrine. *J. Pharmacol. Exp. Therap.* *109:*62 (1953).

120 D. RICHTER: Elimination of amines in man. *Biochem. J. 32:*1763 (1938).

121 J. J. BURNS, M. WEINER, G. SIMSON, and B. B. BRODIE: The biotransformation of ethyl biscoumacetate (Tromexan) in man, rabbit and dog. *J. Pharmacol. Exp. Therap.* *108:*33 (1953).

122 J. H. WEISBURGER, P. H. GRANTHAM, and E. K. WEISBURGER: The metabolism of N-2-fluorenylacetamide in the cat: evidence for glucuronic acid conjugates. *Biochem. Pharmacol. 13:*469 (1964).

compounds cannot be screened in man. One alternative would be to find and utilize an experimental animal that resembles man closely in its handling of all foreign compounds; although no such ideal animal has yet been found, primates are probably most suitable.

Since drug metabolism is mediated by specific enzymes, genetic variations might be expected to occur among individuals of a species. Table 3-11 illustrates pronounced strain differences in the oxidative metabolism of one drug in mice. The data are sleeping times after a single dose of hexobarbital, but it is well known that in mice the duration of action of this drug is determined by the rate of its oxidation. Besides the highly significant differences between strains, another point is evident. The one strain that was not inbred had a much greater variability between animals (as measured by the standard deviation) than did the inbred strains. This is just what one would expect for a trait under genetic control.

Sex differences in rates of drug metabolism are seen prominently in rats. Females sleep considerably longer than males after a given dose of hexobarbital, and they metabolize the drug more slowly. The male-female difference in the rat is seen readily with in vitro systems as well as in vivo. Females pretreated with testosterone show an increase in drug-metabolizing activity, and males pretreated with estradiol show a decrease. Similar differences between male and female rats have been demonstrated for N-demethylation of morphine congeners by microsome preparations in vitro. Curiously, sex differences in the rates of drug metabolism have not been observed in species other than the rat.

TABLE 3-11. **Strain differences in duration of action of hexobarbital in mice**

Male mice, 70 to 80 days old, given hexobarbital (125 mg/kg) intraperitoneally. Figures in parentheses are number of mice in each strain. (Data of Jay,[123] Table 1.)

Strain	Mean sleeping time ± standard deviation (min)
A/LN (25)	48 ± 4
BALB/cAnN (63)	41 ± 2
C57L/HeN (29)	33 ± 3
C3HfB/HeN (30)	22 ± 3
SWR/HeN (38)	18 ± 4
Swiss (non-inbred) (47)	43 ± 15

[123] G. E. JAY, JR.: Variation in response of various mouse strains to hexobarbital (Evipal). *Proc. Soc. Exp. Biol. Med.* 90:378 (1955).

Another good example of genetically determined variation in drug metabolism occurs in rabbits. Certain individuals of this species have an unusual plasma esterase that is capable of hydrolyzing the plant ester alkaloid atropine.[124] Atropine esterase activity has not been found in the plasma of any other species. In rabbits, the gene that controls production of this enzyme is autosomal and autonomous. Thus, each representation of the gene in the diploid organism appears to be expressed independently, so that animals homozygous for the trait have about twice as much enzyme activity as heterozygotes. However, gene expression is delayed; atropine esterase does not appear in the blood of rabbits that have the trait until they are one to two months old. The absence of the enzyme appears to be absolute in animals that lack the trait.[125] There is no immunologically related protein in their blood plasma; and such animals can even be sensitized to purified atropine esterase, further confirming the prior absence of any protein with similar antigenic properties.

In man, few instances of genetic variation in drug metabolism have yet come to light. One that is particularly well documented, the atypical plasma cholinesterase, will be discussed in connection with drug idiosyncrasies in another chapter (p. 434). Here, we shall consider the individual variation in the rate of metabolism of isoniazid (isonicotinic acid hydrazide), a drug used in the chemotherapy of tuberculosis. Isoniazid is metabolized by N-acetylation and, to a lesser extent, by hydrolysis:

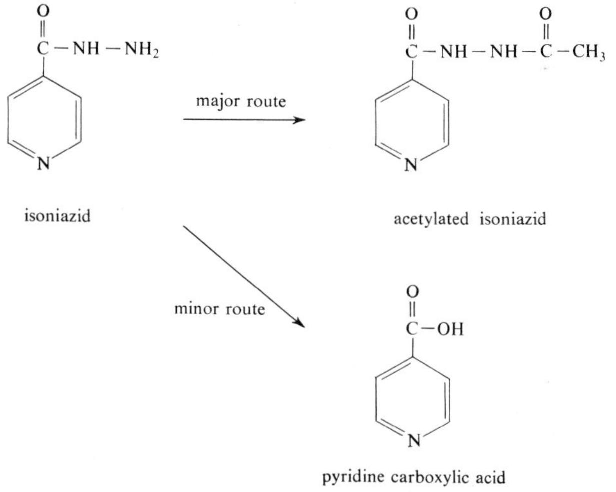

isoniazid acetylated isoniazid

minor route

pyridine carboxylic acid

124 P. B. SAWIN and D. GLICK: Atropinesterase, a genetically determined enzyme in the rabbit. *Proc. Nat. Acad. Sci.* 29:55 (1943).

125 F. MARGOLIS and P. FEIGELSON: Genetic expression and developmental studies with rabbit serum atropinesterase. *Biochim. Biophys. Acta* 90:117 (1964).

When blood concentrations of isoniazid were measured 6 hours after a standard dose in a large number of subjects, a bimodal distribution was found. Some people metabolized this drug very slowly, some rapidly. In a sample of 291 unrelated people, 52.2 per cent metabolized the drug slowly. Age, sex, and race seemed to have no influence. Preliminary familial data suggested that the trait, slow metabolism, was recessive.

In the following analysis we shall designate the allelic genes controlling the metabolism rate as *slow* and *rapid,* the phenotypes as SLOW and RAPID. The hypothesis that a recessive allele was responsible for the slow metabolism of isoniazid could be tested by examining the offspring of a large number of matings. If a recessive trait is expressed phenotypically in fraction q of the population, then the frequency of the recessive allele is $\sqrt{q}$, since the phenotype arises only from matings of q × q, which occur randomly with a probability of q^2.[126] Thus, the allele frequencies here are $\sqrt{0.522} = 0.723$ for the recessive *slow,* and therefore 0.277 for the dominant *rapid.*

Matings of phenotypes SLOW × SLOW should give only SLOW offspring, since *slow-slow* is the only genotype represented.

Matings of phenotypes RAPID × RAPID are more complicated. We have first to know the frequencies of all three possible genotypes, *slow-slow, slow-rapid* (or *rapid-slow*), and *rapid-rapid:*

slow-slow	$(0.723)^2 = 0.522$	[phenotype SLOW]
slow-rapid	$2(0.723 \times 0.277) = 0.401$ ⎫	
rapid-rapid	$(0.277)^2 = 0.077$ ⎭	[phenotype RAPID]
	$\overline{1.000}$	

Now, the sum of the genotype frequencies that make up the phenotype population RAPID is 0.478; therefore the frequency of the genotype *slow-rapid* in this population is $0.401/0.478 = 0.839$. In mating of RAPID × RAPID, the phenotype SLOW (genotype *slow-slow*) can only arise by *slow-rapid* × *slow-rapid,* which will occur with probability $(0.839)^2$, and one-fourth of these matings will yield *slow-slow:*

$$slow\text{-}slow \quad (0.839)^2/4 = 0.174$$

Thus, the phenotypic expectations for matings of the kind RAPID × RAPID are:

SLOW	17.4%
RAPID	82.6%

The expectations for matings of the kind RAPID × SLOW are readily computed in the same way.

126 A full discussion of the Hardy-Weinberg law and balanced polymorphism may be found in C. Stern, *Principles of Human Genetics,* 2nd ed. San Francisco, W. H. Freeman & Co., 1960.

Table 3-12 shows the results of such studies on parents and children. The data reveal a remarkably good agreement between observed and expected outcomes in each category, in confirmation of the hypothesis that slow metabolism of isoniazid is an autosomal recessive trait.

The enzyme responsible for the polymorphism of isoniazid inactivation has been shown, with human liver homogenates, to be an acetyl transferase, using coenzyme A. Sulfamethazine and hydralazine are acetylated by the same enzyme and are therefore subject to the same genetic variation. However, sulfanilamide and *p*-aminobenzoic acid, which appear in human urine in acetylated form, did not show polymorphism, nor were they acetylated by human liver homogenates.[128] Presumably a different enzyme is responsible for the acetylation of these drugs.

The rate of metabolism of the anticoagulant bishydroxycoumarin shows a high degree of individual variation in man.[129] In one subject the plasma level declined at a rate of only 15 per cent per day, while in another the decline was over 90 per cent per day. Other subjects fell between these extremes. There did not seem to be any relationship between these rates and liver disease or age. The half-life of the drug was constant in the same individual tested at different times. Studies in populations and families[130] failed to demonstrate discrete classes of bishydroxycoumarin half-lives. While other factors could well be involved (nutritional status, diet, disease, and so forth), the results are also consistent with a polygenic control. Thus, the numerous genotypes possible would yield a broad distribution of half-lives, rather than the sharp discontinuities seen with single-gene traits.

TABLE 3-12. **Rates of isoniazid metabolism in parents and children**

Numbers in the expected categories are computed on the basis of the hypothesis that slow metabolism of isoniazid is due to a recessive allele, as described in the text. (From Evans et al.,[127] Table X.)

Parental phenotypes	No. of matings	No. of children	No. of children of each phenotype			
			RAPID		SLOW	
			Expected	Observed	Expected	Observed
SLOW × SLOW	16	51	0	0	51	51
RAPID × SLOW	24	70	40.6	42	29.4	28
RAPID × RAPID	13	38	31.3	31	6.7	7
TOTALS	53	159		73		86

---

[127] D. A. P. EVANS, K. A. MANLEY, and V. A. MC KUSICK: Genetic control of isoniazid metabolism in man. *Brit. Med. J.* 2:485 (1960).

[128] D. A. P. EVANS and T. A. WHITE: Human acetylation polymorphism. *J. Lab. Clin. Med.* 63:394 (1964).

[129] M. WEINER, S. SHAPIRO, J. AXELROD, J. R. COOPER, and B. B. BRODIE: The physiological disposition of dicumarol in man. *J. Pharmacol. Exp. Therap.* 99:409 (1950).

[130] A. G. MOTULSKY: Pharmacogenetics. *Progress in Medical Genetics* 3:49 (1964).

EFFECTS OF AGE UPON DRUG METABOLISM

It has long been recognized that the young of humans and other animals may be more sensitive to drugs than are adults. Many enzyme systems change greatly in activity during early life. Figure 3-22 shows the fluctuations in activity of three liver enzymes concerned in amino acid metabolism in fetal and neonatal rats. The tyrosine transaminase had negligible activity before birth, but its activity increased very sharply at 2 hours after birth, reached twice the adult level at 16 hours, and then stabilized at the adult level with the next 12 hours. In contrast, the phenylalanine hydroxylase failed to appear until the second day of life, then increased slowly to adult levels at about eight days. The phenylalanine transaminase was more active in newborn than in adult liver, reached twice the adult level in a few days, and remained above the adult level until about 30 days. In the light of this and similar findings about the lability of enzyme levels in the newborn, attention was focused on the status of the drug-metabolizing enzymes in the neonatal period.

An investigation of the activity of glucuronyl transferase in the microsomes of guinea pig livers revealed some striking differences with age (Fig. 3-23). Enzyme activity for phenolphthalein conjugation was absent or very low in microsomes obtained from fetal or neonatal guinea pig liver. The activity increased markedly during the postnatal period. Similar results were obtained with other substrates, such as *o*-aminophenol and bilirubin.

FIG. 3-22. PATTERNS OF ENZYME ACTIVITY DURING DEVELOPMENT. *Changes in activity of phenylalanine transaminase, tyrosine transaminase, and phenylalanine hydroxylase in rat liver immediately before and after birth. Activity of each enzyme in the adult is assigned the value 1.0. (From Kretchmer, Fig. 5.[131])*

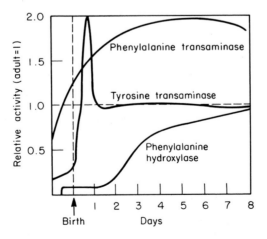

[131] N. KRETCHMER: Enzymatic patterns during development: an approach to a biochemical definition of immaturity. *Pediatrics 23:*606 (1959).

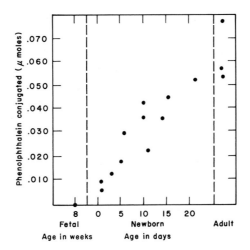

FIG. 3-23. PHENOLPHTHALEIN CONJUGATION BY FETAL, NEONATAL, AND ADULT GUINEA PIG LIVER. *A microsome fraction was prepared from 200 mg liver, UDP-glucuronic acid was added, with 0.15 μmoles of phenolphthalein, and the mixture incubated for 30 minutes at 37°. (From Brown and Zuelzer, Fig. 3.[132])*

These studies have been extended to other drug-metabolizing microsomal enzymes, all of which have been found to be absent, or present in negligible amounts, in early life. The following in vitro reactions have been shown not to occur in liver microsomal preparations obtained from one-day-old guinea pigs or rabbits:[133] N-demethylation (monomethyl-4-amino-antipyrine), O-dealkylation (phenacetin), side chain oxidation (hexobarbital), deamination (amphetamine), aromatic hydroxylation (acetanilid), sulfur oxidation (chlorpromazine), and nitro reduction (*p*-nitrobenzoic acid).[134]

In vivo studies support these conclusions. For example, when acetanilid was administered to newborn infants and to older children, and the plasma levels of N-acetyl-*p*-aminophenol and its glucuronide were measured, it became apparent that the oxidation and conjugation proceeded more slowly in the newborns.[135] Elevated blood bilirubin levels in the newborn (icterus neonatorum) result, in all likelihood, from deficiency of the enzymes responsible for the formation of bilirubin glucuronide.

132 A. K. BROWN and W. W. ZUELZER: Studies on the neonatal development of the glucuronide conjugating system. *J. Clin. Invest. 37:*332 (1958).

133 The drugs in parentheses were used as indicators for the presence or absence of detectable metabolic activity for each particular pathway.

134 J. R. FOUTS and R. H. ADAMSON: Drug metabolism in the newborn rabbit. *Science 129:*897 (1959).

135 M. F. VEST and R. R. STREIFF: Studies on glucuronide formation in newborn infants and older children. *J. Dis. Children 98:*688 (1959).

TABLE 3-13. **Effect of age on metabolism and duration of action of hexobarbital**

In vitro experiments were done with a guinea pig liver microsome system, appropriately fortified with cofactors. In vivo metabolism was measured by giving hexobarbital (1 mg) intraperitoneally to a mouse and then homogenizing the entire animal and determining the residual amount of unchanged drug. Sleeping times were measured in mice only. The number of experiments or animals used are shown in parentheses. (Data of Jondorf et al.,[136] Tables 1, 2, and 3.)

Age (days)	Hexobarbital metabolized in vitro in 1 hr by guinea pigs (%)	Hexobarbital metabolized in vivo in 3 hr by mice (%)	Sleeping time in mice (min)		
			10 mg/kg	50 mg/kg	100 mg/kg
1	0 (3)	0 (6)	> 360 (12)	Died (12)	Died (12)
7	2.5–3.5 (3)	11–24 (6)	107 ± 26 (12)	243 ± 30 (10)	> 360 (12)
21	13–21 (3)	21–33 (6)	27 ± 11 (11)	64 ± 17 (10)	94 ± 27 (12)
Adult	28–39 (5)		< 5 (12)	17 ± 5 (12)	47 ± 11 (12)

136 W. R. JONDORF, R. P. MAIKEL, and B. B. BRODIE: Inability of newborn mice and guinea pigs to metabolize drugs. *Biochem. Pharmacol. 1*:352 (1958).

Further evidence of the correlation between defective drug metabolism in early life and duration of drug action is presented in Table 3-13. In this study, microsomes obtained from one-day-old guinea pigs failed to metabolize hexobarbital, but there was a progressive increase in the oxidation rate in microsomes of older animals. Mice of various ages were injected with hexobarbital, and after 3 hours they were assayed in order to determine how much drug remained. The newborn animals failed to metabolize any of the injected drug over the 3-hour period, seven-day-old mice metabolized about 18 per cent, and three-week-old mice, about 22 per cent. Paralleling this finding, it was observed that sleeping times were much longer in newborn and young mice than in adult animals. However, impaired metabolism alone will not account for the greater sensitivity of young mice to hexobarbital; they seem also to be more sensitive to given tissue and plasma concentrations. Furthermore, very young animals have depressed renal function (p. 200) and an unusually permeable blood-brain barrier.[137]

These findings have some important clinical implications. Infants are likely to be more sensitive to some drugs than are adults, and to show more prolonged effects, even after weight or surface area has been taken into account in arriving at an estimated dosage schedule. There is also special danger in using drugs in obstetrical practice. A drug that is relatively harmless to the mother may cross the placenta and have an adverse effect on the fetus. After parturition, the newborn no longer has the use of a maternal liver system to metabolize the drug, so that very long-lasting effects may then be seen.

The tragic experience with chloramphenicol in newborn infants[138] highlights the serious consequences that can result from deficient drug metabolism. The therapeutic or prophylactic use of chloramphenicol in hospital nurseries led to cases of cyanosis ("gray syndrome"). Some deaths occurred, especially in premature infants, after cardiovascular and respiratory collapse. In the adult human, about 90 per cent of a dose of chloramphenicol is excreted as the monoglucuronide derivative, about 8 per cent as free drug, and traces as the hydrolyzed deacetylated derivative. In newborn infants (and in cats) a small amount of a dehalogenated product is also found.[139-141]

137 S. G. DRISCOLL and D. Y. HSIA: The development of enzyme systems during early infancy. *Pediatrics 22:*785 (1958).

138 C. F. WEISS, A. J. GLAZKO, and J. K. WESTON: Chloramphenicol in the newborn infant: a physiologic explanation of its toxicity when given in excessive dose. *New Engl. J. Med. 262:*787 (1960).

139 A. J. GLAZKO, L. M. WOLF, W. A. DILL, and A. C. BRATTON, JR.: Biochemical studies on chloramphenicol (Chloromycetin). II. Tissue distribution and excretion studies. *J. Pharmacol. Exp. Therap. 96:*445 (1949).

140 A. J. GLAZKO, W. A. DILL, and M. C. REBSTOCK: Biochemical studies on chloramphenicol (Chloromycetin). III. Isolation and identification of metabolic products in urine. *J. Biol. Chem. 183:*679 (1950).

141 W. A. DILL, E. M. THOMPSON, R. A. FISKEN, and A. J. GLAZKO: A new metabolite of chloramphenicol. *Nature 185:*535 (1960).

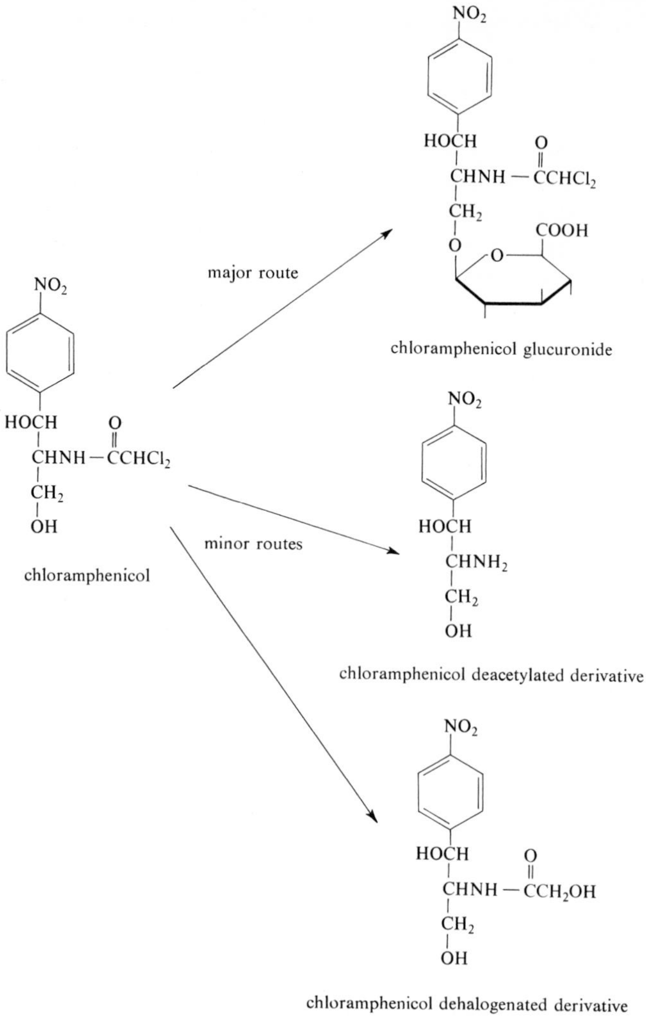

chloramphenicol glucuronide

chloramphenicol deacetylated derivative

chloramphenicol dehalogenated derivative

In premature infants, and during the first week or two of life in normal infants, the mechanism for glucuronide conjugation is grossly deficient. At the same time, renal function (both glomerular filtration and tubular secretion) is also very inefficient. Consequently, an ordinary dose of chloramphenicol leads to a high and prolonged plasma level of the free drug. Plasma glucuronide levels also increase because of the defective tubular secretory mechanism; but, at least in the adult, chloramphenicol monoglucuronide is nontoxic. Repeated doses at intervals that would be suitable in the older infant cause a progressive buildup (cf. p. 309) of the plasma level of chloramphenicol into the range of severe hematologic toxicity.

The production of neonatal kernicterus by bilirubin through depressed glucuronide formation, aggravated by displacement of bilirubin from plasma albumin by certain sulfonamides and vitamin K, was discussed in chapter 2 (p. 143).

Effects of old age on drug metabolism have not been extensively studied. An investigation of hexobarbital sleeping times in male and female rats of different ages revealed some interesting effects of age that could be attributed to the sexual status (Fig. 3-24). Rats begin producing sex hormones (estrogen, testosterone) at about two months of age. It is just at this time that sex differences in sleeping times appear. Thus, male and female rats both slept about 40 minutes at one month of age, but at two months the males slept 15 minutes on the average, while females slept 55 minutes. These differences persisted throughout the period of sexual maturity. Sex hormone production in rats declines at about two years of age. In this experiment, the sex differences in sleeping time disappeared at the same time. In another study rats 30 days of age showed a maximal rate of drug metabolizing activity; then the activity declined progressively until 250 days of age.[143]

FIG. 3-24. EFFECTS OF AGE AND SEX ON THE DURATION OF ACTION OF HEXO-BARBITAL. *Male and female rats, one to 29 months of age, were given a fixed dose of hexobarbital intraperitoneally (75 mg/kg). Each point on the graph represents the mean of a group of six to 12 rats, except at 28 months, when only three males and three females were tested. (From Streicher and Garbus, Fig. 1.[142])*

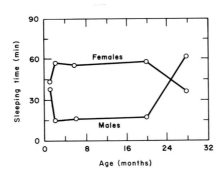

142 E. STREICHER and J. GARBUS: The effect of age and sex on the duration of hexo-barbital anesthesia in rats. *J. Gerontol. 10:*441 (1955).

143 R. KATO, P. VASSANELLI, G. FRONTINO, and E. CHIESARA: Variation in the activity of liver microsomal drug-metabolizing enzymes in rats in relation to the age. *Biochem. Pharmacol. 13:*1037 (1964).

4

THE TIME COURSE OF

DRUG ACTION

RATE OF DRUG ABSORPTION

Drug absorption proceeds either at a constant rate independent of the amount of drug to be absorbed (*zero-order kinetics*) or at a diminishing rate that is always proportional to the amount of drug still to be absorbed (*exponential, or first-order kinetics*). If a drug is injected intravascularly, one cannot really speak of absorption, although in a formal sense we may regard the entire dose as being "absorbed" into the blood stream instantaneously. As we shall see (p. 287), the kinetics of elimination under these conditions are readily analyzed because no simultaneous absorption process complicates matters.

The most straightforward example of constant-rate absorption is that seen with a continuous intravenous infusion, in which the rate of entry of the drug into the vascular system is fixed and maintained at will. Two types of apparatus are employed. The simplest is a gravity-flow intravenous drip, commonly used at the bedside in hospitals. The apparatus is employed to administer blood, plasma, physiologic saline solutions, glucose, and other nutrients. It is a simple matter to add a drug in appropriate concentration. The flow rate is maintained approximately constant by a simple adjustable clamp on the tubing, and the rate is monitored by counting drops in a glass bulb designed for the purpose. A more precise apparatus is the infusion pump, calibrated to deliver solution at a constant rate from a sterile reservoir. The method of continuous infusion has been used extensively and with considerable success for the administration of oxytocin at term to induce labor; here, the exact regulation of dosage is of critical importance. As will be discussed (p. 295), if a constant-rate infusion delivers new drug at a rate that just replaces drug eliminated from the body, a steady-state constant drug level will be maintained throughout the drug's volume of distribution in the body.

Constant-rate absorption may be approximated by various techniques for sustained-release medication. As already shown (p. 113), a subcutaneous pellet in the shape of a flat disc may yield drug into solution at a practically constant rate until it is nearly all dissolved. If the dissolution of the drug can be made the rate-limiting process for absorption (i.e., if the rate of absorption is fast compared with the rate of solution), then the overall absorption rate will be practically constant. The same principle applies to some extent to any insoluble drug in a subcutaneous or intramuscular depot during an initial period, before the total surface area exposed for solution diminishes by much. Protamine zinc insulin and procaine penicillin are examples of drugs whose absorption from depots may proceed at a nearly constant rate for some time after their administration. In sustained-release medications for oral administration, the aim of the manufacturing process is to achieve a nearly constant rate of liberation into the gastrointestinal lumen (cf. p. 127). Generally, in any situation where a supply (or reservoir) of available drug can replace what is absorbed, a constant rate of absorption may be expected. An example would be the application to the skin of a large amount of ointment or cream containing a drug; as the drug penetrates into the deeper layers of the corium, and eventually into the blood stream, it is replaced by diffusion of fresh drug; thus, a continuous gradient of drug concentration is maintained throughout the thickness of the skin, and a constant absorption rate continues as long as drug persists on the surface. Another example is found in the administration of anesthetic gases (p. 323). Here, drug absorbed into the pulmonary blood at the alveoli during each breath is replaced at the next breath from the unlimited supply maintained in the anesthetist's breathing bag.

Except for the rather special cases cited above, both for enteral and parenteral routes of administration, most drug absorption follows first-order kinetics; i.e., a constant fraction of the total drug present is absorbed in each equal interval of time. After intramuscular injection of a drug solution, for example, all the drug is contained in a certain aqueous volume in the interstitial spaces. The probability that a given drug molecule will enter a nearby capillary in a given short period of time depends upon the intrinsic vascularity of the tissue (i.e., how near the capillary is), the permeability of the capillaries to the drug, the local blood flow, and the diffusion rate of the drug. The rate of absorption (molecules per minute) will be the product of this probability times the total number of drug molecules present. As the total amount of drug diminishes, the rate of absorption will obviously decrease proportionately, and the time course of the absorption process can be described by the following equations:

$$\frac{dM}{dt} = -k_a M$$

$$M = M_0 e^{-k_a t}$$

$$\ln \frac{M}{M_0} = -k_a t$$

$$\ln M = \ln M_0 - k_a t$$

$$\log M = \log M_0 - \frac{k_a t}{2.30} \, .$$

where M_0 is the amount of drug placed initially at the absorption site, M is the amount remaining at the absorption site at time t, and k_a is the rate constant for absorption. The last two equations represent straight lines, so if the amount of unabsorbed drug is plotted against time on semilogarithmic coordinates, a line should be obtained with the negative slope $k_a/2.30$ and intercept M_0 on the y-axis. In this treatment back-diffusion from the blood into the depot is neglected. Figure 4-1 presents a good example. Radioactive sodium, as NaCl, was injected intramuscularly in man, and the residual radioactivity was determined for 25 minutes with a Geiger counter at the skin surface. The exponential course of the absorption is clearly demonstrated by the data. Incorporation of epinephrine into the injection markedly reduced the absorption rate (by reducing the local blood flow), but the residual absorption was still first order.

The rate constant of absorption tells us what fraction of remaining drug is absorbed per minute. For the experiment of Fig. 4-1, this rate con-

FIG. 4-1.   ABSORPTION OF ^{24}Na+ FROM AN INTRAMUSCULAR DEPOT IN MAN. *The radioisotope (5 μc) was injected deep into the gastrocnemius muscle. Residual radioactivity was determined by a Geiger counter at the skin. Ordinates represent counts per minute on logarithmic scale but the scale factor (which is irrelevant to the purpose of the graph) is not given. The slope is a measure of* k_a, *the fraction removed per minute.* Lower curve, *control resting muscle,* $k_a = 0.064$ *min*$^{-1}$; upper curve, *epinephrine incorporated in the injection,* $k_a = 0.010$ *min*$^{-1}$. *(From Kety, Fig. 4.[1] By permission of C. V. Mosby.)*

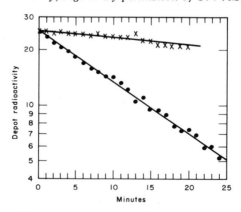

[1] S. S. KETY: Measurement of regional circulation by the local clearance of radioactive sodium. *Amer. Heart J. 38:*321 (1949).

stant, k_a, was 0.064 min^{-1} in the control resting muscle, meaning that 6.4 per cent of the remaining sodium ions were absorbed each minute.

Another useful measure, directly related to k_a, is the *absorption half-time*, $t_{1/2}$, the time when the drug content of the depot has been reduced to half its initial value. As shown above,

$$\ln (M/M_0) = -k_a t.$$

Substituting $M/M_0 = 1/2$, we obtain

$$\ln (1/2) = -k_a t_{1/2}$$

$$t_{1/2} = 0.693/k_a.$$

For sodium absorption, where $k_a = 0.064$ min^{-1}, $t_{1/2} = 11$ min.

RATE OF DRUG ELIMINATION

Elimination refers to all the processes that operate to reduce the effective drug concentration in the body fluids. Depending upon the mechanism of elimination, the course of disappearance of a drug from the body (or the decay of its plasma level) may be zero order (constant rate) or first order (exponential). First-order elimination is the general rule, but if an elimination mechanism can become saturated, then at drug concentrations above the saturation level the elimination will be zero order. An excellent example already discussed is the renal tubular secretion of drugs, for which there is always a maximum tubular transport capacity (T_m). If the plasma level of a drug is so high that T_m is exceeded, zero-order kinetics will obtain until the concentration falls below the saturation level, and then subsequently the elimination rate will decrease with decreasing concentration; at a low enough concentration the elimination will always be first order, i.e., proportional to the concentration. The same principle applies to the secretion of drugs into the bile (p. 203), a process also characterized by a T_m for each drug.

Substrates for drug-metabolizing enzymes may be degraded or conjugated at a constant rate when their concentrations are above saturation levels, or when a coupled reaction is rate limiting. As with renal tubular and biliary transport systems at concentrations just below saturation, complex kinetics apply; then, at low saturation of enzyme (i.e., when most of the enzyme is not in combination with substrate) the reaction becomes first order.[2] From p. 71,

$$v = \frac{dS}{dt} = \frac{S}{(K + S)} V_{max},$$

---

2 Sometimes called *pseudo-first-order* reaction because, although two reactants (substrate and enzyme) have to combine, the latter remains constant and only the changing substrate concentration influences the reaction rate.

and when $v \ll V_{max}$, so that $S \ll K$, we have approximately

$$\frac{dS}{dt} = \frac{V_{max}}{K}\, S,$$

which is obviously the equation of a first-order process, since V_{max}/K is a constant. Initially, therefore, the metabolic elimination of drugs may be zero order or first order, depending upon the drug concentration and the affinity of the particular drug for its metabolizing enzymes. Eventually, as drug levels fall, drug metabolism will become first order.

Figure 4-2 presents a well authenticated instance of a metabolic elimination of two different drugs in the same species by different kinetics. In both cases the metabolic reaction under study was the conjugation of a substituted benzoic acid with endogenous glycine by the mechanism presented on p. 242. In *A*, the drug was anisic acid (*p*-methoxybenzoic acid) and a large excess of glycine was administered simultaneously. The excretion of glycine conjugate in the urine followed a typical exponential course; the rate declined progressively as the level of unconjugated drug in the body declined. In *B*, the drug was *p*-fluorobenzoic acid and no exogenous glycine was furnished. The rate of conjugation of this compound is very much faster than that of anisic acid, but it proceeds at a constant rate (zero order) until very little unconjugated drug remains. The reason is that, because endogenous glycine cannot be made available at a sufficient rate, the glycine supply is rate limiting, so that the overall conjugation rate remains constant. When exogenous glycine was administered simultaneously with *p*-fluorobenzoic acid (not shown in the figure), the initial rate of conjugation was much faster, but it slowed progressively according to first-order kinetics.

An interesting example of zero-order metabolism is the oxidation of ethanol in man and other animals.[4-6] Ethanol is converted to acetaldehyde by the liver alcohol dehydrogenase in a NAD-coupled reaction:

$$CH_3CH_2OH + NAD^+ \rightleftharpoons CH_3CHO + NADH + H^+$$

The acetaldehyde is further metabolized to acetic acid by aldehyde dehydrogenase. The rate of metabolism of ethanol in man is essentially con-

[3] H. G. BRAY, B. G. HUMPHRIS, W. V. THORPE, K. WHITE, and P. B. WOOD: Kinetic studies on the metabolism of foreign organic compounds. 6. Reactions of some nuclear-substituted benzoic acids, benzamides and toluenes in the rabbit. *Biochem. J. 59:*162 (1955).

[4] E. K. MARSHALL, JR. and W. F. FRITZ: The metabolism of ethyl alcohol. *J. Pharmacol. Exper. Therap. 109:*431 (1953).

[5] I. CAMPOS, W. SOLODKOWSKA, E. MUNOZ, N. SEGOVIA-RIQUELME, J. CEMBRANO, and J. MARDONES: Ethanol metabolism in rats with experimental liver cirrhosis. I. Rate of combustion of labeled ethanol and rate of decrease of blood ethanol levels. *Quart. J. Stud. Alcohol 25:*417 (1964).

[6] K. J. ISSELBACHER and N. J. GREENBERGER: Metabolic effects of alcohol on the liver. *New England J. Med. 270:*351, 403 (1964).

stant (about 10 ml per hour) regardless of its concentration; the rate, however, differs considerably from person to person. Alcohol dehydrogenase has been studied extensively, and all the equilibrium constants and reaction rates have been well characterized.[7-10] At physiologic pH the equilibrium constant for the overall reaction is:[11]

$$K = \frac{(CH_3CHO)\ (NADH)}{(CH_3CH_2OH)\ (NAD^+)} = 3 \times 10^{-4}.$$

Thus, the equilibrium for the overall reaction lies far to the left; with equal concentrations of NAD^+ and $NADH$, the equilibrium ratio of ethanol to acetaldehyde will be more than 1000:1. Only the continuous removal of acetaldehyde forces the reaction to completion.

It has been supposed that the reason for the linear rate of oxidation of ethanol in vivo must be the saturation of the liver alcohol dehydrogenase at usual ethanol concentrations. But this is evidently incorrect. The K_m for the interaction of ethanol with the enzyme is about $2 \times 10^{-2}M$. The highest blood ethanol concentration one would normally encounter is about 4 mg/ml (0.4 per cent, $8 \times 10^{-2}M$), and the concentration associated with mild intoxication is about 1 mg/ml (0.1 per cent, $2 \times 10^{-2}M$). Evidently, then, the enzyme is only half-saturated with respect to ethanol during mild intoxication, and by no means fully saturated even at near-lethal ethanol levels.

The zero-order kinetics of ethanol oxidation apparently arise from an insufficient supply of NAD^+, much as the rate of conjugation of fluorobenzoic (Fig. 4-2) was limited by the glycine supply. Here, the rate at which NAD^+ can be regenerated from $NADH$, by transfer of electrons into the mitochondrial cytochrome system, seems to be considerably slower than the rate at which the alcohol dehydrogenase and aldehyde dehydrogenase could function. Indeed, in vivo as well as in vitro, if substrates are furnished that stimulate the $NADH \rightarrow NAD^+$ conversion (e.g., pyruvate, or compounds like alanine, fructose, or glucose which yield pyruvate), the rate of ethanol metabolism can be accelerated.[12, 13]

---

[7] E. NEGELEIN and H.-J. WULFF: Disphosphopyridinproteid, alkohol, acetaldehyd. *Biochem. Z. 293:*351 (1937).

[8] E. RACKER: Crystalline alcohol dehydrogenase from Baker's yeast. *J. Biol. Chem. 184:*313 (1950).

[9] H. THEORELL: Kinetics and equilibria in the liver alcohol dehydrogenase system. *Adv. Enzymol. 20:*31 (1958).

[10] M. M. KINI and J. R. COOPER: Biochemistry of methanol poisoning. III. The enzymic pathway for the conversion of methanol to formaldehyde. *Biochem. Pharmacol. 8:*207 (1961).

[11] If the equilibrium expression is written to include the hydrogen ion concentration at pH 7.4, then the redefined equilibrium constant becomes $3 \times 10^{-4} \times 4 \times 10^{-8} = 1 \times 10^{-11}$.

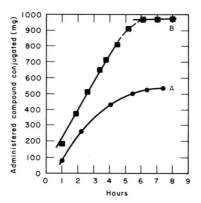

FIG. 4-2.   EXAMPLES OF ZERO-ORDER AND FIRST-ORDER KINETICS IN DRUG ME-
TABOLISM.   *Urinary excretion of glycine conjugates was followed in the rabbit
after administration of 1-g doses of two different compounds:* A, *anisic acid +
glycine (4 g);* B, *p-fluorobenzoic acid.* A *is exponential because excess glycine
is supplied; the drug is also metabolized by other pathways.* B *is linear because
the endogenous glycine supply is rate limiting, nearly to the end of the reaction.*
(*From Bray et al., Fig. 2.*[3])

    Some well-known facts about drinking are logical consequences of
the zero-order kinetics and slow rate of ethanol metabolism. To achieve a
mildly intoxicating level of 1 mg/ml throughout 41 liters of body water
(the volume of distribution for ethanol) will require an intake of about
41 g (55 ml) of absolute ethanol. Most strong liquor contains 40 to 50
per cent ethanol, so the required intake of whiskey, gin, vodka, or similar
drink will be approximately 120 ml, or 4 ounces. This "priming" amount
(cf. p. 301) is often ingested quite rapidly in order to obtain the desired
effect. However, the maximum that can be metabolized is 10 ml/hour, so
that 5 hours would be required to eliminate the 55 ml taken at the outset.
It follows that continuation of the same dosing rate would very soon lead
to progressively higher and more toxic blood levels. The safe maintenance
dose (after priming), to maintain a constant level of mild intoxication, will
be just 10 ml of ethanol (about 20 to 25 ml of liquor) per hour.

    Most elimination mechanisms are approximately first order; a con-
stant fraction of the drug in the body disappears in each equal interval of
time. Typical is the excretion of drugs by glomerular filtration at the
kidneys, as discussed already (p. 194). Other first-order processes are the
excretion of drugs by diffusion and ion trapping at the gastric or intestinal
mucosa, the elimination of volatile drugs at the lungs, and the sequestration

    [12] M. E. SMITH and H. W. NEWMAN: The rate of ethanol metabolism in fed and
fasting animals. *J. Biol. Chem.* 234:1544 (1959).
    [13] W. W. WESTERFELD: The intermediary metabolism of alcohol. *Amer. J. Clin.
Nutr.* 9:426 (1961).

of drugs in various tissues. All these are first order because every drug molecule has a fixed probability of being excreted within a given time; the total rate of excretion is therefore equal to that probability times the total number of drug molecules present. In the case of sequestration, this probability is determined by the blood flow to the tissue concerned and the physicochemical properties of the drug that determine its sequestration. Fat depots are a good example. Their poor blood supply limits the rate of sequestration even when the lipid/water partition coefficient is very high; thus, the blood flow to the fat depots and the partition coefficient both determine what fraction of the total circulating drug will be sequestered each minute.

For first-order (exponential) elimination the familiar equations apply, where X denotes total drug in the body at time t, X_0 the drug present at time zero, and k_e the rate constant for elimination:

$$X = X_0 e^{-k_e t}$$

$$\log X = \log X_0 - k_e t / 2.30$$

$$t_{1/2} = 0.693 / k_e.$$

The half-time for elimination is also called the *biologic half-life.*

Figure 4-3 shows a typical first-order elimination curve after intravenous injection of penicillin into a dog. The decline in the plasma level is almost perfectly linear on semilogarithmic coordinates, i.e., a constant fraction was eliminated in each equal interval of time. The biologic half-life is found by measuring the time required for a given plasma level to decline by one-half, here 25 minutes. The elimination rate constant k_e equals $0.693/25 = 0.028$, or about 3 per cent per minute. Extrapolating

FIG. 4-3.   FIRST-ORDER ELIMINATION OF PENICILLIN FROM PLASMA.   *Penicillin G (50,000 units, 30 mg) was injected intravenously at time zero in a dog weighing about 18 kg. Plasma levels of penicillin were determined periodically, as shown. (Adapted from Beyer et al., Fig. 2.[14])*

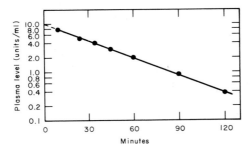

14 K. H. BEYER, H. F. RUSSO, E. K. TILLSON, A. K. MILLER, W. F. VERWEY, and S. R. GASS: 'Benemid,' *p*-(di-*n*-propylsulfamyl)-benzoic acid: its renal affinity and its elimination. *Amer. J. Physiol. 166:*625 (1951).

the curve back to the origin gives an estimate of the concentration that would have been present initially if all the injected material had been distributed in the volume of distribution ultimately attained. To find this V_d, we divide the injected dose (50,000 units) by the extrapolated concentration (10 units/ml) and obtain 5 liters, or 28 per cent of body weight in this animal. The elimination rate is consistent with the renal tubular secretion of a drug whose V_d is somewhat larger than the extracellular fluid volume (cf. Table 2-18 for comparable data in man), and the first-order kinetics indicate that even at the highest concentration observed here, 8 units/ml, the T_m was not exceeded.

Another way of portraying the course of first-order elimination is based upon measurements of cumulative drug excretion in the urine. Let Y' be the total amount of drug eventually excreted, and Y the cumulative excretion to any time t. Then the rate of excretion at any moment will be proportional to the difference between the total amount to be excreted and the amount already excreted at that time, i.e., proportional to the unexcreted fraction. As we have seen,

$$X/X_0 = e^{-k_e t},$$

where X/X_0 is the fraction of initial drug still remaining in the body. Then obviously, the fraction excreted is

$$Y/Y' = 1 - (X/X_0),$$

since the total drug X_0 is identical to the total amount Y' to be excreted.[15] Hence,

$$\ln\left(1 - \frac{Y}{Y'}\right) = -k_e t$$

$$\log\left(1 - \frac{Y}{Y'}\right) = -k_e t / 2.30.$$

When the fraction (or per cent) as yet unexcreted is plotted against time on semilogarithmic coordinates, a straight line should be obtained, from which the half-time for excretion can be read and the elimination rate constant computed. Obviously, if elimination mechanisms other than renal are playing a significant role, the k_e obtained in this way will reflect only the renal contribution to the overall elimination. The method is illustrated in Fig. 4-4 for the sulfonamide drug sulfisoxazole; here, $t_{1/2} = 384$ minutes (6.4 hours).

For a first-order elimination, *the duration of a therapeutically effective drug concentration increases as the logarithm of the amount of drug in the body fluids.* In many instances this means simply that the duration of

---

[15] If routes of elimination other than excretion play a significant role, then Y' will be smaller than X_0, but if all the mechanisms are first order, their sum will also be first order.

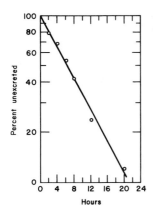

FIG. 4-4. KINETICS OF EXCRETION OF SULFISOXAZOLE IN HUMAN URINE. *Note that vertical scale is logarithmic. The per cent of unexcreted drug* $\left[100 \left(1 - \dfrac{Y}{Y'} \right) \right]$ *is plotted against time;* $k = 0.108 \ hr^{-1}$ *and the biologic half-life is 6.4 hr. (From Nelson and O'Reilly,[16] Fig. 1, redrawn by Nelson, Fig. 3.[17] By permission of Williams & Wilkins and C. V. Mosby.)*

action increases as the logarithm of the dose. This would be true, for example, if the dose were given intravenously; and it would be nearly true whenever the drug is absorbed very rapidly in comparison with its rate of elimination. It is easy to see from the schematic diagram of Fig. 4-5 why this relationship should hold. Let x^* be the threshold concentration for therapeutic effect, established by the distribution of a just-effective dose X^* in its volume of distribution V_d. Let x_1 and x_2 be plasma levels established

FIG. 4-5. SCHEMATIC FIRST-ORDER ELIMINATION CURVES FOR TWO DOSES. *Concentration* x* *is the threshold concentration for therapeutic effect;* x_1 *and* x_2 *are the initial concentrations established by the two doses. It is assumed that absorption is very rapid, or that the doses were administered intravenously.*

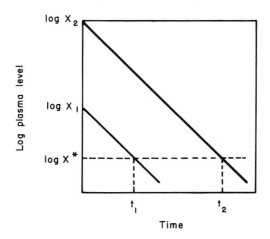

[16] E. NELSON and I. O'REILLY: Kinetics of sulfisoxazole acetylation and excretion in humans. *J. Pharmacol. Exper. Therap. 129:*368 (1960).
[17] E. NELSON: Pharmaceuticals for prolonged action. *Clin. Pharmacol. Therap.* 4:283 (1963).

by the two doses X_1 and X_2. Since V_d is independent of dose, $X_1 = x_1 V_d$, $X_2 = x_2 V_d$, and $X^* = x^* V_d$. The durations of effective concentrations of the two doses are t_1 and t_2; and the slopes of the elimination curves, also independent of dose, are $-k_e/2.30$.[18]

The fundamental equation for first-order elimination (p. 287) and the geometry of Fig. 4-5 yield three equations describing the relationship between duration of effective concentration and dose. First we find t^*, the time required for the concentration to fall from any initial level x_0 to the threshold level x^*, as follows:

$$\log x^*/x_0 = -k_e t^*/2.30$$

and, substituting $x = X/V_d$, cancelling V_d, and inverting, we obtain

$$t^* = (2.30/k_e) \log(X_0/X^*).$$

Also, obviously, for the ratio of effective times after two doses,

$$t_2/t_1 = (\log X_2 - \log X^*)/(\log X_1 - \log X^*),$$

and for the increment in time with the larger dose compared with the smaller,

$$\Delta t^* = t_2 - t_1 = (2.30/k_e)(\log X_2 - \log X_1).$$

These equations, especially the one that gives t^* as a function of dose, have practical importance. The duration of a therapeutic level of a drug depends upon the *ratio of administered dose to the just-effective dose,* and also upon the rate constant of elimination. Evidently, the longer the biologic half-life (i.e., the smaller the value of k_e), the longer the duration for a given dose ratio. Whatever the duration may be at a particular ratio X_1/X^*, geometric increments in the dose will produce only linear increments in the duration of effective drug levels. Suppose, for example, that doubling the threshold dose would result in an effective drug level for 1 hour, i.e., the biologic half-life is 1 hour. Then (Fig. 4-5) the dose would have to be doubled again to achieve an effective level for 2 hours, and doubled yet again to achieve a 3-hour duration. The tolerable limit of geometric increases in drug dosage will be determined by the dose-related toxicity of the particular drug.

Figure 4-6 presents a graphic summary of these relationships for realistic ranges of dose ratio and of k_e. Whatever a just-effective dose may be, it is unlikely, as a general rule, that a dose more than five times greater can be given without grave danger of toxicity; certainly few drugs have this large a margin of safety. Usually one would be restricted to a smaller excess over the just-effective level, perhaps only two- or threefold. Dose ratios X/X^* greater than 5 are therefore not considered here. Values of k_e

---

18 If the ordinates are natural logarithms, ln x, the slopes are simply $-k_e$. If logarithms to the base 10 are used, the slope becomes $-k_e/2.30$ because $\log x = (\ln x)/2.30$.

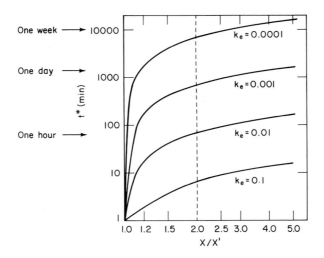

FIG. 4-6. RELATIONSHIP BETWEEN DURATION OF EFFECTIVE THERAPEUTIC LEVELS AND DOSE. *Administered dose* X *is assumed to be absorbed very rapidly, or to be administered intravenously;* X' *is the just-effective dose;* t* *is the time (in minutes) during which the drug concentration in the body fluids exceeds the threshold level. Each curve is for a different value of the rate constant of elimination, as indicated; biologic half-lives are (from top to bottom) 6930, 693, 69, 6.9 minutes. Note that ordinal and abscissal axes are both logarithmic.*

spanning four orders of magnitude are indicated on the curves. Values in the range 0.01 to 0.001 min^{-1} are encountered frequently (biologic half-lives about 1 to 10 hours), since so many drugs are eliminated primarily at the kidneys without significant tubular reabsorption (cf. Table 2-20). Figure 4-6 is shown as a log-log plot in order to encompass the wide range of durations and dose ratios. Note that if twice the just-effective dose is administered (vertical broken line), the duration of therapeutic level will be simply the biologic half-life. This leads to a useful and practical rule: If a drug's effect is to last several hours, to avoid repeated administration at shorter intervals, then that drug must be one whose biologic half-life lasts at least several hours; i.e., it must not be metabolized rapidly or secreted by the renal tubules. Penicillin is a good example of a drug whose biologic half-life is too short (because of its rapid renal tubular secretion), so that ordinary parenteral routes of administration (i.v., i.m.), in which absorption is rapid, may not be practical; sustained-release depot preparations[17] have to be employed instead.

We have referred to the duration of effective therapeutic concentration of a drug as though it were identical to duration of action. Often it is. But there are many exceptions, instances in which a drug's therapeutic action may far outlast its presence in the body fluids. Certain bactericidal drugs kill pathogenic organisms rapidly and then need not be present at all for a certain interval, during which the pathogen population is unable to recover. Alkylating agents usually produce their irreversible chemical effects very quickly, and they may also be quickly destroyed, so that they are not present at all during the subsequent period when the biologic effects develop. Organic phosphate cholinesterase inhibitors are degraded rapidly, but their effects persist until free enzyme is resynthesized. Barbiturates and other centrally acting agents may produce typical actions at a certain threshold concentration, but recovery from these actions may occur at a different concentration; thus, the duration of drug action and the time during which drug concentrations exceed the original threshold may not be the same. Finally, reserpine depletes catecholamines at nerve terminals peripherally, and in brain; the effects are long lasting, until the catecholamine stores can be replenished. Most of the reserpine is eliminated long before the biologic effects wear off, but it is still an open question whether enough reserpine persists at the sites of action to account for the long duration of action.

ZERO-ORDER ABSORPTION, FIRST-ORDER ELIMINATION: THE PLATEAU PRINCIPLE

Derivation of the Principle and Its Application to Constant Infusions

We shall show the derivation of an elementary principle about steady states that has direct application to the kinetics of drug accumulation in the body, and that also has much broader application to fundamental biologic, chemical, and physical processes. If the rate of input into a system is constant and the rate of output from the system is exponential, then the content of the system (here designated by X) will accumulate until a steady state is reached:

$$\xrightarrow{k_{in}} X \xrightarrow{k_{out}}$$

constant input rate $= k_{in}$

output rate $= k_{out} X.$

At the steady state, X will have increased to X', a level at which the output rate is equal to the input rate:

$$k_{out} X' = k_{in}$$

$$X' = k_{in}/k_{out}.$$

In such a system, the steady state can be altered by changing the input rate k_{in} or by changing the output rate constant k_{out}, or both. Any such change will cause a *shift* to a new steady state.

According to the plateau principle, regardless of how a shift is brought about from one steady state to another, *the time course of the shift* (i.e., the rate at which the new plateau level is reached) *is determined solely by* k_{out}, the first-order rate constant of the output process that is operative during the shift. Thus, if the shift is caused by an alteration of k_{in} without change in k_{out}, the sole determinant is the unchanged k_{out}. If the shift is caused wholly or in part by a change in k_{out}, then the sole determinant is the *new* value of k_{out}. In any case, *the rate constant for the shift is equal to* k_{out}, *so the shift half-time is identical to the half-time of the output process,* $0.693/k_{out}$. The same principle applies when the initial value of X is zero and k_{in} is abruptly changed from zero to some finite value; then the shift is simply the establishment of a steady state. And the principle also applies when a steady-state value of X is in effect and k_{in} is abruptly changed to zero (i.e., the input is stopped); then the shift is simply the exponential disappearance of X, resulting in the new "steady state" where $X = 0$.

The plateau principle is fundamental to understanding constant infusions, drug accumulation, dosage regimens, chronic toxicity by drug accumulation, and enzyme induction and stabilization. We shall derive it first, then show its specific applications.[19]

For the change in X,

$$dX/dt = k_{in} - k_{out} X;$$

and at the initial steady state,

$$X'_1 = k_{in_1}/k_{out_1}.$$

Now change k_{in_1} to a new value k_{in_2}, and also change k_{out_1} to a new value k_{out_2}, and consider the time course of the change in X from X'_1 to its new steady-state value X'_2. Accordingly,

$$dX/dt = k_{in_2} - k_{out_2} X,$$

and at the new steady state,

$$X'_2 = k_{in_2}/k_{out_2}.$$

To find X as a function of time after the shift, differentiate with respect to time:

$$\frac{X}{k_{in_2} - k_{out_2}(X)} = dt$$

Rearranging,

$$-\frac{1}{k_{out_2}} \cdot \frac{d[k_{in_2} - k_{out_2}(X)]}{[k_{in_2} - k_{out_2}(X)]} = dt,$$

[19] Much of the work that led to an explicit formulation of the plateau principle was carried out collaboratively with D. B. Goldstein.

and integrating, we obtain

$$\ln [k_{in_2} - k_{out_2}(X)] = -k_{out_2}t + C$$

When $t = 0$, $X = X'$, and the constant of integration, C, is found to be

$$C = \ln [k_{in_2} - k_{out_2} (X_1')]$$

Then substituting, and taking antilogarithms,

$$\frac{k_{in_2} - k_{out_2} (X)}{k_{in_2} - k_{out_2} (X_1')} = e^{-k_{out_2}t}$$

Now we are concerned with the *shift* from one steady state to the other. The total extent of the shift is $(X_2' - X_1')$ and the amount by which X has changed from its initial steady-state value is given by $(X - X_1')$. Thus, the fraction f of the total shift that has been accomplished at any value of X is given by

$$f = \frac{(X - X_1')}{(X_2' - X_1')},$$

and

$$X = fX_2' + X_1' - fX_1'.$$

Substituting this value of X into the equation obtained above, and substituting for k_{in_2} its equivalent value $k_{out_2} (X_2')$, we obtain

$$\frac{X_2' - fX_2' - X_1' + fX_1'}{X_2' - X_1'} = e^{-k_{out_2}t},$$

which simplifies to

$$1 - f = e^{-k_{out_2}t}.$$

This equation makes it evident that the kinetics of the shift are the exponential kinetics of a process with rate constant k_{out_2}. The half-time of the shift is found by setting $f = 0.5$:

$$\ln (0.5) = -k_{out_2}t$$

$$t_{1/2} = -\ln (0.5)/k_{out_2} = 0.693/k_{out_2}.$$

Simply, $t_{1/2}$ is the half-time of the output process.

It may seem paradoxical for the time course of the establishment of a steady state, or of a shift from one steady state to another, to be determined by the output rate constant and to be independent of the input rate. A physical analogy may help to clarify this relationship. Consider a water reservoir with outlet at bottom and outflow rate proportional to the outlet size and the head of water pressure. What are the conditions for establishing a specified steady-state water level? Since the inflow and outflow rates will be equal at the steady state, the inflow rate cannot be chosen at will; only one particular inflow rate will yield the specified level at the steady state. A higher inflow rate will, of course, produce a faster rise of the water level, but then the specified level will be exceeded. A slower inflow rate will produce a slower rise, but then the specified level will not be attained. Only if the outlet size is changed will it become possible to alter the inflow rate so that the specified steady state is approached at a different rate; and clearly, the larger the outlet the more rapidly can the specified steady state be approached.

The same principle applies when no particular steady-state level has been specified. With a given outlet the actual rate of rise of the water level will obviously be greater at high than at low inflow rate, but the steady-state level to be attained will also be proportionately greater. The *relative* rate of rise, measured as fraction of the ultimate level approached (f, as defined earlier), will be the same for all inflow rates. In a given reservoir this relative rate of approach to any steady state will be directly proportional to the outlet size, which is analogous to the rate constant of the drug output process.

Now let us apply the plateau principle to constant infusions. Let V_d be the volume of distribution of a drug (ml); Q a constant rate of infusion of the drug ($mg \cdot min^{-1}$); k_e the first-order rate constant for elimination of the drug (min^{-1}), the rate of change of concentration being given by $k_e x$, where x is the drug concentration in plasma ($mg \cdot ml^{-1}$); and t the elapsed time (min) from the start of the infusion, from the stopping of the infusion, or from any abrupt change in the input or output rate.

Since the elimination rate is expressed in terms of the plasma concentration of the drug rather than of the total drug in the body, k_{in} is represented by Q/V_d, the rate of input per volume of body fluid. Then the equation describing the change in x with time is

$$dx/dt = (Q/V_d) - k_e x.$$

The change in x from the start of the infusion ($x = 0, t = 0$) is given by

$$x = \frac{Q}{k_e V_d} (1 - e^{-k_e t}).$$

This equation shows that with a constant infusion a plasma plateau is eventually reached; for when t becomes infinite, $1 - e^{-k_e t}$ becomes unity, and at the steady state, $x' = Q/k_e V_d$. Rearranging, we have $k_e(x'V_d) = Q$. Here, $x'V_d$ is the total amount of drug in the body, therefore $k_e(x'V_d)$ is the elimination rate, equal to the infusion rate Q.

For any drug administered by constant infusion, therefore, if its volume of distribution and its rate constant of elimination are known, its plateau level can be predicted. The kinetics of attaining the plateau or of shifting from one plateau to another, or of the die-away when the infusion is stopped, are given by the general expression

$$f = 1 - e^{-k_e t},$$

where, in the general case,

$$f = \frac{x - x'_1}{x'_2 - x'_1}.$$

For starting an infusion ($x'_1 = 0$),

$$f = \frac{x}{x'}$$

and for stopping an infusion ($x'_2 = 0$),

$$f = 1 - (x/x').$$

In summary, if the rate of a constant infusion is increased or decreased, or if an infusion is started or stopped, or if the elimination rate constant is increased or decreased, the half-time of the shift to the new steady state is the new elimination half-time (i.e., the biologic half-life of the drug). For discontinuance of an infusion, the time course of the shift is the normal die-away curve of drug concentration.

Figure 4-7 is the generalized graph of the equation for shifting a steady state ($f = 1 - e^{-kt}$). The y-axis is a scale of f, defined as the fraction of the total shift that has been attained. The time axis is generalized to show units of kt rather than of t, and the units themselves are immaterial (minutes, hours, days, etc.) provided k and t are expressed in the same way. To encompass the wide range of times, the x-axis is logarithmic. An example will illustrate the use of this graph. Suppose a drug with elimination $k_e = 0.5$ hr^{-1} is being infused at a constant rate, a steady-state plasma concentration having been established. The infusion rate is now abruptly reduced by one-half. How long will it take to accomplish 75 per cent of the shift to the new and lower steady-state drug level? Observe that k_e has not been changed, so the amount by which the infusion rate was changed is immaterial. The time course of approach to the new steady state will be the same for all changes in the infusion rate. However, the actual level of the new plateau will be determined by the change in the infusion rate. Consulting the graph at $f = 0.75$, we find $kt = 1.4$; and so $t = 1.4/0.5 = 2.8$ hr. The half-time of the shift ($f = 0.5$) would be $0.693/0.5 = 1.4$ hr.

The plateau principle can be applied to experimental constant infusions in order to gain information about the way a drug is disposed of in the body. The rate of infusion is set by the investigator. By periodic determinations of the drug plasma level, the rate of attaining a plateau can be found, and this rate yields an estimate of the elimination rate constant k_e. The actual concentration at the plateau is $Q/k_e V_d$, as we have

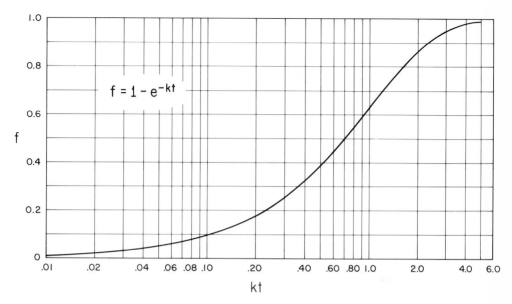

FIG. 4-7. GENERALIZED KINETICS FOR SHIFTING FROM ONE STEADY STATE TO ANOTHER. *This is a graph of equation* $f = 1 - e^{-kt}$, *where* f *is defined as the fractional attainment of the total shift from one steady state to another, for any system with zero-order input and first-order output;* k *is the output rate constant,* t *is time in the same units as* k. *To obtain real time, divide the value of* kt *read from the graph by* k.

seen, from which V_d can also be estimated. By exploring a range of infusion rates leading to widely differing plateau concentrations, it is possible to see whether or not the overall elimination follows first-order kinetics, and it is also possible to see what different mechanisms play the major roles in elimination at different drug concentrations. For example, any experimental procedure that alters k_e will change the plateau level during a constant infusion. If renal excretion is a significant mechanism and the renal arteries are clamped, the plasma drug level will promptly rise, and if other first-order mechanisms are present a new plateau will be attained. By the plateau principle the time course of the shift gives an estimate of the new k_e, as does also the new plateau concentration (provided V_d did not change). If all elimination pathways are blocked or saturated, then continuing the infusion will cause the plasma drug level to rise without limit until toxicity and then death supervene.

An application of this technique is illustrated in Fig. 4-8. Here, neostigmine, a cholinesterase inhibitor, was given to dogs by constant infusion. The plasma neostigmine levels were measured periodically by a method that makes use of the degree of inhibition of the plasma cholinesterase—a given depression of enzyme activity signifies a certain concen-

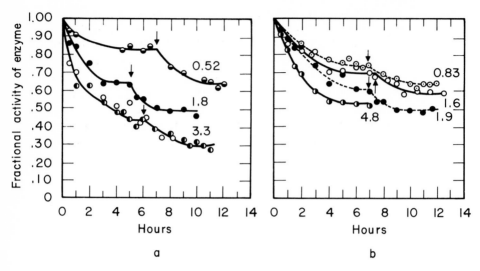

FIG. 4-8.   CONSTANT INTRAVENOUS INFUSIONS OF NEOSTIGMINE IN DOGS.   *Vertical scale is activity of plasma cholinesterase, used as a measure of the concentration of neostigmine, an inhibitor of that enzyme. Since the relationship between inhibitor concentration and observed enzyme activity is complex, curves may only be interpreted semiquantitatively. Each* curve *represents a different infusion rate; values given are to be multiplied by 10^{-10} moles/kg per minute. In graph* a, *renal pedicles were ligated at times shown by* arrows; *in graph* b, *infusion was started in hepatic portal vein instead of femoral vein, then shifted at* arrow *to femoral vein. (From Goldstein et al., Figs. 8 and 11.[20])*

tration of neostigmine, although the relationship is not one of simple proportionality. The data shown on the figure are measurements of enzyme activity, plotted as fractions of the initial uninhibited activity. In Fig. 4-8a we see that plateau levels were established at three different infusion rates into the femoral vein; and in Fig. 4-8b, that infusions into the hepatic portal vein led to a lesser degree of inhibition of the enzyme (i.e., a lower drug concentration) at comparable infusion rates. Qualitatively, this indicates that the liver is a significant site of elimination of neostigmine, a conclusion that was confirmed by shifting the infusion from the portal vein to the femoral vein after the plateau levels were established (Fig. 4-8b); a greater plateau concentration of neostigmine resulted. The effect of tying the renal pedicles (Fig. 4-8a) indicates, in the same way, that the kidneys play a significant role in the overall elimination. The investigators used the difference between the two plateau levels, with and without the kidneys functioning, to obtain a quantitative estimate of the rate constant of renal excretion. This corresponded to a renal clearance for neostigmine of about 100 ml/min, a value consistent with elimination by glomerular filtration in the dog. The renal clearance estimate was confirmed directly by measurements of neostigmine in the urine.

Neostigmine was also administered by constant infusion to human patients suffering from myasthenia gravis, a disease for which it is the drug of choice. Figure 4-9 shows the relationship between the rate of drug infusion at the steady state (equal to the rate of elimination at the steady state) and the neostigmine concentration at the steady state. The data from the experiments with dogs are also shown on the same graph. The method used by the investigators to express the infusion rate is the common one of relating dosage to body weight, since weights of experimental animals or patients vary widely. To be applicable here, the steady-state equation has to be rewritten, dividing both sides by body weight:

$$Q/W = k_e x'(V_d/W) = k_e x'\alpha,$$

where W is the body weight and α is the volume of distribution expressed as a fraction of the body weight. Then

$$\log (Q/W) = \log x' + \log \alpha + \log k_e$$

$$\log k_e + \log \alpha = \log (Q/W) - \log x'.$$

And for any two infusion rates, since α and k_e do not change,

FIG. 4-9. RELATIONSHIP OF ELIMINATION RATE TO THE STEADY-STATE PLASMA LEVEL OF NEOSTIGMINE. Solid circles, *myasthenia gravis patients, for whom neostigmine is the drug of choice.* Open circles, *dogs. Note that this is log-log plot.* Broken line *has a slope of 1. Elimination rate is expressed as moles/kg per minute, neostigmine concentration as moles/liter.* (*From Goldstein et al., Fig. 18.*[20])

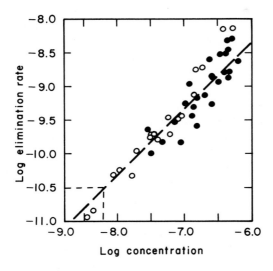

20 A. GOLDSTEIN, O. KRAYER, M. A. ROOT, G. H. ACHESON, and M. E. DOHERTY: Plasma neostigmine levels and cholinesterase inhibition in dogs and myasthenic patients. *J. Pharmacol. Exper. Therap.* 96:56 (1949).

$$log\ (Q_1/W) - log\ (Q_2/W) = log\ x_1' - log\ x_2'$$

$$\text{slope} = \frac{log\ (Q_1/W) - log\ (Q_2/W)}{log\ x_1' - log\ x_2'} = 1.$$

These equations show that if the elimination is first order throughout the range examined, the relationship between log elimination rate and log concentration should be linear, and the slope of the line should be unity. We see from Fig. 4-9 that this seems to be true of neostigmine in both dogs and humans, within the limits of the experimental errors. Since all the points fall approximately on the same line, it follows that the elimination rate constant is about the same in both species, assuming the same manner of distribution into the body fluids. This k_e can be found by applying to Fig. 4-9 the equation $log\ k_e + log\ \alpha = log\ (Q/W) - log\ x'$, then making the subtractions indicated by the dotted lines, and assuming that neostigmine, a quaternary ammonium derivative, is confined to the extracellular fluid ($\alpha = 0.18$, $log\ \alpha = -0.74$):

$$log\ k_e - 0.74 = -10.5 - (-8.2)$$

$$k_e = \text{antilog}\ (-1.56) = 0.0275\ \text{min}^{-1}.$$

Thus, a little less than 3 per cent is eliminated per minute, and

$$t_{1/2} = 0.693/0.0275 = 25\ \text{min}.$$

Dosage Regimens

The plateau principle also provides a fundamental basis for understanding the rationale of dosage schedules and of drug accumulation in the body. When we give a drug we are attempting to establish a certain therapeutic concentration in the body fluids, or a certain total amount of drug in the body. This *effective drug concentration* (EDC) is a characteristic biologic property of the drug, over which we have no control. If the drug level is much below this EDC, the desired drug actions will not occur. If the level is much higher, toxic effects may well become manifest.

Although the EDC has been defined here as a concentration, the argument to follow would apply equally well if EDC were the total amount of drug in the body or the amount of drug fixed at some site of action.

Dosage schedules entail two variables: the magnitude of the single dose and the frequency with which that dose is repeated, usually expressed as a *dosing interval*. For any given dose, the extent to which the drug level in the body will fluctuate within a dosing interval is determined by several factors. For a given rate of elimination, the faster the absorption, the greater the fluctuation. With rapid absorption, the bulk of the drug will enter the circulation rapidly and the drug level will be high at first, then fall relatively fast; whereas with slower absorption, the buildup to a peak will be less rapid and the drug level more sustained, as seen with sustained-release medications (p. 127). For a given rate of absorption, the fluctuation is obviously greater the more rapid the elimination. No generalization will reliably answer the question just how much the drug level may be permitted to fluctuate above and below the desired level; this will depend entirely upon the particular drug. Detailed analysis of the kinetics of the establishment and decay of drug levels after single doses will be deferred to a later section (p. 317).

Here, we shall begin by ignoring the fluctuations. We assume, as a first approximation, that the absorption of a dose proceeds at a practically constant rate throughout each dosing interval, and that it is complete at the end of the dosing interval. In other words, we suppose that the conditions are practically equivalent to those of a constant infusion. Our aim is to establish and maintain the EDC as a steady state. Obviously, if the individual dose were large enough and the dosing interval short enough, the EDC would be reached quickly; but the drug concentration would continue to increase. There must be some lower rate of drug input that would just establish but not exceed the desired EDC; this rate is defined as the *maintenance dose rate*.

A good illustration is found in the use of digitoxin to maintain cardiac compensation in a patient with congestive heart failure; the dose of about 0.1 mg daily, given day after day indefinitely, is the maintenance dose rate for this drug. What determines the maintenance dose rate of a drug, in general? The familiar equation for a constant infusion provides the answer:

$$Q = \text{maintenance dose rate} = k_e(\text{EDC})V_d,$$

where $(\text{EDC})V_d$ is the total amount of drug required in the body at the EDC, determined by the drug's biologic potency and by its distribution in the body. The equation shows that the maintenance dose rate will have to be higher the more rapidly the drug is eliminated.

The time required to establish the EDC with any drug, under the conditions specified, is given by the plateau principle; the half-time will simply be the elimination half-time. Thus, a drug with short biologic half-life can come to the EDC quickly when the maintenance dose is administered from the start. But a drug that is eliminated slowly will necessarily achieve its EDC slowly. If k_e is known, then the whole time course of approach to the EDC is simply that shown in Fig. 4-7.

Once it has been decided to administer a drug, the therapeutic effect is invariably wanted quickly, certainly within a few hours. Yet this is impossible if the drug's half-life is longer than a few hours. The solution to the dosage problem for drugs that are eliminated slowly is to administer relatively large doses initially in order to establish the EDC quickly, and then to continue with the maintenance dose rate thereafter. The large initial doses are called *priming doses*. Note especially that if the priming dose rate were continued, the EDC would be greatly exceeded, at the risk of serious toxicity. A theoretical illustration of this principle is shown in Fig. 4-10. Here, the fluctuations due to the individual doses are shown also; clearly,

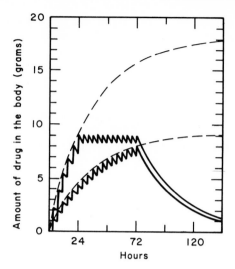

FIG. 4-10.   CURVES OF ACCUMULATION WITH REPEATED DOSAGE AT CONSTANT
INTERVALS.   *Elimination constant* $k_e = 0.0289$ *hr^{-1}, elimination half-time =
24 hr, dosing interval = 4 hr. In lower curve, dose is 1 g; in upper curve, 2 g
for the first six doses, then 1 g.* Solid *curves are computed from the given
parameters;* zig-zag *portions represent fluctuations during period of drug administration.* Broken *curves* indicate course of continued accumulation if drug
administration were continued. Drug stopped at 72 hr. Elimination curve is
seen to be identical to accumulation curve, but inverted. (From Gaddum,
Fig. 1.*[21]*)

the fluctuations can be minimized by subdividing the doses and administering them more frequently, the limit of such dose fragmentation being a
constant infusion. In practice it is inconvenient to administer medication
more often than once every few hours, and the desirability of uninterrupted
sleep at night further demands that the dosing interval be as long as possible. A certain amount of fluctuation is therefore inevitable; and it will be
more extreme the more rapidly the drug is eliminated.

Figure 4-10 is based upon a rigorous theoretical treatment of repeated drug administration leading to attainment of the EDC.[21] Whereas
our application of the plateau principle entailed the assumption that drug
absorption is continuous, this approach takes into account the fluctuations
resulting from drug elimination during the intervals between doses. It assumes, however, that each single dose is absorbed instantaneously. Let M_0
be the dose of a drug, X_0 the resulting drug level in the body (X_0/V_d would
be the plasma concentration), and t^* the dosing interval. Now we give M_0,
at $t = 0$, repeat after t^*, $2t^*$, $3t^*$ . . . nt^*. At $t = 0$, just after the first
dose, $X = X_0$. At $t = t^*$, just before the second dose,

$$X = X_0 e^{-k_e t^*}$$

[21] J. H. GADDUM: Repeated doses of drugs. *Nature 153:*494 (1944).

because of the exponential elimination of the drug during the interval t^*. To simplify the algebra, denote $e^{-k_e t^*}$ by the symbol p. Then just before the second dose, at $t = t^*$,

$$X = X_0 p$$

and just after the instantaneous absorption of the second dose, still at $t = t^*$,

$$X = X_0 + X_0 p = X_0(1 + p).$$

At $2t^*$, just before the third dose,

$$X = X_0(1 + p)p$$

and just after the third dose,

$$X = X_0 + X_0(1 + p)p = X_0(1 + p + p^2).$$

Just after the nth dose,

$$X_n = X_0(1 + p + p^2 + \ldots + p^{n-1}).$$

Solving the series, we obtain

$$X_n = X_0 \frac{(1 - p^n)}{(1 - p)}$$

and eventually, as $n \to \infty$, $p^n \to 0$, since $p < 1$,

$$X_\infty = X_0/(1 - p).$$

For attainment of a certain fraction of the eventual plateau,

$$f = \frac{X_n}{X_\infty} = \frac{X_0(1 - p^n)}{(1 - p)} \cdot \frac{(1 - p)}{X_0} = (1 - p^n)$$

$$f = 1 - e^{-k_e t^* n}$$

Since $t^* n$, the dosing interval times the number of doses, is the same as the total time t, this equation is identical to that derived previously (p. 296) in connection with the plateau principle.

Suppose we wish to compute how many doses will be required at a certain dosing interval to attain a given fraction of the eventual plateau drug level. Rewriting the equation to solve for n, we obtain

$$n = \frac{\ln (1 - f)}{-k_e t^*} = \frac{2.3 \log (1 - f)}{-k_e t^*}.$$

As an example, suppose $k_e = 0.1$ hr^{-1} and $t^* = 4$ hr, and we wish to calculate the number of doses needed to achieve 90 per cent of the plateau. Then

$$n = \frac{2.3 \log (1 - 0.9)}{(-0.1)(4)} = 6 \text{ doses.}$$

Suppose we wish to fix the level of drug in the body and maintain that level. Obviously there will be a direct relationship between the dosing interval and the maintenance dose required. Since the maintenance dose has to replace drug that was eliminated during the dosing interval, the longer the interval, the greater the required dose and the greater also the fluctuation. As shown above,

$$X_\infty = X_0/(1 - p)$$

$$\frac{X_0}{X_\infty} = 1 - e^{-k_e t^*}.$$

This expression gives the fraction of total drug in the body that has to be replaced in each dosing interval. Thus, immediately after the maintenance dose is given (assuming instantaneous absorption), the plateau level is restored,

$$X_0/X_\infty = 1.$$

Just before the next dose, the fraction $(1 - e^{-k_e t^*})$ has been eliminated and must be replaced. This fraction, therefore, represents the maximum fluctuation below the plateau level. Evidently, the smaller the value of k_e and the shorter the dosing interval t^*, the smaller will be the fluctuation.

As an example, suppose we wish to establish and maintain a plasma level of $10\mu g/ml$ with a drug whose volume of distribution is the extracellular fluid, and whose elimination rate constant is 0.001 min^{-1}. If the dosing interval is to be 3 hours, what maintenance dose is required, how long will it take to attain 90 per cent of the desired EDC, and what will be the maximum fluctuation below the EDC?

$$V_d = 12 \times 10^3 \text{ ml}$$

$$X_\infty = V_d(\text{EDC}) = 12 \times 10^3 \times 10 = 120 \text{ mg}$$

$$k_e = 0.001 \text{ min}^{-1}$$

$$t^* = 3 \times 60 = 180 \text{ min}$$

$$\frac{X_0}{X_\infty} = 1 - e^{(-0.001)(180)} = 1 - 0.835 = 0.165$$

$$X_0 = 20 \text{ mg}.$$

The EDC will fluctuate 16.5 per cent below its appropriate level, in other words, from $10\mu g/ml$ to $8.4\mu g/ml$ in each 3-hour interval.

The time required to attain 90 per cent of the EDC if the maintenance dose is administered from the beginning is found readily from the number of doses needed at the fixed 3-hour interval:

$$n = \frac{2.3 \log (1 - 0.9)}{(-0.001)(180)} = \frac{-2.3}{-0.18} = 13 \text{ doses,}$$

and the time required to administer them is 39 hours. This is an undesirably long time. Obviously, the preferable procedure would be to administer the total amount required in the body (120 mg) as a single priming dose or a series of closely spaced priming doses, and then continue with the 20-mg maintenance dose.

Given a drug with $k_e = 0.2$ hr^{-1} and some important reason for minimizing fluctuation. What dosing interval would be required in order to ensure that the drug level does not fall below 90 per cent of the EDC? As shown above, fluctuation is given by the term $(1 - e^{-k_e t^*})$, and here we require

$$1 - e^{-k_e t^*} = 0.10$$

$$e^{-k_e t^*} = 0.9$$

$$t^* = \frac{2.3 \log 0.9}{-k_e} = \frac{-0.106}{-0.2} = 0.53$$

Then the required dosing interval is about ½ hour.

The use of priming doses to overcome the otherwise slow buildup to the EDC with drugs that have long biologic half-lives is exemplified by the procedure known as *digitalization*. One of the commonly used digitalis glycosides, digitoxin, is eliminated very slowly from the body, at a rate of approximately 10 per cent per day; half-life is about seven days. Then if the daily maintenance dose were given from the start, the EDC would not nearly be achieved for weeks, an intolerable situation for a drug whose rapidity of action in congestive heart failure is potentially life saving. Moreover, drugs of this class have a very narrow range between therapeutic and toxic levels, so that large fluctuations cannot be tolerated. Digitalization consists of giving priming doses until the electrocardiographic and clinical signs confirm that the EDC is just being reached, then continuing with the much smaller maintenance dose rate.

An elegant example of the use of priming doses concerns the treatment of malaria with quinacrine. This drug was considered virtually useless for years because of its apparently poor efficacy in acute clinical attacks of malaria, and its seemingly capricious toxicity. During World War II, however, carefully conducted studies[22] of plasma levels and of elimination rates showed clearly that without priming doses the EDC could not be attained quickly enough to be effective in terminating attacks of acute malaria in the erythrocytic phase of the disease. The slow elimination rate of the drug was largely attributable to an extraordinary degree of tissue binding, especially in liver, spleen, skin, and leukocytes (Table 4-1). The binding to leukocytes produced concentrations at least 1000 times those in plasma water, making whole-blood determinations of quinacrine concentration completely misleading. The fractional binding of the drug to plasma proteins was also high—from 0.75 to 0.90. Figure 4-11 shows that when

22 J. A. SHANNON, D. P. EARLE, JR., B. B. BRODIE, J. V. TAGGART, and R. W. BERLINER: The pharmacological basis for the rational use of atabrine in the treatment of malaria. *J. Pharmacol. Exper. Therap. 81:*307 (1944).

TABLE 4-1. **Tissue levels of quinacrine in the dog**

A dog was given quinacrine, 20 mg/kg for 14 days, then sacrificed, and tissue concentrations were determined. (Data of Shannon et al.[22] By permission of Williams & Wilkins.)

Tissue	Quinacrine concentration (mg/kg)
Plasma	0.061
Muscle	55
Lung	310
Spleen	571
Liver	1306

the drug was given to human volunteers at a daily dose of 50 mg, many weeks were required to attain a plasma plateau. When a priming dose was given (200 mg daily for the first five days), an EDC plateau was established (actually somewhat exceeded) at the outset and then maintained by the smaller daily dose.

An interesting calculation can be made, using knowledge of the just-effective priming dosage to estimate V_d. The computation is based

FIG. 4-11. ESTABLISHMENT OF QUINACRINE PLASMA LEVELS IN HUMAN SUB-JECTS. *Vertical scale is plasma quinacrine concentration in μg/liter; horizontal scale gives time in weeks. The points are average values in groups of seven to nine subjects. Drug was given by mouth, 50 mg on each of six successive weekdays, 100 mg on Sundays, total dose 400 mg/wk. In graph* a, *this regimen was pursued from the start. In graph* b, *priming doses were given on the first five days (200 mg daily). (Adapted from Shannon et al., Fig. 1.[22])*

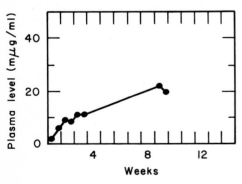 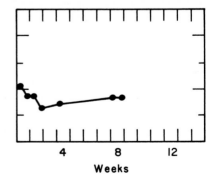

a   b

upon the excess of the priming amount over the maintenance dose, and on the plateau concentration of drug in the plasma. Figure 4-11 shows that during the priming period an excess of 150 mg was given daily for five days, or 750 mg excess. This established a concentration of about $20\mu g$/liter. Then, assuming negligible elimination during this period of time,

$$V_d = X/x = 750 \times 10^3/20 = 3.8 \times 10^4 \text{ liters (sic!)},$$

and applying the general plateau equation,

$$k_e = Q/xV_d$$
$$= (50 \text{ mg day}^{-1}/0.02 \text{ mg liter}^{-1}) \, (3.8 \times 10^4 \text{ liters})$$
$$= 0.07 \text{ day}^{-1}.$$

For the half-time of attaining the plateau without priming doses,

$$t_{1/2} = 0.693/0.07 = 10 \text{ days},$$

and to attain 90 per cent of the desired plateau, from Fig. 4-7, $kt = 2.3$, so that

$$t_{0.9} = 2.3/0.07 = 33 \text{ days}.$$

These calculations make it obvious why quinacrine therapy was so ineffective before the introduction of priming doses.

Obviously, for any drug the dosage during the priming period has to be larger than during the maintenance period. But how much larger? And when maintenance dosage is given from the start, the plateau eventually reached will obviously be higher than the drug level after the first dose. But how much higher? In order to answer these questions we must now specify more rigorously a rational dosage schedule that can be applicable to all drugs, regardless of their rates of elimination. We begin by determining the *dosing interval* t^*. This is dependent upon the amount of fluctuation that is tolerable once the steady state has been established. For illustrative purposes let us limit the range of fluctuation to 10 per cent of the EDC, a reasonable figure for many drugs. This means that t^* must be equal to the time in which one-tenth of the drug amount will be eliminated. Reference to Fig. 4-7 reveals that for $f = 0.1$, $k_e t = 0.1$, and so $t^* = 0.1/k_e$. Also, since $t_{1/2} = 0.693/k_e$, it follows that t^* is almost exactly one-seventh of the elimination half-time, $0.1/0.693$. Now the maintenance dose rate is given by M/t^*, where M is the single dose; and thus, as shown on p. 295,

$$M/t^* = (\text{EDC})V_d k_e$$
$$M = (\text{EDC})V_d k_e t^* = (\text{EDC})V_d/10.$$

This means that if no priming dosage is employed, but the maintenance dosage is used from the start, then the plateau level ultimately established will be ten times that attained during the first dosing interval.[23]

On this dosage schedule we may also estimate, from Fig. 4-7, how many doses will be required to attain 90 per cent of the EDC without priming dosage. For $f = 0.9$, we find $k_e t = 2.3$, $t = 2.3/k_e$. But, as shown above, $1/k_e = 10t^*$; therefore $t = 23t^*$, and 24 doses will be required. If priming dosage is to be used, then, of course, the priming doses have to furnish the total amount of drug needed in the body at the EDC, i.e., $(EDC)V_d$. Therefore, in the present example, the total drug given as priming doses will have to be at least ten times the maintenance dose.[24]

It is interesting to examine the customary dosage schedules for drugs in common use to see whether or not they conform to these rational principles; and if not, to consider why not. Clinical experience alone has served to shape a very suitable dosage schedule for the digitalis glycosides. For digitalis, as pointed out already, $k_e = 0.1$ day^{-1}, i.e., $1/10$ of the amount present is eliminated per day. As shown above, if the fluctuation is to be held within 10 per cent of the EDC, the dosing interval t^* will be $0.1/k_e$, which is equal to one day. Thus, daily administration of the maintenance dose of this drug suffices to achieve the fine degree of control of the drug level that is so essential for this class of drug. If some other, irrational dosage schedule were employed, the therapeutic outcome could be demonstrably worse because toxic signs and symptoms appear at drug levels only slightly higher than the EDC. On the other hand, in congestive failure, even a slight decrease in the plateau level below the EDC will manifest itself in exacerbation of symptoms and clear signs of inadequate dosage.

Now let us consider a hypothetical drug that is eliminated primarily by glomerular filtration, without extensive tissue binding. Here (cf. Table 2-20), if the drug is distributed in body water, $k_e = (0.13$ liter $\cdot$ min$^{-1})/41$ liters $= 0.0032$ min^{-1}. Applying the same criteria as before, that fluctuation is to be held to 10 per cent of the EDC, we find $t^* = 0.1/0.0032 = 31$ minutes. Now as a matter of fact, such a drug would not be given parenterally every ½ hour, but more likely every 4 hours. Thus, a far greater degree of fluctuation is tolerated for the sake of convenience, a dosing interval shorter than several hours for parenteral administration being regarded as impractical. This means either that large fluctuations are tolerable because the EDC can safely be exceeded by a large amount, or that the EDC is simply not maintained continuously and some of the

---

[23] Actually somewhat more than tenfold, because some of the first dose will have been eliminated before all of it is absorbed. For oral or parenteral sustained-release medication, the "single dose" will mean the amount of drug that is absorbed in the interval t*, even though the nominal dosing interval may be longer.

[24] *At least,* because unless the whole priming dosage is given intravenously, some will be eliminated in each dosing interval.

therapeutic effect is sacrificed. Such a drug could, however, be given orally or in a sustained-release form parenterally, if the absorption could be smoothed out over several dosing intervals. Thus, the nominal dose interval might be 4 hours, and the nominal dose would contain eight times as much medication as was required in each 30-minute dosing interval; then if the total administered dose were absorbed evenly over the whole 4 hours, the desired dose rate would be achieved.

There is a limit to the usefulness of periodic dosing. When k_e becomes much larger than 0.003 min^{-1}, (e.g., when the drug is rapidly metabolized), then no dosing interval is practical and the method of constant infusion must be adopted. A good example is the administration of the polypeptide hormone oxytocin to induce labor at term; this drug is destroyed by a peptidase in the blood. Another example is succinylcholine, a neuromuscular blocking agent used in anesthesia. This drug is hydrolyzed rapidly by plasma and liver cholinesterases. Its elimination rate in vivo can be estimated from the increment in duration of effect that is produced by logarithmic dose increments. Thus, for example, in a large number of patients[25] an intravenous dose of 1000 mg caused apnea by paralyzing the muscles of respiration for 17.8 minutes on the average. A dose of 500 mg caused apnea for only 11.9 minutes. The difference, 5.9 minutes, represents the time required for 1000 mg to be decreased by metabolism to only 500 mg, i.e., it is the biologic half-life. Then $k_e = 0.14$ min^{-1}, a much faster rate of elimination than even renal secretory mechanisms could accomplish. Drugs are metabolized at widely varying rates, some even faster than succinylcholine. In all such cases the EDC will be established very soon after starting a constant infusion and can be maintained readily, and the drug effect will disappear within minutes after discontinuing the infusion. Complete elimination of fluctuation and excellent control are the two important advantages gained by the constant infusion of drugs with high k_e values.

Drug Accumulation and Toxicity

The plateau principle also explains why cumulative toxicity sometimes occurs. If a drug's elimination rate is slow, and one attempts nevertheless to achieve a therapeutic effect with a constant dosage schedule (i.e., without priming doses), toxicity is the likely outcome. The reason for this is that one will seek to obtain the therapeutic action quickly; and if the dose rate is chosen to give that result, then the eventual steady-state will greatly exceed the EDC. Let us suppose, for the sake of argument, that a dose rate will always be chosen that suffices to attain one-half the EDC in some convenient time t_1, less than the drug's biologic half-life $t_{1/2}$. One-half

25 W. KALOW and D. R. GUNN: The relation between dose of succinylcholine and duration of apnea in man. *J. Pharmacol. Exper. Therap. 120:*203 (1957).

the eventual plateau will be reached in $t_{1/2}$ if the same constant dose rate is continued. The question is, how much higher than the EDC will the eventual steady-state plateau be? Figure 4-7 provides the answer. At $t_{1/2}$, $kt = 0.693$. We can find the point on the horizontal scale corresponding to kt_1, since we know what fraction t_1 is of t_2; and thus we can determine the value of f at this point. We know that the actual drug level corresponding to this f is one-half the EDC. So $2f$ corresponds to the EDC, and the excessive drug level eventually established will be $1/2f$ times the EDC.

To illustrate, suppose a drug with a half-life of five days is given at a dose rate that gives one-half the EDC in 16 hours (0.67 days). Then $kt_1 = (0.693/5)(0.67) = 0.0929$; and from Fig. 4-7, $f = 0.09$. Therefore the level reached at this dose rate in 16 hours is only 0.09 of the eventual plateau, which will be EDC/0.18, or 6 times the EDC. The half-time of cumulation to this probably toxic level will, of course, be five days.

A very good example of cumulative toxicity with repeated drug administration is seen with bromide ion in man. Bromide used to be relied upon heavily in the chronic treatment of epilepsy, and it was also used as a mild sedative. It is still found in sedative preparations sold across the counter to the general public. The EDC for this drug is about 12 meq/liter. Psychosis and dermatitis, the chief toxic manifestations, occur at concentrations above 20 meq/liter. The bromide ion is distributed in approximately the same volume as the chloride ion, a volume somewhat greater than that of the extracellular fluid, or about 15 liters in the average man. It is handled at the kidneys in much the same way as chloride—filtered at the glomeruli and largely reabsorbed in the tubules. Bromide is actually reabsorbed somewhat more efficiently than chloride; the chloride clearance is about 1.2 liters daily, the bromide clearance about 0.9 liters daily.[26] From the clearance and the volume of distribution we find $k_e = 0.9/15 = 0.06$ day^{-1}; thus, half-life $= 0.693/0.06 = 12$ days. An experimental investigation using radioactive ^{82}Br in ten human subjects and measuring plasma levels twice daily gave exactly this theoretical value for the half-life.[27]

Two conclusions may be drawn from k_e and the half-life. The half-time for achieving the steady state on a constant daily dosage of bromide will be 12 days. And the steady-state level will be about 1/0.06 (or about 16) times the level established on the first day. To use the drug properly, one would compute the maintenance dosage as follows:

$$EDC = 12 \text{ meq/liter}$$

$$V_d = 15 \text{ liters}$$

required amount in body at EDC $= 12 \times 15 = 180$ meq.

[26] J. W. PALMER and H. T. CLARKE: The elimination of bromides from the blood stream. *J. Biol. Chem.* 99:435 (1933).

[27] R. SÖREMARK: The biological half-life of bromide ions in human blood. *Acta Physiol. Scand.* 50:119 (1960).

The maintenance dosage is designated by Q, and

$$Q = k_e(\text{EDC})V_d$$

$$Q = 0.06 \times 180 = 11 \text{ meq} \cdot \text{day}^{-1}, \text{ or about } 0.9 \text{ g} \cdot \text{day}^{-1}.$$

This dose could be given daily for an indefinite period without harm, but it will require 12 days to attain half the EDC, and 40 days (3.3 times the half-time) to achieve 90 per cent of the EDC. Alternatively, the required 180 meq (15 g) could be given within the first few days as a priming dose to establish the EDC, followed by the maintenance dosage thereafter. The reason why toxicity develops so frequently and so insidiously with this drug is that sufficient dosage to produce any sedation at all within a day or two must necessarily be higher than the maintenance dose rate, and so it will inevitably, if continued, produce plasma bromide levels much higher than the EDC.

The bromide half-life can be shortened to three or four days by chloride administration at about 200 meq per day in excess of normal intake. The reason for this is simply that chloride and bromide are treated very much alike at the renal tubules. Increasing the chloride level in the plasma and glomerular filtrate leads to a diminution in the fraction of (chloride + bromide) that is reabsorbed, and thus to an increased bromide clearance.[28]

For the same reasons, cumulative toxicity may develop insidiously with various substances that are not employed therapeutically but to which people may be exposed chronically. Often such poisons are bound tightly at specialized sites in the body. This accumulation in vulnerable tissues causes toxic manifestations, and the low elimination rate associated with extensive binding is responsible for the slow time course of the accumulation. Poisoning by heavy metals follows this pattern. Lead, for example, is present in the urban environment as a result of the combustion of leaded gasoline, and city dwellers breathe it constantly. Because lead is stored in many tissues and deposited in bones, it has a very long half-life in the body. When a human subject was given 2 mg per day of a soluble lead salt, the blood concentration of lead increased from 0.29μg/ml to 0.72μg/ml, with a half-time of about two months.[29] The blood level then remained fairly constant for two years during which the daily intake was maintained. Despite the steady state in the blood and body fluids, a continuous accumulation went on during the whole period of the experiment, as indicated by a persistent small discrepancy between daily intake and daily output (positive lead balance). When the daily dose was discontinued after two years, the

[28] O. BODANSKY and W. MODELL: The differential excretion of bromide and chloride ions and its role in bromide retention. *J. Pharmacol. Exper. Therap.* 73:51 (1941).

[29] R. A. KEHOE, J. C. CHOLAK, O. M. HUBBARD, K. BAMBACH, and R. R. MC NARY: Experimental studies on lead absorption and excretion and their relation to the diagnosis and treatment of lead poisoning. *J. Indust. Hyg. & Toxicol.* 25:71 (1943).

blood level fell with a half-time of two months, but an elevated urine output persisted for much longer. Clearly we are dealing here with complex kinetics. Tissue binding and deposition in bone continue after the fluid compartments are at a steady state, and loss of lead from its sites of very tight binding or deposition continues after the body fluids have nearly eliminated their lead (cf. p. 339 for analogous kinetics concerning the elimination of anesthetic gases). The symptoms of lead poisoning are, initially at least, rather vague; irritability and other mood changes predominate in the early stages, frank psychosis and encephalopathy later. The long biologic half-life results in so slow a buildup of toxic levels in the body that no connection may seem evident between the beginning of exposure to a chronically noxious environment and the development and progression of the symptoms of lead poisoning.

The kidney shows a high affinity for the organic mercurial diuretics. There is good correlation between the renal content of these drugs and the magnitude of diuretic response. Excessive binding, however, leads to typical mercuric ion toxicity, characterized primarily by impaired renal tubular function and ultimately by damage to tubule structure as well. Studies with mercurial diuretics containing ^{203}Hg have shown that after distribution is complete, the concentration in kidney is about 100 times that in plasma.[30] The mercury in the kidney is for the most part bound very tightly to sulfhydryl groups. Bismuth compounds also interact strongly with −SH groups in the kidney and cause toxic effects there; but arsenicals, which also form strong bonds with −SH, deposit largely in liver and skin, causing toxicity in those tissues. The reasons for such tissue-specific differences in binding and accumulation are unknown.

An important site of cumulative storage and toxicity is the widely distributed reticuloendothelial system, which takes up colloidal substances of many kinds. Thorium dioxide was formerly given as a colloidal solution intravenously; its opacity to x-rays made it useful for roentgenographic visualization of the liver, spleen, and blood vessels. However, it is bound so tightly in the reticuloendothelial cells that its excretion is extremely slow. Since thorium is a radioisotope with a very long radioactive half-life, its clinical use has now been abandoned, for the hazards of tissue destruction and of radiation-induced carcinogenesis are increased greatly by the long biologic half-life.

Somewhat similar hazards of cumulative toxicity involving a combination of radioactivity and long biologic half-life are presented by the fallout of debris from nuclear explosions. For example, ^{90}Sr is handled like calcium by the body; it is deposited in bone, and only a minute fraction of the total is excreted daily (cf. p. 407). Therefore, with constant exposure, there is a slow buildup of the body burden. Once the element is

---

[30] R. R. M. BORGHGRAEF and R. F. PITTS: The distribution of chlormerodrin (Neohydrin ®) in tissues of the rat and dog. *J. Clin. Invest.* 35:31 (1956).

stored in the bones, its radioactive decay subjects the erythroblastic tissues and the bone cells to continuous bombardment. Another fallout product of importance is ^{131}I, found widely in milk from cows that have grazed on lands contaminated with fallout debris. This element is concentrated in the thyroid gland by an active transport mechanism and is there incorporated into thyroid hormone. The uptake and incorporation are responsible for the long biologic half-life of iodine, and again the combination of radioactivity, accumulation, and tissue storage intensifies the risk of serious toxicity. For these reasons the potential hazard in the use of ^{131}I for the diagnosis and treatment of thyroid disease is still a matter of controversy among clinicians. Extreme hazards, for similar reasons, are presented by ^{14}C and ^{3}H in chemical forms that permit their incorporation into nucleic acids. A molecule of DNA containing ^{14}C atoms may persist without turnover throughout a person's life, while the radioactivity of this isotope barely diminishes in a human lifetime. If the DNA in question is contained in the germinal cells, mutations resulting from the radioactive disintegrations will present a threat to that person's progeny. Radioactive carbon or tritium present in drugs, intermediate metabolites, or even proteins are far less hazardous because of the relatively short biologic half-lives, in contrast to DNA.

Slow accumulation of drugs and poisons is also seen in the fat depots of the body. The widely used lipid-soluble insecticide DDT has been found regularly in human fat at autopsy, even in people having no known direct contact with it. This is typical of the environmental contamination that affects everyone in cases where continuous exposure can cause slow accumulation over a period of years. Likewise, estrogenic compounds used to promote weight gain in beef cattle have been found in human fat depots at autopsy.

Kinetics of Changes in Enzyme Levels

As pointed out in chapter 3, the enzyme content of an animal tissue is maintained at its normal level by equal rates of enzyme synthesis and enzyme degradation. A drug may increase this steady-state amount of enzyme by speeding its production or slowing its breakdown. Continuous protein synthesis is essential for both of these mechanisms. Therefore, if an enzyme "induction" is abolished by blocking protein synthesis, it cannot be concluded that increased synthesis rather than stabilization was responsible (although activation of existing enzyme can be ruled out as the mechanism of drug action). The "induction" of tryptophan pyrrolase by its substrate, for example, is prevented by puromycin, ethionine, and other inhibitors of protein synthesis; but it is now clear that tryptophan stabilizes the enzyme rather than increasing its rate of synthesis.[31]

31 R. T. SCHIMKE, E. M. SWEENEY, and C. M. BERLIN: The roles of synthesis and degradation in the control of rat liver tryptophan pyrrolase. *J. Biol. Chem.* 240:322 (1965).

The time course of a shift from one steady-state level of enzyme to another is given by the plateau principle; its half-time is simply the turnover half-time (half-life) of the enzyme. Consequently, if an enzyme is to respond quickly to regulatory influences, it must be degraded rapidly. The more rapidly degraded it is, the more rapidly can its level change in response to changes in either the synthesis rate or the degradation rate.[31a]

Much confusion has resulted from failure to recognize this application of the plateau principle. Consider two enzymes, A and B, both subject to regulation by steroid hormones. Enzyme A is rapidly degraded, B is quite stable. Suppose that both rates of synthesis are increased fivefold by hormone treatment. Then both enzyme activities will also have increased fivefold when the new steady state is reached, since (p. 292)

$$X' = k_{in}/k_{out}$$

and we have increased k_{in} by a factor of 5 in both cases. But the rates of increase in enzyme activity will be very different for A and for B. One day after hormone administration is begun, A may already have increased nearly fivefold, whereas B may have changed but little. If the enzyme determinations are performed at this time, therefore, the false conclusion may be drawn that steroid hormones have a much greater effect upon the synthesis of A than upon the synthesis of B. One should always refrain from drawing negative conclusions unless sufficient data are available to be certain that the shift from one steady state to another has been completed.

If a drug that causes increase or decrease in the steady-state level of an enzyme is given as a single injection, interpretation is usually impossible, because there is no way to assess whether or not new steady states have been reached. Figure 4-12 presents an illustrative example. The capacity of rat liver to metabolize zoxazolamine was followed after injections of 3,4-benzpyrene or phenobarbital. The rats that received benzpyrene had a single injection, but the rats that were given phenobarbital had two injections daily for the duration of the experiment. Evidently, the enzyme activity was stimulated by phenobarbital to an increase of about fourfold over the starting level, and a new plateau was reached. The half-time of this shift was about 40 hours, whence it may be concluded that in the presence of phenobarbital the half-time of enzyme degradation was 40 hours. There is no way to decide, from these data alone, whether phenobarbital increases the rate of enzyme synthesis or decreases the rate of enzyme degradation. One might also be tempted to conclude that benzpyrene stimulates the increase in enzyme activity faster than phenobarbital does, but that would not be justified on the basis of the limited data shown. Continuous

---

[31a] C. M. BERLIN and R. T. SCHIMKE: Influence of turnover rates on the responses of enzymes to cortisone. *Mol. Pharmacol. 1:*149 (1965).

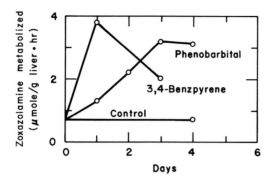

FIG. 4-12.   STIMULATION OF ZOXAZOLAMINE METABOLISM BY BENZPYRENE AND PHENOBARBITAL.   *Weanling rats were injected once with 3,4-benzpyrene (25 mg/kg) or with phenobarbital (38 mg/kg) twice daily for the duration of the experiment. Zoxazolamine metabolism by liver was determined in vitro at the times shown. (From Conney and Burns, Fig. 1.[32])*

administration of benzpyrene might have increased the activity to a much higher level, so the shift half-time could well be identical to that produced by phenobarbital.

The plateau principle can be used as a practical test to distinguish between increased enzyme synthesis and decreased enzyme breakdown as mechanisms underlying a drug-induced increase in enzyme level, assuming that enzyme activation has been ruled out.[32a] The following preconditions must be established: The "inducing" drug must become fully effective quickly and must remain present continuously until the new steady-state enzyme level is clearly established; and the "inducing" action must cease quickly when drug administration is discontinued. Then the half-time of the initial shift is the degradation half-time of the enzyme in the presence of the drug. The half-time of return to the original steady state after the drug is withdrawn is the degradation half-time of the enzyme in the absence of drug. If these two time courses are the same, the drug did not stabilize the enzyme but must have acted by increasing the rate of enzyme synthesis. If the rise is slower than the fall, the drug must have acted, at least in part, by stabilizing the enzyme. The quantitative contributions of the two mechanisms may be estimated from the relationship between the initial and elevated enzyme levels, E_1' and E_2', respectively, as follows:

$$\frac{E_2'}{E_1'} = \frac{Q_2}{Q_1} \cdot \frac{k_1}{k_2},$$

[32] A. H. CONNEY and J. J. BURNS: Factors influencing drug metabolism. *Adv. Pharmacol. 1:*31 (1962).

[32a] H. L. SEGAL and Y. S. KIM: Glucocorticoid stimulation of the biosynthesis of glutamic-alanine transaminase. *Proc. Nat. Acad. Sci. 50:*912 (1963).

where Q_1 and Q_2 are the respective rates of enzyme synthesis (analogous to k_{in}, p. 292), and k_1 and k_2 are the degradation rate constants in the absence and presence of the drug, respectively.

The plateau principle has been applied recently in the manner described above to the problem of analyzing the mechanism whereby continuous administration of phenobarbital increases the amount of liver microsomal barbiturate-oxidizing enzyme.[32b] Phenobarbital was administered daily to rats in dosage sufficient to produce a maximal and sustained shift of the enzyme level. Then the drug was withdrawn and the enzyme level was permitted to return to the original level. The half-time of the shift up was 2.2 days, that of the shift down was 2.6 days. Thus, the enzyme turnover was essentially unaffected by the drug; the main cause of the increase in enzyme level was therefore increased rate of synthesis.

A special case of importance in pharmacology would be the stabilization of an enzyme by its inhibitor, leading to expansion of the total enzyme level at the steady state without any change in the rate of enzyme synthesis. Stated more generally, if the interaction between a drug and its receptor stabilizes that receptor against a normal process of turnover, there will be a compensatory expansion of the steady-state level of receptor molecules. The possible relationship of such a process to drug tolerance and physical dependence is described in chapter 9.

The quantitative description of enzyme expansion by inhibitor interaction is as follows:

Let X be the inhibitor concentration,
  E the free enzyme concentration,
  EX the concentration of inhibited enzyme,
  E_T the total enzyme concentration ($= E + EX$),
  i the fractional inhibition ($= EX/E_T$),
and assume that the reaction of inhibitor with enzyme is very rapid relative to the rate of enzyme degradation.

In the absence of inhibitor,

$$E_1' = E_T' = Q_1/k_E,$$

as already shown, where k_E is the rate constant of degradation of free enzyme. The rate of change in total enzyme after introduction of inhibitor is given by

$$\frac{dE_T}{dt} = Q_1 - k_E E - k_{EX} (EX),$$

where k_{EX} is the rate constant of degradation of EX.

Then substituting $E = (1 - i) \cdot E_T$ and $EX = i \cdot E_T$,

[32b] I. M. ARIAS and A. DE LEON: Estimation of the turnover rate of barbiturate side chain oxidation enzyme in rat liver. *Mol. Pharmacol. 3:*216 (1967).

$$dE_T/dt = Q_1 - k_E \{1 - [1 - (k_{EX}/k_E)] \cdot i\} E_T.$$

At the steady state,

$$E'_{T_2} = \frac{Q_1}{k_E \{1 - [1 - (k_{EX}/k_E)] \cdot i\}}.$$

For the factor of change in *total* enzyme,

$$\frac{E'_{T_2}}{E'_{T_1}} = \frac{1}{1 - [1 - (k_{EX}/k_E)] \cdot i}.$$

For the factor of change in *free* enzyme, substituting for E'_{T_2} its equivalent $E'_2/(1 - i)$,

$$\frac{E'_2}{E'_1} = \frac{1}{1 + (k_{EX}/k_E)[i/(1 - i)]}.$$

Now if the stabilization by inhibitor is considerable, so that k_{EX}/k_E is very small, then the equation for total enzyme becomes, approximately,

$$\frac{E'_{T_2}}{E'_{T_1}} = \frac{1}{1 - i}$$

and the equation for free enzyme becomes, approximately,

$$\frac{E'_2}{E'_1} = 1.$$

In other words, the free enzyme returns nearly to its original steady-state level in the presence of the inhibitor, but the total enzyme at the new steady state is expanded to a level determined by the fractional inhibition. If, at the other extreme, the stabilization by inhibitor is insignificant (k_{EX} nearly equal to k_E), then the enzyme is simply inhibited and not expanded:

$$\frac{E'_{T_2}}{E'_{T_1}} = 1, \quad \frac{E'_2}{E'_1} = 1 - i.$$

For intermediate degrees of stabilization the steady-state level of total enzyme will increase, and at the same time that of free enzyme will decrease.

FIRST-ORDER ABSORPTION, FIRST-ORDER ELIMINATION: KINETICS OF DRUG LEVELS AFTER SINGLE DOSES

We have examined the kinetics of elimination after a drug is introduced intravenously, and the time course of attaining a plateau when a drug is administered at a constant rate. We considered the constant rate to be achieved either rigorously, by a constant infusion, or approximately, by the repetition of a dose at regular intervals. In the latter case we assumed that relative to the whole time course under consideration no serious error would be introduced by ignoring fluctuations due to rapid absorption just after drug administration and progressively slower absorption between doses. Now we shall examine the detailed kinetics of the rise and fall of drug plasma levels after single doses. As is usually found to be the case (cf. p. 280), we assume the absorption process to be first order, and we again assume overall elimination to be first order.

Let M_0 be the dose of a drug, i.e., the amount of drug placed at the site of administration at time zero, and let k_a be the rate constant of absorption. Then at any time t thereafter, the drug remaining at the site of administration is (cf. p. 281):

$$M = M_0 e^{-k_a t}.$$

Now let X be the amount of drug that has been absorbed into the circulation and let k_e be the rate constant of elimination; then

$$\frac{dX}{dt} = k_a M - k_e X$$

and, substituting for M,

$$\frac{dX}{dt} + k_e X = k_a M_0 e^{-k_a t}.$$

This linear first-order differential equation yields the following solution for the case $k_a \neq k_e$, as first shown many years ago in a classical theoretical study of this problem.[33]

$$X = \frac{k_a M_0}{(k_e - k_a)} [e^{-k_a t} - e^{-k_e t}].$$

And for the case $k_a = k_e$, the following equation is obtained:

$$X = k_e M_0 t e^{-k_e t}.$$

These equations are derived as follows:

$$\frac{dX}{dt} = k_a M - k_e X$$

and $$M = M_0 e^{-k_a t}.$$

Equation

$$\frac{dX}{dt} + k_e X = k_a M_0 e^{-k_a t} \text{ is of the form}$$

$$Y' + P(t) Y = Q(t)$$

---

[33] T. TEORELL: Kinetics of distribution of substances administered to the body. I. The extravascular modes of administration. II. The intravascular modes of administration. *Arch. Int. Pharmacodyn.* 57:205, 226 (1937).

Multiply by integrating factor $e^{\int P dt} = e^{\int k_e dt} = e^{k_e t}$, we obtain

$$\frac{d(e^{k_e t} X)}{dt} = e^{k_e t}\left[\frac{dX}{dt} + k_e X\right] = e^{k_e t} \cdot k_a M_0 e^{-k_a t}$$

Then we integrate both sides:

$$e^{k_e t} \cdot X = k_a M_0 \int e^{(k_e - k_a)t} \cdot dt$$

$$e^{k_e t} \cdot X = k_a M_0 \frac{e^{(k_e - k_a)t}}{(k_e - k_a)} + C.$$

When $t = 0$, $X = 0$:

$$C = \frac{-k_a M_0}{(k_e - k_a)}$$

$$e^{k_e t} \cdot X = \frac{k_a M_0 e^{(k_e - k_a)t}}{(k_e - k_a)} - \frac{k_a M_0}{(k_e - k_a)}$$

$$X = \frac{k_a M_0}{(k_e - k_a)} [e^{-k_a t} - e^{-k_e t}]$$

If $k_a = k_e$ then $\int e^{(k_e - k_a)t} \cdot dt = t$, and we proceed as follows from a point midway through the derivation:

$$e^{k_e t} \cdot X = k_a M_0 \int e^{(k_e - k_a)t} \cdot dt.$$

Substituting $k_e = k_a$, we obtain

$$e^{k_e t} \cdot X = k_e M_0 t$$

$$X = k_e M_0 t e^{-k_e t}.$$

Figure 4-13 presents a generalized plot of these equations. Certain normalizing procedures have been followed in order to make a single graph represent all possible relationships between dose administered, rate constant of absorption, and rate constant of elimination. The vertical scale shows X/M_0 rather than X; i.e., regardless of what the actual dose may be, we are following the fractional absorption of that dose into the body tissues from the site of administration. The above equations, showing that the time course of absorption is independent of the dose M_0, justify this procedure. The equations have been solved for various chosen values of the ratio of rate constants, k_e/k_a, and the time scale has consequently been generalized to include one of the rate constants.

The derivation follows:

$$\frac{X}{M_0} = \frac{k_a}{(k_e - k_a)} [e^{-k_a t} - e^{-k_e t}]$$

$$= \frac{1}{\left(\dfrac{k_e}{k_a} - 1\right)} [e^{-k_e t/(k_e/k_a)} - e^{-k_e t}].$$

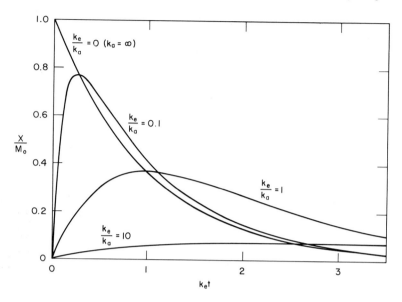

FIG. 4-13.   KINETICS OF FIRST-ORDER ABSORPTION AND FIRST-ORDER ELIMINA-
TION.   *This graph shows the amount of drug in the body* (X) *as fraction of
total drug* (M_0) *placed at an absorption site at time zero. The family of curves
is for different ratios of the rate constant of elimination* (k_e) *to the rate constant of absorption* (k_a). *The abscissal scale includes* k_e; *to convert its values to
actual time* t, *divide by* k_e. See text for complete description.

For any given drug the transformed scale of time, although not
reading directly in minutes, is nevertheless proportional to actual time.
Some important conclusions about the kinetics of drug levels in the body
may be drawn from inspection of this diagram. The curve for $k_a = \infty$
depicts the limiting case of intravenous injection, "absorption" being instantaneous. This shows the usual exponential decay of the drug level. As
absorption becomes slower (k_a smaller) relative to elimination, curves are
obtained that rise to a peak and then fall again. The slower the absorption
relative to elimination, the later is the peak attained and the lower is its
actual value.

In order to transform the time scale to real time, it is only necessary
to divide the values by the elimination rate constant k_e. An example will
serve to illustrate how Fig. 4-13 can be used to predict real behavior of
drugs. Suppose a drug is absorbed from a subcutaneous depot at a rate
of 0.1 min^{-1} and eliminated by excretion and metabolism at a rate of 0.01
min^{-1}. Then $k_e/k_a = 0.1$ and every value on the $k_e t$ scale has to be divided
by 0.01 (so that the scale will read 100, 200, 300 min, etc.). We see that
the peak circulating drug level will be attained in about 25 minutes, and

at that time about 75 per cent of the dose will be distributed into whatever its V_d may be.

Differentiation of the equations yields expressions for the time at which the maximum drug level is attained. For $k_a \neq k_e$,

$$t_{max} = \frac{2.30}{k_a - k_e} \log \frac{k_a}{k_e}$$

and for $k_a = k_e$,

$$t_{max} = 1/k_e.$$

These equations show that the time in which the maximum drug level is achieved is the same regardless of what dose is administered. Substitution of the values of t_{max} into the original equations yield solutions for the maximum amount of drug in the body. For $k_a \neq k_e$, the peak level is given by

$$\frac{X_{max}}{M_0} = \left[\frac{k_e}{k_a}\right]^{k_e/(k_e - k_a)},$$

and for $k_a = k_e$

$$\frac{X_{max}}{M_0} = 0.368,$$

i.e., when the rate constants for absorption and elimination are equal, the peak level in the body is 37 per cent of the dose.

These relationships are derived as follows:

For $k_a \neq k_e$,

$$\frac{X}{M_0} = \frac{k_a}{(k_e - k_a)} [e^{-k_a t} - e^{-k_e t}]$$

$$t_{max} = \frac{1}{(k_a - k_e)} \ln (k_a/k_e)$$

Multiplying and dividing by $e^{-k_e t}$, we obtain

$$\frac{X_{max}}{M_0} = \frac{k_a}{(k_e - k_a)} e^{-k_e t_{max}} [e^{-(k_a - k_e) t_{max}} - 1]$$

$$= \frac{k_a}{(k_e - k_a)} e^{-[k_e/(k_a - k_e)] \ln (k_a/k_e)} [e^{-[(k_a - k_e)/(k_a - k_e)] \ln (k_a/k_e)} - 1]$$

$$= \frac{k_a}{(k_e - k_a)} \left[\frac{k_a}{k_e}\right]^{-k_e/(k_a - k_e)} \left[\frac{k_e}{k_a} - 1\right]$$

$$= \left[\frac{k_a}{k_e}\right]^{k_e/(k_e - k_a)}.$$

For $k_a = k_e$,

$$\frac{X}{M_0} = k_e t e^{-k_e t}$$

$$t_{max} = 1/k_e$$

$$\frac{X_{max}}{M_0} = k_e(1/k_e)e^{-k_e(1/k_e)}$$

$$= e^{-1} = 0.368.$$

These basic equations, transformed in various ways, have been used by several investigators to develop rational approaches to dosage regimens, or to examine how closely observation and theory conform in experimental animals or man.[34-37] An illustration of unusual interest concerns the precursor-product relationship for drugs that are metabolized. If a precursor W is transformed metabolically to a product X, which in turn is further transformed or excreted, then we have

$$W \longrightarrow X \longrightarrow \text{elimination}$$

with a rate constant $k_{W \to X}$ for the first-order transformation reaction, and a rate constant k_e for the first-order elimination of X. Then the kinetics of the rise and fall of X are formally identical to those of sequential first-order absorption and first-order elimination. The same equations apply, and the same characteristic family of curves will be found as in Fig. 4-13. This is illustrated in Fig. 4-14 for anisole (methoxybenzene) transformed to its hydroxylation product p-methoxyphenol, in the rabbit. It can be seen that administration of the precursor will have the same effect as though the product itself had been given by a slow-absorption technique. The curve labelled "Precursor administered" is determined by the relative rate constants, 0.11 hr^{-1} for the hydroxylation and 0.54 hr^{-1} for the elimination (here actually a sulfate conjugation). The curve is simply that predicted by Fig. 4-13 for $k_e/k_a = 5$, and time in hours is $k_e t/0.54$.

Ideally, every drug should be given in such a way as to establish its EDC very rapidly and then maintain it with as little fluctuation as possible. Rapid establishment of the EDC, as we have seen, requires priming dosage if the rate constant of elimination is low. Practically speaking, if the drug level rises quickly and falls quickly, fluctuation can only be smoothed by repeating the dose very frequently; and this may be considered too in-

[34] E. NELSON: Kinetics of drug absorption, distribution, metabolism, and excretion. *J. Pharmaceut. Sci.* 50:181 (1961).

[35] E. NELSON: Kinetics of the excretion of sulfonamides during therapeutic dosage regimens. *J. Theoret. Biol.* 2:193 (1962).

[36] E. KRÜGER-THIEMER and P. BÜNGER: The role of the therapeutic regimen in dosage design. *Chemotherapia* 10:61 (1965/66).

[37] E. KRÜGER-THIEMER and P. BÜNGER: Kumulation und Toxizität bei falscher Dosierung von Sulfanilamiden. *Arzneimittel-Forsch.* 11:867 (1961).

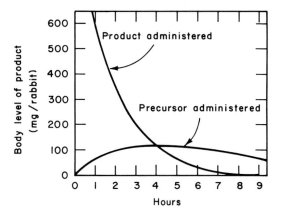

FIG. 4-14.   KINETICS OF PRECURSOR-PRODUCT RELATIONSHIP IN DRUG METABO-
LISM.   *Theoretical diagram of the body level of a product, p-methoxyphenol,
in the rabbit, when its precursor, anisole, is administered, and when it is ad-
minstered itself in equimolar amount. For the O-methylation,* $k = 0.11$ hr^{-1}.
Subsequent conjugation with sulfate proceeds with $k = 0.54$ hr^{-1}. *(From Bray
et al., Fig. 1.[38])*

convenient. Patients do not welcome parenteral administration more often
than every few hours; and even oral medication is unlikely to be taken
reliably more often than that, especially by ambulatory patients. Thus, if a
considerable "overshoot" above the EDC is tolerable, fluctuations may be
preferred to an inconvenient dose schedule. To what extent it may be safe
to exceed the EDC periodically cannot be stated as a general rule; this will
depend upon the range between EDC and toxic levels for each particular
drug. It is absurd, therefore, to administer all drugs on arbitrary fixed
schedules (e.g., with each meal, every 4 hours, etc.). Appropriate dosage
schedules need to be developed for each drug, determined by its k_a, its k_e,
its EDC, and the level at which its toxic effects manifest themselves. If it is
important to obtain a drug's maximum benefit, then it may also be important
to override considerations of convenience and to administer doses as often
as necessary to maintain an effective drug level and at the same time
minimize fluctuations.

KINETICS OF THE UPTAKE AND DISTRIBUTION OF DRUGS ADMINISTERED BY INHALATION: AN APPLICATION OF THE PLATEAU PRINCIPLE TO ANESTHETIC GASES

Introduction

The administration of gases, especially the anesthetic gases, represents a special case of the plateau principle. A constant rate of absorption
across the alveolar membranes into the pulmonary blood is established by

38 H. G. BRAY, W. V. THORPE, and K. WHITE: Kinetic studies of the metabolism of
foreign organic compounds. 5. A mathematical model expressing the metabolic fate of
phenols, benzoic acids and their precursors. *Biochem. J.* 52:423 (1952).

maintaining a constant concentration (partial pressure) of the drug in the inhaled air. The first-order elimination is unusual in that the anesthetic gases are practically not metabolized or excreted by the usual routes; they are eliminated almost entirely at the lungs, the site of their absorption. The net transfer rate from alveoli to blood is initially rapid, then progressively slower as the blood concentration builds up, until finally the rate of transfer from blood to alveoli equals the constant rate of transfer from alveoli to blood, and the net transfer rate becomes zero.

If x_b is the concentration in blood, and x_a that in alveolar air, then

$$dx_b/dt = k_1 x_a - k_2 x_b;$$

and since x_a is held constant, the equation is formally identical to that on p. 293 for zero-order absorption and first-order elimination.

At the steady state (here actually an equilibrium),

$$k_1 x_a = k_2 x_b$$

$$\frac{x_b}{x_a} = \frac{k_1}{k_2} = S,$$

where S is simply the solubility of the gas in blood. The solubility of a gas in a fluid is defined as the ratio of the concentration of dissolved gas to the concentration in the gas phase, at equilibrium. This solubility is also known as the Ostwald coefficient. The definition of solubility is often confusing to the student, but it should be remembered that, unlike solids, gases distribute themselves between a fluid and gas phase so that the amount dissolved increases without limit (theoretically, at least) as the concentration in the gas phase is increased. The only reasonable way to define solubility is, therefore, to relate the amount of gas dissolved in a given volume of fluid to the gas phase concentration required to hold it in solution.

In developing the plateau principle we showed that with a constant rate of drug input the rate of approach to a plateau drug level was determined wholly by the rate constant of elimination; the slower the elimination rate, the slower the approach to the plateau. We shall show in this section that the same thing is true for the anesthetic gases. It will also be shown that the rate constant of elimination is inversely proportional to the solubility of the agent. Therefore, the rate of approach to the plateau depends upon the aqueous (blood) solubility; and the greater the solubility of the gas, the more *slowly* will the plateau (equilibrium) be approached.[39]

> One might suppose, approaching this problem superficially, that a gas with high solubility in blood would achieve equilibrium rapidly because it would pass rapidly from the alveolar air into the blood in the pul-

[39] H. W. HAGGARD: The absorption, distribution, and elimination of ethyl ether. I–V. *J. Biol. Chem.* 59:737, 753, 771, 783, 795 (1924).

monary capillaries. This view, however, fails to take into account how much gas has to be transferred before equilibrium is attained, and the relationship between the total amount to be transferred and the alveolar partial pressure of the gas, which determines the absolute rate of transfer into blood. A full analysis will be presented in the text. The following introductory rationalization may be of interest:

$$dx_b/dt = k_1 x_a - k_2 x_b.$$

Substituting $k_1 = k_2 S$, the expression becomes

$$dx_b/dt = k_2(Sx_a - x_b);$$

and since x_a will be held constant, and letting x_b' designate the eventual plateau at equilibrium,

$$Sx_a = x_b'$$

and

$$dx_b/dt = k_2(x_b' - x_b).$$

And if f is defined as the fraction of the plateau level already attained at any time, $f = x_b/x_b'$, and

$$df/dt = k_2(1 - f).$$

Thus, the rate of increase of f toward equilibrium ($f = 1$) is determined by the value already attained *and by the rate constant of elimination* k_2. Now k_1 is primarily a rate constant of diffusion; it varies relatively little for the various anesthetic gases at a constant temperature. The solubility, on the other hand, is principally a reflection of the interactions of gas molecules (or atoms) with the aqueous medium (blood). A high solubility means a low probability of escape back into the gas phase, i.e., a low k_2. And therefore it follows that a high solubility means a slow approach to equilibrium.

Anesthetic gases vary widely in their solubilities, as shown in Table 4-2; as a result, they also differ very considerably in the rates at which they attain equilibrium in the body fluids.

Since the solubility is a ratio of concentrations, it does not matter in what units these are expressed provided they are the same for both phases. The solubility equation $x_b = S(x_a)$ is simply another way of stating Henry's law, which relates the concentration of dissolved gas to the partial pressure in the gas phase at equilibrium. The transformation of gas concentration to partial pressure is accomplished most simply by means of the gas law,

$$pV = nRT.$$

If the concentration is expressed as moles per liter (n/V), and the partial pressure p is to be obtained in mm Hg, then the gas constant R has the value 62, the temperature T being in absolute degrees.

TABLE 4-2.   Properties of volatile anesthetics

The data of this table are approximate; they are assembled from several sources, and obtained by methods of differing reliability. The expression III_{2-3} means stage III, plane 2–3 anesthesia, a typical depth for abdominal surgery. Most of the data are summarized in Larson et al.[40,41]

	Molecular weight	(S) Solubility in blood at 38°	(x'_b) mM blood at III_{2-3}	(x'_a) mM alveolar air at III_{2-3}	(p) mm Hg at III_{2-3}	mg/ml blood at III_{2-3}	(S_L) oil/water partition coefficient
(Ethanol)	46	1100	88	0.080	1.5	4.0	—
Ether	74	15	20	1.3	25	1.5	3.2
Chloroform	119	7.3	1.8	0.25	4.8	0.21	100
Ethyl chloride	64	2.5	4.6	1.8	35	0.29	—
Halothane	197	2.3	1.0	0.43	8.3	0.21	220
Vinyl ether	70	1.5	2.6	1.7	33	0.18	41
Acetylene	26	0.82	22	27	520	0.57	—
Cyclopropane	42	0.47	4.1	8.7	170	0.17	34
Nitrous oxide	44	0.47	29	61	1200	1.3	3.2
Propylene	42	0.22	4.8	22	420	0.20	—
Ethylene	28	0.14	5.7	41	790	0.16	14

[40] C. P. LARSON, JR., E. I. EGER, II, and J. W. SEVERINGHAUS: The solubility of halothane in blood and tissue homogenates. *Anesthesiology* 23:349 (1962).

[41] C. P. LARSON, JR., E. I. EGER, II, and J. W. SEVERINGHAUS: Ostwald solubility coefficients for anesthetic gases in various fluids and tissues. *Anesthesiology* 23:686 (1962).

Example: What is the partial pressure exerted by a gas at 38° (311° Abs.) whose concentration is 8.70 millimoles per liter?

$$p = (n/V)RT = (8.7 \times 10^{-3})(62)(311) = 168 \text{ mm Hg.}$$

For present purposes we will not distinguish between vapors and gases. Any substance in the gaseous state obeys the gas laws sufficiently well, regardless of whether its boiling point is above or below room temperature. The principal difference arises from the fact that while the concentration of a gas in the inspired air can be varied at will up to 100 per cent, the maximum concentration of a vapor is limited by its vapor pressure at ambient temperature. As this vapor pressure is by definition the partial pressure in equilibrium with the liquid, it follows that no higher partial pressure can exist, any tendency to further evaporation being balanced by re-entry of vapor molecules into the liquid phase. If a liquid is to be a useful volatile anesthetic, it must therefore be potent enough, or volatile enough, so that anesthesia can be produced with a partial pressure (in the inspired air) below its vapor pressure at room temperature.

Example: The vapor pressure of ether at 20° is 442 mm Hg. This is the maximum partial pressure of ether vapor that could be attained. But the partial pressure required to produce surgical anesthesia[42] is only about 25 mm Hg. Establishing a sufficient alveolar ether concentration therefore presents no problem.

Equilibrium in Clinical Anesthesia

The various stages of anesthesia are associated with definite concentrations of each anesthetic agent in the brain and (provided equilibrium has been attained) with definite concentrations in the circulating blood. With a number of anesthetic agents the concentrations in blood and in whole brain have been found to be approximately equal. Because of the precise relationship between depth of anesthesia and blood anesthetic concentration, and because it is impractical to measure the anesthetic concentration in the brain, we shall concern ourselves with blood anesthetic concentration. We shall further limit the discussion by considering that particular blood concentration which, at equilibrium, will produce surgical anesthesia. For any given anesthetic agent there is one and only one such blood concentration, namely, the EDC (effective drug concentration, see p. 300). If the agent is very potent, this required blood concentration will be low; if not very potent, the required blood concentration will be high.

---

[42] Throughout this section, *surgical anesthesia* means stage III, plane 2–3 anesthesia, a suitable level for major surgery without adjuvant muscle relaxants. In actual practice it is common to use many different levels of anesthesia, supplemented by the use of preanesthetic medications, muscle relaxants, and pain-relieving drugs. The reader is referred to textbooks of anesthesiology for details.

Anesthetists sometimes think of potency in connection with the effective concentration in the alveolar air, but this is a very restricted meaning. Rigorously defined, potency refers to the effective molecular concentration of a drug at its site of action, and we use the word in this sense. Low or high, the required blood concentration is determined by the physicochemical properties of the agent on the one hand and the behavior of the central nervous system on the other, both of which are beyond the control of the anesthetist.

At equilibrium there will be a predictable relationship between this concentration in blood (the EDC) and that in the alveolar air, a relationship defined by the solubility of the agent, already discussed above. Because the solubility of any agent in blood at body temperature is a fixed physical property, also beyond the control of the anesthetist, it follows that the concentration of anesthetic required in the alveolar air in order to just reach and then maintain surgical anesthesia is also absolutely fixed and beyond control. If a lower concentration is used, we shall not achieve surgical anesthesia when equilibrium is reached; if a higher concentration is employed, we shall exceed the safe levels of surgical anesthesia and cause respiratory paralysis. The situation is exactly the same as that described for dosage regimens in general, on p. 300.

When equilibrium has been reached, the partial pressure of anesthetic in the alveolar air will obviously be the same as that in the inspired air (for example, in the anesthetist's breathing bag). The concentration in the inspired air, in equilibrium with the EDC in blood, is called the *safe anesthetic gas concentration*. If the anesthetist employs this concentration from the start, then at equilibrium a safe depth of anesthesia will be reliably achieved, and there will be no danger of exceeding this depth. In most of the subsequent discussion we shall assume that the anesthetist makes use of the safe anesthetic concentration from the beginning of the anesthesia, even though for some agents (as we shall see) such a procedure would be impractical.

> *Example 1:* The solubility of ether at 38° is 15. If the concentration in the alveolar air is kept constant at 1.3 mM, what will be the concentration in blood at equilibrium?
>
> $$S = 15$$
>
> $$x_a = 1.3 \text{ mM}$$
>
> $$x_b = S(x_a) = 15 \times 1.3 = 20 \text{ mM}.$$
>
> *Example 2:* At equilibrium, the concentration of chloroform is found to be 1.8 mM in blood (38°), with partial pressure 4.8 mm Hg in the inspired air (20°). What is the solubility of chloroform?
>
> The partial pressure exerted by a gas in a mixture does not change with temperature, provided the sum of all the partial pressures remains

the same (i.e., 760 mm Hg at sea level). Thus, $p = 4.8$ mm Hg also at 38° in alveolar air, and

$$n/V = p/(RT) = 4.8/(62 \times 311) = 0.25 \text{ mM}$$

$$S = x_b/x_a = 1.8/0.25 = 7.3.$$

Example 3: At equilibrium, the concentration of cyclopropane in the inspired air (20°) is found to be 9.2 mM and its solubility is 0.47. What is the blood concentration?

$p = (n/V)RT = (9.2 \times 10^{-3})(62)(293) = 167$ mm Hg. In the alveoli, at 38°, this same partial pressure exists, but because of expansion with increased temperature, the concentration of all gases is lower than in the inspired air. Here,

$$n/V = p/(RT) = 167/[(62)(311)] = 8.7 \text{ mM},$$

or, more simply,

$$n/V = (9.2)(293/311) = 8.7 \text{ mM},$$

whence

$$x'_b = S(x_a) = (0.47)(8.7) = 4.1 \text{ mM}.$$

Rate of Equilibration of Blood and Body Water

EQUILIBRATION AT THE BLOOD-ALVEOLAR MEMBRANE

Let us now consider the factors determining the rate at which the EDC is attained when the anesthetic in the inspired air is maintained at the safe anesthetic gas concentration from the start. As the gaseous anesthetics are all relatively small molecules, they diffuse very rapidly from the blood into all the tissues of the body, and as they are generally lipid soluble, they are able to cross cell membranes rapidly and distribute themselves in intracellular as well as extracellular fluid. Thus, for an average-sized man (70 kg) we shall have to consider the equilibration not of 6 liters of circulating blood but of 41 liters of total body water.

Gas in the alveoli equilibrates almost instantaneously with blood passing through the pulmonary capillary bed. This has been established by careful physiologic studies, most recently by the use of radioactive gases. Let us assume for the moment that it were possible by some kind of special pump to maintain the safe anesthetic concentration in the alveolar air, i.e., to replace continuously all anesthetic that passes over into the pulmonary blood. In that case, all the blood returning from the lungs would continuously carry an equilibrium concentration of anesthetic, namely, the EDC, which will be reached ultimately in all the body water. The entire cardiac output passes through the pulmonary capillary bed, so if the cardiac output is 5 liters per minute and the total body water is 41 liters, it follows, as a first approximation, that the total body water could be brought to equilibrium in about 8 minutes. Actually, this is an underestimate of the time, since the equilibration is asymptotic. As soon as blood returning to the lungs contains some anesthetic, blood leaving the lungs will begin to contribute less toward equilibration of the total body water, because the anesthetic brought to the lungs by blood will simply be carried away again, and the net transfer of anesthetic will be diminished by this amount.

The asymptotic nature of the equilibration process can perhaps best be understood in relation to the total amount of anesthetic needed to bring the body water to equilibrium. If the equilibrium concentration to be achieved is x_b' and the body water amounts to 41 liters, then $41x_b'$ is the amount of anesthetic that must be transferred from the alveoli into the blood in order to reach equilibrium. At the start, when no anesthetic is yet in the blood, the net transfer will be at the rate of $5x_b'$ per minute, as stated above. But now suppose the concentration in the blood and body water has already reached $0.1x_b'$. This will be the concentration in blood arriving at the lungs, while the blood leaving the lungs will always contain the concentration x_b'. The net transfer rate at this point is therefore no longer than $5x_b'$ but $5(x_b' - 0.1x_b')$, or $4.5x_b'$ per minute. Obviously then, the approach to equilibrium will continue to slow down as greater fractions of equilibrium are achieved. Complete equilibrium is only achieved in an infinite time; we can only measure the attainment of a specified *fraction* of equilibrium. The correct estimate of the time required to attain 90 per cent equilibration of body water under these hypothetical conditions is approximately 21 minutes instead of our rough estimate of 8 minutes. The derivation of equations describing this rather complex process is an interesting exercise in the application of mathematics to physiologic problems.[43-46]

LUNG "WASHOUT"

We assumed above that it was somehow possible to establish at once and then to maintain the safe anesthetic concentration in the alveoli. As a matter of fact, respiration is a cyclic process. The amount of anesthetic inhaled in the first breath will be diluted in a considerable lung volume containing no anesthetic whatsoever. The alveolar ventilation is about 0.3 liters. The total effective lung volume after normal inspiration is equal to this

[43] D. S. RIGGS: *The Mathematical Approach to Physiological Problems.* Baltimore, Williams and Wilkins Co., 1963.

[44] D. S. RIGGS and A. GOLDSTEIN: Equation for inert gas exchange which treats ventilation as cyclic. *J. Appl. Physiol. 16:*531 (1961).

[45] S. S. KETY: The physiological and physical factors governing the uptake of anesthetic gases by the body. *Anesthesiology 11:*517 (1950).

[46] S. S. KETY: The theory and applications of the exchange of inert gas at the lungs and tissues. *Pharmacol. Rev. 3:*1 (1951).

volume plus the functional residual capacity and end-expiratory volume, comprising, in all, some 2.8 liters.

Anesthetic taken into the lungs at the first breath $(0.3x_a)$ is therefore diluted immediately so that the alveolar concentration during the inter-respiratory pause is only $(0.3/2.8)x_a$, or $0.11x_a$. Some of the alveolar anesthetic passes into the blood and is carried away, while the rest remains in the lungs to be added to the amount inhaled during the next breath. If very little passes into the blood at each breath, the alveolar concentration will quickly build up in stepwise fashion toward x_a. But if nearly all the anesthetic in the alveoli passes into the blood at each breath, the alveolar concentration after the second, third, and subsequent breaths will not be appreciably greater than after the first breath.

In general, the repeated addition of air carrying anesthetic concentration x_a to the total lung volume containing a lower concentration causes anesthetic to accumulate in the alveoli with each successive breath. Soon, however, each inspiration replaces exactly the amount of anesthetic that passed into the blood during the previous breath. When this state is reached, the alveolar concentration would have risen but little higher than $0.11x_a$ in the case of an agent of very high S, since nearly $0.3x_a$ passes into the blood during each breath, and $0.3x_a$ is the most that can be replaced by a normal inspiration. But the steady-state alveolar concentration would be nearly x_a in the case of an agent of very low S, where very little passes into the blood during each breath. The process whereby the alveolar anesthetic concentration reaches a steady state is termed *lung "washout."* It is virtually complete within less than 2 minutes.

AGENTS OF VERY LOW SOLUBILITY

We have seen that with an agent of very low solubility the alveolar concentration at the end of the washout period is practically the same as that of the inspired air (namely, the safe anesthetic concentration x_a). This anesthetic will distribute itself instantaneously and continuously between alveoli and blood in accordance with its solubility. For example, the anesthetic in 1 ml of alveolar air will bring the same volume of blood to equilibrium without appreciable change in the alveolar concentration. As shown in Fig. 4-15, an agent of solubility 0.1 will have accomplished this when only 1/11 of the total anesthetic in the given volume of alveolar air has passed into an equal volume of blood.

The blood flowing through the lungs during each breath (respiratory rate 20 per minute) is 1/20 of the cardiac output, or 0.25 liters. All this blood leaves the lungs in equilibrium with the alveolar concentration, which is practically x_a. The blood, therefore, carries away a concentration $x_b = S(x_a)$, or an amount equal to $(0.25)(S)(x_a)$ per breath. For an agent of solubility 0.1, this would be $0.025x_a$ per breath, or less than 1 per

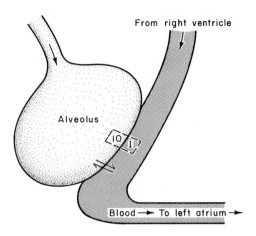

FIG. 4-15. DIAGRAM SHOWING MOMENTARY EQUILIBRIUM BETWEEN EQUAL VOLUMES OF BLOOD AND AIR AT BLOOD-ALVEOLAR MEMBRANE, FOR AN ANESTHETIC AGENT OF SOLUBILITY 0.1.

cent of the total anesthetic in the lungs, an amount that can readily be replaced at the next inspiration.

Because the blood is already carrying all the anesthetic it can, increasing the respiratory rate or minute volume could not significantly increase the transfer of anesthetic into the blood and therefore could not shorten the equilibration time significantly. On the other hand, increasing the cardiac output would markedly increase the rate of removal of anesthetic from the lungs. In fact, doubling the cardiac output would nearly double the rate of removal and thereby nearly halve the equilibration time. Thus, for agents of very low solubility, the cardiac output (and not the respiration) is the major physiologic factor limiting the rate of equilibration. At each breath only a small fraction of the anesthetic in the lungs is removed, and after 3 seconds even this is replenished at the next inspiration. The alveoli continuously contain nearly the safe anesthetic gas concentration, the arterial blood contains the corresponding x_b' (the EDC), and the situation is very much like the hypothetical one discussed earlier (p. 330), where 21 minutes was shown to be a reasonable estimate of the time required to bring the body water to nine-tenths of its equilibrium anesthetic concentration.

AGENTS OF VERY HIGH SOLUBILITY

We have already seen that with an agent of very high solubility so much is transferred to the blood during each breath that little if any remains in the alveoli just before the next inspiration (cf. Fig. 4-15 as it would apply to an agent of solubility 10). The alveolar concentration established at the first inspiration $(0.11x_a)$ is re-established again and again (without appreciable increment) at every succeeding inspiration, and falls practically to zero before the next breath. The arterial anesthetic concentration closely reflects this fluctuating pattern, never exceeding $0.11x_b'$ initially and falling off nearly to zero during every breath. Naturally, the time required to equilibrate the body water with the inspired air will be very much longer than with low-solubility agents. Assuming that the lungs are wholly depleted at each breath, we have $0.3x_a \times 20$, or $6x_a$ entering the blood every minute. Since $S = 10$, this is equal to $0.6x_b'$ per minute, and it would take 68 minutes (at the very least) to carry away from the lungs the $41x_b'$ needed to equilibrate the 41 liters of body water. This calculation ignores the asymptotic nature of the process and is therefore a considerable underestimate, as in the similar example given on p. 330.

The mean alveolar anesthetic concentration (and consequently the arterial concentration) begins to rise only as blood returning from the body tissues to the lungs carries more and more anesthetic. Slightly less is removed from the alveoli during each breath (for the reasons explained before), and the remainder gradually accumulates. With an agent of high solubility, the mean alveolar anesthetic concentration approaches that of the inspired air (x_a) at essentially the same rate as the venous blood approaches equilibrium.

Here, respiration is the principal factor that limits attainment of equilibrium. Because the blood is already removing virtually all anesthetic from the lungs, increasing the cardiac output could not materially shorten the equilibration time. But equilibration can be very substantially hastened by furnishing anesthetic to the alveoli more rapidly (i.e., by increasing the respiratory rate or depth). This is precisely what is accomplished by inhalation of CO_2, a procedure that is primarily useful in accelerating equilibration (and also de-equilibration) with agents of high solubility like ether and chloroform (Table 4-2).

THE TRANSITION ZONE BETWEEN LOW- AND HIGH-SOLUBILITY BEHAVIOR

We have said a good deal about agents of "very low" and "very high" solubility. But what values of S are we justified in regarding as high or low in this connection? As S determines the relative roles of respiratory minute volume and cardiac output in limiting the equilibration rate, it follows that at an intermediate value of S these two physiologic parameters will have equal importance. This critical solubility, which proves to be about 1.2, marks the center of a transition zone between the two types of extreme behavior described. Actually, this zone is fairly broad but as S becomes much smaller or much greater than 1.2, the behavior of the anesthetics will approach more closely that of the prototype low- and high-solubility agents examined in the foregoing discussion. It should be noted that the value $S = 1.2$ is arrived at on the basis of average physiologic data; namely, respiratory rate 20 per minute, alveolar ventilation 0.3 liters, cardiac output 5 liters per minute. A substantial change in any of these values will shift the transition zone toward higher or lower solubilities.

Figure 4-16 shows an arrangement of volatile and gaseous anesthetics according to solubility, on a scale indicating their behavior with respect to equilibration rate. As S increases, the equilibration time becomes longer, without limit. As S decreases, however, a minimum equilibration time is approached (approximately 21 minutes for 90 per cent equilibration, as shown earlier). Thus, agents of very low solubility do not differ materially among themselves in their rates of equilibration.

Figure 4-17 represents the calculated course of equilibration with two agents of different solubility. The change in alveolar anesthetic concentration is plotted in the upper half, the change in anesthetic concentration in body water (or venous blood) in the lower half.

FIG. 4-16.   RELATION OF SOLUBILITY S TO EQUILIBRIUM RATE, SHOWING RELATIVE LIMITATION BY RESPIRATION AND CARDIAC OUTPUT.

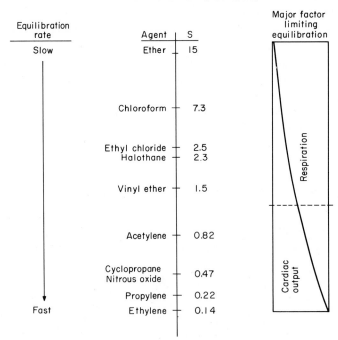

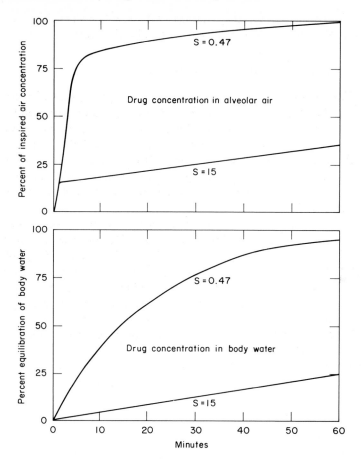

FIG. 4-17. THEORETICAL COURSE OF EQUILIBRATION WITH NITROUS OXIDE (S = 0.47) AND ETHER (S = 15).

DE-EQUILIBRATION

If the anesthetic intake is abruptly stopped, after the EDC has been established, anesthetic begins to be eliminated from the blood into the lungs. The factors affecting de-equilibration of the body water are the same as those already considered in connection with equilibration. An agent of very low solubility can be eliminated almost as fast as the blood delivers it to the lungs. The elimination of an agent of very high solubility is limited by the respiratory rate and minute volume, only a small fraction being removed from the blood during a single passage. Obviously, CO_2 inhalation will be effective in hastening de-equilibration of high-S agents, but will be of no use for this purpose with low-S agents. The curves of de-equilibration are essentially inverted equilibration curves.

POTENCY AND THE AVAILABILITY OF OXYGEN

The potency of an anesthetic is inversely proportional to the EDC. Table 4-2 shows that potency varies widely, and quite independently of solubility. There is a relationship, which is the basis of the Meyer-Overton hypothesis (p. 154), between potency and *lipid solubility*. Anesthetics of high potency (i.e., those that act at low EDC) are generally very soluble in lipid, so that the effective concentrations of all volatile anesthetics in the lipid material of the central nervous system are thought to be approximately the same.

Potency has no bearing on the rates of equilibration or de-equilibration, which depend on S alone. This is a point about which the student is often confused. We can only reasonably compare rates of equilibration when the safe anesthetic gas concentration is consistently employed with all agents. Under these conditions, S represents the relation between how much anesthetic must be transferred into a given volume of blood (i.e., x_b') and what "driving force" is available to accomplish the transfer (i.e., x_a). Naturally, if we arbitrarily increase the alveolar anesthetic concentration, we can force anesthetic into the blood as fast as we wish, but the patient will be dead if we persist. The following tabular summary will illustrate why, when the safe anesthetic gas concentration is used, potency is irrelevant to the rate of equilibration.

	EDC $= x_b'$	S	$x_a \ (= x_b'/S)$
Gas A	1	1	1
Gas B	1	10	0.1
Gas C	10	1	10

Gas A and gas B are equipotent. Yet, because B is ten times more soluble than A, the "driving force" available for achieving the same x_b' is ten times lower with B than with A, and the rate at which x_b' is approached must obviously be considerably lower.

Gas C is ten times less potent than gas A, so the x_b' to be attained is ten times higher. Yet, because S is the same, the "driving force" of C is just ten times greater than that of A, and equilibrium will be reached at the same rate.

The potency of a gaseous anesthetic is immaterial except in one respect that has nothing to do with equilibration rate. If the potency is very low relative to the solubility, the safe anesthetic gas concentration may be so high that there is no room (at ordinary atmospheric pressure) for sufficient oxygen. The minimum O_2 requirement in the inspired air is about

15 per cent, or 114 mm Hg. It follows that the partial pressure of an anesthetic gas may not exceed 646 mm Hg (33.5 mM at 38°). Reference to Table 4-2 will show that by this criterion neither ethylene nor nitrous oxide are suitable agents for producing surgical anesthesia (although they may be useful for lesser degrees of anesthesia), since both require partial pressures greater than 646 mm Hg. The only way to induce surgical anesthesia with either of these agents alone is to employ *total* pressures greater than 760 mm Hg, thereby incorporating oxygen at a partial pressure of at least 114 mm Hg. To the extent it may be thought desirable to furnish oxygen in excess of the minimum 114 mm Hg, other agents may also be found deficient. Acetylene, for example, permits only about 25 per cent of oxygen in the anesthetic mixture. In contrast, anesthesia can be produced with a mixture of 0.7 per cent chloroform and 99.3 per cent oxygen.

Influence of Body Fat

THE ANESTHETIC CONTENT OF THE BODY AT EQUILIBRIUM

Up to this point we have examined the equilibration of body water as though the anesthetics did not dissolve appreciably in other components of the body. However, some of the agents are quite soluble in lipid, and fat constitutes an important fraction of the body weight. In an average person, without prominent fat depots, the fat of the organs and subcutaneous tissues amounts to not less than 15 per cent of the body weight, while it is obvious that in very obese people this fraction may be much higher.[47]

The solubility of an anesthetic in lipids (often estimated approximately from measurements with a vegetable oil) is expressed as a partition coefficient between lipid and blood at 38°:

$$S_L = \frac{x_L}{x_b}.$$

To distinguish between lipid solubility and blood solubility in this section, we shall use the symbol S_b instead of S to denote the latter, S_L to denote lipid solubility.

When the blood and body water attain their equilibrium concentration, x_b', fat will contain $x_L' = S_L(x_b')$. What volume of blood will contain the same amount of anesthetic as a given volume of fat? Obviously this "blood equivalent" of fat is simply S_L. Suppose, for example, $S_L = 10$. This means that any volume of fat at equilibrium will contain ten times as much anesthetic as the same volume of blood, or, in other words, a liter of fat is the equivalent of 10 liters of blood. The effect of body fat is, therefore, to

---

[47] P. R. SCHLOERB, B. J. FRIIS-HANSEN, I. S. EDELMAN, A. K. SOLOMON, and F. O. MOORE: The measurement of total body water in the human subject by deuterium oxide dilution. *J. Clin. Invest.* 29:1296 (1950).

increase the apparent volume of distribution of an anesthetic agent to an
extent that depends on S_L and the volume of fat, and thus to increase the
total amount of anesthetic in the body at equilibrium. An agent of very high
lipid solubility may be distributed largely in the fat depots at equilibrium,
and the total anesthetic content of obese patients may be surprisingly high.

> *Example:* The blood concentration of cyclopropane during surgical
> anesthesia is 4.1 mM. Molecular weight $= 42$, $S_L = 35$. What weight of
> the gas is contained in a 90-kg man, of whom 20 kg is fat?
>   Approximately 20 liters fat is equivalent to (20×35) liters blood.
> Total blood equivalent $= 700$ liters blood $+ 50$ liters body water $= 750$
> liters. Then the weight of gas is: 4.1 mM $\times 750 = 3.08$ moles, or
> (3.08×42) g $= 129$ g. Note that of this total weight of cyclopropane,
> $700/750$, or 93 per cent, is in the fat.

RATE OF UPTAKE OF ANESTHETIC BY FAT DEPOTS

Let us assume that all the arterial blood arriving at a fat depot contains x_b', that the fat contains no anesthetic, and that S_L is high. A high S_L
means that a great deal of anesthetic has to be transferred from blood to
fat, relative to the concentration available in blood. The fat depots of the
body have a relatively poor blood supply. Consequently the blood will be
practically depleted of anesthetic in the proximal portion of the capillaries,
and equilibration will be prolonged until, with the arrival of more and
more blood carrying x_b', enough is finally transferred to bring the whole fat
depot to its equilibrium concentration x_L. This process will be reflected in
the anesthetic content of venous blood draining the fat depot; initially containing practically no anesthetic, its concentration will gradually increase to
x_b' when the fat depot has reached equilibrium. The word "saturate" is very
often misused in this connection. There is never any question of "saturating" the body or fat depots with anesthetic, but only of equilibrating with
a given alveolar anesthetic concentration.

If S_L is low, the amount of anesthetic removed as any portion of the
fat reaches equilibrium may be so small as to leave x_b' practically unchanged; anesthetic transfer from blood to fat can proceed along the whole
length of the capillary, and consequently the whole depot comes to equilibrium as rapidly as the required amount of anesthetic can be delivered by
the arterial blood.

EFFECT OF DEPOT FAT UPON RATES OF EQUILIBRATION AND
DE-EQUILIBRATION OF BODY WATER

The rate of uptake of anesthetic by fat depots is of little interest
in itself, but the question is naturally raised whether fat depots modify the
rate of equilibration (or de-equilibration) of blood and body water. The
maximum effect of depot fat would be observed under circumstances
where all the blood flowing through all the fat depots was cleared of anes-

thetic in a single passage. This would be the case initially, as has already been noted, with agents of high S_L. However, the blood flow through all the fat depots represents so small a fraction of the cardiac output (approximately 3 per cent) that the anesthetic concentration in mixed venous blood would not be substantially lowered even in this extreme case. This conclusion is confirmed by experimental data on nitrogen elimination, showing that the fat depots do not appreciably influence the main course of de-equilibration, but only come into the picture as a slow component after the concentration in mixed venous blood has fallen to a low level.[48,49]

Whatever amount of anesthetic is transferred in a given breath from lungs to blood must be distributed to various organs and tissues in proportion to their respective blood flows. Thus, the rate of uptake by fat cannot exceed a small fraction of the rate of entry from lungs into blood, except possibly in very obese patients, where a larger fraction of the cardiac output flows through fat. The blood, brain, and body water reach near-equilibrium while fat is still far from equilibrium. Anesthetic is then transferred slowly from arterial blood to fat, and replaced at the same rate in the pulmonary capillary blood, without appreciable change in the blood concentration. Thus, once the blood and body water have been practically equilibrated, the anesthetist will be supplying anesthetic to the fat depots, by way of the alveoli and blood, whose anesthetic concentrations remain essentially constant (x_a, and x_b', respectively).

When the anesthetic is discontinued, fat depots have just as little influence on the main course of de-equilibration, and for the same reason (anesthetic flow from fat to blood being similarly limited by the total blood flow through fat). However, after the blood and body water are largely cleared of anesthetic, we should expect a continued leakage from the fat depots, slowest and most prolonged in the case of agents with high S_L. Mixed venous blood should show traces of anesthetic long after the body water is essentially de-equilibrated. Such persistence in the venous blood is observed with cyclopropane (S_b 0.47, S_L 34) and chloroform (S_b 7.3, S_L 100), but not, apparently, with nitrous oxide (S_b 0.47, S_L 3.2) or ether (S_b 15, S_L 3.2).

Speed of Induction and Recovery in Clinical Anesthesia

INDUCTION

The progressive deepening of anesthesia reflects the increasing concentration of anesthetic agent at the sites of action in the brain. By measuring the rate of increase of the concentration in internal jugular (venous) blood as it approaches that of common carotid (arterial) blood, it has been

---

[48] H. B. JONES: Respiratory system: nitrogen elimination. *Med. Phys.* 2:855 (1950).

[49] J. S. ROBERTSON, W. E. SIRI, and H. B. JONES: Lung ventilation patterns determined by analysis of nitrogen elimination rates; use of the mass spectrometer as a continuous gas analyzer. *J. Clin. Invest.* 29:577 (1950).

found that when the anesthetic concentration of arterial blood is kept constant, the brain reaches 90 per cent of equilibrium in about 7 minutes. The rate of blood supply to brain tissue is reported to be 350 ml/kg per minute, while the mean figure for the rest of the body water is approximately 100 ml/liter per minute.[50] One would therefore expect an equilibration rate about 3.5 times faster for brain than for body water as a whole. This conclusion based on the blood-flow/volume ratio agrees pretty well with the theoretical prediction of 21 minutes for 90 per cent equilibration of body water, and the observed time of about 7 minutes for the same fraction of equilibrium in brain, both data for agents of low solubility.

The relative rates of equilibration for both the brain and body water should be the same, regardless of the blood solubility of the anesthetic agent, i.e., regardless of whether the equilibration rate is slow or fast. The rate of induction of anesthesia is therefore determined by the same factors as govern the equilibration of body water, but it is faster. A patient will reach surgical anesthesia while the venous blood and body water are still far from equilibrium, and the fat depots farther still. Thereafter, anesthetic leaves the brain as fast as it arrives, and the patient remains at the same depth of anesthesia while the venous blood and body water (and ultimately the fat depots) come to equilibrium. If a perfect, closed system is being used, one will find that early in anesthesia new anesthetic has to be furnished at a considerable rate. As time goes on, however, less and less has to be added to the system until, eventually, no new anesthetic is required. When the whole body is at equilibrium, the patient can rebreathe the same anesthetic gas while O_2 is supplied and CO_2 is absorbed.

PRACTICAL INDUCTION WITH HIGH-SOLUBILITY AGENTS

For agents of high solubility, like ether and chloroform, the theoretical induction time on our premise of maintaining the safe anesthetic gas concentration from the start would be so long (as shown earlier) that even the use of CO_2 would not make it a practical proposition. The only alternative (and that universally adopted) is to induce with higher gas concentrations, i.e., concentrations that are unsafe in the sense that continued administration would invariably lead to respiratory paralysis and death. At an appropriate time the concentration in the inspired air must be reduced to the safe anesthetic concentration. What the procedure accomplishes is to force large amounts of anesthetic rapidly into the arterial blood and thus establish a desired level of clinical anesthesia quickly. The rest of the body can then equilibrate over a long period of time while the depth of anesthesia is held constant. The procedure is exactly analogous to the use of priming doses (p. 301); it is illustrated diagrammatically in Fig. 4-18 (cf. Fig. 4-10).

[50] S. S. KETY: Quantitative determination of cerebral blood flow in man. *Methods in Medical Research.* 1:204 (1948).

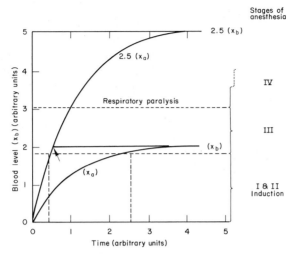

FIG. 4-18. APPROACH TO EQUILIBRIUM IN STAGE III ($x_b = 2$) WHEN SAFE ANES-
THETIC GAS CONCENTRATION IS EMPLOYED FROM START IS SHOWN BY CURVE x_a.
By using $2.5(x_a)$, *the upper curve would theoretically be obtained, approaching*
$x_b = 5$, *but respiratory failure would occur. If at arrow the anesthetic concen-*
tration in the inspired air is reduced to x_a, *blood level* $x_b = 2$ *can be maintained.*
Thus, induction time can be reduced from 2.5 to 0.5 time units.

RECOVERY

The speed of recovery from surgical anesthesia to full consciousness,
reflecting the progressive de-equilibration of the brain, will be influenced
by the same factors that determined the speed of induction. When a low-S
agent is discontinued, the arterial blood concentration falls very quickly as
venous blood is almost completely cleared of anesthetic at the lungs.
A steep concentration gradient is thus provided which, with the high
blood-flow/brain-volume ratio, favors rapid transfer of brain anesthetic to
the cerebral capillary blood, and consciousness is quickly regained.

When a high-S agent is discontinued after equilibration of the body
water, the arterial concentration falls only slowly, and the de-equilibration
of the brain tends to be limited by the rate of elimination of anesthetic
from the whole of the body water. The way to accelerate the otherwise
slow recovery from prolonged anesthesia with a high-S agent is to stimulate
the respiration by administering CO_2; this procedure proves highly effective
in practice.

An excessive concentration of a high-S anesthetic in the blood,
causing too deep an anesthesia, has very different implications depending
upon the circumstances. If anesthesia has just been induced with concentrations greater than the safe anesthetic gas concentration, and the anesthetic
is stopped abruptly as soon as the condition is recognized (e.g., by de-

pressed respiration), there will be a rapid outflow of drug from the brain into the blood, whose concentration is still much lower. Because the bulk of the brain is so small compared with the body water, such a redistribution will readily reduce the danger; indeed, the patient may return toward consciousness with surprising speed. This ability of the body water to act as a "sink" for anesthetic before equilibrium is established serves as a useful safety factor. For the same reason, however, it complicates induction because the depth of anesthesia responds quickly to transient fluctuations in the alveolar anesthetic concentration (e.g., those caused by breath-holding). On the other hand, as the blood and body water approach equilibrium, recovery takes ever longer. Control of the depth of anesthesia becomes easier, but respiratory paralysis late in anesthesia presents a far more serious problem, since now the whole of the body water acts as a buffer opposing outflow of anesthetic from the brain.

5

DRUG TOXICITY

INTRODUCTION

The poisonous properties of drugs have commanded attention since long before the birth of modern pharmacology. Paracelsus (1493–1541) wrote: "All things are poisons, for there is nothing without poisonous qualities. It is only the dose which makes a thing a poison."[1] The first formal lectures that could be said to constitute a course in pharmacology were given at Paris in 1856 by Claude Bernard under the title "Lectures on the Effects of Toxic and Medicinal Substances."[2] These dealt with noxious gases and arrow poisons (curare). Today, that branch of pharmacology known as toxicology encompasses a broad field of investigation and practical application. The variety of effective and potentially toxic drugs in therapeutic use began to increase sharply with the intensive development of synthetic organic chemistry toward the close of the 19th century. New kinds of drugs come into use each year, while a bewildering array of minor modifications are introduced into existing drugs. At the same time, the expanding availability of medical care in all countries results in an increasing exposure of large population groups to drugs. This is most dramatically exemplified by the prophylactic use on a mass scale of such drugs as the antimalarials and the steroid contraceptives.

The increased medical use of drugs leads inevitably to greater hazards of toxicity. All drugs are toxic in overdosage, and people vary greatly in their sensitivity to drugs; so what may be a safe and appropriate dosage for one person can prove to be an overdose for another. Moreover, even in the therapeutic dose range many drugs have unavoidable toxic side effects. Thus, widespread use of a drug is bound to produce a certain number of toxic reactions even if the incidence of toxicity (calculated as per cent of all people treated) is low.

---

[1] Cited in H. E. SIGERIST: *The Great Doctors*. New York, Doubleday & Co., 1958, p. 99.

[2] C. BERNARD: Leçons sur les Effets des Substances Toxiques et Médicamenteuses. Paris, J.-B. Baillière et Fils, 1857.

343

The widespread distribution of drugs is accompanied also by the twin hazards of accidental poisoning and suicide. Accidental poisoning is primarily seen in children; for example, in the United States during 1961, about 90 per cent of the cases reported to a national data-collection center involved children under five years of age.[3] Small children are apt to ingest whatever they find, particularly drugs that are disguised as candy or made up in a sweet-tasting liquid vehicle. The leading causes of drug poisoning in children are aspirin, vitamins, iron preparations, and chocolate-coated laxatives (Table 5-1). Barbiturates lead all drugs used in suicide attempts and are second only to firearms among all the means employed for suicide (Table 5-2). Moreover, data on actual deaths by suicide certainly underestimate the use of barbiturates relative to other methods, for suicide attempts with these drugs often fail. Legally, barbiturates can only be obtained on prescription; therefore physicians and pharmacists bear some responsibility for making these hazardous agents too readily available in lethal quantities.

Beyond the restricted range of drugs in clinical use is the whole gamut of toxic chemicals to which people are exposed in their daily lives. Industrial poisoning continues to be a problem despite increasing concern with worker safety. Each industry presents its own peculiar problems, of which the physician must be aware in order to suspect and diagnose the illnesses, sometimes bizarre, sometimes commonplace, that are caused by exposure to industrial chemicals. In many countries safety precautions in industry, enforced by law and regulated by inspection, have reduced the

TABLE 5-1. **The ten leading causes of accidental poisoning in children under the age of five in 1961**

(Data from the National Clearinghouse for Poison Control Centers.[3])

Type of substance	Per cent of total poisoning cases
1. Aspirin	21.8
2. Insecticides (except mothballs)	5.3
3. Bleach	4.4
4. Detergents, soaps, cleaners	4.3
5. Furniture polish	2.4
6. Kerosene	2.2
7. Vitamins and iron preparations	2.2
8. Disinfectants, deodorizers	2.1
9. Lye, corrosives	2.1
10. Laxatives	1.9

[3] Bulletin of the National Clearinghouse for Poison Control Centers, U.S. Public Health Service, September–October, 1963. Washington, D.C.

TABLE 5-2. **Deaths by suicide in California in 1960**

(Data from California Public Health Statistical Report, Table 36.[4])

Method	No. of suicides
Drugs	
salicylates	12
barbiturates	468
morphine	4
other analgesics	37
unspecified drugs	9
Subtotal, all drugs	**530**
Other poisons (strychnine, phenols, lye, arsenic, fluorides, etc.)	160
Motor vehicle gas	262
Other gases	39
Hanging	296
Drowning	55
Firearms	928
Knives	58
Jumps from high places	81
Unspecified	91
Total, all causes	**2,500**

hazards considerably. Basically, these precautions mean protecting the worker against direct contact with injurious chemicals, by means of adequate clothing and by installing suitable ventilation to remove toxic fumes. About 10,000 different chemicals were employed industrially in the United States in 1960, and production of new chemicals has been increasing at an average annual rate of 7 per cent since 1947.[5] These are incorporated into more than 300,000 potentially toxic trade-named products on the consumer market.[6] Accidental or suicidal poisonings with such materials pose difficult problems for the physician. Until recently, manufacturers were not even required to list all ingredients on the label, so that optimal treatment of acute poisonings was often delayed pending a frantic search for information about the nature of the responsible chemicals.[7] Federal legislation has

[4] California Public Health Statistical Report: *Vital Statistics,* part 1, Table 36, p. 78. 1960. Bureau of Health Education, California State Department of Public Health, Berkeley, Calif.

[5] Manufacturing Chemists Association: *The Chemical Industry Facts Book,* 4th ed., 1960–61. Washington, D.C.

[6] Subcommittee on Interstate and Foreign Commerce, Report 1158: *Hazardous Substances for Household Use.* U.S. Senate, 86th Congress, 2nd session. Washington, D.C.

[7] For a very extensive and well indexed compilation of toxic ingredients in common products, see: M. N. GLEASON, R. E. GOSSELIN, and H. C. HODGE: *Clinical Toxicology of Commercial Products,* 2nd ed. Baltimore, Williams and Wilkins Co., 1963.

now made such listing of ingredients mandatory.[8] Again, as with accidental ingestion of drugs, children under five are often the victims of poisoning by household chemicals. The agents chiefly responsible are chlorine bleaches, kerosene (commonly a solvent for polishes), lye, ammonia, and phenolic disinfectants; kerosene and the strong alkalis account for the greatest number of hospitalizations.[3]

Table 5-3 documents 314 deaths due to accidental poisoning in California during 1960. Throughout the United States, in 1963, there were 2,061 fatal accidental poisonings due to the ingestion of solids or liquids (1,286 of these due to drugs), and another 1,489 due to inhalation of gas.[9] The number of nonfatal poisonings in the United States probably exceeds one million per year.

Many communities have established Poison Control Centers; at the end of 1965, there were about 500 of these in the United States. The ease

TABLE 5-3. Deaths by accidental poisoning in California in 1960

(Data from California Public Health Statistical Report, Table 36.[4])

		By age (years)		
Method	All ages	0–4	5–19	>20
Drugs				
salicylates	12	11		1
barbiturates	62	1	1	60
bromides	3			3
morphine, opium	35	1	3	31
other analgesics, sedatives	24	1		23
other unspecified drugs	16	5		11
Subtotal, all drugs,	**152**	**19**	**4**	**129**
Alcohol	25		2	23
Petroleum products, solvents	3	2		1
Corrosives	2		1	1
Lead	2			2
Arsenic, antimony	5	4		1
Other chemicals, toxins	42	2	1	39
Utility gas (household)	53	4	9	40
Motor vehicle gas	9			9
Other gases	21	1	1	19
Total, all accidental poisonings	**314**	**32**	**18**	**264**

8 Federal Hazardous Substances Labeling Act, Part 191, Chapter I, Title 21, Code of the Federal Regulations; and implementing regulations by Food and Drug Administration, Federal Register, August 12, 1961. Washington, D.C., Government Printing Office.

9 U.S. Department of Health, Education, and Welfare, National Center for Health Statistics: Public Health Service Publication No. 600, *The Facts of Life and Death,* Table 22, p. 20, "Deaths and Death Rates for Accidents." Washington, D.C., Government Printing Office, 1965.

and rapidity of telephone communication means that these centers readily serve the whole population on a 24-hour basis. The centers maintain extensive files on the toxic ingredients of household and commercial products, they supply information and advice on prevention and treatment of poisonings, and most of them also provide treatment facilities. The U.S. Department of Health, Education and Welfare maintains a National Clearinghouse for Poison Control Centers, which publishes a directory as well as regular bulletins about poisonings. Departments of public health in the various states also have divisions concerned with accidental poisonings and occupational hazards. Every physician should be familiar with the use of these consultative facilities; he should also have at his instant disposal a concise reference manual on the general and specific treatment of poisonings.[7,10,10a]

On a still larger scale, society is increasingly faced with the hazards of mass poisoning. Historic precedent is found in the periodic "epidemics" of ergotism known since the Middle Ages in Europe.[11] Ergot is a fungus that grows on rye and produces substances toxic to the blood vessels (causing arteriolar spasm and gangrene) and to the brain (causing hallucinations and psychotic behavior). As recently as 1951, in an outbreak at Pont St. Esprit, France,[12,13] a large part of the population was affected after eating bread made locally from ergot-contaminated flour.

Mass poisonings in the past have been limited, generally, to small population groups because of local production of food. Today, mass production and widespread distribution of food products vastly expand the hazards of mass poisoning. Botulism resulting from a single lot of contaminated canned foods, for example, may affect individuals scattered over the whole world. At Meknès, Morocco, in 1959, a single episode involving cooking oil incapacitated 10,000 people.[14] Olive oil was adulterated with petroleum oil intended for use in high-compression airplane engines at a nearby American air base. The petroleum oil contained triorthocresylphosphate, an organic phosphate derivative with demyelinating effects. Of the 10,000 people who experienced some degree of paralysis, 2,000 required prolonged hospitalization.

Atmospheric pollution by combustion products ("smog") can also produce toxicity on a mass scale. The Donora, Pennsylvania, catastrophe of 1948 resulted in 5,910 cases of illness (43 per cent of the exposed popu-

---

10 R. H. DREISBACH: *Handbook of Poisoning*, 5th ed. Los Altos, Calif., Lange Medical Publications, 1966.

10a W. B. DEICHMANN and H. W. GERARDE: *Symptomatology and Therapy of Toxicological Emergencies.* New York, Academic Press, 1964.

11 G. BARGER: *Ergot and Ergotism.* London, Gurney & Jackson, 1931.

12 A. SUBIACO: Il pane maledetto di Pont St. Esprit. *Clin. Nuova 13:*294 (1951).

13 DRS. GABBAI, LISBONNE, and POURQUIER: Ergot poisoning at Pont St. Esprit. *Brit. Med. J.* 2:650 (1951).

14 DR. FARAJ: Intoxication collective par une huile à base de cresylphosphates. *Semaine Hôp. Paris, Suppl. Med. Monde 36:*2807 (1960).

lation) and 20 fatalities.[15,16] Follow-up studies of the afflicted individuals
have revealed distinctly higher morbidity and mortality rates in the ensuing
years.[17] A similar episode in the greater London area, December 5–9,
1952, apparently claimed several thousand lives. Very large numbers of
people became ill with signs of respiratory distress. A retrospective analysis
of the death records (Fig. 5-1) showed that about 4,000 more deaths occurred at the time of the "fog" than would have been expected on the basis
of data for the previous five years.[18-21] During another London "fog," in
1962, nine patients seen at Guy's Hospital presented signs and symptoms
of acute bronchiolitis without evidence of infection (except in one case).
These patients all had a history of respiratory disease. They all failed to
respond to conventional therapy, and they all improved suddenly on

FIG. 5-1.   DEATHS ASSOCIATED WITH THE LONDON "FOG" OF DECEMBER 1952.
*Solid curve shows weekly number of deaths in Greater London before and
after the "fog." The dates of the "fog" (December 5–9) are shown by hatched
area. Broken curve shows weekly average number of deaths for the preceding
five years. (From Goldsmith, Fig. 1.[18])*

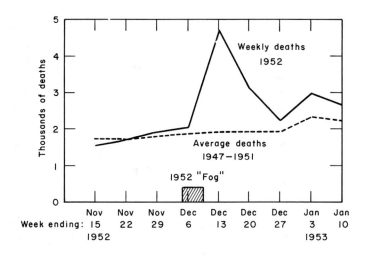

15 B. ROUECHE: "The Fog," in *Eleven Blue Men.* New York, Berkeley Publishing
Corp., 1953, pp. 171–189.

16 H. H. SCHRENK, H. HEIMANN, G. D. CLAYTON, W. M. GAFAFER, and H. WEXLER:
Public Health Bull. No. 306, *Air Pollution in Donora, Pa.* Washington, D.C., 1949.

17 D. J. THOMPSON and A. CIOCCO: Sickness, change of residence, and death. I.
General results of follow-up in two population groups. *Brit. J. Prevent. Social Med. 12:*172
(1958).

18 J. R. GOLDSMITH: "Effect of Air Pollution on Humans," in *Air Pollution,* ed.
by A. C. Stern. New York, Academic Press, 1962, vol. 1, chapt. 10, pp. 335–386.

19 J. FRY: Effects of a severe fog on a general practice. *Lancet 1:*235 (1953).

20 Reports on Public Health and Medical Subjects, No. 95. London, Ministry of
Health, 1954.

21 S. M. FARBER and R. H. L. WILSON, eds.: *The Air We Breathe. A Study of Man
and His Environment.* Springfield, Ill., Charles C Thomas, 1961, p. 414.

December 8, 9, or 10, the days during which the sulfur dioxide content of the air (Fig. 5-2) was falling.[22, 23]

The long-range health hazard associated with air pollution is being evaluated currently. It is unlikely that the reports will be reassuring in view of the crop destruction and enhanced oxidation of rubber that have been observed. The most sensitive organ is almost certain to be the lung. In serious, acute episodes of air pollution (as in those described above), there is always an increase in deaths due to respiratory disease, particularly among people with chronic pulmonary disease. Evidence has been presented that implicates air pollution in lung cancer, bronchial asthma, chronic bronchitis, and pulmonary emphysema.[24]

Thus, toxicity due to drugs and other chemical agents has become a major social problem. Drugs for the treatment of disease, for the prevention of disease, for population control, and as nutritional supplements, food additives, and cosmetics are administered to people intentionally. And people are exposed to industrial chemicals, atmospheric pollutants, pesticides, detergents, and radioactive wastes to the extent that adequate controls have not yet been devised or implemented. The contamination of our environment and the consequent disturbances to the ecologic balances in

FIG. 5-2.   SULFUR DIOXIDE CONTENT OF LONDON "FOGS" 1952 AND 1962.   *SO$_2$ content was recorded daily at noon. The close similarity of these serious smogs is evident; both are mentioned in the text. (From Davies, Fig. 2.[22])*

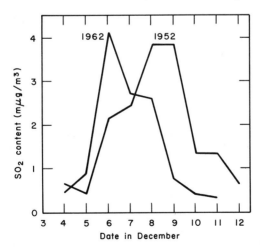

22 G. M. DAVIES: Fog bronchiolitis. *Lancet 1*:580 (1963).

23 There need not necessarily be a cause-and-effect relationship between SO$_2$ content and the disease. Sulfur dioxide was merely used as one index for measuring the intensity of the smog. Smogs have complex compositions; carbon monoxide, total oxidants, and total smoke content are also used as convenient indices of intensity.

24 T. A. GLENN, JR.: Regional air pollution warning system. *J. Air Pollution Control Assoc. 16*:22 (1966).

nature present serious challenges to society.[25] For all these many man-made hazards, toxicity data have to be obtained and acceptable limits of exposure have to be worked out. The problem of drug toxicity is one facet of this broader issue.

THE EVALUATION OF DRUG TOXICITY IN LOWER ANIMALS AND IN MAN

Broadly speaking, any adverse drug effect may be thought of as a manifestation of drug toxicity. It will be useful, however, to consider separately and in considerable detail, in later chapters, the following special categories of adverse drug effect: idiosyncrasy, drug allergy, tolerance and physical dependence, mutagenesis, teratogenesis, and carcinogenesis. In this chapter, we shall discuss the principles that guide toxicity evaluations in general, and we shall focus attention upon the common kinds of dose-related harmful effects of drugs upon the various organ systems of the body.

Sometimes a toxic effect is simply an extension of the therapeutic effect at a higher dose level. Coumarin anticoagulants, for example, prolong the clotting time of the blood. Overdosage leads to a bleeding tendency from excessive prolongation of the clotting time. Often, on the other hand, toxicity takes the form of a *side effect* more or less unrelated to the primary drug action. Examples are the nausea and vomiting seen frequently with the cardiac glycosides, and the gastrointestinal distress that often accompanies the ingestion of ferrous sulfate.

If quantitative estimates of efficacy and toxicity could be carried out routinely in humans, the decision whether a new drug should be adopted for clinical use would be a fairly straightforward task. We would begin at a low dosage, and increase the dose cautiously, watching carefully for toxic effects. If the desired therapeutic effect could be obtained with little or no toxicity in a large number of patients, we would accept the drug as efficacious and safe. In order to determine the margin of safety, we might increase the dosage well beyond the therapeutically effective range, with the aim of seeing by how much the therapeutic dose could be exceeded before toxicity ensued. Consider the following hypothetical illustration:

	Effective daily dose	Daily dose causing a toxic effect
Drug A	1 mg	2 mg
Drug B	100 mg	500 mg

We assume that A and B, at their effective doses, have equally useful therapeutic actions. In the usual situation, the two drugs being compared would be congeners with the same mechanism of action but different poten-

---

[25] R. CARSON: *Silent Spring*. Boston, Houghton Mifflin Co., 1962.

cies. Here, A is 100 times more potent than B, yet it is relatively more toxic. Drug A produces toxicity at only twice its therapeutic dose, whereas B can be given safely up to five times its therapeutic dose.

Obviously, such deliberate exploration of toxic doses in humans is out of the question. Therefore the initial evaluations have to be based upon experiments with lower animals, and these have to explore the qualitative as well as the quantitative aspects of toxicity. It is important at this stage to find out what kinds of harmful effect may be expected, and at what dosages they may be manifested. Because species differences are considerable, several animal species have to be used. A convenient measure of potency is the *median effective dose* (ED50), that dose which would produce the specified effect in 50 per cent of all subjects. If the effect being measured is death, the corresponding measure is the *median lethal dose* (LD50), and if the effect is a toxic one, the expression *median toxic dose* (TD50) is appropriate. Because of biologic variation it is meaningless to speak of "minimum lethal dose," "minimum toxic dose," or "maximum tolerated dose," as was customary at one time.

Drug potency, in itself, may concern the medicinal chemist or pharmacologist who wishes to investigate the relationship between chemical structure and biologic activity, but drug potency is clinically of no great practical importance. It usually matters little whether the ordinary dose of a drug is 10 micrograms or 10 milligrams. The essential attribute we seek in a drug is not potency, but efficacy at a safe dose. Ideally, this means that there should be a wide range of dosage between the effective and the toxic dose. The ratio TD50/ED50 (or often, in animals, LD50/ED50) is called the *therapeutic ratio* (also "therapeutic index"). A low ED50 characterizes a potent drug; but if the TD50 is also low, the margin of safety may be wholly inadequate. The therapeutic ratio is an initial crude indication of how safe a drug is likely to be. It is especially useful in a congeneric series, where molecular modifications are likely to alter both potency and toxicity but not necessarily to the same extent.

One problem in applying the therapeutic ratio concept is that few drugs are without some toxic side effect even at ordinary therapeutic dosage. The seriousness of the disease, the benefit likely to be derived from using the drug, and the degree of damage likely to be sustained as a result of drug toxicity all have to be weighed. A "minimum loss approach" has been proposed, which would give appropriate weight to these factors.[26] Curiously, some of our most useful drugs are also among the most toxic; neither digitalis glycosides nor the opiate analgesics can be said to have favorable therapeutic ratios.

A simple procedure for a preliminary assessment of the toxicity of a drug is the determination of lethal dosage in mice. The method will

[26] M. A. SCHNEIDERMAN, M. H. MYERS, Y. S. SATHE, and P. KOFFSKY: Toxicity, the therapeutic index, and the ranking of drugs. *Science 144:*1212 (1964).

be described in some detail because it is applicable to any estimation of a quantal drug effect. *Quantal effects* (in contrast to graded effects, cf. chapter 1) are all-or-none responses. Each individual is categorized as responding or not responding, according to whatever criterion of response has been adopted. In studies of lethal toxicity each animal is classified as dead or alive at a specified time after drug administration. For any toxic agent there will be some low dose that kills no animals, some high dose that is uniformly lethal, and an intermediate dosage range in which a varying fraction of a population will be killed.

Some animals in a population will be sensitive to a drug, some will be resistant. As a rule, the sensitivity of animals to different doses of a drug is distributed normally with respect to the logarithm of the dose. If log dose is plotted on the horizontal axis and the relative frequency of animals sensitive to the various doses is plotted on the vertical axis, a gaussian (normal) distribution is usually approximated. This is illustrated in Fig. 5-3 for three hypothetical drugs. The doses are expressed as $\mu g/kg$ and the logarithms are plotted on the x-axis. The y-axis shows relative frequencies of animals dying at the different dose levels. The mean (also median) sensitivity is the dose at which one-half the animals die (the LD50), i.e., all animals sensitive to a lower dose are killed, whereas all animals sensitive to a higher dose survive. Curve A represents a drug that is lethal to one-half the animals at a dose of $10\mu g/kg$ (log dose = 1). A small fraction of the population is killed even at doses below $1\mu g/kg$ (log dose = 0). Another small fraction is not killed until the dose is raised

FIG. 5-3.   THEORETICAL DISTRIBUTIONS OF SENSITIVITIES TO THE LETHAL EFFECTS OF DRUGS IN A POPULATION.   *The mean (and median) sensitivity to drug A is 1.0 log unit, i.e., $10\mu g/kg$, and the standard deviation is ±0.5 log units. The mean sensitivity to drug B is 2.2 log units, i.e., $160\mu g/kg$, and the standard deviation is the same as for drug A. Drug C has the same median lethal dose as drug A, but the population is much more homogeneous with respect to the drug's lethal action; the standard deviation is only ±0.16 log units.*

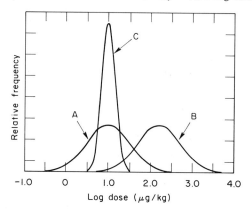

above 100μg/kg (log dose = 2.0). The standard deviation for this drug is ± 0.5 log units; thus, two-thirds of the population of animals is killed at doses between 0.5 and 1.5 on the log scale, or between one-third and three times the LD50.

Curve B represents a drug for which the standard deviation of sensitivities is exactly the same as for drug A, but whose toxicity is much lower. The LD50 is at 2.2 log units, or 160μg/kg, so this drug is only 1/16 as toxic as drug A.

Finally, curve C represents a drug that has the same toxicity as drug A, but to which the population responds in a much more homogeneous way. The standard deviation is only ± 0.16 log units. The antilog of 0.16 is 1.45; thus, two-thirds of the population are killed by this drug in the dosage range from 1/1.45 to 1.45 times the LD50 (between 69 and 145 per cent of the LD50) or at doses between 6.9 and 14.5μg/kg.

All quantal log dose-response (LDR) curves can be made identical by simply stretching or contracting the log dose scale. The convenient way to do this is to choose the standard deviation as the unit for this scale, and to designate the median lethal dose as zero. This is shown in Fig. 5-4,

FIG. 5-4. THE QUANTAL LOG DOSE-RESPONSE CURVE. *The horizontal axis shows log dose in units of the standard deviation; the graph is therefore perfectly general.* Curve 1 *represents the normal distribution of sensitivities of individual animals to the drug;* curve 2 *is the cumulative normal distribution;* μ *represents the mean (also median) sensitivity,* σ *the standard deviation of sensitivities. For responses in general, the ED50 is the median effective dose; when death is the criterion of response, the median effective dose is called median lethal dose (LD50).*

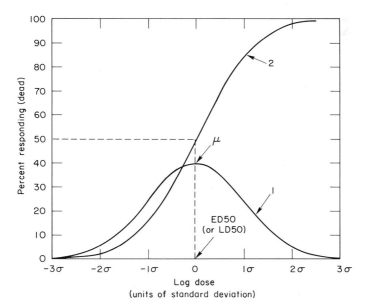

curve 1. In reality, actual doses would be indicated on the new generalized scale. Thus, curves A and B of Fig. 5-3 would be drawn identically in the center of such a graph, except that the actual central value of log dose for curve A would be 1.0, whereas that for B would be 2.2. The central value for curve C would be 1.0, but the log dose values would be spread out to make the smaller standard deviation, 0.16, occupy the same linear distance as the standard deviation 0.5 of the other two curves.

In practice, what one determines is not the sensitivities of individual animals, but rather the cumulative number of animals that respond as the dosage is increased. Therefore, a more useful form of graphic presentation is the cumulative (integral) form of the normal distribution (Fig. 5-4, curve 2). This is the total area of the gaussian curve summed from left to right and expressed as per cent of the total area. Thus, at any dose the cumulative curve gives the per cent of animals responding to that dose and to all lower doses. These curves and their rationale are the same as those presented in chapter 1, Fig. 1-70, where we discussed an interpretation of the LDR curve as a quantal distribution of receptor sensitivities.

In the normalized form shown here, the position, shape, and slope of the quantal LDR curve (curve 2) are fixed. At one standard deviation below the ED50, 16 per cent respond; at one standard deviation above the ED50, 84 per cent respond. At $-\sigma/2$, 31 per cent respond; at $+\sigma/2$, 69 per cent respond. These fixed relationships provide the basis for transforming quantal LDR curves to straight lines, which can be analyzed readily by statistical procedures. Instead of showing "per cent responding" on the y-axis, each per cent response is converted to a *normal equivalent deviation* (N.E.D.), i.e., to the corresponding multiple of the standard deviation, as shown below:

Per cent response	N.E.D.
2	-2.0
7	-1.5
16	-1.0
31	-0.5
50	0
69	$+0.5$
84	$+1.0$
93	$+1.5$
98	$+2.0$

This is the same procedure used to construct "probability graph paper"; the normal equivalent deviations are equally spaced on the y-axis, but for convenience the "per cent" scale is retained. On such paper a cumulative gaussian normal distribution assumes the form of a straight line throughout its entire range.

In order to circumvent the use of negative numbers, integer 5 is added to every N.E.D. The resulting new units are called *probits* (for "probability units") (Table 5-4). Thus, 50 per cent response (N.E.D. = 0) corresponds to probit 5; 16 per cent response (N.E.D. = −1.0) corresponds to probit 4; 93 per cent response (N.E.D. = +1.5) corresponds to probit 6.5; and so on. From a practical standpoint one is rarely concerned with probit values smaller than 2 or greater than 8, since these represent per cent responses well below 1 per cent and above 99 per cent, respectively.

Figure 5-5 presents log dose-probit curves for three hypothetical drugs. In the theoretical normalized curve (Fig. 5-4, curve 2) the log dose scale was in units of the standard deviation; the corresponding probit curve would be a straight line with slope 1.0. In Fig. 5-5, we represent the logarithms of actual doses as abscissas, so that the position on the log dose axis reflects the potency of the drug. The customary measure of potency, the ED50, is the point on the log dose scale corresponding to probit 5. Drug A is evidently the most potent; its ED50 is antilog 1.3 = 20 mg. The slope of a log dose-probit line is determined by the biologic variation in sensitivity to the drug; it is equal to $1/\sigma$, so the more homogeneous the population the steeper will be the line. In general, the standard deviation

TABLE 5-4. Conversion of per cent to probit

Each row of the table contains the probits corresponding to a decade of per cents. To find, for example, the probit corresponding to 23 per cent, enter the row labeled 20; under column headed 3 find probit 4.26. (Adapted from Finney,[28] Table I, originally Fisher and Yates,[28a] Table IX. By permission of Cambridge University Press and Oliver and Boyd.)

%	0	1	2	3	4	5	6	7	8	9
0	—	2.67	2.95	3.12	3.25	3.36	3.45	3.52	3.59	3.66
10	3.72	3.77	3.82	3.87	3.92	3.96	4.01	4.05	4.08	4.12
20	4.16	4.19	4.23	4.26	4.29	4.33	4.36	4.39	4.42	4.45
30	4.48	4.50	4.53	4.56	4.59	4.61	4.64	4.67	4.69	4.72
40	4.75	4.77	4.80	4.82	4.85	4.87	4.90	4.92	4.95	4.97
50	5.00	5.03	5.05	5.08	5.10	5.13	5.15	5.18	5.20	5.23
60	5.25	5.28	5.31	5.33	5.36	5.39	5.41	5.44	5.47	5.50
70	5.52	5.55	5.58	5.61	5.64	5.67	5.71	5.74	5.77	5.81
80	5.84	5.88	5.92	5.95	5.99	6.04	6.08	6.13	6.18	6.23
90	6.28	6.34	6.41	6.48	6.55	6.64	6.75	6.88	7.05	7.33

[27] J. W. TREVAN: The error of determination of toxicity. *Proc. Roy. Soc. B. 101*:483 (1927).

[28] D. J. FINNEY: *Probit Analysis,* 2nd ed. London, Cambridge University Press, 1952.

[28a] R. A. FISHER and F. YATES: *Statistical Tables for Biological, Agricultural and Medical Research.* London, Oliver and Boyd, 1938.

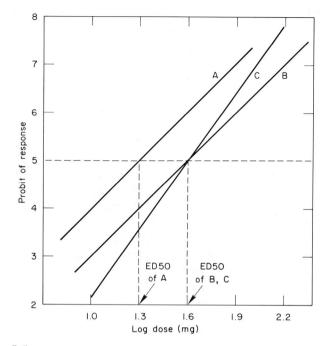

FIG. 5-5.   LOG DOSE-PROBIT CURVES FOR THREE HYPOTHETICAL DRUGS.

may be found readily on a probit plot as the difference in log dose corresponding to a change of 1 probit. Thus, the standard deviation of sensitivities to drug A is found to be 0.3 log unit on the dose scale, i.e., a doubling of dosage.

We can never study a whole population experimentally. We can only examine a sample. The statistical problem is always to estimate the population parameters (e.g., the LD50 and standard deviation) from sample statistics.[27] To estimate the LD50 of drug A in mice, we would administer the drug to groups of animals at different doses. The per cent mortality in each group would be plotted as probit against log dose, and the best line would be drawn through these experimental points.

Accurate determination of the best line requires special weighting of the points. Obviously, the data on per cent response are most reliable in the region of 50 per cent response and quite unreliable at the extremes of the curve, where per cent response is strongly affected by chance factors that influence the responses of a very few animals. For example, the difference of one animal responding between 10/20 and 11/20 (the ratios of numbers of animals affected to total number tested) results in a change from 50 per cent to 55 per cent, and from probit 5.00 to probit 5.13. The difference between 1/20 and 2/20, also one animal responding, results in a change from 5 per cent to 10 per cent, and, since this is in the flat tail of the normal distribution, a change from probit 3.36 to 3.72. The weighting factors compensate for these effects.[27, 29, 30]

By applying appropriate procedures the true LD50 and its confidence limits can be estimated. Obviously, as in all statistical estimations, the smaller the variability of the data (i.e., the steeper the slope) and the larger the sample size, the more accurate will be the estimate of the LD50, and the smaller will be its confidence range. The whole technique of statistical analysis of quantal LDR data is known as *probit analysis*. For a full working knowledge of this technique the reader is referred elsewhere.[28, 29] Especially popular is a short-cut method employing nomograms in place of rather elaborate computations.[30] In the remainder of this discussion we shall examine some illustrative applications of the method to toxicity and efficacy evaluations.

Table 5-5 and Fig. 5-6 present the results of a series of determinations on the lethal toxicity of an organophosphate cholinesterase inhibitor, guthion, in mice. The drug was given intraperitoneally to groups of eight or ten animals. At sufficient dosage the mice died from respiratory depression and other manifestations of central and peripheral acetylcholine accumulation. The entire experiment was replicated five times. The data illustrate the greater variability encountered in small groups, and the "smoothing" effect of pooling all the data into a single large sample. In these graphs the dose scale is logarithmic, but actual doses (rather than their logarithms) are indicated; this is often convenient where log probability (or probit) paper is readily available. From the probit plot for the pooled data we see that the LD50 is estimated to be 7.0 mg/kg. At probit 4.0, the corresponding dosage is 5.4 mg/kg. Now the ratio of these doses, corresponding to a difference of one probit, is $7.0/5.4 = 1.30$, and log $1.30 = 0.114$; this is our estimate of σ. This standard deviation is remarkably small. The entire range from 2 per cent mortality (probit 3) to 98 per cent mortality (probit 7), 4 probits in all, is spanned by less than a threefold range of dosage ($4 \times 0.114 = 0.456$; antilog $0.456 = 2.86$). Consequently, with this drug, even small groups of mice yield acceptable confidence limits for the LD50, as shown in Table 5-5; and the confidence range for the pooled data is narrower still.

Let us now return to Fig. 5-5. Curve B represents a drug that is less potent than A but has the same slope. One might wish, typically, to compare the toxicities of A and B quantitatively. From data obtained in groups of mice one will ask: "Is A really more toxic than B, or does the separation of sample lines on a log dose-probit plot arise by chance?" "If there is a

29 A. GOLDSTEIN: *Biostatistics: An Introductory Text.* New York, Macmillan Co., 1964.

30 J. T. LITCHFIELD, JR., and F. WILCOXON: A simplified method of evaluating dose-effect experiments. *J. Pharmacol. Exper. Therap. 96*:99 (1949).

TABLE 5-5.   Toxicity of guthion in mice

The drug was administered intraperitoneally, dissolved in 50% dimethylsulfoxide, to female mice. The number dead were recorded after 90 minutes. Data are number dead/total. LD50 values and confidence limits computed according to Litchfield and Wilcoxon.[30] (Data from student laboratory exercise, Department of Pharmacology, Stanford University School of Medicine, 1966)

Dose	Raw data					
	Experiment number					
(mg/kg)	1	2	3	4	5	Totals
4	—	0/10	—	0/10	1/10	1/30
5	0/8	1/10	0/8	1/10	1/10	3/46
6	3/8	2/10	2/8	2/10	4/10	13/46
7	3/8	5/10	5/8	5/10	5/10	23/46
8	7/8	5/10	7/8	5/10	5/10	29/46
10	8/8	10/10	7/8	10/10	9/10	44/46

LD50 values and confidence limits

Exp. no.	LD50 (mg/kg)	95% confidence limits	
		Lower	Upper
1	6.8	6.15	7.50
2	7.4	6.55	8.35
3	6.7	6.00	7.40
4	7.6	6.66	8.67
5	6.8	5.80	7.95
Pooled	7.0	6.59	7.43

real difference, how much more toxic is A than B?" "What is the true potency ratio (or toxicity ratio) of the two drugs, and what confidence limits can be placed on such a ratio?" Illustrative examples of such comparative toxicity evaluations will be presented, but again the reader is referred elsewhere for details of the procedures for arriving at these estimates.

If two log dose-probit curves are not parallel, it makes no sense to compare their potencies. Consider B and C in Fig. 5-5. Evidently the two drugs do not kill mice by the same mechanism, for the population responds more uniformly to C than to B. At probit 5 (LD50), both have the same potency. At probit 6 (84 per cent lethality), C is more potent; at probit 4 (16 per cent lethality), B is more potent. Any statement about comparative toxicity would have to be qualified by specifying what portion of the dose-mortality curve was under consideration.

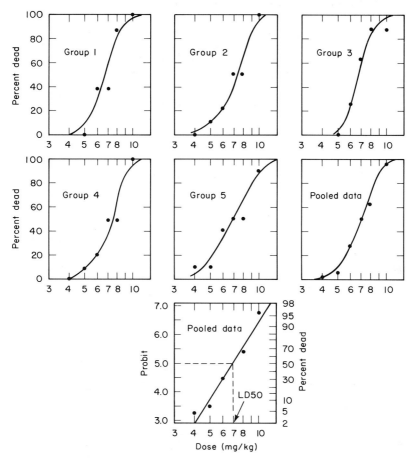

FIG. 5-6. TOXICITY OF GUTHION IN MICE. *The data of Table 5-5 are plotted as log dose-per cent mortality curves for each group of mice and for the pooled data. Horizontal scale is logarithmic, but actual doses are indicated. The log dose-probit curve for the pooled data is shown at bottom.*

Initial toxicity tests are often carried out just as described above. Even while determining the mouse LD50 values, however, important clues may be obtained about mechanisms of toxicity. Do the animals convulse before death? Does respiration cease before the heart fails? Are there signs of gastrointestinal disturbance? Does muscular paralysis occur? Although species often differ from each other, a particular toxic effect may nevertheless occur universally, so that information gathered in any species should guide one's eventual testing of a drug in man.[31]

[31] G. ZBINDEN: Experimental and Clinical Aspects of Drug Toxicity. *Adv. Pharmacol.* 2:1 (1963).

In order to arrive at an estimate of the therapeutic ratio, a method must be chosen for demonstrating the therapeutic effect in test animals, if that is possible. Here, the most appropriate species can be used, not necessarily the same as for the toxicity tests. It might be thought that a meaningful comparison of therapeutic and toxic doses would have to be carried out in one and the same species. However, even if lethal and therapeutic effects were both measured in mice, the therapeutic ratio thus arrived at could not be assumed to apply to man. The whole procedure should rather be regarded as an arbitrary one, primarily useful for comparing different drugs. Thus, two agents might be studied for their ability to reduce blood sugar levels in diabetic dogs. The dose required to bring about some specified effect, such as lowering the blood sugar concentration to some arbitrary value within a certain time, would be determined in a series of dogs, so that an ED50 value could be found for each drug. The LD50 values for the same two drugs would be obtained in mice, as already described. Then that drug with the greatest ratio [LD50 (mice)]/[ED50 (hypoglycemia, dogs)] would be considered the most promising in this particular evaluation.

It has been argued that to express the margin of safety as the therapeutic ratio LD50/ED50 is wholly unrealistic. Certainly in man the median lethal dose is of academic interest only. Even the median toxic dose would not be a useful measure because one is interested in obtaining therapeutic effects in nearly all patients, if possible, at a dosage that is toxic to practically none. The criterion we really want is a therapeutic ratio based on a dose that is toxic to perhaps 1 per cent of patients, and a dose that is effective in 99 per cent of patients. We might look for the ratio LD1/ED99 in animal tests. If all quantal LDR curves had the same slopes, then it would make no difference what ratio were chosen; the ratio LD1/ED99, for example, would always be a fixed fraction of the ratio LD50/ED50. But variation of slopes with different drugs and even different effects of the same drug complicates the situation.

Figure 5-7 illustrates theoretically how slopes influence the interpretation of a therapeutic ratio. Judged by the TD50/ED50 criterion, drug A appears safer; its therapeutic ratio is 2 dose units on the log scale, whereas the therapeutic ratio for B is only 1 dose unit. Because the slopes in A are rather flat, however, there is a larger overlap of efficacy and toxicity. The ED90 dose (probit 6.28), for example, corresponds to TD10 (probit 3.72); thus, at a dose effective in 90 per cent of those treated, 10 per cent of the animals would experience drug toxicity. In contrast, with drug B, despite the smaller margin of safety at probit 5, one can select a dose that is effective in 99 per cent (probit 7.33) yet causes toxicity in only 1 per cent (probit 2.67). Drug B seems preferable because the steep slopes of its log dose-effect and log dose-toxicity curves reduce the extent of overlap. But from a practical standpoint steep curves have serious disadvantages. Fluctuations in drug level are inevitable because of variation in drug ab-

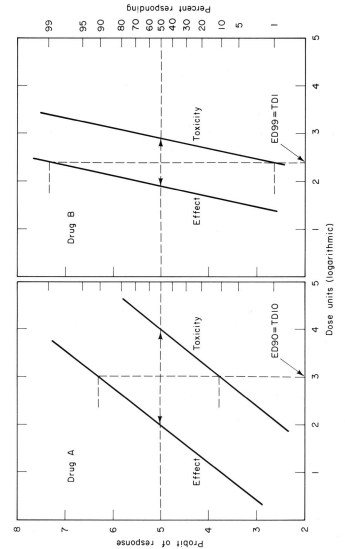

FIG. 5-7. EFFECT OF SLOPE ON THE METHOD OF EXPRESSING THE THERAPEUTIC RATIO. *Log dose-probit curves for two hypothetical drugs, A and B, showing relationship between therapeutic effect and toxicity. These curves are steeper for drug B than for drug A. Scale of abscissas is in equal logarithmic increments of dosage. See text for analysis.*

sorption and elimination and because of periodicity of dosage schedules (cf. chapter 4). The steeper the curve, the more readily can overshoot occur into the toxic range. Thus, inadvertent overdosage would be more hazardous with B than with A because a relatively smaller dose range lies between the TD1 and TD99. The situation becomes even more complex if, as frequently happens, the effect and toxicity curves are not even parallel.

A comparison of two barbiturates in mice, based upon the concept of ED99 and LD1, is shown in Fig. 5-8. Here, aprobarbital appears to offer a greater margin of safety because, although the two drugs did not differ greatly in lethal potency, aprobarbital was considerably more potent in producing sleep. The therapeutic ratio LD50/ED50 was 5.3 for aprobarbital, 2.6 for phenobarbital. Because of differences in slope, however, the two drugs appear more nearly the same when LD1/ED99 values are

FIG. 5-8.   COMPARISON OF THERAPEUTIC RATIOS OF TWO BARBITURATES IN MICE. *Groups of 20 mice were injected with each dose subcutaneously. Sleep was defined as loss of righting reflex. Deaths were recorded at 24 hours. The log dose-probit lines are calculated, using appropriate weighting factors for the points at various probit values. (Adapted from Foster, Figs. 1 and 2.[32])*

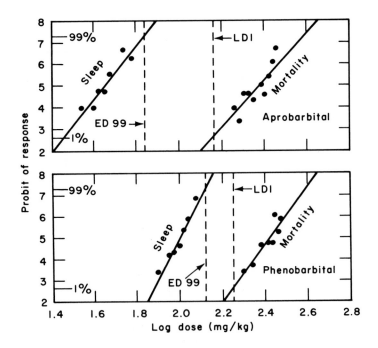

[32] R. H. K. FOSTER: Standardization of safety margin. *J. Pharmacol. Exper. Therap.* 65:1 (1939).

considered: the respective ratios now become 2.0 and 1.3. Small differences in therapeutic ratio may be of minor importance relative to other considerations such as duration of action, which do not enter into the computation of a therapeutic ratio.

Similar data on efficacy and toxicity in man are presented in Fig. 5-9. Digitoxin was administered therapeutically to patients with atrial fibrillation. A reduction of 40 to 50 per cent in heart rate was the criterion of therapeutic response, vomiting was the criterion of toxic response. The curves are of great interest because few such quantal LDR studies have been carried out in human subjects. The rather flat slopes indicate how variable human responses are likely to be. Here, the standard deviation is 0.21 on the log scale, corresponding to a dose factor of 1.6 (antilog

FIG. 5-9. THERAPEUTIC RATIO OF DIGITOXIN IN MAN. *Ten patients with atrial fibrillation were given a single oral dose of digitoxin at intervals of one week. The per cent of patients showing a decrease of 40 to 50% in heart rate is shown in curve at* left, *the per cent responding with nausea and vomiting is shown in curve at* right. *The dose scale on the x-axis is shown in three ways. At top the unit dose is 5μg/kg, and successive doublings of this dose are indicated by integers 1, 2, 3, 4. On middle line is scale of actual doses spaced logarithmically. On bottom scale are logarithms of doses. (Redrawn from Marsh, Fig. 7.[33] By permission of Charles C Thomas.)*

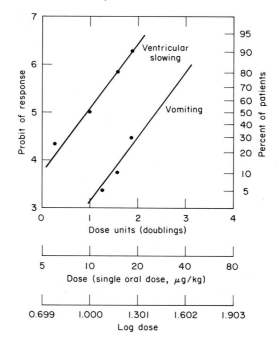

[33] D. F. MARSH: *Outline of Fundamental Pharmacology.* Springfield, Ill., Charles C Thomas, 1951.

0.21 = 1.6). At a dose of 10μg/kg, a therapeutic response would be obtained in only one-half of all patients. At 16μg/kg, only 84 per cent would respond; at 6.2μg/kg, 16 per cent would respond. The therapeutic ratio is not large. Measured at probit 5, TD50 = antilog 1.42, and ED50 = antilog 0.98; therefore TD50/ED50 = antilog (1.42 − 0.98) = 2.8. But the overlap of the curves is so great that a therapeutic ratio computed as TD1/ED99 would be much smaller than unity, i.e., at a dosage producing a therapeutic result in 99 per cent of patients, vomiting would occur in much more than 1 per cent. As a matter of fact, even at the ED50 three patients in every 100 would display this toxic symptom. Thus digitoxin has to be administered very cautiously, and the dosage has to be individualized. A cardiac glycoside with a larger therapeutic ratio would be a very useful drug, and pharmaceutical firms have spent much money and effort on the search. But, although many compounds with digitalis-like activity are known, none has yet been found to have a therapeutic ratio substantially greater than that of digitoxin.

A comparative study of two analgesic drugs in man is presented in Fig. 5-10. These are not quantal LDR curves; responses are averages of measured graded effects in a large number of patients. Studies of pain relief in man are extraordinarily difficult to carry out properly. Subjects and drug sequences have to be randomized, double-blind technique is essential, and placebo reactions must be taken into account[35] (cf. chapter 14). Nevertheless, some clear-cut results have been obtained, as in these experiments. About 68 mg of dihydrocodeine was equivalent to 10 mg of morphine in analgesic potency, indicating that dihydrocodeine is the less potent drug by a factor of 7. However, it might well be superior for clinical use if it could be shown, at doses producing the same degree of analgesia, to be less potent in causing respiratory depression, a serious side effect of morphine. The figure shows clearly, however, that the relative potencies of the two drugs in producing respiratory depression were just about the same as for their analgesic effects. Moreover, both drugs produced some degree of respiratory depression even at the lowest analgesic doses. As with nausea and vomiting in the case of the digitalis glycosides, so also here in the series of morphine-like analgesics it has not yet been possible to separate the major side effect from the desired therapeutic action.

Information about the metabolism of a drug is important in the evaluation of its toxicity. As pointed out in chapter 3, drugs may be metabolized quite differently in different species; not only do rates vary, but the pathways may be dissimilar. No firm predictions can be made about this from one species to another; and although there is probably a general similarity between man and the other primates, even here no systematic

34 J. C. SEED, S. L. WALLENSTEIN, R. W. HOUDE, and J. W. BELLVILLE: A comparison of the analgesic and respiratory effects of dihydrocodeine and morphine in man. *Arch. Int. Pharmacodyn. 116:*293 (1958).

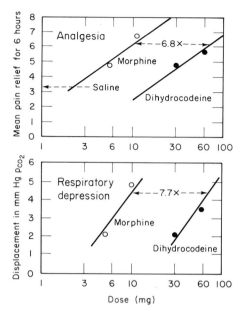

FIG. 5-10.   COMPARISON OF ANALGESIC AND RESPIRATORY DEPRESSANT EFFECTS
OF MORPHINE AND DIHYDROCODEINE IN MAN.   *Patients with pathologic pain
were used. Pain relief was scored on an arbitrary scale for 6 hours after drug
administration. Average pain relief for 68 administrations of each drug at two
doses is shown in* upper *curves. Respiratory depression was measured by the
diminished sensitivity of alveolar ventilation to CO_2; reults are shown in* lower
curves. (Adapted from Seed et al., Figs. 2 and 4.[34])

proofs have been adduced. The mode of drug metabolism can affect the
toxicity in several ways. Sometimes a metabolite is responsible for the principal toxic effects. Then if the preclinical testing is conducted in animals
that do not form a toxic metabolite, whereas humans do, serious toxicity
may be discovered unexpectedly during the clinical trials. Conversely, if
the species used for testing does form such a metabolite, but man does not,
a potentially safe and useful drug might be discarded. Another source of
misleading information is species variation in rates of drug metabolism
(p. 266). Yet another problem is raised by the development of drug
tolerance when a drug induces an increase in the level of the microsomal
drug-metabolizing enzymes, and the drug itself is a substrate, so that its
rate of metabolism increases with continuing administration. Tolbutamide
is a good example. This drug induces the synthesis of microsomal drug-

[35] R. W. HOUDE, S. L. WALLENSTEIN, and W. T. BEAVER: "Clinical Measurement of
Pain," in *Analgetics,* ed. by G. deStevens. New York, Academic Press, 1965.

metabolizing enzymes in man, and also in rats and rabbits; however, it is not itself metabolized in any of these species. But in the dog tolbutamide not only induces the enzymes, but is also degraded by them. For such a drug, preclinical testing in the dog would lead to completely false predictions about toxicity and efficacy in man.[36]

In addition to acute lethality determinations in mice, and animal tests of biologic effectiveness, new compounds that are candidates for clinical evaluation must undergo a rigorous series of acute and chronic toxicity tests. These tests, now largely prescribed by the Food and Drug Administration, are carried out in a variety of laboratory animals, the highest dose level being set sufficiently high to produce clear-cut toxicity. Hematologic studies and liver and kidney function tests are done routinely, and complete autopsy and histologic examinations are performed. Specially designed experiments seek carcinogenic activity or teratogenic effects in pregnant animals. Table 5-6 summarizes the usual procedures carried out in the stage of preclinical testing.

TABLE 5-6.   Toxicologic procedures in animals

(From Abrams et al.,[37] Table II. By permission of C. V. Mosby.)

I. ACUTE
1. LD50 determination in rats or mice
2. Pyramiding single-dose studies in dogs
3. Local effects (topical or parenteral agents)

II. SUBACUTE
1. Six to 13 weeks' administration to 40 rats (three dose levels)
2. Four to 13 weeks' administration to six dogs (three dose levels)

III. CHRONIC
1. One year's administration to rats (three dose levels)
2. Six months' administration to dogs (three dose levels)
3. Six months' administration to a third species
4. Reproduction experiments in rats and rabbits

IV. SPECIAL STUDIES
1. Metabolism: absorption, blood, and tissue levels, transportation across membranes, excretion
2. Effects on physiologic functions: blood pressure, cardiac output, respiration, renal function, central nervous system activity, hormonal effects, influences on appetite
3. Histochemical studies when indicated

[36] H. REMMER: Panel discussion, in Symposium: Evaluation and mechanisms of drug toxicity. *Ann. New York Acad. Sci. 123:*305 (1965).

[37] W. B. ABRAMS, R. E. BAGDON, and G. ZBINDEN: Drug toxicity and its impact on drug evaluation in man. *Clin. Pharmacol. Therap. 5:*273 (1964).

The usefulness of so much routine toxicologic testing has been questioned sharply,[31,38,39,39a] but it could also be argued from unfortunate experiences of recent years that extraordinary caution is justified before allowing new drugs to be introduced for widespread use in humans. The only relevant data that could help decide how much testing and what kinds of testing are useful would come from retrospective studies of drugs after their introduction into clinical use. Looking back through the results of animal testing at that stage, one could then get some index of predictability for human toxicity. Unfortunately, this has rarely been done. In one study of this kind[40] six unrelated drugs were considered: a glucocorticoid, a central depressant, an agent that blocks the oxidation of alcohol, a synthetic antibacterial drug, an antibiotic, and a tranquilizer. Each had been subjected to the usual routine acute and chronic toxicity tests, and each had been used in at least 500 patients. Some results are shown in Table 5-7. In the first part, toxic signs are compared in rat, dog, and man. Only those effects are included that would have been detected in all three species; vomiting, for example, which does not occur in the rat, is omitted from consideration. Evidently, certain effects were common to all three species, others were observed only in dog and man. For these types of toxicity the preclinical testing in the two species had obvious predictive value. On the other hand, some adverse effects occurred only in the dog, and others were seen only in man. The second part of Table 5-7 shows a detailed analysis of the toxic actions of one drug in dog and in man. This agent was characterized by a predominance of effects on the central nervous system, and no sign or symptom category was excluded. Here, as might have been expected, fewer of the human effects were predictable from the animal experience.

For all six drugs in these retrospective analyses, an attempt was made to estimate the proportion of right and wrong predictions that could have been made about human toxicity. The following prediction rule was hypothesized: If a toxic sign occurs in both the dog and the rat, it will also occur in man, but not otherwise. On this basis, 68 per cent of the positive predictions (i.e., that a toxic effect would occur in man) were correct, and 79 per cent of the negative predictions were correct. This analysis, however, excluded (as in the first part of Table 5-7) all signs and symptoms

38 J. M. BARNES and F. A. DENZ: Experimental methods used in determining chronic toxicity. *Pharmacol. Rev.* 6:191 (1954).

39 G. ZBINDEN: The problem of the toxicologic examination of drugs in animals and their safety in man. *Clin. Pharmacol. Therap.* 5:537 (1964).

39a G. ZBINDEN: Animal toxicity studies: a critical evaluation. *Appl. Therap.* 8:128 (1966).

40 J. T. LITCHFIELD, JR.: Evaluation of the safety of new drugs by means of tests in animals. *Clin. Pharmacol. Therap.* 3:665 (1962).

41 H. KALTER: Experimental investigation of teratogenic action. *Ann. New York Acad. Sci.* 123:287 (1965).

TABLE 5-7.   **Retrospective analysis of toxicity in animals and man**

In part *a,* only those toxic signs were considered which could occur in all three species. Effects peculiar to man, or subjective effects that could not be evaluated in animals, were excluded. In part *b,* all effects of one drug were inlcuded. (From Litchfield,[40] Tables I and II. By permission of C. V. Mosby.)

a. Toxic signs, all six drugs		b. Toxic signs and symptoms, one drug only	
Signs	**Animal**	**Signs and symptoms**	**Animal**
Low food intake		SIGNS	
Weight loss or impaired gain		Gastroduodenal ulcers	
Adrenal, lymphoid, and	Rat	Diarrhea	
muscle atrophy	Dog	Leukopenia	
Lymphocytopenia and	Man	Lymphocytopenia	
eosinopenia		Hyperthermia	Dog
Hyperglycemia		Salvation	
		Dyspnea	
Myositis	Dog	Ataxia	
Gastroduodenal ulcer	Man	Abnormal electrocardiogram	
Bacterial invasion			
		Rash	
Liver damage		Pimples	
Anemia		Chills	Man
Neutrophil increase	Dog only	Gooseflesh	
Polydipsia		Nasal congestion	
Polyuria			
Parasitic invasion		SYMPTOMS	
		Drowsiness	
Purpura	Man only	Headache	
Localized fat deposition		Dullness	
		Depression	
		Lethargy	
		Fatigue	
		Nightmare	
		Tinnitus	Man
		Giddiness	
		Metallic taste	
		Epigastric pain	
		Heartburn	
		Impotence	
		Loss of libido	

that could not possibly have been observed in the experimental animals because they are peculiar to man. Of 89 different toxic drug actions observed, 33 fell into this category.

The study discussed above shows how characteristic differences in species responses to drugs can diminish the predictive value of animal testing. Even more perplexing is the finding that the same toxic effect may occur in many species, but under different conditions and in response to different drugs. The evaluation of teratogenic action is plagued by this problem. As illustrated at length in chapter 12, there seems to be no reliable way to predict for a new drug whether or not it is likely to cause fetal malformations in the human, even though it often turns out to be easy enough to demonstrate such an action in some animal under some condition, once the teratogenicity in the human has become evident. If salicylates, for example, were tested under optimal conditions in the rat, they would be classed as teratogens, whereas in mice and humans they are almost certainly not teratogenic. On the other hand, thalidomide, which is a potent teratogen in the human, does not produce fetal malformations in rats.[41] It is likely that in this important area testing in other primates may yield the most consistent correlations with the human.[42]

In summary, the whole subject of preclinical testing is in a state of flux. It would be foolish to require a lengthy set of routine tests that will have no predictive value. On the other hand, enough is known about the unpredictability of species differences to suggest that testing in the lower animals should include many species. Certainly in many cases a pattern of toxicity will emerge that can serve as a guide for what to expect in man. This is especially true of certain kinds of toxicity involving physiologic and biochemical processes that are equally important in all animal life. Examples are interference with protein and nucleic acid synthesis, steroid metabolism, neurotransmitter function, blood formation, renal tubular absorption and secretion, myocardial contractility, and so on. Increasingly, monkeys will have to be used for toxicity tests, because of their close phylogenetic relationship to man. In general, the best approach would seem to be a flexible one, determined largely by the potential benefit of the new agent. Delay in the introduction of a new drug incident to exhaustive preclinical testing is of no great consequence for patients if effective drugs of the same type are already available. However, in the rare instance where a new agent promises great benefit or even life-saving properties in a disease for which no adequate remedy exists, more risk is obviously acceptable, and the preclinical testing phase should be shortened.

Once a drug has been subjected to a certain amount of preclinical testing, and its animal toxicity is known, it can be evaluated for therapeutic effect in man. Generally, the first humans to receive a new drug are exposed to little or no danger. A dose is selected that is well below what has been found to have any effect at all in animals. The subjects are under the constant supervision of clinical investigators who are on their guard for signs of untoward reactions. Naturally, the number of subjects is small, and doses are carefully increased to the point where the desired therapeutic effect is obtained or signs of toxicity appear. It is later on, when tight con-

42 C. S. DELAHUNT and L. J. LASSEN: Thalidomide syndrome in monkeys. *Science* *146:*1300 (1964).

trol of the drug is relaxed, and it becomes more widely available for clinical use under less rigidly controlled conditions, that difficulties often arise.

Regulations of the Food and Drug Administration prescribe appropriate procedures to be followed and the kind of information that must be accumulated and submitted before approval is given for wider distribution of a drug. Nevertheless, it has been a recurring theme, documented amply in the medical literature, that a drug heralded as having little or no toxicity when first introduced turns out to have significant toxic effects. Several reasons may be suggested for this consistent underestimation of the toxicity of new agents.

1. *The toxic reaction may be a rare event.* Suppose the incidence of toxicity is only one in 1,000. It is very unlikely to be picked up in preliminary testing, but it will surely emerge after the drug has been used widely. Drug toxicity associated with idiosyncratic responses based on genetic abnormalities falls into this class. Examples are the prolonged apnea occasionally seen after succinylcholine administration (p. 434), the primaquine-induced hemolytic anemias (p. 444), and the porphyrias caused by drugs (p. 453). But many rare toxicities are not known to have a genetic basis. The antibiotic chloramphenicol was used extensively for two years before it was realized that at high dosage it could cause severe agranulocytosis and aplastic anemia, sometimes fatal; the incidence was only one out of 50,000 or 100,000 patients.[43,44] After chloramphenicol had been in use for 17 years it was discovered that its prolonged use could lead to visual impairment.[45,46] Of course, a useful drug should be retained in clinical use even when it is found to have rare toxic effects. On the other hand, such a drug should not be used for trivial purposes, or if a safer compound will serve equally well.

Rare or sporadic toxicity may sometimes be attributable to impurities irregularly associated with a drug, rather than to the drug itself. The volatile anesthetic halothane provides an instructive example. This agent has been in extensive use in both Europe and the United States for about a decade. Severe liver damage following halothane anesthesia has been reported at an incidence of about one in 10,000 administrations. An analysis of commercially available halothane by the powerful technique of gas chromatography (Fig. 5-11) revealed the presence of several con-

---

[43] P. R. MC CURDY: Chloramphenicol bone marrow toxicity. *J. Am. Med. Ass.* *176:*588 (1961).

[44] A. A. SHARP: Chloramphenicol-induced blood dyscrasias: analysis of 40 cases. *Brit. Med. J. 1:*735 (1963).

[45] J. G. COCKE, JR., R. E. BROWN, and L. J. GEPPERT: Optic neuritis with prolonged use of chloramphenicol. *J. Pediat. 68:*27 (1966).

[46] N. N. HUANG, R. D. HARLEY, V. PROMADHATTAVEDI, and A. SPROUL: Visual disturbances in cystic fibrosis following chloramphenicol administration. *J. Pediat. 68:*32 (1966).

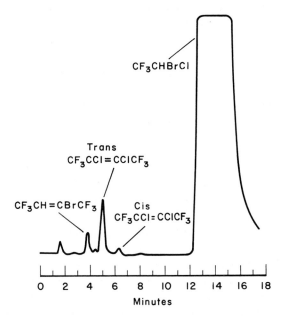

FIG. 5-11. GAS CHROMATOGRAPHIC ANALYSIS OF COMMERCIAL HALOTHANE. *One microliter of halothane was placed on the column. Several peaks representing impurities are seen to emerge ahead of the main halothane peak. (From Cohen et al., Fig. 3.[47])*

taminants, one of which (dichlorohexafluorobutene) was present to the extent of about 0.02 per cent:[47]

halothane   dichlorohexafluorobutene

Under the usual conditions of halothane administration, the concentration of the butene impurity in the vaporizer was found to increase severalfold during the course of anesthesia.[48] The impurity is known to be very toxic, and there are indications that the occasional liver toxicity reported with halothane administration was caused by it rather than by halothane itself. The commercial synthesis of halothane has been altered to eliminate the

[47] E. N. COHEN, H. W. BREWER, J. W. BELLVILLE, and R. SHER: The chemistry and toxicology of dichlorohexafluorobutene. *Anesthesiology 26:*140 (1965).
[48] E. N. COHEN, J. W. BELLVILLE, H. BUDZIKIEWICZ, and D. H. WILLIAMS: Impurity in halothane anesthetic. *Science 141:*899 (1963).

butene compound, and precautions are now taken against the accumulation of butene derivatives in the anesthetic vaporizers; it remains to be seen if this will eliminate the hepatotoxicity. The halothane experience raises a general question: Might other drug toxicities also be due to impurities, by-products, isomers, and so on, not ordinarily removed by conventional procedures for drug synthesis or isolation? Obviously, the standards of purity that were acceptable 25 years ago have to be revised to conform to modern analytical and preparative techniques.

A major problem associated with rare toxicities is the difficulty of collecting adequate information. Suppose a physician observes that one of his patients develops a blood dyscrasia. Is it a manifestation of the existing disease? Is it a sign of a new disease process? Or is it caused by a drug; and if so, by which of several drugs the patient may have been taking? The blood disorder may even appear well after drug therapy has been terminated, and the history of previous medication may be uncertain. Unless the physician suspects a particular drug, the case is not likely to be reported at all. Occasionally, a physician will write a letter of inquiry to the pharmaceutical firm that markets the drug, asking if other physicians have had similar experiences. Only recently have regulations of the Food and Drug Administration required pharmaceutical firms to make their files of such letters available to inspectors.

Some organized attempts have been made to collect information on untoward drug effects. For example, the Registry of Blood Dyscrasias, under the auspices of the American Medical Association, solicited information for several years about blood disorders associated with drug administration and frequently published pooled data and interpretations. Table 5-8 lists drugs reported to be associated with various blood dyscrasias. The table does not indicate the frequency of toxic reaction to the individual drugs; to develop such information, it would be necessary to know the relative extent to which each drug is used. And without such information about relative use, no useful correlations can be deduced about the hazard or relative safety of a particular drug.

This data-collection and evaluation service of the AMA, under the new name of Registry of Adverse Drug Reactions,[50] has now been expanded to include all drugs. Other data-collection mechanisms have been established to assess teratogenic hazards (Perinatal Collaborative Study), the toxicity of halothane anesthesia (National Halothane Study), and so forth. Extensive tabulations of rare untoward drug reactions have been published.[51] What the public welfare really requires, in place of these ad hoc procedures, is a nationwide or worldwide data-collection system,

[49] Registry on Blood Dyscrasias. Report to the Council on Drugs. *J. Am. Med. Ass. 179:*888 (1962).

[50] Council on Drugs, American Medical Association. Publications of the Registry on Adverse Reactions, vol. 1. Chicago, 1964–65.

[51] P. S. NORMAN and L. E. CLUFF: "Adverse Drug Reactions and Alternative Drugs of Choice," in *Drugs of Choice, 1964–65,* ed. by W. Modell. St. Louis, C. V. Mosby Co., 1964, chapt. 3, pp. 50–65.

feeding into a computerized monitoring program. Such a mechanism, for which the technology is already at hand, would detect unusual associations between particular drugs and adverse effects. Whenever such an association occurred at a frequency greater than expected by chance, attention would be called quickly and automatically to the potential hazard. It is evident in retrospect that such a mechanism would have alerted us at least a year in advance to the chloramphenicol toxicity and to the serious teratogenic effects of thalidomide (p. 727).

2. *The toxic reaction may appear only after prolonged drug administration.* This presents a thorny problem because, if chronic toxicity studies in animals are carried to an extreme, the introduction of useful new drugs will inevitably be delayed. And even after a drug fails to cause any harm to animals in a prolonged toxicity test, it may nevertheless still produce damage on long-term administration to humans. With respect to any new drug that is to be used constantly, year in and year out, in humans, the argument could be made that safety on long-term administration remains unproved. At the time of their introduction into widespread use, this could have been said about vitamins, hormone preparations, antimalarials, food additives, steroid oral contraceptives, and even the chlorination or fluoridation of water supplies.

Possible carcinogenicity epitomizes the dilemma. The conservative point of view, now in effect, is that any compound, at any dose, that causes cancer in animals (usually mice) is liable to be prohibited for human use. It is not known, however, whether the human is more or less susceptible to carcinogenic agents than are mice. Nor is it known if an agent that causes a low incidence of tumors in mice poses any real threat to man, especially when given only infrequently, at lower relative dosage, to adults who may already have lived more than one-half their life span. A parenteral iron preparation (iron dextran injection, Imferon) was withdrawn from the market because it was found to cause cancer under some conditions in mice. Subsequently, because it was considered to be of value therapeutically, its re-introduction was permitted. Nevertheless, as with chloramphenicol, the wise physician will keep the possible toxicity in mind and not use such a drug if safer ones can be used instead. Thus, the standard orally administered iron preparations are usually adequate; only in special circumstances is a parenteral iron preparation called for.

Chronic administration of streptomycin results in a high incidence of neurologic damage, manifested by hearing deficit and disorders of equilibrium. Yet the great potential benefit of this drug in tuberculosis and other infections often outweighs even so serious a hazard.

At the other extreme we have instances in which toxic new drugs were introduced, and serious damage was caused without valid evidence of therapeutic efficacy. A notorious recent example is triparanol (MER-29), an agent that was shown to inhibit the reductive conversion of desmosterol (24-dehydrocholesterol) to cholesterol. Administration of this drug lowers

TABLE 5-8. **Drugs or chemicals shown by direct or circumstantial evidence to be associated with blood dyscrasias**

(Data from the Registry on Blood Dyscrasias.[49])

	Hemolytic anemia	Pancyto-penia	Thrombocy-topenia	Leuko-penia	Anemia
Acetanilid	X				
Acetazolamide			X		
Acetophenetidin	X				
Allylisopropylacetylurea			X		
Aminopyrine	X			X	
Arsphenamine		X	X	X	X
Benzene		X	X	X	X
Carbutamide		X	X	X	X
Chloramphenicol		X	X	X	X
Chlordane		X	X	X	X
Chlorothiazide			X	X	
Chlorpromazine				X	
Chlorpropamide		X	X	X	X
Colchicine		X	X	X	X
Diphenylhydantoin sodium					X
Dipyrone				X	
Gamma benzene hexachloride		X	X	X	X
Gold salts		X	X	X	X
Imipramine				X	
Lead					X
Mepazine				X	
Meprobamate		X	X	X	X
Methimazole				X	
Methylphenylethyl hydantoin		X	X	X	X
Naphthalene	X				
Nitrofurantoin	X				
Pamaquine	X				

blood cholesterol levels and accordingly raises blood desmosterol levels.[52] It might have been predicted, a priori, that an inhibitor of cholesterol biosynthesis would have widespread effects on the body, including a decrease in the production of corticosteroids. Nevertheless, the drug was introduced and vigorously promoted for the treatment of hypercholesterolemia, especially in atherosclerotic individuals. Only later did it become apparent that triparanol caused severe chronic toxicity, including cataracts, ichthyosis, alopecia, leukopenia, and diminished libido.[53, 54] As a result, the drug

[52] J. AVIGAN, D. STEINBERG, H. E. VROMAN, M. J. THOMPSON, and E. MOSETTIG: Studies of cholesterol biosynthesis. I. The identification of desmosterol in serum and tissues of animals and man treated with MER-29. *J. Biol. Chem. 235:*3123 (1960).

[53] R. W. P. ACHOR, R. K. WINKELMANN, and H. O. PERRY: Cutaneous side effects from use of triparanol (MER-29): preliminary data on ichthyosis and loss of hair. *Proc. Staff Meetings Mayo Clinic 36:*217 (1961).

[54] R. C. LAUGHLIN and T. F. CAREY: Cataracts in patients treated with triparanol. *J. Am. Med. Ass. 181:*339 (1962).

TABLE 5-8 **(Continued)**

	Hemolytic anemia	Pancyto-penia	Thrombocy-topenia	Leuko-penia	Anemia
Para-aminosalicylic acid	X				
Phenindione				X	
Phenylbutazone		X	X	X	X
Phenylhydrazine	X				
Primaquine	X				
Primidone					X
Probenecid	X				
Promazine				X	
Pyrimethamine			X	X	X
Quinacrine		X	X	X	X
Quinidine	X		X		
Quinine			X		
Ristocetin			X		
Stibophen	X				
Streptomycin		X	X	X	X
Sulfacetamide	X				
Sulfadiazine				X	
Sulfamethoxypyridazine	X	X	X	X	X
Sulfanilamide	X			X	
Sulfisoxazole			X	X	
Sulfoxone	X				
Thiazolsulfone	X				
Thiobarbital				X	
Thiouracils				X	
Tolbutamide		X	X	X	X
Trimethadione		X	X	X	X
Trinitrotoluene		X	X	X	X

was removed from the market. The therapeutic efficacy of this drug in atherosclerosis had never been established. True, it lowered cholesterol levels, but there was never proof that any patients would benefit from lower cholesterol (and higher desmosterol) levels. Curiously, too, the manufacturer's reports on the preclinical tests gave little indication of chronic toxicity, yet animal experiments afterwards clearly demonstrated severe chronic toxicity in rats.[55] Subsequently it was charged in the courts that evidence of chronic toxicity had been concealed; the defendants pleaded no contest and were heavily fined.[56, 57] It seems fair to point out that episodes like this, coupled with abuses in drug promotion and advertising, helped create the atmosphere in which legislation was passed (in 1962) giving stricter regulatory powers to the Food and Drug Administration.

[55] L. VON SALLMAN, P. GRIMES, and E. COLLINS: Triparanol induced cataracts in rats. *Arch. Ophthalmol.* 70:522 (1963).

[56] New York Times, June 5, 1964, p. 11.

[57] M. MINTZ: *The Therapeutic Nightmare.* Boston, Houghton Mifflin Co., 1965.

3. *The toxic effect may not have been detected in any of the animal species used for preclinical testing.* The effect may even be unique to man, or to some particular period of human life. The failure of animal testing to reveal toxicity is characteristic of the nonlethal adverse effects that commonly limit the use of drugs in man. Examples of reactions not readily observable in experimental animals are headache, nausea, insomnia, and psychotic disturbances. Some toxic manifestations in humans may be utterly bizarre and unexpected. The thalidomide episode (p. 727) is typical of this class of toxic reaction. The drug causes fetal malformations when taken by pregnant women. Prior to the epidemic of human toxicity, no laboratory tests for teratogenic effects had been developed. Many animal species are not affected. Even now it is by no means certain that similar incidents can be prevented. Another example of wholly unexpected, bizarre toxicity is that caused by the monoamine oxidase inhibitor tranylcypromine in people who eat cheeses rich in tyramine or whose intake of sympathomimetic amines is otherwise enhanced (cf. p. 258).

The newborn infant is peculiarly vulnerable to certain types of drug toxicity. He has a low level of drug-metabolizing enzymes, and his renal system does not work as efficiently as that of the older child or adult. Drug toxicities in the newborn, that once seemed inexplicable, are now better understood and can be avoided. These include chloramphenicol toxicity (p. 277), and kernicterus caused by vitamin K or sulfonamides displacing unconjugated bilirubin from plasma proteins (p. 143). Another interesting example of the vulnerability of the very young to otherwise innocuous agents is the often-fatal methemoglobinemia seen in infants less than six months old, whose feeding formulas are made with water (usually rural well water) containing inorganic nitrate. A nitrate concentration as low as 50 mg per liter may be toxic. Three factors are responsible. First, the less acid stomach contents of infants permit invasion of the upper gastrointestinal tract by nitrate-reducing bacteria. The resulting nitrite is absorbed, and it is the direct cause of the methemoglobinemia.[58] Second, fetal hemoglobin is more easily converted to methemoglobin than is the adult form, and young infants still have considerable amounts of fetal hemoglobin in their blood. Third, infants are less able than older children to reduce methemoglobin back to the ferrous form, because they are deficient in the essential enzymes.[59] These last two factors also explain why the young infant is more prone to develop methemoglobinemia from various agents like sulfonamides, ethylaminobenzoate, *p*-nitroaniline, and aniline dyes.[60]

[58] M. CORNBLATH and A. F. HARTMANN: Methemoglobinemia in young infants. *J. Pediat. 33:*421 (1948).

[59] J. D. ROSS and J. F. DESFORGES: Reduction of methemoglobin by erythrocytes from cord blood: further evidence of deficient enzyme activity in the newborn period. *Pediatrics 23:*718 (1959)

[60] F. RIEDERS: Noxious Gases and Vapors I: Carbon Monoxide, Cyanides, Methemoglobin, and Sulfhemoglobin," in *Drill's Pharmacology in Medicine,* 3rd ed., ed. by J. R. DiPalma. New York, McGraw-Hill, 1965, chapt. 58.

TREATMENT OF TOXICITY

Principles of Nonspecific Therapy

Certain immediate measures are called for in every case of poisoning, regardless of the cause.[10] First attention is given to maintaining respiration and circulation. Then it is important to find out what drug was taken, and how much of it, so that rational procedures can be followed. Further absorption of the toxic agent into the circulation should be stopped or retarded, but the appropriate steps depend upon the route of administration. If the drug was ingested and the patient remains conscious, vomiting should be induced. Various means may be employed, such as mechanical gagging, emetics (e.g., syrup of ipecac, mustard powder) by mouth, and injection of apomorphine. However, vomiting should not be induced if the toxic agent is corrosive (lye, kerosene, etc.), for it may cause hemorrhage or perforation of the esophagus or stomach. If the patient is unconscious, and a noncorrosive agent was ingested, then gastric lavage may be carried out, but only after insertion of an endotracheal tube, to avoid the possibility of asphyxiation by inhalation of vomitus. Activated charcoal or large amounts of protein may be given by mouth to adsorb toxic material and retard its further absorption from the gastrointestinal tract. Quantitative studies on the absorption of various substances have shown that plain activated charcoal is more effective than the so-called "universal antidote" containing magnesium oxide and tannic acid as well.[60a, 60b] If the drug was given subcutaneously or intramuscularly, attempts may be made to delay its absorption by applying tourniquets proximal to the injection site, as in the first-aid treatment of snake bite. Obviously, if the toxic substance is being absorbed through the skin, thorough washing is indicated.

The most important reason for ascertaining exactly what agent is responsible for the toxic effects is that some poisons can be treated with specific antidotes. If a patient is found unconscious and no further information can be obtained, then general supportive therapy will be initiated, the principles of which are discussed below. But the prognosis may be improved greatly, indeed the victim's condition may even be changed for the better in a moment, if the poison is identified and the specific antidote is given. Unfortunately, in all too many cases it is hard to find out what poison was taken. It is not yet customary to label prescription medications. Frequently, a child or a person attempting suicide has emptied a container that bears no indication of the nature of the contents. Time has to be wasted in frantic telephone calls to relatives, pharmacists and physi-

60a R. E. GOSSELIN and R. P. SMITH: Trends in the therapy of acute poisonings. *Clin. Pharmacol. Therap. 7:*279 (1966).

60b A. L. PICCHIONI, L. CHIN, H. L. VERHULST, and B. DIETERLE: Activated charcoal vs. "universal antidote" as an antidote for poisons. *Toxicol. Appl. Pharmacol. 8:*447 (1966).

cians in the attempt to identify the medication. All medications should be labeled. This is accomplished very simply; the physician has only to request it on the prescription blank. Household and commercial products that are potentially toxic are now required to bear appropriate cautionary labels and to name the toxic ingredients. Poison control centers have useful files of information about toxic substances in household and commercial use.

Inasmuch as no specific antidotes are known for most drugs and poisons, the aims of treatment are to support the vital functions and hasten drug elimination. These essentials of nonspecific treatment are illustrated well by the management of poisoning due to barbiturates, the agents most frequently used in suicide attempts. Because here the life-threatening toxic effects are central respiratory depression and secondary circulatory collapse, primary attention is directed to maintaining a free airway and administering artificial respiration as required. Gastric lavage is never undertaken in an unconscious patient unless a cuffed endotracheal or tracheotomy tube is in place, to avoid any possibility of airway occlusion by vomitus. Even when the airway is protected, gastric lavage is limited to those occasions when the poison has been ingested very recently and is known not to be corrosive to the mucosa of the esophagus and stomach.

There has been much controversy over the use of analeptic drugs in poisonings by barbiturates or other central depressant drugs. These analeptics (pentylenetetrazol, picrotoxin, bemegride) are certainly capable of stimulating the respiration of experimental animals depressed by barbiturates; and when the depression is mild, they also show an awakening effect. However, their effectiveness is much diminished at deeper levels of barbiturate depression. About 20 years ago in Denmark, a concerted attack on the problem of poisoning by central depressants was initiated.[61-63] Treatment was centralized in certain hospitals, where emergency teams stood ready day and night. Emphasis was placed upon restoring and maintaining the vital functions, and experts were trained in the important techniques. The mortality rate fell dramatically (Fig. 5-12). When analeptics were completely abandoned (in 1949), the results continued to improve. Over a period of 15 years the mortality was reduced from 25 per cent to less than 1 per cent. It is difficult to attribute this impressive accomplishment to any single factor; and it is also difficult to prove conclusively from data of this kind that analeptics make matters worse, as the Danish workers claim. It is fair to say that the only important result one could hope for in analeptic treatment would be restoration of respiratory function, and this

    [61] C. CLEMMESEN and E. NILSSON: Therapeutic trends in the treatment of barbiturate poisoning. The Scandinavian method. *Clin. Pharmacol. Therap. 2*:220 (1961).
    [62] A. MYSCHETZKY and N. A. LASSEN: Urea-induced, osmotic diuresis and alkalization of urine in acute barbiturate intoxication. *J. Am. Med. Ass. 185*:936 (1963).
    [63] C. CLEMMESEN: Treatment of narcotic intoxication. *Danish Med. Bull. 10*:97 (1963), and other papers in the same volume, pp. 100–144.

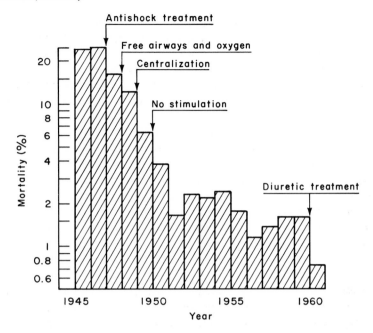

FIG. 5-12. MORTALITY TREND IN POISONINGS DUE TO CENTRAL DEPRESSANTS UPON IMPROVEMENT OF NONSPECIFIC TREATMENT METHODS IN COPENHAGEN. *Barbiturates accounted for more than 75 per cent of the poisonings. Scale of ordinates is logarithmic. The figures are from the official Danish medicostatistical bureau; only hospitalized patients were included. "Centralization" refers to the treatment of all cases of poisoning at a few designated centers. (From Myschetzky and Lassen, Fig. 5.[62])*

can be achieved more reliably and with better quantitative control by mechanical means. The "awakening" effect is of no consequence, since the patient will awaken spontaneously when the barbiturate has been eliminated; and the danger of excessive analeptic action, namely convulsions, is a real one. Moreover, the proper use of analeptics, to ensure a sufficient effect yet avoid overstimulation, would require constant intravenous infusion of a short-acting compound (e.g., pentylenetetrazol), with constant monitoring and regulation, a task that should only be undertaken by an expert. The consensus today supports the Danish view that analeptics should never (or almost never) be used.

If adequate oxygenation is maintained by artificial respiration, the blood pressure can usually be supported by intravenous fluids. The use of pressor amines in hemorrhagic and traumatic shock has been abandoned in recent years[64-65] in favor of agents like isoproterenol, which strengthen

[64] R. C. LILLEHEI, J. K. LONGERBEAM, J. H. BLOCH, and W. G. MANAX: The nature of irreversible shock: experimental and clinical observations. *Ann. Surgery 160:*682 (1964).
    [65] M. NICKERSON: Sympathetic blockade in the therapy of shock. *Amer. J. Cardiol. 12:*619 (1963).

myocardial contractility and cause peripheral vasodilation, and of α-adrenergic blocking agents like phenoxybenzamine, which relax arterioles and thereby promote better tissue perfusion. In hemorrhagic and traumatic shock the arterioles are constricted reflexly, the catecholamine content of the blood is very high, and blood volume is diminished; despite high peripheral resistance blood pressure is low, so that blood flow through the tissues is poor and venous return and cardiac output are low. It is still somewhat uncertain to what extent the same physiologic disturbances are present in barbiturate overdosage, and to what extent the hypotension may be caused by loss of sympathetic tone at the arterioles, resulting from depression of central vasomotor outflow. In barbiturate poisoning, if intravenous fluids alone will not restore an adequate blood pressure, it may be rational to use pressor amines. However, the increasing tendency is to avoid complicating a relatively simple problem of central depression by administering additional drugs, each with its own potential toxicity. Moreover, systolic blood pressures as low as 60 mm Hg are compatible with adequate perfusion of the vital organs. Attention is properly focused upon the central venous pressure (measured by a polyethylene catheter threaded up the antecubital vein to the vena cava) and the urine output (measured by an indwelling catheter), rather than upon blood pressure alone.[66, 66a]

Another significant advance of recent years has been the employment of hemodialysis and, more important, peritoneal dialysis. Use of the ion-trapping principle (p. 121) in conjunction with peritoneal dialysis has proved very effective in accelerating the removal of weak electrolytes. It is interesting to note that the original artificial kidney was designed by J. J. Abel (1857–1938), the first American pharmacologist, with a view to the treatment of drug poisoning.[67] The modern artificial kidney has been used successfully to remove salicylates, barbiturates, glutethimide, bromide, methanol, and numerous other drugs from the blood. The efficacy of hemodialysis in removing salicylate from the body was illustrated in Fig. 2-40. Unfortunately, the artificial kidney is a complicated, expensive apparatus, not without hazard to the patient, and generally available only at the largest medical centers. Peritoneal dialysis is less complicated but less efficient; an isotonic fluid is introduced into the peritoneal cavity, then evacuated and replaced periodically.[68] Figure 5-13 shows how effective this

66 H. SHUBIN and M. H. WEIL: The mechanism of shock following suicidal doses of barbiturates, narcotics and tranquilizer drugs, with observations on the effects of treatment. Amer. J. Med. 38:853 (1965).

66a L. WEINSTEIN and A. S. KLAINER: Management of emergencies. IV. Septic shock—pathogenesis and treatment. New England J. Med. 274:950 (1966).

67 J. J. ABEL, L. G. ROWNTREE, and B. B. TURNER: On the removal of diffusible substances from the circulating blood of living animals by dialysis. J. Pharmacol. Exper. Therap. 5:275 (1914).

68 J. P. KNOCHEL, L. E. CLAYTON, W. L. SMITH, and K. G. BARRY: Intraperitoneal THAM: an effective method to enhance phenobarbital removal during peritoneal dialysis. J. Lab. Clin. Med. 64:257 (1964).

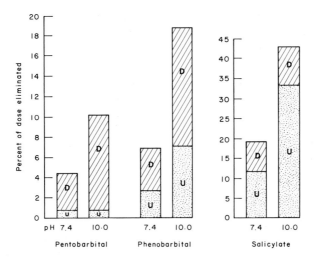

FIG. 5-13. ELIMINATION OF DRUGS BY PERITONEAL DIALYSIS IN DOGS. Dogs *were given pentobarbital (35 mg/kg), phenobarbital (100 mg/kg), or sodium salicylate (100 mg/kg). Peritoneal dialysis was performed with ordinary glucose-Ringer solution at body pH or with an alkaline buffer solution at pH 10 (tromethamine, tris(hydroxymethylamino)methane, THAM). The dialysis fluid was changed every 30 minutes for 3 hours. The total amounts of drug excreted into urine (U) and into the dialysis fluid (D) were measured and expressed here as per cent of the total dose. (Adapted from Nahas et al., Figs. 5 and 6.[69] By permission of C. V. Mosby.)*

procedure can be. Studies were carried out in dogs poisoned with pentobarbital ($pK_a = 7.8$), phenobarbital ($pK_a = 7.2$), and salicylate ($pK_a = 3.0$). Two kinds of dialysis fluid were compared: ordinary unbuffered Ringer-glucose, and a solution of tromethamine (tris(hydroxymethylamino)methane) buffered at pH 10. Since tromethamine diffuses only slowly across membranes and thus tends to stay within the peritoneal cavity, it serves to make the peritoneal fluid into an "ion trap" for diffusible weak acids. The figure indicates that more than ten times as much pentobarbital was eliminated into the alkaline, buffered solution as into urine over a 3-hour period, and that the buffered solution was always more effective than the unbuffered solution. Peritoneal dialysis, while far simpler than hemodialysis, also requires very careful attention to fluid and electrolyte balance.[69, 70]

The beneficial effects of acidosis or alkalosis in promoting the redistribution of weak acids or bases in the various body compartments have

69 G. G. NAHAS, J. GJESSING, J. J. GIROUX, M. VEROSKY, and L. C. MARK: The passage of THAM across the peritoneum during dialysis. *Clin. Pharmacol. Therap.* 6:560 (1965).

70 J. F. MAHER and G. E. SCHREINER: Hazards and complications of dialysis. *New England J. Med.* 273:370 (1965).

already been considered in detail (p. 157). Thus, administration of bicarbonate results in a transient plasma alkalosis, which promotes a shift of barbiturate out of the brain (and other tissues) into the plasma by the ion-trapping mechanism. This effect of altered plasma pH upon the distribution of a weak electrolyte between tissues and plasma was illustrated in Fig. 2-22. Since the nonionized form of a drug is at the same concentration on both sides of biologic membranes, it follows that the magnitude of the inequality of *total* drug concentration will depend upon two factors, the pH gradient and the pK_a of the drug. The limits between which the plasma and urine pH values can be manipulated are narrow—a few tenths of a pH unit for the plasma, a few pH units for urine. The proportional rate of change of the nonionized form with respect to pH is given by the following equation,[71] obtained by differentiating the Henderson-Hasselbalch equation (cf. p. 26):

$$\frac{d(HA)/d(pH)}{(HA)} = -\ln 10 \left[\frac{10^{pH}}{10^{pH} + 10^{pK}} \right]$$

This expression gives the change of (HA) relative to the concentration already present. When the equation is solved for pH 7.4 and the proportional change in (HA) is plotted as a function of pK_a, the curve shown in Fig. 5-14 is obtained. It can be seen that the maximal proportional rate of change is obtained with agents whose pK_a is about 6 or lower, and the minimal value is attained with drugs whose pK_a is about 8 or higher. This shows quantitatively how much more effective is alkalinization of plasma,

FIG. 5-14. PROPORTIONAL RATE OF CHANGE WITH pH OF THE NONIONIZED FORM OF A WEAK ACID AT pH 7.4. *The curve is plotted from the equation given above. Proportional rate of change of the nonionized form of the acid is given as ordinates, pK_a' as abscissas. The* dotted line *is the asymptote approached by the function as pK_a' decreases. (From Waddell and Butler, Fig. 1.[71])*

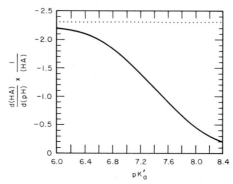

[71] W. J. WADDELL and T. C. BUTLER: The distribution and excretion of phenobarbital. *J. Clin. Invest.* 36:1217 (1957).

urine, or peritoneal wash fluids for removing the more acidic drugs (like salicylates or even phenobarbital [pK$_a$ = 7.2]) than acids that are weaker than phenobarbital. In the barbiturate class, it so happens that most of the short-acting compounds, like pentobarbital and secobarbital, have pK$_a$ values in the range 7.6 to 8.0,[72] and are therefore more difficult to eliminate by ion-trapping mechanisms.

The shifting of acidic drugs from tissues into plasma by producing a transient metabolic alkalosis would be of no long-term benefit were it not for the corresponding effect on reabsorption from tubular urine; the excreted bicarbonate alkalinizes the urine, so that the back-diffusion of the drug is greatly retarded and the total drug output in the urine is increased. Quite apart from the influence of alkalinization, forced diuresis in itself significantly increases the renal clearance of any drug that is largely reabsorbed under conditions of low urine output.[73] This phenomenon is shown clearly in Fig. 5-15. At both acid and alkaline urine pH, the renal clearance of phenobarbital was found to be a linear function of the urine flow. The osmotic diuretics, urea or mannitol, are commonly used to pro-

FIG. 5-15. RENAL CLEARANCE OF PHENOBARBITAL AS A FUNCTION OF URINE FLOW IN DOGS. *Diuresis was induced by oral water, intravenous mercapto-merin, or intravenous sodium sulfate. In* lower curve, *urine pH was below 7.0; in the experiments shown in* upper curve, *sodium bicarbonate was given intravenously so that urine pH was 7.8 to 8.0. Clearances were computed from the concentration of unbound drug in plasma. (From Waddell and Butler, Fig. 4.[71])*

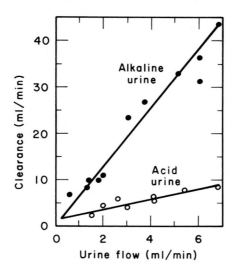

[72] M. E. KRAHL: The effect of variation in ionic strength and temperature on the apparent dissociation constants of thirty substituted barbituric acids. *J. Phys. Chem.* **44**:449 (1940).

[73] J. C. STRICKLER: Forced diuresis in the management of barbiturate intoxication. *Clin. Pharmacol. Therap.* **6**:693 (1965).

TABLE 5-9.   Efficiency of various types of active treatment of acute barbiturate intoxication

Values shown below are approximate only, and are estimates from various studies with long-acting barbiturates. The values given for hemodialysis assume 8 hours of dialysis plus 16 hours of spontaneous clearance per 24 hours. (Data of Myschetzky,[62] Table 6.)

Treatment	Urine volume (liters/24 hr)	pH	Clearance (ml/min)	(liters/24 hr)
Spontaneous	1.5	6	1	1.5
Diuretics				
mercurials, fluids	5	6	3.5	5
mannitol	9	6	6	9
osmotic diuretic plus				
alkalinization	12	7.5–8	17	24
Hemodialysis (8 hours only)			35	18

mote a diuresis as great as 12 liters in 24 hours, alkalinization being achieved with bicarbonate or lactate. Such a regimen has been shown to reduce the period of barbiturate coma by two-thirds, compared with patients not so treated; the need for tracheotomy was reduced by one-half, and the overall mortality was further reduced compared with that achieved by respiratory management alone.[62, 74] Of course, forced diuresis of any type is not employed in the presence of anuria or serious renal damage occasioned by the toxic material. Alkaline diuresis and peritoneal dialysis become distinctly less advantageous with increasing pK_a value of the barbiturate; thus, pentobarbital ($pK_a = 7.8$) is more poorly eliminated by these procedures than is phenobarbital ($pK_a = 7.2$).[72, 75, 76]

The efficiency of various techniques of promoting the clearance of long-acting barbiturates is summarized in Table 5-9. Hemodialysis effects the greatest increase in clearance, but since it is used intermittently, the total amount of barbiturate removed per day is about the same as with alkaline diuresis.

Principles of Antidotal Treatment

The limited number of specific antidotes that are available[77] are listed in Table 5-10. They will be discussed as examples of the various mechanisms of antidotal action. As more information becomes available

---

[74] N. A. LASSEN: Treatment of severe acute barbiturate poisoning by forced diuresis and alkalinisation of the urine. *Lancet 2:*338 (1960).

[75] H. F. BUNN and G. D. LUBASH: A controlled study of induced diuresis in barbiturate intoxication. *Ann. Int. Med. 62:*246 (1965).

[76] H. A. BLOOMER: Limited usefulness of alkaline diuresis and peritoneal dialysis in pentobarbital intoxication. *New England J. Med. 272:*1309 (1965).

[77] A. K. DONE: Clinical pharmacology of systemic antidotes. *Clin. Pharmacol. Therap. 2:*750 (1961).

TABLE 5-10. Toxic agents, specific antidotes, and mechanisms of antidotal action

Toxic agent	Specific antidote
Mechanism 1: Antidote complexes with poison, rendering it inert	
Arsenic, mercury	Dimercaprol (BAL)
Lead, plutonium, uranium	Calcium disodium edetate (EDTA); diethylenetriamine pentaacetic acid (DTPA)
Iron	Sodium ferrocyanide (by mouth); DTPA (?)[a]; desferrioxamine (?)[a]
Copper	Penicillamine
Thallium	Dithizone (?)[a]
Formaldehyde	Ammonia (by mouth)
Heparin	Protamine; hexadimethrine
Botulinus toxin and other toxins	Botulinus antitoxin and other antitoxins
Cholinesterase inhibitors	Pralidoxime
Cyanide	Methemoglobin (formed by nitrite administration)
Mechanism 2: Antidote accelerates metabolic conversion of poison to nontoxic product	
Cyanide	Thiosulfate
Mechanism 3: Antidote blocks metabolic formation of poison from less toxic precursor	
Methanol	Ethanol
Selenocystathionine	Cystine
Fluoroacetate	Acetate; monoacetin
Mechanism 4: Antidote specifically accelerates excretion of poison	
Bromide	Chloride
Strontium, radium	Calcium salts
Mechanism 5: Antidote competes with poison for essential receptors	
Carbon monoxide	Oxygen
Curare (tubocurarine)	Neostigmine; edrophonium
Coumarin anticoagulants	Vitamin K
Morphine, related narcotics	Nalorphine; related antagonists
Thallium	Potassium salts (?)[a]
Amino acid analogues	Amino acids
Mechanism 6: Antidote blocks receptors that are responsible for toxic effect	
Cholinesterase inhibitors	Atropine
Mechanism 7: Antidote restores normal function by repairing or by-passing effect of poison	
Agents that produce methemoglobinemia	Methylene blue
Digitalis glycosides	Potassium salts; α-adrenergic blocking agents; procaine amide; disodium EDTA (?)[a]
Methotrexate, other folic acid antagonists	Folinic acid; thymidine + purine + glycine
5-Fluorouracil	Thymidine
6-Mercaptopurine	Purines

[a] (?) indicates practical efficacy of antidote not well established, or doubtful.

about the biochemical mechanisms of toxicity, more such antidotes will undoubtedly be developed. Unlike the discovery of new drug actions, where chance has often been more important than foresight, rational selection and even deliberate synthesis have played important roles in the development of specific antidotes.

MECHANISM 1. ANTIDOTE COMPLEXES WITH POISON, RENDERING IT INERT

Heavy Metals. The treatment of poisoning due to heavy metals offers the simplest example of this mechanism. Chelating agents are used to form tightly bound nontoxic complexes with the metal ions. This reduces the concentration of free metal ions in the body fluids and thus promotes the dissociation of bound metal from tissue enzymes and other functional macromolecules. Typically the metal-chelate complexes are water soluble and can be excreted by the kidney. Thus the total body load of metal is reduced. The principles of chelation, with some examples, have already been presented in chapter 1.

Poisoning by arsenic or mercury is specifically combatted by dimercaprol. This antidote was developed during World War II for protection against the arsenical gas lewisite; hence the original designation British anti-lewisite (BAL).[78] This compound holds the distinction of being the first antidotal agent synthesized on a rational basis. Arsenic was known to inhibit enzymes containing essential sulfhydryl groups, and small SH-containing molecules like cysteine and glutathione were found to offer some protection to experimental animals. The principle of chelation in stable five-membered or six-membered ring compounds (cf. chapter 1) suggested that dithiols might complex arsenic more firmly than monothiols do. Out of many compounds tested, dimercaprol (dimercaptopropanol) proved most effective. The vicinal sulfhydryl groups form a stable mercaptide ring with appropriate metal ions, while the alcohol group serves to confer water solubility upon the whole complex.

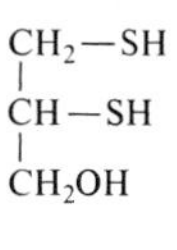

$$
\begin{array}{ll}
\mathrm{CH_2-SH} & \mathrm{CH_2-S} \\
| & | \quad\!\!\!\diagdown \!\! \mathrm{As-R} \\
\mathrm{CH-SH} & \mathrm{CH-S}\diagup \\
| & | \\
\mathrm{CH_2OH} & \mathrm{CH_2OH}
\end{array}
$$

dimercaprol 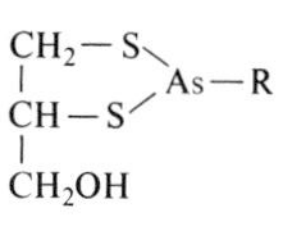   arsenic mercaptide

Dimercaprol finds use chiefly in arsenic and mercury poisonings, but it is also effective in the less common poisonings by gold, bismuth, cadmium, and polonium. Scattered reports indicate its probable usefulness in antimony, chromium, and nickel poisonings. Unfortunately, like other thiols,

[78] L. A. STOCKEN and R. H. S. THOMPSON: Reactions of British anti-lewisite with arsenic and other metals in living systems. *Physiol. Rev. 29:*168 (1949).

it has considerable toxicity of its own, so that it has to be administered very cautiously. No exact dosage can be stated. Enough has to be given to complex stoichiometrically with all the toxic metal ions, but a large excess over this has to be avoided. The difficulty of choosing a correct dose is increased by the complicated time course to be expected; free metal ions in the body fluids will be complexed immediately, but the withdrawal of bound metal from the tissues proceeds much more slowly.

Lead poisoning is an industrial hazard for the many factory workers whose occupations bring them into contact with this metal, and for garage employees who are exposed to leaded gasoline. Among children there is still a considerable amount of lead poisoning from the ingestion of leaded paints and plaster, even though the general use of leaded paint was banned a quarter-century ago. The specific antidote to lead poisoning is calcium disodium edetate (EDTA), the structure and properties of which were presented earlier (p. 14). The very high stability constants of EDTA for lead, nickel, cobalt, and several other metals were shown in Table 1-3. The relatively nontoxic calcium disodium complex, rather than EDTA itself, is used clinically to avoid complexing the essential ionized calcium in the blood plasma. Thus, only metals with greater affinity than calcium will be bound, by displacing Ca^{++} from the $CaNa_2$-EDTA complex. The stability constant for the complex with Pb^{++} is 10^7 times greater than that for the Ca^{++} complex.

Radioactive metals present special toxicity problems. The amounts in the body are likely to be small, but the long biologic and radioactive half-lives of these elements enhance their toxicity. Plutonium is most effectively removed from the body by complexing it with diethylenetriamine-pentaacetic acid (DTPA), a compound closely related to EDTA. Treatment is most successful when it is carried out shortly after exposure and before the plutonium is entirely sequestered in bone.[79, 80] Uranium is complexed and removed effectively by calcium disodium edetate.[81] Alkalinization of the urine by administration of bicarbonate also promotes excretion of the uranyl ion, apparently as a nontoxic bicarbonate complex. Strontium and radium are difficult to remove by the known chelating agents, because their binding constants for EDTA and similar compounds are too close to that of calcium; a different principle, competitive displacement, is employed (p. 407).

Iron. Iron poisoning occurs frequently in young children who eat toxic amounts of ferrous sulfate tablets intended for the treatment of iron deficiency anemias in an adult member of the household. The high stability

[79] M. W. ROSENTHAL, J. F. MARKLEY, A. LINDENBAUM, and J. SCHUBERT: Influence of DTPA therapy on long-term effects of retained plutonium. *Health Phys.* 8:741 (1962).

[80] W. D. NORWOOD: Therapeutic removal of plutonium in humans. *Health Phys.* 8:747 (1962).

[81] R. DAGIRMANJIAN, E. A. MAYNARD, and H. C. HODGE: The effects of calcium disodium ethylenediamine tetraacetate on uranium poisoning in rats. *J. Pharmacol. Exper. Therap. 117:*20 (1956).

constants of the complexes between iron and EDTA or DTPA (Table 1-3) suggest that calcium disodium edetate ought to be the agent of choice in treating iron poisoning or diseases in which there is abnormal deposition of iron in the tissues. Experimental studies, confirmed by clinical experience, indicate that, although there may be some protective effect with early enough administration, reliable antidotal action cannot be achieved. The reason probably is that iron is bound even more firmly to naturally occurring chelating compounds in the body, such as transferrin, ferritin, and the heme proteins.

The absorption of iron from the gastrointestinal tract can be blocked, and its local deleterious actions prevented, by the oral administration of complexing agents. The most promising, in experimental studies, is sodium ferrocyanide $(Na_4Fe(CN)_6)$.[82] The ferrocyanide ion is capable of associating with another iron atom (either Fe^{++} or Fe^{+++}) to form a complex that is extremely insoluble throughout the pH range encountered in the gastrointestinal tract. The EDTA chelates, in contrast, tend to dissociate in an acid medium. Ferrocyanide itself appears to have a very low toxicity when administered by mouth. Clinical reports on the usefulness of this antidote have not yet appeared.

A newly introduced agent for the systemic treatment of iron poisoning is desferrioxamine,[83] obtained by isolation of a siderochrome pigment from a streptomycete and removal of the bound iron by a chemical procedure. The structure of this compound is shown in Fig. 5-16. It chelates iron in an octahedral complex, as shown; and the stability constant of the complex is greater than 10^{30}. Desferrioxamine will remove iron from transferrin and from ferritin, but not from hemoglobin or the cytochromes, to which the metal is bound even more tightly. Thus the chelate stability constant is just in the right range for the removal of excessive iron without disrupting the biologically indispensable iron compounds. Initial reports on the use of this compound have been favorable,[84-86] but not enough information is yet available to permit a balanced assessment of its clinical value.

Copper. Copper poisoning is unusual; when it occurs, dimercaprol may be used. There is, however, a rare genetic disease (Wilson's disease) (cf. chapter 6) characterized by deficiency of the copper-binding plasma

82 V. NIGROVIĆ and A. CATSCH: Tierexperimentelle Untersuchungen zur Behandlung der akuten Eisenvergiftung. *Arch. exper. Pathol. Pharmakol. 251:*225 (1965).

83 V. H. BICKEL, E. GÄUMANN, W. KELLER-SCHIERLEIN, V. PRELOG, E. VISCHER, A. WETTSTEIN, and H. ZÄHNER: Über eisenhaltige Wachstumsfaktoren, die Sideramine, und ihre Antagonisten, die eisenhaltigen Antibiotika Sideromycine. *Experientia 16:*129 (1960).

84 S. MOESCHLIN and U. SCHNIDER: Treatment of primary and secondary hemochromatosis and acute iron poisoning with a new, potent iron-eliminating agent (desferrioxamine-B). *New England J. Med. 269:*57 (1963).

85 J. JACOBS, H. GREENE, and B. R. GENDEL: Acute iron intoxication. *New England J. Med. 273:*1124 (1965).

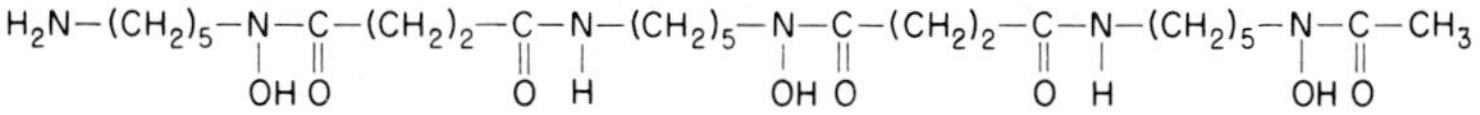

$$H_2N-(CH_2)_5-N-C-(CH_2)_2-C-N-(CH_2)_5-N-C-(CH_2)_2-C-N-(CH_2)_5-N-C-CH_3$$

a

Structure of desferrioxamine.

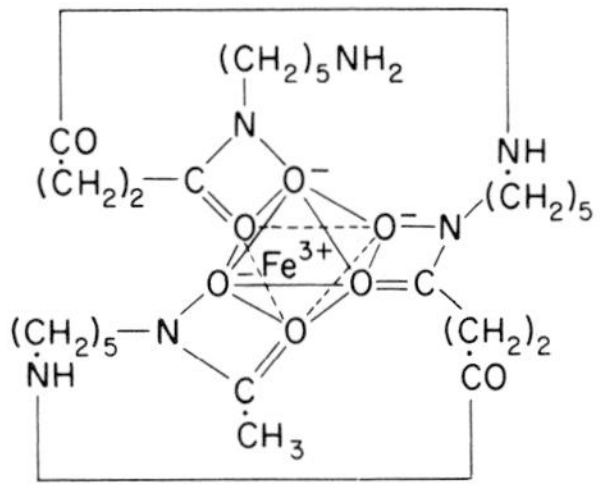

b

Structure of the iron-desferrioxamine chelate.

FIG. 5-16. DESFERRIOXAMINE AND ITS COMPLEX WITH IRON. (*From Moeschlin and Schnider, Fig. 1.*[84])

protein, ceruloplasmin, and deposition of copper in the tissues (especially liver and brain). Here, once the disease is diagnosed, large amounts of copper have to be mobilized and excreted, and then the same therapy must be continued on a lifelong basis. Dimercaprol would be ill suited for this because it is toxic, as pointed out earlier, and also because it has to be administered parenterally. What is required here is a safer and orally effective copper-binding agent. Such a compound is penicillamine:[86a]

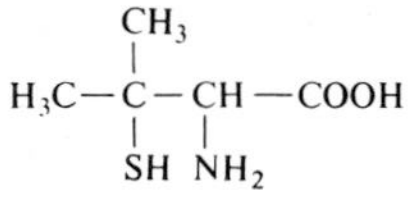

$$H_3C-C-CH-COOH$$

penicillamine (*β, β*-dimethylcysteine)

Penicillamine chelates copper about as effectively as does its parent compound cysteine (p. 101). The methyl substituents on the *β*-carbon atom, however, render the agent more resistant to degradation by cysteine desulfhydrase or L-amino acid oxidase, thus prolonging its biologic half-life.[87] Allergic sensitization is the major drawback to its use.

[86] C. F. WHITTEN, G. W. GIBSON, M. H. GOOD, J. F. GOODWIN, and A. J. BROUGH: Studies in acute iron poisoning. I. Desferrioxamine in the treatment of acute iron poisoning: clinical observations, experimental studies, and theoretical considerations. *Pediatrics 36:*322 (1965).

[86a] I. STERNLIEB and I. H. SCHEINBERG: Penicillamine therapy for hepatolenticular degeneration. *J. Am. Med. Ass. 189:*748 (1964).

[87] H. V. APOSHIAN: Biochemical and pharmacological properties of the metal-binding agent penicillamine. *Fed. Proc. 20:*185 (1961).

Thallium. Thallium acetate and sulfate are used as rodenticides and as poisons for ants and roaches. Thallium acetate has also been used in Europe as a depilatory agent, especially in children with ringworm. Thus, occasionally, accidental ingestion of thallium salts occurs. The only chelating agent shown to be effective for this metal is diphenylthiocarbazone (dithizone):

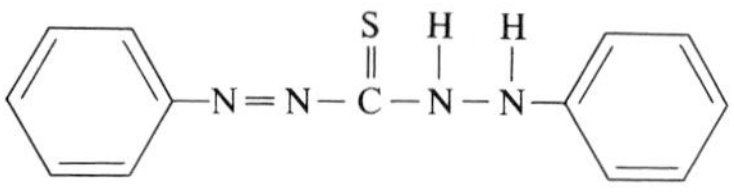

dithizone

In rats poisoned experimentally by thallium, this compound enhanced urinary excretion of the metal and had a life-saving action within a certain dosage range.[88] Its protective action is illustrated in Table 5-11. Dithizone was highly effective up to 100 mg/kg, but at the still higher dose it was toxic in its own right. The high toxicity makes this a hazardous antidote for use in man; nevertheless, in severe thallium poisoning good results have been claimed.[89] Table 5-11 also shows some beneficial effects of potassium salts.

Formaldehyde. Inactivation of a toxic agent by a specific antidote, in the gastrointestinal tract, was illustrated above by the action of ferrocyanide ion in precipitating ferrous (or ferric) ions by complexing with them. A similar instance is the use of ammonia as antidote to the oral

TABLE 5-11.   **Treatment of experimental thallium poisoning**

Rats were poisoned with thallous sulfate, subcutaneously, at the various dosages shown, then treated as indicated. Figures are numbers of animals dead/total in each group. (Data of Lund,[88] Tables 1 and 2.)

Treatment	Dose of thallous sulfate (mg/kg)			
	13	**20**	**25**	**30**
None	1/12	16/24	25/28	25/25
NaCl, 0.6% in drinking water		3/6	6/6	
KCl, 0.75% in drinking water		0/6	1/10	5/6
Dithizone, daily for 4 days by mouth				
33 mg/kg		0/6	0/6	2/6
100 mg/kg		0/6	0/6	0/6
270 mg/kg		0/6	2/6	1/6

[88] A. LUND: The effect of various substances on the excretion and the toxicity of thallium in the rat. *Acta Pharmacol. Toxicol. 12*:260 (1956).

[89] P. H. CHAMBERLAIN, W. B. STAVINOHA, H. DAVIS, W. T. KINKER, and T. C. PANOS: Thallium poisoning. *Pediatrics 22*:1170 (1958).

ingestion of formaldehyde. Formaldehyde reacts with ammonia, provided the pH is greater than about 8, to form hexamethylenetetramine (methenamine):

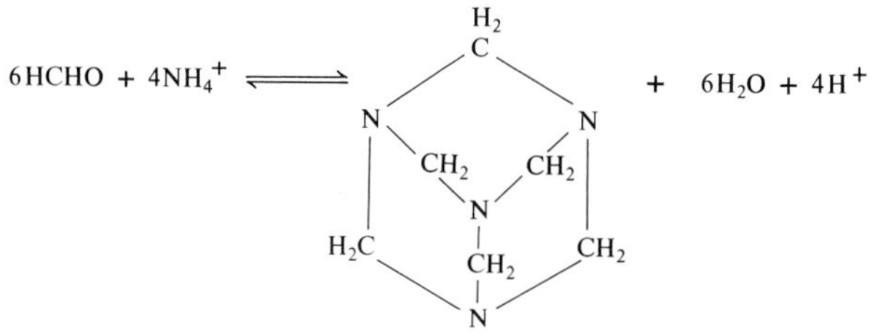

$$6\,HCHO + 4NH_4{}^+ \rightleftharpoons \qquad + \quad 6H_2O + 4H^+$$

methenamine

This reaction is more commonly employed in the use of methenamine as a urinary antiseptic. Here, the compound is administered by mouth and excreted into the urine, which must be kept acid in order to drive the reaction to the left, liberating formaldehyde, the presumed antibacterial agent. If a patient has swallowed formaldehyde, the administration of dilute ammonia or of ammonium salts in an alkaline buffered medium should eliminate the highly toxic free formaldehyde from the gastrointestinal tract by driving the same reaction to the right.[90] However, formaldehyde is so reactive that even a short delay would probably make the antidote useless. Formaldehyde poisoning is so rare that clinical experience with the antidotal treatment has not been sufficient to indicate how effective it really is.

Heparin. Direct combination between an antidote and the toxic agent is also illustrated by the treatment of toxicity due to heparin. This and related polysulfonated polysaccharides interfere with blood coagulation directly, in vitro as well as in vivo. They are believed to block the conversion of prothrombin to thrombin, and also the thrombin-mediated conversion of fibrinogen to fibrin. Their toxicity, manifested as hemorrhages and the consequences of hemorrhages, is primarily an extension of their therapeutic action. Several polycations react directly with heparin in vivo or in vitro, forming nontoxic complexes that are pharmacologically inert. The low-molecular-weight, basic protein protamine, for example, terminates the effects of heparin rapidly when injected intravenously in approximately equimolar amounts.[91] The protamine-heparin complex is excreted by glomerular filtration. In open heart surgery, where heparin is used most commonly, it is desirable to terminate the anticoagulant effects promptly at

---

[90] A. LUND: Rational treatment of formaldehyde poisoning. *Acta Pharmacol. Toxicol. 3:*323 (1947).

[91] T. W. PARKIN and W. F. KVALE: Neutralization of the anticoagulant effects of heparin with protamine (salmine). *Amer. Heart J. 37:*333 (1949).

the conclusion of the operative procedure. A synthetic polybasic substance, hexadimethrine bromide (Polybrene), is being tried as a heparin antagonist to avoid some of the undesirable side effects of protamine, notably the anticoagulant action of protamine itself in large doses:[92, 93]

$$\left[\begin{array}{c} CH_3 \quad\quad CH_3 \\ | \quad\quad\quad\quad | \\ -N-(CH_2)_6-N-(CH_2)_3- \\ | \quad\quad\quad\quad | \\ CH_3 \quad\quad CH_3 \end{array}\right]_n^{++} \bullet 2n\,Br^-$$

hexadimethrine bromide

Botulinus Toxin.   The specific antitoxins, although more often considered to lie within the realm of immunology than pharmacology, are certainly germane to this discussion of specific antidotes. The principle of neutralizing a toxin in vivo by an antitoxin represents the most specific example of the direct complexing mechanism whereby the poison is rendered inert. Botulinus toxin is chosen as prototype for consideration here because so much is understood about its mode of action. However, the same immunologically specific mechanism underlies the antidotal procedures for combatting poisoning by other toxins (e.g., diphtheria, tetanus) or by snake venoms.

Botulinus toxin is the most potent poison known. Its lethal dose in the mouse is less than $10^{-4}\mu g$, and it has been estimated that $0.3\mu g$ is lethal in man.[94] The toxin has been obtained as a crystalline protein, and its mode of action has been elucidated in recent years. It is absorbed from the gastrointestinal tract and then acts specifically upon the nervous system. There are central effects, apparently in spinal pathways,[95] but its most prominent toxic action is muscular paralysis. Structures innervated by cholinergic fibers in the autonomic system are also affected. The muscles and other end-organs remain responsive to electrical stimulation and to acetylcholine (AcCh). At motor nerve endings, the toxin not only blocks the transmission of nerve impulses across the neuromuscular junction, but it also abolishes the spontaneous miniature end-plate potentials.[96] The significance of this is that these randomly occurring miniature potentials represent the spontaneous, uncoordinated release of "packets" of AcCh.

[92] N. G. ROTHNIE and J. B. KINMONTH: The neutralization of heparin after perfusion. *Brit. Med. J.* 2:1194 (1960).

[93] C. HOUGIE: Anticoagulant action of protamine sulphate. *Proc. Soc. Exper. Biol. Med.* 98:130 (1958).

[94] C. LAMANNA: The most poisonous poison. *Science 130:*763 (1959).

[95] H. R. TYLER: Botulinus toxin: effect on the central nervous system of man. *Science 139:*847 (1963).

[96] V. B. BROOKS: An intracellular study of the action of repetitive nerve volleys and of botulinum toxin on miniature end-plate potentials. *J. Physiol. 134:*264 (1956).

Thus, AcCh release is prevented, not only in response to the arrival of a nerve impulse in the region of the nerve terminals, but at all other times as well. If a nerve-muscle preparation in vitro is exposed to a toxin-antitoxin mixture, no abnormality ensues. If the same preparation is exposed to toxin alone, there is a lag of about 30 minutes, after which the typical neuromuscular blockade develops. After the toxin has been in contact with the tissue, the blockade will develop inevitably, even in the presence of antitoxin. Thus, something that antitoxin cannot reverse happens rapidly, only to become evident later. Evidently, the fundamental effect of the toxin is to inactivate the mechanism for release of stored AcCh.

Botulism is a rare but frequently fatal disease, acquired by eating preserved foods (often meat or fish) in which the causative organism (*Clostridium botulinum*) has grown because of faulty sterilization.[97] At least four antigenically different strains (A, B, E, F) are commonly involved. Antitoxin is prepared in horses by repeated challenge and eventual collection of blood serum. Multivalent antitoxin, effective against all four strains, is now available; it is obviously indicated whenever doubt exists as to the antigenic type of the toxin.

There has been an element of fatalism about the treatment of this disease, conditioned largely by the difficulty of proving conclusively that the antitoxin is useful. The total number of cases seen annually in the whole world is very small, and certainly no one would deliberately conduct a placebo-controlled trial on desperately ill patients who might be saved by antitoxin (cf. chapter 14). Moreover, the experimental indications that the toxin quickly produces irreversible effects have led to the opinion that once symptoms are manifested it is already too late to treat. Probably this pessimism is unfounded. Whatever the explanation may be, some dramatic recoveries have been seen after antitoxin treatment, even in patients who seemed to be running an inexorably lethal course.[98] That the antitoxin combines directly with toxin in the manner of a typical antibody-antigen interaction seems clear enough. There have been some indications that slow absorption of toxin from the intestinal tract might be responsible for the protracted downhill course of some patients. If that were so, it would be easier to understand how antitoxin, even late in the disease, could block further progression of symptoms by complexing free toxin entering the circulation.

Cholinesterase Inhibitors. A somewhat more complex illustration of an antidote's action by combining with the poison and simultaneously

---

[97] C. S. PETTY: Botulism: The disease and the toxin. *Amer. J. Med. Sci. 249:*345 (1965).

[98] R. L. WHITTAKER, R. B. GILBERTSON, and A. S. GARRETT, JR.: Botulism, Type E. Report of eight simultaneous cases. *Ann. Int. Med. 61:*448 (1964).

[99] B. HOLMSTEDT: Pharmacology of organophosphorus cholinesterase inhibitors. *Pharmacol. Rev. 11:*567 (1959).

removing it from receptors is provided by the treatment of poisoning due to cholinesterase inhibitors. Here, a specific reagent, pralidoxime, was "tailor-made" to remove the inhibitors from the active site of the enzyme by a nucleophilic attack, and simultaneously to interact with them and form an inert complex.

The organic phosphate cholinesterase inhibitors were developed initially as insecticides and later were investigated as chemical warfare agents ("nerve gases"). Some of these compounds and their LD50 values are shown in Table 5-12. Accidental poisoning occurs frequently, especially

TABLE 5-12.   **Some organic phosphate anticholinesterases**

LD50 values were determined in mice, intraperitoneally or sub-cutaneously. From Holmstedt,[99] Tables A–E.

LD50	Structure
Diisopropyl fluorophosphate (DFP) 4 mg/kg i.p.	$\begin{array}{c} CH_3 \quad\quad F \quad\quad CH_3 \\ \diagdown \quad\quad | \quad\quad \diagup \\ CH-O-P-O-CH \\ \diagup \quad\quad || \quad\quad \diagdown \\ CH_3 \quad\quad O \quad\quad CH_3 \end{array}$
Tetraethyl pyrophosphate (TEPP) 0.7 mg/kg i.p.	$\begin{array}{c} C_2H_5O \quad O \quad\quad O \quad OC_2H_5 \\ \diagdown \; || \quad\quad || \; \diagup \\ P-O-P \\ \diagup \quad\quad\quad\quad \diagdown \\ C_2H_5O \quad\quad\quad\quad OC_2H_5 \end{array}$
Isopropyl methyl phosphonofluoridate (Sarin, GB) 0.42 mg/kg i.p.	$\begin{array}{c} F \quad\quad CH_3 \\ | \quad\quad \diagup \\ CH_3-P-O-CH \\ || \quad\quad \diagdown \\ O \quad\quad CH_3 \end{array}$
Methylfluorophosphorylcholine 0.1 mg/kg i.p.	$(CH_3)_3N^+-CH_2-CH_2-O-\underset{\underset{O}{\overset{\overset{F}{|}}{||}}}{P}-CH_3$
Diethyl 4-nitrophenyl thionophosphate (parathion) 10–12 mg/kg s.c.	$\begin{array}{c} C_2H_5O \quad\quad S \\ \diagdown \quad\quad || \\ P \\ \diagup \quad\quad \diagdown \\ C_2H_5O \quad\quad O-\!\!\!\bigcirc\!\!\!-NO_2 \end{array}$
Diethyl 4–nitrophenyl phosphate (paraoxon) 0.6–0.8 mg/kg s.c.	$\begin{array}{c} C_2H_5O \quad\quad \dot{O} \\ \diagdown \quad\quad || \\ P \\ \diagup \quad\quad \diagdown \\ C_2H_5O \quad\quad O-\!\!\!\bigcirc\!\!\!-NO_2 \end{array}$

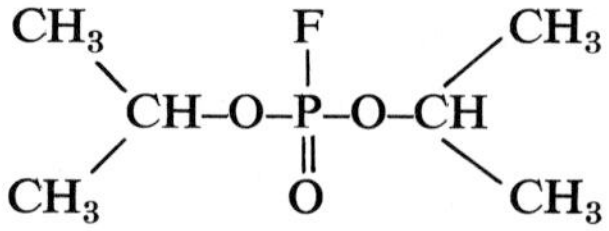

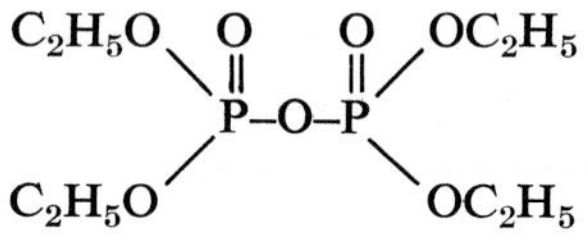

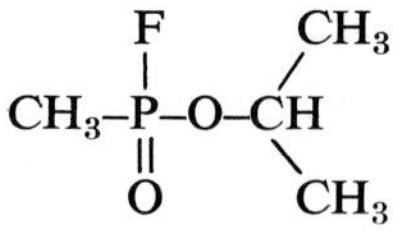

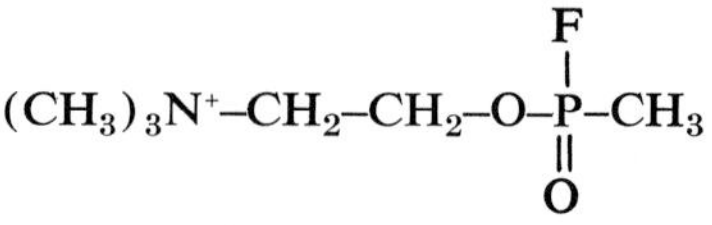

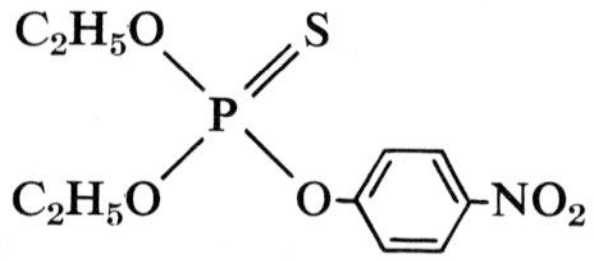

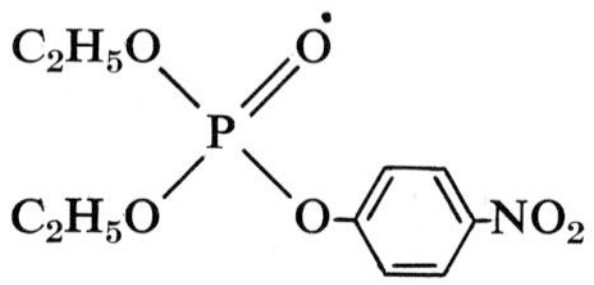

among agricultural workers. During 1963, in California, there were 345 instances of occupational poisoning of all types; 267 of these were due to a single insecticide, the organic phosphate compound parathion. Occasionally parathion causes mass poisoning; in one instance in 1963, 94 peach pickers were affected.[100]

The organic phosphates act by phosphorylating and thereby inactivating the "serine enzymes," as described in chapter 1. Toxic manifestations are due to inactivation of acetylcholinesterase. Plasma cholinesterase is also inactivated; this seems to do no harm in itself, but the activity of the plasma enzyme provides a convenient assay by which to judge the extent of poisoning. Acetylcholinesterase is found in erythrocytes (where its function is unknown), at parasympathetically innervated effector organs (smooth muscles, glands), at the skeletal muscle end-plates, at autonomic ganglia, and in the central nervous system. At all these sites, the enzyme normally hydrolyzes and thus terminates the action of the neurotransmitter acetylcholine (AcCh). Symptoms of accumulation of AcCh appear if the acetylcholinesterase activity is reduced by about one-half, and death ensues if the enzyme activity falls below 10 to 20 per cent of normal activity.[101] When death occurs, it is usually due to respiratory failure, caused in part by neuromuscular paralysis, in part by central depression.

The immediate treatment of poisoning due to cholinesterase inhibition relies upon the principle (to be discussed later) of blocking the receptors upon which the excessive AcCh acts, and the specific antidote employed for this purpose is atropine (p. 89). In severe poisoning, however, a real problem is that the spontaneous recovery of enzyme activity is very slow. The phosphoryl-enzyme bond (Fig. 1-5) is hydrolyzed spontaneously at a negligible rate. The main contribution to spontaneous recovery appears to be the generation of new enzyme protein. Figure 5-17 shows, for example, an experiment in which the plasma cholinesterase, synthesized in the liver, recovered with a half-time of about ten days, a rate comparable to that of the synthesis rates of several other liver proteins. The erythrocyte acetylcholinesterase activity recovered at a rate of about 1 per cent per day, a time course typical of the formation of new red blood cells.

If a more powerful nucleophilic reagent than water could be employed, it might be possible to rupture the phosphoryl-enzyme bond and regenerate active enzyme. Hydroxylamine does this in vitro. When acetylcholinesterase was inhibited by tetraethyl pyrophosphate and allowed to recover its activity by spontaneous hydrolysis, less than 5 per cent of the control activity returned in seven days, only 50 per cent in 28 days.

[100] Occupational Disease in California Attributed to Pesticides and other Agricultural Chemicals, 1963. Report prepared by G. D. Kleinman. State of California Department of Public Health, Bureau of Occupational Health. Berkeley, Calif.

[101] D. GROB and J. C. HARVEY: Effects in man of the anticholinesterase compound sarin (isopropyl methyl phosphonofluoridate). *J. Clin. Invest. 37:*350 (1958).

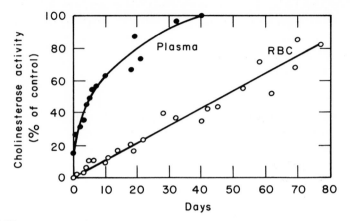

FIG. 5-17. RATE OF RESTORATION OF PLASMA AND RED BLOOD CELL CHOLIN-ESTERASE ACTIVITY AFTER INHIBITION BY SARIN. *Data are average values obtained in ten human subjects. Sarin administration was stopped at day zero, and recovery of enzyme activities was followed for 80 days. (From Grob and Harvey, Fig. 9.[101])*

Hydroxylamine caused a rapid regeneration of active enzyme. Even in 30 minutes, as shown in Fig. 5-18, reactivation occurred, to a variable extent depending upon the concentration of hydroxylamine, with complete reactivation at 0.5*M*.

FIG. 5-18. REACTIVATION OF ACETYLCHOLINESTERASE BY HYDROXYLAMINE IN VITRO. *Enzyme was inhibited with tetraethyl pyrophosphate, then treated for 30 minutes with different concentrations of hydroxylamine at pH 7 and 23°. Curve shows per cent of the original enzyme activity that was recovered at each hydroxylamine concentration. (From Wilson, Fig. 1.[102])*

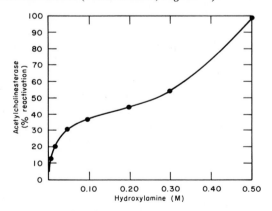

102 I. B. WILSON: Acetylcholinesterase. XIII. Reactivation of alkyl phosphate-inhibited enzyme. *J. Biol. Chem. 199:*113 (1952).

The sequence of reactions between the enzyme and a fluorophosphate inhibitor may be represented as follows, where —G: signifies the
| H

electron-rich group in the esteratic site:

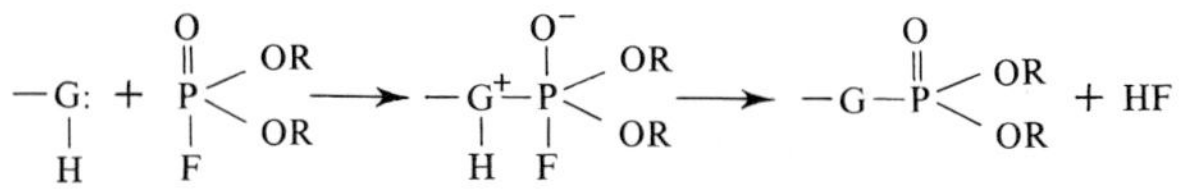

formation of phosphorylated enzyme

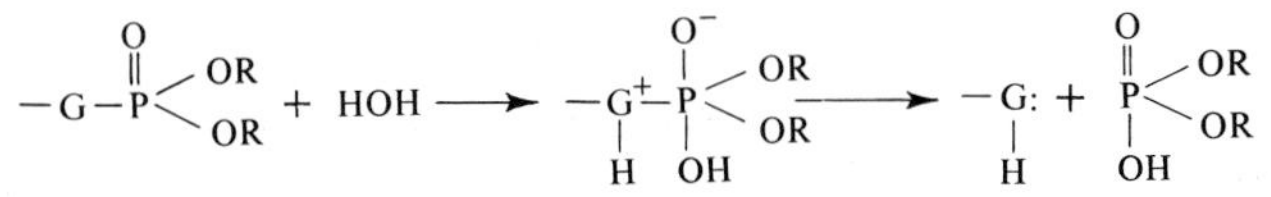

hydrolysis of phosphorylated enzyme (very slow)

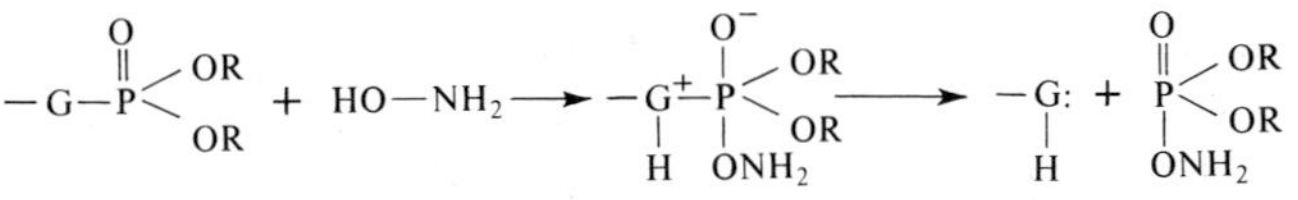

reactivation of phosphorylated enzyme by hydroxylamine (fast)

High concentrations of hydroxylamine are not tolerated in vivo, but it has been reasoned[103] that if such a nucleophilic reagent could be combined with a molecular structure that was specific for the active site of the enzyme, a therapeutically useful reactivating agent might well be formed. Working from the knowledge that in acetylcholinesterase an anionic site is disposed at 7 A distance from the esteratic site (cf. chapter 1), hydroxylamine was incorporated into a molecular structure having a quaternary nitrogen atom at the appropriate distance.[104] Several such oximes have been synthesized. One of these, pralidoxime (N-methylpyridinium 2-aldoxime, formerly known as 2-PAM), is now widely used as an antidote to cholinesterase inhibitors. Under certain conditions pralidoxime is almost a million times more potent than hydroxylamine. Yet, as might be expected on theoretical grounds, it is not much better than hydroxylamine in reactivat-

103 I. B. WILSON: Molecular complementarity and antidotes for alkylphosphate poisoning. *Fed. Proc. 18:*752 (1959).

104 An organic phosphate compound that included a quaternary nitrogen atom 7 A from the electronegative phosphorus atom should be very effective as an inhibitor. Thus, methylfluorophosphorylcholine (Table 5-12), an analogue of AcCh, is one of the most potent anticholinesterases known.

ing other phosphorylated serine enzymes (e.g., chymotrypsin) whose substrate specificities imply an entirely different molecular architecture at their active sites. The structures of pralidoxime and some congeners are shown in Fig. 5-19. The practical efficacy of pralidoxime combined with atropine is illustrated in Table 5-13. Atropine alone increased the LD50 of sarin in rabbits. Combined treatment with pralidoxime and another oxime (TMB4), but without atropine, was ineffective. But the pralidoxime-atropine combination protected the animals against 90 LD50 doses of sarin.

The same principles apply to poisoning by the carbamate inhibitors of acetylcholinesterase (e.g., neostigmine, physostigmine), which are often used clinically. These inhibitors form carbamylated enzymes analogous to the phosphorylated enzymes discussed above (cf. Fig. 1-5), except that their rates of spontaneous hydrolysis are much faster. In theory, the reactivation rate (i.e., the hydrolysis rate of the carbamyl-enzyme bond) should be independent of the nature of the noncarbamate portion of the inhibitor molecule. Since only the substituted carbamyl group itself is attached to the enzyme, and not the organic alcohol to which it was originally linked, all monomethyl carbamates should yield the same rate of enzyme reactivation, all dimethyl carbamates another rate, and so on. Table 5-14 confirms this and also shows that all the rates were accelerated in vitro by hydroxylamine. Thus, on theoretical grounds, pralidoxime should be as useful for reactivation here as with the organic phosphates. The difference is, however, that the spontaneous hydrolysis of the carbamates is very much faster, so that in practice atropine and supportive treatment suffice and no reactivating-complexing antidote is needed.

FIG. 5-19. OXIMES USED IN ANTICHOLINESTERASE POISONING. *In upper row associated anions are not shown. 2-PAM is available as the iodide or chloride, TMB-4 as the chloride.*

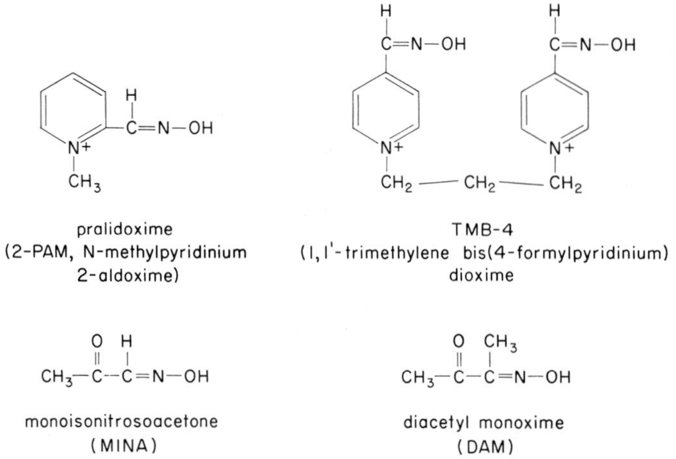

pralidoxime
(2-PAM, N-methylpyridinium
2-aldoxime)

TMB-4
(1,1'-trimethylene bis(4-formylpyridinium)
dioxime)

monoisonitrosoacetone
(MINA)

diacetyl monoxime
(DAM)

TABLE 5-13. Antagonism of the lethal effects of sarin by intravenous oximes and atropine

Rabbits were injected i.v. with graded doses of sarin, followed by various combinations of oximes and atropine 30 seconds later, also i.v. (From O'Leary et al.,[105] Table 2.)

Antidotal treatment	Sarin LD50 (μg/kg) (95% confidence limits)	Multiples of untreated sarin LD50
None	14.7 (12.6–17.4)	1.0
Atropine, 2 mg/kg	38.0 (24.5–48.8)	2.6
2-PAM chloride, 7.5 mg/kg +		
TMB4 chloride, 7.5 mg/kg	18.4 (16.3–20.9)	1.3
Atropine plus 2-PAM chloride, 5 mg/kg	365 (342–400)	25
Atropine plus 2-PAM chloride, 10 mg/kg	1321 (985–1770)	90

Cyanide. A final illustration of antidotal action by complexing and removing the toxic agent is found in the treatment of cyanide poisoning. Here, the mechanism is more intricate than those discussed above because the actual complexing agent is produced within the body. The antidote is methemoglobin, produced in vivo by the action of sodium nitrite,

TABLE 5-14. The half-lives of carbamyl derivatives of purified acetylcholinesterase

(Data of Wilson et al.,[106] Table 1.)

Acetylcholinesterase inhibitor	$t_{1/2}$ (min)	
	In aqueous solution	In 1M NH$_2$OH
CARBAMATES		
carbamylcholine	ca. 2	ca. 1
METHYL CARBAMATES		
methylcarbamylcholine	38	5
physostigmine	38	5
DIMETHYL CARBAMATES		
dimethylcarbamyl fluoride	26	13
dimethylcarbamylcholine	26	14
neostigmine	28	13
pyridostigmine	26	14

[105] J. F. O'LEARY, A. M. KUNKEL, and A. H. JONES: Efficacy and limitations of oxime-atropine treatment of organophosphorus anticholinesterase poisoning. *J. Pharmacol. Exper. Therap. 132:*50 (1961).

[106] I. B. WILSON, M. A. HARRISON, and S. GINSBURG: Carbamyl derivatives of acetylcholinesterase. *J. Biol. Chem. 236:*1498 (1961).

which converts hemoglobin to methemoglobin. Methemoglobin, in turn, complexes cyanide ion. Another but equally important part of the treatment makes use of a different principle—acceleration of the metabolic conversion of cyanide to a nontoxic product—and it will be discussed fully later (p. 401).

Cyanide combines with the ferric iron atom in heme proteins in the tissues, destroying their capacity to undergo oxidation and reduction in the normal electron transport process. Contrary to popular impression, cyanide is not a very potent poison, but it can cause death extremely rapidly, primarily by inactivating cytochrome oxidase in tissues. Administration of oxygen, theoretically at least, should do no good, since the utilization of O_2 at the tissue level is impaired, not the oxygen supply; hemoglobin remains fully oxygenated in cyanide poisoning.

The first aim of treatment is to bind as much cyanide ion as possible in an inert form. This is accomplished by converting a portion of the blood hemoglobin to methemoglobin, thus making a large amount of ferric heme available for interaction with CN^-. The affinity of CN^- for cytochrome oxidase is actually greater than for methemoglobin;[107] nevertheless, a very large total amount of methemoglobin can withdraw enough cyanide from tissue cytochrome oxidase to be life saving. A normal adult has nearly 1,000 g of blood hemoglobin, containing about 4 g of iron. Thus, if 50 per cent of the hemoglobin is converted to methemoglobin, binding capacity is created for almost 1 g of cyanide ion, more than the fatal dose in man. Serious symptoms of anoxia due to methemoglobinemia are not seen until more than one-half of the total amount of hemoglobin has been oxidized.

The mechanism whereby nitrites oxidize hemoglobin to methemoglobin is still imperfectly understood. There may be a coupled oxidation of NO_2^- to NO_3^-, and of oxyhemoglobin to methemoglobin hydroxide, with simultaneous reduction of water,[108] as follows:

$$Hb^{++} \cdot O_2 \longrightarrow Hb^{+++} + e^- + O_2$$

$$Hb^{++} \cdot O_2 \longrightarrow Hb^{+++} + e^- + [O] + [O]$$

$$NO_2^- + [O] \longrightarrow NO_3^-$$

$$H^+ + [O] + 2e^- \rightarrow OH^-$$

$$OH^- = OH^-.$$

[107] H. G. ALBAUM, J. TEPPERMAN, and O. BODANSKY: A spectrophotometric study of competition of methemoglobin and cytochrome oxidase for cyanide in vitro. *J. Biol. Chem. 163:*641 (1946).

[108] K. BETKE, I. GREINACHER, and O. TIETZE: Oxydation menschlicher und tierischer Oxyhämoglobine durch Natriumnitrit. *Arch. exper. Pathol. Pharmakol. 229:*220 (1956).

Although the exact mechanism is still not known, these steps yield the overall reaction

$$NO_2^- + 2Hb^{++}\cdot O_2 + H_2O \longrightarrow NO_3^- + 2Hb^{+++}\cdot OH^- + O_2.$$

Because speed is essential, sodium nitrite is injected intravenously. There would be considerable advantage in a first-aid antidote that could be administered quickly by anyone. It has been suggested, therefore, that the vapor of amyl nitrite be inhaled; small ampoules of the volatile liquid are available. Although this is probably better than nothing, the rate of production of methemoglobin by this means is unavoidably slow, and the total amount that can be produced even in several minutes of amyl nitrite inhalation is but a fraction of the desirable amount.

MECHANISM 2. ANTIDOTE ACCELERATES METABOLIC CONVERSION OF POISON TO NONTOXIC PRODUCT

Cyanide. The second aim in the treatment of cyanide poisoning exemplifies this mechanism. The CN^- ion is normally converted in vivo to the innocuous thiocyanate (CNS^-) by the cyanide-thiosulfate sulfur transferase (p. 248). However, the rate of this reaction is ordinarily slow because the requisite sulfur donors (such as thiosulfate) are present in the body in limiting amounts. The reaction can be accelerated considerably by administering thiosulfate. Experiments with dogs have shown that the LD50 of cyanide can be increased threefold by sodium thiosulfate alone, fivefold by sodium nitrite alone, and 18-fold by a combination of both antidotes.[109] Thus, two different mechanisms of antidotal action together form the basis of the treatment of cyanide toxicity: nitrite to form methemoglobin and complex the cyanide, thiosulfate to accelerate the metabolic conversion of cyanide to thiocyanate. In experimental animals, a further degree of protection was obtained by injecting the sulfur transferase enzyme together with thiosulfate;[110] but pure preparations of the enzyme are not available for clinical use.

In addition to the two antidotal mechanisms already described, a third approach appears to yield beneficial results in cyanide poisoning: administration of oxygen. As already noted, the hemoglobin is fully saturated in cyanide poisoning, so that oxygen would not be expected to be useful. Apparently, however, increasing the physically dissolved plasma O_2 tension bypasses some of the cyanide blockade of tissue O_2 utilization (see mechanism 7). Table 5-15 summarizes clear-cut experiments in mice.

109 K. K. CHEN, C. L. ROSE, and G. H. A. CLOWES: Comparative values of several antidotes in cyanid poisoning. *Amer. J. Med. Sci. 188:*767 (1934).

110 C.-J. CLEMEDSON, H. I. HULTMAN, and B. SORBO: The antidote effect of some sulfur compounds and rhodanese in experimental cyanide poisoning. *Acta Physiol. Scand.* 32:245 (1954).

TABLE 5-15.   **Antidotal effects in cyanide poisoning in mice**

Groups of ten Swiss-Webster male mice were used to determine the ĿD50 of KCN (administered subcutaneously) by the method of Litchfield and Wilcoxon.[30] NaNO$_2$ (100 mg/kg) was administered subcutaneously, Na$_2$S$_2$O$_3$ (1.0 g/kg) intraperitoneally; O$_2$ was given as a mixture of 95 per cent O$_2$, 5 per cent CO$_2$. The 95 per cent confidence limits for slope and for LD50 are given in parentheses. (From Way et al.,[111] Table 1. By permission of American Association for the Advancement of Science.)

Exp.	Treatment before KCN	Slope function	LD50(mg/kg)
1	Control (air)	1.27 (1.03–1.56)	8.50 (7.73–9.44)
2	O$_2$	1.28 (1.02–1.70)	11.3 (10.3–12.4)[a]
3	NaNO$_2$	1.13 (1.06–1.21)	21.2 (19.9–22.6)
4	NaNO$_2$ + O$_2$	1.10 (1.02–1.20)	22.5 (21.4–23.6)[b]
5	Na$_2$S$_2$O$_3$	1.33 (0.98–1.70)	34.6 (30.2–39.1)
6	Na$_2$S$_2$O$_3$ + O$_2$	1.15 (1.06–1.24)	42.2 (40.0–44.5)[a]
7	NaNO$_2$ + Na$_2$S$_2$O$_3$	1.12 (1.03–1.26)	53.5 (51.2–55.6)
8	NaNO$_2$ + Na$_2$S$_2$O$_3$ + O$_2$	1.12 (0.96–1.31)	73.0 (69.8–76.8)[a]

[a] Significantly different from experiments 1, 5, and 7.
[b] Not significantly different from experiment 3.

Groups of ten animals were used to determine the LD50 of potassium cyanide alone, and with various treatments. Eight different conditions were studied. The slopes of all the quantal LDR curves were substantially the same, as shown in the third column. The LD50 values and their 95 per cent confidence limits are given in the last column. The protective effects of nitrite and of thiosulfate individually and the increased protection afforded by both together are shown in experiments 1, 3, 5, and 7. The effect of furnishing 95 per cent oxygen is indicated in experiments 2, 4, 6, and especially in experiment 8 as compared with experiment 7. Even though the mechanism is unknown, it would seem appropriate to furnish O$_2$, possibly even at increased pressure, as part of the treatment of severe cyanide poisoning.

MECHANISM 3. ANTIDOTE BLOCKS METABOLIC FORMATION OF POISON FROM LESS TOXIC PRECURSOR

Methanol.   This mechanism is illustrated by the treatment of methanol poisoning with ethanol. Methanol poisoning is principally due to the consumption of alcoholic beverages that have been adulterated with methanol. Mass poisonings occur sporadically, as in Georgia in 1951, when 323 people were poisoned, of whom 41 died.[112] Methyl alcohol in large

[111] J. L. WAY, S. L. GIBBON, and M. SHEEHY: Cyanide intoxication: protection with oxygen. *Science 152*:210 (1966).

[112] M. N. COOPER, G. L. MITCHELL, JR., I. L. BENNETT, JR., and F. H. CARY: Methyl alcohol poisoning: an account of the 1951 Atlanta epidemic. *J. Med. Assoc. Georgia 41*:48 (1952).

doses is a depressant of the central nervous system in all animals, a property it shares with other aliphatic alcohols. This general depressant action is rarely the cause of death in methanol poisoning. The two characteristic and serious toxic effects of methanol are due to metabolites of the alcohol—formaldehyde and formic acid. Formaldehyde selectively damages retinal cells, causing blindness; formic acid produces acidosis. Both of these toxic actions are seen only in man and other primates, so experimental investigations have been rather difficult.[113]

Ethanol and methanol are oxidized by the same enzyme system; alcohol dehydrogenase converts alcohol to aldehyde (acetaldehyde, formaldehyde), then aldehyde dehydrogenase converts aldehyde to acid (acetic acid, formic acid). This provides the basis for the use of competitive substrate inhibition to block the conversion of methanol to the more toxic formaldehyde and formic acid.[114] The formaldehyde that is responsible for retinal damage may be formed in the retina itself rather than in the liver, since alcohol dehydrogenase is present in retinal cells, where it normally catalyzes the reversible oxidation of vitamin A, an alcohol, to the aldehyde retinene.[115] The rate of metabolism of methanol is independent of concentration over a wide range, just as with ethanol (cf. p. 284).[116] Methanol oxidation was studied in a purified system with alcohol dehydrogenase from monkey liver. Ethanol competitively inhibited the reaction, and its affinity for the enzyme was about tenfold that of methanol.[117] In the body, methanol is oxidized very slowly, only about one-seventh as rapidly as ethanol, so the antidotal treatment with ethanol has to be prolonged for several days.

There is good evidence that another system, involving hydrogen peroxide and catalase, also plays a part in the oxidation of methanol to formaldehyde.[118,119] The purified catalase, like the alcohol dehydrogenase, is active with ethanol as substrate and is inhibited competitively by ethanol when methanol is the substrate.[118] Apparently, in vivo, methanol is metabolized slowly by both pathways. Ethanol, on the other hand, is primarily oxidized by alcohol dehydrogenase; but it has a greater affinity than methanol for both catalase and alcohol dehydrogenase. Consequently,

113 J. R. COOPER and M. M. KINI: Biochemical aspects of methanol poisoning. *Biochem. Pharmacol. 11:*405 (1962).

114 O. RÖE: The roles of alkaline salts and ethyl alcohol in the treatment of methanol poisoning. *Quart. J. Studies Alcoholism 11:*107 (1950).

115 M. M. KINI and J. R. COOPER: Biochemistry of methanol poisoning. 4. The effect of methanol and its metabolites on retinal metabolism. *Biochem. J. 82:*164 (1962).

116 G. R. BARTLETT: Combustion of C14 labeled methanol in intact rat and its isolated tissues. *Amer. J. Physiol. 163:*614 (1950).

117 M. M. KINI and J. R. COOPER: Biochemistry of methanol poisoning. 3. The enzymic pathway for the conversion of methanol to formaldehyde. *Biochem. Pharmacol. 8:*207 (1961).

118 M. E. SMITH: Interrelations in ethanol and methanol metabolism. *J. Pharmacol. Exper. Therap. 134:*233 (1961).

119 T. R. TEPHLY, R. E. PARKS, JR., and G. J. MANNERING: Methanol metabolism in the rat. *J. Pharmacol. Exper. Therap. 143:*292 (1964).

ethanol can inhibit the oxidation of methanol, whereas methanol has but little effect upon ethanol oxidation.

Selenocystathionine. A more unusual instance of this antidotal mechanism is found in the treatment of poisoning due to selenocystathionine. Selenium analogues of the sulfur-containing amino acids occur in nature and cause poisoning in livestock and occasionally in man. These compounds occur in certain plants growing in seleniferous soils of the western United States[120] and in the nuts of *Lecythis ollaria,* a Venezuelan tree.[121] The compounds found in plants include selenomethionine, selenomethylcysteine, and selenocystathionine. The toxic syndrome of selenocystathionine poisoning in man is characterized by nausea, vomiting, dizziness, and fainting. In rats (and possibly in man) there is liver damage. Characteristically, a week or two after ingestion of selenocystathionine, there is generalized loss of hair. The livestock disease ("alkali disease," "blind staggers") is also characterized by hair loss and by deformation of keratinized structures like the hoof. In mammalian cells growing in vitro, cystine blocks the cytotoxic effect. Cystine is a competitive inhibitor of cystathionase, a pyridoxal enzyme that cleaves and deaminates cystathionine (or selenocystathionine) to cysteine (or selenocysteine) and α-ketobutyric acid.

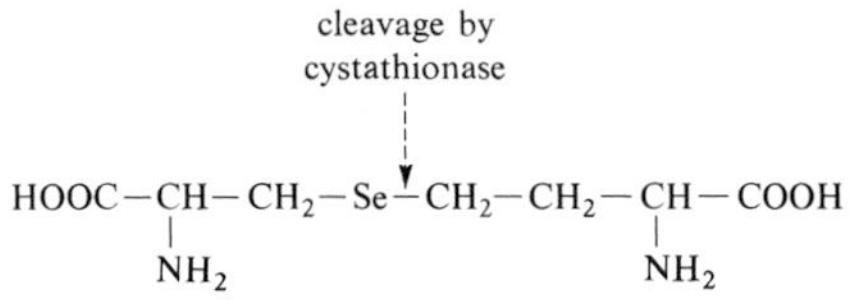

$$\text{cleavage by}$$
$$\text{cystathionase}$$

$$HOOC-CH-CH_2-Se-CH_2-CH_2-CH-COOH$$
$$\quad\quad\;\; | \quad\quad\quad\quad\quad\quad\quad\quad\quad\quad\;\; |$$
$$\quad\quad\;\; NH_2 \quad\quad\quad\quad\quad\quad\quad\quad\;\; NH_2$$

selenocystathionine

Cells that lack this enzyme are not sensitive to selenocystathionine.[122] Thus, in poisoning by this substance, the actual toxic agent appears to be the cleavage product selenocysteine. By competing with selenocystathionine for the active site of cystathionase, cystine blocks conversion to the toxic product. Apparently, cystine also antagonizes the toxicity by supplying intracellular cysteine, which in turn competes with selenocysteine for incorporation into protein (mechanism 5). This competition, presumably, takes place at the active site of the cysteine-activating enzyme, which couples cysteine (or selenocysteine) to the appropriate transfer-RNA

120 I. ROSENFELD and O. A. BEATH: *Selenium: Geobotany, Biochemistry, Toxicity, and Nutrition.* New York, Academic Press, 1964.

121 L. ARONOW and F. KERDEL-VEGAS: Cytotoxic and depilatory effects of extracts of *Lecythis ollaria. Nature 205:*1185 (1965).

122 L. ARONOW: Metabolism of seleno-cystathionine and effects on mammalian cells growing in vitro. *Fed. Proc. 25:*196 (1966).

molecule. Although the antidotal effects of cystine described here have been observed only in cell cultures, it seems likely that cystine will prove a useful antidote in poisoning by the selenium amino acid analogues in man and animals.

Fluoroacetate. Another illustration of antidotal action by blocking the metabolic conversion of a precursor to a toxic product is seen in the treatment of fluoroacetate toxicity. This halogenated acetic acid derivative (CFH_2COOH) is found as a toxic constituent of *Dichapetalum cymosum,* a plant indigenous to South Africa, where it constitutes a hazard to livestock. The compound has been used as a rodenticide (under the designation "1080"), and thus several cases of accidental human poisoning have occurred. There is invariably a latent period after fluoroacetate administration. Then, after a delay of 1 or 2 hours, symptoms of myocardial and central nervous system malfunction appear. These include nausea, apprehension, convulsions, and defects of cardiac rhythm which can culminate in ventricular fibrillation. The metabolism of fluoroacetate has been studied thoroughly.[123] The compound enters the tricarboxylic acid cycle in competition with acetate, and is then metabolized to fluorocitrate. Fluorocitrate inhibits aconitase, the enzyme responsible for the conversion of citrate to isocitrate.[124] Thus, both citrate and fluorocitrate accumulate after fluoroacetate administration. These relationships are illustrated in Fig. 5-20. The

FIG. 5-20.   METABOLISM AND SITE OF ACTION OF FLUOROACETATE.   (*Adapted from Peters.*[124])

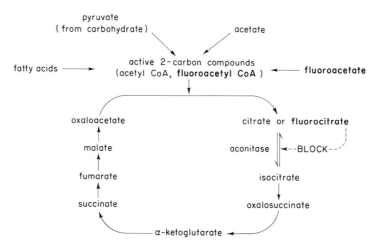

123 R. A. PETERS: Mechanism of the ,toxicity of the active constituent of *Dichapetalum cymosum* and related compounds. *Adv. Enzymol. 18:*113 (1957).

124 R. A. PETERS: Biochemistry of some toxic agents. II. Some recent work in the field of fluoroacetate compounds. *Bull. Johns Hopkins Hosp. 97:*21 (1955).

toxic effects seem to result from the disruption of energy supply consequent to the blockade in the tricarboxylic acid cycle.

Acetate, or acetate precursors (ethanol, acetamide), serve as antidotes by competing with fluoroacetate, as would be expected, and such compounds have had a limited but definite protective action in experimental fluoroacetate poisoning by diminishing the accumulation of citrate and of fluorocitrate.[125,126] Best results have been obtained with monoacetin, the monoacetate ester of glycerol.[127]

MECHANISM 4. ANTIDOTE SPECIFICALLY ACCELERATES EXCRETION OF POISON

Bromide. An example is the effect of chloride ions in accelerating the removal of bromide ions from the body. Accumulation of bromide in the extracellular fluids leads to a toxic syndrome characterized by disturbances of function in the central nervous system. Early symptoms are impaired mental processes, drowsiness, dizziness, irritability, and emotional instability. More severe effects include mania, delirium, delusions, hallucinations, and coma. Neurologic disorders are also typical (tremors, motor incoordination, slurred speech), as well as dermatitis, abnormal function of the exocrine glands, and gastrointestinal disturbances. The slow time course of the accumulation of bromide in the body, which accounts for the insidious development of bromism, has been discussed fully in chapter 4. The specific antidotal administration of chloride was also described there. It depends upon the nearly identical handling of the chloride and bromide anions in the kidney. Increased chloride intake results in chloride diuresis. The excretion of bromide will be in nearly the same ratio to chloride as in the extracellular fluid.

As a specific illustration of the chloride-bromide relationship, assume the following:

Cl^- concentration (extracellular fluid) = 100 meq/liter = 36 g/liter; total body Cl^- = 36 g × 12 liters extracellular fluid = 432 g; daily excretion of Cl^- in urine = daily Cl^- intake = 5 g, or 5/432 (about 1 per cent) of the total body Cl^-;

Br^- concentration, mild toxic level = 10 meq/liter, or 10 per cent of the chloride concentration, on a molar basis.

If the chloride intake and output remained unchanged, then about 1 per cent of the body bromide would be excreted daily, because this is the frac-

[125] R. A. PETERS and R. W. WAKELIN: The synthesis of fluorocitric acid and its inhibition by acetate. *Biochem. J.* 67:280 (1957).

[126] S. GITTER: The influence of acetamide on citrate accumulation after fluoroacetate poisoning. *Biochem. J.* 63:182 (1956).

[127] M. B. CHENOWETH, A. KANDEL, L. B. JOHNSON, and D. R. BENNETT: Factors influencing fluoroacetate poisoning. Practical treatment with glycerol monoacetate. *J. Pharmacol. Exper. Therap.* 102:31 (1951).

tion of body chloride that is excreted daily. If an additional 5 g of chloride is administered each day, this excess will also be excreted, since the kidney functions to maintain a constant halide concentration in the extracellular fluid. Thus, as total halide excretion doubles, the excretion of bromide will be doubled, from 1 per cent per day to 2 per cent per day. It is not difficult to administer 5 to 10 g of sodium chloride or ammonium chloride daily, but very much larger amounts are impractical; thus the maximum effect that can be achieved is to increase the rate of bromide excretion several-fold. However, since bromide poisoning rarely presents itself as an acute emergency, slow elimination of the poison is usually not a serious handicap.

Strontium and Radium. Another example of the same principle is the accelerated removal of strontium and radium by the administration of calcium. Both metals compete with calcium for the mechanisms that mediate absorption, binding to proteins, transport across membranes, deposition in bone, and renal excretion.[128] Most recent investigations have concerned strontium, because radioactive ^{90}Sr is a product of nuclear explosions. It appears in fallout debris and thus may make its way into the human body by the oral and inhalation routes. The isotope is a beta emitter with a radioactive half-life of 28 years; its effective half-life after deposition in bone (taking account of both radioactive and biologic half-lives) is about seven years. The corresponding figure for ^{226}Ra is 44 years. Neither of these metals can be removed from the body efficiently by chelating agents of the EDTA type because the binding constants are too close to those of calcium, which is always present in great excess over the traces of strontium or radium that would be of concern.

The absorption of strontium from the gastrointestinal tract is less efficient than that of calcium. Investigations in man, using ^{85}Sr (a gamma emitter, radioactive half-life 64 days) and ^{45}Ca showed that even on a low-calcium diet the molar absorption of calcium was two to three times that of strontium; and higher calcium intakes correspondingly reduced the absorption of strontium.[129] Milk is an important source of calcium in man; inasmuch as youngsters drink more milk than adults, they should be protected better. But because milk from cows exposed to fallout may be a prime source of ^{90}Sr intake, the situation is complex.[130]

Preferential transport of calcium relative to strontium occurs in the renal tubules as well as the gastrointestinal tract. Consequently, although both are almost completely reabsorbed, a smaller fraction of strontium than of calcium in tubular urine is reabsorbed. Experiments in

128 A. ENGSTRÖM, R. BJÖRNERSTEDT, C. J. CLEMEDSON, and A. NELSON: *Bone and Radiostrontium.* New York, Wiley, 1958.

129 H. SPENCER, M. LI, J. SAMACHSON, and D. LASZLO: Metabolism of strontium-85 and calcium-45 in man. *Metabolism* 9:916 (1960).

130 F. C. GRAN and R. NICOLAYSEN: A theoretical analysis of radio-strontium metabolism and deposition in humans. *Acta Physiol. Scand.* 61:Suppl. 223 (1964).

TABLE 5-16.   **Renal tubular reabsorption of strontium and calcium in man**

85Sr was used, and plasma and urine concentrations were determined by radioactivity; Ca was determined titrimetrically. The three rows of data are from experiments with increasing calcium intake. (Data of Samachson and Spencer-Laszlo,[131] Table 4.)

Clearance (liters/day)			Tubular reabsorption (%)	
Ca	Sr	Sr/Ca	Ca	Sr
0.2	1.06	5.3	99.78	99.01
0.8	3.50	4.4	99.10	96.76
2.0	6.50	3.3	97.76	93.99

man[131] showed that with low calcium intake the calcium clearance was low, and the clearance ratio of strontium to calcium was about 5 to 1 (Table 5-16). Raising the calcium intake by a factor of 10 caused a corresponding increase in the calcium clearance, since the tubular reabsorption mechanisms operate to maintain calcium homeostasis in the plasma. At the same time there was a sixfold increase in strontium clearance. These effects are similar, in principle, to those of increased chloride intake upon bromide excretion, except that the renal clearance of strontium is considerably greater than that of calcium, whereas the bromide clearance is slightly less than that of chloride (p. 310). The excretion of strontium can also be increased by metabolic acidosis, causing demineralization of bone, and thereby promoting the mobilization of bone calcium and sequestered strontium. In man, the excretion of strontium is accelerated by calcium gluconate or by acidosis produced by ammonium chloride, and more so by administering both together.[132] Nonspecific ways of accelerating the excretion of a poison from the body are important in the treatment of toxicity when no specific antidotes are available, and they are also appropriate in conjunction with specific antidotes. These procedures (hemodialysis, peritoneal dialysis, ion trapping) were discussed at the beginning of this chapter.

MECHANISM 5. ANTIDOTE COMPETES WITH POISON FOR ESSENTIAL RECEPTORS

Carbon Monoxide.   The treatment of carbon monoxide poisoning by administration of oxygen exemplifies this mechanism. Carbon monoxide

131 J. SAMACHSON and H. SPENCER-LASZLO: Urinary excretion of calcium and strontium 85 in man. *J. Appl. Physiol.* 17:525 (1962).

132 H. SPENCER and J. SAMACHSON: Removal of radiostrontium in man by orally administered ammonium chloride two weeks after exposure: the effect of low and high calcium intake. *Clin. Sci.* 20:333 (1961).

is a product of combustion, so it is found wherever the internal combustion engine is in use. It is an industrial hazard, and it causes accidental poisoning in households where it is present in cooking gas. Suicide by the use of automobile exhaust gas is common. About 5,000 deaths annually in the United States are caused by carbon monoxide.

Carbon monoxide may be considered an antimetabolite of oxygen. It combines reversibly with hemoglobin to form carboxyhemoglobin. There are two consequences of importance. First, a certain number of binding sites for oxygen are occupied, so the oxygen-carrying capacity of the blood is decreased. Second, the binding of one or more molecules of CO to a molecule of hemoglobin with its four heme groups increases the affinity of the remaining sites for oxygen. The basis of this action is apparently the same as the well-known effect of one bound oxygen molecule upon the affinity of hemoglobin for the next one, namely, an induced allosteric modification of the protein (p. 91).[133] Thus, the ability of hemoglobin in the erythrocytes to give up oxygen to the tissues at low partial pressures of oxygen is seriously interfered with. This shifting of the oxyhemoglobin dissociation curve to the left (Fig. 5-21) causes a degree of tissue anoxia far greater than could be accounted for by the simple loss of oxygen-carrying capacity. Dogs were poisoned with CO until 75 per cent of their hemo-

FIG. 5-21. EFFECT OF CARBON MONOXIDE ON OXYHEMOGLOBIN DISSOCIATION. *Vertical axis shows oxyhemoglobin as per cent of total hemoglobin not com-*

$$bined\ with\ CO,\ \left(\frac{oxyhemoglobin}{oxyhemoglobin + hemoglobin} \times 100\right).\ Horizontal\ axis\ shows$$

partial pressure of O_2 in mm Hg. Curve at right, in the absence of CO; that at left, in the presence of 32 per cent carboxyhemoglobin. (From Roughton and Darling, Fig. 2.[134])

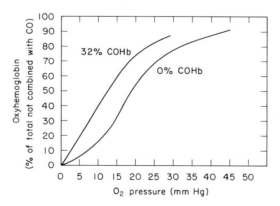

[133] J. WYMAN, JR.: Linked functions and reciprocal effects in hemoglobin: a second look. *Adv. Prot. Chem. 19*:223 (1964).

[134] F. J. W. ROUGHTON and R. C. DARLING: The effect of carbon monoxide on the oxyhemoglobin dissociation curve. *Amer. J. Physiol. 141*:17 (1944).

globin was carboxyhemoglobin. The animals collapsed, and those that survived showed serious damage from tissue anoxia. In contrast, transfusion experiments showed that 75 per cent of the blood could be replaced with CO-saturated blood without serious consequence.[135]

In man, little effect is seen with concentrations of carboxyhemoglobin up to about 35 per cent of the total hemoglobin. As the concentration approaches 50 per cent, headache, flushing, weakness, vomiting, and collapse occur. The color of the patient's skin may become cherry-red because of peripheral vasodilation and the bright-red color of carboxyhemoglobin itself. At still higher concentration, coma, intermittent convulsions, and respiratory failure are seen.

The affinity of CO for hemoglobin is about 250 times that of O_2. This means that the dangerous level of 50 per cent carboxyhemoglobin (i.e., equal parts CO-hemoglobin and O_2-hemoglobin) will be reached when the concentration of CO in the inspired air is only $1/250$ that of O_2, or 0.08 per cent. The uptake of CO and the kinetics of its equilibration and elimination are governed by the same principles as those already discussed in connection with anesthetic gases (chapter 4). Although the aqueous solubility of CO is low, its solubility in blood is very high because of its binding to hemoglobin; therefore its behavior is that of a typical high-solubility agent. Like the high-S anesthetic gases, it attains equilibrium slowly, and its uptake rate is very sensitive to changes in respiratory minute volume. Thus an active person, with a high respiratory exchange, will absorb CO faster (and be poisoned faster) than a person at rest.

The patient is removed from the contaminated environment and kept at rest, avoiding all stimulants, in order to reduce tissue oxygen demand to the lowest possible level. Respiration is maintained artificially, if necessary, with administration of pure O_2 or a mixture of 95 per cent O_2, with 5 per cent CO_2, to promote the competitive displacement of CO. Raising the O_2 concentration in the inspired air from 20 per cent to 100 per cent reduces the biologic half-life of carboxyhemoglobin in man from 250 minutes to about 40 minutes, as would be expected.[136] Use of a compression chamber at two atmospheres O_2 pressure works faster still and also helps correct tissue anoxia by supplying enough O_2 in solution in the plasma to maintain tissue oxygen requirements.[137] In severe poisoning, exchange transfusion is indicated to furnish an immediate supply of fresh hemoglobin.

Curare. In curare poisoning, the competition between the poison and acetylcholine at receptors in the skeletal muscle end-plate provides the

[135] D. L. DRABKIN, F. H. LEWEY, S. BELLET, and W. H. EHRICH: The effect of replacement of normal blood by erythrocytes saturated with carbon monoxide. *Amer. J. Med. Sci. 205:*755 (1943).

[136] F. J. W. ROUGHTON and W. S. ROOT: The fate of CO in the body during recovery from mild carbon monoxide poisoning in man. *Amer. J. Physiol. 145:*239 (1945).

[137] A. L. BARACH: Hyperbaric oxygen and current medical uses of oxygen. *New York J. Med. 63:*2775 (1963).

basis for antidotal action by a competitive displacement mechanism. Tubocurarine, the active principle of curare, is used as a muscle relaxant in surgery. The major effect of overdosage is a prolonged flaccid paralysis of striated muscles, secondary to a stabilization of the membrane potential at the end-plate (cf. chapter 1). In the presence of tubocurarine the usual amounts of AcCh released by motor nerve terminals no longer produce a sufficient local depolarization at the end-plate to trigger a propagated muscle action potential, so the muscle does not contract. It can be shown, with isolated nerve-muscle preparations, that higher concentrations of AcCh will provoke a response in the curarized end-plate, and the relationship between tubocurarine and AcCh appears to be competitive over a wide dose range (cf. chapter 1). It is not practical to administer AcCh itself as an antidote. First, it is destroyed almost at once by the circulating plasma and erythrocyte cholinesterases. Second, its access from the circulation to the muscle end-plate is somewhat restricted by lipid membrane barriers. The antidotal procedure, therefore, is to administer a cholinesterase inhibitor. Neostigmine, physostigmine, and similar drugs, by retarding the destruction of AcCh liberated by nerve impulses, allow a higher steady-state level of AcCh to accumulate locally. Thus, for any given rate of arrival of nerve impulses at the motor nerve terminals, the local AcCh concentration will be higher in the presence of a cholinesterase inhibitor. The organic phosphate cholinesterase inhibitors would act in the same way, but their effects would long outlast the period of curare-induced paralysis. The most useful antidote in the class of cholinesterase inhibitors is neostigmine; its efficacy is attributed not only to cholinesterase inhibition, but also to a mild direct stimulatory action on the muscle end-plate.

Edrophonium is a structural analogue of neostigmine; but it is not a carbamate ester, and it is a very poor inhibitor of cholinesterase:

edrophonium   neostigmine

Edrophonium reverses the paralysis caused by tubocurarine even faster than does neostigmine. In contrast to neostigmine, which has a long duration of action, the effect of a single dose of edrophonium wears off very quickly. The exact mechanism of edrophonium action remains uncertain, but its direct stimulatory actions on the end-plate presumably play a role.

Possibly edrophonium and neostigmine both displace tubocurarine from AcCh receptor sites in the muscle end-plate.[138]

Coumarin. Another instance of this mechanism, the competitive reversal of toxic effect by the antidote, is the treatment of coumarin toxicity by vitamin K. The coumarins are anticoagulants; the most frequently used are bishydroxycoumarin, warfarin, and phenindione (Fig. 5-22). They are employed therapeutically to depress the coagulability of blood in order to prevent thrombosis in coronary artery disease and other conditions.[139] Because they are also widely used as rodenticides, poisoning sometimes occurs in children. The coumarins act by depressing the synthesis of four plasma protein factors (the so-called prothrombin complex—factors II, VII, IX, and X) required in the normal process of blood coagulation. These proteins are synthesized in the liver, but only in the presence of adequate levels of vitamin K. The exact role of vitamin K in promoting the synthesis of these proteins is not known, but studies with perfused rat livers have shown that the vitamin K effect is not blocked by actinomycin D, whereas it is inhibited by puromycin and other inhibitors of protein synthesis.[140]

FIG. 5-22.   THE COUMARIN ANTICOAGULANTS AND VITAMIN K.

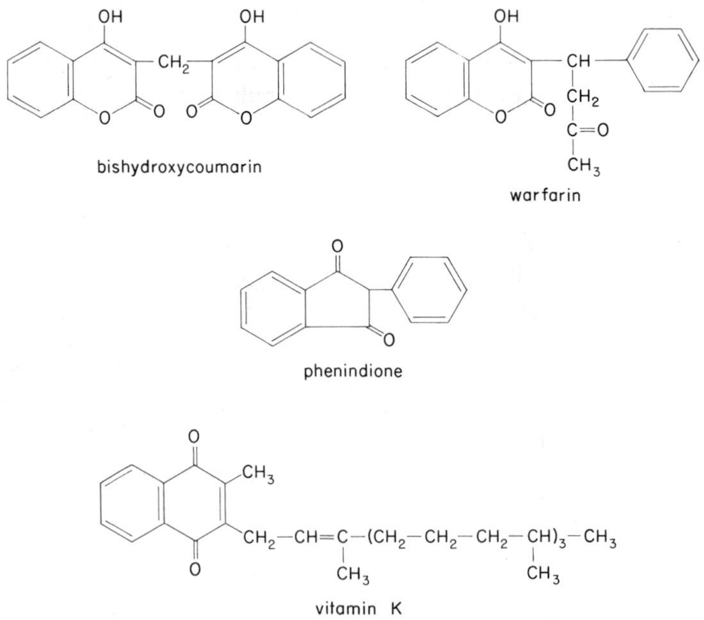

bishydroxycoumarin

warfarin

phenindione

vitamin K

[138] P. G. WASER: The cholinergic receptor. *J. Pharm. Pharmacol. 12:*577 (1960).
[139] G. I. C. INGRAM: Anticoagulant therapy. *Pharmacol. Rev. 13:*279 (1961).
[140] J. W. SUTTIE: Control of prothrombin and factor VII biosynthesis by vitamin K. *Arch. Biochem. Biophys. 118:*166 (1967).

This suggests that the vitamin promotes some aspect of protein synthesis subsequent to transcription of the genetic message into specific messenger RNA.

The coumarins may be regarded as structural analogues of vitamin K (Fig. 5-22). They behave as antimetabolites of the vitamin, and their effects are tantamount to vitamin K depletion. This is exemplified in Table 5-17, showing that vitamin K deficiency and warfarin administration in rats both depressed the ability of their livers to synthesize factor VII in vitro. The effects were specific; despite the considerable depression of this synthesis by both treatments, there was no general decline in the rate of protein synthesis. Administration of vitamin K in vivo restored the synthetic capacity in both groups.

The coumarin anticoagulants act slowly, as would be expected. They have no effect whatsoever upon blood clotting when added in vitro. Their actions take several days to develop, so acute toxicity is not usually a problem. Serious toxicity can develop with long-term use and inadequate control of the prothrombin time. A cause of toxic overdosage might be an unanticipated decrease in the rate of coumarin metabolism secondary to changes in the intake of other drugs, as described earlier (p. 265). Poisoning could be the result of ingesting coumarin rat poisons. The toxic manifestations are principally hemorrhagic episodes affecting various organs. Vitamin K derivatives are specific antidotes, but one cannot expect an immediate response; sufficient time must elapse for some new protein synthesis to occur. The lipid-soluble vitamin K_1 is more effective than the water-soluble analogues,[142] and it acts within a few hours.

TABLE 5-17. **Effects of vitamin K deficiency and warfarin on Factor VII synthesis by rat liver slices**

Rats were placed on a vitamin K-free diet or were given warfarin (25 mg/kg, i.v.) 2 hours before sacrifice. Factor VII production was then studied in liver slices in vitro, as well as ^{14}C-glycine incorporation into total protein in the same slices. (From Pool and Borchgrevink,[141] Tables 1 and 4.)

Treatment	Factor VII production (units/g in 3 hr)	Protein synthesis (cpm/mg protein)
None	225	3.3
Vitamin K-free diet	58	3.3
Warfarin	12	4.3

141 J. G. POOL and C. F. BORCHGREVINK: Comparison of rat liver response to coumarin administered in vivo versus in vitro. *Amer. J. Physiol. 206:*229 (1964).

142 A. S. DOUGLAS and A. BROWN: Effect of vitamin-K preparations on hypoprothrombinæmia induced by dicoumarol and tromexan. *Brit. Med. J. 1:*412 (1952).

Morphine and Morphine-like Narcotics.   The mechanism of competition for a receptor site also seems to explain the dramatic antidotal actions of nalorphine in poisoning by morphine and morphine-like narcotics. The agents that stereospecifically antagonize the analgesic and narcotic effects of morphine and related drugs were discussed in chapter 1. Figure 1-43 showed the structure of morphine and its antagonist nalorphine. The only difference in chemical structure is a replacement of the N-methyl group of morphine by N-allyl. Levallorphan, another antagonist, bears an identical relationship to levorphanol, whose structure was shown in Fig. 1-41.

Morphine poisoning usually occurs as a result of self-administered overdosage in an addict. The victim will be in a deep stupor or coma, with severely depressed respiration. Nalorphine can be life saving in these circumstances. It reverses all the narcotic effects promptly, and marked stimulation of respiration is seen. Nalorphine can also provoke a severe withdrawal syndrome in an addicted individual. Very small doses are used in a test for addiction; pupillary dilation is produced in addicted individuals but not in others. Nalorphine is also used to treat respiratory depression in infants born to mothers who have been using narcotics, but here caution is required. The newborn infant may possibly be dependent on morphine, so that nalorphine could precipitate a severe, even fatal withdrawal syndrome.

The antagonistic effects of nalorphine and of levallorphan to the analgesia produced by morphine-like narcotics were studied in rats. The tail-flick method was used to determine ED50 values for several analgesic agents. These were found to vary in potency over a thousandfold range; the smallest ED50 was 0.125 mg/kg, the largest was 120 mg/kg.[143] The same tests were repeated after administration of nalorphine or levallorphan. Some very clear-cut results were obtained. The slopes of all the quantal log dose-response curves were the same; in the presence of an antagonist they were only shifted to the right (i.e., to higher doses).[144] For a given antagonist the extent of this shift was always the same, no matter which narcotic analgesic was under test; but the two antagonists differed somewhat in potency. Thus, a fixed dose of nalorphine (92μg/kg), given prior to an ED80 dose of an analgesic, reduced the effect so that only 40 per cent of the animals instead of 80 per cent showed analgesic response; and this dose of nalorphine produced this same modification of analgesic response for all the narcotic agents tested. Exactly the same was true of levallorphan, ex-

[143] L. GRUMBACH and H. I. CHERNOV: The analgesic effect of opiate-opiate antagonist combinations in the rat. *J. Pharmacol. Exper. Therap. 149:*385 (1965).

[144] B. M. COX and M. WEINSTOCK: Quantitative studies of the antagonism by nalorphine of some of the actions of morphine-like analgesic drugs. *Brit. J. Pharmacol. 22:*289 (1964).

cept that it was about twice as potent as nalorphine, $44\mu g/kg$ producing the same reductions in analgesic response. The behavior is that to be expected of antagonists and agonists competing for the same receptor site.[145]

Figure 5-23 presents the results of an interesting experiment on two meperidine derivatives. The analgesic ED80 dose was first determined by subcutaneous administration in rats; criterion of response was failure of tail flick despite the application of heat for a period of 20 seconds. The ED80 doses proved to be $1.16\mu mole/kg$ for the less potent compound (A), $0.31\mu mole/kg$ for the more potent one (B). The ratio of these doses is 3.7. Now the analgesic doses were increased, and in each instance the amount of nalorphine required to antagonize the increased analgesic effect was determined. Each dose pair for constant effect was plotted as a single point, the nalorphine dosage on the horizontal axis, the analgesic dosage on the vertical axis. Straight lines that diverged from the origin resulted. Thus,

FIG. 5-23. COMPETITIVE ANTAGONISM OF NALORPHINE AGAINST TWO NARCOTIC ANALGESICS. *Rats were tested by the tail-flick method. The ED80 doses for two phenylpiperidine derivatives were $1.16\mu mole/kg$ for drug A, $0.31\mu mole/kg$ for drug B; the ratio of potencies was 3.7. For each increment of the analgesic dose, an amount of nalorphine was found that would just antagonize the increased analgesia, and this dose of nalorphine* (abscissa) *was plotted against the total dose of the analgesic* (ordinate). *The ratios of the slopes of the two straight lines is 3.7. (From Grumbach and Chernov, Fig. 3.[143])*

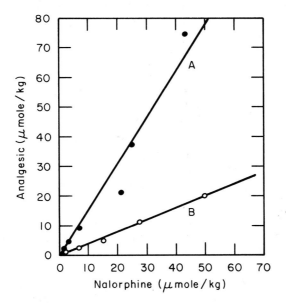

[145] The characteristic effect of a competitive antagonist upon the position but not the slope of a graded LDR curve was discussed exhaustively in chapter 1. The same principles are applicable here.

for a given drug there was an invariable antagonistic ratio. For example, 1μmole of nalorphine always antagonized 1.5μmole of drug A, but only 0.4μmole of the more potent drug B. Remarkably, the slopes of the two straight lines have the same ratio, 3.7, as the ED80 doses of the two drugs. These findings again imply a strictly competitive interaction between narcotic agent and narcotic antagonist, as though differences in affinities for the same receptor site were involved. Similar results were obtained when levallorphan was used as the antagonist.

Although the narcotic antagonists have little or no analgesic effects of their own in experimental animals, they produce analgesia in man. Surprisingly, although nalorphine at low doses antagonizes morphine effects, at doses comparable with those of morphine, it has analgesic effects of its own.[146,147] But severe side effects, especially psychotomimetic ones, rule out its clinical use as a morphine substitute. Tolerance to and physical dependence on nalorphine also occur.[148]

Just as opiate-induced analgesia can be blocked by nalorphine, so also can the development of physical dependence on the opiates be prevented. If monkeys are given an opiate regularly, dependence will eventually be established. Deprivation of the drug will then cause a typical withdrawal syndrome. Monkeys were given morphine every 4 hours for 35 days at the fixed dose of 5 mg/kg. The antagonist levallorphan was given with each morphine injection, a different dose being administered to each animal. After 35 days the injections were stopped and the intensity of withdrawal symptoms was noted. As Fig. 5-24 shows, levallorphan blocked the establishment of the physical dependence in a dose-related fashion; complete antagonism occurred at an approximately equimolar ratio.

The relief of opiate-induced respiratory depression by nalorphine is the basis of its life-saving capability in severe narcotic poisoning.[150] Yet nalorphine itself is not a respiratory stimulant but a respiratory depressant, like morphine. At high doses, however, nalorphine (unlike morphine) seems incapable of producing very severe respiratory depression.[151] Possibly the mechanism of antagonism here, as with analgesia, is the displacement of morphine from its receptor sites, as discussed at length in chapter 1 (p. 56). Thus, the severe respiratory depression caused by morphine would be replaced by a milder depression caused by nalorphine.

146 L. LASAGNA and H. K. BEECHER: The analgesic effectiveness of nalorphine and nalorphine-morphine combinations in man. *J. Pharmacol. Exper. Therap. 112:*356 (1954).

147 A. S. KEATS and J. TELFORD: Nalorphine, a potent analgesic in man. *J. Pharmacol. Exper. Therap. 117:*190 (1956).

148 W. R. MARTIN and C. W. GORODETZKY: Demonstration of tolerance to and physical dependence on N-allylnormorphine (nalorphine). *J. Pharmacol. Exper. Therap. 150:*437 (1965).

149 M. H. SEEVERS and G. A. DENEAU: A critique of the "dual action" hypothesis of morphine physical dependence. *Arch. Int. Pharmacodyn. 140:*514 (1962).

150 J. E. ECKENHOFF and S. R. OECH: The effects of narcotics and antagonists upon respiration and circulation in man. *Clin. Pharmacol. Therap. 1:*483 (1960).

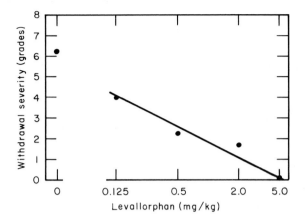

FIG. 5-24.   PREVENTION OF PHYSICAL DEPENDENCE ON MORPHINE BY LEVAL-
LORPHAN.   *Levallorphan at various doses was administered simultaneously with
morphine sulfate (5 mg/kg) every 4 hours, subcutaneously, to monkeys
(Macaca mulatta). After 35 days the drugs were stopped and the intensity of
withdrawal symptoms was assessed on an arbitrary grading scale. Note logarithmic dose scale. (From Seevers and Deneau, Fig. 1.[149])*

Thallium.   Some ion antagonisms may represent competition at
receptor sites on membranes or enzyme active centers. In thallium poisoning, for example, potassium ion has been found to counteract many of the
toxic actions and also to promote the renal excretion of thallium. The
protective effect of KCl administration in rats poisoned with Tl_2CO_4 is
shown in Table 5-11; in the same experiments NaCl was without effect.
In addition, it has been shown that the cytotoxic effect of thallium salts on
mouse fibroblasts growing in cell culture is partially blocked by potassium
salts.[152] Although the mechanisms are still unknown, the chemical similarities between Tl^+ and K^+ lend plausibility to a hypothesis of competition
for the same receptor sites.

Amino Acid Analogues.   Finally, amino acid analogues (e.g.,
ethionine, fluorophenylalanine), which have been investigated as potential
anticancer agents, are all toxic. The analogous natural amino acids are
effective antidotes; they compete for incorporation into protein, as described for selenocysteine (p. 404).

MECHANISM 6. ANTIDOTE BLOCKS RECEPTORS THAT ARE RESPON-
SIBLE FOR TOXIC EFFECT

Cholinesterase Inhibitors.   A good example is the use of atropine
to prevent the toxic effects of cholinesterase inhibitors. It interacts with

151 A. S. KEATS and J. TELFORD: Studies of analgesic drugs. X. Respiratory effects
of narcotic antagonists. *J. Pharmacol. Exper. Therap. 151*:126 (1966).
152 L. HELLENGA and L. ARONOW: unpublished observations.

AcCh receptors, rendering them insensitive to the large amounts of AcCh that accumulate in this type of poisoning. Atropine acts upon receptors at the parasympathetic effector organs and in the central nervous system; it has but slight action at autonomic ganglia and practically none at the neuromuscular junction. Atropine should be given liberally to counteract the effects of cholinesterase inhibitors, certainly in dosage sufficient to produce clear signs of atropinization, e.g., mydriasis, tachycardia, dry hands and mouth, and hot, flushed skin. From the competitive relationship between atropine and AcCh (Fig. 1-65) it may be deduced that much more atropine will be required in anticholinesterase poisoning than is needed to atropinize a normal person. Atropine is especially helpful in antagonizing the life-threatening bronchiolar constriction and excessive bronchial secretions produced by AcCh accumulation.

Atropine alone can protect experimental animals against several LD50 doses of an organic phosphate cholinesterase inhibitor. However, since the neuromuscular junction is not responsive to atropine, the paralysis of the respiratory muscles produced by excessive AcCh will not be relieved. Prompt artificial respiration is therefore called for. As was shown in Table 5-13, atropine and the reactivating agent pralidoxime each have some protective effects, and the antidotal action is greatly enhanced when both agents are used together; combination therapy is now standard.

MECHANISM 7. ANTIDOTE RESTORES NORMAL FUNCTION BY REPAIR-
ING OR BYPASSING EFFECT OF POISON

Agents that Produce Methemoglobinemia. The use of methylene blue to combat methemoglobinemia illustrates the repair of a damaged receptor by an antidote. The oxidized, ferric form of hemoglobin is a chocolate-colored pigment called methemoglobin. Erythrocytes normally contain small amounts of methemoglobin, presumably a steady-state level resulting from spontaneous oxidation. They also contain two enzyme systems that reduce methemoglobin back to hemoglobin; these are methemoglobin diaphorase (diaphorase I), using NADH as coenzyme, and methemoglobin reductase (diaphorase II), using NADPH. A great many substances can produce methemoglobin,[153] for example, nitrites, chlorates, phenacetin, acetanilid, sulfanilamide, nitrobenzene, quinones, aniline, and aniline dyes. The production of methemoglobin by acetanilid and by aniline metabolites (p. 209), and the sensitivity of infants to nitrate in their drinking water and to aniline dyes (p. 376) have been discussed. Nitrites are probably the commonest cause of methemoglobinemia; the reader is referred to a fascinating account of medical detection in a mass poisoning caused by the substitution of sodium nitrite for table salt.[154]

    153 O. BODANSKY: Methemoglobinemia and methemoglobin-producing compounds. *Pharmacol. Rev. 3:*144 (1951).
    154 B. ROUECHÉ: "Eleven Blue Men," in *Eleven Blue Men.* New York, Berkeley Publishing Corp., 1953, pp. 78–89.

Methemoglobin will not carry oxygen; therefore extensive methemoglobinemia is incompatible with life. When one or more of the four iron atoms in a hemoglobin molecule is oxidized to the ferric state, the affinity of O_2 for the other sites is increased. The oxyhemoglobin dissociation curve is shifted to the left, as with carboxyhemoglobin (but not so markedly) (Fig. 5-21), so the delivery of O_2 to the tissues is impaired.[155] Patients with methemoglobinemia are therefore more anoxic than they would be if an equivalent loss of hemoglobin were sustained by hemorrhage. Early symptoms of anoxia may be seen below 50 per cent methemoglobin, but oxygenation becomes seriously inadequate only at higher levels; the lethal concentration is apparently above 70 per cent.[156]

Methylene blue causes the reduction of methemoglobin to hemoglobin, and it is an effective antidote for methemoglobinemia, regardless of its cause. The dye acts as an intermediate electron acceptor between NADPH and methemoglobin; it undergoes a cyclic reduction to its colorless form, leucomethylene blue:

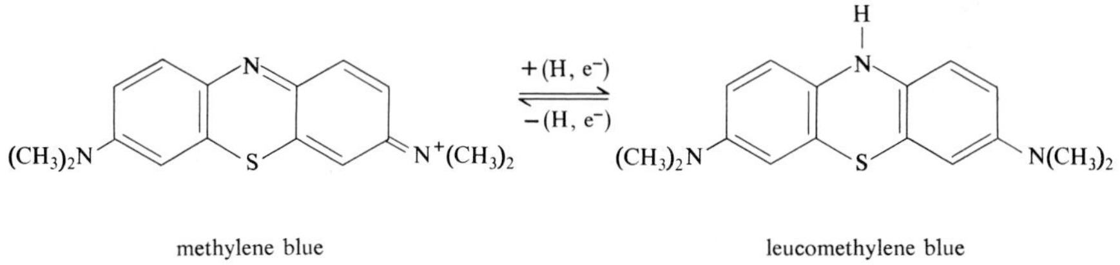

methylene blue   leucomethylene blue

The direct reaction between NADPH and methemoglobin is catalyzed by methemoglobin reductase (diaphorase II), as already noted, and this reaction is accelerated by the intervention of methylene blue.[157] The electron transport sequence is as follows:[158]

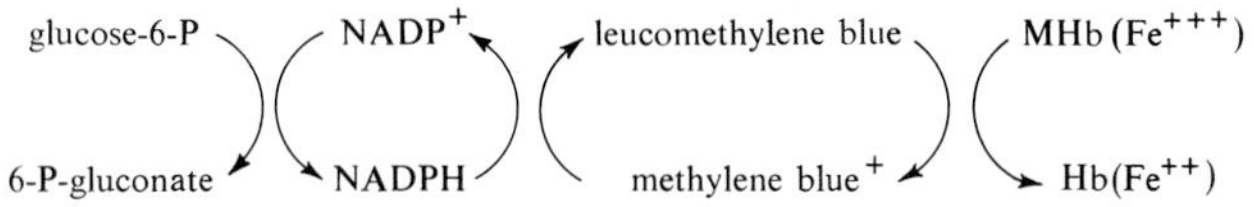

In the absence of methemoglobin, oxygen will serve as a terminal electron acceptor, oxidizing leucomethylene blue; thus, for example, methylene blue stimulates glucose oxidation by erythrocytes.

[155] R. C. DARLING and F. J. W. ROUGHTON: The effect of methemoglobin on the equilibrium between oxygen and hemoglobin. *Amer. J. Physiol.* 137:56 (1942).

[156] O. BODANSKY and H. GUTMANN: Treatment of methemoglobinemia. *J. Pharmacol. Exper. Therap.* 90:46 (1947).

[157] F. M. HUENNEKENS, R. W. CAFFREY, R. E. BASFORD, and B. W. GABRIO: Erythrocyte metabolism. IV. Isolation and properties of methemoglobin reductase. *J. Biol. Chem.* 227:261 (1957).

[158] E. BEUTLER and M. C. BALUDA: Methemoglobin reduction. Studies of the interaction between cell populations and of the role of methylene blue. *Blood* 22:323 (1963).

The effectiveness of intravenous methylene blue in treating severe methemoglobinemia has been demonstrated experimentally in dogs;[156] at methemoglobin concentrations in excess of 80 per cent, only one dog out of 12 survived in a control series, but eight out of nine treated animals recovered rapidly and completely. The efficacy of methylene blue in man has also been shown.[159] Care should be exercised in the use of methylene blue, as higher doses paradoxically cause methemoglobinemia (by direct oxidation), as well as producing hemolysis and central nervous system depression.[160] Oxygen administration is also indicated, to increase the concentration of physically dissolved O_2 carried to the tissues in the plasma.

Digitalis. Another example of an antidote repairing or bypassing the effect of a poison is seen in the treatment of digitalis toxicity. Were this poisoning not so common an occurrence, it might well be omitted here entirely because the antidotal mechanisms (and for that matter the mechanisms of the therapeutic or toxic actions of digitalis) are still so poorly understood. Nevertheless, there are clearly specific, effective antidotes, which will be discussed.

Digitalis toxicity occurs frequently and is difficult to avoid, for two reasons. First, as explained in chapter 4, the drug has a very long biologic half-life, so it tends to accumulate, with an equally long half-time. Second, because the therapeutic ratio is very small, as shown earlier in this chapter, relatively small overshoots beyond the intended plateau, or unpredictable fluctuations of the drug level or of the patient's sensitivity to the drug can have serious consequences.

There are three major types of toxic manifestation.[161] These were well described in 1775 by Withering,[162] who introduced this drug into medicine:

> "I found him [a Yorkshire tradesman] incessantly vomiting, his vision indistinct, his pulse forty in a minute. Upon enquiry, it came out that his wife had stewed a large handful of green foxglove leaves in a half pint of water and given him the liquor which he drank at one draught . . . this good woman knew the medicine of her country, but not the dose of it, for the husband narrowly escaped with his life."

Gastrointestinal disturbances, especially nausea, vomiting, and diarrhea, tend to occur early, and may serve as significant warning signs. Neurologic and ophthalmologic disorders are common; these include flicker-

---

[159] A. F. MANGELSDORFF: Treatment of methemoglobinemia. *A.M.A. Arch. Ind. Health 14:*148 (1956).

[160] N. GOLUBOFF and R. WHEATON: Methylene blue induced cyanosis and acute hemolytic anemia complicating the treatment of methemoglobinemia. *J. Pediat. 58:*86 (1961).

[161] A. P. SOMLYO: The toxicology of digitalis. *Amer. J. Cardiol. 5:*523 (1960).

[162] W. WITHERING: "An Account of the Foxglove, and Some of Its Medical Uses; with Practical Remarks on Dropsy, and Other Diseases." Reproduced in its entirety in *Medical Classics 2:*305 (1937).

ing sensations, colored vision, photophobia, and a variety of central manifestations such as vertigo, headache, drowsiness, restlessness, irritability, weakness, convulsions, delusions, and stupor. The third class of toxic action comprises the cardiac effects proper, mainly depressed conduction and many kinds of cardiac arrhythmia.[163] The appearance of an irregularity of the pulse not previously present in a patient receiving a digitalis glycoside is very serious, because it has been shown in animal experiments that such effects do not occur until about 60 per cent of the fatal dose has been given. The increased automaticity of the cardiac tissues may be expressed as paroxysmal or nonparoxysmal atrial tachycardia, premature ventricular beats, bigeminal pulse, nodal tachycardia, or ventricular tachycardia, with various degrees of associated heart block. Fatal ventricular fibrillation may supervene abruptly. It has been estimated that in as many as one-half of all cases one of these cardiac arrhythmias is the first sign of toxicity, without any premonitory gastrointestinal or neurologic symptoms.[164] The pattern of toxic effects is rather variable, not only between patients, but even in the same patient on different occasions. On the other hand, there is no evidence of any regular patterns of toxicity distinguishing one digitalis glycoside from another.[165]

It would seem elementary that signs of digitalis toxicity should call for immediate discontinuance of the drug. Surprisingly, this is not always done. Since many arrhythmias arise from the primary cardiac disease under treatment, the dose of digitalis may even be increased in the mistaken opinion that insufficient therapeutic effect has been obtained.[166] Recognition of the toxic arrhythmias, sometimes only possible by means of the electrocardiogram, is therefore the primary key to effective treatment.

Discontinuing the administration of digitalis is essential, but it is unlikely to have any immediate effect because the drug is eliminated so very slowly (p. 305). The most important antidote is potassium ion. It is still unclear exactly what roles the monovalent and divalent cations play in cardiac contraction or impulse initiation and conduction. There is no doubt, however, that administration of digitalis in toxic doses leads to an abnormal efflux of potassium from the heart. Conversely, the sensitivity of the heart to the toxic effects of digitalis glycosides is increased by lowering the perfusing potassium concentration (in animal experiments), and diminished by raising the potassium level.[167] These animal observations led

[163] C. FISCH, K. GREENSPAN, S. B. KNOEBEL, and H. FEIGENBAUM: Effect of digitalis on conduction of the heart. *Progr. Cardiovasc. Dis.* 6:343 (1964).

[164] P. L. RODENSKY and F. WASSERMAN: Observations on digitalis intoxication. *Arch. Int. Med.* 108:171 (1961).

[165] G. CHURCH, L. SCHAMROTH, N. L. SCHWARTZ, and H. J. L. MARRIOTT: Deliberate digitalis intoxication. A comparison of the toxic effects of four glycoside preparations. *Ann. Int. Med.* 57:946 (1962).

[166] B. LOWN and H. D. LEVINE: *Atrial Arrhythmias, Digitalis and Potassium.* New York, Landsberger Medical Books, 1958.

[167] E. BRAUNWALD and F. J. KLOCKE: Digitalis. *Ann. Rev. Med.* 16:371 (1965).

to clinical experimentation and controlled observation, which revealed similar actions in man.[166,168] A significant precipitating cause of digitalis toxicity may be the hypokalemia produced by the vigorous use of diuretics in cardiac patients. Arrhythmias caused by digitalis (particularly atrial tachycardias) can often be abolished by oral or slow intravenous administration of KCl or other potassium salts.[166,169] The amount required is about 50 to 100 meq (3 to 7 g of KCl). This increases the plasma K^+ to 1 or 2 meq/liter above its normal level of 3.5 to 5.0 meq/liter, and presumably restores potassium to the depleted heart. On theoretical grounds (cf. chapter 2), better control can be maintained by continuous intravenous infusion of a dilute solution of a potassium salt than by oral administration; and fine control is important here because excessive potassium levels are dangerous.

It has been shown in experimental animals that the cardiac actions of digitalis require the presence of calcium, and some evidence has been adduced that digitalis toxicity can be antagonized by lowering the plasma calcium concentration. This has been attempted with the sodium salt of EDTA, and some success has been claimed[170,171] in terminating digitalis-induced arrhythmias. It is difficult, however, to induce the desired degree of hypocalcemia while avoiding tetany, and the efficacy of the procedure remains controversial.

Other methods are effective in combatting digitalis toxicity on the heart. It has long been known that epinephrine and related catecholamines can precipitate cardiac arrhythmias, especially in the digitalized heart, and that sympathetic denervation reduces the sensitivity of the heart to the toxic actions of digitalis. These findings have led to the introduction of beta-receptor blocking agents in the treatment of digitalis toxicity, apparently with some success.[172] Procaine amide, a derivative of the local anesthetic procaine, also has proved useful in reducing cardiac arrhythmias, especially ventricular ectopic beats, caused by digitalis.

Folic Acid Antagonists. The bypass mechanism of antidotal action is also well illustrated in the field of chemotherapy, where the toxic effects of antimetabolites can be antagonized by end-products of the inhibited reactions. Investigations on the mode of action of sulfonamides in certain bacteria revealed that their action is antagonized competitively by

168 J. J. SAMPSON, E. C. ALBERTON, and B. KONDO: The effect on man of potassium administration in relation to digitalis glycosides, with special reference to blood serum potassium, the electrocardiogram, and ectopic beats. *Amer. Heart J. 26:*164 (1943).

169 B. M. COHEN: Digitalis poisoning and its treatment. *New England J. Med. 246:*225, 254 (1952).

170 R. S. ELIOT and S. G. BLOUNT, JR.: Calcium, chelates, and digitalis: a clinical study. *Amer. Heart J. 62:*7 (1961).

171 J. L. ROSENBAUM, D. MASON, and M. J. SEVEN: The effect of disodium EDTA on digitalis intoxication. *Amer. J. Med. Sci. 240:*77 (1960).

172 J. P. P. STOCK and N. DALE: Beta-adrenergic receptor blockade in cardiac arrhythmias. *Brit. Med. J. 2:*1230 (1963).

p-aminobenzoic acid (PABA).[173] Evidently, the sulfonamides act as competitive substrates for the first reaction utilizing PABA—its condensation with a dihydropteridine derivative to form dihydropteroic acid, as shown in Fig. 5-25.[174] Folic acid, the end-product of the pathway inhibited by the sulfonamides, antagonizes their action noncompetitively. These contrasting modes of antagonism are illustrated in Fig. 5-26. The concentrations of antagonist required to produce half-maximal growth of the test organism are plotted on the vertical axis against various sulfonamide concentrations on the horizontal axis. The straight line, with slope 1.0, indicates that with PABA there was a fixed competitive ratio; thus, for example, a tenfold increase of sulfonamide could be overcome by a tenfold increase in PABA. With either folic acid compound, on the other hand, the same amount that was needed to sustain growth in the absence of sulfonamide was effective at all sulfonamide concentrations. In other words, in the presence of folic

FIG. 5-25.   PATHWAY OF FOLIC ACID SYNTHESIS IN MICROORGANISMS.

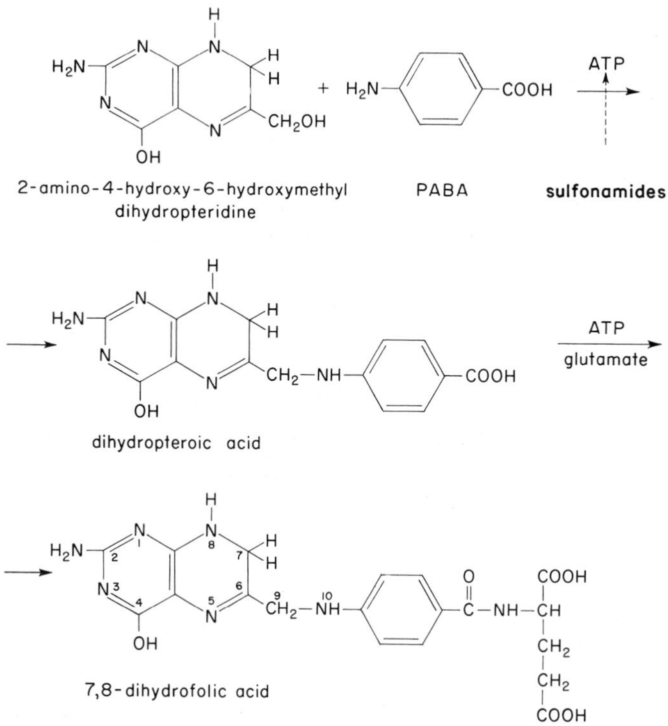

2-amino-4-hydroxy-6-hydroxymethyl
dihydropteridine   PABA   **sulfonamides**

dihydropteroic acid

7,8-dihydrofolic acid

[173] D. D. WOODS: The relation of *p*-aminobenzoic acid to the mechanism of the action of sulphanilamide. *Brit. J. Exper. Pathol.* 21:74 (1940).

[174] G. M. BROWN: The biosynthesis of folic acid. II. Inhibition by sulfonamides. *J. Biol. Chem.* 237:536 (1962).

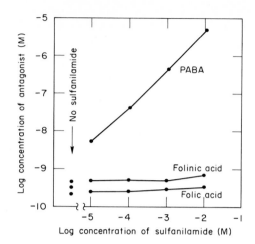

FIG. 5-26. COMPETITIVE AND NONCOMPETITIVE ANTAGONISM OF SULFONAMIDE
ACTION. *The data were obtained in a bacterial strain* (Clostridium tetanomor-
phum) *that requires* p-aminobenzoic acid *(PABA) for growth. The normal
requirement in the absence of sulfanilamide is indicated by the three points at
left. The concentrations of PABA, folic acid, or folinic acid required to restore
half-maximal growth in the presence of various concentrations of sulfanilamide
are plotted. The strictly competitive antagonism by PABA contrasts with the
noncompetitive product inhibition by folic acid and its formyltetrahydro derivative (leucovorin, citrovorum factor, folinic acid). (From Woods, Fig. 8.*[175]* *By
permission of Cambridge University Press.*)

acid, the sulfonamide drug no longer had any effect, because folic acid is
the sole essential product of the inhibited reaction. The same principle
applies to any toxic agent. If all end-products of the pathways blocked by
the agent are made available, then the toxicity is effectively bypassed.

Several reduced derivatives of folic acid serve as cofactors in the
transfer of single carbon atoms. Figure 5-27 shows the pathways in mammalian cells. Folic acid undergoes two reduction steps, to the 7,8-dihydro
derivative (FAH_2) and then to 5,6,7,8-tetrahydrofolic acid (FAH_4), which
is directly involved in formyl and methyl transfers. Folinic acid (leucovorin,
citrovorum factor) is N^5-formyl FAH_4 (not shown), which is readily converted in the body to N^5,N^{10}-anhydroformyl FAH_4. These folic acid derivatives are essential for the interconversion of glycine and serine, for the
synthesis of thymidylic acid from deoxyuridylic acid, and for two different
steps in the purine biosynthetic pathway, as illustrated in Fig. 5-27.[176,177]

[175] D. D. WOODS: The biochemical mode of action of the sulphonamide drugs.
J. Gen. Microbiol. 29:687 (1962).

[176] J. L. STOKES: Substitutions of thymine for "folic acid" in the nutrition of
lactic acid bacteria. *J. Bacteriol.* 48:201 (1944).

[177] In bacteria, the histidine and methionine biosynthetic pathways involve single-
carbon transfers in which folic acid is involved. In mammalian cells, however, these amino
acids are not synthesized but have to be furnished exogenously.

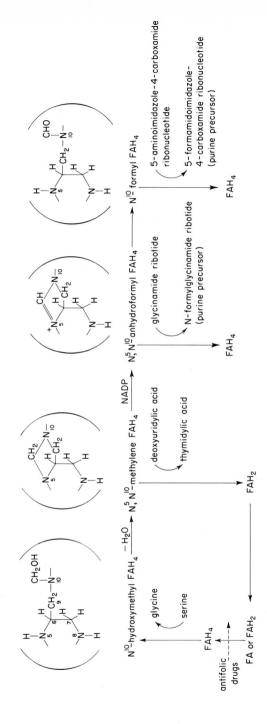

FIG. 5-27. PATHWAY OF FOLIC ACID METABOLISM IN MAMMALS. FA, *folic acid*; FAH$_2$, *7,8-dihydrofolic acid*; FAH$_4$, *5,6,7,8-tetrahydrofolic acid*.

In the synthesis of thymidylic acid, FAH_4 acts as a reducing agent, since the formyl group is converted to a methyl group; and consequently the continuous regeneration of FAH_4 from FAH_2, mediated by folic acid reductase, becomes essential.

The folic acid antagonists are the first drugs to have been used with some degree of success in cancer chemotherapy,[178] and they are still widely employed in the treatment of childhood leukemia. Because they interfere with essential functions in all cells, they have a high toxicity. *Methotrexate* (Fig. 5-28), the drug of this class in common use today, combines reversibly but very tightly with folic acid reductase and inactivates it. The combination is practically stoichiometric, with a dissociation constant of only $3 \times 10^{-11}M$, representing an affinity 10^5 times greater than that of folic acid for the same enzyme.[179] The effect, as would be predicted from Fig. 5-27, is primarily to block endogenous synthesis of glycine, thymidylate, and the purines.[180]

Folic acid is of no value in overcoming the toxic effects of excess methotrexate, because it is unable to displace the drug from the active center of the reductase. Better results are obtained with folinic acid, which is converted readily to one of the active FAH_4 compounds in the body. If the sole action of methotrexate were to block the reduction of FA or FAH_2 to FAH_4, then an antagonist like folinic acid should act noncompetitively, since it would be furnishing the product of the inhibited reaction. Actually, the antagonism is strictly competitive, suggesting another site of methotrexate action beyond folic acid reductase,[181] or possibly a competition for cellular uptake processes.[182] On the other hand, the end-products of single carbon transfer overcome the methotrexate toxicity completely and noncompetitively. This can be accomplished by a mixture of thymidine (which generates thymidylic acid in the cell), of a purine such as hypoxanthine or adenine, and of glycine; cells growing in vitro in such a mixture are indifferent to all concentrations of methotrexate.[183]

5-Fluorouracil and 5-Fluorodeoxyuridine. 5-Fluorouracil and 5-fluorodeoxyuridine (Fig. 5-28) participate in normal intermediary metab-

178 S. FARBER, L. K. DIAMOND, R. D. MERCER, R. F. SYLVESTER, JR., and J. A. WOLFF: Temporary remissions in acute leukemia in children produced by folic acid antagonist, 4-aminopteroyl-glutamic acid (Aminopterin). *New England J. Med. 238:*787 (1948).

179 W. C. WERKHEISER: Specific binding of 4-amino folic acid analogs by folic acid reductase. *J. Biol. Chem. 236:*888 (1961).

180 W. C. WERKHEISER: The biochemical, cellular, and pharmacological action and effects of the folic acid antagonists. *Cancer Res. 23:*1277 (1963).

181 L. ARONOW: Studies on drug resistance in mammalian cells. I. Amethopterin resistance in mouse fibroblasts. *J. Pharmacol. Exper. Therap. 127:*116 (1959).

182 J. R. BERTINO: The mechanism of action of the folate antagonists in man. *Cancer Res. 23:*1286 (1963).

183 M. T. HAKALA and E. TAYLOR: The ability of purine and thymine derivatives and of glycine to support the growth of mammalian cells in culture. *J. Biol. Chem. 234:*126 (1959).

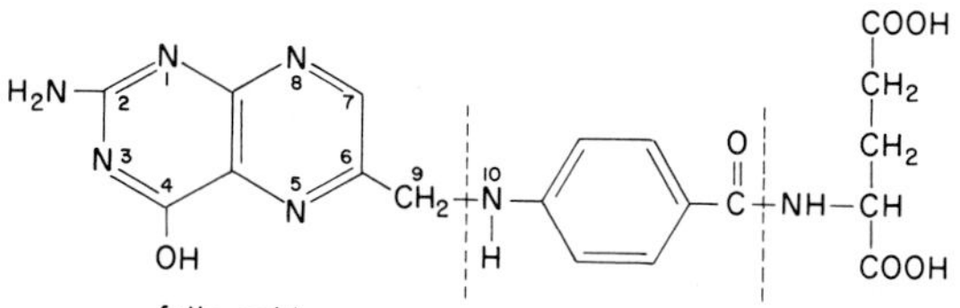

folic acid

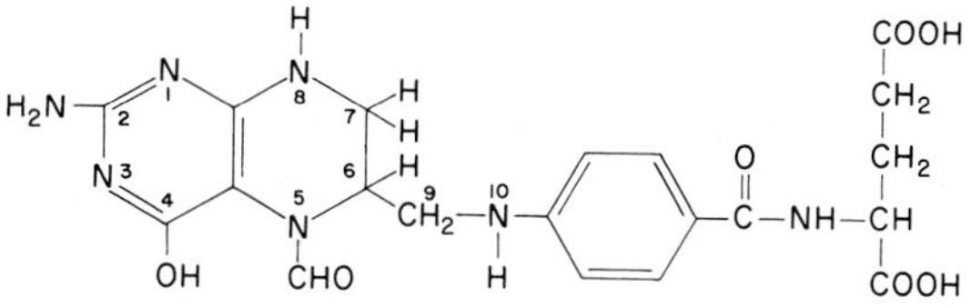

N^5-formyltetrahydrofolic acid
(folinic acid, leucovorin, citrovorum factor)

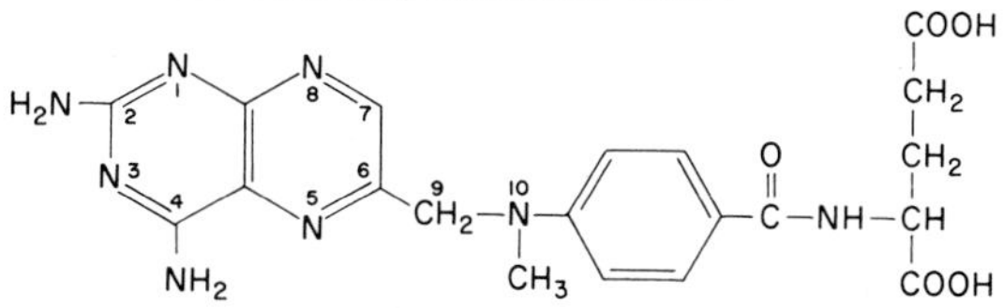

methotrexate

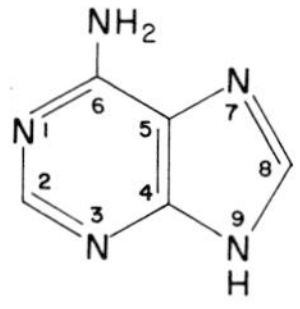

adenine

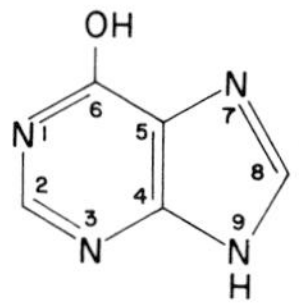

hypoxanthine

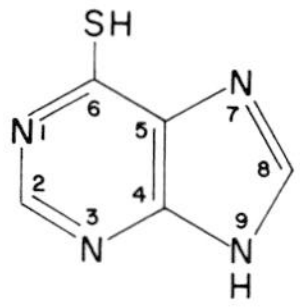

6-mercaptopurine

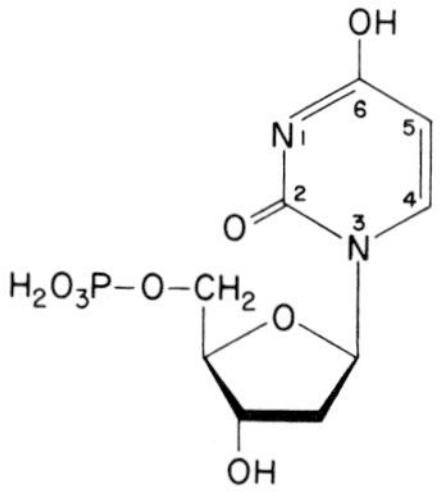

deoxyuridylic acid

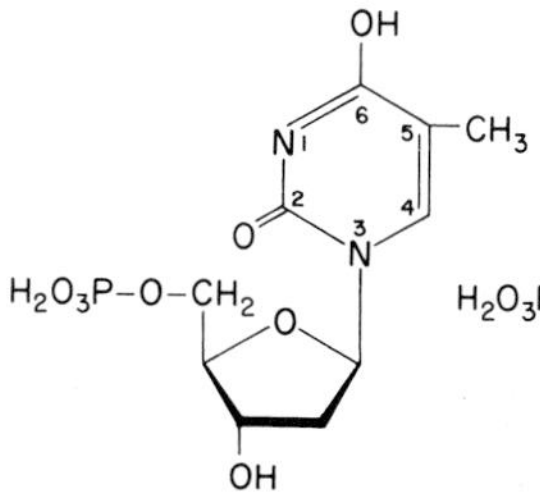

thymidylic acid

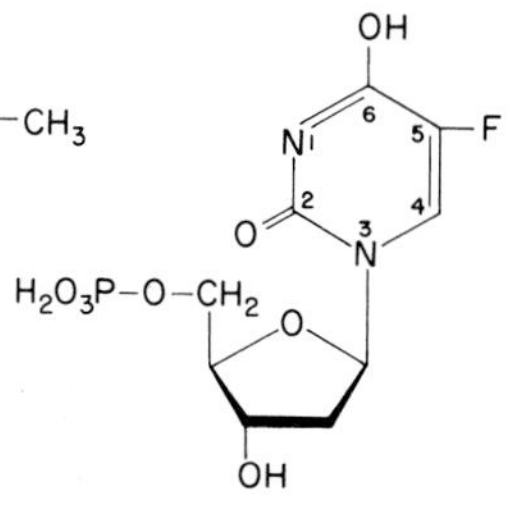

5-fluorodeoxyuridylic acid

FIG. 5-28. SOME ESSENTIAL METABOLITES, AND THEIR ANTIMETABOLITES USED IN CANCER CHEMOTHERAPY.

olism, forming ribonucleosides and phosphorylated derivatives. The anti-tumor effect of these compounds can be attributed to inhibition of DNA synthesis secondary to a block of thymidylate synthesis. Both agents are converted to 5'-fluoro-2'-deoxyuridine 5'-monophosphate (FUdRP), which inhibits the enzyme thymidylate synthetase competitively.[184] Since thymidine is converted readily to thymidylic acid by a kinase, thymidine acts as a specific and effective antidote; in the presence of thymidine, the need for de novo thymidylate synthesis is obviated.

6-Mercaptopurine. Another inhibitor of DNA synthesis is 6-mercaptopurine (Fig. 5-28). The active compound is apparently the derivative 6-mercaptopurine ribonucleoside 5'-phosphate, formed within the cell. The primary mechanism of action of this compound in cancer chemotherapy is its inhibition of the conversion of inosinic acid to adenine and guanine nucleotides.[185] Both hypoxanthine and adenine are effective antidotes. Guanine is less effective, probably because of its rapid degradation and limited capacity for conversion to adenine nucleotides in the cells.

[184] P. REYES and C. HEIDELBERGER: Fluorinated pyrimidines 26. Mammalian thymidylate synthetase: its mechanism of action and inhibition by fluorinated nucleotides. *Mol. Pharmacol. 1:*14 (1965).

[185] J. S. SALSER and M. E. BALIS: The mechanism of action of 6-mercaptopurine. I. Biochemical effects. *Cancer Res. 25:*539 (1965).

6

DRUG IDIOSYNCRASY

AND PHARMACOGENETICS

INTRODUCTION

Idiosyncrasy is defined as "a peculiarity of physical or mental constitution or temperament; a characteristic distinguishing an individual; characteristic susceptibility; eccentricity."[1] The word has long been used in pharmacology to describe peculiar drug reactions resulting from abnormal reactivity of the individuals in whom they occur. Idiosyncrasy may take the form of extreme sensitivity to small doses, with drug effects of the same kind that usually occur at much higher doses. Or the reactions may be of a unique kind not ordinarily seen at any dose. The classification of any particular untoward drug reaction as idiosyncratic is likely to be rather uncertain as long as the mechanism remains obscure. However, recent advances in pharmacogenetics have exposed the precise mechanism of some idiosyncratic responses and give promise of clarifying others eventually.[2-4] We may now define idiosyncrasy more precisely as a *genetically determined* abnormal reactivity to a drug. A full understanding of an idiosyncratic reaction requires elucidation of the mechanism whereby the usual drug effect is altered in the genetically abnormal person, of the biochemical abnormality that constitutes the phenotypic expression of the genetic defect, and also of the pattern of inheritance of the genotype.

Idiosyncrasy should not be a catchall classification for unexpected reactions to drugs. Accidental overdosage, inadvertent injection into a vein, or excessively rapid intravenous administration may all provoke severe or

[1] *Webster's New International Dictionary of the English Language,* 2d ed. Springfield, Mass., G. and C. Merriam Co., 1949.

[2] W. KALOW: *Pharmacogenetics: Heredity and the Response to Drugs.* Philadelphia, W. B. Saunders, 1962.

[3] J. B. STANBURY, J. B. WYNGAARDEN, and D. S. FREDRICKSON, eds.: *The Metabolic Basis of Inherited Disease,* 2nd ed. New York, McGraw-Hill, 1966.

[4] B. N. LA DU: Altered drug response in hereditary disease. *Fed. Proc. 24:* 1287 (1965).

even fatal reactions. Insoluble preparations of penicillin, for example, meant for depot use but introduced into a vein by accident, can cause massive pulmonary embolism. Too rapid intravenous injection of mercurial diuretics may cause ventricular fibrillation. A special kind of acute un-toward reaction results from the rapid intravenous administration of drugs that are capable of releasing histamine from tissues. Sudden onset of intense generalized itching and burning sensations, lacrimation, erythema, blood pressure collapse, tachycardia, vomiting, and urticaria may present an alarming picture. In asthmatic patients a severe asthmatic crisis may be precipitated. Allergic reactions to drugs present a special pattern of responses, discussed in the next chapter. Strange and surprising as all these kinds of adverse reactions may be, they have nothing to do with idiosyn-crasy.

Mere sensitivity to a low dose of a drug or resistance to a high dose does not qualify as idiosyncrasy. Population heterogeneity is an obvious feature of all dose-response relationships, so that a wide dose range may separate the most sensitive from the least sensitive individuals. When guinea pigs were pretreated with an antihistamine drug and then exposed to a lethal dose of histamine, the dose required to protect 84 per cent of the animals was ten times greater than that which protected 16 per cent of them.[5] The remarkably wide variation in human response to digitoxin was illustrated in Fig. 5-9. It is likely that this commonly observed biologic variation in responsiveness to drugs has a genetic basis, a conclusion that is strengthened by the fact that variation is substantially less in inbred strains of animal than in cross-breeding wild strains (Table 3-11). The characteristic feature in idiosyncratic sensitivity to low doses or resistance to high doses is a discontinuity from the ordinary distribution of dose sensi-tivities.

Abnormal sensitivity to drugs in infancy should not be confused with idiosyncrasy. Very small doses of aniline dyes, for example, no more than are used in inks for marking diapers, may cause methemoglobinemia in the newborn. And the sensitivity of infants to chloramphenicol and to small amounts of nitrates in well water falls into the same category. As discussed in chapters 3 and 5, enzyme systems in the newborn, including drug-metabolizing enzymes, are often quantitatively (and sometimes quali-tatively) different from those in the adult. Such differences can account readily for most of the well-documented instances of infant sensitivity to drugs.[6]

---

[5] J. T. LITCHFIELD, JR., and F. WILCOXON: A simplified method of evaluating dose-effect experiments. *J. Pharmacol. Exp. Therap. 96*:99 (1949).

[6] Unsubstantiated descriptions of bizarre drug reactions abound in the literature and are repeated in textbooks. It is alleged, for example, without adequate documentation, that infants are extraordinarily sensitive to morphine, and also that they are frequently ex-cited rather than sedated by barbiturates. Likewise, some adults are said to be extraordinarily sensitive to quinine, exhibiting full-blown toxicity of the central nervous system (cinchonism) at fantastically small doses.

That gene mutations may abolish the synthesis of specific proteins or cause the production of altered proteins is now well established. Although the complete absence of a given protein need not necessarily be incompatible with life, it will often be so. Therefore, the mutations that find phenotypic expression as genetically abnormal individuals are only a selection of all possible mutations. Included are those protein deletions that are not lethal, as well as a wide variety of modified proteins, usually altered by single amino acid substitutions. Prototypic of this kind of genetic modification is the slight alteration of hemoglobin structure that causes sickle cell anemia.[7] Here, one amino acid (valine) is substituted for another (glutamic acid) at position 6 on the β-chain. Although this new *hemoglobin S* is functional in oxygen transport, it undergoes an abnormal molecular aggregation, damaging to the integrity of the erythrocyte, at low oxygen tension.[8, 8a] Isozymes fall into the same category. These are modified enzymes, still functional, but displaying altered affinities for substrates and inhibitors, altered reaction velocities, changes in state of aggregation or allosteric interaction, or modified responses to temperature and ionic environment.

In view of the importance of proteins to all aspects of drug action it is not surprising that an altered phenotype should be the basis of an idiosyncratic drug reaction. Indeed, the phenotypic abnormality is often first revealed by a person's abnormal response to a drug, so that drugs prove to be excellent tools for the discovery of hitherto unsuspected hereditary defects. We can devise, a priori, a classification of mechanisms of drug idiosyncrasy, based upon the general principles relating drugs to proteins. Thus, for example, if a drug's action is terminated primarily by metabolic degradation, then genetic modification of the degradative enzyme could prolong or shorten the drug action to an abnormal degree. Table 6-1 lists six mechanisms, with examples of each one. The list includes all the drug idiosyncrasies whose mechanisms are at all well understood. These will be discussed in the remainder of this section.

First a few words of explanation are in order about the nomenclature used to describe the mode of inheritance of a drug idiosyncrasy.[9] The term *sex linked* describes a trait carried on the X chromosome. If the male (whose sex chromosome pattern is XY) carries one allele for the trait, he has no normal allele; he is said to be *hemizygous*. The female (XX) carrying a sex-linked abnormality may be *heterozygous* or *homozygous* for the trait. The term *autosomal* refers to a trait carried on any of the 22

[7] L. PAULING, H. A. ITANO, S. J. SINGER, and I. C. WELLS: Sickle cell anemia, a molecular disease. *Science 110:*543 (1949).

[8] M. F. PERUTZ: *Proteins and Nucleic Acids.* Amsterdam, Elsevier Publishing Co., 1962.

[8a] M. MURAYAMA: Molecular mechanism of red cell 'sickling." *Science 153:*145 (1966).

[9] C. STERN: *Principles of Human Genetics,* 2nd ed. San Francisco, W. H. Freeman, 1960.

TABLE 6-1. Mechanisms and examples of drug idiosyncrasies

Type of pharmacologic abnormality	Drug	Genetic basis	Disease or trait	Mode of hereditary transmission
1. Abnormally prolonged drug effect	Succinylcholine	Altered plasma cholinesterase	Succinylcholine apnea of long duration	Autosomal autonomous
	Nitrites and other drugs that cause methemoglobinemia	Deficient NADH methemoglobin reductase	Hereditary methemoglobinemia	Autosomal recessive
	Isoniazid, certain other drugs that are metabolized by acetylation	Deficient liver acetyl transferase	Increased toxicity of isoniazid and related drugs	Autosomal recessive
2. Increased sensitivity to drug effect	Nitrites and other drugs that cause methemoglobinemia	Abnormal hemoglobins (S and H)	Propensity to develop methemoglobinemia	Autosomal; hemoglobin S autonomous, not known if heterozygotes sensitive to methemoglobinemia-producing drugs; hemoglobin H recessive
3. Novel drug effect	Primaquine and other drugs	Deficient glucose-6-phosphate dehydrogenase in erythrocytes	Favism, drug-induced hemolytic anemia	Sex-linked autonomous
	Barbiturates and other drugs	Abnormal inducibility of δ-aminolevulinic acid synthetase	Hepatic porphyria	Autosomal dominant
4. Decreased responsiveness to drug	Coumarin anticoagulants	?	Warfarin resistance	Autosomal dominant

	Vitamin D (calcium?)	?	Vitamin D-resistant rickets	Sex-linked dominant
	Phenylthiourea (PTC)	Altered chemoreceptors?	Nontasters (association with thyroid disease?)	Autosomal recessive
	Vitamin B$_{12}$	Absence of intrinsic factor	Poor absorption of vitamin B$_{12}$ = juvenile pernicious anemia	?
	Succinylcholine	Isozyme of plasma cholinesterase with high activity	Resistance to succinylcholine paralysis	Autosomal autonomous
	Atropine	Presence of atropine esterase (rabbits)	Atropine resistance	Autosomal autonomous
	Insulin	Presence of insulinase (mice)	Insulin resistance	Multigenic
	Mydriatic agents	?	Racial differences in drug effectiveness	?
5. Abnormal distribution of drug	Copper	Deficient ceruloplasmin	Wilson's disease	Autosomal recessive
	Iron	Increased tissue ferritin (hemosiderin)	Hemochromatosis	?
	Thyroxine	Increased or decreased thyroid-binding globulin	Elevated or depressed protein-bound iodine	Autosomal dominant
6. Differences in use of and response to psychotropic drugs (?)	Caffeine, nicotine, others	?	Differences in drug habituation and abuse (?)	?

pairs of chromosomes (in man) other than X or Y; here, the ordinary principles of heterozygosity or homozygosity apply to both sexes. With reference to the inheritance of a trait, the terms *dominant, codominant, recessive* are meaningful. If the trait is expressed in heterozygotes as well as in homozygotes, it is called dominant. If alternative expressions of the trait are possible, each independent of the others, it is called codominant; a classical example is blood group, in which alleles A and B are codominant over O, so that genotypes AO and BO belong to blood groups A and B, respectively (dominance), but genotype AB has both blood group antigens A and B (codominance). Finally, if the trait is only expressed in homozygotes, or (if sex linked) in hemizygotes, it is called recessive.

Difficulties arise in applying the terminology of classical genetics to traits in which the underlying molecular abnormalities are understood. Let us consider a drug idiosyncrasy that depends upon the presence of an altered enzyme. And suppose, as is often true, that alleles for altered forms of the enzyme are independently expressed, i.e., that the allelic forms of the gene are *autonomous,* so that each gives rise to its corresponding gene product, the enzyme. At the molecular level the abnormalities are inherited without dominance (autonomously); but if one looks at the drug idiosyncrasy, various results are possible. The heterozygote will contain normal enzyme and altered enzyme. If the normal enzyme suffices to protect against expression of the idiosyncrasy, then responses to the drug will be normal in heterozygotes and abnormal in homozygotes, and the trait will be described as recessive. On the other hand, if the presence of altered enzyme suffices to confer the idiosyncratic response, then heterozygotes and homozygotes will both display the trait, and it will be described as dominant. Finally, in the same example, if attention is focused upon the enzymes (as upon blood group substances in the earlier example), then the inheritance would be described as "without dominance," or codominant, since each allelic form of the gene is independently expressed. Whenever use of the older nomenclature would be confusing, we shall avoid terminologic ambiguities by stating in which genotypes each drug idiosyncrasy is expressed, and then describing separately how the gene products are determined, if known.

ABNORMALLY PROLONGED DRUG EFFECT

Succinylcholine Hydrolysis

This drug is a depolarizing type of neuromuscular blocking agent, widely used to produce muscular relaxation during surgical procedures (p. 49). The deserved popularity of succinylcholine rests upon its very rapid metabolic degradation by the cholinesterase of plasma and liver (acylcholine acyl-hydrolase, sometimes called "pseudocholinesterase").

The drug level, established quickly by intravenous infusion and maintained readily, drops rapidly within a few minutes after the infusion is discontinued. The degradative reaction is a simple hydrolysis to the pharmacologically inert succinylmonocholine:

$$(CH_3)_3\overset{+}{N}-CH_2CH_2-O\underset{\uparrow}{-}\overset{O}{\overset{\|}{C}}CH_2CH_2\overset{O}{\overset{\|}{C}}-O-CH_2CH_2-\overset{+}{N}(CH_3)_3$$

choline $\underset{\text{hydrolysis}}{\uparrow}$ succinylmonocholine

succinylcholine (succinyldicholine)

Occasional patients manifest a bizarre response to succinylcholine, a prolonged muscular relaxation and apnea lasting as long as several hours after discontinuance of the infusion. Investigation revealed that many of these individuals have an atypical plasma cholinesterase.[2]

The atypical cholinesterase hydrolyzes various substrates at considerably reduced rates. This alone might suggest merely that the amount of enzyme is reduced. However, the entire pattern of affinities for substrates and inhibitors differs from the normal. Figure 6-1 illustrates this pattern for succinylcholine as a substrate (Fig. 6-1a), and also for succinylcholine as an inhibitor of the hydrolysis of benzoylcholine (Fig. 6-1b). It can be seen that the affinity of the atypical enzyme for succinylcholine is more than 100-fold decreased compared with the normal. The concentrations of succinylcholine that are used clinically to produce neuromuscular paralysis during anesthesia are well below those required to saturate the enzyme. Consequently, the reduced affinity of the abnormal enzyme for succinylcholine is sufficient cause of the abnormally prolonged duration of action of the drug in patients with atypical cholinesterase.

It has proved convenient to use dibucaine, a local anesthetic that is completely stable in the presence of cholinesterase, to characterize the enzyme. The affinity of dibucaine as an inhibitor of the normal cholinesterase is about 20 times its affinity for the atypical enzyme. Under arbitrarily standardized conditions, with benzoylcholine as substrate and dibucaine at $10^{-5}M$, the rate of hydrolysis of benzoylcholine by the normal enzyme is inhibited about 80 per cent, but the atypical cholinesterase is but little affected. The per cent inhibition by dibucaine under these conditions is called the "dibucaine number." The results of testing a large number of randomly selected people are shown in Fig. 6-2a. Most of the subjects clustered in a roughly normal distribution around dibucaine number 78, with a remarkably small coefficient of variation (about 4 per cent). A small group had intermediate dibucaine numbers in the range 40 to 70; there was no overlap with the normal range. Two subjects had very low dibucaine numbers (less than 20). In investigations on an even larger scale it has been found that the incidence of very low dibucaine numbers is about

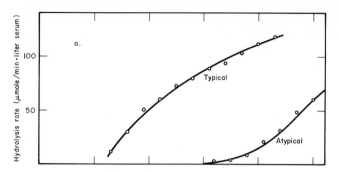

Succinylcholine was used as substrate. Hydrolysis rate was measured by a titrimetric procedure at pH 7.0 and 30°; results for the typical enzyme are shown at left, those for the atypical enzyme at right.

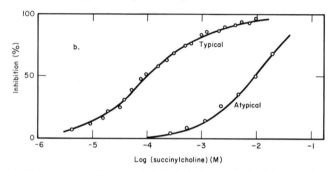

Succinylcholine was used as an inhibitor of the hydrolysis of benzoylcholine, measured by a spetrophotometric method. Results with typical enzyme are shown at left, results with atypical enzyme at right.

FIG. 6-1.   INTERACTIONS OF SUCCINYLCHOLINE WITH PLASMA CHOLINESTERASE. (*From Kalow, Figs. 19 and 21.*[2])

1 in 3,000, and these people invariably respond to succinylcholine by prolonged paralysis.

Family studies leave little doubt that the presence of atypical cholinesterase is a genetically determined characteristic. Very low dibucaine numbers correspond to the homozygous condition. Intermediate values apparently arise from plasma containing a mixture of normal and atypical enzyme. This is indicated, for example, in Fig. 6-3, where inhibition curves are shown for plasma with normal, intermediate, and low dibucaine numbers. The behavior of the "intermediate" plasma is what would be expected of a mixture; inhibition is first manifested at the very low inhibitor concentration to which the normal plasma responds, but complete inhibition is approached only at the very high concentrations required by the atypical enzyme. Figure 6-2b shows the results of dibucaine studies of families of subjects with low or intermediate dibucaine numbers. The frequencies of low and intermediate dibucaine numbers are very much greater than in the population as a whole. All the data are compatible with the existence

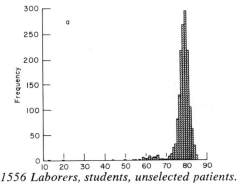

1556 Laborers, students, unselected patients.

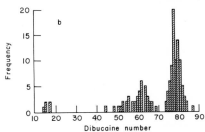

135 Members of 9 families of individuals known to have low or intermediate dibucaine numbers.

FIG. 6-2. FREQUENCY DISTRIBUTION OF DIBUCAINE NUMBERS. *Dibucaine numbers represent per cent inhibition of plasma cholinesterase activity by dibucaine at a fixed concentration in a standardized test, with benzoylcholine as substrate. (From Kalow, Fig. 22.[2])*

of two allelic autosomal autonomous genes. Thus, the defect occurs in, and is transmitted by, both sexes. Homozygous normals produce a given quantity of the normal enzyme, individuals homozygous for the abnormal gene produce only atypical cholinesterase. Heterozygotes produce a mixture of the enzymes, much as carriers of sickle cell trait produce both hemoglobins A and S.[9] The primary amino acid sequence of the enzyme has not yet been determined, and the exact nature of the genetic abnormality is not yet clarified at the molecular level.

The gene for atypical cholinesterase has a widespread distribution throughout the world. Application of the Hardy-Weinberg law (p. 272) to the frequencies of the phenotypes leads to estimates of the gene frequency of about 2 per cent in all the population groups studied, including British, Greek, Portuguese, North African, Jewish, and Asiatic ethnic groups, and Australian aboriginals.[10] This uniformity is rather unusual and contrasts sharply with some of the drug idiosyncrasies to be discussed

[10] H. LEHMANN and J. LIDDELL: "Genetical variants of human serum pseudo-cholinesterase," *Progress in Medical Genetics, 3:*75 (1964).

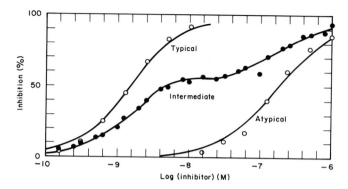

FIG. 6-3.   INHIBITION OF PLASMA CHOLINESTERASE BY A NEOSTIGMINE ANA-
LOGUE.   *The inhibitor used was an analogue of neostigmine known by the code
name Ro2-0683. The substrate was benzoylcholine. The per cent inhibition of
enzyme activity is shown for three kinds of plasma. At left, typical plasma; at*
right, *atypical plasma;* middle curve, *plasma with intermediate dibucaine number. (Modified from Kalow, Fig. 25.[2])*

later. It implies lack of any selective pressure related to geographic or
ethnic differences.

Other variants of the plasma cholinesterase have been discovered.
The atypical cholinesterase already discussed is relatively insensitive to a
number of inhibitors other than dibucaine; one of these is the fluoride ion.
In family studies it was found that some individuals had enzyme with
normal or almost normal sensitivity to dibucaine inhibition but resistance
to fluoride inhibition. The fluoride resistance was shown to be determined
by an independent allele by demonstrating its segregation, as follows. In
two families fluoride-resistant, dibucaine-resistant males mated to homozygous normal females had two kinds of children: fluoride-resistant but not
dibucaine-resistant, or dibucaine-resistant but not fluoride-resistant; of ten
children of such matings not one was of the same phenotype as either
parent. Only the homozygote for fluoride resistance exhibits prolonged
apnea when exposed to succinylcholine,[11, 12] just as is true of the dibucaine-
resistant atypical enzyme variant.

Another variant discovered through family studies is the so-called
"silent" gene, apparently an *amorphic* allele for this enzyme, i.e., one that
determines no gene product at all or an enzyme protein so altered as to be
completely inactive. Evidence for the presence of this allele is the existence
of individuals who should be heterozygotes according to the presumed
genotypes of their parents, yet who seem to be homozygotes. Figure 6-4a
presents an illustration of this variant. The two females III-1 and III-2
(the *propositi,* i.e., the subjects who first came to the attention of the in-

[11] J. LIDDELL, H. LEHMANN, and D. DAVIES: Harris and Whittaker's pseudocholinesterase variant with increased resistance to fluoride. *Acta Genet. Statist. Med. 13:*95 (1963).
[12] M. WHITTAKER: The pseudocholinesterase variants: esterase levels and increased
resistance to fluoride. *Acta Genet. Statist. Med. 14:*281 (1964).

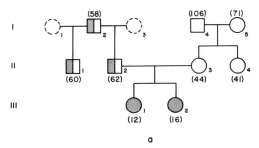

Classification of the phenotypes according to dibucaine number. Squares, *males;* circles, *females;* open symbols, *normal dibucaine number* (*presumed normal homozygote*); shaded symbols, *abnormally low dibucaine number* (*presumed abnormal homozygote*); half-shaded symbols, *intermediate dibucaine number* (*presumed heterozygote*). *Numbers in parenthesis are not dibucaine numbers but units of activity of the plasma cholinesterase, normal range 60 to 125. Symbols shown with* broken lines *signify individuals not tested.*

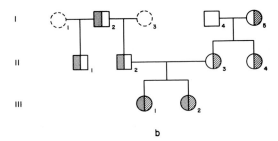

Same family as above, reclassified according to the hypothesis of an amorphic allele. Here, open symbols signify normal allele, solid symbols atypical allele, and hatched symbols amorphic allele.

FIG. 6-4. INHERITANCE OF THE AMORPHIC ALLELE OF THE PLASMA CHOLIN-ESTERASE GENE. (*From Lehmann and Liddell, Figs. 12 and 13.*[10] *By permission of Grune & Stratton.*)

vestigators) had abnormally low dibucaine numbers and extremely low enzyme activity; they appeared to be atypical homozygotes. Their father (II-2), their grandfather (I-2), and their paternal uncle (II-1) all were, as expected, heterozygotes for the atypical enzyme (dibucaine numbers and enzyme activities were both intermediate). Their mother (II-3), however, and their maternal grandmother (I-5) and maternal aunt (II-4) presented an unusual pattern. They had enzyme activities in the intermediate range; but their dibucaine numbers were normal rather than intermediate (as would have been expected for ordinary heterozygotes). This and other instances of a peculiar inheritance pattern[12a] has led to the interpretation

12a H. W. GOEDDE, D. GEHRING and R. A. HOFMANN: Biochemische Untersuchungen zur Frage der Existenz eines "silent Gene" im Polymorphismus der Pseudocholinesterasen. *Humangenetik 1:*607 (1965).

diagrammed in Fig. 6-4b. It is assumed that the individuals with low cholinesterase activity but normal sensitivity to dibucaine have one allele for normal cholinesterase and one amorphic ("silent") allele. Then, as shown, the paradoxes are resolved; the two daughters carry one atypical allele and one amorphic allele. The concept of a "silent" allele is supported strongly by the discovery of a woman completely lacking in plasma cholinesterase activity, presumably a homozygote for this allele. Married to a normal homozygote, this subject has given birth to two children, both with low plasma cholinesterase activity.

The role of the various genotypes in determining the idiosyncratic response to succinylcholine is indicated in a recent study of 78 patients who displayed prolonged apnea after receiving the drug.[13] Enzyme activity was determined with acetylcholine as substrate; in this method the normal range is 72 to 166 units. Dibucaine and fluoride numbers were also determined. The genotypes were deduced from the results of these determinations and confirmed in family studies in about one-quarter of the cases. The frequencies of the various genotypes and the activities of plasma cholinesterase in each group are shown in Table 6-2; note that these genotype frequencies refer to the special patient group, not to the population as a whole. Atypical homozygotes comprised 38 per cent of the patient group, whereas the frequency of this genotype in the population as a whole is about 1 in 3,000. Curiously, one-third of all the patients who experienced prolonged apnea were of normal genotype with normal plasma cholinesterase activity.

TABLE 6-2.   Genotype frequencies and cholinesterase activity in patients with succinylcholine apnea

Cholinesterase activity was determined with acetylcholine as substrate; normal range is 72 to 166 units. Mean ± standard deviation is shown. Genotypes were deduced from inhibition studies with dibucaine and fluoride. (From Thompson and Whittaker,[13] Table I.)

Genotype	Plasma cholinesterase activity	Per cent of total
Normal-normal	86.1 ± 25.4	32.1
Normal-atypical	62.7 ± 19.6	12.8
Normal-fluoride resistant	88.0 ± 29.4	7.7
Atypical-fluoride resistant	64.7 ± 15.0	9.1
Atypical-atypical	40.5 ± 8.6	38.5

[13] J. C. THOMPSON and M. WHITTAKER: A study of the pseudocholinesterase in 78 cases of apnoea following suxamethonium. *Acta Genet. Statist. Med.* 16:209 (1966).

Electrophoretic investigations have revealed yet another cholinesterase variant. In normal plasma the cholinesterase activity migrates in an electrophoretic field as four bands. Chromatography of these bands by a molecular sieving technique revealed that molecules of different sizes were represented.[14,15] Presumably these are isozymes of the normal enzyme, perhaps in different states of aggregation. Occasionally, a plasma was found that yielded an additional band in electrophoresis. The cholinesterase activity in such cases was about 30 per cent higher than normal; the sensitivity to inhibition by dibucaine or fluoride was not decreased. Since normal cholinesterase is present as well as an additional activity represented by the unusual electrophoretic band, it could not be expected that these individuals would show any unusual response to succinylcholine; an increase of this magnitude in the rate of destruction of succinylcholine would in all likelihood escape detection in view of its already rapid metabolism. Family studies indicated that the abnormality was transmitted as an autosomal autonomous characteristic. About 5 per cent of healthy British subjects had this variant in their plasma.[16]

The current state of knowledge about plasma cholinesterase variants and their relationship to succinylcholine idiosyncrasy is summarized in Table 6-3.

Hereditary Methemoglobinemia

A somewhat different example of how an abnormally prolonged drug effect can arise on the basis of a genetic defect is found in hereditary methemoglobinemia.[17,18] Here, nitrites and other drugs that cause methemoglobinemia (e.g., aniline derivatives) have an unexpectedly long duration of action because one of the enzymes involved in the reduction of methemoglobin to hemoglobin in erythrocytes is absent. Ordinarily, there is a small steady-state level of methemoglobin (about 1 per cent of total hemoglobin), presumably arising by spontaneous oxidation of Fe^{++} to Fe^{+++} in the hemoglobin molecules. The ferric iron is continuously re-

---

14 H. HARRIS, D. A. HOPKINSON, and E. B. ROBSON: Two-dimensional electrophoresis of pseudocholinesterase components in normal human serum. *Nature* 196:1296 (1962).

15 H. HARRIS and E. B. ROBSON: Fractionation of human serum cholinesterase components by gel filtration. *Biochim. Biophys. Acta* 73:649 (1963).

16 H. HARRIS, D. A. HOPKINSON, E. B. ROBSON, and M. WHITTAKER: Genetical studies on a new variant of serum cholinesterase detected by electrophoresis. *Ann. Human Genet.* 26:359 (1963).

17 P. S. GERALD and E. M. SCOTT: "The Hereditary Methemoglobinemias," in *The Metabolic Basis of Inherited Disease,* 2nd ed., ed. by J. B. Stanbury, J. B. Wyngaarden, and D. S. Fredrickson. New York, McGraw-Hill, 1966, pp. 1090–1099.

18 W. KALOW: "Human Hereditary Defects with Altered Drug Response," in *Pharmacogenetics: Heredity and the Response to Drugs,* Philadelphia, W. B. Saunders, 1962, pp. 146–205.

TABLE 6-3.   The principal variants of plasma cholinesterase

Enzyme activity was measured with benzoylcholine as substrate. Dibucaine and fluoride numbers are per cent inhibition by these substances under standard conditions. (Data compiled from Lehmann and Liddell, Table 4[10] and Harris et al.[16] By permission of Grune & Stratton.)

Type of enzyme	Enzyme activity (units/ml)	Subject's response to succinylcholine	Dibucaine number	Fluoride number
Normal	60–125	Rapid hydrolysis	71–83	57–68
"Atypical"				
heterozygote	26–90	Rapid hydrolysis	52–69	42–55
homozygote	< 35	Prolonged apnea	15–25	20–25
"Fluoride-resistant"				
heterozygote	Normal	Rapid hydrolysis	71–78	50–55
homozygote	Normal	Prolonged apnea	64,67	34,35
"Silent gene"				
heterozygote	Variably decreased	Rapid hydrolysis		
homozygote (1 case)	None	Prolonged apnea		
Electrophoretic variant (five bands instead of four)	About 30% higher than normal	Rapid hydrolysis	Normal	Normal

duced again by four different reductive mechanisms in the red cell.[19] Three of these mechanisms utilize ascorbic acid, glutathione, or NADPH as the reducing agents. The fourth and most important is NADH methemoglobin reductase. This enzyme is alternately oxidized by methemoglobin and reduced by NADH, whereby methemoglobin is reduced to hemoglobin. In hereditary methemoglobinemia the NADH methemoglobin reductase is absent.[20] The trait is due to an autosomal recessive allele, so the disease is manifested in homozygotes of either sex. It is ordinarily detected by the presence of cyanosis at birth. Any drug that tends to produce methemoglobin can be dangerous in subjects with this genetic defect and should be avoided if possible. A listing of such drugs is provided in Table 6-4.

Figure 6-5 illustrates the effect of a single dose of sodium nitrite in a person with hereditary methemoglobinemia and in a normal person. The amount of methemoglobin formed was about the same in both subjects, but whereas it had all but disappeared within 6 hours in the normal, there was no conversion whatsoever in the abnormal subject. The thera-

[19] J. W. HARRIS: *The Red Cell.* Cambridge, Harvard University Press, 1963.

[20] E. M. SCOTT: The relation of diaphorase of human erythrocytes to inheritance of methemoglobinemia. *J. Clin. Invest. 39:*1176 (1960).

TABLE 6-4. **Drugs that can cause methemogobinemia**

(Adapted from Prankerd,[21] tables pp. 139, 140. By permission of Charles C Thomas.)

Direct oxidants (effective in vitro and in vivo)
nitrites
nitrates (reduced to nitrite by bacteria in gut)
chlorates
quinones
methylene blue (high doses)

Indirect oxidants (scarcely effective in vitro, but effective in vivo)
arylamino and arylnitro compounds
aniline
acetanilid
acetophenetidin
nitrobenzenes
nitrotoluenes
sulfonamides

peutic management of methemoglobinemia in these individuals follows the principles outlined elsewhere (p. 419); methylene blue and oxygen are the agents of choice.

Slow Metabolism of Isoniazid

Isoniazid and related drugs are inactivated by acetylation. The slow acetylation phenomenon, resulting from a genetically determined reduced

FIG. 6-5. EFFECT OF NITRITE UPON A PATIENT WITH HEREDITARY METHEMO-GLOBINEMIA. *At zero time 0.5 g sodium nitrite was injected intravenously in a normal subject and in a patient with this hereditary disease. Increase in blood methemoglobin content is shown on vertical axis. (From Eder et al., Fig. 5.[22])*

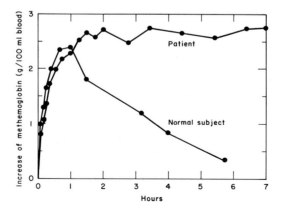

21 T. A. J. PRANKERD: *The Red Cell.* Springfield, Mass., Charles C Thomas, 1961.
22 H. A. EDER, C. FINCH, and R. W. MC KEE: Congenital methemoglobinemia. A clinical and biochemical study of a case. *J. Clin. Invest. 28:*265 (1949).

amount of a liver acetyl transferase,[22a, 22b] has been discussed fully in chapter 3. When isoniazid is given in ordinary doses to people with this enzyme deficiency, it accumulates to toxic levels and serious neuropathies can result.[23] The defect is transmitted as an autosomal recessive trait.

INCREASED SENSITIVITY TO DRUG

Abnormal Hemoglobins

The genetically altered hemoglobins may confer abnormal sensitivity to nitrites and other drugs that cause methemoglobinemia, even though the reductive processes in the erythrocytes are normally operative. In sickle cell anemia the replacement of glutamic acid by valine at position 6 in both β-chains results in a hemoglobin that appears to be normal when it is carrying oxygen, but forms molecular aggregates in the absence of oxygen.[8a] This change in the properties of hemoglobin causes a grossly visible "sickling" of the erythrocytes at low oxygen tension; and such erythrocytes agglutinate in the capillaries and are subject to lysis. The details of the dependence of erythrocyte integrity upon the properties of hemoglobin are still not worked out. Hemoglobin M, like hemoglobin S, differs from normal hemoglobin A by a single amino acid residue,[8] but the replacement may occur at several different positions. Histidine at position 58 on the α-chain or position 63 on the β-chain may be replaced by tyrosine; valine at position 67 on the β-chain may be replaced by glutamic acid; and there are other forms of this abnormal hemoglobin. At least two of the four iron atoms in hemoglobin M are very readily oxidized to the ferric state. Hemoglobin H consists of four β-chains instead of the usual two α- and two β-subunits. This abnormal hemoglobin is also unusually sensitive to oxidation. The life span of the affected erythrocytes is about 40 days instead of the usual 120 days. Methemoglobin accumulates in the older cells, and they become much more susceptible to lysis. In people with either of these hemoglobin anomalies, the drugs listed in Table 6-4 can be dangerous; sulfonamides, for example, may cause hemolytic anemia.

NOVEL DRUG EFFECT

Primaquine Sensitivity

The antimalarial drug primaquine can ordinarily be administered at a dosage of 30 mg daily with only insignificant side effects. About 5 to

22a J. H. PETERS, K. S. MILLER and P. BROWN: Studies on the metabolic basis for the genetically determined capacities for isoniazid inactivation in man. *J. Pharmacol. Exper. Therap.* 150:298 (1965).

22b J. W. JENNE: Partial purification and properties of the isoniazid transacetylase in human liver. Its relationship to the acetylation of p-aminosalicylic acid. *J. Clin. Invest.* 44:1992 (1965).

23 S. DEVADATTA, P. R. J. GANGADHARAM, R. H. ANDREWS, W. FOX, C. V. RAMAKRISHNAN, J. B. SELKON, and S. VELU: Peripheral neuritis due to isoniazid. *Bull. World Health Organ.* 23:587 (1960).

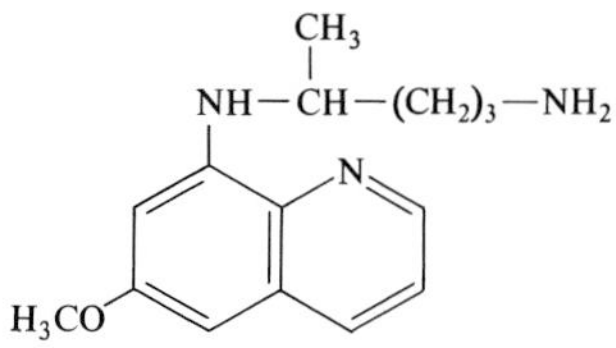

$$\text{H}_3\text{CO} \diagdown \quad \text{NH}-\overset{\overset{\displaystyle \text{CH}_3}{|}}{\text{CH}}-(\text{CH}_2)_3-\text{NH}_2$$

primaquine

10 per cent of Negro males given this normal dosage of primaquine develop a profound acute hemolytic anemia. The response is not merely an exaggerated sensitivity to an ordinary side effect of the drug; even at much higher doses no comparable hemolytic crises could be provoked in white patients of Northern European stock, nor in certain other ethnic groups, although very mild degrees of hemolysis could be detected by laboratory tests.

Radioactive chromic ion (^{51}Cr) is bound so tightly to erythrocytes that it can be used conveniently as a tag to follow the fate of infused red cells. With this technique for studying the defect in primaquine idiosyncrasy, it could be shown[24] that, when cells from reactors were transfused into normal individuals and primaquine was then administered, hemolysis of these labeled erythrocytes occurred. On the other hand, normal cells transfused into reactors were unaffected by the drug. Thus, the abnormality is localized to the erythrocyte.

Radioactive iron (^{59}Fe) can be used to label the newest erythrocytes differentially. With this technique it was shown that in a primaquine reaction only erythrocytes older than about 55 days are hemolyzed. A single dose of ^{59}Fe was administered. A few days later a challenging dose of primaquine caused hemolysis but no release of ^{59}Fe. Thus, only the older erythrocytes were lysed, not those that had been produced in the presence of the radioactive iron. By giving the primaquine challenge to different subjects at various times after the ^{59}Fe, it was found that radioactive cells were lysed after about 55 days. This explained the clinical observation that even massive hemolytic episodes were self-limiting; recovery occurs despite continued drug administration (Fig. 6-6). After a long enough drug-free interval, however, primaquine is again capable of inducing a hemolytic crisis.

Reactors develop hemolytic anemia not only in response to primaquine, but also to acetanilid and other aniline derivatives including sulfanilamide, to naphthalene and its metabolites, to nitrofurantoin and some other nitro compounds. An unidentified compound present in fava beans also provokes a hemolytic crisis in sensitive individuals; hence the name *favism*

---

24 E. BEUTLER: The hemolytic effect of primaquine and related compounds: a review. *Blood 14*:103 (1959).

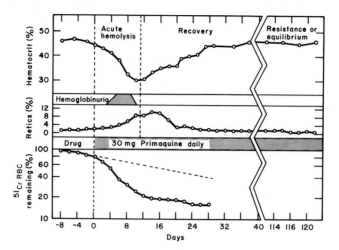

FIG. 6-6. CLINICAL COURSE OF PRIMAQUINE-INDUCED HEMOLYTIC ANEMIA. *Composite data from three Negro male reactors with similar degree of glucose-6-phosphate dehydrogenase (G6PD) deficiency. Primaquine was started at day zero. Eight days before, each subject had been injected with a sample of his own erythrocytes labeled with ^{51}Cr. Hematocrit is shown at* top, *reticulocytes at* middle, *red cell survival at* bottom. Broken line *represents normal course of erythrocyte destruction. Note hemoglobinuria at height of hemolytic crisis. (From Kellermeyer et al., Fig. 1.[25] By permission of C. V. Mosby, originally from the* Bulletin of the World Health Organization 22:625, 1960.)

is also given to this genetic anomaly. A list of agents that can induce hemolytic anemia in this condition is given in Table 6-5.

Some of the active compounds cause hemolysis of reactor cells in vitro, but others evidently have to be metabolized first, since they are inactive in vitro. Naphthalene is in this latter category, whereas its oxidation products, α- and β-naphthol, are active both in vivo and in vitro. Primaquine itself is not very effective in vitro; presumably a metabolite is the active hemolytic agent. It has long been known that aniline and nitro compounds are capable of causing hemolytic anemia; therefore it is of great practical importance to recognize that all these hemolytic reactions, as well as favism, can be manifestations of the same idiosyncrasy. On the other hand, some of the same drugs at very high doses can cause hemolysis of normal erythrocytes. Primaquine itself can produce some hemolysis in normal subjects at 120 mg daily, four times the usual dosage. Combined with high doses of acetanilid, it regularly causes a severe hemolytic reaction. Finally, phenylhydrazine, in high dosage, is well known to cause serious

    25 R. W. KELLERMEYER, A. R. TARLOV, S. L. SCHRIER, P. E. CARSON, and A. S. ALVING: The hemolytic effect of primaquines. XIII. Gradient susceptibility to hemolysis of prima-quine-sensitive erythrocyte. *J. Lab. Clin. Med.* 58:225 (1961).

TABLE 6-5. **Agents reported to be capable of inducing hemolytic anemia in subjects with genetically determined idiosyncratic susceptibility**

(Adapted from Marks and Banks,[26] Table 3.)

Primaquine	Quinine
Pamaquine	Quinidine
Pentaquine	*p*-Aminosalicylic acid
Quinocide	Antipyrine
Sulfanilamide	Probenecid
Sulfapyridine	Acetanilid
Sulfisoxazole	Phenylhydrazine
Sulfacetamide	Acetophenetidin
Sulfamethoxypyridazine	Pyramidone
Salicylazosulfapyridine	Chloroquine
Sulfones (sulfoxone)	Chloramphenicol
Naphthalene	Fava bean
Methylene blue	Viral respiratory infections
Vitamin K	Infectious hepatitis
Acetylsalicylic acid	Infectious mononucleosis
Nitrofurantoin	Bacterial pneumonias and septicemias (e.g.,
Furazoladone	typhoid)
	Diabetic acidosis
	Uremia

hemolytic crises in all exposed individuals; indeed, in animals it is used experimentally to destroy red cells and thereby provoke a massive synthesis of reticulocytes.

One of the most effective hemolytic agents, acetylphenylhydrazine, can be used in vitro for identification of reactor erythrocytes. Under appropriate conditions, in the presence of oxygen and glucose, normal erythrocytes incubated with acetylphenylhydrazine maintain normal levels of reduced glutathione (GSH). Under the same conditions GSH levels of reactor cells show a profound decline (Fig. 6-7), presumably through conversion to oxidized glutathione (GSSG). Apparently, deficiency of sulfhydryl compounds like GSH in the red cells can cause hemolysis, because agents that bind or oxidize —SH groups are hemolytic for both normal and reactor cells. The in vitro acetylphenylhydrazine test has proved extremely useful in predicting those who will react adversely to primaquine and related drugs, and in carrying out family studies to establish the genetic basis of the abnormality.

The basis of the curious GSH instability in response to hemolytic drugs remained obscure until it was discovered that reactor cells have a

26 P. A. MARKS and J. BANKS: Drug-induced hemolytic anemias associated with glucose-6-phosphate dehydrogenase deficiency: a genetically heterogeneous trait. *Ann. N. Y. Acad. Sci. 123:*198 (1965).

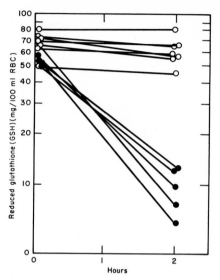

FIG. 6-7. THE ACETYLPHENYLHYDRAZINE TEST FOR PRIMAQUINE SENSITIVITY
OF ERYTHROCYTES. *Gluthathione content was measured initially and after 2
hours of incubation with acetylphenylhydrazine (5 mg/ml).* Open circles *are
erythrocytes from normal subjects,* solid circles *are erythrocytes from primaquine-sensitive subjects. (From Beutler, Fig. 4.*[24] *By permission of Grune &
Stratton.)*

deficiency in the enzyme glucose-6-phosphate dehydrogenase (G6PD).
No other enzyme activity thus far examined is depressed. Glutathione reductase and G6PD are apparently coupled systems:

$$GSSG + NADPH + H^+ \xrightarrow[\text{reductase}]{\text{GSSG}} 2\,GSH + NADP^+$$

$$\text{glucose-6-phosphate} + NADP^+ \xrightarrow{\text{G6PD}}$$
$$\text{6-phosphogluconic acid} + NADPH$$

Figure 6-8 shows the amount of reduced glutathione formed in dialyzed
homogenates of normal and primaquine-sensitive erythrocytes under three
different conditions. In part a, NADPH was supplied, so that the activity
of the glutathione reductase could be measured directly; the homogenates
from the primaquine-sensitive cells behaved normally. In part b, glucose-
6-phosphate and NADP were supplied, so that the reduction of NADP
was prerequisite to the reduction of oxidized glutathione (as shown in the
equation above). Since glucose-6-phosphate was the only other substrate
in the system, its oxidation had to furnish the hydrogen for NADP reduction, and thus the whole reaction was made to depend upon the activity
of the enzyme G6PD. The primaquine-sensitive erythrocytes were obviously

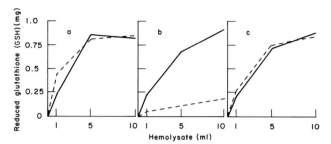

FIG. 6-8. THREE ENZYME ACTIVITIES IN ERYTHROCYTES FROM NORMAL AND PRIMAQUINE-SENSITIVE SUBJECTS. *The amount of reduced glutathione formed from a fixed amount of oxidized glutathione in a fixed time was measured, as a function of the amount of dialyzed hemolysate used. Solid curves are for normal subject, dashed curves are for primaquine-sensitive subject.* a, *NADPH was supplied and the activity of glutathione reductase was measured directly.* b, *Glucose-6-phosphate and NADP were supplied; therefore the reduction of GSSG to GSH was coupled to the activity of G6PD.* c, *6-Phosphogluconate was supplied instead of glucose-6-phosphate, so the GSSG reduction depended on the activity of 6-phosphogluconic dehydrogenase. (From Carson et al., Fig. 1.*[27] *By permission of the American Association for the Advancement of Science.)*

deficient in this enzyme. Finally, in part c, 6-phosphogluconate was supplied; its oxidation now furnished NADPH, and again the homogenates from primaquine-sensitive cells behaved normally. In this way the defect was localized to G6PD alone. Thus, the specific enzyme defect in reactor cells is now known, and a reasonable connection has been established between the resulting inability to utilize glucose in the oxidative pathway to pentose and the inability to maintain GSH needed for the integrity of the erythrocyte.

Random testing of erythrocytes in vitro from Negro subjects has revealed a clear bimodality among males with respect to the residual GSH values at the end of the acetylphenylhydrazine test. Most of the population values clustered at about 60 mg per 100 ml of erythrocytes, with a spread from about 35 to about 100; there were no values at all in the range 20 to 35, but about 15 per cent of the males had GSH contents below 20. In females the results were different. There was a much greater dispersion of data; only about 2 per cent had very low values, and about 5 per cent fell into an intermediate group distinct from the highs and the lows. Families of primaquine reactors were found to have a much higher incidence of low values among males and females, and a much higher incidence of intermediate values among females, than the population as a whole. Primaquine-sensitive fathers had normal sons, but passed the trait to all their daughters. A few color-blind primaquine-sensitive males passed both defective genes

27 P. E. CARSON, C. L. FLANAGAN, C. E. ICKES, and A. S. ALVING: Enzymatic deficiency in primaquine-sensitive erythrocytes. *Science 124:*484 (1956).

together to their daughters (color blindness is known to be carried on the X chromosome).

The pattern of inheritance of this trait is that of an autonomous sex-linked defect. Because males carry the defect on their single X chromosome (they are hemizygous), it is necessarily expressed phenotypically; these are the primaquine-sensitive group, with very low GSH values in the in vitro test. Female heterozygotes have intermediate values because the normal gene on one X chromosome and the defective allele on the other are both expressed. Obviously, heterozygous females will pass the defect to half their sons. Affected males have normal sons because they pass only their Y chromosome to them; and they have heterozygous daughters because they pass the defective X chromosome to all of them. If there were really complete phenotypic expression without dominance, then heterozygotes should fall into a well defined intermediate group, and the frequency of the intermediates would be mathematically determined by the known gene frequency. This does not seem to occur. In the populations studied, more women were found with normal values in the GSH test than would be expected from the frequency of affected males (which, for a sex-linked trait, is the same as the gene frequency). This finding, and the wide dispersion of values, suggest that there is variable expression (variable penetrance), i.e., some other factors influence the degree to which the trait is expressed in identical genotypes.

Subsequent studies have shown that G6PD deficiency is not a simple absence of the enzyme but rather a heterogeneous trait. The levels of enzyme activity, the presence or absence of enzyme in white cells, the affinity of the enzyme for glucose-6-phosphate and for NADP, and the enzyme's pH optimum, thermal stability, and electrophoretic mobility all vary greatly in affected individuals belonging to different ethnic groups (Table 6-6). Evidently the defect can assume a number of allelic forms.

The G6PD abnormality itself appears to be without adverse effect unless the erythrocytes are challenged by certain drugs. From the point of view of genetic theory, however, high incidence of an abnormal gene in a given ethnic group implies some significant survival value for the heterozygotic carrier females.[9] Analogous reasoning with respect to carriers of the sickling trait led to the discovery[28] that such heterozygotes are more resistant to serious forms of malaria than is the normal population. Prepubertal (especially infant) mortality from malaria is considerably lower in those individuals. Reactors to primaquine and fava beans are also found predominantly among groups which live in, or trace their ancestry to, malaria-hyperendemic areas (Table 6-7).[29, 30]

[28] A. C. ALLISON: Malaria in carriers of the sickle-cell trait and in newborn children. *Exper. Parasitol.* 6:418 (1957).

[29] A. C. ALLISON: Glucose-6-phosphate dehydrogenase deficiency in red blood cells of East Africans. *Nature* 186:531 (1960).

[30] A. R. TARLOV, G. J. BREWER, P. E. CARSON, and A. S. ALVING: Primaquine sensitivity. Glucose-6-phosphate dehydrogenase deficiency: an inborn error of metabolism of medical and biological significance. *Arch. Int. Med.* 109:209 (1962).

TABLE 6-6. Properties of glucose-6-phosphate dehydrogenase (G6PD) in deficient subjects belonging to different population groups

Enzyme activity is expressed as per cent of normal. Michaelis constants are indicated for reaction with substrate (G6P) and with coenzyme (NADP). Stability is the thermal stability of enzyme activity when whole hemolysates are incubated. Electrophoretic mobility was measured in starch gel. (Adapted from Marks and Banks,[26] Table 2.)

Ethnic or geographic group	Enzyme activity (% of normal)		Substrate affinities		Stability	Electrophoretic mobility
	Red cells	White cells	K_m G6P	K_m NADP		
Negro males	10–15	Normal or slightly decreased	Normal	Normal	Decreased	Normal fast component missing
Barbieri, males[a] (Northern Italian)	50	Normal	Slightly increased	Increased	Normal	Fast[b]
Sicilian	1–4	Decreased	Slightly increased	Increased	Decreased	—
Sardinian	<1	Decreased	—	—	Decreased markedly	Fast[b]
Sephardic Jew	3–6	Decreased	Slightly decreased	Slightly decreased	Decreased	Normal

[a] An Italian family with a particular kind of G6PD deficiency.
[b] Normal fast and slow components missing; new very fast component present.

TABLE 6-7.   **Incidence of glucose-6-phosphate dehydrogenase deficiency**

(From Marks and Banks,[26] Table 1.)

Group	Incidence (%)
ASHKENAZIC JEWS (males)	0.4
SEPHARDIC JEWS (males)	
Kurds	53
Iraq	24
Persia	15
Cochin	10
Yemen	5
North Africa	< 1–4
ARABS	4
IRANIANS	8
SARDINIANS (males)	4–30
GREEKS (including Cyprus and Crete)	0.7–3
NEGROES	
American	13
Nigerians	10
Bantu	20
Leopoldville	18–23
Bashi	14
Pygmies	4
Watutsi	1–2
ASIATICS	
Chinese	2
Filipinos	13
Indians—Parsees	16
Javanese	3
Micronesians	0–1
AMERICAN INDIANS	
Oyana (males)	16
Carib (males)	2
Peruvian (males)	0
ESKIMOS	0

A curious by-product of the investigations on primaquine was the finding that all newborn infants are susceptible to drug-induced hemolytic anemia.[31] Among the eliciting drugs is menadione and other vitamin K analogues, which are naphthoquinone derivatives; these drugs, given to prevent neonatal hemorrhage, can cause hemolysis. There is apparently no G6PD defect in the erythrocytes of normal infants, but low GSH levels are found. The abnormality persists for only a week or two.

31 W. H. ZINKHAM and B. CHILDS: Effect of vitamin K and naphthalene metabolites on glutathione metabolism of erythrocytes from normal newborns and patients with naphthalene hemolytic anemia. *Amer. J. Dis. Children* 94:420 (1957).

Porphyria

Another example of idiosyncrasy causing a novel response to a drug is the precipitation of acute attacks of porphyria by barbiturates and other drugs.[2] The porphyrias are genetic abnormalities of the regulation of heme synthesis (Fig. 6-9), in which large amounts of heme precursors (δ-aminolevulinic acid and porphobilinogen) are excreted in the urine. These are transformed to porphyrins with deep-red color; and thus the urine of patients with acute porphyria may turn dark on standing, a useful diagnostic criterion. The two main forms of the disease are acute intermittent porphyria (Swedish porphyria) and porphyria cutanea tarda (South African porphyria). Acute attacks are manifested by neurologic disturbances of many kinds (e.g., paralysis, psychosis, peripheral neuritis), acute abdominal pain, hypertension, and tachycardia. In the South African form, there are photosensitivity and cutaneous lesions, and an abnormally high excretion of uroporphyrin I and coproporphyrin I. In the Swedish form, porphobilinogen and δ-aminolevulinic acid are excreted. Both genetic defects are transmitted as autosomal dominant traits. The incidence of the Swedish form is about 1.5 per 100,000 people in Sweden and Australia, much higher in Lapland. The South African form, which can be traced to one Dutch emigrant who settled in Capetown in 1686,[9] may affect as many as 1 per cent of Afrikaners.

Acute attacks of porphyria in people who have the trait can be caused by drugs, and these attacks are sometimes fatal. Most frequently the barbiturates are involved.[32] Drugs that cause this idiosyncratic reaction belong to different chemical classes, but the allyl group is common to many of them. Diallylbarbiturate, allylisopropylbarbiturate, and allylmethylbutylbarbiturate all provoke great increases in porphyrin excretion; and allylisopropylacetylurea (Sedormid) was one of the earliest known offenders. Chloroquine, sulfonamides, aminopyrine, hexachlorobenzene, and other drugs without the allyl group have also been implicated.[33] For obvious reasons it is important to know which drugs do *not* induce attacks of porphyria; known to meet this criterion are ether, morphine, chloral hydrate, and penicillin. A catalogue of "safe" drugs would be useful, not only for patients with porphyria, but for all who have genetic defects in which drug idiosyncrasy is prone to occur.

The biochemical basis of porphyria is evidently an uncontrolled overproduction of porphyrins, principally porphobilinogen, the first pyrrole on the pathway of heme biosynthesis (Fig. 6-9). The enzyme responsible

---

[32] L. EALES and G. C. LINDER: Porphyria—the acute attack. An analysis of 80 cases. *South African Med. J. 36:*284 (1962).

[33] S. GRANICK: Hepatic porphyria and drug-induced or chemical porphyria. *Ann. N. Y. Acad. Sci. 123:*188 (1965).

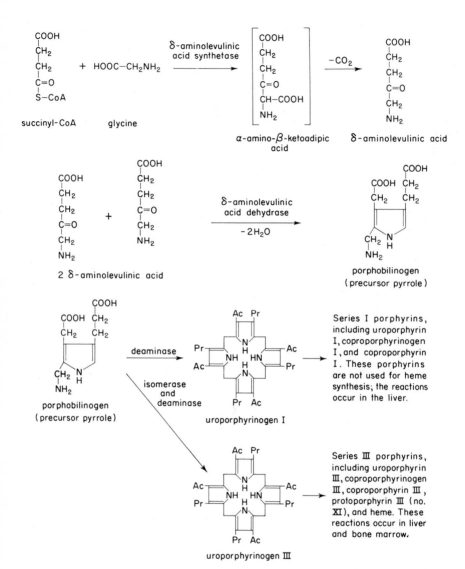

FIG. 6-9. THE PATHWAY OF HEME SYNTHESIS. *The single enzyme carrying out the first two steps of the pathway, δ-aminolevulinic acid synthetase, requires pyridoxal phosphate. The precursor pyrrole, porphobilinogen, is polymerized into either the series I or series III porphyrins. Ac, acetic acid residue; Pr, propionic acid residue.*

for the condensation of glycine and succinyl-CoA is δ-aminolevulinic acid synthetase (ALA synthetase). In the subsequent step, two molecules of δ-aminolevulinic acid are condensed by a second enzyme, δ-aminolevulinic acid dehydrase, to form porphobilinogen. Further enzymic transformations join four porphobilinogen molecules to form a porphyrin skeleton. Side chain modifications yield the several uroporphyrinogens and corresponding uroporphyrins, and the coproporphyrinogens and corresponding coproporphyrins. Eventually, protoporphyrin IX combines with Fe^{++} to form heme.[34] The step mediated by ALA synthetase is rate limiting for the whole pathway. Thus, an increased activity of this enzyme would lead to an increased rate of biosynthesis of the heme precursors.

Several agents that produce acute porphyria in vivo have been shown to cause a large increase in the level of ALA synthetase in the liver of experimental animals.[35] Studies with embryonic chick liver cells in vitro have been especially interesting.[36] Addition of drugs such as mentioned above led to the production of porphyrins detectable by fluorescence microscopy. Porphyrins were also readily formed if δ-aminolevulinic acid was added. Actinomycin D, added to the cultures, blocked the drug-induced porphyrin formation but not that caused by δ-aminolevulinic acid. Since the effect of actinomycin is to prevent DNA-dependent RNA synthesis, it would appear that the direct effect of the drugs was to induce the synthesis of ALA synthetase, and thereby to cause an increase in porphyrin production.

Further elegant studies with the same system of chick-embryo liver cells have considerably strengthened this interpretation.[37] The induction of ALA synthetase was shown to occur only in liver cells and to be reversible on withdrawal of the inducing agents. During induction of this enzyme there was no general increase in protein synthesis, i.e., the inducing effect was a specific one. Moreover, the inducing agents did not prevent the normal breakdown of ALA synthetase, the half-life of which was 4 to 6 hours in the presence or absence of inducers. It is postulated that heme synthesis is normally controlled by a regulatory mechanism that represses the synthesis of ALA synthetase and thereby maintains a low rate of

[34] S. GRANICK and D. MAUZERALL: Porphyrin biosynthesis in erythrocytes. II. Enzymes converting δ-aminolevulinic acid to coproporphyrinogen. *J. Biol. Chem.* 232:1119 (1958).

[35] S. GRANICK and G. URATA: Increase in activity of δ-aminolevulinic acid synthetase in liver mitochondria induced by feeding of 3,5-dicarbethoxy-1,4-dihydrocollidine. *J. Biol. Chem.* 238:821 (1963).

[36] S. GRANICK: Induction of the synthesis of δ-aminolevulinic acid synthetase in liver parenchyma cells in culture by chemicals that induce acute porphyria. *J. Biol. Chem.* 238:PC2247 (1963).

[37] S. GRANICK: The induction in vitro of the synthesis of δ-aminolevulinic acid synthetase in chemical porphyria: a response to certain drugs, sex hormones, and foreign chemicals. *J. Biol. Chem.* 241:1359 (1966).

synthesis of heme. Heme itself is supposed to be the repressor, combining specifically with an aporepressor protein to shut down the function of the operator, so that the operon coding for ALA synthetase will not be transcribed, or will be transcribed at a very low rate.[38] According to this model, the inducing drugs might be expected to displace heme from the aporepressor and thereby increase the rate of transcription. It would be predicted, therefore, that heme itself should be able to overcome the effects of inducers; this has been demonstrated in vitro in the liver cell system.[37] Finally, as shown in Fig. 6-10, a chemical similarity has been proposed, whereby the effective inducers could mimic a part of the heme structure and thereby occupy a portion of the heme site on the aporepressor.

These investigations suggest that the drug idiosyncrasy in porphyria might be the consequence of an altered regulatory mechanism, in which the aporepressor became much more sensitive to derepression by exogenous agents. If it could be shown that the primary amino acid sequence of the synthetase enzyme in patients with porphyria is normal, whereas the amount of enzyme protein is elevated, then the argument that a control

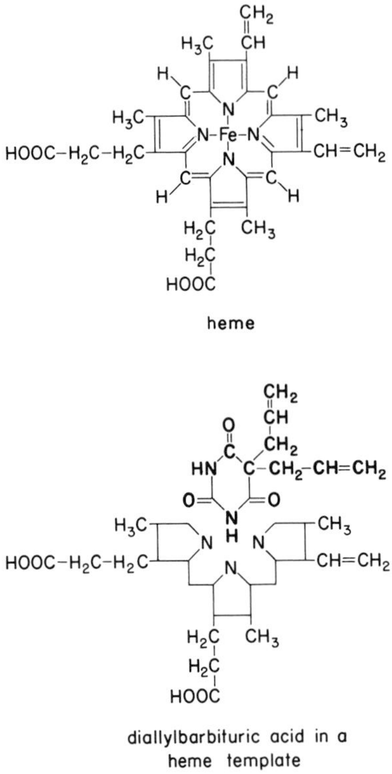

heme

diallylbarbituric acid in a
heme template

FIG. 6-10. POSTULATED CHEMICAL RELATIONSHIP BETWEEN HEME AND A CHEMICAL INDUCER OF PORPHYRIA. *The compound shown below in bold face is diallybarbituric acid, an inducer of porphyria in genetically prone subjects. The structure below shows how the diallybarbituric acid structure could fit into a heme template on the aporepressor. (After Granick, Fig. 6.[37])*

[38] F. JACOB and J. MONOD: Genetic regulatory mechanisms in the synthesis of proteins. *J. Mol. Biol.* 3:318 (1961).

gene has mutated would be strengthened. There are noteworthy differences between hepatic porphyria and most other genetic diseases of man, perhaps again suggesting that an unusual genetic mechanism is at work. The disease is determined by a dominant gene, i.e., the normal allele does not confer protection, as it usually would against a defective protein. The disease may not become apparent until adult life, whereas many genetic defects are manifest at birth. Finally, the disease is characterized by increased activity of an enzyme, whereas most genetic diseases are due to absence or reduced activity of an enzyme or other functional protein.

DECREASED RESPONSIVENESS TO DRUG

Coumarin Resistance

The coumarin anticoagulants inhibit blood clotting by blocking the synthesis of four proteins essential to the clotting process: factors II (prothrombin), VII (proconvertin), IX (plasma thromboplastin component), and X (Stuart-Prower factor). Vitamin K is required for the synthesis of these specific proteins in the liver, and the coumarins antagonize vitamin K competitively. The structures of these compounds were presented in Fig. 5-21, where the close chemical similarity between the coumarins and vitamin K is apparent.

The recent observation[39] that a patient required 20 times the average daily dose of warfarin to maintain the desired prolongation of prothrombin clotting time led to the discovery of a genetic trait that confers resistance to all the coumarins. Figure 6-11 shows a comparison of the

FIG. 6-11. DOSE-RESPONSE RELATIONSHIP FOR WARFARIN IN A NORMAL AND A RESISTANT SUBJECT. *Response is expressed as the minimum level of prothrombin complex activity attained after a single dose, in terms of per cent of normal activity.* Circles *are oral doses,* triangles *are intravenous doses. (From O'Reilly et al., Fig. 2.[39])*

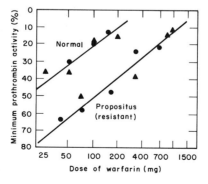

[39] R. A. O'REILLY, P. M. AGGELER, M. S. HOAG, L. S. LEONG, and M. L. KROPATKIN: Hereditary transmission of exceptional resistance to coumarin anticoagulant drugs. The first reported kindred. *New Engl. J. Med. 271:*809 (1964).

responses to warfarin in this patient (the propositus) and a normal subject. The minimum level of prothrombin activity achieved after each dose is plotted against log dose. The striking insensitivity of the propositus is apparent. Since oral and intravenous doses produced equivalent responses, both in the normal subject and in the propositus, it follows that defective absorption is not to blame for the warfarin resistance. Moreover, the rate of disappearance of warfarin, as judged by the return of prothrombin activity to normal levels after discontinuing the drug, was found to be exactly the same in the propositus and in the normal subject. Nor was the extent of protein binding of warfarin unusual in the propositus.

Figure 6-12 shows the effects of a fixed dose of warfarin in normal subjects and in the family of the propositus. Here, the plasma concentration of warfarin and the reduction in prothrombin complex activity were measured 48 hours after a single dose of warfarin (1.5 mg/kg). The familial character of the warfarin resistance is obvious.

Figure 6-13 shows the pedigree of the same family. Individuals displaying warfarin resistance are represented by black symbols. We have

FIG. 6-12. NORMAL AND ABNORMAL RESPONSES TO WARFARIN. *Plasma concentrations of warfarin and prothrombin complex activity were measured 48 hours after single doses of warfarin (1.5 mg/kg) in 16 normal subjects (above), and in eight members of the family of the warfarin-resistant subject (propositus) of Fig. 6-11 (below). Open circles are initial levels of prothrombin complex activity, solid circles are levels after warfarin. Roman and Arabic numerals identify generation and individual respectively, in the coumarin-resistant kindred (cf. Fig. 6-13). (From O'Reilly et al., Fig. 5.[39])*

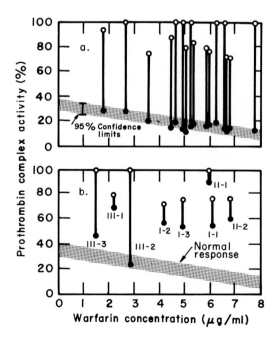

here a trait that (*1*) appears in successive generations, (*2*) appears in both sexes, (*3*) is transmitted by both sexes, and (*4*) in matings between affected and normal individuals is sometimes transmitted and sometimes not. This trait is exceedingly rare. Many thousands of people have been given coumarin anticoagulants, and most of them have been under rigorous laboratory control of their prothrombin clotting times. Yet this family is the only known instance of coumarin resistance. For a rare trait the demonstrated pattern of inheritance can only mean that the trait is autosomal and dominant, for the following reason. If a trait is recessive, then the rarer it is, the lower the probability that the mate of an affected individual will also be carrying the abnormal allele; thus the offspring would be heterozygotes and phenotypically normal. Therefore, a trait that is very rare and appears in successive generations (as in this family) is probably not recessive, and affected individuals are probably heterozygotes. This is a second example (cf. drug-induced porphyria) of an idiosyncratic reaction to drugs determined by a dominant gene.

It has been postulated that vitamin K induces transcription of the messenger-RNA upon which the clotting factor proteins are synthesized.[40] If so, the competitive antagonism by warfarin presumably involves an interaction with the receptor that mediates the action of vitamin K. This receptor could be the DNA itself, or a protein repressor with which vitamin K normally interacts to derepress (i.e., stimulate synthesis of) the prothrombin complex of proteins. According to this view, vitamin K competitively displaces the endogenous repressor (as yet undiscovered), and the coumarin anticoagulants in turn displace vitamin K. The genetic defect would be a modification of this receptor, reducing its affinity for warfarin but not significantly changing its affinity for the vitamin. Such a differential

FIG. 6-13. KINSHIP OF THE COUMARIN-RESISTANT PROPOSITUS OF FIG. 6-11. (*From O'Reilly et al., Fig. 6.*[39])

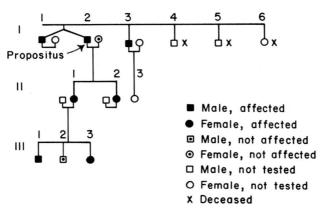

■ Male, affected
● Female, affected
▣ Male, not affected
◉ Female, not affected
□ Male, not tested
○ Female, not tested
X Deceased

40 R. E. OLSON: Vitamin K induced prothrombin formation: antagonism by actinomycin D. *Science 145:*926 (1964).

change of relative affinity for two compounds is analogous to one mechanism of genetically determined sulfonamide resistance in bacteria.[41] The enzyme that normally interacts with *p*-aminobenzoic acid and is inhibited by sulfonamides undergoes a mutational change whereby its affinity for sulfonamides is greatly reduced without a comparable change in its affinity for *p*-aminobenzoic acid. In the case of coumarin resistance, the mutational change appears to affect a regulatory protein rather than any protein involved directly in the clotting process.

Warfarin has been in use as a rodenticide for nearly a quarter of a century. Recently, warfarin resistance has been observed in wild rats in Scotland[42,43] and in Denmark.[44] The same principle applies here as with insect resistance to insecticides and bacterial resistance to antibiotics. If an agent is lethal to most of a population, and if genes conferring resistance are present at all, the strong selective pressure will lead to replacement of the original sensitive population by a resistant one.

Vitamin D-Resistant Rickets

Another instance of decreased responsiveness to a drug is the special form of rickets that is resistant to vitamin D. Now that improved nutrition and vitamin supplementation have reducd the incidence of classical rickets, this form of the disease is recognized more readily. It is characterized by retarded growth and low plasma phosphate levels, with or without skeletal deformities.[45,46] The plasma calcium level is usually not abnormally low, but there is a profound renal loss of phosphate. These abnormalities do not respond to ordinary doses of vitamin D even when given systematically; but huge doses of vitamin D, more than 1,000 times the usual amount, are effective. Intravenous infusion of a calcium salt temporarily restores the renal tubular reabsorption of phosphate to normal, and massive oral doses of calcium have the same effect.

By measuring plasma phosphate levels in families of affected individuals it was established that the disease is familial.[47,48] The trait was found in both men and women. Seven affected males had ten sons, all of them normal, and 15 daughters, all with the disease. This shows conclu-

41 B. D. DAVIS and W. K. MAAS: Analysis of biochemical mechanism of drug resistance in certain bacterial mutants. *Proc. Nat. Acad. Sci. U.S.A. 38:*775 (1952).

42 C. M. BOYLE: Case of apparent resistance of *Rattus norvegicus* Berkenhout to anticoagulant poisons. *Nature 188:*517 (1960).

43 J. H. CUTHBERT: Further evidence of resistance to warfarin in rats. *Nature 198:*807 (1963).

44 M. LUND: Resistance to warfarin in the common rat. *Nature 203:*778 (1964).

45 F. ALBRIGHT, A. M. BUTLER, and E. BLOOMBERG: Rickets resistant to vitamin D therapy. *Amer. J. Dis. Children 54:*529 (1937).

46 T. F. WILLIAMS, R. W. WINTERS, and C. H. BURNETT: "Familial (Hereditary) Vitamin D-resistant Rickets with Hypophosphatemia," *The Metabolic Basis of Inherited Disease,* 2nd ed., ed. by J. B. Stanbury, J. B. Wyngaarden, and D. S. Fredrickson. New York, McGraw-Hill, 1966, pp. 1179–1204.

sively that the disease is inherited as a sex-linked, dominant trait. A male carries the defective gene for this disease on his single X chromosome, which will be passed to his daughters but not to his sons. That the daughters, who must have been heterozygotes, were affected, shows that the trait is dominant.

The pathogenesis of vitamin D-resistant rickets remains controversial. Probably many of the manifest abnormalities are secondary to excessive parathyroid activity. Thus, for example, if poor calcium absorption from the intestine were the primary defect, lower plasma calcium levels would be expected. But feedback control mechanisms, including increased output of parathyroid hormone, would tend to raise plasma calcium by improving calcium absorption and promoting bone resorption.[49] The secondary hyperparathyroidism would also be responsible for the decreased renal tubular reabsorption of phosphate and the consequent hypophosphatemia. If a protein involved in calcium transport across the intestinal wall were synthesized under the influence of vitamin D, as suggested by recent experiments,[50] then the abnormality could be analogous to that postulated for coumarin resistance; here, the gene defect would yield a modified receptor with poor affinity for vitamin D. Further speculation on the mechanism is fruitless until more is learned about the normal function of vitamin D at the level of molecular interactions.

Inability to Taste Phenylthiourea

Receptors with a high degree of stereospecificity for chemical agents mediate the senses of taste and olfaction, acting somehow as transducers between the chemical stimuli and the specific sensory signals that are transmitted to the brain. It is not surprising, therefore, that genetic defects should cause altered responsiveness in these systems. Such hereditary abnormalities are known for both taste and smell. We shall discuss the one best understood by geneticists—the inability to taste phenylthiourea (phenylthiocarbamide, PTC):

phenylthiourea (PTC)

[47] R. W. WINTERS, J. B. GRAHAM, T. F. WILLIAMS, V. W. MC FALLS, and C. H. BURNETT: A genetic study of familial hypophosphatemia and vitamin D resistant rickets. *Trans. Ass. Amer. Physicians 70:*234 (1957).

[48] J. B. GRAHAM, V. W. MC FALLS, and R. W. WINTERS: Familial hypophosphatemia with vitamin D resistant rickets. II. Three additional kindreds of the sex-linked dominant type with a genetic analysis of four such families. *Amer. J. Human Genet. 11:*311 (1959).

[49] F. W. LAFFERTY, C. H. HERNDON, and O. H. PEARSON: Pathogenesis of vitamin D-resistant rickets and the response to a high calcium intake. *J. Clin. Endocrinol. 23:*903 (1963).

[50] R. H. WASSERMAN and A. N. TAYLOR: Vitamin D_3-induced calcium-binding protein in chick intestinal mucosa. *Science 152:*791 (1966).

PTC is perceived by most subjects as a very bitter substance at concentrations less than 0.15m*M,* but a minority note no bitterness at all until much higher concentrations (sometimes 100 times higher) are reached. With a dilution series test, each concentration differing by a factor of 2 from the one before, a fairly reproducible taste threshold can be established for each subject. Figure 6-14 presents the frequency distributions obtained in one investigation with PTC (top) and with quinine (bottom) in the same subjects. The bimodality found with PTC but not with quinine shows that all bitter tastes do not activate the same chemoreceptors, and that people who are deficient in their ability to taste PTC may nevertheless taste quinine quite normally. For convenience, the subjects who taste PTC only at very high concentrations are categorized as "nontasters."

The question of whether the trait is dominant or recessive can be settled by means of mating analysis and application of the Hardy-Weinberg law, as was illustrated for isoniazid metabolism in Table 3-12. The reader is referred to that discussion for the detailed derivation. Here (Table 6-8),

FIG. 6-14. DISTRIBUTION OF TASTE THRESHOLDS FOR PHENYLTHIOUREA (PTC) AND QUININE. *The most concentrated solutions are numbered 1 (0.13 per cent PTC or 0.0187 per cent quinine sulfate). The sets of increasing integers (toward left on the x-axes) represents serial twofold dilutions. Category labeled <1 represents subjects unable to taste even the most concentrated solution. Tests were performed with a Belgian population of 225 males and 200 females. (From Leguebe, Figs. 1-4.*[51])

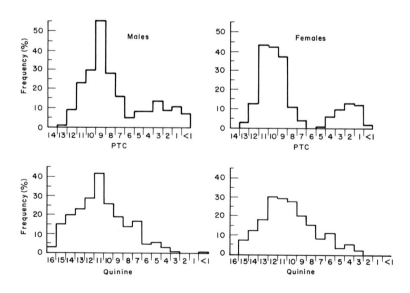

[51] A. LEGUEBE: Génétique et anthropologie de la sensibilité à la phenylthiocarbamide. I. Fréquence du gène dans la population belge. *Bull. Inst. Roy. Sci. Nat. Belgique* 36: article 27 (1960).

TABLE 6-8.   Inheritance of the inability to taste phenylthiourea

The expected fraction of nontasters was computed from the Hardy-Weinberg law on the assumption that it is a recessive trait, as described in the text. (From Stern,[9] Table 20; by permission of W. H. Freeman. Adapted from L. H. Snyder, *Ohio J. Sci. 32:*436, 1937.)

Parents	No. of families	Offspring		Fraction of nontasters	
		Tasters	Nontasters	Observed	Expected
Taster × taster	425	929	130	0.123	0.124
Taster × nontaster	289	483	278	0.366	0.354
Nontaster × nontaster	86	5	218	0.978	1.000

we see that matings between tasters yielded both tasters and nontasters in large numbers, whereas matings between nontasters yielded almost entirely nontaster offspring (the few exceptions in studies like this could be due to misclassification or illegitimacy). This finding indicates that the nontaster trait is recessive, the taster character dominant. Quantitative

FIG. 6-15.   TASTE THRESHOLDS FOR PHENYLTHIOUREA (PTC) IN THREE ETHNIC GROUPS.   *Thresholds were measured in 155 English males, 74 African Negroes, and 66 Chinese. Frequencies are plotted as per cent of total in each group. The concentrations and serial dilutions were the same as in Fig. 6-14. (From Barnicot, Fig. 1.*[52] *By permission of Cambridge University Press.)*

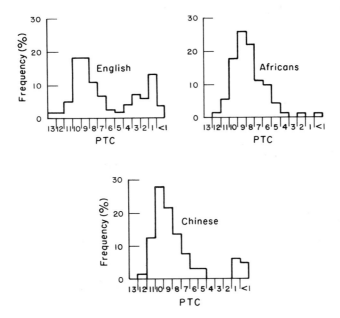

52 N. A. BARNICOT: Taste deficiency for phenylthiourea in African Negroes and Chinese. *Ann. Eugenics 15:*248 (1950–51).

agreement with this hypothesis is tested as outlined in chapter 3, using the frequency of nontasters in the whole population (0.298, based on more than 3,000 persons tested) to estimate the gene frequencies. Thus, $q^2 = 0.298$, $q = 0.545$, where q is the frequency of the nontaster allele. The computations for matings of tasters and nontasters, and for matings of tasters and tasters, yield, for the expected fraction of nontasters, $q/(1 + q)$ and $[q/(1 + q)]^2$, respectively. The results, in Table 6-8, agree so nearly perfectly with the observed data that the postulated mode of inheritance (recessive) can be accepted. The random occurrence of the trait among both sexes showed that it was autosomal.

As shown above, the nontaster allele is carried by more than one-half of the American white population tested. Figure 6-15 shows the distribution of PTC-tasting ability in three different ethnic groups widely separated geographically. The frequency of tasters among American Indians (not shown in Fig. 6-15) was found to be 98 per cent, among Arabs only 63 per cent. As with other drug idiosyncrasies, the implication of such differences is that some property directly or indirectly associated with the allele has been subject to long-term selective pressures of differing degree in the several geographic environments. The PTC nontaster trait is also found in primates other than man; 8 of 28 chimpanzees were judged to be nontasters.

An analogue of PTC is a formerly widely used sweetening agent, ethoxyphenylurea:

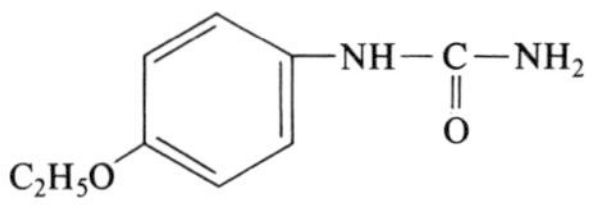

ethoxyphenylurea

When sulfur is substituted for oxygen in the urea moiety of this compound, the taste changes from sweet to bitter. It is concluded that the bitter taste of PTC is due to the grouping $-NH-\underset{\underset{S}{\|}}{C}-NH_2$. The same grouping is found in the thiouracil family of drugs, which block the synthesis of thyroid hormones:

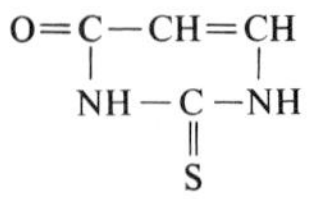

thiouracil

This relationship suggested that a genetic abnormality involving an altered chemoreceptor for the thiouracil grouping might in some way also lead to defective thyroid function. Although the rationale seems far-fetched, surveys have shown that there is indeed a significant increase over random expectation in the incidence of nodular goiter among male nontasters,[53] and also in the number of nontasters among a group of athyrotic cretins.[54] The significance of these findings remains obscure.

Juvenile Pernicious Anemia

Defective vitamin absorption is the cause of pernicious anemia. The juvenile form of this disease clearly has a genetic basis, whereas the role of heredity in adult pernicious anemia has not been worked out. The fundamental defect in pernicious anemia is inability to absorb vitamin B_{12} from the gastrointestinal tract. The absorption is dependent upon the presence of a mucoprotein synthesized in the gastric mucosa and secreted into the stomach. This protein, of molecular weight about 50,000, is called "intrinsic factor."[55] It binds to the mucosa of the ileum, and if it is carrying a molecule of B_{12}, the vitamin is transported across the mucosal cells and absorbed directly into the blood. In pernicious anemia this specific protein is absent. The treatment of choice is vitamin B_{12} given parenterally, but intrinsic factor from a domestic animal (usually hog) may also be effective. Massive doses of B_{12} by mouth result in some degree of absorption even in the absence of intrinsic factor.

Juvenile pernicious anemia has an early onset, before two years of age in 15 of 26 recorded cases, whereas the adult form is rarely seen before age 35. Megaloblastic anemia and neurologic disturbances are characteristic of both types of the disease, but gastric achlorhydria, present in the adult, does not occur in the majority of the juveniles. The genetic basis of the juvenile disease is indicated by the very high incidence among siblings—five pairs among the 26 cases.[56] Analogous genetic diseases probably exist, characterized by deficient absorption from the gastrointestinal tract. In cystic fibrosis, for example, there is known to be deficient production of digestive enzymes with poor absorption of fats and the fat-soluble vitamins.

Resistance to Succinylcholine

Decreased responsiveness to succinylcholine has been reported,[57] in contrast to the prolonged effect of the drug in patients with atypical

53 F. D. KITCHIN, W. HOWEL-EVANS, C. A. CLARKE, R. B. MC CONNELL, and P. M. SHEPPARD: P.T.C. taste response and thyroid disease. *Brit. Med. J. 1:*1069 (1959).

54 G. R. FRASER: Cretinism and taste sensitivity to phenylthiocarbamide. *Lancet 1:*964 (1961).

55 V. HERBERT and W. B. CASTLE: Intrinsic factor. *New Engl. J. Med. 270:*1181 (1964).

56 O. R. MC INTYRE, L. W. SULLIVAN, G. H. JEFFRIES, and R. H. SILVER: Pernicious anemia in childhood. *New Engl. J. Med. 272:*981 (1965).

57 H. W. NEITLICH: Increased plasma cholinesterase activity and succinylcholine resistance: a genetic variant. *J. Clin. Invest. 45:*380 (1966).

cholinesterase. The propositus, a 29-year-old male, was unaffected by a dose of succinylcholine that reduced grip strength (as measured by a hand dynamometer) of control subjects to about 10 per cent of normal within a minute. At twice the test dose, there was only a transient 50 per cent reduction in his grip strength. Analysis of his plasma cholinesterase by electrophoresis revealed a new component with mobility not normally observed. The enzyme activity was three times normal, a much greater increase than in the electrophoretic variants described earlier (p. 441). The same plasma cholinesterase abnormalities were found in the mother, one sister, and one daughter, but not in three other siblings or a son. One brother and one daughter were not tested. The abnormal enzyme is evidently inherited as an autosomal autonomous characteristic. Inasmuch as one representation of the allele is sufficient to cause an excessively rapid destruction of succinylcholine, the succinylcholine resistance behaves as a dominant trait. The allele that controls synthesis of the earlier discussed atypical cholinesterase has to be present on both homologous chromosomes for the succinylcholine apnea to be manifested, because any normal enzyme suffices to destroy the drug rapidly enough. Consequently, succinylcholine apnea appears to be a recessive trait. This illustrates well the semantic difficulties discussed on p. 434.

The unusual electrophoretic mobility of the genetically abnormal cholinesterase in succinylcholine-resistant subjects indicated that the high cholinesterase activity did not result simply from an increased amount of the normal enzyme. Quantitative inhibition studies with the irreversible organic-phosphate cholinesterase inhibitor diisopropylfluorophosphate (DFP), used to "titrate" the number of active centers of the enzyme, revealed that the velocity of substrate hydrolysis by each active center (i.e., the substrate turnover number) was higher than in the normal cholinesterase.

Atropine Resistance (Rabbits)

It has already been noted (p. 271) that many rabbits have an idiosyncratic resistance to the pharmacologic actions of atropine. This is attributable to the presence of a plasma enzyme, atropine esterase (atropine acyl hydrolase). The recognition of this enzyme as genetically determined, and the elucidation of its mode of inheritance, was among the earliest pioneering achievements in biochemical genetics.[58] The presence of the enzyme is determined by an autonomous autosomal gene. Homozygotes contain about twice as high an enzyme activity in their plasma as do heterozygotes. Atropine esterase has not been found in any other species thus far examined, including man.

---

[58] P. B. SAWIN and D. GLICK: Atropinesterase, a genetically determined enzyme in the rabbit. *Proc. Nat. Acad. Sci. U.S.A. 29:*55 (1943).

Insulin Resistance (Mice)

A strain of mice is known that is resistant to insulin, tolerating about 100 times the dose that causes fatal hypoglycemia in normal mice.[59] Breeding experiments have indicated that there are multigenic determinants; one factor is the presence in the livers of resistant animals of a high level of a degradative enzyme.[60]

Racial Differences in Drug Response

Finally, there are numerous racial differences in response to drugs in man, indicating that genetic influences play a role. Very few of these are well documented as yet. One clear example is the difference in response to *mydriatic agents*.[61] Whites of European stock display what we generally regard as the typical dilation of the pupil when ephedrine and similar agents are applied in the conjunctival sac. At the same drug concentration Negroes show practically no response. A similar insensitivity of Negroes to the mydriatic effect of atropine was also reported.[62] Since ephedrine and atropine produce mydriasis by completely different mechanisms, it seems likely that the difference between the racial groups arises more from some anatomic or physiologic peculiarity of the iris than from any drug-specific alteration of a receptor.

ABNORMAL DISTRIBUTION OF DRUG

Copper (Wilson's Disease)

A genetically determined abnormality of copper metabolism, resulting in copper deposition in tissues, is known as Wilson's disease or *hepatolenticular degeneration*.[63, 64] A specific copper-containing protein, the α_2-globulin called ceruloplasmin, is deficient or absent from the plasma. The disease is inherited as an autosomal recessive trait. It is exceedingly rare; there are probably only a few cases per million population. The accumulation and deposition of copper occurs in all tissues but is especially

59 H. B. CHASE, M. S. GUNTHER, J. MILLER, and D. WOLFFSON: High insulin tolerance in an inbred strain of mice. *Science 107:*297 (1948).

60 R. E. BEYER: A study of insulin metabolism in an insulin tolerant strain of mice. *Acta Endocrinol. 19:*309 (1955).

61 K. K. CHEN and E.J. POTH: Racial differences as illustrated by the mydriatic action of cocaine, euphthalmine and ephedrine. *J. Pharmacol. Exp. Therap. 36:*429 (1929).

62 T. G. SCOTT: The eye of the West African Negro. *Brit. J. Ophthalmol. 29:*12 (1945).

63 I. H. SCHEINBERG and I. STERNLIEB: Wilson's disease. *Annu. Rev. Med. 16:*119 (1965).

64 A. G. BEARN: "Wilson's Disease," *The Metabolic Basis of Inherited Disease,* 2nd ed., ed. by J. B. Stanbury, J. B. Wyngaarden and D. S. Fredrickson. New York, McGraw-Hill, 1966, pp. 761–779.

marked in the liver and brain. The pathologic changes in these organs largely account for the disease symptoms, which are cirrhosis and numerous manifestations of neurologic disorder, including psychosis. The excessive amounts of copper in the tissues are largely bound to the various tissue proteins, which appear to be quite normal otherwise. Moreover, ceruloplasmin is evidently the only copper protein that is deficient in this disease; others like tyrosinase and erythrocuprein are present in normal amounts.

Ceruloplasmin normally contains about 98 per cent of the plasma copper, not reversibly bound but incorporated into the protein structure at the time of synthesis. The daily intake of copper in the diet amounts to a few milligrams, more or less, depending upon what foods are eaten. Of this amount approximately 1 mg is normally absorbed, and this corresponds roughly to the amount of copper incorporated daily into newly synthesized ceruloplasmin. Thus, the plasma water and tissues normally contain only negligible amounts of free copper. In the normal steady state, the same amount of ceruloplasmin that is synthesized each day is also destroyed and eliminated daily. It is presumably excreted into the intestine together with its associated copper, although the exact relationship between ceruloplasmin breakdown and copper excretion has not yet been elucidated.

When ceruloplasmin is absent, or present in insufficient amount, a decreased total amount of copper is found in the plasma, but a much greater than normal amount of free copper. Copper ions therefore escape from the circulation into the tissue water, where they become bound to various tissue components. Incidentally, more copper becomes available for renal excretion, so that more appears in the urine; but despite this increased urinary output the patient with Wilson's disease is in positive copper balance. Figure 6-16 shows the characteristic abnormalities of copper content in plasma and urine. The daily retention of copper in Wilson's disease may be as little as 50 μg; this would account for the accumulation of nearly 200 mg in the tissues of a ten-year-old child affected by the disease. Because the process of accumulation is slow, and symptoms do not develop until considerable copper deposition has occurred, the clinical manifestations of this disease are rarely seen before the age of six, and sometimes not until much later in life.

The specific drug for treatment or prevention is penicillamine,[65] which chelates copper and eliminates it from the body, as described already in chapters 1 and 5. Because penicillamine is highly effective, it is all the more important to detect ceruloplasmin deficiency as early in life as possible. Routine screening of all infants might not be considered practical in view of the rarity of the condition; but certainly all relatives of patients in whom the diagnosis has been made should be investigated thoroughly and treated if evidence of the abnormality is found.

[65] I. STERNLIEB and I. H. SCHEINBERG: Penicillamine therapy for hepatolenticular degeneration. *J. Amer. Med. Ass. 189:*748 (1964).

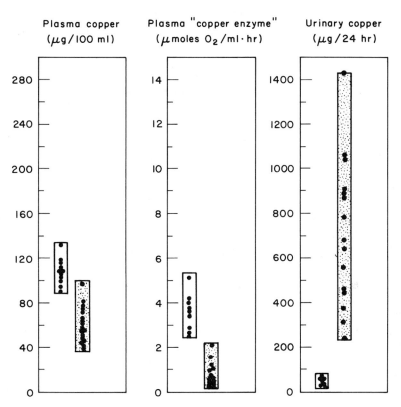

Plasma copper
(μg/100 ml)

Plasma "copper enzyme"
(μmoles O_2/ml·hr)

Urinary copper
(μg/24 hr)

FIG. 6-16.   PLASMA COPPER, PLASMA CERULOPLASMIN, AND URINARY COPPER IN NORMAL SUBJECTS AND IN PATIENTS WITH WILSON'S DISEASE.   *At* left, *total plasma copper;* middle, *plasma ceruloplasmin, assayed by a method using a copper oxidase activity as the measure of ceruloplasmin;* right, *total urinary copper, daily output. Data from individual subjects are represented by solid dots within vertical bars showing range.* Open bars, *normal subjects;* stippled bars, *patients with Wilson's disease.* (*Modified from Bearn, Fig. 5.[66]*)

Iron (Primary Hemochromatosis)

Genetically determined abnormal distribution of iron characterizes the disease known as primary ("idiopathic") hemochromatosis.[67, 68] Here, there is a progressive accumulation of iron in the tissues. In the normal young adult, the body contains about 1 g of iron, and this amount remains fairly constant throughout life. In the patient with hemochromatosis, the

[66] A. G. BEARN: Genetic and biochemical aspects of Wilson's disease. *Amer. J. Med. 15:*442 (1953).

[67] T. H. BOTHWELL and C. A. FINCH: *Iron Metabolism.* Boston, Little, Brown and Co., 1962.

[68] J.-C. DREYFUS and G. SCHAPIRA: "Iron Overload. The Metabolism of Iron in Hœmochromatosis," *Iron Metabolism,* a CIBA Symposium, ed. by F. Gross. Berlin, Springer-Verlag, 1964, pp. 296–325.

steady state is somehow disturbed, and there is a daily excess of iron absorption over iron excretion in the amount of about 2 mg. The disease is rarely seen until middle age, presumably because so many years are required for the iron content of tissues to reach damaging levels. In patients the total body iron reaches 20 to 40 g. Most of the excess iron is deposited as hemosiderin, a complex pigment containing ferritin. In liver and pancreas, the iron content may reach 50 to 100 times the normal, and lesser degrees of accumulation are seen in the thyroid gland and in skin, spleen, kidney, and stomach. The pancreas shows degeneration of acinar tissue and scarring of the islets, and diabetes is a common manifestation of the disease. There is usually portal cirrhosis of the liver, accompanied by liver insufficiency. The skin becomes pigmented, with increased melanin as well as hemosiderin deposits. The pancreatic and skin involvement account for the older name, "bronze diabetes."

One distinguishing feature of primary hemochromatosis is an elevation of the plasma iron concentration, resulting in an abnormally high saturation of transferrin, the plasma iron-binding protein. Transferrin is capable of binding essentially all plasma iron up to concentrations of about $350\mu g/ml$. In the normal adult the plasma iron concentration is approximately $120\mu g/ml$, representing a transferrin saturation of 35 per cent. In the patient with hemochromatosis, the plasma iron and the transferrin saturation are both twice normal. The total plasma transferrin is not increased, and there is no evident change in its affinity for iron. Given the high plasma iron concentration, the clinical manifestations of the disease are not remarkable; iron overload after prolonged therapy of refractory anemia leads to the same syndrome of cirrhosis, diabetes, and skin pigmentation.

There is a question whether the positive iron balance and high plasma iron concentration in hemochromatosis arise from increased absorption or decreased excretion. What data are available indicate that the rate of elimination of iron is not diminished in this disease. The nature of the primary defect is not yet known; presumably it is an abnormality of the mechanism that prevents the net absorption from dietary sources of more iron than is required to meet the very small daily needs of the body. Therapy of hemochromatosis entails the removal of iron from the body. Hitherto this has been attempted by periodic bleeding, but recently trials have been initiated with iron-binding compounds like desferrioxamine (p. 388).

The recognition of primary hemochromatosis as a genetically determined disease was delayed for several reasons. The late development of the clinical manifestations in patients means that members of antecedent generations of patients' families are often not available for study. The incidence of the disease is very low—less than 1 in 20,000 hospital admissions. Criteria for distinguishing the disease from other kinds of iron overload ("hemosiderosis" from multiple blood transfusions, dietary overload in Bantu tribesmen) have only recently been worked out. Now, measurements of plasma iron and transferrin saturation permit identification of the trait even in young subjects many years before symptoms appear. Investigations by this method show a very high frequency of abnormality in families of patients with overt disease.

Hemochromatosis is much more common in males than in females, but in this instance the sex difference may have no genetic connotation. Women lose iron through pregnancy, lactation, and menstruation. The loss attributed to menstruation, when prorated over the whole month, amounts to no less than 0.8 mg per day,[69] which is nearly one-half the daily overload of 2 mg in hemochromatosis. Accordingly, the disease usually develops later in women than in men, so that the apparent incidence in a population containing both sexes and all ages would be higher among males.

One family study[70] spans four generations (Fig. 6-17). The wife in the first generation (I-2) had developed diabetes at age 49 and died of cardiac failure (cardiac damage occurs frequently in hemochromatosis); she was also said to have developed pigmentation of the skin. There was no evidence of disease in her husband (I-1). Of nine children, all but one showed some indication, more or less severe, of hemochromatosis. In the third generation, eight of 15 subjects had elevated plasma iron levels, although none yet showed signs of disease. Finally, four of seven children in

FIG. 6-17. A FAMILY PEDIGREE OF PRIMARY HEMOCHROMATOSIS. Squares *are males,* circles *females.* Open symbols, *normal;* solid symbols, *"bronze diabetes,"* i.e., *frank hemochromatosis with pigmentation;* symbols containing X, *subjects with one or two signs of hemochromatosis;* symbols containing dot, *subjects with elevated plasma iron level and no other demonstrable abnormality.* (*With modifications, from Boulin and Bamberger, chart p. 3158.*[70])

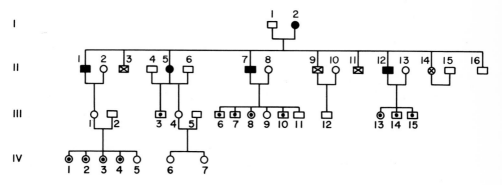

69 J. MILLIS: The iron losses of healthy women during consecutive menstrual cycles. *Med. J. Australia* 2:874 (1951).

70 R. BOULIN and J. BAMBERGER: L'Hémochromatose familiale. *Sem. Hôp. Paris* 29:3153 (1953).

the fourth generation also had elevated plasma iron levels. Throughout the kindred, the abnormal trait appeared in both males and females. The same arguments that applied to the analysis of the mode of inheritance of coumarin resistance (Fig. 6-13) apply here. A trait that is very rare and that appears in successive generations is probably not recessive; and affected individuals are probably heterozygotes. In this case primary hemochromatosis would be autosomal and dominant. But then the classification of II-9 as normal is anomalous; and since his mother carried the trait, illegitimacy cannot be invoked as an explanation. Moreover, the appearance of the trait in the fourth generation among children whose parents both were normal is also incompatible with the proposed mode of inheritance. More family studies are required.

Increased or Decreased Thyroxine-Binding Globulin

Another genetic abnormality in the binding of a drug to a plasma protein concerns thyroxine. This hormone is carried in the plasma bound in roughly equal amounts to three kinds of plasma protein: (*1*) albumin, (*2*) a protein ("prealbumin") that migrates more rapidly toward the anode than does albumin, and (*3*) thyroxine-binding α-globulin (TBG).[71] TBG also binds triiodothyronine.[72] Its affinity is much greater for thyroxine than for triiodothyronine, and this probably explains why triiodothyronine is distributed so much more readily into the tissues. Less than 0.1 per cent of total plasma thyroxine is present in the free form.[73]

During a routine health examination a man with normal thyroid function was found to have a greatly elevated serum protein-bound iodine (PBI) level, about 12 to $16\mu g$ per 100 ml of plasma over a nine-month period, compared with the normal range of 4 to $7\mu g$. Electrophoretic studies established that his thyroxine-binding globulin could bind about twice as much thyroxine as normal. There were no concomitant abnormalities of thyroxine binding to plasma albumin or "prealbumin," and the turnover rate of thyroxine in the plasma did not seem to be abnormal. Follow-up studies on the family[74] revealed the same abnormality in eight of 29 people, including three females and five males. The results are shown in Fig. 6-18. No qualitative difference in electrophoretic behavior of the abnormal TBG could be discerned.[75] The pattern of inheritance was consistent with an autosomal dominant trait.

Deficiency of TBG capacity has also been found. In two patients with clinically normal thyroid function given ^{131}I-labeled thyroxine the amount of radioactivity associated with TBG was determined.[71,76] No ab-

71 W. R. BEISEL, H. ZAINAL, S. HANE, V. C. DI RAIMONDO, and P. H. FORSHAM: Low thyroidal iodine uptake with euthyroidism associated with deficient thyroid-binding globulin but normal cortisol binding. *J. Clin. Endocrinol. 22:*1165 (1962).

72 A. H. GORDON, J. GROSS, D. O'CONNOR, and R. PITT-RIVERS: Nature of the circulating thyroid hormone-plasma protein complex. *Nature 169:*19 (1952).

normality was observed in the electrophoretic pattern of the plasma proteins, and there was no alteration of binding of the labeled thyroxine in the "prealbumin" and albumin regions. However, only a trace of radioactivity migrated with the electrophoretic mobility of TBG. Estrogen treatment, which usually increases the thyroxine-binding capacity of TBG, had no effect. The apparent volume of distribution of thyroxine was only slightly increased over control values, but the plasma half-life of the ^{131}I-labeled hormone was shorter than normal by about 50 per cent. Total daily excretion of thyroid hormones into the urine was within normal limits. Evidently, the rate of entry of labeled thyroxine into tissues (especially liver) was increased as a result of the TBG deficiency.[77] Since plasma

FIG. 6-18. THYROXINE-BINDING CAPACITY OF PLASMA α-GLOBULIN IN NORMAL SUBJECTS AND THE "ELEVATED TBG" KINSHIP. *Horizontal scale shows thyroxine-binding capacity in μg thyroxine per ml of serum, vertical axis shows frequency. Squares are males, circles are females. (Modified from Beierwaltes et al., Fig. 2.[75])*

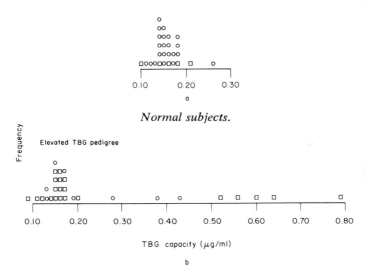

Subjects in kinship of individuals with elevated TBG capacity.

[73] J. E. RALL, J. ROBBINS, and C. G. LEWALLEN: "The Thyroid," *The Hormones,* vol. 5, ed. by G. Pincus, K. V. Thimann, and E. B. Astwood. New York, Academic Press, 1964, pp. 159–439.

[74] W. H. BEIERWALTES and J. ROBBINS: Familial increase in the thyroxine-binding sites in serum alpha globulin. *J. Clin. Invest. 38:*1683 (1959).

[75] W. H. BEIERWALTES, E. A. CARR, JR., and R. L. HUNTER: Hereditary increase in the thyroxine-binding sites in the serum alpha globulin. *Trans. Ass. Amer. Physicians 74:*170 (1961).

[76] S. H. INGBAR: Clinical and physiological observations in a patient with an idiopathic decrease in the thyroxine-binding globulin of plasma. *J. Clin. Invest. 40:*2053 (1961).

[77] R. R. CAVALIERI and G. L. SEARLE: The kinetics of distribution between plasma and liver of ^{131}I-labeled L-thyroxine in man: observations of subjects with normal and decreased serum thyroxine-binding globulin. *J. Clin. Invest. 45:*939 (1966).

binding would normally retard the passage of a substance from the blood plasma into the tissues, it seems reasonable that a decreased binding of thyroxine should lead to an increased rate of its passage into tissues. Studies of two families have shown clearly that the defect is genetically determined and consistent with an autosomal dominant mode of inheritance; however, sex linkage is not yet ruled out.[78,79]

DIFFERENCES IN USE OF AND RESPONSE TO PSYCHOTROPIC DRUGS

Most drug idiosyncrasies are discovered by chance when a drug is administered to a person who happens to carry a genetic trait determining the idiosyncratic response. Psychotropic drugs have the special property that they are sought out for self-administration by people who wish to experience a particular effect. The sought-after action may be euphoria, stimulation, tranquilization, or other modifications of mood or behavior. The multiplicity of genetic determinants of brain function, and the manifold actions of the psychotropic drugs, caution against oversimplified approaches. Suppose, however, that there were intrinsic differences in response to the psychotropic agents. Then one would also expect to find corresponding differences in the habitual use of these drugs, for if a person failed to obtain the desired effect he would not continue to resort to that drug. It is well known, for example, that most people react with extreme displeasure to an initial dose of an opiate narcotic, both nausea and dysphoria being common responses. It was once supposed that administration of opiates in legitimate medical practice might "create" addicts. There is no valid evidence of this claim, although it is true that the incidence of addiction is high in the health professions, where there is easy access to addicting drugs.[79a] It is quite obvious, however, that of the many millions of patients who receive morphine, an insignificantly small fraction ever seek to take the drug again. Likewise, in the population as a whole, very few of those who could obtain morphine or heroin illegally, if they wished, become addicts. It is noteworthy that although D-amphetamine has been used very widely to counteract fatigue and sleeplessness, only an occasional person who used it became habituated to it. And despite the nearly universal exposure of the population to the "legal" psychotropic drugs (alcohol, caffeine, and nicotine), some become habituated and some do not. Certainly socioenvironmental reasons can be found, ex post facto, to

78 J. S. MARSHALL, R. P. LEVY, and A. G. STEINBERG: Human thyroxine-binding globulin deficiency. A genetic study. *New Engl. J. Med. 274:*1469 (1966).

79 J. T. NICOLOFF, J. T. DOWLING, and D. D. PATTON: Inheritance of decreased thyroxine-binding by the thyroxine-binding globulin. *J. Clin. Endocrinol. 24:*294 (1964).

79a H. ISBELL: Methods and results of studying experimental human addiction to the newer synthetic analgesics. *Ann. N.Y. Acad. Sci. 51:*108 (1948).

explain each case of addiction to heroin, the barbiturates, or alcohol, or of habituation to lysergic acid diethylamide, marijuana, nicotine, or amphetamine. But most people afflicted by the same adverse environmental circumstances do not seek escape through drug abuse. Despite the present paucity of evidence, therefore, the possibility should be entertained that the characteristic effects of psychotropic drugs upon mood, which underlie the development of drug abuse, may be at least in part genetically determined.

Investigation in this field has not yet transcended the difficulties of designing experiments free of self-selection or other kinds of bias, and of working out methods suitable for quantitation of subjective responses. It has been found, for example, that housewives who drink large amounts of coffee responded entirely differently to a test dose of caffeine in a placebo-controlled experiment than did housewives who never drink coffee.[80] The coffee drinkers felt more alert and had a sense of well-being after caffeine, as compared with placebo. The nondrinkers obtained significantly fewer effects of this kind; on the other hand, caffeine made them feel nervous and "jittery." But it is not known if the group habituated to coffee would have reacted in the same way at an earlier age, before their first exposure to caffeine. Large individual differences are observed in the sensitivity of people to the sleep-disturbing actions of caffeine,[81,82] but again it is not clear whether or not these are innate differences, independent of any prior exposure to caffeine. One investigation on the coffee-drinking and smoking habits of monozygotic and dizygotic twins suggests that these two kinds of drug-seeking behavior[83] are subject to genetic influences.

[80] A. GOLDSTEIN and S. KAIZER: Unpublished observations.

[81] A. GOLDSTEIN, R. WARREN, and S. KAIZER: Psychotropic effects of caffeine in man. I. Individual differences in sensitivity to caffeine-induced wakefulness. *J. Pharmacol. Exp. Therap. 149:*156 (1965).

[82] A. GOLDSTEIN, S. KAIZER, and R. WARREN: Psychotropic effects of caffeine in man. II. Alertness, psychomotor coordination, and mood. *J. Pharmacol. Exp. Therap. 150:*146 (1965).

[83] F. CONTERIO and B. CHIARELLI: Study of the inheritance of some daily life habits. *Heredity 17:*347 (1962).

7

DRUG ALLERGY

INTRODUCTION

Allergy is defined as an "altered degree of susceptibility caused by a primary inoculation or treatment, as with a specific germ or foreign substance, and manifested in reaction to a subsequent inoculation or treatment with the same thing. . . ."[1] The term "hypersensitivity" is often used to describe the allergic state. This word is inappropriate as applied to drug allergy, because its literal meaning invites confusion with other kinds of adverse drug reaction. One could properly describe as "hypersensitive" the normal therapeutic responses of the people at the lower end of the frequency distribution in a quantal log dose-response curve, i.e., those individuals who are sensitive to a very low dose of a drug. One could also reasonably describe as "hypersensitivity" an idiosyncratic response, at a low dosage level, to the therapeutic or toxic effects of a drug in a genetically predisposed person. There has been a lack of precision in the diagnosis of drug allergies and often a failure to apply clear-cut criteria to their classification. Ambiguous terminology adds to the confusion. We shall avoid the term "hypersensitivity" and describe as drug allergy those drug reactions that have an obvious (or inferred) immunologic basis.[2-5]

In order for a drug to produce an allergic reaction, a prior *sensitizing* contact is required, either with the same drug or with one closely related chemically. A period of time is required—usually about 7 to 10 days—for the synthesis of drug-specific antibodies. Then exposure to the drug (the *eliciting* contact)[5a] results in an antigen-antibody interaction, which pro-

---

[1] *Webster's New International Dictionary of the English Language,* 2nd ed. Springfield, Mass., G. and C. Merriam Co., 1949.

[2] W. C. BOYD: *Fundamentals of Immunology,* 3rd ed. New York, Interscience Publishers, 1956.

[3] E. A. CARR, JR.: Drug allergy. *Pharmacol. Rev.* 6:365 (1954).

[4] M. SAMTER and H. L. ALEXANDER, eds.: *Immunological Diseases.* Boston, Little, Brown and Co., 1965.

[5] M. L. ROSENHEIM and R. MOULTON, eds.: *Sensitivity Reactions to Drugs.* Springfield, Ill., Charles C Thomas, 1958.

[5a] There need be no drug-free interval between the sensitizing contact and the eliciting contact; thus, allergic sensitization could occur in the early part of a course of treatment, and allergic response at a later time, during the same course of treatment.

vokes the typical manifestations of allergy. These manifestations are numerous. They involve various organ systems, and they range in severity from minor skin lesions to fatal anaphylactic shock. The pattern of allergic response differs in different species. In man, involvement of the skin is most common, whereas in the guinea pig, for example, bronchiolar constriction leading to asphyxia is typical. The pattern of response is somewhat conditioned by the route of sensitization and the route of subsequent administration, and also by the particular drug employed. A certain drug may preferentially elicit one or a few responses from among the whole pattern of possible responses. Sulfonamide allergy, for example, is usually manifested by dermatitis, conjunctivitis, or fever; penicillin, on the other hand, most frequently elicits urticaria ("hives") and generalized itching. Despite these differences between drugs, the allergic response pattern as a whole is nonspecific with respect to any particular chemical structure. Many different agents, wholly unrelated chemically, once they have sensitized, may be equally capable of eliciting a given allergic response—for example, dermatitis, anaphylaxis, or angio-edema. In a given species, under given conditions, the allergic response is a consequence of antigen-antibody interaction; it has nothing directly to do with the chemical structure of the eliciting drug.

Drug allergy can usually be distinguished clearly from ordinary drug toxicity and from drug idiosyncrasy on the following grounds:

1. *Occurrence.* All three kinds of adverse drug reaction may be unusual. Toxic side effects are unusual if the therapeutic action of a drug is ordinarily obtained at a dose much lower than the toxic dose, i.e., if the drug has a high therapeutic ratio. But the incidence of toxic side effects can be increased at will until, at sufficient dosage, everyone reacts. Idiosyncrasy is manifested only in genetically susceptible individuals, regardless of dosage. Idiosyncrasy is usually rare, because any given abnormal genotype is likely to be rare. But some genetic polymorphisms are fairly prevalent, and if these determine drug idiosyncrasy, then the idiosyncrasy may be quite widespread (e.g., PTC nontasters, p. 461). Although drug allergy is usually seen in no more than a few per cent of all people who receive a given drug, some chemicals can cause allergic sensitization in nearly everyone exposed to them. Probably a genetic predisposition to allergy is required;[6-8] but those who are predisposed are capable of being sensitized to many different allergens. The genetic predisposition to idiosyncrasy is a

6 A. S. WIENER, I. ZIEVE, and J. H. FRIES: The inheritance of allergic disease. *Ann. Eugenics* 7:141 (1936).

7 P. F. DE GARA: "The Hereditary Predisposition in Man to develop Hypersensitivity: A Critical Review," in *Mechanisms of Hypersensitivity,* International Symposium, Henry Ford Hospital, ed. by J. H. Shaffer, G. A. LoGrippo, and M. W. Chase. Boston, Little, Brown and Co., 1958, pp. 703–712.

8 J. H. SANG and W. R. SOBEY: The genetic control of response to antigenic stimuli. *J. Immunol.* 72:52 (1954).

sensitivity to a particular drug or class of drugs, but the genetic predisposition to allergy is much more general.

2. *Dose relationship*. Toxic side effects are clearly dose related, as are idiosyncratic responses in susceptible individuals. In both cases the usual dose-effect principles apply, since the responses are mediated directly by specific drug-receptor interactions. In contrast, allergic responses have an erratic relationship to dosage. It is known that extremely small doses (e.g., traces of antibiotics in foodstuffs) suffice to sensitize in some cases. It is also clear that minute doses can elicit allergic responses in previously sensitized individuals, and the magnitude of the response has little to do with the size of the eliciting dose. Sometimes a mere trace of drug (e.g., an amount of only a fraction of a microgram contaminating a syringe) elicits life-threatening manifestations of allergy; and sometimes full therapeutic doses evoke only mild allergic effects. It appears that the magnitude of an allergic response is determined primarily by immunologic factors in the individual and that the drug (at whatever dose) may serve chiefly to "trigger" the reaction.

3. *Prior contact with drug*. Although prior exposure to a drug is not necessary for toxic side effects or idiosyncratic responses, it is essential for allergic reactions. However, sensitization may occur covertly by environmental or dietary exposure (e.g., penicillin in cow's milk), so that allergic responses may occur without known prior exposure.

4. *Chemical specificity*. Toxic side effects and drug idiosyncrasies are directly and specifically determined by the chemical structure of the drug, and typical structure-activity relationships can be established. In drug allergy, the responses are determined by antigen-antibody reactions, and they are largely independent of which drug molecule elicits them. If for ordinary drug effects the analogy to specific keys fitting pre-existing locks is appropriate, then in drug allergy the key (sensitizing drug) is presented to a locksmith who, after a while, makes some locks to fit the key, and installs these locks in doors labeled "dermatitis," "anaphylaxis," and so on. Here, the structure-activity relationships concern the chemical structures of the sensitizing drug (the original key) and the eliciting drugs (identical or similar keys). Some drugs are more capable of sensitizing than others. If a particular drug does sensitize, then only this drug or closely related congeners will elicit the allergic response.

5. *Mechanisms*. In drug allergy, the immunologic basis can often be established by demonstrating circulating antibodies in serum or altered immunologic responses in tissues. The antibodies are specific for the sensitizing drug and closely related compounds; but, as already indicated, the manifestations of drug allergy are unrelated to any particular drug. In contrast, the nature of a toxic or idiosyncratic reaction to a drug is determined by that drug. A corollary is that toxic or idiosyncratic reactions

are overcome or prevented by antagonists that are specific for the drug that precipitated the reaction. In drug allergy, on the other hand, specific drug antagonists are useless, but drugs like antihistamines, epinephrine, and hydrocortisone, whose actions are directed toward the general manifestations of the allergic response, may be effective.

IMMUNOLOGIC BASIS OF DRUG ALLERGY

In the classic development of immunologic theory,[2,4,9-11] foreign proteins with antigenic properties were found to induce the formation of antibody proteins rather specifically directed against the sensitizing antigens. A variety of methods could be employed to demonstrate the presence and specificity of these antibodies. Precipitin reactions reflected the direct combination of antibody with antigen to form an insoluble complex. Hemagglutination revealed the presence of antibody by an alteration of the surface properties of erythrocytes, usually mediated by complement.[12] Antibodies fixed in the skin or carried there by lymphoid cells were demonstrable by local erythema and wheal formation elicited by application of the specific sensitizing antigen.

Allergic responses are classified as *immediate* or *delayed*. The terms refer to the time that intervenes, in a sensitized subject, between the eliciting dose and the response. The immediate-type reaction usually occurs within minutes. Circulating humoral antibodies can be demonstrated by precipitin reactions. Sensitization can be brought about by a systemic route of drug administration. The delayed-type reaction (also called "tuberculin type") appears hours to days after the eliciting dose has been administered. Serum antibodies are not demonstrable, but tissue antibodies are evidently present, and the allergic sensitivity can often be transferred passively by cells of the lymphoid series. In this type, the skin is the major route of sensitization and the chief site of allergic reaction.

Covalently Bonded Drug-Protein Conjugates

Drugs that provoke allergic reactions are usually small molecules rather than proteins, so that special techniques had to be developed to investigate the immunologic basis of drug allergies. These techniques were worked out in the course of a remarkable series of experiments, largely in

---

9 E. A. BROWN: "Reactions to Drugs," *International Textbook of Allergy*, ed. by J. M. Jamar. Springfield, Ill., Charles C Thomas, 1959, pp. 609–623.

10 D. H. CAMPBELL, J. S. GARVEY, N. E. CREMER, and D. H. SUSSDORF: *Methods in Immunology: A Laboratory Text for Instruction and Research*. New York, W. A. Benjamin, 1963.

11 S. COHEN and R. R. PORTER: Structure and biological activity of immunoglobulins. *Advance. Immunol.* 4:287 (1964).

12 *Complement* is the name given to a mixture of globulins present in normal plasma. By combining with antigen-antibody complexes, complement can make manifest certain effects (e.g., lysis of red blood cells) that would otherwise not occur.

the laboratory of Karl Landsteiner (1892–1943), who summarized the methods and results in a classic treatise.[13] Prior to these experiments it was assumed that antigen specificity resided entirely in the protein used as antigen. The basic discovery that upset this idea and opened the way to further progress was the finding that when proteins were acylated[14] they would display altered specificity as antigens. Immune serum prepared against an acylated protein would react more strongly with the acylated protein than with the same protein that had not been acylated. Numerous compounds of low molecular weight could be linked to proteins by acylation or by diazo coupling reactions (to tyrosine, histidine, or lysine residues) to form "artificial conjugated antigens." The simple chemicals thus conjugated to proteins were called *haptens*.

Hapten-protein conjugates could be used to sensitize experimental animals so that antibodies would develop in their sera. These sera would then give precipitin reactions with the same antigen that had been used to sensitize, but would react only weakly with the unconjugated protein. Of greater interest, these sera would give precipitin reactions with the same hapten coupled to an entirely different protein. Thus, the ordinary precipitin reactions to foreign proteins could be avoided, and the hapten-directed specificity enhanced, by using one kind of protein to sensitize and a different kind to test the immune sera. Hapten conjugates, for example, were made with horse serum, and these were injected into rabbits to produce immune sera. Each immune serum was then tested by mixing it with a hapten conjugate of chicken serum. The antibodies produced in the rabbit that were directed against horse serum proteins would not precipitate the chicken serum. But antibodies directed against the hapten would give positive precipitin reactions with protein conjugates of that hapten, regardless of the source of the protein. In this way it was shown quite dramatically that immunologic reactivity could be directed specifically against the hapten.

In these investigations the specificity of the antibody was found to be directed not only toward the hapten but often in varying degree toward other small molecules related chemically to the hapten. Sometimes, the antibody specificity was even directed toward a particular grouping or small segment of the hapten molecule, for example, toward the 2-chlorobenzene portion of a complex azobenzene derivative.

Table 7-1 presents an illustrative example of these experimental results. Each of the antigens listed vertically at the left was diazotized and reacted with chicken serum; the protein was then precipitated with salt, washed, and stored for use in the testing procedure. Four of the same com-

---

[13] K. LANDSTEINER: *The Specificity of Serological Reactions.* Cambridge, Mass. Harvard University Press, 1945.

[14] Acylation was carried out with the anhydrides or chlorides of butyric, isobutyric, trichloroacetic, and anisic acids; these groups were coupled chiefly to ε-amino groups of lysine residues.

pounds, shown across the top of the table, were diazotized and reacted with horse serum. The precipitated and washed proteins were then used to immunize groups of rabbits. Tests of the immune sera were carried out by adding a few drops of it to a dilute solution of the chicken serum azoprotein. The amount of precipitation was scored, from none $(-)$ to intense flocculence $(++++)$. The tabulated results show at a glance the high degree of specificity of the immune sera. For example, the immune serum prepared against o-aminocinnamic acid (A) yielded a precipitin reaction only against chicken serum protein containing the same hapten and not against any of the others, even o-aminosulfonic acid (E), which has a fairly close chemical relationship. The column of results under m-aminosulfonic acid (B) is interesting because it shows both specificity and cross-reactivity. The strongest precipitin reaction was against chicken serum containing the same compound; and there was considerable reaction also with the ortho isomer (E), but none with the para isomer (C). The reactivity toward the ortho isomer (E) was slightly diminished when the antigen contained a methyl group para to the amino group (F), and became weaker still when the ring had a chlorine substituent (H). Immune serum directed against p-aminosulfonic acid (C) reacted weakly with the meta isomer (B) but not at all with the ortho isomer (E). The presence of a methyl group ortho to the amino group (D) did not hinder the reactivity much, but the additional presence of a bromine substituent (G) abolished it. The last column shows that when toluidine sulfonic acid (D) was used to prepare the immune serum, the strongest precipitin reaction was obtained with the homologous antigen (D). Strong cross-reactivity was obtained against the same antigen lacking the methyl group (C), and weak cross-reactivity against the meta isomer lacking the methyl group (B), but none against the ortho compound (E). Here, the bromine substituent (G) does not interfere with reactivity, in contrast to the analogous cross-reaction under column (C). This behavior suggests that the antigenic determinant of (D) may be the set of substituents on the right-hand side of the molecule as drawn $(-NH_2, -CH_3, -H, -SO_3H)$. Since these same groups are present in the antigen (G), the presence or absence of the bromine atom is irrelevant. One could hypothesize that antibodies were formed against the simpler compound, p-aminosulfonic acid (C), in the same manner; here, the antigenic determinants are $-NH_2, -H, -H,$ $-SO_3H$. When the antigen contains a methyl group (D), destroying this pattern on one side, the pattern remains the same on the other so the antigen-antibody reaction can still occur. But when $-CH_3$ is placed on one side and $-Br$ on the other (G), the distinctive pattern to which the immune serum is directed no longer remains, and the antigen-antibody reaction is prevented.

A modification of the technique described above permits the use of hapten molecules themselves in the testing procedure. If an immune

TABLE 7-1. Specificity and cross-reactivity of immune sera to azoprotein antigens

The compounds shown at top (A to D) were diazotized and coupled to horse serum proteins. These were used to immunize rabbits, and the rabbit antisera were used in the tests. The same four compounds and four others (A to H) were diazotized and coupled to chicken serum proteins; these were used as antigens in the tests. The testing procedure consisted of adding a few drops of an immune serum to a dilute solution of the hapten-protein antigen and recording the intensity of precipitation (0 to ++++). (Modified after Landsteiner and Lampl,[15] Table III. By permission of Springer.)

Antigens	Immune sera			
	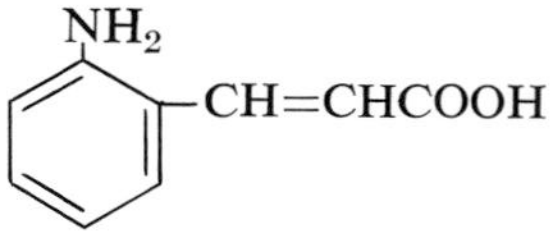 (A) NH₂ / CH=CHCOOH	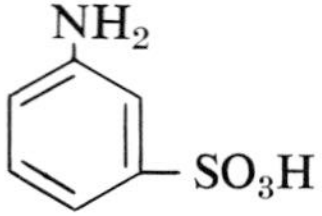 (B) NH₂ / SO₃H	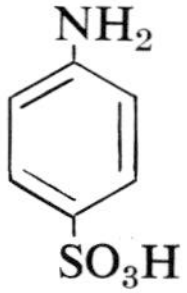 (C) NH₂ / SO₃H	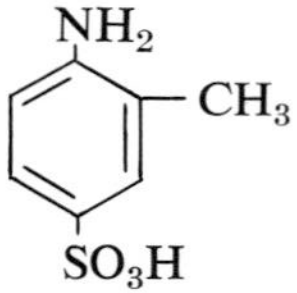 (D) NH₂ / CH₃ / SO₃H
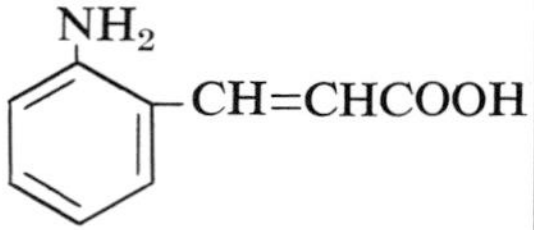 (A) NH₂ / CH=CHCOOH	+++	0	0	0
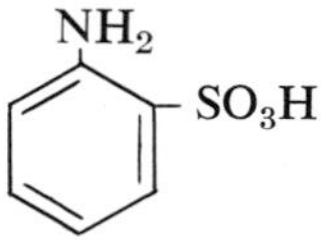 (E) NH₂ / SO₃H	0	+++	0	0
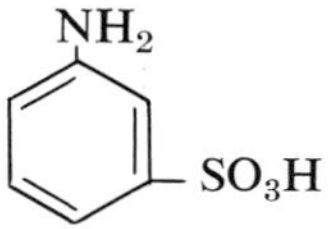 (B) NH₂ / SO₃H	0	++++	+	+

Compound					
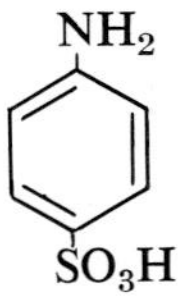 (C) NH$_2$–C$_6$H$_4$–SO$_3$H	0		0	++++	+++
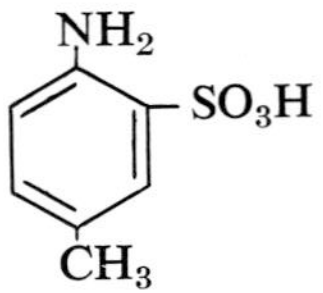 (F) NH$_2$, SO$_3$H, CH$_3$	0		++	0	0
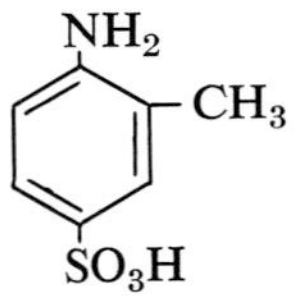 (D) NH$_2$, CH$_3$, SO$_3$H	0		0	+++	++++
(G) NH$_2$, CH$_3$, Br, SO$_3$H	0		0	0	+++
(H) NH$_2$, SO$_3$H, Cl	0		+	0	0

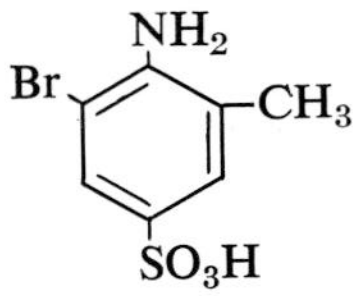

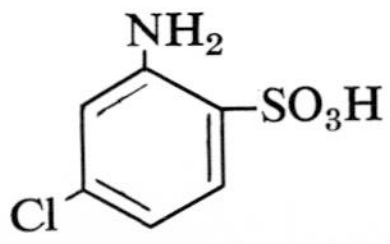

serum has been prepared against a certain hapten-protein conjugate, and the same hapten is introduced into the incubation mixture at the time of testing, the precipitin reaction will be inhibited. Here, although the pure hapten is not capable of forming an insoluble complex with the antiserum, it nevertheless combines with the antibody molecules and thereby blocks their combination with the hapten-protein conjugate. This phenomenon is called *hapten inhibition*.

A procedure developed recently permits allergic hemagglutination reactions to be tested and quantitated in vitro. A hapten-erythrocyte conjugate, which can be formed in vitro, is used to sensitize an appropriate animal (usually a rabbit). The antibodies that appear in the rabbit serum will then react in vitro with erythrocytes bearing hapten molecules, causing their agglutination.[16] The usefulness of this technique in studying the basis of allergic drug phenomena is illustrated by investigations on penicillin allergy, discussed later (p. 486).

The principles developed in the pioneering studies cited above were further applied in investigations dealing with skin sensitization in guinea pigs.[17] Picryl chloride (2,4,6-trinitrochlorobenzene), 2,4-dinitrochlorobenzene, and 2,4-dinitrofluorobenzene were used. These compounds form covalent linkages with free amino groups; 2-4-dinitrofluorobenzene is the same reagent used to establish the primary sequence of proteins by combining with the NH_2-group of the terminal amino acid at each step of a sequential degradation.[18] When such reagents were injected intradermally into guinea pigs, local sensitization resulted, and skin reactions could be elicited subsequently by reapplication of the same reagent. Sensitization of the skin could also be brought about by intraperitoneal injection of the allergenic agent, accompanied by killed mycobacteria as an "adjuvant."[18a] Even better skin sensitization resulted from coupling the reactive chemical to erythrocyte stromata and injecting this artificial conjugate intraperitoneally. Combined injection of the artificial conjugates with mycobacteria in paraffin oil led to sensitization when the intramuscular route was used. The sensitivity to delayed-type contact dermatitis thus induced could be passively transferred to a recipient animal by lymphocytes or by cell

[15] K. LANDSTEINER and H. LAMPL: Über die Abhängigkeit der serologischen Spezifität von der chemischen Struktur. (Darstellung von Antigenen mit bekannter chemischer Konstitution der spezifischen Gruppen). XII. Mitteilung über Antigene. *Biochem. Z.* 86:343 (1918).

[16] W. E. BULLOCK and F. S. KANTOR: Hemagglutination reactions of human erythrocytes conjugated covalently with dinitrophenyl groups. *J. Immunol.* 94:317 (1965).

[17] M. W. CHASE: Experimental sensitization with particular reference to picryl chloride. *Int. Arch. Allergy Appl. Immunol.* 5:163 (1954).

[18] F. SANGER and H. TUPPY: The amino-acid sequence in the phenylalanyl chain of insulin. 1. The identification of lower peptides from partial hydrolysates. *Biochem. J.* 49:463 (1951).

[18a] An adjuvant is a substance, usually not antigenic in itself, that enhances antibody formation in response to an antigen.

exudates from lymphocytes.[19] After injection of such cellular material, the skin of the recipient, which had never been exposed to the allergenic chemical, acquired specific sensitivity within 12 hours to two days.

These studies of sensitization of the skin are of interest because they appear to mimic so closely the course of events in human contact dermatitis. Sensitization appears to be most effective by direct application of the allergen to the skin, presumably because conjugates have to be formed with the skin proteins. Subsequently, the dermatitis can be elicited either by topical reapplication of the allergen or by its administration via a systemic route. It has been shown[20] that when dinitrochlorobenzene is applied to guinea pig skin, nearly all of it that becomes fixed in the epidermis is bound to lysine groups in the proteins of the Malpighian layer, at the junction of the epidermis and corium. This binding is thought to be essential for the development of the typical delayed-type skin allergy. Dinitrochlorobenzene conjugates with homologous (i.e., guinea pig) serum or with heterologous protein (egg albumin) caused sensitization of the immediate type, with circulating antibodies demonstrable, but no skin allergy. On the other hand, conjugates of the same hapten with guinea pig skin protein, injected into the foot pad of the guinea pig, led to a typical delayed-type allergy of the contact dermatitis type; no circulating antibodies developed, but passive transfer could be achieved with lymphoid cells. Thus, it appears that the development of allergic contact dermatitis requires sensitization with a conjugate of hapten and skin protein.

The success of these experimental approaches in producing suitable models of drug allergy raised the question whether a hapten must necessarily form a covalent linkage to a protein in order to act as an antigen. In one study[21] a series of reactive chemicals was tested on rabbits to see if there was any correlation between antigenicity and the ability to combine with free amino groups of proteins. The highest antibody titers were found with those compounds that were capable of forming covalent bonds at body pH and at low temperature and were not readily metabolized. A similar and even more dramatic indication of the importance of covalent attachment came from experiments with 2,4-dinitrochlorobenzene.[13] This compound causes an allergic contact dermatitis in factory workers exposed to it; and, as indicated above, guinea pigs can also be sensitized to it. There are approximately 90 chloro- and nitro-substituted benzenes. In experiments carried out with 17 of these, it was found that guinea pigs could be

[19] M. W. CHASE, W. DAMESHEK, S. HABERMAN, M. SAMTER, and T. L. SQUIER: A symposium on the role of the formed elements of the blood in allergy and hypersensitivity. *J. Allergy* 26:219 (1955).

[20] S. B. SALVIN: Contact hypersensitivity, circulating antibody, and immunologic unresponsiveness. *Fed. Proc.* 24:40 (1965).

[21] P. G. H. GELL, C. R. HARRINGTON, and R. P. RIVERS: The antigenic function of simple chemical compounds: production of precipitins in rabbits. *Brit. J. Exper. Pathol.* 27:267 (1946).

sensitized to ten. Not one of the seven inert compounds would combine with the amino group of aniline in vitro, but all ten that sensitized were able to do so. On the other hand, most drugs in therapeutic use, including many that are prone to cause allergic sensitization, are not chemically reactive compounds, certainly not comparable with the diazotizing, acylating, or amine-combining reagents used experimentally. This paradox has led to the proposal that allergenic drugs are transformed in vivo to more reactive derivatives. These, according to this view, are the true allergens, forming covalent bonds with body proteins, analogous to the artificial conjugates used to produce experimental allergy.

The strongest evidence for covalent binding in hapten-protein interactions in vivo comes from recent investigations on penicillin allergy.[22-25] It has been shown that both in vitro and in vivo penicillin undergoes slow transformation to much more reactive derivatives. Figure 7-1 shows the initial molecular rearrangement of penicillin to penicillenic acid, and the subsequent transformation of this intermediate to penicilloic acid. Penicillenic acid can react with amino groups (e.g., ϵ-amino groups of lysine residues in proteins) prior to molecular rearrangement, as shown by the broken arrow, to yield α-amide derivatives of the penicilloic acid structure. A number of lines of investigation have implicated these penicilloic acid-protein conjugates as the probable sensitizing antigens in penicillin allergy.

Typical evidence is presented in Fig. 7-2. The method of hemagglutination was used. Erythrocytes were incubated with penicillin and then added to a reaction mixture containing penicillin antiserum, produced by repeated injection of penicillin into a rabbit. The penicillin-treated red blood cells were agglutinated by the antiserum at dilutions up to 1/64. The technique of hapten inhibition was then used to assess the specificity of the antibodies and antigens in the reaction. Addition of the same hapten to which the antibodies were formed inhibits the hemagglutination by saturating the antibody molecules. The hapten inhibition was quantitated by finding what hapten concentration was needed to inhibit the agglutination completely at various serum dilutions. Obviously, the less the serum is diluted (i.e., the more concentrated the antibodies), the more hapten is required. The resulting curves in Fig. 7-2 are remarkable because they show clearly that the compounds whose structures were illustrated in Fig. 7-1 fall into three distinct classes. Penicillin itself, penicillenic acid, and penicilloic acid (a, b, and c) were by no means the most effective in-

[22] C. W. PARKER: Immunochemical mechanisms in penicillin allergy. *Fed. Proc.* 24:51 (1965).

[23] A. L. DE WECK: Studies on penicillin hypersensitivity. I. The specificity of rabbit "anti-penicillin" antibodies. *Int. Arch. Allergy Appl. Immunol. 21:*20 (1962).

[24] A. L. DE WECK: Studies on penicillin hypersensitivity. II. The role of the side chain in penicillin antigenicity. *Int. Arch. Allergy Appl. Immunol. 21:*38 (1962).

[25] B. B. LEVINE: Immunochemical mechanisms involved in pencillin hypersensitivity in experimental animals and in human beings. *Fed. Proc.* 24:45 (1965).

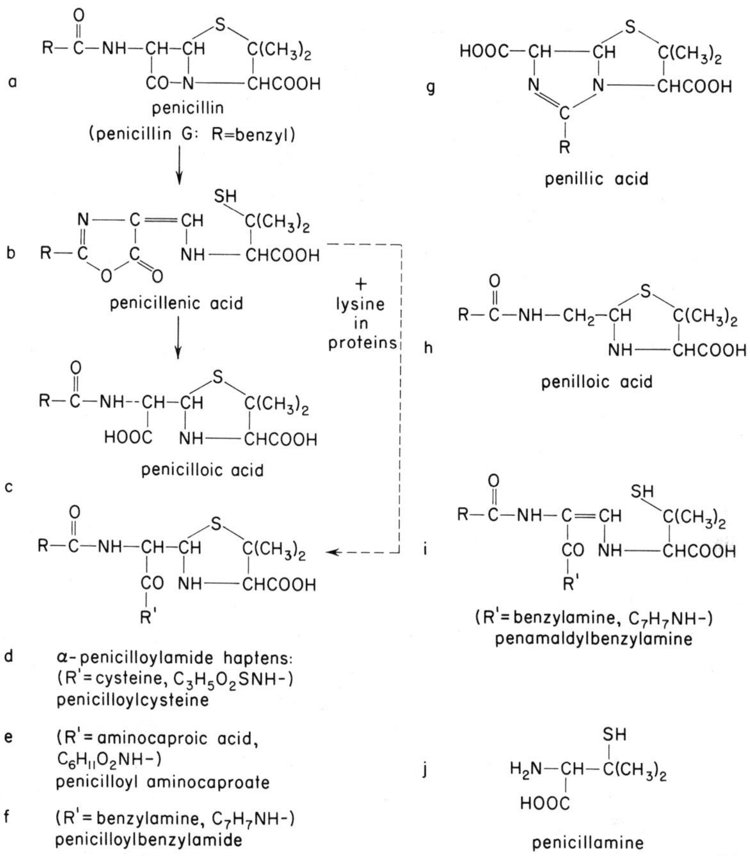

FIG. 7-1. STRUCTURES OF PENICILLIN AND DERIVATIVES. Arrows *indicate spontaneous transformations of the penicillin structure. The derivatives shown here are referred to in Fig. 7-2. (Adapted from de Weck, Fig. 1.*[28])

hibitors of the hemagglutination, and four related compounds (g, h, i, and j) were entirely ineffective. But the three α-penicilloylamide haptens tested were about 100 times more effective than penicillin itself or its two breakdown products. These results imply very strongly that the penicillin antiserum was really directed against such a penicilloyl derivative, and thus, by inference, that a penicilloyl conjugate was the actual sensitizing agent in vivo. Other investigations have led to the same conclusion, except that in man there seem to be other antigenic determinants in addition to the penicilloylamide conjugates.[22, 24, 25]

In summary, the argument that covalently bonded conjugates between drug and a body protein are necessary for the development of drug allergy rests on two kinds of evidence. First, experimental allergy in animals has been produced readily with reagents capable of forming covalent

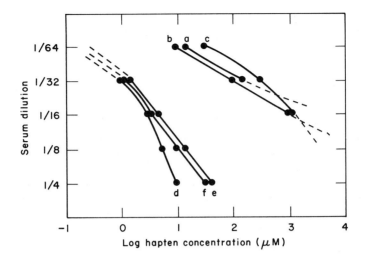

FIG. 7-2.   INHIBITION OF HEMAGGLUTINATION BY HAPTENS RELATED TO PENICIL-
LIN.   *The designation of the various haptens refers to Fig. 7-1. A suspension of
erythrocytes was preincubated with benzylpenicillin (a, Fig. 7-1), then added
to rabbit benzylpenicillin antiserum. Hemagglutination resulted up to serum
dilution 1/64. Addition of hapten to the reaction mixture could inhibit hemagglutination by combining with the serum antibody. Each experimental point
here represents the hapten concentration needed to achieve complete inhibition
of hemagglutination at the given serum dilution. With haptens g, h, i, and j (not
shown), no inhibition resulted even at 10^{-3}M, the highest concentration tested.
(Modified after de Weck, Fig. 4.[23])*

bonds with proteins, whereas attempts to make animals allergic to drugs
that are not particularly reactive have been unsuccessful. Second, the
antigenic determinants in penicillin allergy, both in animals and in man,
appear to be penicilloyl or related covalent conjugates with proteins (as
described above) rather than the original penicillin molecule itself. These
findings certainly show that penicillin derivatives are capable of acting as
allergens when combined covalently with proteins; but they do not exclude
the possibility that penicillin itself could become an antigen by interacting
reversibly with a protein. In this connection it is interesting that some
patients experiencing allergic reactions to penicillin contain in their serum
antibodies that cause passive sensitization of recipient skin to crystalline
penicillin (benzylpenicillin) but not to any of the derivatives or conjugates.[25] Insofar as other drugs are concerned, especially nonreactive ones
(e.g., sulfonamides, salicylates) that can cause allergy in man, nothing can
be said about the formation or nonformation of covalently bonded conjugates until relevant experiments are carried out. Since we know so little
about the molecular mechanisms involved in the synthesis of specific antibodies in response to the presence of antigens, it is impossible to judge
a priori whether or not a fairly tight but reversible binding of a drug to

plasma albumin or to other proteins in the body might create a sufficiently stable antigenic determinant to produce allergic sensitization.

Affinity Labeling

Recent investigations into the structure of antibody active sites[26] have employed an ingenious technique known as *affinity labeling*. An animal is sensitized to a diazotized hapten-protein conjugate, as in the methods described earlier, and specific antibody proteins (γ-globulins) are prepared from the animal's serum. A labeling reagent is then used, which is capable of forming covalent bonds with tyrosine residues, and which is also related closely enough to the sensitizing hapten so that it will interact specifically with the antibody active site. Thus, a tyrosine residue in the active site can be labeled specifically. For example, if sensitization was carried out with *p*-azobenzenearsonate, then the corresponding reactive diazonium derivative, *p*-(arsonic acid)benzenediazonium fluoborate, is used as the labeling reagent. Three pairs of sensitizing conjugates and corresponding labeling reagents are shown in Table 7-2.

The diazo complex of the labeling reagent with tyrosine in the protein could be determined spectrophotometrically. When a labeling reagent was allowed to react with γ-globulins synthesized in response to sensitization with the homologous hapten conjugate, the azotyrosine was readily measurable. But when the labeling reagent was allowed to react under the same conditions with nonantibody γ-globulin or with γ-globulin of different antibody specificity, there was virtually no complex formation. Moreover, if the antibody sites were first saturated by the homologous hapten, the complex formation with labeling reagent was prevented. Thus, the labeling reagent appears to combine with a tyrosine residue in the antibody active site.

This technique has been used to study the composition of the antibody active site by disrupting the S—S bonds that hold together the two light and two heavy chains of the immunoglobulin molecule. The chains were subjected to tryptic or chymotryptic digestion, followed by various analyses of the peptide fragments. The heavy chains (molecular weight 50,000) and the light chains (molecular weight 25,000) both were found to be labeled in tyrosine residues, and the labeling in both types of chain could be prevented by saturation with homologous hapten. The labeled peptide fragments from both kinds of chain were found to be very similar in average size and in containing an unusually high content of amino acids with hydrophobic side chains. Antibody molecules of the same specificity were found to be heterogeneous with respect to amino acid sequence in the vicinity of the labeled tyrosine residue of each chain. The manner in which particular regions of the light and heavy chains combine to form antibody

[26] S. J. SINGER and R. F. DOOLITTLE: Antibody active sites and immunoglobulin molecules. *Science 153:*13 (1966).

TABLE 7-2.   Affinity-labeling systems

Homologous pairs of hapten conjugates were used to sensitize, and labeling reagents to label the antibody active site. The cationic portions of the fluoborate salts used as labeling reagents are shown below. (From Singer and Doolittle,[26] Table 1. By permission of the American Association for Advancement of Science.)

Sensitizing conjugate	Labeling reagent cation
HO_3S——N=N $\begin{cases} tyr \\ his \\ lys \end{cases}$	HO_3S——$\overset{+}{N}\equiv N$
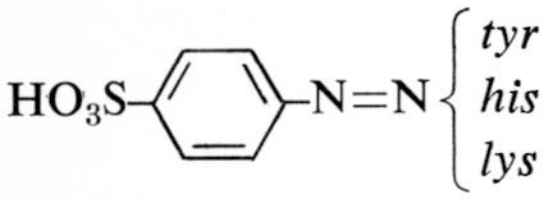 *p*-azobenzenearsonic acid conjugate	 *p*-(arsonic acid)benzenediazonium
O_2N——lys, NO_2	O_2N——$\overset{+}{N}\equiv N$
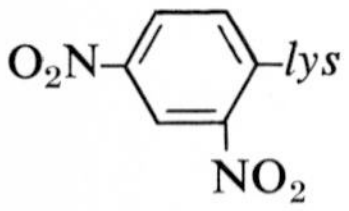 2,4-dinitrophenyl conjugate	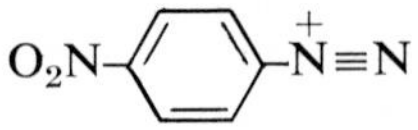 *p*-nitrobenzenediazonium
	——$\overset{+}{N}\equiv N$, NO_2
	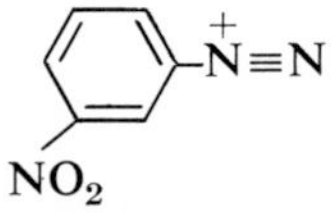 *m*-nitrobenzenediazonium
$(CH_3)_3\overset{+}{N}$——N=N $\begin{cases} tyr \\ his \\ lys \end{cases}$	$(CH_3)_3\overset{+}{N}$——$\overset{+}{N}\equiv N$
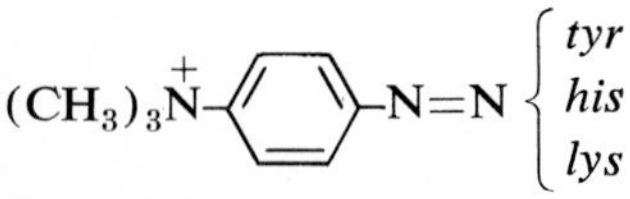 *p*-azotrimethylphenylammonium conjugate	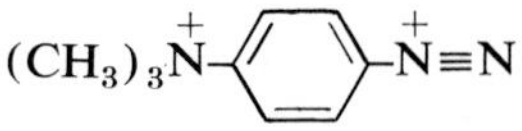 *p*-(trimethylammonium)benzenediazonium

active sites with characteristic specificities remains to be elucidated. The process of antibody synthesis during sensitization to a hapten is thought to involve the selective proliferation of those cells that can make light and heavy chains with the right amino acid sequences to form an antibody active site specific to the sensitizing hapten.[27]

DRUG ALLERGY IN MAN

In this section we shall consider (*1*) the various manifestations of drug allergy, (*2*) the frequency of allergic drug reactions in human populations and the factors that determine this frequency, (*3*) the methods of

[27] F. M. BURNET: *The Clonal Selection Theory of Acquired Immunity.* Nashville, Tenn., Vanderbilt University Press, 1959.

predicting allergic sensitivity in individual patients, (*4*) the methods of desensitizing, and (*5*) the management of allergic reactions. There is little doubt that penicillin is the leading cause of allergic drug reactions in general and also of serious systemic reactions.[28-30] Consequently, a great deal of the research on drug allergy in man deals with this drug. And because penicillin has been administered to millions of patients, often under controlled conditions in teaching hospitals and clinics, conclusions from such studies are often soundly based on statistically valid data.

Manifestations of Drug Allergy

Allergic reactions in man may be localized or widespread. Spasm of smooth muscle, edema of the mucous membranes, and vascular damage characterize the immediate-type response. Target organs are the respiratory and gastrointestinal tracts, the blood vessels, and skin. The most dangerous allergic reaction, anaphylaxis, is of the immediate type.[31] Symptoms develop with alarming rapidity after an eliciting dose, which may be extremely small. Anxiety and a sensation of generalized warmth is followed by complaints of substernal pressure, difficulty in breathing, collapse of blood pressure, and anoxia. Death can occur within a few minutes. This fatal syndrome has occurred after the sting of a single bee, and after the administration of a test dose of less than $1\mu g$ of penicillin. Necropsy findings show obstructive edema of the upper respiratory tract; this, and also laryngospasm and bronchospasm, are the usual causes of death.

Bronchial asthma alone may appear as an immediate allergic response unaccompanied by the more severe symptoms of anaphylaxis. There is experimental evidence that histamine is released during the allergic reaction. Human bronchial strips freshly obtained at autopsy were suspended in a tissue bath so that contractions of the smooth muscle could be recorded.[32] Bronchial strips from asthmatic subjects contracted in response to the same antigens (pollens, house dust) that had precipitated asthmatic attacks during life. At the same time, histamine was released into the bath. Control strips from nonallergic subjects did not contract, neither did they release histamine in response to the same allergens. But normal as well as allergic strips contracted when histamine was added to the bath. Antihistaminics completely blocked the response to added histamine but were ineffective

[28] R. A. KERN and N. A. WIMBERLEY, JR.: Penicillin reactions: their nature, growing importance, recognition, management, and prevention. *Amer. J. Med. Sci. 226:*357 (1953).

[29] C. D. CALNAN: Cutaneous reactions to penicillin. *Postgrad. Med. 40: Supplement 152* (1964).

[30] S. M. FEINBERG and A. R. FEINBERG: Allergy to penicillin. *J. Amer. Med. Ass. 160:*778 (1956).

[31] L. P. JAMES, JR., and K. F. AUSTEN: Fatal systemic anaphylaxis in man. *New Engl. J. Med. 270:*597 (1964).

[32] H. O. SCHILD, D. F. HAWKINS, J. L. MONGAR, and H. HERXHEIMER: Reactions of isolated human asthmatic lung and bronchial tissue to a specific antigen. Histamine release and muscular contraction. *Lancet 2:*376 (1951).

against the contradictions caused by allergens in sensitized strips. These experiments suggest that an antigen-antibody response in the previously sensitized tissue releases histamine, but they do not show that histamine is responsible for the muscle spasm. Possibly some other mechanism is the immediate cause of the antigen-induced contraction. These findings essentially confirm in human tissues the principle underlying the classical Schultz-Dale phenomenon,[33] in which histamine release and muscle spasm are both elicited in guinea pig uterus in a tissue bath by specific antigens to which the animal had previously been sensitized. Consistent with the experimental in vitro results cited above, antihistamines are not effective in vivo in anaphylaxis or drug-induced asthma in man. Moreover, antihistamines themselves can cause bronchoconstriction in man, and they have been shown to cause contraction of isolated strips of guinea pig tracheal smooth muscle at concentrations in the usual therapeutic range.[34]

Other manifestations of the immediate type are conjunctivitis and rhinitis (as in hay fever), generalized urticaria with itching, and angioedema of various tissues.[35]

Not readily classified as immediate or delayed is the "serum sickness syndrome," so called because it was first recognized as a response to antitoxin preparations containing horse serum. It is often elicited by foreign proteins as well as by drugs. The syndrome consists of fever, lymphadenopathy, and arthralgia, sometimes accompanied by urticaria. Polyarteritis nodosa and other collagen diseases may develop. Drug fever may often be seen alone, without the other reactions of the "serum sickness" group.

Dermatitis is a delayed response. The allergic reactions to systemic drug administration vary from trivial fixed eruptions[36] to widespread and fatal exfoliative dermatitis, and the skin manifestations may assume a variety of forms. Contact dermatitis is the allergic response of skin to direct application of an eliciting drug. Lymphocytes infiltrate the cutis underlying the area of contact, and there is vascular dilation manifested by erythema. Vesicles form in the epidermis. Severe contact dermatitis may be accompanied by systemic allergic reactions such as polyarteritis or other collagen diseases.[37] The role of histamine in allergic skin reactions is better established than in asthmatic and anaphylactic responses. Histamine is certainly

---

[33] H. H. DALE: The anaphylactic reaction of plain muscle in the guinea-pig. *J. Pharmacol. Exp. Therap.* 4:167 (1913).

[34] D. F. HAWKINS: Bronchoconstrictor and bronchodilator actions of antihistamine drugs. *Brit. J. Pharmacol.* 10:230 (1955).

[35] Angio-edema (also called angioneurotic edema) consists of swellings of the face, hands, feet, genitalia, and other regions. The syndrome is caused by dilation (and presumably altered permeability) of small blood vessels, chiefly in the subcutaneous tissues.

[36] These lesions are remarkable. They occur in precisely the same cutaneous areas, sometimes no bigger than a fingertip, whenever the eliciting drug is given.

[37] D. M. PILLSBURY, W. B. SHELLEY, and A. M. KLIGMAN: "Drug Allergy" and "Contact Dermatitis of the Allergic Type," in *Dermatology*. Philadelphia, W. B. Saunders, 1956, chaps. 17 and 18.

released from skin as a consequence of the antigen-antibody reaction, and the blood level of histamine may be elevated.[38] Injection of histamine into the skin produces the "triple response" of erythema, wheal formation, and flare that also characterizes the delayed type of skin allergy.[13, 39, 40] Moreover, antihistaminic drugs are effective in antagonizing these phenomena when they occur as part of an allergic syndrome.

Many drugs have been held responsible for allergic disorders of the blood and the blood-forming tissues, such as hemolytic anemia, granulocytopenia (reduced number of circulating granulocytic leukocytes), and thrombocytopenia (reduced number of platelets).[41] Often there is a mere coincidence in time between administration of the drug and onset of the disease, without rigorous proof of an allergic basis. And frequently the disorder is actually an idiosyncratic one, as, for example, the hemolytic anemia due to primaquine. In some instances, however, it has been possible to demonstrate that drug allergy underlies the pathologic changes, by demonstrating the presence of an antibody that reacts specifically with the suspected drug in a manner that can account for the destruction of blood cells. A few such examples will be cited.

A patient receiving the antischistosome drug stibophen (sodium antimony bis-pyrocatechol-2,4-disulfonate) developed an acute hemolytic anemia. Standard hematologic tests showed that the patient's serum, in vitro, could cause agglutination and hemolysis of his own or normal erythrocytes, but only in the presence of the drug. Serum from an unsensitized individual had no such effect.[42]

The antipyretic drug aminopyrine has been implicated in an allergic reaction leading to granulocytopenia.[43] The mechanism is an agglutination of leukocytes, which presumably leads to their more rapid destruction. Three hours after a dose of aminopyrine, a patient developed pronounced leukopenia. At this time, 300 ml of the patient's whole blood was transfused into a normal recipient of the same blood group. The white blood cell count of the recipient fell precipitously (from 5,000 to 1,000 per cubic millimeter) soon after the transfusion. The decrease occurred mainly in neutrophils, eosinophils, monocytes, and, to a lesser degree, in lymphocytes. One week later, the recipient was given 300 ml of normal blood, and no

38 M. W. CHASE: "Antibodies to Drugs," in *Sensitivity Reactions to Drugs,* ed. by M. L. Rosenheim and R. Moulton. Springfield, Ill. Charles C Thomas, 1958, pp. 125–134.

39 H. H. DALE and P. P. LAIDLAW: The physiological action of β-iminazolylethylamine. *J. Physiol. 41:*318 (1910).

40 T. LEWIS: *The Blood Vessels of the Human Skin and Their Responses.* London, Shaw and Sons, 1927.

41 E. A. CARR, JR., and G. A. ASTE: Recent laboratory studies and clinical observations on hypersensitivity to drugs and use of drugs in allergy. *Annu. Rev. Pharmacol. 1:*105 (1961).

42 J. W. HARRIS: Studies on the mechanism of a drug-induced hemolytic anemia. *J. Lab. Clin. Med. 47:*760 (1956).

43 S. MOESCHLIN and K. WAGNER: Agranulocytosis due to the occurrence of leukocyte-agglutinins (pyramidon and cold agglutinins). *Acta Haematol. 8:*29 (1952).

decline in the white cell count occurred. Administration of aminopyrine itself to the recipient did not cause agranulocytosis. When a second recipient was tested with blood from the aminopyrine-sensitive donor, similar results were obtained; agglutination of the patient's own leukocytes or of normal leukocytes occurred when the patient's serum was added in vitro. Clearly, the sensitive individual had something in his blood, after aminopyrine injection, that could agglutinate his own or others' leukocytes. The site of destruction of agglutinated cells in the body in allergic drug reactions is not known with certainty. Studies with ^{32}P-labeled leukocytes indicated that during virus infections destruction of leukocytes occurs mainly in the lungs.

Blood platelets have been implicated as targets of allergic drug reactions.[44] This has been shown for allylisopropylacetylurea (Sedormid), a sedative formerly in very wide use in Europe. An antibody to the drug has been demonstrated in the serum of patients who, while taking this compound, developed thrombocytopenic purpura, a bleeding tendency caused by platelet deficiency. When a patient's serum, drug, platelets from the patient or from a normal donor, and complement[12] were incubated together, platelet lysis occurred. Without complement, the platelets agglutinated but did not lyse. Without drug, there was neither lysis nor agglutination. The factor in the patient's serum responsible for these immune reactions was a γ-globulin. A very similar result was obtained with the antihistaminic drug 2-(N-phenyl-N-benzylaminomethyl)imidazoline (Antazoline), also capable of causing thrombocytopenic purpura. Other drugs, notably quinidine, have also been implicated in this disorder, but the evidence for an allergic basis is not conclusive.

A controversy has raged for years about the rare aplastic anemia seen in patients treated with chloramphenicol. The infrequency of the reaction suggested to some that its basis was allergic, but rigorous criteria were never met. The reaction was known to occur most frequently in patients who had been undergoing prolonged therapy with the drug, a surprising finding for an allergic response, since previously sensitized patients would have been expected to react promptly. A careful clinical study has now shown[45] that the bone marrow toxicity is strictly dose related. A reversible depression of erythrocyte production could be produced in most patients at sufficient dosage. Inasmuch as chloramphenicol at high concentration does inhibit protein synthesis in mammalian cells in vitro, it seems likely that the aplastic anemia observed occasionally in patients is a direct toxic effect (or possibly in some patients an idiosyncratic sensitivity), but not an instance of drug allergy.

        [44] J. F. ACKROYD: "The Pathogenesis of Purpura," in *Lectures on Haematology*, ed. by F. G. J. Hayhoe. London, Cambridge University Press, 1959, p. 217.
        [45] J. L. SCOTT, S. M. FINEGOLD, G. A. BELKIN, and J. S. LAWRENCE: A controlled double-blind study of the hematologic toxicity of chloramphenicol. *New Engl. J. Med.* 272:1137 (1965).

In some well-documented cases, the lymphoid system is the main target of drug allergy, and lymphadenopathy mimicking Hodgkin's disease may develop. In one case, a patient developed allergy to sulfisoxazole, diphenylhydantoin, primidone, and phenobarbital; circulating antibodies were demonstrated against all but the last of these.[46]

Involvement of the liver in an allergic drug reaction is apparently very rare, if indeed it occurs at all. Drugs do cause the two main types of liver injury: parenchymal cell damage or inflammation, and obstructive jaundice associated with inflammation of the bile canaliculi.[41] Iproniazid has been associated with parenchymal damage. The phenothiazines have been associated with injury of the obstructive-jaundice type.[47] In no case of liver injury caused by a drug has there been unequivocal evidence of an allergic reaction, but there is often presumptive evidence. For example, the liver damage may not occur during a first exposure to a drug, but only on readministration. Or there may be an associated dermatitis. Until specific antibodies are demonstrated in tissue or serum, judgment should be withheld about the allergic basis of a particular hepatotoxicity.

Frequency of Allergic Reactions to Drugs

The frequency of drug allergy in man is dependent upon the nature of the drug, the route of administration, the genetic predisposition of those who receive the drug, and the extent of prior exposure and of cross-reactivity to the same or related drugs.[48] There is really no way at present to arrive at a valid estimate of the frequency of allergic reactions to all drugs. There is not even universal agreement about the criteria for classification of a drug reaction as allergic. Consequently, many toxic or idiosyncratic reactions are considered allergic, while many allergic reactions are attributed to some other cause. Even were there no diagnostic difficulty, however, the pertinent statistical questions could not be answered. One would like to know what fraction of all patients treated with a given drug develop symptoms of allergy. One would like to know which of two drugs is less likely to cause allergy. Retrospective fact-gathering and haphazard reporting of reactions lead to distorted impressions. The only useful sort of investigation includes all patients who receive a drug, and all have to be followed to determine who has an allergic reaction and, equally important, who has not. As matters now stand, the mild allergic reactions, which are undoubtedly more common than the severe ones, are usually not even reported; they are treated by physicians everywhere, and the information is nowhere pooled or analyzed. Severe allergic reactions often result in

[46] D. S. ROBINSON, M. G. MAC DONALD, and F. P. HOBIN: Sodium diphenylhydantoin reaction with evidence of circulating antibodies. *J. Amer. Med. Ass. 192:*171 (1965).

[47] J. REICHEL, S. B. GOLDBERG, M. ELLENBERG, and F. SCHAFFNER: Intrahepatic cholestasis following administration of chlorpropamide. Report of a case with electron microscopic observations. *Amer. J. Med. 28:*654 (1960).

[48] H. L. ALEXANDER: *Reactions with Drug Therapy.* Philadelphia, W. B. Saunders, 1955.

hospitalization, hence are more likely to come to general attention. But knowing how many severe allergic reactions are attributable to a given drug does not help one assess the relative risk of using that drug unless one also knows how frequently the drug is administered. The number of allergic drug reactions, as an isolated statistic, is about as informative as the number of Fords, Chevrolets, and Alfa Romeos involved in automobile accidents in a year without knowledge of the number or kinds of cars on the highways or the miles driven per car.

Nevertheless, there is no doubt that some drugs are more allergenic than others. Caffeine is certainly more widely used than aspirin, and aspirin more so than penicillin; yet allergy to penicillin is fairly common, allergy to aspirin is rare, and allergy to caffeine is unknown.

Drug allergy may be induced by any route of administration, but not with equal efficiency. The oral route seems to be associated with a lower incidence of allergic sensitization than any other, whereas topical application of drugs to the skin is especially prone to sensitize. Industrial exposure to chemicals often results in the development of contact dermatitis among production workers. In one survey of more than 3,000 cases of dermatitis due to occupational exposure, approximately one-sixth could be attributed to allergenic substances.[49] The number of compounds that are capable of causing contact dermatitis is extremely large and continually increases as new chemicals are synthesized. The list in Table 7-3 is taken from a textbook of occupational medicine. It is incomplete, but it serves to show the diversity of allergenic compounds to which people may be exposed. Contact dermatitis in workers engaged in the production of a new drug may serve as an omen of the probable development of drug allergy later, in patients, after the drug is introduced for therapeutic use.

There are very great individual differences, as well as species differences, in the ability to become sensitized to drugs, and this "allergic predisposition" probably has a genetic basis.[6-8] Guinea pigs can be bred for high or low susceptibility to skin sensitization with 2,4-dinitrochlorobenzene.[51] Attempts were made to sensitize human subjects to contact dermatitis with p-nitrosodimethylaniline and 2,4-dinitrochlorobenzene. Subjects were found to vary considerably in their susceptibility to sensitization by either compound; moreover, some became sensitized exclusively to one or the other, some to both, some to neither.[52]

[49] J. V. KLAUDER: Actual causes of certain occupational dermatoses. *Arch. Dermatol.* 85:441 (1962).

[50] A. J. FLEMING: "Chemical Health Hazards," *Modern Occupational Medicine,* 2nd ed., ed. by A. J. Fleming, C. A. D'Alonzo, and J. A. Zapp, Philadelphia, Lea & Febiger, 1960, pp. 365–418.

[51] M. W. CHASE: Inheritance in guinea pigs of the susceptibility to skin sensitization with simple chemical compounds. *J. Exper. Med.* 73:711 (1941).

[52] K. LANDSTEINER, A. ROSTENBERG, JR., and M. B. SULZBERGER: Individual differences in susceptibility to eczematous sensitization with simple chemical substances. *J. Invest. Dermatol.* 2:25 (1939).

TABLE 7-3.   Compounds that may cause contact dermatitis in industrial workers

The list, by no means complete, indicates the diversity of allergenic substances to which industrial workers may be exposed. (From Fleming et al.,[50] p. 381.)

Acetaldehyde	Methyl *m*-amino-*p*-oxybenzoate
Acetyl nitrate	(ortho form)
Amido azobenzene	Methyl salicylate
Amido azotoluene	Monomethyl-*p*-aminophenol sulfate
Aniline black	Nickel
Biacetyl	Nitrobenzene
Bromides	Nitrosodimethylaniline
N-cetyltrimethylammonium bromide	Nitrosomethylurethan
Chromates	N,N-di-*sec*-butyl-*p*-phenylenediamine
ammonium, potassium, and sodium	*p*-Aminoacetanilid coupled with *p*-
Cobalt	cresol (dye)
Cyanines and isocyanines	*p*- and *m*-Toluenediamine (dye)
Cyclohexanone	*p*-Nitroaniline coupled with aniline
Dichlorobenzene	(dye)
Dichloroethyl sulfide	*p*- and *o*-Amidophenol
Dicyanines	*p*- and *o*-Toluidine
Diethylene glycol abietate	*p*-Phenylenediamine
Dinitrochlorobenzene	Phenyldiiodoarsine
Dinitrophenol	Phenylhydrazine
Diphenylamine	Phthalic anhydride
Diphenyloloctadecane	Picryl chloride
Emetine hydrochloride	Pinacyanols
Eosin	Polyhydric phenols
Formaldehyde	Quinhone azide
Guanidines	Rhodamine B dye (derived from
Hexamethylene tetramine	diethyl-*m*-aminophenol [2 moles]
Hydroabietyl alcohol	and phthalic anhydride)
Hydroabietyl diglycolate	Tetrabromofluorescein
Hydroquinone	Tetramethylthiuram mono- and di-
Hydroxylamine hydrochloride	sulfide
Mercaptobenzthiazole	*tert*-Butylcatechol
Mercury compounds, organic and in-	Thioglycolic acid
organic	Vinyl acetate
Methyl heptine carbonate	Vinyl carbazole

We have already seen that prior exposure to a drug is essential for the sensitization that must precede an allergic response. But it should be borne in mind that mere absence of a recorded history of previous exposure by no means rules out the possibility of allergy, since histories of this kind are notoriously unreliable. Patients are commonly unaware of what medication they receive, multiple irrational drug mixtures abound, and memories tend to be much less persistent than antibody-forming capacity. Moreover, enough is known about cross-sensitization to make it apparent that the initial exposure may have been to a different but related drug or environmental chemical.

An investigation was conducted on the effect of prior exposure to sulfonamides upon the incidence of allergy.[53,54] The allergic responses considered were those characteristic of the sulfonamide compounds—drug fever, dermatitis, and conjunctivitis. Three sulfonamides were used: sulfathiazole, sulfapyridine, and sulfadiazine. Before starting a course of therapy, a careful history was taken to see if the patient had previously been exposed to any sulfonamide and, if so, to which one; and also to ascertain if the previous exposure had resulted in an allergic reaction. The results are summarized in Table 7-4. In a very large series of patients receiving a sulfonamide for the first time (control series), the incidence of allergic reactions developing during the course of therapy was 5.0 per cent. In most of these, presumably, the drug was administered for weeks, long enough for sensitization and subsequent elicitation of the reaction to occur. Patients who had had previous treatment with a different drug and had not reacted to it were no more likely to develop an allergic reaction during their second course of treatment (incidence 3.6 per cent) than if they were receiving the drug for the first time. But if the second course involved administration of the same drug as during the first course, even though there had been no reaction during the first course, the incidence of allergy was increased (to 11.1 per cent). If there had been a reaction to the first course, then the incidence of reaction during the second course was still higher (16.7 per

TABLE 7-4.   **Frequencies of several allergic responses to sulfonamides during first and second courses of drug treatment**

The allergic responses considered here were drug fever, dermatitis, and conjunctivitis. (From Dowling et al.,[54] Table III.)

Reaction to first course	Sulfonamides administered during second course	Total no. of patients	Patients developing allergic reactions during second course	
			Number	Per cent
No	Different drug	169	6	3.6
No	Same drug	144	16	11.1
Yes	Different drug	30	5	16.7
Yes	Same drug	48	33	68.8
	Control series of persons receiving one course only	737	37	5.0

[53] H. F. DOWLING and M. H. LEPPER: "Drug fever" accompanying second courses of sulfathiazole, sulfadiazine and sulfapyridine. *Amer. J. Med. Sci.* 207:349 (1944).

[54] H. F. DOWLING, H. L. HIRSH, and M. H. LEPPER: Toxic reactions accompanying second courses of sulfonamides in patients developing toxic reactions during a previous course. *Ann. Int. Med.* 24:629 (1946).

cent), even when a different drug was used. Most significant, if the same drug that had caused an allergic reaction during the first course was administered again at a second course, the incidence of allergy jumped to 68.8 per cent. The evidence is therefore clear that in the sulfonamide series there is both specificity and cross-reactivity. A patient sensitized to one drug is more likely to react to a second drug than if he had never been sensitized at all, but he is less likely to react to the second drug than to the one that sensitized him.

The extent of cross-reactivity after prior exposure in the penicillin group is less clearly worked out and more controversial. Several semi-synthetic derivatives have been made in recent years by adding various side groups to the 6-aminopenicillanic acid skeleton (Fig. 7-3). Extravagant claims were made for some of these at the time of their introduction; for example, that they could be given safely to patients who were allergic to penicillin G. In general, such claims have not been borne out, and cross-reactivity is the rule rather than the exception. Such cross-reaction has been demonstrated by actual allergic manifestations in patients, and also by skin tests or red cell agglutination.[55,56] Conversely, patients who tolerate the new congeners usually show no positive skin test or hemagglutination with other types of penicillin, even though they might once have had an allergic

FIG. 7-3. STRUCTURES OF SOME PENICILLINS. *The basic penicillin structure is shown above as 6-aminopenicillanic acid with an R substituent. Several R groups are shown below.*

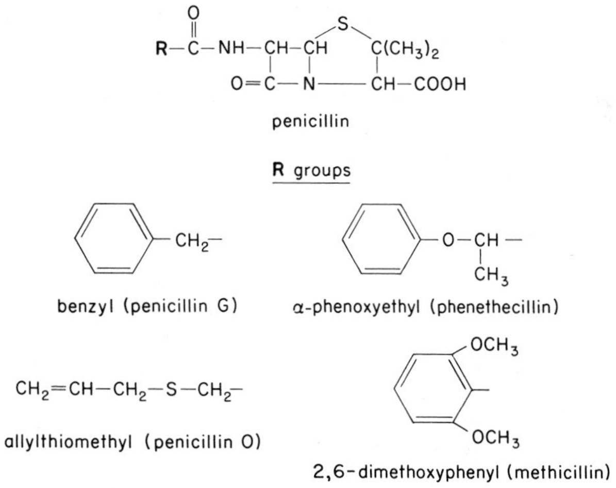

penicillin

R groups

benzyl (penicillin G)   α-phenoxyethyl (phenethecillin)

$CH_2=CH-CH_2-S-CH_2-$

allylthiomethyl (penicillin O)

2,6-dimethoxyphenyl (methicillin)

[55] R. H. SCHWARTZ and J. H. VAUGHAN: Immunologic responsiveness of man to penicillin. *J. Amer. Med. Ass. 186:*1151 (1963).

[56] G. T. STEWART: Cross-allergenicity of penicillin G and related substances. *Lancet 1:*509 (1962).

reaction.[57] One of the methodologic difficulties here is that a patient who previously had an allergic reaction to penicillin might not necessarily react at the next challenge, even with the same drug. Thus, sound conclusions can only be obtained in large-scale well-controlled studies, of which there have been but few. Most careful investigations have revealed cross-reactivity in some patients, absence of cross-reactivity in others.[58, 59]

This heterogeneity of allergic response is consistent with the experimental finding that there may be several antigenic determinants, even to a single drug. Moreover, one person may form antibodies directed toward a particular part of the drug molecule, another toward different chemical groups. If a patient happened to be allergically sensitized in a specific way toward benzylpenicillin, then a derivative with a different R group might well fail to elicit the reaction. But another patient, in whom benzylpenicillin was also the sensitizing drug, could have developed a less specific kind of allergic responsiveness, and therefore react to any other penicillanic acid derivative. The reasons for such individual differences are unknown; one could speculate that they are determined genetically. The practical consequence of this is that one cannot really predict how an individual patient will respond; it is therefore considered safest to avoid penicillin altogether if there is reason to fear a serious allergic response.[60]

The incidence of allergic reaction to penicillin among all patients receiving it ranges from less than 1 per cent to nearly 10 per cent in various studies. In an extensive survey conducted in Australia,[61] 1.3 per cent of nearly 7,000 patients given systemic penicillin were reported to have an allergic reaction; probably some mild reactions were not reported. About one-tenth of the reported reactions could be considered life threatening, although there were no fatalities in this series. Table 7-5 shows that the reactions most commonly were of the delayed type, and Table 7-6 classifies all symptoms and signs, giving the frequency of each. The majority of all the reported reactions involved the skin (urticaria and erythema).

A controlled study with over 2,000 college students[62] revealed an incidence of allergic reactions of 3.3 per cent. These were principally urticaria, angio-edema, skin eruptions, and serum sickness. Of the 70 reactions, 27 were of the immediate type, the remainder delayed.

[57] P. P. VAN ARSDEL, JR.: Allergic reactions to penicillin. *J. Amer. Med. Ass. 191*:238 (1965).

[58] E. F. LUTON: Methicillin tolerance after penicillin G anaphylaxis. *J. Amer. Med. Ass. 190*:39 (1964).

[59] C. W. PARKER and J. A. THIEL: Studies in human penicillin allergy: a comparison of various penicilloyl-polylysines. *J. Lab. Clin. Med. 62*:482 (1963).

[60] Anon.: Penicillin allergy. *Medical Letter 6*:77 (1964).

[61] Research Committee of the New South Wales Faculty of the Australian College of General Practitioners: Report on a survey of allergic reactions to penicillin. *Med J. Australia 1*:827 (1959).

[62] K. P. MATHEWS, F. M. HEMPHILL, R. G. LOVELL, W. E. FORSYTHE, and J. M. SHELDON: A controlled study on the use of parenteral and oral antihistamines in preventing penicillin reactions. *J. Allergy 27*:1 (1956).

TABLE 7-5. Immediate and delayed reactions in penicillin allergy

Survey of 6,832 patients receiving penicillin. (From Research Committee of the New South Wales Faculty,[61] Table I.)

Reaction	Number of cases
IMMEDIATE	7
DELAYED	
less than 24 hours	24
1 to 7 days	33
8 to 14 days	14
over 14 days	3
period not specified	10
Total	91

Venereal disease clinics provide a good source of information about the frequency of allergic reactions to penicillin among the population as a whole, since groups attending these clinics (unlike those in a skin clinic, for example) are not likely to include an unusual number of indi-

TABLE 7-6. Symptoms and signs in penicillin allergy

Survey of 6,832 patients receiving penicillin. (From Research Committee of the New South Wales Faculty,[61] Table III.)

Clinical features	Number of cases
FEVER	9
ARTHRALGIA	20
SKIN SIGNS	
bullae	4
erythema	46
purpuric spots	1
urticaria	64
subsequent desquamation	11
MOUTH SIGNS	
dryness	3
oral bullae	1
RESPIRATORY SIGNS	
laryngeal obstruction	2
bronchospasm	2
GENERAL COLLAPSE (coldness, sweating, etc.)	9
PARESTHESIAS	2

viduals prone to allergic reactivity. Results of such surveys indicate a reaction rate of a few per cent, based upon very large numbers of people. For example, among more than 25,000 patients receiving penicillin in venereal disease clinics in 1959, 0.5 per cent developed urticaria; and there were eight instances of systemic anaphylaxis.[63] Very similar data on the overall incidence of allergic reaction to penicillin were obtained in a British study of nearly 900 patients treated for venereal disease.[64]

Prolonged treatment with penicillin may result in a high frequency of allergic reaction, and the allergy may develop unpredictably at any time during the course of therapy. For example, 32 adult patients were treated with benzathine penicillin G, a repository preparation, as part of a rheumatic fever prophylaxis program.[65] The drug was given intramuscularly once a month. Six patients developed some kind of allergic response, one at the first injection, others after several months. One patient, who had displayed no previous sign of allergy, died within a few minutes after her 20th injection, presumably from an anaphylactic reaction. The autopsy revealed no embolism in the lungs, such as would have resulted from inadvertent intravenous injection of the insoluble benzathine penicillin.

Penicillin is thought to be the major cause of anaphylaxis in man. A nationwide survey,[66] covering 29 per cent of all general hospital beds in the country over a three-year period, revealed 1,070 cases of life-threatening drug reactions, of which 901 (84 per cent) were caused by penicillin. Of these 901 cases, 83 died, a fatality rate of nearly 10 per cent. The frequency of severe reactions to penicillin showed no unusual distribution by age or sex. The route of administration emerged as a significant factor. There were 611 anaphylactoid reactions following intramuscular injection, of which 10 per cent were fatal; after oral administration, there were 49 reactions and none was fatal. Because the intramuscular route is the commonest route of administration of penicillin, it is impossible to say whether or not the greater number of reactions by this route is of any significance. But there is little doubt that the reactions after the oral route were less severe, presumably because of the slower entry of the drug into the circulation (cf. chapter 2). Since the survey covered about one-third of all hospital beds in the country, but included three years of data, it would appear that there were somewhat less than 100 fatalities per year in the country as a whole.

[63] W. J. BROWN, W. G. SIMPSON, and E. V. PRICE: Reevaluation of reactions to penicillin in venereal disease clinic patients. *Public Health Rep. 76:*189 (1961).

[64] R. R. WILLCOX and G. R. FRYERS: Sensitivity to repository penicillins. *Brit. J. Venereal Dis. 33:*209 (1957).

[65] I. HSU and J. M. EVANS: Untoward reactions to benzathine penicillin G in a study of rheumatic-fever prophylaxis in adults. *New Engl. J. Med. 259:*581 (1958).

[66] H. WELCH, C. N. LEWIS, H. I. WEINSTEIN, and B. B. BOECKMAN: Severe reactions to antibiotics. A nationwide survey. *Antibiot. Med. 4:*800 (1957).

Tests for Predicting Drug Allergies

In view of the potential seriousness of drug allergies, it would obviously be valuable to have a reliable and safe method of testing for allergic sensitivity before administering a drug. For many years, skin and conjunctival tests were in vogue, whereby a very small amount of the drug solution was injected intradermally or dropped into the conjunctival sac. Local erythema or conjunctival inflammation was taken as sign of allergic sensitivity. These tests fell into disrepute for two reasons. First, they were unreliable in a capricious way. Patients with positive tests who were nevertheless given the drug therapeutically because of serious need often did not have allergic reactions, whereas patients with negative tests might have reactions of life-threatening severity. Second, the test itself could precipitate a full-blown anaphylactic response in some patients; indeed, deaths have been recorded as a result of skin testing, even though the amount used was only a minute fraction of the usual therapeutic dose. Recently, however, advances in identification of the true antigenic determinants for penicillin sensitization (p. 486) have led to the development of a more reliable skin test using penicilloyl-polylysine as the reagent.[67] The test consists of intradermal injection of the synthetic antigen, followed by appraisal of the size of the wheal and erythema at the test site 20 minutes later. Some danger still persists; for example, four out of 16,239 patients tested developed generalized skin reactions after the test, and one had bronchospasm.

The predictive value of the penicilloyl-polylysine test can be assessed in the data presented in Table 7-7 and Fig. 7-4. If history of prior contact with penicillin is ignored, then a strong correlation between skin test result and subsequent allergic reaction is seen (Table 7-7). Among those with negative skin test, only 0.5 per cent experienced any reaction. The per cent experiencing an allergic reaction increased with increasing positivity of the skin test, to 10.2 per cent among the group that had reacted most strongly. On the other hand, it is interesting that even in this strongly positive group, nine out of ten patients given penicillin therapeutically did not react adversely.

Figure 7-4 shows that the predictive value was even greater when previous history was taken into account. Of the patients with a history of penicillin sensitivity as well as a positive skin test, more than one in four experienced an allergic reaction; in the remaining categories, the response frequency was graded in an orderly manner. A meaningful way of summarizing these studies is to say that if a person without any history of penicillin allergy reacts positively to the skin test, the probability is in-

[67] B. C. BROWN, E. V. PRICE, and M. B. MOORE, JR.: Penicilloyl-polylysine as an intradermal test of penicillin sensitivity. *J. Amer. Med. Ass.* 189:599 (1964).

TABLE 7-7.   Relationship between skin test result and subsequent reaction to penicillin

The skin test with penicilloyl-polylysine was scored according to size of wheal and erythema (—: negative response; ±: ambiguous response, wheal less than 12 mm in diameter; 2+: positive, wheal 12 to 20 mm in diameter; 4+: strongly positive, wheal more than 20 mm in diameter). Patients with 2+ or 4+ skin tests were given penicillin therapeutically only when it was felt that the need outweighed the risk. (Table constructed from data of Brown et al.,[67] text and Fig. 3.)

Skin test response	No. of patients given penicillin therapeutically	Per cent of patients reacting allergically to therapeutic course
—	13,530	0.5
±	782	1.3
2+	212	4.2
4+	206	10.2

creased greatly that he will experience an allergic reaction to therapeutically administered penicillin, as compared with one whose skin test is negative. In these experiments, "allergic reactions" included angio-edema, urticaria, generalized itching, erythematous skin eruptions, and anaphylaxis.

FIG. 7-4.   RELATIONSHIP BETWEEN PREVIOUS HISTORY OF PENICILLIN ALLERGY, SKIN TEST RESPONSE, AND SUBSEQUENT ALLERGIC REACTION TO PENICILLIN. *The per cent of patients reacting to a therapeutic course of penicillin is shown as a function of previous history of allergic reaction to penicillin, and of reaction to the penicilloyl-polylysine skin test. These results are those of the patients analyzed in Table 7-7, and the meaning of skin test categories is the same as given there. (From Brown et al., Fig. 4.[67])*

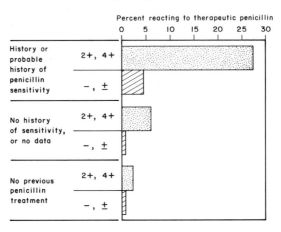

The large number of patients giving positive histories but negative skin tests can be rationalized in numerous ways, the most likely of which are that the antigenic determinants were different in the previous episode, and that the patient may have lost his allergic sensitivity with the passage of time.[29]

Desensitization

If it is very important to give a drug to which a patient is known to be sensitive, and no alternative drug is available, then desensitization may be attempted. In at least some cases this technique has been successful. Precautions against anaphylaxis must be taken; epinephrine, oxygen, and equipment for tracheostomy should be at hand. A very small amount of the drug (e.g., a few micrograms of penicillin) can be given intracutaneously. Every half hour the dose can be doubled, and eventually administration is switched to the subcutaneous route, using a location that permits application of a tourniquet above the injection site. Finally, if therapeutic doses can be achieved without adverse reaction, the procedure may be considered successful.[60]

The scientific basis of desensitization remains uncertain. By mechanisms not yet clarified, if a large amount of the allergen can be introduced without triggering the allergic reaction, the allergic state is somehow inhibited. Perhaps this is related to the phenomenon of hapten inhibition already described (p. 484). In animals, some striking examples have been demonstrated. When guinea pigs were fed 2,4-dinitrochlorobenzene for several weeks and then given a typical sensitizing course intracutaneously, there was a dramatic inhibition of the expected development of allergic sensitivity.[68] The protection was manifest even six months later. The protective effect of prefeeding was highly specific for the particular antigen; another hapten, *o*-chlorobenzoyl chloride, sensitized as usual even when it was given at the same time as the ineffective 2,4-dinitrochlorobenzene. Similar experiments with neoarsphenamine had been conducted many years before, with essentially the same result.[69] In all such cases, the protective feeding of hapten has to precede the attempted sensitization; the allergic responses cannot be modified once sensitization has occurred.

Another possible approach to desensitization is suggested by the experimental work on immunologic paralysis in skin homograft reactions. Tolerance to skin homografts can be induced in various species by prior injection of donor cells during fetal life of the recipient.[70] It would be of

68 M. W. CHASE: Inhibition of experimental drug allergy by prior feeding of the sensitizing agent. *Proc. Soc. Exp. Biol. Med. 61*:257 (1946).

69 M. B. SULZBERGER: Hypersensitiveness to arsphenamine in guinea-pigs. I. Experiments in prevention and in desensitization. *Arch. Dermatol. 20*:669 (1929).

70 N. A. MITCHISON: Immunological tolerance and immunological paralysis. *Brit. Med. Bull. 17*:102 (1961).

interest to ascertain whether prenatal exposure of the mother to certain allergenic drugs could reduce the incidence of allergic reactions to those same drugs later in the offspring.

Management of Drug Allergies

In the mild types of allergic reaction, the signs and symptoms subside when the drug is withdrawn. Antihistamines are helpful in relieving urticaria and itching. Anti-inflammatory steroids are effective in suppressing annoying skin reactions and are probably useful also when collagen is involved.

Life-threatening allergic manifestations develop very quickly and require instantaneous action. The important measures are to delay further drug absorption, to ensure an adequate airway, and to administer epinephrine for bronchodilation. Antihistamines are useless and possibly harmful in that they may cause bronchoconstriction. In penicillin anaphylaxis, the intravenous injection of penicillinase has been advocated, with the purpose of destroying the drug. This is irrational because (*a*) the patient's life is in jeopardy from an antigen-antibody reaction that has already occurred and cannot be reversed, (*b*) the probable antigenic determinant of the allergic response (e.g., a penicilloyl derivative) is not a substrate for penicillinase, and (*c*) penicillinase is a foreign protein, which could cause further allergic reactions.

A tragic aspect of so many anaphylactic deaths is that the administration of penicillin was wholly unnecessary. For example, in a survey of 30 fatal anaphylactic reactions to penicillin,[71] the drug had been given in one case each for a nonspecific skin eruption, a sprained toe, a traumatic injury to the finger, dermatitis associated with venous stasis, and prophylactically after intranasal surgery. In 12 of these fatal cases, the penicillin had been administered for an upper respiratory infection without fever. Penicillin could have served no useful purpose in any of these instances. It is also appalling that in systemic anaphylaxis tracheostomy is rarely performed; yet the cause of death is often laryngeal edema or laryngospasm, and establishing an airway would save a life.

Although subcutaneous administration of epinephrine is the best treatment for anaphylaxis, there is bound to be some delay, even when a physician is at hand; and the procedure is altogether impractical in the absence of a physician. An excellent first-aid treatment is the inhalation of an epinephrine aerosol. A stable suspension of epinephrine microcrystals, of particle size 3-5 microns (cf. chapter 2), is available in an automatic aerosol dispenser.[72] Each dose of the inhalation delivers 0.16 mg of

[71] A. ROSENTHAL: Follow-up study of fatal penicillin reactions. *J. Amer. Med. Ass. 167:*1118 (1958).

[72] A. SELTZER: A useful device for treating acute allergic drug reactions—the Medihaler-Epi. *Med. Ann. Dist. Columbia 27:*131 (1958).

epinephrine to the respiratory tract, where it can act on the laryngeal tissues to prevent edema and on the bronchial tree to prevent smooth-muscle constriction. At the same time the systemic absorption of the epinephrine is rather limited; thus, even five or more inhalations may produce only slight cardiovascular effects. Such an epinephrine aerosol device should obviously be included in any emergency kit and should also be carried by people known to be prone to anaphylactic reactions from drugs, foods, bee stings, and so on.[73]

[73] J. H. SHAFFER: Stinging insects—a threat to life. *J. Amer. Med. Ass.* 177:473 (1961).

8

DRUG RESISTANCE

ORIGIN OF ACQUIRED DRUG RESISTANCE

Drug resistance is a state of insensitivity or of decreased sensitivity to drugs that ordinarily cause growth inhibition or cell death. The term is customarily used in reference to microorganisms or to cell populations (notably neoplasms) undergoing continuous growth in higher organisms. We are concerned here with *acquired* resistance, i.e., with populations initially sensitive that undergo a change in the direction of insensitivity.[1]

The Mutation-Selection Mechanism

The typical course of events in the development of drug resistance is that a strain of bacteria exposed to a growth-inhibitory or lethal drug responds normally at first. The growth rate is reduced or the population size is diminished. Eventually, however, although the drug is still present, growth resumes. The organisms that display this renewed growth are no longer susceptible to the same drug concentration. If the organism is a pathogen and the resistance has developed in a patient under treatment, the patient relapses and the infection becomes refractory to the old drug regimen. This phenomenon has been recognized since the latter part of the 19th century in microorganisms, and within the past decade in mammalian cells in vitro and some kinds of cancer cells in vivo. Acquired drug resistance is an important limitation to the use of antibiotics and many other antimicrobial and anticancer agents.

For a long time it was assumed that the drug played some directive role in causing a biochemical adaptation in the cells. It has become clear, however, in most cases that have been studied adequately, that this view is incorrect. Instead, spontaneous mutants, which differ genetically from the original population in that they are already resistant to the drug action, survive and give rise to a wholly new, drug-resistant population. The drug provides a strong selective pressure in favor of the resistant cell by pre-

---

[1] R. J. SCHNITZER: "Drug Resistance in Chemotherapy," in *Experimental Chemotherapy,* Volume I, R. J. Schnitzer and F. Hawking, eds. New York, Academic Press, 1963.

venting growth of all the nonmutant wild-type sensitive cells. Thus, in acquired resistance the bulk of the initial cell population usually does not become resistant. It responds to drug in the expected way, and it is then replaced by cells of a different kind, which are less sensitive to the drug action.[1a, 2] Occasionally, a growth-inhibitory drug may have mutagenic properties and thus nonspecifically increase the probabilities of many kinds of mutation; no example is known of a drug that selectively increases the mutation rate at the particular gene locus concerned with sensitivity and resistance to itself.

Evidence for the Mutational Origins of Drug Resistance

The question whether or not exposure to a drug is instrumental in causing development of resistance to that drug remained controversial for a long time. The difficulty arose from the fact that the drug necessarily had to be present in order to demonstrate drug resistance. How, then, could one tell if it had played a part in causing the altered cell response? Was drug resistance an adaptation to the drug, or a spontaneous change having survival value? The first solution to this problem was reached by means of an ingenious statistical approach known as a *fluctuation test*.[3] In its original form, this test was used to prove that acquired resistance of bacteria to bacteriophage arose spontaneously, before contact with the phage. Later, the same procedure was applied to determine the origin of bacterial resistance to a number of antibacterial drugs.

The design of the fluctuation test is illustrated in Fig. 8-1. It was applied as follows to streptomycin resistance.[4] A drug-sensitive culture was diluted so that very small inocula (50 to 300 cells) could be placed in each of a series of culture tubes. By plating an appropriate portion of the original culture on an agar test plate containing a lethal concentration of streptomycin, the frequency of drug-resistant cells in the original culture was estimated; each resistant cell would give rise to a resistant colony on the test plate, whereas no other cells would grow. It could then be asserted with confidence that none of the small inocula contained any cells already resistant to streptomycin; for example, if the frequency of resistant cells was 10^{-5}, then there would be only one chance in 1,000 that a given inoculum of 100 cells contained a resistant cell. The culture tubes were incubated to permit multiplication of the small inocula to full-grown cultures (10^8 to 10^9 cells). Then came the critical step in the test. A sample from each culture tube was plated on a single test plate containing drug;

[1a] V. BRYSON and M. DEMEREC: Bacterial resistance. *Amer. J. Med. 18:*723 (1955).

[2] V. BRYSON and W. SZYBALSKI: Microbial drug resistance. *Advance. Genet. 7:*1 (1955).

[3] S. E. LURIA and M. DELBRÜCK: Mutations of bacteria from virus sensitivity to virus resistance. *Genetics 28:*491 (1943).

[4] M. DEMEREC: Origin of bacterial resistance to antibiotics. *J. Bacteriol. 56:*63 (1948).

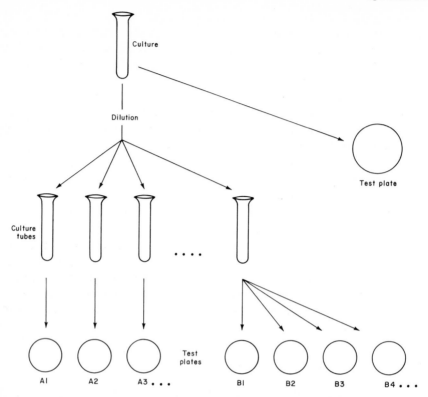

FIG. 8-1.   FLUCTUATION TEST TO DETERMINE ORIGIN OF DRUG RESISTANCE. *Small numbers of bacteria are inoculated into culture tubes. After growing out, they are plated onto test plates. Only the test plates contain drug. The numbers of drug-resistant colonies on the plates of series A are compared with those of series B. (After Luria and Delbrück.[3])*

about 20 culture tubes were thus plated (series A). From the 21st tube, identical platings were made onto 15 more test plates containing drug (series B). Now the plates of both series were incubated, and the numbers of resistant colonies were counted.

Let us suppose that drug resistance arises only after contact of bacteria with drug. Then in this experimental design drug resistance would arise on the test plates. Since all test plates received equal inocula, the numbers of resistant colonies should be approximately the same on them all. On the other hand, if the drug resistance arose prior to contact with drug (i.e., in the culture tubes), then there might well be differences in the numbers of drug-resistant cells in the different tubes. If a spontaneous event leading to drug resistance occurred early in the growth of a culture, then by the time of plating onto the test plates, a sizeable clone of resistant cells would have developed. If the spontaneous event occurred late, then only a few resistant cells would be present in that tube when it was plated. The variation between plates in series B affords a measure of the random fluctuations to be expected from the experimental technique itself, when all platings are made from the same culture.

The question, then, is whether the variation in series A is substantially greater than the variation in series B. The answer was unambiguous. Table 8-1 shows that, although the mean number of resistant colonies was very similar in both series, the variation was much greater in series A. When numbers of items or events are counted, the random variation in repeated counts is expected to be such that the variance will be equal to the mean. This was approximately true in series B, but the variance in series A was much greater than could reasonably have come about by chance ($P <$ 0.001). In other words, events in the tubes, but not in the plates, determined the numbers of drug-resistant cells obtained. Thus, it was concluded that phage resistance, streptomycin resistance, and so on, owed their origins to spontaneous random events occurring during growth of a culture of microorganisms. Several variants of the fluctuation test, some much simpler to perform, all led to the same conclusions.[5] An interesting application of the same concept to mice with transplantable leukemia yielded a

TABLE 8-1. **Fluctuation test on streptomycin resistance**

Platings onto streptomycin plates from independent cultures are tabulated at left (series A), platings from a single culture are tabulated at right (series B). Numbers of streptomycin-resistant colonies on each plate are given. (From Demerec,[4] Table 1.)

Series A				Series B			
Samples from independent cultures				Samples from single culture			
Culture no.	No. of resistant bacteria	Culture no.	No. of resistant bacteria	Sample no.	No. of resistant bacteria	Sample no.	No. of resistant bacteria
1	67	11	56	1	142	11	110
2	159	12	91	2	155	12	125
3	135	13	123	3	132	13	135
4	291	14	97	4	123	14	121
5	75	15	48	5	140	15	112
6	117	16	52	6	146		
7	73	17	54	7	141		
8	129	18	89	8	137		
9	86	19	111	9	128		
10	101	20	164	10	121		
Mean			105.9				131.2
Variance			2913.9				151.1

[5] H. B. NEWCOMBE and R. HAWIRKO: Spontaneous mutation to streptomycin resistance and dependence in *Escherichia coli. J. Bacteriol.* 57:565 (1949).

similar indication about the origin of drug resistance of the leukemic cells to a cancer chemotherapeutic agent.[6]

A more direct and perhaps more convincing way of showing that resistant variants are present prior to contact with a drug is by means of the *replica plate technique*.[7] A culture of bacteria is spread uniformly over the surface of an ordinary nutrient agar plate and incubated until confluent heavy growth is present. This master plate is then pressed onto a sterile velvet surface, so that many cells from every part of the plate are transferred to the pile of the fabric. Fresh agar plates are then pressed, in succession, onto the same velvet surface; a few cells from every part of the velvet are thus transferred onto the surface of each "replica" plate. The replica plates (but not the master plate) contain the growth-inhibitory drug or antibacterial agent, so only resistant cells will be able to grow. Figure 8-2 shows the outcome of such an experiment, in which the antibacterial agent was phage. Eleven resistant colonies grew on one replica plate, eight on the other. Of these colonies, five pairs occupied identical locations on the two plates. Obviously, in these same positions on the master plate (which contained no phage) small clones of resistant cells must have been already present. It was concluded, therefore, that phage resistance arose spontaneously prior to contact with the selective antibacterial agent. Similar results have been obtained with streptomycin, penicillin, and other antibacterial drugs.

FIG. 8-2.   REPLICA PLATE DEMONSTRATION OF ORIGIN OF RESISTANCE. *Plates a and* b *were spread with phage. By means of velvet, as described in the text, a master plate with confluent growth of a phage-sensitive bacterial population was replicated onto plates* a *and* b. *All phage-resistant colonies are shown;* arrows indicate those in congruent positions on both plates. (From Lederberg and Lederberg, Fig. 2.[7])

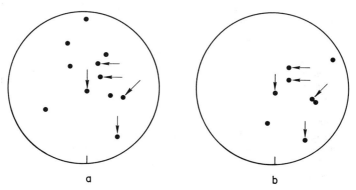

a   b

[6] L. W. LAW: Origin of the resistance of leukæmic cells to folic acid antagonists. *Nature 169*:628 (1952).

[7] J. LEDERBERG and E. M. LEDERBERG: Replica plating and indirect selection of bacterial mutants. *J. Bacteriol. 63*:399 (1952).

An extension of the replica plate procedure permitted the isolation of a pure strain of streptomycin-resistant *Escherichia coli* that had never been exposed to streptomycin at any stage of the procedure. Replica plating was used to locate a position on the master plate corresponding to that of a resistant colony on a replica plate. A bacteriologic loop was used to transfer cells from this position into a culture tube containing broth. After incubation, this culture was used to prepare a fresh master plate, and the entire procedure of replica plating was repeated. A larger number of resistant colonies was now obtained on the replica plates. Again, cells were taken from a position on the new master plate corresponding to a resistant colony on the replica plate, and the whole procedure was repeated. Eventually, a pure culture of a streptomycin-resistant strain was obtained in this way, despite the fact that the cells had never been in contact with streptomycin. The drug was contained only in the replica plates; the cultures, progressively enriched for resistant cells, were grown only on master plates and in broth tubes containing no drug.

Drug resistance, like other genetic properties, can be transferred in the laboratory between cells of the same or closely related species by mechanisms that mediate the intercellular transfer of DNA.[8] Thus, specific drug resistance "markers" have been used in transformation experiments, in which DNA of the resistant strain is used to transform the genotype of some cells of a sensitive strain. Drug resistance has also been transduced by means of a phage, which carries over a portion of the genome of the resistant cell; this is then integrated into the genetic apparatus of the recipient, drug-sensitive cell. Drug resistance has also been transferred by mating techniques, in which DNA of a donor cell is introduced into a recipient cell by direct contact of the two.

Of interest is the recent finding,[9] which may have important practical implications for chemotherapy, that drug resistance (especially among the enteric bacteria) can also be transferred infectiously. This transfer of resistance occurs between cells of the same strain, different strains of the same species, and even different species. The carrier of the resistance trait is an episome, an extrachromosomal self-replicating fragment of DNA. The typical pattern is a simultaneous transfer of multiple drug resistance, for example to sulfonamides, streptomycin, tetracyclines, and chloramphenicol.

Patterns of Emergence and Spread of Drug Resistance

There are two patterns in the mutational development of drug resistance: the multiple-step ("penicillin type") and the facultative large-step ("streptomycin type") patterns. In the *multiple-step pattern,*[10] each

[8] W. BRAUN: *Bacterial Genetics,* 2nd ed. Philadelphia, W. B. Saunders, 1965.

[9] T. WATANABE: Infective heredity of multiple drug resistance in bacteria. *Bacteriol. Rev. 27:*87 (1963).

[10] H. EAGLE: The multiple mechanisms of penicillin resistance. *J. Bacteriol. 68:*610 (1954).

isolation of resistant organisms in the laboratory leads only to a small increase in the degree of resistance. If a culture is placed in contact with a very high concentration of drug, all cells are affected, none will grow. At a suitable low concentration, while most of the population is held in check, a few resistant mutants will grow. These mutants are still sensitive to the drug at a somewhat higher concentration. Evidently no possible mutation can confer a high degree of resistance. On the other hand, if the population of mutants having a low level of resistance is grown in the presence of a somewhat higher drug concentration, one can select for another mutation, superimposed on the first, which will confer a higher degree of resistance. In this way, step by step, quite high levels of resistance can be achieved. It was formerly thought that this pattern necessarily implied a multigenic determination of resistance (i.e., that each mutation affected one gene and that many such genes were concerned in the action of the drug), so that the effects of successive mutations would be more or less additive. Our present understanding of mutation mechanisms makes an alternative view likely—that a single gene could well be involved but that mutations at different sites within this gene can lead to corresponding alterations at different positions on the gene product (presumably protein).[11] Consider an enzyme, the target of the drug action. The configuration of the combining site will be subject to modification by amino acid substitutions throughout the protein, and the configurational change might be expected to show additive effects when several substitutions are introduced. Each small change could reduce the affinity for the drug by a small amount, and these affinity decrements could be additive. That this reasoning has concrete applicability to drug-sensitive enzymes in microorganisms will be shown later (p. 535).

The *facultative large-step pattern* in mutational development of drug resistance is seen typically with streptomycin. If a sensitive culture is plated on a low concentration of the antibiotic, resistant colonies of different kinds can be obtained. Some are resistant only to a low concentration of drug, others to a high concentration; some few are completely insensitive to streptomycin at any concentration. It has been shown by recombination techniques that the various kinds of resistant genotypes represent alleles of the same gene locus. Evidently, mutational substitution at certain sites leads to much greater change in drug sensitivity than at others. The biochemical basis of streptomycin resistance will be discussed in detail later (p. 549).

The large-step pattern is a far more serious threat to successful chemotherapy than is the multiple-step pattern; for, where it applies, an infectious disease may escape from drug control abruptly and completely at any time. For this reason, combined chemotherapy is especially indicated with drugs and organisms showing this pattern. The treatment of tuber-

---

[11] B. WOLF and R. D. HOTCHKISS: Genetically modified folic acid synthesizing enzymes of Pneumococcus. *Biochemistry* 2:145 (1963).

culosis illustrates the point. The basis of combined chemotherapy is the complete independence of the mutational events leading to resistance to different drugs, provided that the drugs are not simply congeners acting by the same mechanism. Suppose two drugs, X and Y, which inhibit the growth of a pathogen, and a spontaneous mutation rate 10^{-6} for resistance to each of these. If 10^6 cells divide once, there will arise, on the average, one mutant resistant to X, and one mutant resistant to Y. But because the mutational events are independent, the probability is vanishingly small (10^{-12}) that a cell resistant to both drugs will arise. Thus, X-resistant mutants will be killed by Y, Y-resistant mutants will be killed by X, and the disease will be kept under control. This is the rationale for the combined treatment of tuberculosis with streptomycin plus isoniazid, streptomycin plus *p*-aminosalicylic acid, or isoniazid plus *p*-aminosalicylic acid.

It would appear that the logic of combined chemotherapy applies to all infections. But where control is readily accomplished with a single drug, and large-step resistance is not a problem (e.g., treatment of gonorrhea or syphilis with penicillin), a second drug will not offer sufficient advantage to outweigh its additional risks. The recently recognized problem of infectious episome-mediated multiple drug resistance (p. 513) may well frustrate the attack on drug resistance by the means outlined here; for, obviously, if organisms can become resistant simultaneously to several drugs, combined chemotherapy with those same drugs would fail.

Important factors determining the ease with which drug resistance makes its appearance and then spreads in a human or animal population are (*1*) the intensity of endemic or epidemic infection in that population, and (*2*) the extent of drug usage. If the total number of parasites harbored in the host population is high and the drug is widely used, opportunity is provided for the occurrence of mutations conferring resistance as well as for selection of the resistant genotype so that it becomes dominant. This principle frequently operates in shifts from sensitivity to resistance among numerous pathogenic microorganisms.

An example studied particularly carefully[12,13] is summarized in Fig. 8-3. In preparation for the introduction of the then new antibiotic erythromycin at a contagious disease hospital in Chicago, nose and throat cultures were obtained from all patients and from all personnel concerned with patient care. Whenever staphylococci were found, their sensitivity to erythromycin was determined in vitro. On September 28, 1952, the use of erythromycin was begun. Nose and throat cultures were made periodically. In February the use of erythromycin was discontinued. The figure

[12] H. F. DOWLING, M. H. LEPPER, and G. G. JACKSON: Clinical significance of antibiotic-resistant bacteria. *J. Amer. Med. Ass. 157:*327 (1955).

[13] M. H. LEPPER, B. MOULTON, H. F. DOWLING, G. G. JACKSON, and S. KOFMAN: "Epidemiology of Erythromycin-Resistant Staphylococci in a Hospital Population—Effect on Therapeutic Activity of Erythromycin," in *Antibiotics Annual 1953–54*, 1953, p. 308.

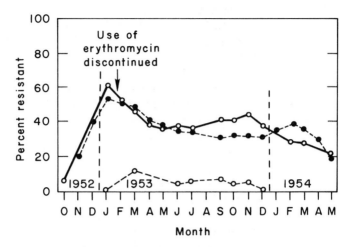

FIG. 8-3.   ERYTHROMYCIN RESISTANCE AMONG STRAINS OF *Staphylococcus* IN A HOSPITAL POPULATION.   *Nose and throat culture data collected periodically at a large hospital for contagious diseases. Resistance of staphylococci to high concentration of erythromycin (100μg/ml) was determined. (Sensitive strains responded to 1μg/ml.) Erythromycin was introduced at the end of September 1952 and discontinued in February 1953.* Vertical axis *shows per cent of all strains isolated that were resistant to the drug;* horizontal axis *shows month and year.* Solid curve, *hospital personnel;* upper broken curve, *patients at time of discharge from hospital;* lower broken curve, *patients on admission to hospital.* (*From Dowling et al., Fig. 1.*[12])

shows that at the outset, the incidence of erythromycin resistance was negligible. It rose quickly, so that by January 60 per cent of the staphylococci cultured from hospital personnel were resistant. The incidence among patients on discharge exactly paralleled this trend. For the first several months, no resistant organisms were harbored by patients at the time of their admission to the hospital. By March 1953, however, this was no longer true, presumably because of the widespread use of the antibiotic in the community by that time. The data show clearly that the resistant strains were being transmitted from hospital personnel to the patients, and that the bacterial flora in the carriers became resistant to erythromycin coincident with its introduction into use in the hospital. The conclusions about transmission of the resistant strains were confirmed by detailed analyses of the serologic types of the organisms. Following discontinuance of erythromycin, there was a gradual decline in the frequency of resistant strains. Similar observations on the rise and decline of bacterial resistance associated with intensity of therapeutic use have been made with penicillin, tetracyclines, and other antibiotics.

The prophylaxis of malaria provides another illustration of how mass use of a drug can encourage the development of drug resistance if conditions are favorable. In mice infected with *Plasmodium berghei,* the antifolic drug pyrimethamine is an effective antimalarial agent. At low levels of infection in the mice, drug treatment is very successful and drug resistance rarely occurs. But when the degree of parasitemia is high (e.g., 40 to 50 per cent of the red blood cells parasitized), resistance occurs readily.[14,15]

Similar findings were reported from field trials on human malaria in East Africa.[16] In an isolated village of 130 people parasitemia (*P. falciparum*) was demonstrated in 84 of them. Mosquito carriers abounded; the intensity of transmission was estimated at about one infective bite per person per night. Pyrimethamine, whose biologic half-life is only a day or two, was administered once monthly. The parasitemia rate fell from 64 per cent to 23 per cent in the first month, and to 21 per cent by the end of the second month. But then it started to climb, and had returned to pre-treatment levels by the end of the sixth month despite continuation of the pyrimethamine regimen. The malarial infections in this village were now unresponsive to the drug. But in two other villages in the same geographic region, where no pyrimethamine had been used, the plasmodia were still drug sensitive. An effective chemotherapeutic attack on any disease that infects a large part of the population requires sufficiently vigorous and continuous treatment to reduce the number of infectious organisms to a very low level. This principle was epitomized by Ehrlich, in the early days of chemotherapy, in the injunction, "Frapper fort et frapper vite!"[17] It is also essential to take stimultaneous measures (such as mosquito eradication in malaria) to block the transmission of the disease, in order to prevent the spread of drug-resistant organisms.

It would be useful to have reliable means for suppressing the emergence of drug resistance during chemotherapeutic treatment of infections or of cancer. The measures already discussed are (*1*) the use of a combination of drugs, and (*2*) the attempt to treat intensively so as to eradicate the infectious organisms quickly. Another possible approach would be the use of antimutagenic agents, which would suppress the spontaneous mutation rate and thereby decrease the frequency of emergence of drug-resistant mutants. Adenosine and guanosine, under certain special circumstances in vitro, have been shown to act as antimutagens,[18] but no practical application has developed. Recently, it has been claimed that the

---

[14] I. M. ROLLO: 'Daraprim' resistance in experimental malarial infections. *Nature* *170:*415 (1952).

[15] G. H. HITCHINGS: Pyrimethamine. The use of an antimetabolite in the chemotherapy of malaria and other infections. *Clin. Pharmacol. Therap. 1:*570 (1960).

[16] D. CLYDE and G. T. SHUTE: Resistance of East African varieties of *Plasmodium falciparum* to pyrimethamine. *Trans. Roy. Soc. Trop. Med. Hyg. 48:*495 (1954).

[17] P. EHRLICH: Chemotherapeutics: scientific principles, methods, and results. *Lancet 2:*445 (1913).

[18] A. NOVICK: Mutagens and antimutagens. *Brookhaven Symp. 8:*201 (1956).

antimalarial drug quinacrine has the ability to suppress the development of bacterial resistance to a number of antibacterial drugs.[19] The experiments were designed in such a way, however, that it is impossible to tell whether quinacrine was acting as an antimutagen or whether it was preventing the growth of resistant mutants in some way.

BIOCHEMICAL MECHANISMS OF DRUG RESISTANCE

That individual cells can become drug resistant by mutation implies that deletion or modification of an enzyme, or alteration of the properties of some other cell component whose synthesis is under gene control, can be responsible for the altered response to drug.[20-22] A number of possible general mechanisms have been suggested,[23] which are used as a basis for the following classification of mechanisms.

Mechanism 1. Decreased Intracellular Drug Level

D-SERINE

The decrease of drug concentration inside cells could come about by altered permeability of the cells, so that the rate of drug entry by diffusion is reduced. Or, if the drug is actively transported into the cell, a defect in an enzyme (permease) or protein carrier that participates in this process could reduce the intracellular drug concentration. D-Serine resistance in *E. coli* exemplifies this mechanism.[20] This amino acid isomer inhibits growth of sensitive cells. Resistant cells no longer take it up, nor can they concentrate glycine from the medium, as do the wild-type cells. Evidently, a glycine permease is responsible for the entry of both glycine and D-serine into the sensitive cell, and this activity is lost in the resistant cells. Since the endogenous pathway of glycine synthesis in this organism remains intact, the permease is dispensable and the D-serine-resistant cells are able to grow.

SULFONAMIDES, METHOTREXATE, AND 6-MERCAPTOPURINE

An investigation into sulfonamide resistance in *E. coli* revealed two kinds of resistance.[24] In one kind, an enzyme with altered affinity for sulfon-

---

[19] M. G. SEVAG and B. ASHTON: Evolution and prevention of drug-resistance. *Nature* 203:1323 (1964).

[20] H. S. MOYED: Biochemical mechanisms of drug resistance. *Annu. Rev. Microbiol.* 18:347 (1964).

[21] R. J. SCHNITZER and E. GRUNBERG: *Drug Resistance of Microorganisms.* New York, Academic Press, 1957.

[22] G. E. W. WOLSTENHOLME and C. M. O'CONNOR, eds.: *Drug Resistance in Microorganisms.* Ciba Foundation Symposium. Boston, Little, Brown and Co., 1957.

[23] B. D. DAVIS and W. K. MAAS: Analysis of the biochemical mechanism of drug resistance in certain bacterial mutants. *Proc. Nat. Acad. Sci. U.S.A. 38:*775 (1952).

[24] M. L. PATO and G. M. BROWN: Mechanisms of resistance of *Escherichia coli* to sulfonamides. *Arch. Biochem. Biophys. 103:*443 (1963).

amide was isolated from the cells (cf. p. 537). In the other kind, although the cells were resistant to sulfonamides, the cell-free extracts (including sulfonamide-sensitive enzyme) displayed no differences from the wild type. It was concluded that the explanation of resistance must be the failure of the sulfonamide to enter the cells; however, no direct proof was offered. Permeability changes have been implicated more directly in the acquired resistance of mouse leukemia cells to methotrexate (amethopterin), a potent inhibitor of dihydrofolate reductase (p. 426).[25] Decreased permeability has also been postulated to explain resistance to 6-mercaptopurine in a certain subline of ascitic carcinoma in mice. Cell-free extracts were able to form 6-mercaptopurine ribonucleotide, the actual toxic agent. Yet whole cells failed to achieve levels of the ribonucleotide as high as those observed in sensitive cell strains.[26]

CHLOROQUINE

Recent investigations into the mechanism of resistance of malaria parasites to chloroquine implicate impeded uptake of drug by organisms.[27,28] Chloroquine complexes with DNA and thus inhibits reactions that require the participation of DNA. Inhibition of DNA replication is thought to be the primary drug effect. The DNA-dependent RNA polymerase reaction (i.e., genetic transcription) is also inhibited, in vitro, regardless of whether the cell-free system is derived from chloroquine-sensitive or chloroquine-resistant organisms. In whole bacterial cells, it has been shown that a chloroquine-sensitive strain, *Bacillus megaterium,* takes up about ten times more of the drug than a chloroquine-insensitive strain, *Bacillus cereus.* Direct evidence relating uptake of drug to acquired resistance comes from experiments in mice, using *Plasmodium berghei.* A drug-resistant strain was developed by serial passage in mice for 17 months in the presence of increasing concentrations of chloroquine. Uptake studies were carried out with ^{14}C-chloroquine labeled in the quinoline ring. Figure 8-4 shows the relationship between the dose of drug and its concentration in red blood cells after 4 hours, when the maximum was attained. Since the uptake by normal unparasitized erythrocytes was negligibly small, it is assumed that the content of drug in parasitized cells reflects its uptake by the plasmodia. The greatly diminished concentration in the resistant plasmodia as compared with sensitive plasmodia is evident. The highest level that could be attained in the resistant organisms, with a 40-mg/kg

[25] G. A. FISCHER: Defective transport of amethopterin (methotrexate) as a mechanism of resistance to the antimetabolite in L5178Y leukemic cells. *Biochem. Pharmacol.* *11:*1233 (1962).

[26] A. R. P. PATERSON: Resistance to 6-mercaptopurine. II. The synthesis of thioinosinate in a 6-mercaptopurine-resistant subline of Ehrlich ascites carcinoma. *Canad. J. Biochem. Physiol.* 40:195 (1962).

[27] J. CIAK and F. E. HAHN: Chloroquine: mode of action. *Science* 151:347 (1966).

[28] P. B. MACOMBER, R. L. O'BRIEN, and F. E. HAHN: Chloroquine: physiological basis of drug resistance in *Plasmodium berghei. Science* 152:1374 (1966).

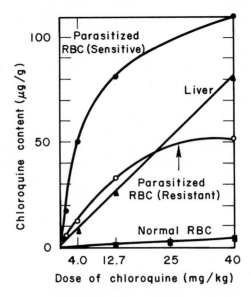

FIG. 8-4. UPTAKE OF CHLOROQUINE BY SENSITIVE AND RESISTANT PLASMODIA. *¹⁴C-chloroquine was given intraperitoneally to uninfected mice and to mice infected with a sensitive or resistant strain of* Plasmodium berghei. *The data for infected mice refer only to parasitized red cells, the parasitized fraction having been determined by microscopic observation. The cells infected with resistant plasmodia contained 1.6 times more parasites per cell than the cells infected with sensitive parasites; thus, the drug content* per parasite *differs, between resistant and sensitive parasites, even more than shown. Chloroquine concentration in liver increased linearly with dose. (From Macomber et al., Fig. 3.[28] By permission of the American Association for the Advancement of Science.)*

dose of chloroquine, was the same as would be achieved at one-tenth the dose in sensitive plasmodia. The uptake curve for liver shows that the drug concentration in this organ increased linearly with dose. The selective toxicity and satisfactory therapeutic ratio of chloroquine acting upon sensitive plasmodia may well be related to the steep uptake curve for parasitized red cells at drug dosages so low that very little drug is taken up by vital organs of the host.

ARSENITE

A somewhat surprising but well-documented example of drug resistance attributable to decreased intracellular concentration of drug concerns growth inhibition of bacteria by arsenite.[29,30] This heavy metal

[29] K. ARIMA and M. BEPPU: Induction and mechanisms of arsenite resistance in *Pseudomonas pseudomallei. J. Bacteriol. 88:*143 (1964).

[30] M. BEPPU and K. ARIMA: Decreased permeability as the mechanism of arsenite resistance in *Pseudomonas pseudomallei. J. Bacteriol. 88:*151 (1964).

anion strongly inhibits essential sulfhydryl enzymes like pyruvate (or α-ketoglutarate) dehydrogenase. A sample of soil was plated on a medium containing $10^{-2}M$ arsenite. One of the organisms that grew (a *Pseudomonas*) was studied to see how it was affected by arsenite. It was found that if this organism was grown in the absence of arsenite and then inoculated into a medium containing arsenite, there was always a lag before growth began. The growth rate, however, was the same up to very high concentrations of arsenite ($> 10^{-2}M$). When the cells that had grown in the presence of arsenite were inoculated into fresh medium containing arsenite at the same concentration, growth began without any lag. It was apparent, then, that the organisms as isolated from soil had the genetic endowment to adapt to the presence of arsenite. In this respect, they were analogous to strains of *Micrococcus* capable of becoming resistant to penicillin by producing penicillinase when exposed to penicillin.

The inhibition of dehydrogenase activities by arsenite was examined in *Pseudomonas* cells grown in the presence of arsenite and in cells grown in its absence. Figure 8-5 shows this comparison for the oxidation of α-ketoglutarate. The large difference observed here was seen also when pyruvate, succinate, or malate was the substrate. However, when these same dehydrogenase activities were tested in cell-free extracts, the difference between the two kinds of cells disappeared, i.e., the arsenite resistance was abolished by cell lysis. These findings seemed to implicate some kind of exclusion mechanism at the cell membrane as the cause of arsenite re-

FIG. 8-5. EFFECT OF ARSENITE ON OXIDATION OF α-KETOGLUTARATE IN SENSITIVE AND RESISTANT PSEUDOMONAS CELLS. Solid circles, *cells grown in ordinary medium;* open circles, *cells grown in presence of $10^{-2}M$ arsenite. (From Arima and Beppu, Fig. 4.*[29])

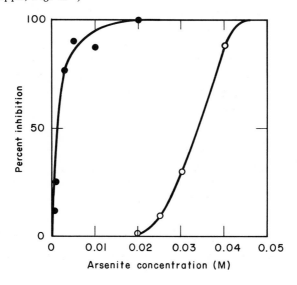

sistance. Direct measurements confirmed this. Cells that had been grown in the presence or absence of arsenite ($10^{-2}M$) were equilibrated with several different concentrations of radioactive arsenite, and the uptake of radioactivity was measured. Results are shown in Fig. 8-6 on a double-reciprocal plot. At any given arsenite concentration, the uptake by the population of resistant cells was smaller than that by sensitive cells. But the intercept on the y-axis, representing the maximum uptake at "infinite" arsenite concentration, was the same for both kinds of cell. As in the use of this type of graph to analyze enzyme inhibition (p. 72), the identical y-axis intercepts (analogous to V_{max}) signify the presence of a saturable process. Here, despite the exclusion of arsenite from resistant cells at low external arsenite concentrations, at very high concentrations the exclusion mechanism is, in effect, overwhelmed. The underlying molecular processes are still unknown,

FIG. 8-6.   UPTAKE OF ARSENITE BY SENSITIVE AND RESISTANT PSEUDOMONOS CELLS. Solid circles, *cells taken from ordinary medium;* open circles, *cells that had been grown in presence of 10^{-2}M arsenite. For the measurement of uptake radioactive arsenite was used and 20 minutes was allowed for equilibration. In the double-reciprocal plot shown here, the intercept on the y-axis represents the maximum uptake at "infinite" external arsenite concentration. (From Beppu and Arima, Fig. 3.[30])*

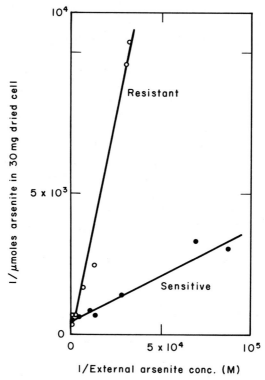

but the findings would be consistent with the presence of an inducible transport "pump" for extruding arsenite from the cells. The resistance develops within a period of only one or two cell generations, and it is lost quickly in the absence of arsenite. In this instance, therefore, the acquired drug resistance must be attributed to a phenotypic modification, and it is present in all cells of the resistant strain after exposure to arsenite.

Acquired resistance of trypanosomes to organic arsenicals has also been shown to depend upon decreased penetration by the drugs.[31] Of particular interest was the finding that the diminished uptake of arsenic by the cells occurred only with those arsenosobenzene compounds containing an amide substituent, to which the resistance had developed, but not to other organic arsenicals to which there was no cross-resistance. The acquired resistance of *E. coli* to selenate may possibly also be attributed to lack of uptake of the drug.[32]

Mechanism 2. Increased Destruction of Drug

PENICILLIN

The best-documented example of resistance due to increased destruction of drug in microorganisms is the resistance of certain strains of *Micrococcus* (*Staphylococcus aureus*) to penicillins.[33] Penicillinase (β-lactamase) is an inducible enzyme, which hydrolyzes the $C-N$ bond in the lactam ring of the penicillins; the resulting penicilloic acid products are inactive. Resistance on this basis can only develop in strains that have the genetic potential to produce this enzyme, and only under certain conditions. The mere presence of penicillinase in a single cell will not protect that cell against the lethal effects of penicillin when a sufficient supply of the drug is present to maintain effective concentrations. On the other hand, a whole population of penicillinase-containing cells acts cooperatively to reduce the ambient penicillin concentration, so that cell survival and multiplication may occur. The amount of penicillinase per cell plays an important role, and this is subject to the usual regulatory controls. Mutation can render the enzyme constitutive instead of inducible, so that a much larger amount is produced, even in the absence of the drug; and thus an immediate rather than a delayed resistance can be manifested upon first exposure to penicillin. New modified forms of penicillin, resistant to the hydrolytic action of penicillinase, have recently been introduced into therapeutic use (cf. chapter 13).

[31] H. EAGLE and H. J. MAGNUSON: The spontaneous development of arsenic-resistance in *Trypanosoma equiperdum,* and its mechanism. *J. Pharmacol. Exp. Therap.* 82:137 (1944).

[32] A. SHRIFT and E. KELLY: Adaptation of *Escherichia coli* to selenate. *Nature* 195:732 (1962).

[33] A. V. S. DE REUCK and M. P. CAMERON, eds.: *Resistance of Bacteria to the Penicillins.* Ciba Foundation Study Group No. 13. Boston, Little Brown and Co., 1962.

INSECTICIDES

Several good illustrations of this mechanism are to be found in the acquired resistance of insects to insecticides. An example was presented in chapter 3 (Table 3-5), showing that houseflies resistant to chlorophenothane (DDT) demonstrated a greatly enhanced capacity to inactivate the toxic compound by dehydrochlorination. Houseflies resistant to carbamate insecticides have been shown to degrade these compounds more rapidly than do the sensitive strains.[34] The most extensive studies in insects have dealt with resistance to organophosphate cholinesterase inhibitors like malathion. As in the case of parathion (p. 229), malathion becomes

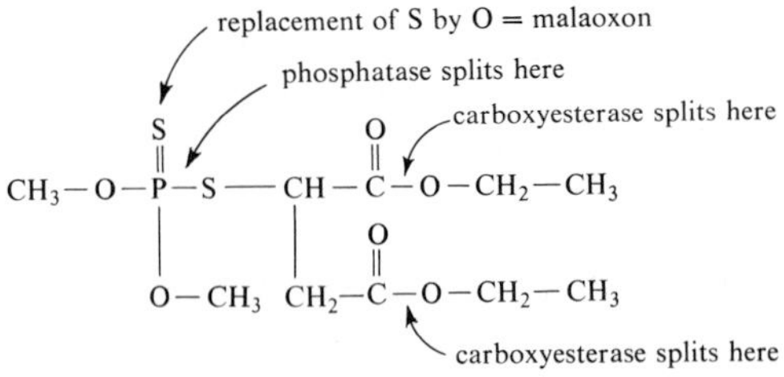

replacement of S by O = malaoxon

phosphatase splits here

carboxyesterase splits here

$$CH_3-O-\overset{\overset{\displaystyle S}{\|}}{\underset{\underset{\displaystyle O-CH_3}{|}}{P}}-S \longrightarrow \underset{\underset{\displaystyle CH_2-\overset{\overset{\displaystyle O}{\|}}{C}-O-CH_2-CH_3}{|}}{CH}-\overset{\overset{\displaystyle O}{\|}}{C}-O-CH_2-CH_3$$

carboxyesterase splits here

malathion

an active inhibitor only upon its conversion to an oxygen analogue known as malaoxon. Both malathion and malaoxon can be degraded, by a phosphatase and by a carboxyesterase, as indicated in the structural formula above.

During the widespread use of malathion as a larvicide against mosquitoes, a resistant strain emerged.[35] Larvae of this strain were found to contain greatly increased activity of a mitochondrial carboxyesterase that degraded malathion to the monoester and the succinic acid derivative. Thus, less malathion remained available for conversion to malaoxon. The degradation of malaoxon was also increased in this strain, compared with the sensitive strain. The enhanced esterase activity was thought to be due to an increased amount of the normal enzyme, since no alterations in affinity for malathion were found. However, affinities for other substrates were not studied, nor were pH optima or thermal stability.

Mating experiments showed that the increased carboxyesterase activity was inseparable from the malathion resistance. The data are shown in Table 8-2. The resistant larvae required 42 times higher malathion

34 G. P. GEORGHIOU and R. L. METCALF: The absorption and metabolism of 3-isopropylphenyl *N*-methylcarbamate by susceptible and carbamate-selected strains of house flies. *J. Econ. Entomol. 54:*231 (1961).

35 F. MATSUMURA and A. W. A. BROWN: Biochemistry of malathion resistance in *Culex tarsalis. J. Econ. Entomol. 54:*1176 (1961).

TABLE 8-2. Carboxyesterase activity and malathion resistance in mosquito larvae

Larvae of *Culex tarsalis* were tested for sensitivity to malathion by determining the LC50 (concentration, in parts per million, killing 50 per cent of the larvae). Carboxyesterase and phosphatase products were measured by an in vitro assay using radioactive malathion and identifying products by a chloroform extraction procedure; the data are per cent of total radioactivity found in products in 30 minutes at 23°. (From Matsumura and Brown,[35] Table 12.)

Larvae	Malathion LC50 (ppm)	Carboxyesterase products (%)	Phosphatase products (%)
Resistant	1.8	4.4 ± 0.6	4.3 ± 0.8
Sensitive	0.043	0.8 ± 0.3	3.2 ± 0.9
F_1 hybrid	0.80	4.5 ± 1.0	
B_1 back-cross	0.75	4.2 ± 0.4	
B_2 back-cross	0.80	5.4 ± 0.6	

concentration for 50 per cent kill than did the sensitive strain; and under the conditions of the assay, the carboxyesterase activity was 5.5 times higher. There was no difference in phosphatase activity between the two strains. The first-generation hybrid (F_1) showed a resistance level somewhat lower than the resistant strain, and a high carboxyesterase activity. Selection for malathion resistance was carried out among the F_1 hybrids. Survivors of exposure to malathion (1 part per million) were crossed back to the sensitive line to obtain strain B_1. The same procedure was repeated with B_1, survivors being mated with the sensitive strain to obtain B_2. The table shows that the high carboxyesterase activity was retained in B_1 and B_2 strains, despite their genomes being ¾ and ⅞, respectively, derived from the sensitive stock. Thus, selection for malathion resistance resulted in associated high activity of this particular degradative enzyme. It was concluded that the gene conferring malathion resistance is an allele of the wild-type gene that determines carboxyesterase activity.

A similar investigation[36] of malathion resistance in houseflies showed that although resistance was accompanied by increased esterase activity toward malathion or malaoxon, there was decreased activity toward other ester substrates (e.g., methoxybutyrate). In mating experiments, this decreased activity was inseparable from the increased activity toward malathion or the resistance to malathion. Thus, it seems likely that the enhanced ability to degrade the insecticide resulted from a qualitatively altered enzyme rather than a simple increase in amount of a normal enzyme. The increase in esterase activity toward malathion and the con-

36 F. J. OPPENOORTH and K. VAN ASPEREN: Allelic genes in the housefly producing modified enzymes that cause organophosphate resistance. *Science 132:*298 (1960).

comitant decrease in activity toward methoxybutyrate suggested that the resistant strain might prove to be sensitive to a methyl ester analogue of malathion; this was demonstrated to be true.[37] Thus, resistance to one particular insecticide does not necessarily confer cross-resistance, even to closely related congeners.

Mechanism 3. Decreased Conversion of Drug to a More Active Compound

p-FLUOROPHENYLALANINE

An interesting example of this mechanism in bacteria is the acquired resistance to *p*-fluorophenylalanine (cf. p. 104). The active form of this drug is its complex with the phenylalanine transfer-RNA, a complex that is formed because the phenylalanine-activating enzyme accepts the fluoro analogue. Once attached to transfer-RNA, the drug is incorporated into proteins instead of the natural amino acid, with deleterious consequences for the bacteria, presumably because the analogue-containing proteins cannot function normally. Phenylalanine-activating enzyme was purified from wild-type cells and from resistant mutants.[38] The purified wild-type enzyme functioned with either phenylalanine or fluorophenylalanine as substrate. The enzyme from the resistant organism was completely inactive toward fluorophenylalanine when tested in a cell-free system containing phenylalanine transfer-RNA, ATP, and Mg^{++}. The K_m values for phenylalanine, however, and for ATP were the same as for the normal enzyme. In addition to its inactivity toward fluorophenylalanine, the mutant enzyme had a much greater thermal stability than did the wild-type enzyme. It is supposed, therefore, that a mutation in the structural gene controlling the amino acid sequence of the activating enzyme was responsible for the acquired resistance to the drug. Presumably, a configurational change resulting from the amino acid replacement rendered the fluoro derivative incapable of combining, whereas the enzyme was still able to activate the natural amino acid.

PURINE AND PYRIMIDINE ANALOGUES

Purine and pyrimidine analogues, when they act by incorporation into nucleic acids, have to be converted to nucleotides first; fluorouridylic acid, for example, is the active form of 5-fluorouracil. Changes in the enzymes mediating such conversions may be responsible for drug resistance. For example, ascites tumors in mice are inhibited by 5-fluorouracil. Several resistant sublines of ascites cell were studied to ascertain the mechanism

---

[37] W. C. DAUTERMAN and F. MATSUMURA: Effect of malathion analogs upon resistant and susceptible *Culex tarsalis* mosquitoes. *Science 138:*694 (1962).

[38] W. L. FANGMAN and F. C. NEIDHARDT: Demonstration of an altered aminoacyl ribonucleic acid synthetase in a mutant of *Escherichia coli. J. Biol. Chem. 239:*1839 (1964).

of drug resistance.[39] The activity of the enzyme uridine kinase was found to be drastically decreased in resistant cells. This enzyme catalyzes the phosphorylation of uridine to uridylic acid and of fluorouridine to fluoro-uridylic acid, with ATP as phosphate donor; so its deficiency would decrease the conversion of 5-fluorouracil to its active form. Uridine kinase was isolated and purified from wild-type and resistant cells. The enzyme from resistant cells precipitated at a lower concentration of ammonium sulfate than that from wild-type cells, it was more difficult to elute from an anion exchange column at pH 7.4, and it was more readily inactivated by heat. Thus, the presumptive basis of the decreased enzyme activity is a mutational alteration in enzyme structure.

A similar illustration is provided by resistance to the adenine analogue, 2,6-diaminopurine by a *Salmonella* species.[40] The drug is a growth inhibitor in this organism, and resistant mutants can be obtained in its presence. The enzymes that convert purine bases to the corresponding nucleotides catalyze the transfer of a ribose phosphate moiety from phos-phoribosyl pyrophosphate (PRPP), splitting out pyrophosphate; they are therefore called nucleotide pyrophosphorylases. These enzymes were purified and eluted from a DEAE-cellulose anion exchange column, the enzyme activity of each fraction being tested for pyrophosphorylase activity with adenine, 2,6-diaminopurine, and hypoxanthine. The results are shown in Fig. 8-7. The extract from wild-type *Salmonella* cells (top) yielded two distinct peaks of enzyme activity—one for adenine, forming adenosine monophosphate (AMP), the other for hypoxanthine, forming inosine monophosphate (IMP). The adenylic pyrophosphorylase also converted diaminopurine to its nucleotide. The extract from resistant cells (middle) showed two alterations: (*1*) the adenylate enzyme was eluted sooner from the column, whereas the IMP enzyme behaved normally in this respect; and (*2*) all trace of activity toward diaminopurine had disappeared. An equal mixture of the two extracts (bottom) illustrates the expected additive effects, showing that the resistant extract did not contain any inhibitor that would interfere with detection of diaminopurine pyrophosphorylase activity if it were present. Thus, it is reasonable to conclude that the acquired resistance to diaminopurine is due to a mutational modification of the adenylic acid pyrophosphorylase. The effect of the genetic change is to alter its ionic properties somewhat and to abolish its ability to interact with 2,6-diaminopurine as a substrate, without altering its activity toward adenine.

An analogous example of this mechanism is of some importance in cancer chemotherapy. The purine analogue 6-mercaptopurine (6-MP) is

[39] O. SKÖLD: Studies on resistance against 5-fluorouracil. IV. Evidence for an altered uridine kinase in resistant cells. *Biochim. Biophys. Acta* 76:160 (1963).

[40] G. P. KALLE and J. S. GOTS: Genetic alteration of adenylic pyrophosphorylase in *Salmonella. Science* 142:680 (1963).

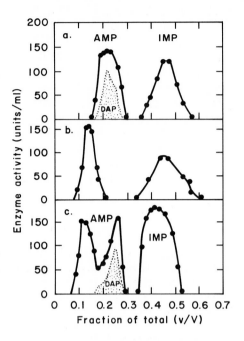

FIG. 8-7. ELUTION OF SALMONELLA PYROPHOSPHORYLASES FROM AN ANION EXCHANGE COLUMN. *DEAE-cellulose column elution by linear NaCl gradient from 0 to 0.5M in pH 7.6 buffer.* Horizontal axis *shows fraction of the total 400-ml volume run through the column;* vertical axis *shows enzyme activities. Each fraction was assayed for pyrophosphorylase activity with PRPP as donor and adenine, 2,6-diaminopurine, and hypoxanthine individually as acceptors; thus, AMP, diaminopurine. nucleotide (DAP), and IMP were formed. a, wild-type extract; b, diaminopurine-resistant extract; c, mixture of a and b. (From Kalle and Gots, Fig. 1.*[40] By permission of the American Association for the Advancement of Science.)*

converted to the corresponding nucleotide by the "salvage pathway" in mammalian cells, involving the same reaction with PRPP just described for bacteria. In numerous instances in transplantable murine tumors and in other mammalian cells growing in vitro, acquired resistance to 6-MP entails loss of the nucleotide pyrophosphorylase.[41] Here, the relevant enzyme is inosinic (or guanylic) acid pyrophosphorylase, which is active with hypoxanthine, guanine, 6-MP, thioguanine, and azaguanine as substrates. As with 2,6-diaminopurine resistance in bacteria, the adenylate pyrophosphorylase here is usually not affected. It is by no means established that drug failures with 6-MP in clinical cancer chemotherapy are due to acquired resistance of this kind.[42] The de novo pathway of purine biosynthe-

41 R. W. BROCKMAN: Resistance to purine antagonists in experimental leukemia systems. *Cancer Res. 25:*1596 (1965).

42 J. D. DAVIDSON: Formal discussion on resistance to purine antagonists in experimental leukemia systems. *Cancer Res. 25:*1606 (1965).

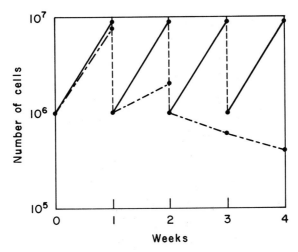

FIG. 8-8.   SELECTIVE INHIBITION OF GROWTH OF MOUSE FIBROBLASTS RESISTANT
TO 6-MERCAPTOPURINE.   *Weekly multiplication of cells in vitro, subcultured
each week.* Horizontal axis *is number of weeks;* vertical axis *is number of cells,
plotted on a logarithmic scale. The medium contained methotrexate (10^{-6}M),
hypoxanthine and thymidine (3×10^{-5}M), and glycine (10^{-4}M).* Solid line,
normal cells; broken line, *cell line resistant to 6-mercaptopurine. Cells were diluted and subcultured weekly as indicated by* vertical broken lines. *When adenine was substituted for hypoxanthine, both cell lines grew well (not shown).*
(From Tomizawa and Aronow, data of Table 4.[43])

sis, beginning with donation of an amine group from glutamine to PRPP,
is quite distinct from the nucleotide pyrophosphorylase reaction in that the
ribose phosphate grouping is present from the beginning. Consequently, the
nucleotide pyrophosphorylases are dispensable enzymes; purine synthesis
continues in their absence.

A model has been proposed for the possible exploitation, in cancer
chemotherapy, of the property causing drug resistance.[43] A line of mouse
fibroblasts resistant to 6-MP was developed in vitro, and the cause of the
resistance was shown to be deficient conversion of 6-MP to the nucleotide.
Such resistant cells should be unable to utilize exogenous purines like
hypoxanthine and be completely dependent upon their de novo pathway
of purine biosynthesis. The de novo pathway can be blocked by antifolic
drugs, which block single-carbon transfers, since single-carbon transfers are
essential in biosynthesis of the purine ring. If cells are exposed to one of
these antifolic drugs, methotrexate, and at the same time glycine, thymidine,
and a purine are supplied, wild-type cells will be able to grow (cf. p. 426).
The methotrexate inhibition will be overcome because all the end-products
of the single-carbon transfer reactions are furnished, and the purine can

43 S. TOMIZAWA and L. ARONOW: Studies on drug resistance in mammalian cells.
II. 6-Mercaptopurine resistance in mouse fibroblasts. *J. Pharmacol. Exp. Therap.* 128:107
(1960).

be utilized by means of the "salvage pathway." The cells resistant to 6-MP, on the other hand, should be unable to grow in a hypoxanthine-supplemented medium because they cannot utilize this exogenous purine, and their endogenous synthesis of purines ·is shut off by methotrexate. The experiment is shown in Fig. 8-8. The outcome was as expected; the resistant cell line eventually failed to grow in a medium containing methotrexate, hypoxanthine, thymidine, and glycine, whereas the normal cell line continued to multiply under these conditions. When adenine was substituted for hypoxanthine, however, the resistant cells grew perfectly well.

Mechanism 4. Increased Concentration of Metabolite Antagonizing the Drug Action

One of the earliest investigations of sulfonamide resistance disclosed a striking example of this mechanism.[44] When the amount of *p*-aminobenzoic acid in resistant mutants of *Staphylococcus* was compared with that in the sensitive parent strains, an increase on the order of 100-fold was found in the resistant cells. This increase was sufficient to account for the observed degree of resistance by competitive antagonism of the sulfonamide inhibition. Few other examples of this mechanism have come to light, and even for sulfonamide resistance it is not the most frequent mechanism. Overproduction of a metabolite implies that there has been a mutational loss of control in a pathway that is subject to regulation by end-product ("feedback") inhibition or by end-product repression of enzymes. Several illustrations will be given on p. 539 of drug resistance due to mutational modification of enzymes subject to end-product inhibition. In these instances, the resulting increased metabolite levels seem to be incidental to the drug resistance rather than to be its cause.

Mechanism 5. Increased Amount of Target Enzyme

Enzyme levels in cells are regulated to meet the needs of the organism by controls exerted upon the processes of transcription (messenger-RNA synthesis) and translation (assembly of nascent protein).[45] Enzyme induction by a substrate or substrate analogue illustrates the expansion of enzyme capacity by specific *derepression* of the gene, resulting in an increased rate of enzyme synthesis. The *repressor* is thought to be a protein, which interacts with the genetic apparatus and prevents (or reduces the frequency of) its transcription. Combination of an *inducer* with this protein releases the repression. Mutational alterations of several kinds can

[44] M. LANDY, N. W. LARKUM, E. J. OSWALD, and F. STREIGHTOFF: Increased synthesis of *p*-aminobenzoic acid associated with the development of sulfonamide resistance in *Staphylococcus aureus. Science* 97:265 (1943).

[45] J. D. WATSON: Molecular Biology of the Gene. New York, W. A. Benjamin, 1965.

affect these control mechanisms. Complete release of repression, perhaps due to mutation in the regulatory gene that controls synthesis of the repressor, results in *constitutive formation* of an enzyme that is normally inducible; a great increase in its rate of synthesis results, and therefore its steady-state level in the cell becomes greatly elevated. Mutational modification of repressor configuration is also possible, resulting in altered affinities for inducers.

Whatever the detailed mechanisms of enzyme regulation may turn out to be, it is clear already that mutational alterations in regulatory systems can lead to acquired drug resistance. If the drug happens to be a reversible inhibitor of a given enzyme, and if the amount of that enzyme per cell increases, then the same drug concentration, producing the same per cent inhibition, will no longer prevent growth. The actual enzyme activity in the presence of the drug will be greater than in the wild type, and the products of the enzyme reaction will be formed at a rate more than sufficient to meet the needs of the cell. If the drug happens to be an irreversible inhibitor, then a stoichiometric equivalent of drug will be required to produce any given inhibition; and this will obviously require more drug when more enzyme is present.

ANTIFOLIC DRUGS

This mechanism (increased amount of target enzyme) has been identified as a cause of acquired resistance to antifolic drugs in bacteria, in mammalian cells in culture, and in transplanted leukemic cells in vivo.[46] However, it is still uncertain whether treatment failure of human leukemia with antifolic agents is to be attributed to this cause.[47] The target of action of the antifolic drug is the enzyme dihydrofolate reductase, which catalyzes the reduction of dihydrofolate to the active tetrahydrofolate (p. 423). In the experiment shown in Fig. 8-9, sarcoma-180 cells were grown in vitro and sublines resistant to methotrexate were isolated.[48] The activity of the enzyme was measured in cell extracts from sensitive and resistant cells. It can be seen that the activity of dihydrofolate reductase was much higher in the resistant than in the sensitive cell lines. A comparison was made between the degree of resistance and the extent of increase in enzyme activity. Calculation showed that cells of the "AH" line were 67-fold more resistant to methotrexate than the wild type, and the enzyme activity was found to have increased 65-fold. The "AT" line was 174 times more resistant to the drug than was the wild type, and its enzyme activity had

[46] G. A. FISCHER: Increased levels of folic acid reductase as a mechanism of resistance to amethopterin in leukemic cells. *Biochem. Pharmacol.* 7:75 (1961).

[47] J. R. BERTINO: Current studies of the folate antagonists in patients with acute leukemia. *Cancer Res.* 25:1614 (1965).

[48] M. T. HAKALA, S. F. ZAKRZEWSKI, and C. A. NICHOL: Relation of folic acid reductase to amethopterin resistance in cultured mammalian cells. *J. Biol. Chem.* 236:952 (1961).

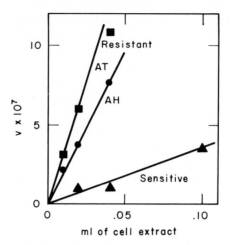

FIG. 8-9.   DIHYDROFOLATE REDUCTASE ACTIVITY IN EXTRACTS OF NORMAL AND
METHOTREXATE-RESISTANT MAMMALIAN CELLS.   *Sarcoma-180 cells were grown
in vitro and methotrexate-resistant sublines were isolated. Extracts were assayed
at 37° for 15 minutes with folic acid as substrate and NADPH as hydrogen
donor. One milliliter of the diluted extract corresponded to 43.5 mg of resistant
AH cells, 60 mg of resistant AT cells, and 352 mg of sensitive cells. Ordinates
are reaction velocity* (v, *in moles of NADPH per liter per minute*). (*From
Hakala et al., Fig. 3.*[48])

increased 155-fold. Moreover, the extent of increase in enzyme activity in
the two resistant strains was exactly paralleled by the degree of increase in
binding capacity of the extracts for methotrexate. At the same time, it was
shown that the K_m for folic acid and the rate of conversion of substrate per
drug-binding site (i.e., per active center) were the same for the resistant
and wild-type enzyme. Sublines of mouse sarcoma have been developed
with much greater degrees of methotrexate resistance than those discussed
above. One cell line was resistant to 3,000 times the usually effective concentration of methotrexate, and it contained 300 to 400 times the normal
amount of dihydrofolate reductase.[49] In cells like these, as much as 5 per
cent of the total protein may be represented by this one enzyme.[50]

A very thorough study of the properties of dihydrofolate reductase
from methotrexate-resistant bacteria (*Diplococcus pneumoniae*) revealed
two distinct types of resistance.[51] In one type, the properties of the enzyme
were altered; this will be discussed later. In the other type, two different
mutations mapped genetically to about the same region of the genome led
to very large increases in the amount of enzyme, but there was no detectable

[49] M. T. HAKALA and T. ISHIHARA: Chromosomal constitution and amethopterin
resistance in cultured mouse cells. *Cancer Res.* 22:987 (1962).

[50] M. T. HAKALA and E. M. SUOLINNA: Specific protection of folate reductase against
chemical and proteolytic inactivation. *Mol. Pharmacol.* 2:465 (1966).

[51] F. M. SIROTNAK, G. J. DONATI, and D. J. HUTCHISON: Genetic modification of
the structure and amount of dihydrofolate reductase in amethopterin-resistant *Diplococcus
pneumoniae. J. Biol. Chem.* 239:4298 (1964).

change in its properties. The level of drug resistance was measured by determining the amount of drug required to give the same degree of growth inhibition with wild-type and resistant cells and expressing this as a ratio. The two strains were 15 and 20 times more resistant, respectively, than the wild type. The K_m values for dihydrofolate and for NADPH were the same for the enzyme from the two resistant strains as for the wild-type enzyme; and the pH optimum was also the same, 7.3. The enzyme activity per milligram of cell protein (expressed as moles of dihydrofolate reduced per minute) of the two strains was 14 and 18 times greater, respectively, than that of the wild-type enzyme. Finally, because methotrexate is bound very tightly to the enzyme, the number of drug-binding sites can be measured directly by determining the maximum amount of drug that can be bound per milligram of protein in the extract. This estimate agreed remarkably well with that based upon enzyme activity; the increase was 16-fold and 22-fold, respectively, over the wild-type enzyme. It seems justifiable to conclude, therefore, in these two cases, that the observed degree of resistance to methotrexate was accounted for by a comparable increase in the amount of the target enzyme per cell, without significant change in the properties of the enzyme.

NEOSTIGMINE

An unusual example of this mechanism is the acquired resistance of a strain of *Pseudomonas* to neostigmine.[52] This organism contains a cholinesterase. It can utilize simple sources of carbon and nitrogen (e.g., glucose and ammonia) for growth, but its growth can be made to depend upon the cholinesterase by furnishing a choline ester as sole source of carbon or nitrogen. Thus, if acetylcholine has to be utilized, the cholinesterase activity becomes rate limiting for growth. Under these conditions, neostigmine, a cholinesterase inhibitor, acted as a growth inhibitor; when choline and acetate were furnished instead of acetylcholine, neostigmine had no growth-inhibitory effect whatsoever. Mutants resistant to neostigmine were obtained. These proved to contain a greatly increased amount of cholinesterase. All the properties of the enzyme that were measured proved to be identical with those of the wild-type cholinesterase. Thus, the acquired drug resistance could be attributed to an increased amount of the target enzyme.

Mechanism 6. Decreased Requirement for Product of Drug-Sensitive Enzyme (Hypothetical)

This mechanism is included for the sake of completeness, since it is logically plausible, although no examples have been discovered. Consider the reaction $X \rightarrow Y$, catalyzed by an enzyme that is subject to inhibition by

[52] B. W. SEARLE and A. GOLDSTEIN: Mutation to neostigmine resistance in a cholinesterase-containing *Pseudomonas*. *J. Bacteriol. 83:*789 (1962).

a drug. A certain rate of production of Y is essential to the needs of the cell; and thus the drug, by inhibiting the reaction, inhibits cell growth in the wild type. One can imagine the following way for this mechanism of resistance to operate. Suppose that in the wild-type cell, Y is being degraded (or drawn off into nonessential reactions) so that its steady-state level is kept low. In other words, the rate of the reaction $X \rightarrow Y$ is assumed to be considerably greater than the rate at which Y has to be synthesized to meet growth needs. Under these conditions, mutational loss of an enzyme responsible for the degradation (or diversion) of Y could result in drug resistance. For then, even when it was largely inhibited by the drug, the reaction $X \rightarrow Y$ would produce Y fast enough to satisfy growth requirements. A similar argument would apply if a mechanism developed for the more efficient utilization of Y for the growth needs of the cell. On the other hand, there is no basis for supposing that Y could become nonessential to the cell. One might argue that by mutation, the drug-sensitive enzyme could be deleted, and the cell would then use an exogenous supply of Y. But if the wild-type cell was capable of deriving Y from an exogenous source, it would not have been inhibited by the drug. The mutation, then, would have to have opened a pathway, not previously operative, for utilizing an exogenous metabolite. The implausibility of an "alternative metabolic pathway" as a mechanism of acquired drug resistance is discussed below (mechanism 7).

Mechanism 7. Alternative Metabolic Pathway Bypassing the Drug-Sensitive Reaction (Hypothetical)

In order to explain acquired drug resistance on this basis, we have to postulate some rather special conditions. Certainly, the bypass pathway could not have been present in wild-type cells; because if it were, the organism would have been drug-resistant in the first place. And if the genetic specifications for the supposed alternative pathway were not present before, they could hardly be expected to spring up, fully formed, as the result of a single mutational step. It would have to be imagined, then, that the wild type contained inactive DNA corresponding to the enzymes for the alternative pathway. Possibly the genes were present in a form that could be activated by mutation. Possibly the pathway was repressed and could be derepressed by mutation in a regulatory gene. Because the idea of bypassing a drug-sensitive step is simple and attractive, this mechanism has often been cited as the most likely explanation for acquired drug resistance. It seems, on the contrary, to be the least likely, and no examples of it have yet come to light.

Mechanism 8. Decreased Relative Affinity of Enzyme for Drug Compared with Substrate

Our present understanding[45] of the dependence of protein configuration upon amino acid sequence, and the recognition of induced allosteric modifications of protein structure, make this mechanism seem a plausible one. Random mutations in the structural gene controlling the target enzyme result in many kinds of alteration. Some mutations may be "nonsense," interrupting the translation of the message because the altered codon corresponds to no amino acid. Other mutations may lead to gross changes in amino acid composition and sequence, as by the "frame shift" mechanism (p. 640), so that no enzyme is formed. And some single amino-acid replacements are probably incompatible with the folding of the polypeptide chain into an enzymically active conformation. But a great many different amino acid substitutions will yield functional but altered enzyme. From among the cells containing these altered enzymes, the drug will select in favor of those with functional enzyme whose relative affinity for drug (compared with substrate) is decreased.

p-NITROBENZOIC ACID

There are now numerous examples of this mechanism, in which the altered affinity of the target enzyme has been demonstrated, much as was done with enzymes responsible for nucleotide formation (cf. p. 527). Remarkably, the first demonstration of this mechanism was accomplished years ago in whole cells by means of an elegant experiment.[23] A design was conceived that could rule out all plausible alternatives to the implication that resistance must be due to a target enzyme with altered affinity for the drug. The growth of *E. coli* is inhibited by *p*-nitrobenzoic acid (PNB), and this agent was found to compete with the utilization of two structurally similar metabolites, *p*-aminobenzoic acid (PAB) and *p*-hydroxybenzoic acid (POB). These metabolites have quite different functions in the cell, and both are required to reverse the inhibition caused by PNB. Thus, PNB evidently interacts with two distinct enzymes, a PAB enzyme and a POB enzyme. These relationships are represented diagrammatically in Fig. 8-10.

In the experiment, wild-type cells were plated on inhibitory concentrations of PNB under two different conditions: (*1*) in the presence of PAB, and (*2*) in the presence of POB. Since both metabolites are required to overcome the action of PNB, growth was inhibited under both conditions. However, a few colonies resistant to the drug action appeared on both kinds of plate. The resistant cells isolated in the presence of PAB were still inhibited by PNB in the presence of POB; and, likewise, the cells isolated in the presence of POB were still sensitive to PNB in the presence of PAB. In other words, resistance developed independently to the two different actions—anti-PAB and anti-POB—of one and the same drug, PNB. This finding ruled out any mechanism of resistance (mechanisms 1 to 3) that depends upon decreased penetration, increased destruction, or decreased conversion of the drug since all of the drug actions would then have been altered equally.

Sulfathiazole was known to inhibit *E. coli* growth by acting as a competitive antagonist to PAB. The corresponding hydroxy compound,

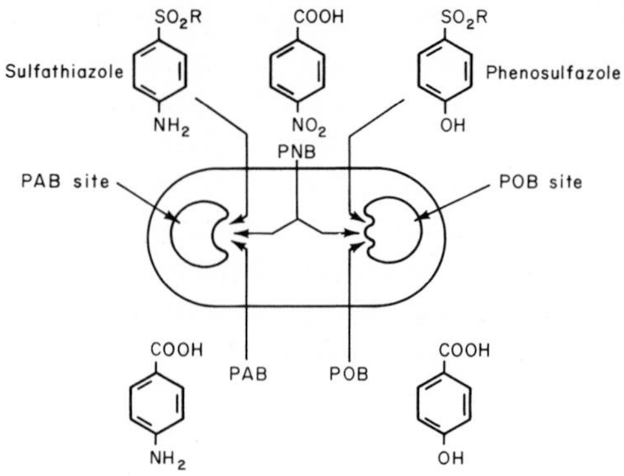

FIG. 8-10. MODEL SHOWING INDEPENDENT ENZYMES FOR UTILIZATION OF
p-AMINOBENZOIC ACID (PAB) and p-HYDROXYBENZOIC ACID (POB) IN *Escherichia
coli.* *Both enzymes are shown inhibited by* p-nitrobenzoic acid (PNB), *each is
inhibited independently by the sulfonamides corresponding to PAB and POB,
respectively.* (R *represents the substituted amide groupings of sulfathiazole and
phenosulfazole.*) (*Modified from Davis and Maas, Fig. 1.*[23])

phenosulfazole, was found to inhibit growth by competing with POB (see
Fig. 8-10). Mutants selected for resistance to each of these compounds
displayed the following behavior: The mutants resistant to sulfathiazole
were not resistant to phenosulfazole. They were also not resistant to PNB
even when POB was present; i.e., they were still sensitive to the anti-PAB
action of PNB, despite their resistance to the anti-PAB action of sulfathiazole. The mutants resistant to phenosulfazole showed analogous properties. They were not resistant to sulfathiazole or PNB in the presence of
PAB. Moreover, the mutants originally isolated on PNB also failed to
show cross-resistance; neither the organism resistant to the anti-PAB
action of PNB nor the one resistant to the anti-POB action of PNB was
resistant to sulfathiazole or phenosulfazole. Thus, resistance at a single site
can be specific for one inhibitor of that site. This finding rules out mechanisms 4 to 7. If, for example, the resistance were due to an increased concentration of the metabolite antagonizing the drug (mechanism 4), then
resistance at the PAB site (or the POB site) would mean resistance to all
competitive inhibitors at that same site. A similar argument applies to the
other postulated mechanisms. Only mechanism 8, an altered target enzyme,
is compatible with these experimental observations, for the loss of affinity
resulting from a change in enzyme configuration could be specific for the
chemical structure of one or another inhibitor.

SULFONAMIDES

The isolation of the target enzyme for sulfonamide action[53] made
it possible to examine directly the question of altered enzymes in sulfon-

[53] G. M. BROWN: The biosynthesis of folic acid. II. Inhibition by sulfonamides.
J. Biol. Chem. 237:536 (1962).

amide resistance. The synthesis of compounds with biologic activity characteristic of folic acid was studied in cell-free extracts by furnishing PAB, 2-amino-4-hydroxy-6-hydroxymethyldihydropteridine (the pteridine portion of the folic acid structure), ATP, Mg^{++}, and a cell extract. After incubation the mixture was assayed for folate by means of a bioassay with *Streptococcus faecalis* as test organism. Sulfonamides block the synthesis of folate in this cell-free system, and PAB overcomes the block. Extracts from sulfathiazole-resistant mutants of *E. coli* had approximately normal enzyme activity; but this activity was much less readily inhibited by sulfathiazole. The resistant extract was tested against four other sulfonamides and found to be resistant to them all; but the degree of resistance varied for the different compounds and for different mutants.[24] This is illustrated in Table 8-3. The top line shows the ratio of each drug to PAB that was required to produce 50 per cent inhibition in the extract of wild-type cells. The smaller the number, the more potent the sulfonamide. The second and third lines give the same data for two resistant mutants. Clearly, the quantitative change in resistance was not the same with respect to every drug. The enzyme from mutant A, for example, shows a fivefold change in the drug/PAB ratio with sulfanilamide, but only a little more than a twofold change with sulfacetamide. Mutant B, on the other hand, displays a lesser degree of resistance to sulfanilamide, but a greater degree to sulfacetamide. The enzyme system from mutant A was completely inactivated in 10 minutes at 46°, whereas the wild-type enzyme was stable under these conditions.

It seems clear that qualitatively altered enzymes can be responsible for sulfonamide resistance. A rather more detailed investigation into the

TABLE 8-3. **Resistance of cell-free extracts of *Escherichia coli* to sulfonamides**

Cell-free extracts were prepared as described in the text, and the conversion of *p*-aminobenzoic acid (PAB) and a pteridine to biologically active folate compounds was measured. The ratio of inhibitor to PAB for 50 per cent inhibition of the reaction velocity was measured in each case. The smaller the ratio, the more potent the inhibitor of the conversion reaction. Two mutants (A and B), isolated for resistance to sulfathiazole, were compared with the wild type. (Adapted from Pato and Brown,[24] Table III.)

	Inhibitor				
Source of extract	Sulfa-thiazole	Sulfa-benzamide	Sulfa-cetamide	Sulfa-diazine	Sulfa-nilamide
	(Inhibitor/PAB for 50% inhibition)				
E. coli B (wild type)	0.71	0.95	7.9	1.6	20
Sulfathiazole-resistant mutant A	2.5	5.3	18	5.0	110
Sulfathiazole-resistant mutant B	4.2	2.6	23	6.0	54

folic acid-synthesizing enzymes of *Pneumococcus* led to the same conclusions,[11] but showed further by genetic analysis that different mutations in a single gene can lead to modified forms of the same enzyme, whose properties (including degree of resistance to sulfonamides) are altered in individually distinctive ways.

ANTIFOLIC DRUGS

In the study of methotrexate resistance in bacteria in which increased amounts of dihydrofolate reductase were found (p. 531), some of the mutant strains were shown to have qualtitatively different enzyme.[51] Strain R5 is a good example. This mutant had a resistance level 40 times greater than the wild type. The activity of dihydrofolate reductase in extracts was almost identical with that of the wild type, and the K_m values for dihydrofolate and for NADPH were nearly the same as those of the wild-type enzyme. However, the affinity of this enzyme for methotrexate was drastically reduced; indeed, the apparent mode of inhibition was changed from noncompetitive to competitive. This is illustrated in Fig. 8-11. The velocity of the dihydrofolate reduction was measured at various substrate concentrations, in the absence and presence of methotrexate, and the results were plotted by the double-reciprocal method (p. 72). The wild-type enzyme and the resistant mutant R6 both yielded straight lines intersecting on the x-axis, typical of noncompetitive inhibition. The result for R5 was quite different. The methotrexate concentration had to be increased more than tenfold in order to inhibit the reaction sufficiently; and then the lines intersected on the y-axis, as is typical of competitive inhibition. Further investigation of this enzyme revealed that the pH optimum

FIG. 8-11.   INHIBITION OF DIHYDROFOLATE REDUCTASE ACTIVITY IN EXTRACTS OF WILD-TYPE AND METHOTREXATE-RESISTANT CELLS.   *Several mutant strains of* Diplococcus pneumoniae *were studied. Double-reciprocal plots are shown in the customary way, reciprocal substrate concentration (dihydrofolate) on the x-axis, reciprocal velocity (moles dihydrofolate reduced per minute) on the y-axis. At left, wild-type extract;* center, *extract from resistant mutant R6;* at right, *extract from resistant mutant R5. Solid circles,* reaction in the absence of methotrexate; open circles, *with methotrexate, 3.2 × 10⁻¹⁰M for wild and R6, 6.45 × 10⁻⁹M for R5. (Adapted from Sirotnak et al., Figs. 1 and 2.[51])*

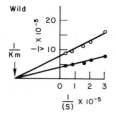
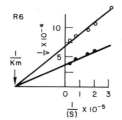
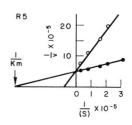

was 0.6 units lower than that of the wild-type enzyme. The heat stability of this enzyme was indistinguishable from that of the wild type, but another resistant mutant yielded enzyme with reduced affinity for drug, shift to competitive inhibition, altered pH optimum, and markedly increased rate of heat inactivation at 45°.

"FALSE FEEDBACK INHIBITORS"

An interesting mechanism of drug resistance that also depends upon modified enzyme structure involves end-product inhibition, an important mechanism in the regulation of intermediary metabolism.[20] Many instances of end-product inhibition are now known to be mediated by allosteric interactions, the allosteric site being distinct from the substrate site. Some growth inhibitors act as "false feedback inhibitors," i.e., by mimicking the action of the endogenous feedback inhibitor and thereby shutting off an essential biosynthetic pathway. Resistance to this kind of inhibition can occur by mutational modification of the allosteric site. Thus, the enzyme becomes insensitive to the drug; but at the same time it may lose its ability to respond to the normal endogenous end-product inhibitor. The result is drug resistance, if the cell can survive the accompanying overproduction of end-products in the affected pathway. The classic example is valine resistance in *E. coli*.[54] In strain K12 of this organism, valine is a potent growth inhibitor, and the inhibition is overcome noncompetitively by isoleucine. It has been shown that a single enzyme catalyzes the synthesis of two different α-acetohydroxy acids that serve as precursors to valine and isoleucine, respectively; these are α-acetolactate and acetohydroxybutyrate. Valine acts as a feedback inhibitor of the acetohydroxy acid synthetase enzyme:

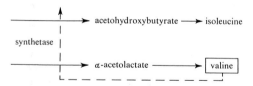

The enzyme has been isolated from valine-resistant mutants and shown to be resistant to valine inhibition. Table 8-4 shows a comparison of wild-type strain K12 with a valine-resistant mutant. The reaction mixture contained pyruvate when acetolactate formation was measured, α-keto-butyrate when acetohydroxybutyrate formation was measured. The amount of product formed in the absence of valine was approximately the same in

    [54] R. I. LEAVITT and H. E. UMBARGER: Isoleucine and valine metabolism in *Escherichia coli*. XI. Valine inhibition of the growth of *Escherichia coli* strain K-12. *J. Bacteriol.* *83*:624 (1962).

TABLE 8-4.   Valine inhibition of acetohydroxy acid formation

Reaction mixture contained pyruvate or α-ketobutyrate, thiamine pyro-
phosphate, Mg^{++}, pH 8.0, and extract from wild-type or valine-resistant
Escherichia coli K12. Incubation was for 15 minutes at 37° in air.
(Modified from Leavitt and Umbarger,[54] Table 2.)

		Wild type		Valine-resistant	
Compound formed	Valine	Amount formed (μmoles)	Inhibition (%)	Amount formed (μmoles)	Inhibition (%)
Acetolactate	none	0.54	—	0.46	—
	$5.0 \times 10^{-5}M$	0.25	55	0.46	—
	$1.0 \times 10^{-4}M$	0.12	78	0.42	8
	$2.0 \times 10^{-4}M$	0.07	87	0.39	11
Acetohydroxy-	none	0.39	—	0.35	—
butyrate	$5.0 \times 10^{-5}M$	0.20	48	0.35	—
	$1.0 \times 10^{-4}M$	0.14	63	0.31	12
	$2.0 \times 10^{-4}M$	0.07	82	0.29	15

both extracts, but the extract from valine-resistant cells was resistant to
the valine inhibition. In general, mutational modification of an allosteric
site can occur without simultaneous alteration of the substrate site; indeed,
as described elsewhere (p. 91), these sites can be on physically distinct
subunits of a multimeric enzyme molecule.

Tryptophan acts as a feedback inhibitor of its own synthesis by
blocking a step in the conversion of shikimic acid 5-phosphate to anthranilic acid,[55] as illustrated in Fig. 8-12. The amino acid analogue 5-methyl-
tryptophan (also shown in the figure) mimics the feedback inhibition
caused by tryptophan, and thus shuts off tryptophan synthesis. Since the
analogue cannot be utilized for protein synthesis, it serves as a growth-
inhibitory drug. Mutants of *E. coli* were selected for resistance to the
growth inhibition caused by 5-methyltryptophan. Extracts of these mutants
were compared with wild-type extracts in a cell-free system for the conversion of shikimic acid phosphate to anthranilic acid in the presence of
glutamine (as amino group donor), Mg^{++}, and NAD. Results are shown
in Fig. 8-13. The concentration-dependent inhibition of anthranilic acid
synthesis by both tryptophan and 5-methyltryptophan is apparent in the
wild-type extract. The resistant extract shows a greatly diminished sensitivity
not only to inhibition by 5-methyltryptophan but also to inhibition by
tryptophan. A by-product of the acquired resistance to the 5-methyl analogue was therefore loss of regulatory control by tryptophan and a consequent overproduction of that amino acid and its excretion into the medium.

[55] H. S. MOYED: False feedback inhibition: inhibition of tryptophan biosynthesis
by 5-methyltryptophan. *J. Biol. Chem. 235:*1098 (1960).

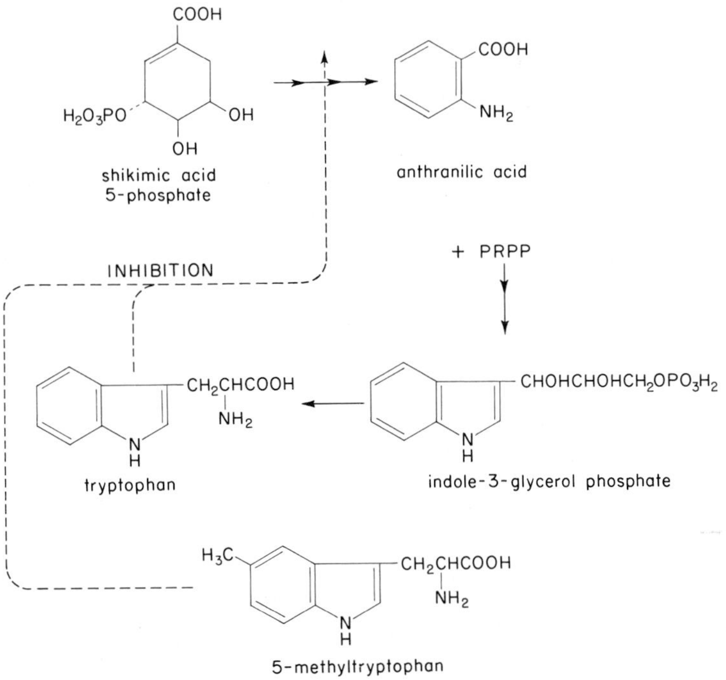

FIG. 8-12. FEEDBACK INHIBITION BY TRYPTOPHAN AND 5-METHYLTRYPTOPHAN. *The pathway of tryptophan biosynthesis is shown, from shikimic acid. Shikimic acid is a branch point, serving also as precursor to other aromatic metabolites. Compound arrows indicate intermediary reactions not shown. The site of feedback inhibition is one of the steps in the conversion of shikimic acid phosphate to anthranilic acid. (After Meister.[56])*

A similar example of acquired resistance to a feedback inhibitor concerns 2-thiazolealanine, an analogue of histidine.[57] In a manner similar to that described for tryptophan, histidine regulates its own synthesis by inhibiting an early reaction, in this case the coupling of adenosine triphosphate (ATP) with ribose phosphate derived from 5-phosphoribosyl-1 pyrophosphate (PRPP). This feedback inhibition is illustrated in Fig. 8-14. The pyrophosphorylase that catalyzes this reaction is specifically inhibited by histidine, and also by 2-thiazolealanine. Growth inhibition is the consequence of the resulting histidine deficiency. The inhibition of histidine synthesis, either by histidine itself or by its analogue, is noncompetitive with respect to the substrates (ATP, PRPP), and the inhibitory site can be distinguished clearly from the substrate site by treating the enzyme with

56 A. MEISTER: *Biochemistry of the Amino Acids,* 2nd ed. New York, Academic Press, 1965.

57 H. S. MOYED: Interference with the feed-back control of histidine biosynthesis. *J. Biol. Chem.* 236:2261 (1961).

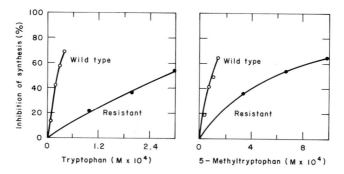

FIG. 8-13. INHIBITION OF ANTHRANILIC ACID SYNTHESIS BY TRYPTOPHAN AND 5-METHYLTRYPTOPHAN. *Inhibition of anthranilic acid synthesis by cell-free extracts was measured as described in the text. The resistant strain was a mutant selected for resistance to growth inhibition by 5-methyltryptophan.* (*From Moyed, Figs. 2 and 3.*[55])

mercuric ions. Figure 8-15 shows that although mercuric ion had no effect upon the enzyme activity in the absence of histidine, it abolished histidine inhibition in a concentration-dependent manner; at $10^{-5}M$ mercuric chloride, the effects of histidine were completely overcome. This could not have been due to a complexing of histidine by mercuric ion inasmuch as there was a 100-fold excess of histidine. Thorough removal of mercuric ions by means of a sulfhydryl compound was found to restore the sensitivity of the enzyme to inhibition by histidine. Other experiments showed that the enzyme was composed of subunits. Thus, the feedback inhibition is evidently brought about by combination of histidine (or 2-thiazolealanine) at an allosteric site.

A resistant mutant of *Escherichia coli* was isolated by the usual selection procedures. The pyrophosphorylase of these cells was found no longer to be sensitive to inhibition, either by 2-thiazolealanine or by histidine. Presumably, a mutation has altered the allosteric site or has affected the mode of interaction of the enzyme subunits so that allosteric inhibition is no longer possible. The mutant, therefore, not only grows despite the presence of the inhibitor but also overproduces histidine and excretes it into the culture medium.

In addition to this genetic mechanism of resistance to 2-thiazole-alanine, an interesting phenotypic resistance has been demonstrated.[57] Histidine biosynthesis is regulated not only by feedback inhibition but also by end-product repression of some of the biosynthetic enzymes in the pathway. Under certain conditions, especially at low concentrations of 2-thiazolealanine, wild-type cells undergo the following adaptation. The histidine deficiency caused by the "false feedback inhibition" releases the enzymes from repression and an increased rate of enzyme synthesis ensues. Thus, the target enzyme, the pyrophosphorylase upon which the inhibitor

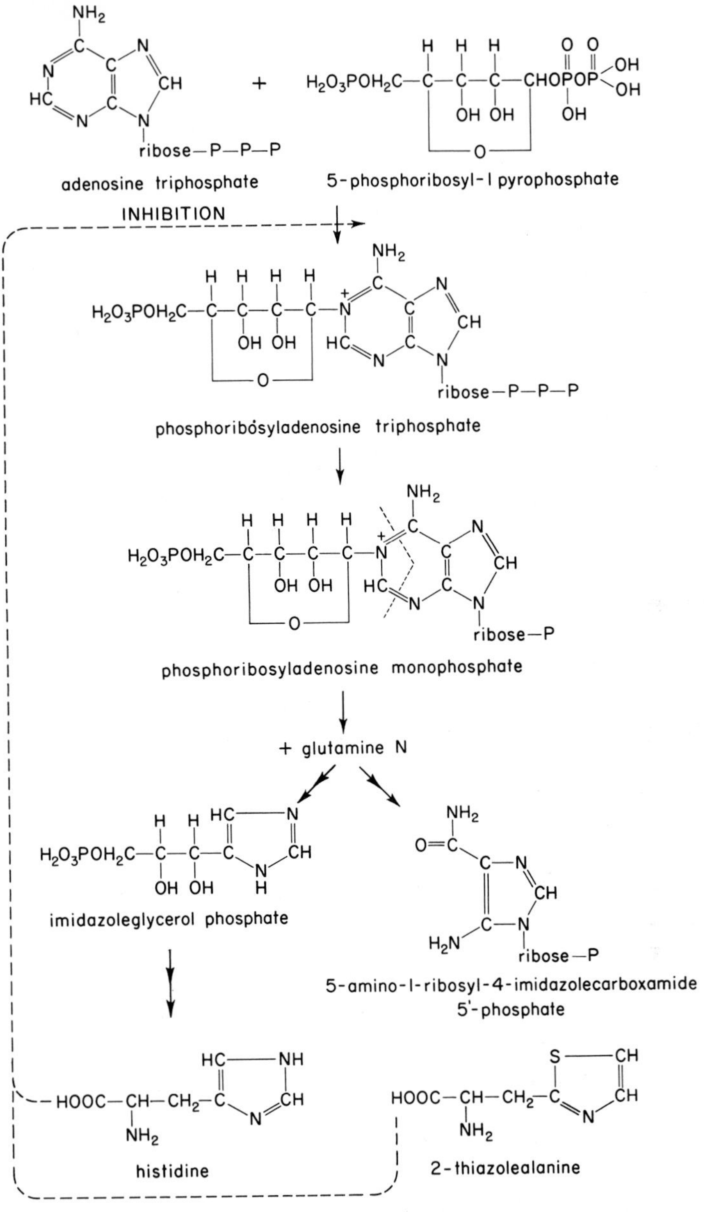

FIG. 8-14. FEEDBACK INHIBITION BY HISTIDINE AND 2-THIAZOLEALANINE. *The pathway of histidine biosynthesis is shown.* Compound arrows *indicate intermediate steps not shown. The site of feedback inhibition by histidine or by its analogue, 2-thiazolealanine, is the phosphoribosyladenosine triphosphate pyrophosphorylase, which catalyzes addition of the phosphoribosyl moiety to ATP. Carbon atoms of ribose, nitrogen and carbon atoms from adenine, and nitrogen from glutamine form the imidazole ring. (After Smith and Ames.*[58]*)

58 D. W. E. SMITH and B. N. AMES: Phosphoribosyladenosine monophosphate, an intermediate in histidine biosynthesis. *J. Biol. Chem.* 240:3056 (1965).

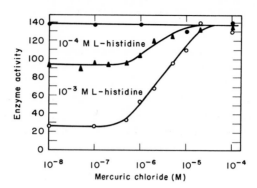

FIG. 8-15.   MERCURIC ION REVERSAL OF FEEDBACK INHIBITION.   *The activity of phosphoribosyladenosine triphosphate pyrophosphorylase was measured; units of enzyme activity on the y-axis are changes in optical absorbancy in a 4-minute incubation. The enzyme was assayed in the presence of two histidine concentrations and various concentrations of mercuric chloride. Line at top shows activity of the enzyme in the absence of histidine. (From Martin, Fig. 9.[59])*

acts, is greatly increased in amount. Despite the continued presence of the inhibitor, conversion of substrate to product now proceeds at a rate sufficient to meet the histidine needs of the cell, and growth is resumed. Figure 8-16 illustrates the considerable increase in enzyme level in the wild type

FIG. 8-16.   ENZYME DEREPRESSION CAUSED BY 2-THIAZOLEALANINE IN WILD-TYPE CELLS OF *Escherichia coli*.   *Wild-type cells and a mutant strain resistant to 2-thiazolealanine were grown to the same cell mass in the presence of various concentrations of 2-thiazolealanine. Extracts were prepared and assayed for their ability to form an early product in the histidine pathway. In effect, the assay measures the pyrophosphorylase that catalyzes formation of phosphoribosyl-ATP from ATP and PRPP. Vertical axis gives enzyme activity; horizontal axis gives concentrations of 2-thiazolealanine in which cells were grown. (Modified from Moyed, Fig. 6.[57])*

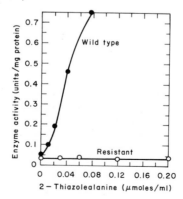

in the presence of 2-thiazolealanine. No such effect is to be expected in the genetically resistant strain, and none occurs.

STREPTOMYCIN DEPENDENCE

A rare and remarkable special kind of acquired drug resistance is that known as *drug dependence*. Here, the cells not only tolerate a growth-inhibitory drug but specifically require that drug for their growth. The phenomenon has been described for chloramphenicol and for isoniazid; but the best-known and best-understood instance is streptomycin dependence.

Streptomycin-dependent strains of bacteria can be isolated on medium containing the drug by the usual procedures for selecting resistant mutants. On subculture, these organisms will grow only in the presence of streptomycin or very closely related congeners. The specificity of the requirement for streptomycin suggested that the drug must have played some directive role in the development of the dependent state, for it was hard to imagine that a specific requirement for a foreign substance could develop spontaneously. Nevertheless, it has been shown conclusively by the replica plating technique[60] that streptomycin dependence arises by spontaneous mutation. Despite the superficial similarity to physical dependence in higher organisms (p. 578), this phenomenon has essentially the same genetic basis as the more usual kind of acquired drug resistance. Streptomycin sensitivity, various degrees of resistance, and dependence are determined by alleles of a single genetic locus.[61] There is a widespread misconception that dependence is an extreme form of resistance, that a cell becomes "more and more resistant and eventually becomes dependent." This is not correct. A sensitive cell may become resistant or dependent by a single mutational step.

Protein Synthesis and the Genetic Code

The primary effect of streptomycin is to inhibit protein synthesis.[62, 63] Figure 8-17 provides a framework for understanding the mode of action of this drug at the molecular level, and for considering the basis of resistance and dependence. The messenger-RNA (mRNA) has a polarity that is determined by the fact that each phosphodiester bond between

59 R. G. MARTIN: The first enzyme in histidine biosynthesis: the nature of feedback inhibition by histidine. *J. Biol. Chem. 238:*257 (1963).

60 A. GOLDSTEIN: The origin of streptomycin-dependent variants of *Escherichia coli. J. Pharmacol. Exp. Therap. 112:*326 (1954).

61 D. A. MITCHISON: Microbial genetics and chemotherapy. *Brit. Med. Bull. 18:*74 (1962).

62 C. R. SPOTTS and R. Y. STANIER: Mechanism of streptomycin action on bacteria: a unitary hypothesis. *Nature 192:*633 (1961).

63 C. R. SPOTTS: Physiological and biochemical studies on streptomycin dependence in *Escherichia coli. J. Gen. Microbiol. 28:*347 (1962).

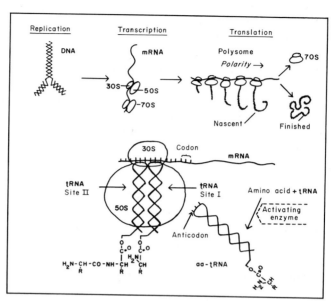

FIG. 8-17.   MECHANISM OF PROTEIN SYNTHESIS.   *At* top, *transcription of the genetic message, and attachment of ribosomes to messenger-RNA. These may attach and begin translation of the message before transcription is completed. Nascent proteins are shown as hanging free from the ribosomes. At* bottom, *a magnified view of events on the single ribosome. The configuration of transfer-RNA is, in reality, more complex than represented here. (From Das et al., Fig. 12.*[64]*)*

adjacent nucleotides extends from the 5'-hydroxyl group of one ribose residue to the 3'-hydroxyl group of the adjacent ribose residue. Thus, at one end of the polynucleotide chain is a free 5'-hydroxyl group, at the other end a free 3'-hydroxyl group. These ends are referred to, respectively, as the 5'- and 3'-ends. The ribosomes are compound particles with sedimentation coefficient 70S. Each is composed of a 50S and a 30S subunit. The ribosomes attach to 5'-ends of mRNA strands and move in the direction 5'→3' as they translate the genetic message and assemble the nascent protein.[65]

The magnified diagram of a single ribosome in the polysome array indicates how the two subunits collaborate to form a matrix on which the translation of the genetic message can take place. In the diagram, the 5'-end of the mRNA strand is to the left, corresponding to the NH_2-terminal end of the nascent protein. The ribosome will move from left to right as it adds

[64] H. K. DAS, A. GOLDSTEIN, and L. C. KANNER: Inhibition by chloramphenicol of the growth of nascent protein chains in *Escherichia coli. Mol. Pharmacol. 2:*158 (1966).

[65] A. GOLDSTEIN, J. B. KIRSCHBAUM, and A. ROMAN: Direction of synthesis of messenger RNA in cells of *Escherichia coli. Proc. Nat. Acad. Sci. U.S.A. 54:*1669 (1965).

new amino acids to the —COOH terminus of the nascent protein chain.[65a] The 30S subunit is known to bind mRNA; the 50S and 30S subunits probably both bind transfer-RNA (tRNA). The nascent protein is attached to the tRNA molecule that carried its carboxy-terminal amino acid into the ribosomal assembly site; this attachment is formed by an ester bond between the α-carboxyl group of the amino acid and the 3'-hydroxyl group of adenosine ribose at the end of every tRNA molecule. The tRNA that carries the nascent protein is very firmly bound to the ribosome; the site of its attachment is designated "site II." The next amino acid to be added to the nascent protein is carried on its appropriate tRNA molecule into a site (designated "site I") where it fits perfectly into position for peptide bond formation. The transfer of the acyl group of the nascent chain to the amino group of the amino acid in site I (i.e., the formation of the peptide bond) transfers the entire nascent protein chain to the tRNA in site I, and simultaneously liberates the tRNA from site II. The physical movement of the ribosome to the right, a distance corresponding to one codon (three nucleotides, approximately 10 A), could be brought about by the peptidyl-tRNA "jumping" from site I into site II, or by a rolling movement of the ribosome that brings a new binding site into position.

The general principles of the genetic code appear to be solidly established, and the 64 codon assignments are pretty well worked out. They are presented in Table 8-5. Each triplet is presented with its 5'-terminal at the left, 3'-terminal at the right, so the reading is from left to right. The codons represent bases in mRNA; these are derived, of course, from a complementary strand (the "sense" strand) of the DNA by the classical base-pairing mechanism. The actual translation of the sequence of codons in mRNA is mediated by specific base pairing between the base triplet in the codon and a complementary triplet (anticodon) in the appropriate tRNA molecule. Complete primary base sequences in a few tRNA molecules[68, 69] reveal certain essential features of this structure. Although there is a considerable degree of internal base pairing, the tRNA

[65a] A. GOLDSTEIN, D. B. GOLDSTEIN, and L. I. LOWNEY: Protein synthesis at 0° C in *Escherichia coli. J. Mol. Biol. 9:*213 (1964).

[66] D. SÖLL, E. OHTSUKA, D. S. JONES, R. LOHRMANN, H. HAYATSU, S. NISHIMURA, and H. G. KHORANA: Studies on polynucleotides. XLIX. Stimulation of the binding of aminoacyl-sRNA's to ribosomes by ribotrinucleotides and a survey of codon assignments for 20 amino acids. *Proc. Nat. Acad. Sci. U.S.A. 54:*1378 (1965).

[67] R. BRIMACOMBE, J. TRUPIN, M. NIRENBERG, P. LEDER, M. BERNFIELD, and T. JAOUNI: RNA codewords and protein synthesis. VIII. Nucleotide sequences of synonym codons for arginine, valine, cysteine, and alanine. *Proc. Nat. Acad. Sci. U.S.A. 54:*954 (1965).

[68] R. W. HOLLEY, J. APGAR, G. A. EVERETT, J. T. MADISON, M. MARQUISEE, S. H. MERRILL, J. R. PENSWICK, and A. ZAMIR: Structure of a ribonucleic acid. *Science 147:*1462 (1965).

[69] J. T. MADISON, G. A. EVERETT, and H. KUNG: Nucleotide sequence of a yeast tyrosine transfer RNA. *Science 153:*531 (1966).

TABLE 8-5.   The genetic code

Assignments for the triplets shown in parentheses were somewhat
uncertain at the time this table was compiled. Each triplet codon is
shown with its 5'-terminal nucleotide to the left, 3'-terminal to the
right. The codons are translated from left to right. The codons UAA
and UAG appear to code for N-formylmethionine; they are involved
in initiating and terminating polypeptide chains. (After Söll et al.[66]
and Brimacombe et al.[67])

UUU UUC	Phe	UCU UCC UCA UCG	Ser	UAU UAC	Tyr	UGU UGC	Cys
(UUA) UUG	Leu			UAA UAG	start/stop	(UGA) UGG	Trp
CUU CUC (CUA) CUG	Leu	CCU CCC CCA CCG	Pro	CAU CAC	His	CGU CGC CGA CGG	Arg
				CAA CAG	Gln		
AUU AUC	Ile	ACU ACC ACA ACG	Thr	AAU AAC	Asn	AGU AGC	Ser
(AUA) AUG	Met			AAA AAG	Lys	AGA (AGG)	Arg
GUU GUC GUA GUG	Val	GCU GCC GCA GCG	Ala	GAU GAC	Asp	GGU GGC GGA GGG	Gly
				GAA GAG	Glu		

molecule has a rather complex structure, perhaps ensuring its recognition
by the correct activating enzyme. Little is yet known about this recognition
mechanism, which determines how each activating enzyme attaches a particular amino acid to the tRNA molecule containing the anticodon that
corresponds to that particular amino acid.

Figure 8-18 shows the probable structures of two different tRNA
molecules from yeast. The occurrence, at a central position of these and
other tRNA molecules, of a base triplet complementary to the known codon
for the appropriate amino acid makes the anticodon hypothesis inescapable.
Thus, for example, a codon assignment for alanine had been known to be
GCC. The expected anticodon (written in the direction 3'→5') would
therefore be CGG, and the sequence CGI actually appears at the middle
loop of alanine tRNA. The base-pairing properties of I (hypoxanthine) are
similar to those of G (guanine). Similarly, UAC is a codon for tyrosine, and
the complementary sequence AΨG is found in the same position in the
middle loop of tyrosine tRNA. Ψ (pseudouracil) has the same base-pairing
properties as U (uracil).

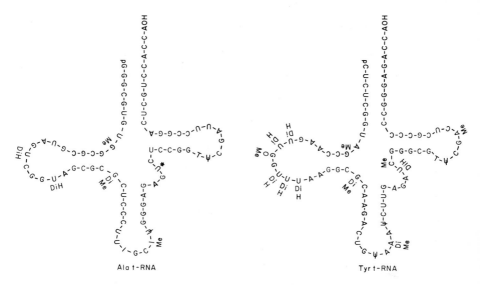

FIG. 8-18. PRIMARY STRUCTURE AND PROBABLE HIGHER-ORDER STRUCTURE OF TWO TRANSFER-RNA MOLECULES, ALANINE AND TYROSINE tRNA FROM YEAST. MeG, *Methyl guanine;* DiMeG, *dimethylguanine;* DiHU, *dihydrouracil;* I, *inosine = hypoxanthine riboside;* MeI, *methyl inosine;* ψ, *pseudouracil;* U*, *mixture of uracil and dihydrouracil;* T, *thymine riboside;* MeOG, O-*methylguanine;* DiMeA, *dimethyladenine;* MeC, *methylcytosine;* A, *adenine;* G, *guanine;* C, *cytosine;* U, *uracil;* p, *phosphate;* OH, *3'-hydroxyl.* (*From Madison et al., Fig. 2.*[69] *By permission of the American Association for the Advancement of Science.*)

Disturbance of Translation by Streptomycin

The correct assembly of every protein in the cell according to the specifications of the genetic code (the translation of the genetic message) depends upon a high degree of fidelity in the matching of anticodon to codon. The structure of the ribosome, which provides the matrix for this matching process, evidently plays a role in assuring the necessary fidelity. And the available evidence implicates streptomycin as a distorting agent in the translation process. The first concrete evidence pointing to a ribosomal site of action of this drug came from experiments on the incorporation of phenylalanine into polypeptide by a cell-free system consisting of bacterial ribosomes, polyuridylic acid (polyU) functioning as a synthetic mRNA, and the appropriate activating and transfer enzymes.[70,71] In this

[70] J. E. DAVIES: Studies on the ribosomes of streptomycin-sensitive and resistant strains of *Escherichia coli. Proc. Nat. Acad. Sci. U.S.A. 51:*659 (1964).

[71] E. C. COX, J. R. WHITE, and J. G. FLAKS: Streptomycin action and the ribosome. *Proc. Nat. Acad. Sci. U.S.A. 51:*703 (1964).

system, little effect of the drug was seen unless it was added before the polyU, suggesting that in order to exert its effect it has to combine with ribosomes before the ribosomes attach to mRNA.

The result of such an experiment is shown in Fig. 8-19. In the control extract (left), the sucrose gradient centrifugation illustrates the typical pattern of distribution of the RNA, measured by optical density at 260 mμ: a prominent 70S peak of ribosome monomers about tube 22, and a large amount of material at the top of the gradient (4S and below). The polyU, containing ^{14}C, all appeared in a peak in the 100 to 200S region, corresponding to polysomes. Likewise, the amino acid–incorporating capacity (as indicated by the ability of the fractions to incorporate radioactive phenylalanine) was concentrated in the polysome region. In the presence of streptomycin (right), there was no significant effect upon the optical density pattern or upon the distribution and amount of polyU in the polysomes. But there was a profound decrease in the capacity of the polysomes to incorporate the amino acid.

These findings, and the well-known ability of the cationic streptomycin molecule to complex with nucleic acids, suggested, as had been proposed on theoretical grounds,[62,63] that the ribosomes might be the sites of streptomycin action. This proved to be true. The ribosomes from sensi-

FIG. 8-19.   EFFECT OF STREPTOMYCIN UPON POLYSOME FUNCTION IN A CELL-FREE SYSTEM.   *Radioactive polyuridylic acid (polyU) was added to a crude extract of* Escherichia coli, *allowed to stand 30 minutes at 0°, then run 2 hours on a sucrose density gradient. Optical density at 260μ (i.e., nucleic acid) and polyU radioactivity were measured in each fraction, and the capacity of each fraction to incorporate radioactive phenylalanine was also determined. Bottoms of gradients are to left.* Left, *control;* right, *streptomycin (10⁻⁴M) added 5 minutes before polyU, and also contained in the gradient. (From Davies, Figs. 1 and 3.[70])*

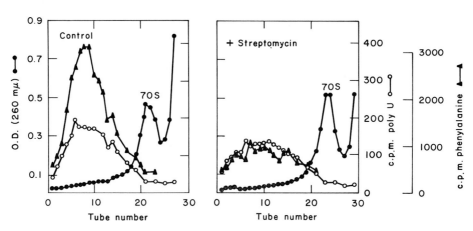

tive organisms bind about one molecule of streptomycin each, whereas ribosomes from resistant strains neither bind the drug nor are affected by it in a cell-free incorporating system.[72] Moreover, if the ribosomes are dissociated into 30S and 50S subunits and then recombined in a crossover experiment, the 30S subunit carries the resistance or sensitivity to streptomycin; the 50S subunit is indifferent. Evidently, the genetic locus concerned with sensitivity, resistance, or dependence involves the structure of the 30S ribosomal subunit.

Evidence has now accumulated which shows that in the presence of streptomycin, ribosomes from streptomycin-sensitive cells bind the drug in such a way that the specific codon-anticodon interactions are distorted.[73, 74] Thus, the "wrong" tRNA is permitted, at a fairly high frequency, to enter site I, and consequently the "wrong" amino acid is incorporated into the nascent protein. This misreading effect, in a cell-free system, is illustrated in Table 8-6. Under the experimental conditions em-

TABLE 8-6. Misreading of codons caused by streptomycin

The cell-free system contained an extract of streptomycin-sensitive *Escherichia coli* supplemented with excess transfer-RNA. Reaction mixture contained: 12.5mM Mg^{++}; polyuridylic acid (polyU), 10μg per 0.25 ml; polycytidylic acid (polyC), 15μg to 20μg per 0. 25 ml. Incorporation into acid-insoluble material (protein) was measured. The control incorporation of *Phe* (set equal to 100) was 500$\mu\mu$moles, that of *Pro* was 200$\mu\mu$moles. (Data of Davies et al.,[73] Tables 2 and 3.)

	Control	Streptomycin (4μg/ml)
polyU		
Phe	100	60
Leu	5	10
Ile	8	30
Ser	4	20
Tyr	26	38
polyC		
Pro	100	230
His	1	12
Thr	17	41
Leu	1	3
Ala	1	4
Ser		55

ployed, phenylalanine was principally incorporated when polyU was used as messenger (UUU is the codon for *Phe*); there was also significant incorporation of tyrosine, very little of leucine, isoleucine, or serine. Addition of streptomycin reduced the incorporation of *Phe,* as already shown, but it greatly increased the incorporation of *Leu, Ile,* and *Ser.* When polyC was used as messenger (CCC is the codon for *Pro*) streptomycin caused an increase in the incorporation of proline, rather than an inhibition; but there was a dramatic and disproportionate increase in the incorporation of serine and histidine. The pattern that emerges from these misreadings of the genetic code appears in most cases to be a disturbance in the reading of the base in the 5′-position in the codon, but sometimes the base in the middle position is affected. The experimental observations in Table 8-6 are understandable by reference to the genetic code (Table 8-5) on the premise that the binding of streptomycin to the 30S ribosome subunit distorts the fit between tRNA and mRNA so that normal hydrogen bonding distances are altered. Thus, we might have UUU (*Phe*) read as though it were AUU (*Ile*), CUU (*Leu*), or UCU (*Ser*); or CCC (*Pro*) read as though it were UCC (*Ser*), CAC (*His*), and so on. Numerous misreadings in vivo would lead to the insertion of many wrong amino acids, or even to the premature termination of nascent protein chains (e.g., by misreading of an amino acid codon as the terminating triplet UAG or UAA). Clearly, normal protein synthesis would be completely disrupted and cell death would probably result.

In the light of these findings about the site of action of streptomycin, it might be supposed that streptomycin resistance could arise from mutation in a gene controlling the structure of the 30S ribosomal subunit, presumably one of its protein components. That the alteration which confers resistance occurred on the 30S particle was shown when, by recombining 50S particles from sensitive cells with 30S particles from resistant cells, the resulting hybrid ribosomes were resistant to the drug effect.[70, 71]

Phenotypic Suppression and the "Misreading" Hypothesis

Strong support for the "misreading" hypothesis of streptomycin action and a plausible explanation of streptomycin dependence come from experiments on phenotypic suppression.[75, 76] Among certain strains of

[72] S. PESTKA, R. MARSHALL, and M. NIRENBERG: RNA codewords and protein synthesis. V. Effect of streptomycin on the formation of ribosome-sRNA complexes. *Proc. Nat. Acad. Sci. U.S.A.* 53:639 (1965).

[73] J. DAVIES, L. GORINI, and B. D. DAVIS: Misreading of RNA codewords induced by aminoglycoside antibiotics. *Mol. Pharmacol.* 1:93 (1965).

[74] J. DAVIES, D. S. JONES, and H. G. KHORANA: A further study of misreading of codons induced by streptomycin and neomycin using ribopolynucleotides containing two nucleotides in alternating sequence as templates. *J. Mol. Biol.* 18:48 (1966).

[75] J. DAVIES, W. GILBERT, and L. GORINI: Streptomycin, suppression, and the code. *Proc. Nat. Acad. Sci. U.S.A.* 51:883 (1964).

[76] L. GORINI and E. KATAJA: Phenotypic repair by streptomycin of defective genotypes in *E. coli. Proc. Nat. Acad. Sci. U.S.A.* 51:487 (1964).

streptomycin-resistant bacteria it has been possible to select for mutations that are suppressible by streptomycin. A concrete example will illustrate. An arginine-requiring mutant was isolated from a strain of *E. coli* with moderate resistance to streptomycin. The mutant was completely lacking in active ornithine transcarbamylase, the enzyme converting ornithine to citrulline in the biosynthetic pathway leading to arginine. Naturally, the organism was able to grow when arginine was supplied. However, it was also able to grow when streptomycin was furnished in appropriate concentration, regardless of whether arginine was present or not. When grown on streptomycin, the cells produced active ornithine transcarbamylase, i.e., the effects of the mutation were suppressed. Mating experiments showed that the site of the suppressible mutation was indeed in the ornithine transcarbamylase structural gene. Phenotypic suppression could also be demonstrated in streptomycin-sensitive organisms, provided very low concentrations of the drug were employed.

The interpretation of phenotypic suppression by streptomycin is as follows: The mutation in the structural gene had resulted in an altered codon specifying an amino acid replacement, at that particular position in the sequence, that was not compatible with a functional state of the protein. Alternatively, the altered codon might specify no amino acid at all ("nonsense"). By inducing misreading, streptomycin then caused the defective codon to be read in a tolerable way (i.e., as an amino acid compatible with enzyme function) with a certain frequency, and so a partial repair of the defective protein was effected. A hypothetical example, based upon the information in Tables 8-5 and 8-6, may be cited. Suppose a triplet UCC, coding for serine in the wild-type enzyme, had mutated to CCC by a U→C transition.[77] Then, in the mutant organism, proline is inserted at that position instead of serine, producing (let us assume) a protein that is unable to fold into the correct tertiary configuration and is therefore inactive. Streptomycin induces the misreading of CCC as serine with a high frequency (Table 8-6), and thus the correct amino acid will be inserted sometimes in the mutant organism. Some functional enzyme molecules will be formed, and some growth will occur in the presence of streptomycin. The misreading effect, of course, is rather general, so the partial restoration of activity of the mutated enzyme is accompanied by reduced activity of other enzymes.[78, 79]

---

[77] As will be explained in chapter 10, in the discussion of chemical mutagenesis, a *transition* is an induced change of one DNA purine or pyrimidine for another. Suppose the wild-type DNA had a base pair T-A, the A being in the "sense" strand that will determine the mRNA formed during transcription. Then, by the normal pairing process, A will determine U at that position in the mRNA. The mutational transition T-A → C-G will yield C instead of U in the mRNA.

[78] L. GORINI: Streptomycin and the ambiguity of the genetic code. *New Scientist* 24:776 (1964).

[79] W. F. ANDERSON, L. GORINI, and L. BRECKENRIDGE: Role of ribosomes in streptomycin-activated suppression. *Proc. Nat. Acad. Sci. U.S.A.* 54:1076 (1965).

Mutants of the kind described above are classified as "conditionally streptomycin dependent" because a metabolite can substitute for streptomycin in supporting growth. Streptomycin seems to act in its usual way (inducing misreading) when it remedies the phenotypic defect caused by the mutation. It is assumed that in the classical type of streptomycin dependence, where only the drug itself is effective, the 30S ribosome structure has been altered in such a way that misreading occurs in the absence of drug, to an extent that disrupts protein synthesis completely. Then, binding of streptomycin to the defective 30S particle would restore a more normal configuration, permit a higher frequency of correct codon-anticodon interactions, and thereby permit cell growth to occur.

SELECTION OF DRUG-RESISTANT CELLS IN ANIMALS AND MAN

To what extent might selection of resistant cells play a role in the development of drug tolerance in animals and man? Such a mechanism would presumably be operative only in tissues characterized by a high rate of cell renewal, in which a drug-resistant or drug-dependent variant could generate a clone sufficiently large to replace an original drug-sensitive cell population. Such tissues are principally the blood-forming elements of bone marrow, the gastrointestinal epithelium, male germinal cells, embryonic tissues, and neoplasms.[80]

Tolerance to massive acute hemolysis produced by primaquine, after the initial occurrence, could be thought of as resulting from a selection mechanism, although no resistant mutants are involved. In individuals who are genetically prone to react in this way (p. 444), the older erythrocites are sensitive, the younger cells are resistant. The first dose of primaquine therefore wipes out the older cell population, and the individual is then tolerant to further doses. If a regular dosage schedule is maintained, a certain small fraction of the total erythrocyte population will be lysed every day as new cells come of age; but massive acute hemolysis will not be manifested again unless primaquine is first discontinued for long enough to permit re-establishment of the normal age distribution of the erythrocyte population.

According to the clonal selection theory of immunologic tolerance,[81] mutation and selection underlie the development of a person's immunologic reactivity and his ability to recognize and not reject his own proteins. Lymphoid cells of the embryo are thought to become specialized, through mutation, for the production of a variety of immunoglobulins; each cell synthesizes one or a few of such antibody proteins. Exposure to endogenous antigens during fetal development is postulated to cause the elimi-

---

[80] C. P. LEBLOND and B. E. WALKER: Renewal of cell populations. *Physiol. Rev.* *36*:255 (1956).

[81] F. M. BURNET: Immunological recognition of self. *Science 133*:307 (1961).

nation of all those cells whose antibodies would interact with these antigens. As a result of this selection process, the cells that remain, resistant (in a sense) to endogenous proteins, stand ready to be stimulated by foreign antigens during postfetal life.[82] When this occurs, they proliferate and thus greatly increase the production of particular antibodies. As suggested already in connection with the discussion of drug allergy (chapter 7), it may be possible that exposure to a drug during fetal life confers protection in later life against that drug's producing an allergic response.

Dogs that recover after massive destruction of liver and kidney tissue caused by uranium salts subsequently display tolerance to uranium toxicity. The tissue regenerates in a peculiar way, as judged by its microscopic morphology. Apparently, the cells damaged by the toxic action of uranium are replaced by an ingrowth of quite different cells, which nevertheless seem to be functionally competent. In both liver and kidney, these new cells appear to be more resistant not only to uranium but to other toxic agents as well. Dogs that have recovered from a toxic dose of uranium tolerate another dose several times larger than the first, without further injury, and their livers are also more resistant to damage by chloroform.[83, 84] Tolerance to arsenic administration is discussed later (p. 580) in connection with cellular mechanisms of tolerance.

Neoplasms that have a rapid growth rate might be expected to provide good examples of the mutation-selection process in the origin of drug resistance.[85] This is true of transplantable leukemia and ascitic carcinoma of mice; instances of acquired resistance to antifolic compounds or purine analogues have been presented earlier in this chapter. But acquired resistance of leukemia or of a solid malignant neoplasm to drug therapy may have complex causes. Sometimes, although the disease becomes refractory, the cancer cells themselves may show little or no evidence of drug resistance. In one experiment,[86] mice were inoculated with leukemia cells and then treated with methotrexate. These animals survived about twice as long as untreated controls, but they died despite continuous drug therapy. Leukemia cells obtained from such animals at death and reinjected into fresh mice were found to be sensitive to methotrexate. Thus, the cause of death was certainly not the emergence of a drug-resistant

82 P. B. MEDAWAR: Immunological tolerance. *Science 133:*303 (1961).

83 W. DE B. MAC NIDER: A study of the acquired resistance of fixed tissue cells morphologically altered through processes of repair. I. The liver injury induced by uranium nitrate. A consideration of the type of epithelial repair which imparts to the liver resistance against subsequent uranium intoxications. *J. Pharmacol. Exp. Therap. 56:*359 (1936).

84 W. DE B. MAC NIDER: A study of the acquired resistance of fixed tissue cells morphologically altered through processes of repair. II. The resistance of liver epithelium altered morphologically as a result of an injury from uranium, followed by repair, to the hepatoxic action of chloroform. *J. Pharmacol. Exp. Therap. 56:*373 (1936).

85 R. W. BROCKMAN and E. P. ANDERSON: Biochemistry of cancer (metabolic aspects). *Annu. Rev. Biochem. 32:*463 (1963).

86 L. W. LAW: Differences between cancers in terms of evolution of drug resistance. *Cancer Res. 16:*698 (1956).

mutant line of leukemia cells. Only after repeated animal passage in the presence of methotrexate was it possible to obtain a population of drug-resistant cells that would be indifferent to methotrexate when inoculated into fresh animals.

Figure 8-20 shows an experiment[87] in which ascites tumor cells were counted regularly by washing out the peritoneal cavities of the mice. Methotrexate administration on alternate days caused regular sharp declines in the cell number. Nevertheless, the treated groups died 12 days after injection of the tumor cells, with cell count about 30 million in the ascitic fluid. The untreated groups succumbed within six days, with cell count around 80 million. Cells recovered from the treated mice at death were not drug resistant, as proved by reinoculation into fresh animals. The most probable explanation for the death of the treated mice in this experiment is that the neoplastic cells had spread from the abdominal cavity to vital organs elsewhere in the body, where they were inaccessible to the drug.

Drugs like methotrexate, 6-mercaptopurine, and glucocorticoids can produce striking amelioration of the condition of patients with certain kinds of cancer. But the neoplastic process eventually becomes refractory to the drug therapy. It has often been assumed that drug failure under these conditions must be due to selection of genetically altered tumor cell lines,

FIG. 8-20.   EFFECT OF METHOTREXATE ON GROWTH OF TUMOR CELLS IN MICE. *An ascitic form of mouse leukemia was used. Mice were injected initially with about 3 million methotrexate-sensitive cells.* Solid line *shows cell counts from the abdominal cavity in untreated controls, which died by six days after injection.* Broken line *shows cell counts in mice treated with methotrexate (3 mg/kg) on days 2, 4, 6, 8, and 10. The treated animals were all dead by the 12th day. (From Welch, Chart 1.*[87])

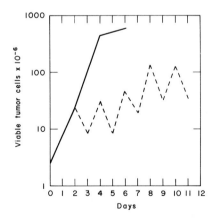

[87] A. D. WELCH: The problem of drug resistance in cancer chemotherapy. *Cancer Res. 19:*359 (1959).

much as described earlier for microorganisms and transplantable murine tumors. Extensive data on "drug-resistant" human cancers have not yet been obtained, but it is interesting that thus far, at least, not a single convincing instance of drug resistance due to mutation and selection has come to light. Clearly, many other factors can account for therapeutic failure.[88, 47, 42] The drugs used in cancer chemotherapy, for example, have very poor therapeutic ratios. Therefore, they have to be used at maximum tolerated dosage, so that any increase of dose is likely to produce serious toxicity. Under these conditions, any change in the patient's circulation that reduces the efficiency of delivery of the drug to the tumor site may result in drug failure. Or a part of the tumor itself may be poorly vascularized and consequently receive too little drug. Invasion of the central nervous system by tumor cells can protect them from drugs unable to pass the drug-brain barrier readily. Alterations in metabolism or excretion of the drug may also contribute to the drug-refractory state.

[88] Symposium: Conference on obstacles to the control of acute leukemia. *Cancer Res.* 25:1469–1679 (1965).

9

DRUG TOLERANCE AND

PHYSICAL DEPENDENCE

Drug tolerance is a state of decreased responsiveness to any pharmacologic effect in animals or man, resulting from prior exposure to a given drug or to its congener. The degree of tolerance may vary within wide limits. Usually in the tolerant organism, although the ordinarily effective drug dose is less effective than it had been, or even entirely ineffective, an increased dosage will again elicit the typical drug response. In some kinds of tolerance, however, the response can no longer be obtained at any dosage.

Physical dependence is a phenomenon sometimes associated with drug tolerance, in which an organism requires the presence of a drug in order to function normally. Tolerance is invariably present, for the drug no longer produces its usual biologic effect. The state of physical dependence is revealed by withdrawing the drug. This elicits various pathophysiologic disturbances known collectively as a *withdrawal syndrome* (also "abstinence syndrome"). All manifestations of the withdrawal syndrome can be terminated abruptly and dramatically by readministering the drug.

TOLERANCE BY INDIRECT MECHANISMS

There are two mechanisms whereby an animal can become tolerant to a drug even though the sensitivity of the cellular (or subcellular) site of drug action does not change. *First,* the concentration of free drug in contact with the receptors may be held within normal limits even while the total drug dosage to the animal increases. This could occur by a reduction in the efficiency of drug absorption into the body, an increase in the rate of drug elimination, a diminution in the passage of drug across biologic membranes that separate the sites of action from the plasma water, or an increased amount of binding of the drug into an inert complex. *Second,* the biologic effect of the drug may be increasingly antagonized, through homeostatic mechanisms, even though the drug continues to manifest its usual action upon its cellular receptors. Examples of both types of mechanism will be presented.

Reduction of the Effective Drug Concentration

In the only well-documented instances of this mechanism, tolerance results from an increased rate of drug metabolism. Progressively diminished absorption from the gastrointestinal tract has been cited as the cause of tolerance in arsenic eaters,[1] but the data are fragmentary and inconclusive.[2-4] It has been claimed that when polypeptides like parathyroid hormone or insulin are given as drugs, antibodies may sometimes form and inactivate them by direct combination, thus producing a state of tolerance; but the evidence for this is unconvincing.

There is no doubt that tolerance develops toward any drug that induces synthesis of enzymes responsible for its own degradation, as described fully in chapter 3. This kind of tolerance has a unique characteristic —its magnitude is strongly dependent upon the route of drug administration and upon the criteria of drug effect. Suppose such a drug is given intravenously to a "naive" animal and to one that has been pretreated with the drug for a long time. The maximum intensity of drug effect should be the same in both animals, but the effect should be terminated more quickly in the pretreated animal. This should be so because the dose distributes into the same volume of distribution and produces the same drug level in the body fluids of both animals. But the increased rate of metabolism in the pretreated animal will cause the level to fall faster. If lethality were the measure of drug action, we should probably not find any difference in LD50 between pretreated and naive animals. But if the total area under an effect-duration curve were the criterion (as for analgesia, p. 598), then the animal that degrades the drug faster will seem to have become tolerant. The situation is different when the drug is given by a route of slow absorption, for here the peak level attained after a single dose is determined by

---

[1] About a century ago, this peculiar form of drug abuse was prevalent among the peasants of the province of Styria and elsewhere in Austria. Solid arsenic trioxide was eaten, usually in powdered form, in gradually increasing dosage. It was supposed to produce a ruddier complexion and an appearance of healthy well-being, and to increase the endurance in mountain climbing.

[2] J. J. VON TSCHUDI: Uber die Giftesser. *Wiener Med. Wochenschr. 1:*453 (1851); *3:*8 (1853).

[3] W. HAUSMANN: Uber die Arsenikesser in Steiermark. *Arch. Int. Pharmacodyn. 11:*483 (1903).

[4] H. E. ROSCOE: "On the Alleged Practice of Arsenic-Eating in Styria," in *Memoirs of the Literary and Philosophical Society of Manchester,* 3rd Series. London, H. Bailliere, 1862, vol. 1, p. 208.

the balance between absorption rate and elimination rate (cf. Fig. 4-13). As the rate of drug metabolism increases, therefore, the peak intensity of drug effect will be reduced, and ever larger doses will be required.

Tolerance to barbiturates and to ethyl alcohol arises in part from cellular adaptations, to be discussed later (p. 584), and in part from an increased rate of drug metabolism, as already illustrated for pentobarbital in Table 3-7. In the experiment summarized there, the biologic half-life of the drug in rats was about 79 minutes after the first dose, only 26 minutes after the fourth dose. There was a corresponding reduction in sleeping time, but the plasma barbiturate level at the time of awakening was essentially the same in the naive and tolerant animals. These data are consistent with the finding[5] that tolerance to the sedative-hypnotic effects of barbiturates is not necessarily accompanied by an increase in the LD50. The rate of development of this kind of tolerance depends, as might be expected, upon the particular barbiturate and the species. It appears that a sufficiently high blood level has to be maintained for a certain length of time in order to cause an increased rate of synthesis of the liver microsomal enzymes. Rats and rabbits, for example, which metabolize hexobarbital very rapidly, had to be given that drug twice daily for several days in order to develop tolerance; dogs, which metabolize hexobarbital much more slowly, developed tolerance after a single dose.[6]

An increased rate of metabolism of ethyl alcohol, associated with the tolerant state, is illustrated in Fig. 9-1. Six male subjects, addicted to alcohol, were studied under carefully controlled conditions on a hospital ward.[7] Their nutrition was adequate during the course of the experiment, and they received vitamin supplements daily. After a four-day predrinking period they were given a small test dose of ethyl alcohol by mouth and, 30 minutes later, an intravenous injection of $10\mu c$ of ethanol-1-^{14}C. Blood ethanol levels were followed, and carbon dioxide in the expired air was measured and its radioactivity determined. The specific radioactivity of the CO_2 served as a measure of the rate of oxidation of ethanol. The subjects were then given alcohol in large amounts regularly for seven days. At the end of that time, another test dose was given. The data for one subject are summarized in the figure. At the left (a), it can be seen that the blood level established by the test dose declined much faster after the seven-day period of drinking than before. At the right (b), the specific radioactivity of carbon dioxide in the first 2 hours after the test dose is seen to be much

[5] C. M. GRUBER and G. F. KEYSER: A study on the development of tolerance and cross tolerance to barbiturates in experimental animals. *J. Pharmacol. Exp. Therap. 86:*186 (1946).

[6] H. REMMER: Gewöhnung an Hexobarbital durch beschleunigten Abbau. *Arch. Int. Pharmacodyn. 152:*346 (1964).

[7] J. H. MENDELSON, S. STEIN, and N. K. MELLO: Effects of experimentally induced intoxication on metabolism of ethanol-1-C14 in alcoholic subjects. *Metabolism 14:*1255 (1965).

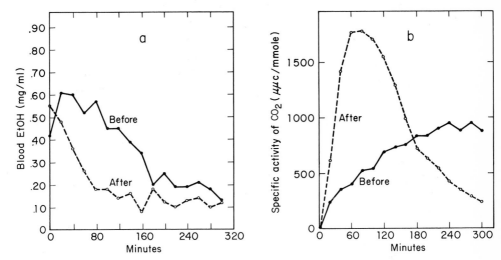

FIG. 9-1. INCREASED METABOLISM OF ETHANOL DURING TOLERANCE. *Data from one subject, before and after a seven-day period of alcohol ingestion, during which the subject received 3.2 g of ethanol per kg per day in divided doses. A test dose of ethanol was given by mouth, and ½ hour later 10μc of ethanol-1-14C was given intravenously. At 20-minute intervals, blood samples were removed for ethanol determination, and samples of expired air were collected for CO_2 assay and radioactivity determination. a, blood ethanol concentrations; b, specific radioactivity of CO_2. Solid lines, test before the seven-day period of drinking; broken lines, test after seven-day period of drinking. (Modified from Mendelson et al., Figs. 3 and 7.[7] By permission of Grune & Stratton.)*

higher after the drinking period than before. Evidently, as has also been shown in rats,[8] the administration of ethanol induces a large increase in activity of liver alcohol dehydrogenase, the rate-limiting enzyme in the oxidative pathway for ethanol.

Homeostatic Adjustments Antagonizing the Drug Action

Tolerance to exogenous hormones frequently develops as a consequence of the operation of homeostatic adjustments. Two examples may be cited. Administration of thyroid hormone to a normal individual leads initially to the characteristic stimulation of tissue metabolism. But feedback of the higher circulating hormone levels upon the pituitary gland reduces the output of thyroid-stimulating hormone. This, in turn, causes a diminution of endogenous hormone secretion from the thyroid gland, and the net result is a reduction in the blood levels of thyroid hormone. Similar ad-

---

[8] R. M. DAJANI, J. DANIELSKI, and J. M. ORTEN: The utilization of ethanol. II. The alcohol-acetaldehyde dehydrogenase systems in the livers of alcohol-treated rats. *J. Nutrition* 80:196 (1963).

justments occur with the adrenal steroids. Thus, a degree of apparent tolerance develops to the administration of both these hormones.[9]

A homeostatic adjustment in the renal mechanisms for maintaining acid-base balance accounts for the tolerance that develops to the diuretic action of ammonium chloride. Administration of this drug to a patient with edema results in an initial loss of sodium and potassium, with their osmotic equivalent of water. However, within a few days, the diuresis stops despite continued administration of the drug. The phenomenon is illustrated in Fig. 9-2, representing an experiment in a human subject maintained on a diet of constant electrolyte composition.[10] After a control period of five days, a regimen of 15 g of ammonium chloride daily was started. Since the NH_4^+ ion is converted to neutral urea in the liver, each molecule of ammonium chloride absorbed adds one hydrogen ion to the

FIG. 9-2. DEVELOPMENT OF TOLERANCE TO DIURESIS CAUSED BY AMMONIUM CHLORIDE. *The subject of this experiment was maintained on a diet of constant composition throughout the experiment. Daily excretion of chloride is shown on* top line, *excretion of ammonia, titratable acid, sodium, and potassium at* bottom. *For convenience the scale for cation excretion is inverted. Units are milliequivalents. (From Pitts, Fig. 26.[10] By permission of Charles C Thomas.)*

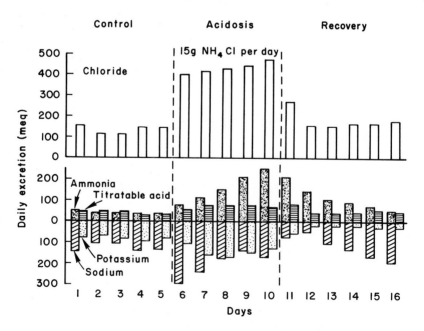

[9] H. CLEGG, ed.: *Drugs in the Treatment of Disease.* London, British Medical Association, 1961, pp. 276, 289.

[10] R. F. PITTS: *The Physiological Basis of Diuretic Therapy.* Springfield, Ill., Charles C Thomas, 1959.

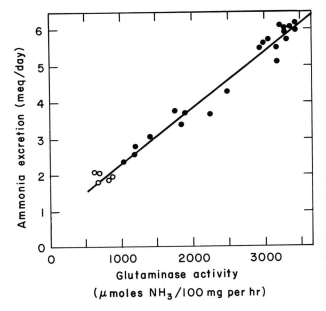

FIG. 9-3. RELATIONSHIP OF AMMONIA EXCRETION TO RENAL GLUTAMINASE ACTIVITY. *Rats were maintained on a standard electrolyte-deficient diet* (open circles) *supplemented with from 2 to 6 millimoles of ammonium chloride per day* (solid circles). *Daily ammonia excretion was measured* (ordinates), *and renal glutaminase activity was determined* (abscissas) *and expressed as micromoles of ammonia produced per hour by 100 mg dry weight of tissue.* (*From Rector et al., Fig. 2.[11]*)

body fluids. The daily dose of 15 g amounts to 280 milliequivalents of protons and chloride ions. The acidosis is compensated by the bicarbonate buffer system of the extracellular fluids, resulting in decreased plasma bicarbonate and increased plasma chloride. The increased chloride load presented to the renal tubules in the glomerular filtrate results in increased chloride excretion and an accompanying increased excretion of Na+. Potassium excretion (from intracellular fluid) tends to rise after a day or two. By the second day of drug administration, the urinary ammonia excretion starts to increase; and as it does, the sodium and potassium excretions return to control levels. Thus, by the fifth day of ammonium chloride administration, the additional chloride excretion is being accompanied by a nearly stoichiometric equivalent of ammonia and hydrogen ions. The body is then in a state of compensated metabolic acidosis. The urine is acid (not shown), and the daily ammonium chloride intake is balanced by an equal ammonium chloride excretion. Complete tolerance has developed to the diuretic action of ammonium chloride. The reversibility of the various compensatory mechanisms is shown in the excretion pattern during the six-day recovery period after cessation of drug administration.

The biochemical basis of the development of tolerance to ammonium chloride diuresis was demonstrated in rats.[11] Groups of animals were maintained on standard diets supplemented with various amounts of ammonium chloride. Measurements were made of urinary ammonia excretion and also of the activity of a renal enzyme, glutaminase (since urinary ammonia is derived from glutamine). The glutaminase activity increased in a few days to a new plateau that was proportional to the intake of ammonium chloride. This is shown in Fig. 9-3, where the ammonia excretion is plotted against the glutaminase activity of kidney homogenates, and each point represents one rat. The cluster of points at low enzyme activity and low ammonia excretion represents untreated control rats; the other points are data from rats on the ammonium chloride regimen. A perfectly linear relationship was found. The higher the daily dose of ammonium chloride, the higher the new steady-state level of renal glutaminase, and the higher the ammonia excretion. Evidently, the key to the development of tolerance to ammonium chloride diuresis is an increased rate of synthesis (or decreased rate of degradation) of this kidney enzyme in response to acidosis.

TOLERANCE AT THE CELLULAR SITES OF DRUG ACTION

Several criteria serve to distinguish this type of tolerance from that due to selection of drug-tolerant cells from a population of drug-sensitive cells, and also from tolerance displayed by a whole animal in which the sensitivity of the target cells remains unchanged.

A selection mechanism can often be ruled out on the basis that too little time has elapsed, provided the rate of cell renewal at the sites of drug action is approximately known. Thus, acute tolerance (*tachyphylaxis*) to some drugs may develop within a few minutes. Tolerance can sometimes be produced in isolated tissues in an organ bath, where no cell divisions occur and where all mechanisms involving the whole animal can be excluded. In the most striking instances of drug tolerance, the site of drug action is in the brain, where no cell renewal occurs, so that the cells becoming tolerant are necessarily the same ones that were formerly drug sensitive.

When drug tolerance is accompanied by physical dependence, all simple explanations such as the mere exclusion of drug from the sites of action, or the inactivation or destruction of the drug, become inadequate. The mere absence of drug from the sites of action could not account for the functional changes that necessarily underlie the dependent state. And the disturbances that ensue if the drug is withdrawn attest to its having

---

[11] F. C. RECTOR, JR., D. W. SELDIN, and J. H. COPENHAVER: The mechanism of ammonia excretion during ammonium chloride acidosis. *J. Clin. Invest. 34:*20 (1955).

been present and active at cellular sites of action during the period of drug tolerance.

Finally, the presence of a cellular tolerance may be established unequivocally by direct measurement of drug concentrations in the appropriate body fluids. It may be demonstrated that sufficient drug is in contact with the target cells, yet no pharmacologic effect results. And it may be shown further that a typical response to the drug can be elicited if the ambient drug concentration is raised to a level much higher than is ordinarily required (or than was formerly required in the same animal).

Acute Tolerance (Tachyphylaxis)

SYMPATHOMIMETIC AMINES

It has been known for many years that repeated intravenous doses of certain sympathomimetic amines elicit smaller and smaller cardiovascular responses. Figure 9-4 shows a typical experiment with ephedrine.[12] A dog was anesthetized with a barbiturate and atropinized to block vagal effects, then given ephedrine sulfate, 3 mg/kg intravenously. There was a very large increase in the mean blood pressure, due principally to arteriolar constriction and partly to increased cardiac output. Twenty-five minutes later

FIG. 9-4.   EPHEDRINE TACHYPHYLAXIS IN THE DOG.   *A 5-kg male dog was given barbiturate anesthesia and atropinized. The record, obtained on a kymograph drum, reads from left to right. Mean blood pressure is shown on the* vertical axis, *time on the* horizontal axis. *The long* upper tracing *is the response to the first injection of ephedrine sulfate (3 mg/kg intravenously). The second injection of ephedrine* (lower tracing) *was given 25 minutes after the first; subsequent injections were made at 10-minute intervals. (From Chen and Meek, Fig. 1.[12])*

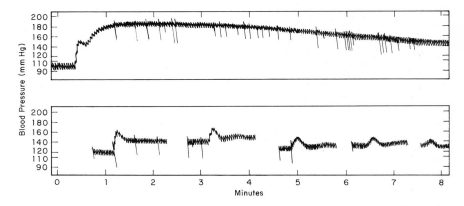

12 K. K. CHEN and W. J. MEEK: Further studies of the effect of ephedrine on the circulation. *J. Pharmacol. Exp. Therap. 28:*31 (1926).

the same dose was repeated, with much diminished effect; both the intensity of the response and its duration were reduced. Further repetition of the injection at 10-minute intervals led quickly to a state of nearly complete tolerance to the drug. Similar effects have been demonstrated in many sympathetically innervated tissues outside the cardiovascular system, such as uterus, intestine, bronchioles, and nasal mucous membranes.[13]

In experiments like that depicted in Fig. 9-4, it has been found that even after the establishment of tachyphylaxis to ephedrine, other agents (e.g., epinephrine) continued to manifest their usual pressor actions. The tolerance, therefore, could not be attributed to any general exhaustion of the contractile capacity of the arteriolar smooth muscle. The only alternative explanation seemed to be that there were receptors specific for each kind of sympathomimetic agent, and that these different classes of receptors became "saturated" more or less easily. Somehow, it was supposed, the occupancy of ephedrine receptors by ephedrine made them unresponsive to further ephedrine administration, while other receptors (e.g., those responsive to epinephrine) continued functioning.[13]

The concept of independent receptors appeared more and more dubious as the number of known sympathomimetic agents increased, for each one appeared to have its own pattern of tachyphylaxis. Among the phenylethylamines, for example, those with α-methyl groups (ephedrine, amphetamine) produced tachyphylaxis more readily than unsubstituted compounds like tyramine; and the catecholamines themselves (epinephrine, norepinephrine) were found to produce little or no tachyphylaxis.[14] The chemical structures of these compounds and others to be discussed are shown in Fig. 9-5.

Our current understanding of the mechanism of tachyphylaxis is based upon the discovery that many sympathomimetic amines of the phenylethylamine structure have no vasoconstrictor actions of their own but act indirectly by releasing norepinephrine (NE) from storage sites in adrenergic nerve endings.[15] Reserpine, which depletes the neuronal stores of NE almost completely, was used as a tool to classify the various sympathomimetic agents according to their modes of action.[16] In reserpinized animals, some of these compounds, like NE, retained full potency, i.e., they acted directly upon the NE receptors on the postjunctional effector cells. Some had diminished effects, indicating a mixed action, partly dependent

[13] C. V. WINDER, M. M. ANDERSON, and H. C. PARKE: Comparative properties of six phenethylamines, with observations on the nature of tachyphylaxis. *J. Pharmacol. Exp. Therap. 93:*63 (1948).

[14] M. D. DAY and M. J. RAND: Tachyphylaxis to some sympathomimetic amines in relation to monoamine oxidase. *Brit. J. Pharmacol. 21:*84 (1963).

[15] J. H. BURN and M. J. RAND: The action of sympathomimetic amines in animals treated with reserpine. *J. Physiol. 144:*314 (1958).

[16] U. TRENDELENBURG, A. MUSKUS, W. W. FLEMING, and B. GOMEZ ALONSO DE LA SIERRA: Modification by reserpine of the action of sympathomimetic amines in spinal cats; a classification of sympathomimetic amines. *J. Pharmacol. Exp. Therap. 138:*170 (1962).

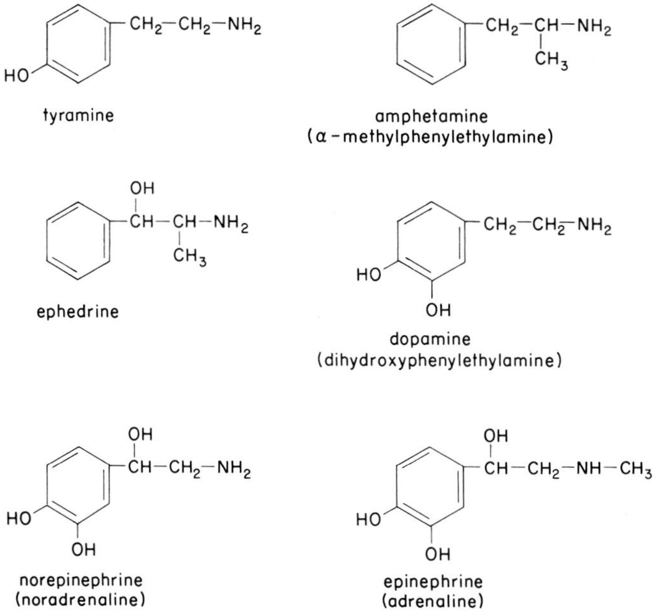

FIG. 9-5.   STRUCTURES OF SOME PHENYLETHYLAMINE DERIVATIVES.

upon the presence of NE stores in the nerve ending. Some agents, like tyramine, were devoid of their usual cardiovascular effects in reserpinized animals, i.e., their whole action seemed to be due to their ability to release NE from its storage sites.

Figure 9-6 illustrates the approximately parallel effects of NE depletion upon nerve stimulation and upon the actions of tyramine. The experiment was done in cats whose spinal cords had been transected in the cervical region in order to eliminate tonic sympathetic activity.[17] The effects of supramaximal preganglionic stimulation at various frequencies were compared with those of tyramine at increasing dosage, using the contraction of the nictitating membrane as criterion of response. The control animals received no reserpine; a group was given reserpine (0.1 mg/kg) 24 hours prior to the testing; another group was given a higher dose of reserpine (3 mg/kg) 48 and 24 hours prior to the testing. The results show the systematic reduction of response to a given stimulus frequency or a given dose of tyramine by the increasing doses of reserpine. In other words, both nerve stimulation and tyramine work by releasing NE. Prior depletion of NE by reserpine diminishes the amount of NE that can be released effectively by either means. And increasing stimulus frequency or increasing tyramine

[17] U. TRENDELENBURG: Modification of the effect of tyramine by various agents and procedures. *J. Pharmacol. Exp. Therap. 134:*8 (1961).

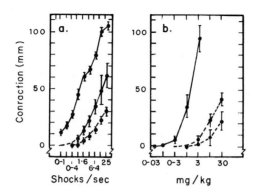

FIG. 9-6.   EFFECT OF PRETREATMENT WITH RESERPINE ON RESPONSE TO NERVE
STIMULATION AND TYRAMINE.   *Spinal cats were pretreated with reserpine, 3
mg/kg 48 and 24 hours before testing* (bottom curves), *or 0.1 mg/kg 24 hours
before testing* (middle curves). *Controls were not reserpinized* (upper curves).
Vertical axis, *contraction of nictitating membrane, mm deflection on drum
record.* Horizontal axis, (a) = *stimulus frequency to preganglionic sympathetic
chain, shocks/sec;* (b) = *tyramine dose, mg/kg. Vertical ranges are ± standard
error. (From Trendelenburg, Fig. 1.*[17])

dosage partly overcomes the deficit caused by reserpine. In the same experiments, the blood pressure and heart rate responses to tyramine (not shown) were similarly reduced by the reserpine pretreatment, and partially restored by increasing doses of tyramine.

The observations cited above illustrate a mechanism whereby treatment with one drug (reserpine) produces tolerance to another (tyramine). Can tachyphylaxis to tyramine itself be explained in the same way, i.e., that tyramine depletes all the NE and therefore becomes ineffective? There is no doubt that tyramine releases NE and that the development of tachyphylaxis is associated with diminished NE release. Figure 9-7 illustrates this with the perfused isolated rat heart.[18] The experiment makes use of the fact that sympathetic nerve endings take up exogenous NE. This uptake and binding mechanism normally plays an important role in terminating the action of NE released into the region of the nerve-effector junction by a nerve stimulus. The stores of NE that are capable of being released by nerve stimuli can be labeled with radioactive NE taken up from the circulation. In the experiment, ^{3}H-NE was given by way of the perfusion fluid for a few minutes, following which 1-minute samples of the perfusate effluent were collected for determination of

[18] J. AXELROD, E. GORDON, G. HERTTING, I. J. KOPIN, and L. T. POTTER: On the mechanism of tachyphylaxis to tyramine in the isolated rat heart. *Brit. J. Pharmacol.* **19**:56 (1962).

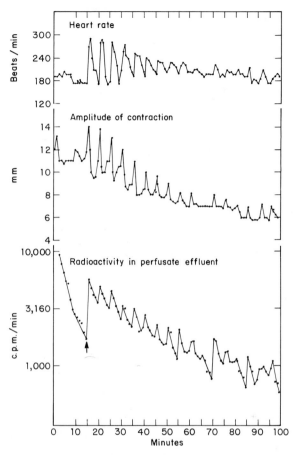

FIG. 9-7. TYRAMINE TACHYPHYLAXIS AND THE RATE OF RELEASE OF ^{3}H-NOREPI-
NEPHRINE FROM PERFUSED RAT HEART. *Rat hearts were perfused in vitro and
the amplitude and rate of contraction were measured. At the outset, ^{3}H-norepi-
nephrine was infused for 2 to 4 minutes. Then at 15 minutes* (arrow) *and every
5 minutes thereafter, an injection of tyramine (10μg) was made into the perfusion cannula. The perfusate effluent was collected in 1-minute fractions and
radioactivity was determined; about 85 per cent of this effluent radioactivity was
identified as catecholamine. Note logarithmic scale of radioactivity. (Modified
from Axelrod et al., Fig. 1.*[18] *By permission of the British Medical Association.)*

radioactivity. At the same time, the heart rate and amplitude of contraction
were measured. During the initial period, the heart rate and contraction
amplitude were fairly stable, and there was a rapid outflow of the recently
infused ^{3}H-NE. An injection of tyramine at 15 minutes caused a sharp rise
in heart rate and contraction amplitude and simultaneously a considerable
additional outflow of ^{3}H-NE. Repeated injections of tyramine at 5-minute
intervals resulted (after the second or third injection) in ever smaller

responses of the heart. Although each injection continued to cause a measurable release of ^{3}H-NE, the actual amounts released became smaller at the same time that tolerance was developing to the biologic effects. In this connection it is important to note that the scale of radioactivity in the figure is logarithmic, so that equal vertical distances represent smaller amounts of radioactivity near the bottom of the chart than near the top. Thus, whereas the initial tyramine injection, at 15 minutes, released about 4,000 cpm additional radioactivity into the perfusion effluent, the injection at 20 minutes released only 1,600 cpm, and the injection at 85 minutes only 600 cpm.

The experiment described above might seem to support the simple view that tolerance to tyramine results from complete depletion of the neuronal NE. When residual NE was actually measured, however, by a chemical procedure, a considerable amount was found even after tyramine had become ineffective. Some of this residual NE was releasable by nerve stimulation; and biologic responses to such stimulation were obtainable during tyramine tachyphylaxis, although their magnitudes were reduced (especially at low stimulus frequencies). The NE that was easily releasable by tyramine could be distinguished from the remainder of the neuronal stores by varying the conditions of administration of radioactive NE. Figure 9-8 shows such an experiment.[19] Rats were given ^{3}H-NE intravenously and killed 1 hour later; their hearts were assayed for catecholamine content by means of a fluorometric procedure, and catecholamine radioactivity was determined. Other animals were treated in the same way but were given a dose of tyramine 30 minutes after the ^{3}H-NE injection. The left panels (*a*) show that tyramine caused a depletion of about 40 per cent in the catecholamine content and a decrease of about the same extent in the radioactivity, compared with control hearts. On the other hand, if the radioactive NE was given 48 hours prior to the tyramine injection, and the animals were killed as before, 30 minutes after tyramine (right panels, *b*), there was relatively less loss of radioactivity. In other words, the exogenous NE was readily releasable by tyramine soon after it was taken up; but there were also stores of NE, more slowly labeled in this experiment, which were resistant to release by tyramine.[20, 21]

Tachyphylaxis to tyramine and related agents, as well as the tolerance to tyramine that is produced by reserpine, can be overcome by infusion of NE.[18] The administered catecholamine is taken up by sympathetic neurons and stored (as already discussed) in a "labile pool," whence it is

19 L. T. POTTER, J. AXELROD, and I. J. KOPIN: Differential binding and release of norepinephrine and tachyphylaxis. *Biochem. Pharmacol. 11:*254 (1962).

20 L. T. POTTER and J. AXELROD: Studies on the storage of norepinephrine and the effect of drugs. *J. Pharmacol. Exp. Therap. 140:*199 (1963).

21 R. KUNTZMAN and M. M. JACOBSON: On the mechanism of heart norepinephrine depletion by tyramine, guanethidine and reserpine. *J. Pharmacol. Exp. Therap. 144:*399 (1964).

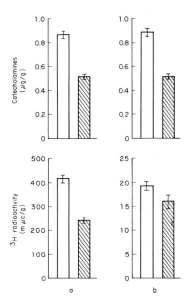

FIG. 9-8. DIFFERENTIAL RELEASE OF RECENTLY LABELED NOREPINEPHRINE BY TYRAMINE. *Rats were given 10μc of ³H-norepinephrine per 100 g body weight intravenously. Either 30 minutes later (a) or 48 hours later (b), some of the rats received tyramine (10 mg/kg) intravenously, and 30 minutes afterwards they were sacrificed. Heart catecholamine and radioactive catecholamine were determined; these data are given per gram of heart tissue ± standard errors.* Open histograms, *controls;* hatched histograms, *tyramine-injected rats.* (*From data of Potter et al., Table 1.*[19])

easily released by tyramine. However, as might be expected, tachyphylaxis reappears very quickly under these circumstances, for the newly bound NE is rapidly depleted.[22]

How do agents like tyramine release NE from the neuronal stores? It has been shown that tyramine itself is taken up and bound at the catecholamine storage sites, displacing NE in the process.[18] This bound tyramine is then releasable, either by nerve stimulation or by subsequent doses of tyramine. The releasable tyramine acts as a "false neurotransmitter." Since tyramine does not stimulate the catecholamine receptors in postjunctional effector cells, the diminished response in the tachyphylactic state is understandable; what is released as tachyphylaxis develops is a mixture containing tyramine and a decreasing amount of NE.[23]

22 J. R. CROUT, A. J. MUSKUS, and U. TRENDELENBURG: Effect of tyramine on isolated guinea-pig atria in relation to their noradrenaline stores. *Brit. J. Pharmacol. 18:*600 (1962).

23 J. M. MUSACCHIO, I. J. KOPIN, and V. K. WEISE: Subcellular distribution of some sympathomimetic amines and their β-hydroxylated derivatives in the rat heart. *J. Pharmacol. Exp. Therap. 148:*22 (1965).

The enzymes of catecholamine metabolism can influence the development and duration of tachyphylaxis.[24] Present concepts are illustrated diagrammatically in Fig. 9-9, and the biochemical pathways of synthesis and degradation of the catecholamines are shown in Fig. 9-10. Extraneuronal metabolism of the catecholamines is evidently mediated by catechol-O-methyl transferase (COMT); the major portion of exogenously administered catecholamines as well as the NE released by nerve stimulation or by tyramine are converted to O-methyl derivatives. Catecholamines within the neurons are metabolized principally by monoamine oxidase (MAO) located in the mitochondria. The NE released by reserpine is oxidized by this enzyme, and very little of it escapes to exert a pharmacologic action upon the effector cells. But in the presence of MAO inhibitors, the NE escapes and reserpine acquires sympathomimetic stimulant properties. Tyramine is also metabolized by MAO, and MAO inhibitors accelerate the development of tachyphylaxis to this compound,[14] presumably by permitting a greater buildup of tyramine stores in the catecholamine granules. The α-methyl derivatives of phenylethylamines are not substrates of MAO, and consequently tachyphylaxis develops much more readily to them than to tyramine.

Another complexity is revealed by studies on the dependence of tachyphylaxis upon dose and time. As might be expected, low doses of tyramine, widely spaced in time, produce no tachyphylaxis; presumably

FIG. 9-9.   SCHEMATIC DIAGRAM OF CATECHOLAMINE TRANSFORMATIONS IN THE ADRENERGIC NEURON.   *Synthesis of norepinephrine (NE) and its incorporation into storage granules takes place in the adrenergic neuron. Intraneuronal oxidation to deaminated products is catalyzed by monoamine oxidase (MAO) in mitochondria. Metabolism of released NE is catalyzed by catechol-O-methyl transferase (COMT) located in the postjunctional tissue. Reserpine releases NE intraneuronally, tyramine releases it from the neuron.*

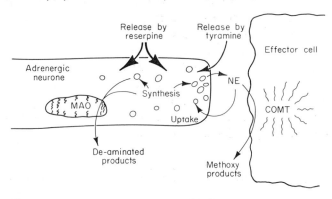

24 I. J. KOPIN: Storage and metabolism of catecholamines: the role of monoamine oxidase. *Pharmacol. Rev. 16:*179 (1964).

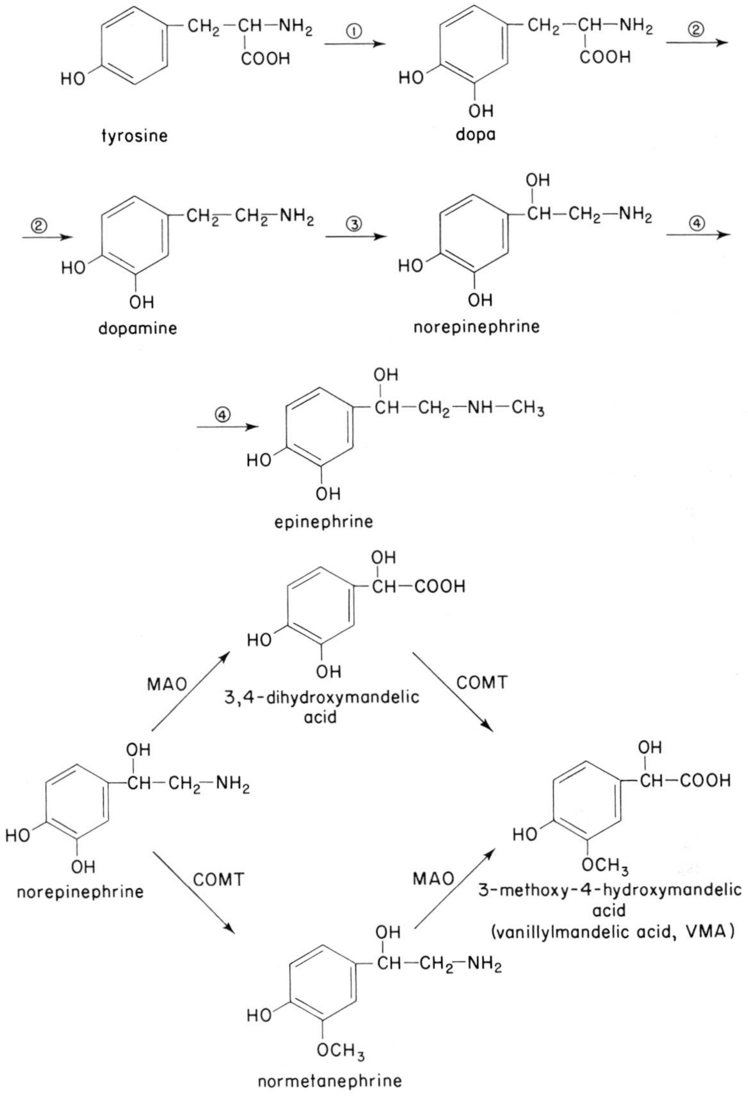

FIG. 9-10. PATHWAYS OF SYNTHESIS AND METABOLISM OF THE CATECHOL-AMINES. *The synthetic pathway from tyrosine is shown above; enzyme 1 (tyrosine hydroxylase) appears to be the rate-limiting enzyme. The alternative degradative pathways for norepinephrine are shown below. Epinephrine is handled in analogous fashion. Several minor metabolites and conjugates, not shown here, are also found in the urine. Enzymes: 1, tyrosine hydroxylase; 2, dopa decarboxylase; 3, dopamine β-hydroxylase; 4, phenylethanolamine-N-methyl transferase; MAO, monoamine oxidase; COMT, catechol-O-methyl transferase.*

the accumulation of tyramine in the storage granules is limited, under these conditions, by its constant metabolic removal by MAO. Tolerance to high doses given at short intervals develops rapidly, and persists. At intermediate doses, however, a peculiar effect has been described.[25] Tachyphylaxis develops after several doses, but this is followed by an "escape," i.e., a return of responsiveness to tyramine. The phenomenon is illustrated in Fig. 9-11. The upper panel shows pressor responses in a spinal cat after the third and ninth injection of tyramine at 15-minute intervals, and the return of a pressor effect at the 16th injection. The lower panel shows that the cardiac catecholamine content continued to decline throughout the injection series. These results are thought to be explained by the fact that tyramine depletion of NE pools can stimulate the synthesis of NE. Continued administration of tyramine could therefore furnish easily releasable NE, in amounts sufficient to restore pressor action, without significantly replenishing the total NE store. This hypothesis gains some support from the finding that the escape from tachyphylaxis can be pre-

FIG. 9-11.   ESCAPE FROM TYRAMINE TACHYPHYLAXIS IN THE SPINAL CAT.   *Tyramine (800μg/kg) was injected intravenously into spinal cats at 15-minute intervals and blood pressure was recorded. Groups of cats were sacrificed at different times and the cardiac catecholamine contents were determined. Typical blood pressure tracings after the 3rd, 9th, and 16th tyramine dose are shown in upper panel. Mean catecholamine contents ± standard errors are shown in lower panel. (From Bhagat et al., Figs. 1 and 2.[25])*

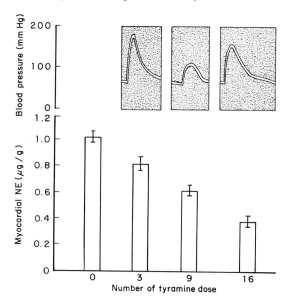

[25] B. BHAGAT, E. K. GORDON, and I. J. KOPIN: Norepinephrine synthesis and the pressor responses to tyramine in the spinal cat. *J. Pharmacol. Exp. Therap. 147*:319 (1965).

vented by agents (e.g., disulfiram, p. 253) that block the β-hydroxylation of dopamine, an essential step in the pathway of NE synthesis (Fig. 9-10).[26]

OTHER DRUGS THAT PROVOKE ACUTE TOLERANCE

Stimulants of Neuroeffector Systems. Drugs like acetylcholine and nicotine, which act by depolarizing a membrane to trigger an action potential, may cause a response initially and then block their own actions.[27,28] This effect is readily demonstrable by the local application of nicotine to a sympathetic ganglion. If the superior cervical ganglion of the cat is exposed and the contractions of the nictitating membrane are recorded, the application of a high concentration of nicotine to the ganglion will cause a maximum sustained contraction, which will spontaneously subside. The ganglion is then blocked, and application of nicotine or of carbachol will not elicit a further contraction of the nictitating membrane. A similar demonstration can be made with acetylcholine on smooth or striated muscle that is responsive to it. A rat uterus is suspended in a tissue bath, under slight tension, in a special low-calcium medium that will inhibit spontaneous contractility. Small doses of acetylcholine now will produce brief contractions; a very large dose of acetylcholine causes a maximum sustained contraction, which (like that of the nictitating membrane) spontaneously subsides. Thereafter, the uterus will be completely unresponsive to acetylcholine. Repeated washing of the tissue gradually restores the sensitivity. In these instances, the acute tolerance is largely the consequence of persistent depolarization at the sites of action, in the continued presence of the drug. A new response is impossible until the membrane at the ganglion cell, muscle end-plate, or smooth muscle cell can repolarize.

Histamine. Acute and chronic tolerance to histamine has been the subject of periodic study in the past, but the mechanisms have not been elucidated. In a typical experiment on an anesthetized cat, the administration of 10 μg of histamine intravenously produced a moderate fall of blood pressure. Repeated injections of histamine, in increasingly larger doses, elicited diminishing hypotensive responses, so that within hours the dosage could be increased more than 100-fold.[29]

---

[26] J. M. MUSACCHIO, M. GOLDSTEIN, B. ANAGNOSTE, G. POCH, and I. J. KOPIN: Inhibition of dopamine-β-hydroxylase by disulfiram *in vivo. J. Pharmacol. Exp. Therap. 152:*56 (1966).

[27] W. D. M. PATON and E. J. ZAIMIS: The methonium compounds. *Pharmacol. Rev. 4:*219 (1952).

[28] W. D. M. PATON: Transmission and block in autonomic ganglia. *Pharmacol. Rev. 6:*59 (1954).

[29] ST. KARÁDY: Über experimentelle Tieruntersuchungen zur Frage der Histamintachyphylaxie und Histaminresistenz. *Arch. Exp. Pathol. Pharmakol. 180:*283 (1936).

In another investigation,[30] in guinea pigs, single daily histamine doses of 0.5 mg/kg were given subcutaneously. After a week, the daily dosage was increased by 0.5 mg/kg, and then a further increase of the same magnitude was made each subsequent week for eight weeks. Two effects of histamine were chosen for study—bronchiolar constriction and stimulation of gastric acid secretion. Initially, and at the end of the eight-week period, the animals were tested for their sensitivity to the pulmonary effect of histamine by placing them in an aerosol chamber and noting how much time was required for them to cough and become dyspneic. An increase in this time represents a decrease in sensitivity to the drug; but since no information is available about the rate of increase of the local histamine concentration in the bronchioles, no conclusions can be drawn about the quantitative aspects of tolerance. In control animals, the average time was 1 to 1½ minutes, and this was not significantly different in untreated animals retested after eight weeks. In contrast, the animals that had received daily injections of histamine for eight weeks showed a significant increase in time, to more than 3 minutes. Free gastric acidity in untreated animals at the end of the experiment was 21.5 meq per liter (standard error ± 4.1) after a test dose of histamine, but in the histamine-treated animals it was only 2.6 meq per liter (standard error ± 1.8). Thus, a striking degree of tolerance developed to this histamine action. An antihistamine drug given before each histamine injection did not prevent the development of tolerance in these guinea pigs.

Histamine releasers (e.g., tubocurarine, morphine) may at first produce hypotension and other effects attributable to histamine, but the effects diminish on repeated administration.[31] Presumably, the tolerance to these agents results in part from histamine depletion from storage sites in the skin and elsewhere, and in part reflects the onset of tolerance to histamine itself. After tachyphylaxis has developed fully, there is no further release of histamine, although the histamine stores in tissues are by no means depleted.[32]

Nitrites. It has long been common knowledge that workers engaged in nitroglycerin production or in the handling of dynamite (which contains nitroglycerin) experience throbbing headache, nausea, and other unpleasant symptoms upon first exposure, but become readily "accustomed" to the compound.[33, 34] The tolerance wears off in a few days, so that the

[30] J. L. AMBRUS, C. M. AMBRUS, and J. W. E. HARRISSON: Effect of histamine desensitization on histamine induced gastric secretion of guinea pigs. *Gastroenterology 18:*249 (1951).

[31] W. D. M. PATON: Compound 48/80: a potent histamine liberator. *Brit. J. Pharmacol. 6:*499 (1951).

[32] J. L. MONGAR and H. O. SCHILD: A comparison of the effects of anaphylactic shock and of chemical histamine releasers. *J. Physiol. 118:*461 (1952).

[33] G. E. EBRIGHT: The effects of nitroglycerin on those engaged in its manufacture. *J. Amer. Med. Ass. 62:*201 (1914).

[34] A. M. SCHWARTZ: The cause, relief and prevention of headaches arising from contact with dynamite. *New Engl. J. Med. 235:*541 (1946).

term "Monday disease" has been used[35] to describe the renewed symptoms after a weekend off the job; and workers are said to avert this "disease" by carrying a small amount of nitroglycerin home with them in order to maintain their state of tolerance. Tolerance to this and other nitrite esters was studied in human volunteers.[36] Erythritol tetranitrate was given by mouth, glyceryl trinitrate (nitroglycerin) and ethylene glycol dinitrate by rubbing onto the skin, and methyl nitrate and amyl nitrite by inhalation. A "headache dose" was determined, which would just produce a moderately uncomfortable headache. When repetition of the dose failed to elicit headache, the dose was increased. In this way, tolerance was produced to all these esters, although the degree of tolerance could not be ascertained accurately. The investigators asserted thtat complete tolerance to one or two "headache doses" could be produced. Cross-tolerance was the rule for all the nitrites and nitrates mentioned above, but not for the hypotensive actions of unrelated drugs like histamine. In dogs in which tolerance to the nitrate esters was established,[37] it was found that the red blood cells had lost much of their ability to hydrolyze the esters. Since it is thought that the nitrate esters act pharmacologically as free nitrite, this decreased hydrolytic capacity could explain the tolerance. It would not, however, explain cross-tolerance to sodium nitrite, which was regularly observed.[38, 36]

Urethane. Acute tolerance to urethane has been demonstrated in isolated tissue.[39] A piece of rabbit ileum was suspended in an organ bath and its movements recorded by means of a lever and kymograph. When urethane (3 to 5 mg/ml) was added to the Ringer solution in the bath, the characteristic spontaneous pendular movements stopped immediately. Within 15 minutes, however, the movements began again and had returned to control levels an hour later. At this time, fresh urethane solution was without effect. However, replacement of the urethane solution with fresh Ringer solution caused a considerable increase in the amplitude of the contractions, as though some compensatory mechanism operating in the presence of the drug was unmasked by its removal.

Atropine. Atropine tolerance has been demonstrated in dogs with isolated loops of intestine (Thiery-Vella loops) in which peristaltic activity was measured by pressure changes in small balloons within the gut lumen.[40]

35 J. C. MUNCH, B. FRIEDLAND, and M. SHEPARD: Glyceryl trinitrate. II. Chronic toxicity. *Industr. Med. Surg. 34:*940 (1965).

36 L. A. CRANDALL, JR., C. D. LEAKE, A. S. LOEVENHART, and C. W. MUEHLBERGER: Acquired tolerance to and cross tolerance between the nitrous and nitric acid esters and sodium nitrite in man. *J. Pharmacol. Exp. Therap. 41:*103 (1931).

37 L. A. CRANDALL, JR.: The fate of glyceryl trinitrate in the tolerant and non-tolerant animal. *J. Pharmacol. Exp. Therap. 48:*127 (1933).

38 H. B. MYERS and V. T. AUSTIN: Nitrite toleration. *J. Pharmacol. Exp. Therap. 36:*227 (1929).

39 K. HECHT: Untersuchungen über Giftgewöhnung. *Arch. Exp. Pathol. Pharmakol. 113:*338 (1926).

40 G. W. GRAY and M. H. SEEVERS: In vivo observations on the nature of atropine tachyphylaxis exhibited by intestinal smooth muscle. *J. Pharmacol. Exp. Therap. 113:*319 (1955).

When atropine was first administered, the typical depression of motility was observed; but after three or four doses at 30-minute intervals, the drug became wholly ineffectual. The peristaltic activity was then also resistant ("cross-tachyphylaxis") to atropine congeners, but not to unrelated drugs like cocaine, nitrites, and ganglionic blocking agents, which still produced their usual inhibitory effects. Moreover, the tachyphylaxis to atropine developed even when the inhibitory effects of atropine were antagonized by simultaneous administration of methacholine, and also when atropine was given repeatedly in doses too small to produce any inhibitory effects on the intestinal motility. The investigators proposed that atropine induced tolerance by occupying receptors persistently "in the face of a compensatory change" in the tissue; but no direct evidence has been adduced.

Tolerance and Physical Dependence in the Central Nervous System

From prehistoric times, and in all ethnic groups, people have sought out drugs that would furnish pleasure and satisfaction, allay anxiety, or influence the psyche in other ways considered desirable. Among these agents are a great many to which tolerance may develop, and also some upon which the user becomes physically dependent. Because of the confusion of legal, popular, and scientific meanings of "habituation" and "addiction," the Expert Committee of the World Health Organization considering nomenclature decided to abandon these older terms and to substitute a single more inclusive term, namely *drug dependence*.[41]

Drug dependence includes three quite distinct and independent components: tolerance, physical dependence, and compulsive abuse (psychic craving). Different drugs show these features to various degrees.[42] Marihuana is subject to compulsive abuse, but tolerance and physical dependence do not occur.[43] A low degree of tolerance to cocaine, nicotine, and caffeine develops, and also mild physical dependence.[44] The psychic craving for these stimulants may be very intense, as in habitual cigarette smokers who try to "break the habit." Similar craving, withdrawal headache, and behavioral changes such as irritability and restlessness are seen when a prolonged high intake of caffeine is suddenly stopped.[45] D-Amphetamine (dextroamphetamine, d-amphetamine, D(+)-amphetamine) and

---

[41] WORLD HEALTH ORGANIZATION, Expert Committee on Drugs Liable to Produce Addiction: Report on the Thirteenth Session. WHO Tech. Rep. Ser. 273, Geneva, 1964, p. 9.

[42] Evaluation of Dependence-Producing Drugs. Report of a WHO Scientific Group. WHO Tech. Rep. Ser. 287, Geneva, 1964.

[43] G. E. W. WOLSTENHOLME and J. KNIGHT, eds.: *Hashish: Its Chemistry and Pharmacology*. Ciba Foundation Study Group No. 21. Boston, Little, Brown and Co., 1965.

[44] G. A. DENEAU and M. H. SEEVERS: Pharmacological aspects of drug dependence. *Advance. Pharmacol. 3:*267 (1964).

[45] R. H. DREISBACH and C. PFEIFFER: Caffeine-withdrawal headache. *J. Lab. Clin. Med.* 28:1212 (1943).

d-lysergic acid diethylamide (LSD) are both subject to compulsive abuse; and tolerance to them develops, but without physical dependence.[46,47] An example of tolerance and physical dependence without compulsive abuse is provided by the morphine congener and antagonist nalorphine. This drug has been given experimentally to human subjects; but although the dosage was raised progressively, and a withdrawal syndrome ensued when administration was stopped, no psychic craving developed; moreover, nalorphine is not sought after by addicts.[48] Alcohol, barbiturates, and the opiate narcotics display all three components of drug dependence to so intense a degree as to create major problems for the individual and for society. We shall later discuss these drugs in detail, since they have been investigated most intensively with respect to tolerance and physical dependence.

The social evils of drug addiction are intensified when addiction is treated as a crime rather than a disease. Compulsive abuse originates in the strong pleasurable (euphoriant) actions of a drug that tend to reinforce the drug-seeking behavior in certain individuals.[49,50] The development of a high degree of tolerance forces the addict to very much higher dosages in order to obtain the desired effects. Eventually, even though he no longer obtains any pleasurable result because of tolerance, physical dependence compels him to continue taking the drug at all costs to ward off the withdrawal syndrome. The illegal status of the drug drives its price to exorbitant heights in the black market; and to sustain his needs, the victim of drug dependence is often forced into a life of criminality.[51]

Experimentation on tolerance and physical dependence requires that a clearly recognizable drug effect be studied, preferably one that can be measured quantitatively. The drug must then be administered on a regular schedule over a long period of time, in order to establish whether or not tolerance develops with respect to the chosen criterion. A straightforward approach in animal experimentation is to choose a drug effect that can be localized to a particular region of the brain and that produces an objectively measurable change in a body function. Among the many such actions drugs can cause are vomiting, respiratory depression or stimulation, convulsive seizures, stimulation or depression of coordinated motor activity, and alteration of temperature control.

[46] C. D. LEAKE: *The Amphetamines.* Springfield, Ill., Charles C Thomas, 1958.

[47] D. E. ROSENBERG, A. B. WOLBACH, JR., E. J. MINER, and H. ISBELL: Observations on direct and cross tolerance with LSD and D-amphetamine in man. *Psychopharmacologia* 5:1 (1963).

[48] W. R. MARTIN and C. W. GORODETZKY: Demonstration of tolerance to and physical dependence on N-allylnormorphine (nalorphine). *J. Pharmacol. Exp. Therap.* 150:437 (1965).

[49] L. KOLB: Types and characteristics of drug addicts. *Mental Hygiene* 9:300 (1925).

[50] A. WIKLER and R. W. RASOR: Psychiatric aspects of drug addiction. *Amer. J. Med.* 14:566 (1953).

[51] J. A. O'DONNELL and J. C. BALL, eds.: *Narcotic Addiction.* New York, Harper & Row, 1966.

Drug-induced hypothermia is a good example. An early experiment using this criterion demonstrated the development of tolerance to arsenite in rats.[52] Although the site of drug action was not studied, it seems likely to have been upon the hypothalamic temperature-regulating center. When a lethal dose (10 mg/kg) of sodium arsenite was given intraperitoneally, death was preceded by a profound fall in body temperature. A smaller dose (6 mg/kg), which produced transient hypothermia, was given daily for 18 days to a group of four rats. Figure 9-12 shows the hypothermic responses to the first, sixth, 11th, and 18th injection, each response smaller than the previous one. Animals that had been made tolerant in this way could then be given 10 mg/kg daily without displaying any toxic symptoms. Other rats were made tolerant to 12 mg/kg, a dose at which all control animals, which had never received a previous injection, displayed marked hypothermia and died. Measurements of residual arsenic in the abdominal cavity showed that lack of absorption of the material could not have been the cause of tolerance. A similar technique has been used recently to demonstrate tolerance with a promazine tranquilizer in mice[53] and to localize the site of the hypothermic action of morphine by intracerebral microinjection in rats[54,55] (p. 600).

FIG. 9-12. TOLERANCE TO ARSENITE HYPOTHERMIA IN THE RAT. *Four female rats were maintained at constant ambient temperature (24° to 26°) and given a daily dose of sodium arsenite, 6 mg/kg, intraperitoneally. The body temperature curve is shown after the first, sixth, 11th, and 18th injection. (From Norris and Elliott, Fig. 2.[52])*

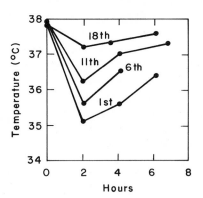

[52] E. R. NORRIS and H. W. ELLIOTT: Tolerance to arsenic trioxide in the albino rat. *Amer. J. Physiol. 143:*635 (1945).

[53] K. LAGERSPETZ: The induction of physiological tolerance to promazine in mice. II. The development of induced tolerance. *Ann. Med. Exper. Biol. Fenniae 41:*214 (1963).

[54] V. J. LOTTI, P. LOMAX, and R. GEORGE: Temperature responses in the rat following intracerebral microinjection of morphine. *J. Pharmacol. Exper. Therap. 150:*135 (1965).

[55] V. J. LOTTI, P. LOMAX, and R. GEORGE: N-Allylnormorphine antagonism of the hypothermic effect of morphine in the rat following intracerebral and systemic administration. *J. Pharmacol. Exp. Therap. 150:*420 (1965).

Modern quantitative methods of investigating animal behavior, especially operant conditioning and conditioned avoidance techniques, have been useful in studying tolerance and physical dependence because they are often quite sensitive to disruption by centrally acting drugs.[56,57] The return to normal patterns of behavior despite continued drug administration becomes an indicator of tolerance; further disturbance of the behavior pattern on withdrawal may be viewed as the equivalent of a withdrawal syndrome. Behavioral phenomena, however, are subject to adaptive modification by numerous influences, such as the repetition of a testing procedure or uncontrolled variations in external stimuli; these changes must be clearly distinguished, by means of adequate controls, from pharmacologic tolerance.[58] Recent applications of these methods to the problem of drug tolerance have established that the cat becomes tolerant to meprobamate,[59] and that rats can be made tolerant to D-amphetamine,[60] LSD,[61,62] and alcohol.[63]

Many of the characteristic subjective effects of centrally acting drugs can only be studied in humans because, if they occur in other species, we have no way to detect or measure them. Only in recent years have the techniques of the controlled clinical trial (cf. chapter 14) been applied to the study of drug tolerance and physical dependence. A great deal of our present understanding in this field is derived from investigations on human volunteers carried out over a number of years at the U.S. Public Health Service hospital for addicts at Lexington, Kentucky. A very important advantage of this locale is that the patient-prisoners who volunteer to be subjects are under restraint, the wards can be locked, and external sources of drugs can be effectively cut off. Without these safeguards, one might well wonder if experimental conditions can actually be observed faithfully. Many examples in the remainder of this chapter will be drawn from this extraordinary series of clinical-pharmacologic experiments.

As a prototype of this kind of study, let us examine in detail an experiment carried out to see if tolerance could develop to LSD or to D-amphetamine in man.[47] A second question concerned the mechanism of action of these stimulant drugs. If they acted in the same way, upon the same receptors, then tolerance to one would presumably confer tolerance to the other. The experiment was designed so that cross-tolerance could be tested as well as direct tolerance to the drug that had been administered

56 P. B. DEWS and W. H. MORSE: Behavioral pharmacology. *Annu. Rev. Pharmacol.* *1*:145 (1961).

57 H. STEINBERG, A. V. S. DE REUCK, and J. KNIGHT, eds.: *Animal Behaviour and Drug Action*. Ciba Foundation Symposium. Boston, Little, Brown and Co., 1964.

58 S. IRWIN: Influence of external factors and arousal mechanisms on the rate of drug tolerance development. *Arch. Int. Pharmacodyn. 142*:152 (1963).

59 M. RICHELLE: A note on behavioral tolerance to meprobamate. *J. Exper. Anal. Behavior 8*:45 (1965).

60 C. R. SCHUSTER and J. ZIMMERMAN: Timing behavior during prolonged treatment with *dl*-amphetamine. *J. Exper. Anal. Behavior 4*:327 (1961).

61 D. X. FREEDMAN, J. B. APPEL, F. R. HARTMAN, and M. E. MOLLIVER: Tolerance to behavioral effects of LSD-25 in rat. *J. Pharmacol. Exp. Therap. 143*:309 (1964).

chronically. The subjects were ten former opiate addicts who had received no narcotic drugs for at least six months. The drugs, including a placebo control, were given "blind," i.e., without the subjects being aware of their nature. The subjects were divided into two groups. At first, over a period of a few weeks, test doses of placebo, D-amphetamine, and LSD were given to both groups. Various measurements were made at hourly intervals, twice before the test dose and eight times thereafter; these included body temperature, pulse rate, blood pressure, pupillary diameter, and kneejerk. In addition, the subject was asked to respond to a series of questions about his mood, feelings, and sensations. Two doses of LSD (0.5 μg/kg and 1.5 μg/kg) and a single dose of D-amphetamine (0.6 mg/kg) were used. At the higher dose of LSD, as compared with placebo, there was a significant rise in temperature, pulse rate, blood pressure, and pupillary diameter, and a significant reduction of the threshold stimulus required to elicit the kneejerk. Moreover, there were significantly more positive answers to the questions about mood (e.g., "Do you have a weird feeling?") after the higher dose of LSD than after placebo. "Clinical grades" assigned by physician observers, based on the subjects' general behavior, were also significantly increased relative to placebo. With D-amphetamine, the significant changes were a rise in blood pressure, an increase in the number of positive answers on the questionnaire (e.g., "Does your memory seem sharper to you than usual?"), and increased "clinical grades."

One group of subjects was then given LSD, another group D-amphetamine, on a regular schedule, beginning with smaller doses and building up to 1.5μg/kg of LSD and 0.6 mg/kg of D-amphetamine (the same as the test doses) daily for 13 days. The tests were then repeated on two successive days, using both drugs for each group of subjects. Thus, the group that had been receiving D-amphetamine chronically was tested for direct tolerance to D-amphetamine, and also for cross-tolerance to LSD. The group that had received LSD chronically was tested for direct tolerance to LSD and cross-tolerance to D-amphetamine. A rest period of two weeks was then allowed to permit the tolerance to wane. Now the entire experiment was repeated with the same subjects, including a repeat of the initial testing, the period of chronic administration, and the final testing, except that the drugs were crossed over. The subjects that had been made tolerant to D-amphetamine in the first stage were now made tolerant to LSD, and vice versa.

The results of this experiment were extraordinarily clear-cut. After chronic administration of LSD, the effect of the test dose of LSD was diminished on all the variables measured, especially the pupillary dilation.

62 D. X. FREEDMAN, G. K. AGHAJANIAN, E. M. ORNITZ, and B. S. ROSNER: Patterns of tolerance to lysergic acid diethylamide and mescaline in rats. *Science 127:*1173 (1958).

63 H. MOSKOWITZ and M. WAPNER: Studies on the acquisition of behavioral tolerance to alcohol. *Quart. J. Stud. Alc. 25:*619 (1964).

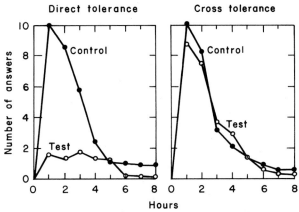

FIG. 9-13. TOLERANCE TO D-AMPHETAMINE IN MAN. *The data are subjective positive responses to a questionnaire about the effects of D-amphetamine on mood. Time after administration of 0.6 mg/kg D-amphetamine is shown on x-axis. Direct tolerance (left) is shown by diminution of response after chronic administration of D-amphetamine for 13 days as compared with initial control. Absence of cross-tolerance (right) is shown by nearly identical response to the control after chronic administration of LSD for 13 days. Both parts of the experiment were carried out at different times in the same subjects in a cross-over design. (From Rosenberg et al., Fig. 3.[47] By permission of Springer.)*

The subjective actions of LSD also decreased greatly. The effects of a test dose of D-amphetamine, however, remained essentially unchanged. After chronic administration of D-amphetamine, on the other hand, direct tolerance developed with respect to the blood pressure elevation and the subjective effects, and there was no cross-tolerance to LSD. The striking results obtained for the questionnaire responses in one part of this experiment are presented in Fig. 9-13. The results with D-amphetamine during control periods are shown as the number of positive answers in the questionnaire as a function of time after administration of the test dose, in the curves labeled *Control*. The curve labeled *Test,* on the left, represents the responses to the test dose of D-amphetamine after the period of chronic administration of D-amphetamine; direct tolerance is essentially complete. On the right is seen the action of D-amphetamine in the same subjects, after they had been made tolerant to LSD. There was no cross-tolerance to D-amphetamine whatsoever. When similar curves were plotted (not shown) for the effects of test doses of LSD in LSD-tolerant and D-amphetamine-tolerant subjects, they looked very much like these. The clear conclusion is that although D-amphetamine and LSD have some similarities as stimulant drugs, their mechanisms of action are quite different. In contrast, cross-tolerance does develop between LSD and two other hallucinogens, mescaline and psilocybin.

ALCOHOL, BARBITURATES, AND MEPROBAMATE

These central depressants produce a kind of tolerance and physical dependence that is more dangerous to the addict and to society than occurs with the opiate narcotics.[64,65,65a] The desired effects with these agents are often obtained at the expense of motor incoordination, boisterous and aggressive behavior, and loss of judgment. The antisocial aspects of alcoholism are nowhere more evident than in the high mortality and injury rates associated with drunken driving. Yet our society imposes no penalties upon the use of alcohol. At the same time, it classes addicts to morphine or heroin as criminals, although no demonstrable antisocial behavior is associated with the pharmacologic actions of these drugs.

It was shown many years ago that tolerance to alcohol has a cellular basis, for both in animals and in man repeated administration leads to diminishing effects at given levels of alcohol in the blood. Dogs, for example, were given as much alcohol as they would tolerate for a period of 55 weeks.[66] Alcohol concentrations in the blood and cerebrospinal fluid were measured periodically. Throughout the range of blood levels, established by administering different doses of alcohol, there was less manifest intoxication at each blood level after habituation than before. In an experiment with human subjects[67] it was initially found that signs of intoxication appeared at blood alcohol levels of about 2 mg/ml. But then, although the administration of alcohol was continued and the blood levels were maintained, the subjects nevertheless became sober within a period of 4 to 10 hours.

The essential features of delirium tremens were known for years. But considerable controversy raged as to whether this psychosis was caused by chronic intoxication or by withdrawal. A well-controlled experiment by the group at Lexington settled the question.[68] Ten former morphine addicts were used for the study. They were furnished enough alcohol to maintain the "maximum state of intoxication compatible with safe ambulatory management" for a period of up to 13 weeks, followed by abrupt and complete withdrawal. The average daily dose was around ¼ to ½ liter of 95 per cent ethanol daily. To avoid any complications due to malnutrition, the

---

[64] H. ISBELL and H. F. FRASER: Addiction to analgesics and barbiturates. *Pharmacol. Rev.* 2:355 (1950).

[65] M. VICTOR and R. D. ADAMS: The effect of alcohol on the nervous system. *Res. Publ. Ass. Res. Nerv. Ment. Dis.* 32:526 (1953).

[65a] E. M. JELLINEK: Phases of alcohol addiction. *Quart. J. Stud. Alc.* 13:673 (1952).

[66] H. W. NEWMAN: Acquired tolerance to ethyl alcohol. *Quart. J. Stud. Alc.* 2:453 (1941).

[67] I. A. MIRSKY, P. PIKER, M. ROSENBAUM, and H. LEDERER: "Adaptation" of the central nervous system to varying concentrations of alcohol in the blood. *Quart. J. Stud. Alc.* 2:35 (1941).

subjects were kept on a high-calorie diet well supplemented with vitamins throughout the experiment.

Figure 9-14 shows the data obtained with one subject during the whole period of alcohol administration. The "degree of intoxication" was evaluated by trained observers, using an arbitrary scale from 0 to 4. The record shows a fairly good agreement between blood levels and the estimated degree of intoxication. Initially, during the period required for buildup of the blood level, as the daily intake was being increased very cautiously, there was no evidence of intoxication. Then, as the blood concentration rose past 1 mg/ml, the subject became boisterous, noisy, and silly. During the third week, a curious fall in the blood alcohol concentration occurred, without any change in the daily intake. This phenomenon was observed in all the subjects consistently. Its cause was not investigated, but it might reflect the appearance of increased activity of the liver enzymes that metabolize ethanol (cf. p. 232). As the blood alcohol level declined at this time, sobriety returned. When the daily dose was now increased, the

FIG. 9-14. INTOXICATION AND BLOOD ALCOHOL CONCENTRATIONS IN ONE SUBJECT DURING CHRONIC ADMINISTRATION OF ALCOHOL. *Alcohol was given by mouth in divided doses, in the amounts shown. Dilute alcohol solutions were used but the amounts are expressed as ml of 95% ethanol. Degree of intoxication was rated on an arbitrary scale, according to the subject's behavior; each point represents an average of 3 daily ratings. Alcohol intake was adjusted as required to maintain as nearly as possible the maximum degree of intoxication compatible with safe ambulatory management (about grade 2). (Modified from Isbell et al., Fig. 1.*[68] *By permission of* Journal of Studies on Alcohol.)

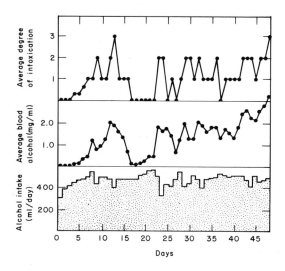

[68] H. ISBELL, H. F. FRASER, A. WIKLER, R. E. BELLEVILLE, and A. J. EISENMAN: An experimental study of the etiology of "rum fits" and delirium tremens. *Quart. J. Stud. Alc.* 16:1 (1955).

blood level rose again, and the state of intoxication returned. Subsequently, the blood level continued to rise as the daily intake was adjusted upward, but the degree of intoxication lagged behind. For example, on day 13, a blood level of 2 mg/ml produced grade-3 intoxication; but on the final day of the experiment, a blood level of about 3.5 mg/ml was required for the same degree of intoxication. Tolerance was demonstrable on electroencephalograph records as well as by these gross evaluations. An increase of slow-wave activity occurred initially at the higher blood levels, but this effect became less marked as the experiment proceeded, despite the rising blood levels in the final weeks.

Despite their state of chronic intoxication, none of the subjects developed any hallucinatory or convulsive behavior during the period of alcohol intake. The onset of withdrawal symptoms upon discontinuance of alcohol administration was quite rapid. About 8 hours after their last drink, the subjects became nervous, apprehensive, and very weak. Some suffered retching and vomiting. All six of the patients who had been drinking for 48 days or more manifested tremor, weakness, perspiration, nausea, vomiting, diarrhea, elevated blood pressure and insomnia. Delirium and hallucinations occurred in four of the subjects. Convulsions of the grand mal type developed in two; one of these became so seriously ill he had to be treated with barbiturates. All the symptoms waned after a number of days, and three months later the subjects appeared to be quite normal in all respects. Three subjects who withdrew from the experiment within the first month developed only slight tremor and anorexia.

It is clear from this and similar experiments[69] that delirium tremens is a typical withdrawal syndrome manifested after prolonged intake of ethyl alcohol; that a severe degree of physical dependence may occur; and that the intensity of the withdrawal syndrome depends upon the duration of exposure to alcohol and, presumably, the dosage schedule.

Tolerance to the barbiturates and physical dependence on them present a picture rather similar to what is seen with alcohol.[70,71] In both cases, experiments in animals have shown that although a contribution to tolerance is made by increased drug metabolism due to induction of enzymes, the main feature of tolerance is an adaptation of the brain to higher drug levels. Neither with the barbiturates nor with alcohol does one see the impressive degree of tolerance that can develop with the narcotics; nevertheless, the tolerance is readily demonstrable. For example, rats were given barbital in daily doses of 200 mg/kg subcutaneously, a sufficient dose

[69] J. H. MENDELSON, special ed.: Experimentally induced chronic intoxication and withdrawal in alcoholics. *Quart. J. Stud. Alc.* 25:Suppl. 2, 1964.

[70] M. H. WULFF: *The Barbiturate Withdrawal Syndrome.* Suppl. No. 14, EEG and Clinical Neurophysiology. Copenhagen, Munksgaard, 1959.

[71] H. ISBELL: Addiction to barbiturates and the barbiturate abstinence syndrome. *Ann. Intern. Med.* 33:108 (1950).

to produce anesthesia.[72] At the instant of awakening, each rat was sacrificed and the drug concentration was determined in its brain. In a group of animals thus killed after the second daily dose, the mean brain concentration was 184 mg/kg. After the fifth injection, the concentration at awakening was 248 mg/kg, a statistically significant increase ($P<0.01$).

Tolerance development is favored by the continuous presence of drug in adequate concentration; and therefore phenobarbital and barbital, which are not metabolized rapidly, lead to tolerance more readily than those barbiturates that have short biologic half-lives. When phenobarbital or barbital was administered to rats on alternate days for two weeks, no tolerance was produced. But when the same doses were given daily for two weeks, a moderate degree of tolerance was established, the waking drug concentration in the brain being about 35 per cent higher than initially, as described above.[72]

In another investigation,[73] rats were pretreated with increasing doses of barbital for 13 days. A test dose of barbital (200 mg/kg) was then administered to these animals and to controls that had never received barbital. The pretreated animals awakened significantly sooner than the others; their average sleeping times, in duplicate runs, were 284 and 319 minutes, respectively, compared with 387 and 393 minutes for the naive rats. Then the tolerant rats and nontolerant controls were each given a single dose of ^{14}C-barbital (150 mg/kg). Brain, plasma, and urine radioactivities were measured at 10, 30, and 60 minutes, and at 3 and 6 hours. These determinations are shown in Fig. 9-15. There were no differences of any consequence in the data between the tolerant and nontolerant rats. But, despite identical barbital brain levels at 60 minutes, three of the five control rats were asleep, but all four tolerant rats were awake. The material measured here was nearly all barbital, identified chromatographically in the urine; only about 5 per cent of the drug was metabolized. Under these conditions, therefore, no part of the tolerance could be attributed to increased drug destruction or excretion.

Physical dependence upon barbiturates has been produced very rapidly in experimental animals under conditions of intensive drug treatment.[74] Groups of cats were given three or four doses of pentobarbital intravenously daily, each sufficient to produce deep anesthesia. Then, after different durations of this barbiturate pretreatment, groups of the cats were tested to determine their thresholds for the induction of convulsive seizures with pentylenetetrazol. The periods of pentobarbital administration studied

[72] H. REMMER, M. SIEGERT, H. R. NITZE, and I. KIRSTEN: Die Gewöhnung an langwirkende Barbiturate. *Arch. Exp. Pathol. Pharmakol. 243:*468 (1962).

[73] A. G. EBERT, G. K. W. YIM, and T. S. MIYA: Distribution and metabolism of barbital-14C in tolerant and nontolerant rats. *Biochem. Pharmacol. 13:*1267 (1964).

[74] J. H. JAFFE and S. K. SHARPLESS: The rapid development of physical dependence on barbiturates. *J. Pharmacol. Exp. Therap. 150:*140 (1965).

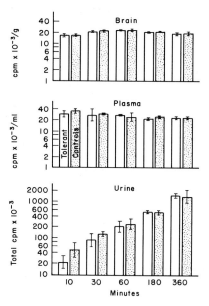

FIG. 9-15. BARBITAL LEVELS IN NONTOLERANT AND TOLERANT RATS. *Rats were pretreated for 13 days to establish tolerance. A single dose of 150 mg/kg of ^{14}C-barbital was then given intraperitoneally to these animals and to naive controls. Groups of four or five rats were killed at each time after administration of the drug, and radioactivity was determined in brain, plasma, and urine as shown.* Open histograms, *tolerant rats;* stippled histograms, *controls. Note logarithmic scales of radioactivity.* Brackets *represent ± 2 standard errors above and below the means. None of the tolerant animals slept; but in the control groups, one of five was asleep at 30 minutes, three of five at 60 minutes, and one of five at 180 minutes. (Modified from Ebert et al., Fig. 1.*[73]*)

were from one day to three weeks. As the experiment continued, tolerance was manifested by a shortening of the duration of anesthesia, and it became necessary to increase the dosage to establish the same degree of anesthesia. On abrupt termination of the barbiturate injections, except in the group intoxicated for only one day, typical withdrawal syndromes developed. The cats showed increased hyperexcitability, tremors, startle responses, myoclonic jerks, and in at least one animal a spontaneous grand mal seizure. The pentylenetetrazol seizure thresholds were determined by infusing this convulsant drug intravenously at a slow constant rate and measuring the amount required to produce the onset of the tonic phase of muscular movements. The results are given in Table 9-1. They show that even after intoxication with pentobarbital for only 26 hours, although no spontaneous signs of withdrawal could be detected, the seizure threshold was already lowered, compared with initial thresholds determined in the same cats. After longer periods of intoxication, the lowering of seizure

TABLE 9-1. **Lowering of seizure threshold during barbiturate withdrawal in cats**

Cats were given pentobarbital intravenously three to four times daily, in doses sufficient to cause deep anesthesia. Prior to the injections, seizure threshold was determined in each cat by infusing pentylene-tetrazol intravenously and measuring how much was required to produce tonic muscular contractions. Then, after various durations of barbiturate intoxication, seizure threshold was again determined 20 and 90 hours after pentobarbital was discontinued. The data are average thresholds, as per cents of initial threshold for each animal group. All the depressed thresholds differ significantly ($P<0.05$) from the pretreatment value. (Data from Jaffe and Sharpless,[74] Table 1.)

| | | Threshold for pentylenetetrazol-induced seizures (% of pretreatment threshold) | |
| | Duration of barbiturate treatment | 20 hrs after terminating barbiturate | 90 hrs after terminating barbiturate |
No. of animals			
8	26 hrs	82	101
7	56 hrs	72	107
7	5 days	46	103
4	3 weeks	31	59

threshold during the withdrawal period was very marked, and it persisted for several days.

In man, tolerance to barbiturates is well known. A false impression long prevailed that physical dependence upon these agents did not develop, until experiments with human subjects,[75,76] very much like those on alcohol, dispelled this impression. The experiments demonstrated that abrupt withdrawal from barbiturates precipitates a particularly violent withdrawal syndrome, characterized by weakness, tremor, insomnia, anxiety, vomiting, loss of weight, increased pulse and respiratory rates, increased blood pressure, convulsions of the grand mal type, and a psychosis closely resembling alcoholic delirium tremens. The withdrawal syndrome is so severe that abrupt withdrawal of barbiturates from an addicted patient must never be undertaken; the dosage has to be reduced very gradually over a long period of time.

New centrally acting drugs are too often introduced and used widely before the hazards of tolerance and physical dependence are fully realized. This was true of the mild tranquilizing agent meprobamate. Eventually, in a well-designed clinical trial, the withdrawal syndrome was

[75] H. ISBELL, S. ALTSCHUL, C. H. KORNETSKY, A. J. EISENMAN, H. G. FLANARY, and H. F. FRASER: Chronic barbiturate intoxication: an experimental study. *Arch. Neurol. Psychiatr.* 64:1 (1950).

[76] H. F. FRASER, H. ISBELL, A. J. EISENMAN, A. WIKLER, and F. T. PESCOR: Chronic barbiturate intoxication: further studies. *Arch. Intern. Med.* 94:34 (1954).

demonstrated unequivocally.[77] Groups of about 25 patients each were
given either placebo or meprobamate (3.2 or 4.6 g) daily for 40 days. The
design of the experiment was "double blind," i.e., neither the patients nor
the observers knew the assignment of medications. Severe sedative effects
were observed at both dosages of meprobamate; 35 out of the 47 patients
receiving the drug had a staggering gait or could not stand unsupported.
Over a period of about a week, however, despite continued dosage, tolerance developed, and these effects wore off. After 40 days, placebo was substituted for drug, in identical capsules, so patients were unaware that medications were being changed. A variety of withdrawal symptoms ensued, of
varying degrees of severity, involving 44 of the 47 patients. Insomnia and
tremors were the most common; others included vomiting, severe anxiety,
loss of appetite, hallucinations, and delusions resembling those seen after
alcohol withdrawal. Three patients had grand mal convulsive seizures. The
data are summarized in Table 9-2. It is clear that patients who had been
receiving placebo for the first 40 days experienced no "withdrawal" effects,
whereas the severity of the syndrome in the patients from whom meprobamate was withdrawn bore a direct relationship to the dosage previously
administered.

Physical dependence upon alcohol, barbiturates, or meprobamate
entails no cross-dependence upon the opiate narcotics, but there seems
to be complete cross-dependence within this group, and possibly even to
other depressants. Paraldehyde, for example, has been used traditionally in
alcoholic delirium tremens, and barbiturates are also effective in this
condition. To a large extent, the success of such agents may be due not

TABLE 9-2.   **Withdrawal syndrome after 40 days on meprobamate**

Patients were given meprobamate or placebo for 40 days. Then,
placebo was abruptly substituted for meprobamate and careful observations were made over the next several days. The intensity of
abstinence symptoms was graded by physician observers. Data are
numbers of patients in each category. (From Haizlip and Ewing,[77]
Table 4.)

	Intensity of withdrawal syndrome				Total no. of pts.
	None	**Mild**	**Moderate**	**Severe**	
Placebo	22	2	0	0	24
Meprobamate, 3.2 g daily	2	17	3	1	23
Meprobamate, 6.4 g daily	1	11	9	3	24

[77] T. M. HAIZLIP and J. A. EWING: Meprobamate habituation. A controlled clinical
study. *New Engl. J. Med.* 258:1181 (1958).

so much to their own sedative properties as to their specific relief of the withdrawal syndrome by substituting for alcohol, and then permitting a more gradual withdrawal to be accomplished.[68]

NARCOTICS

Pharmacologic Effects of the Narcotics.   This group of compounds comprises the natural opium alkaloids, of which morphine is the prototype, and related synthetic and semisynthetic drugs. Sometimes these are called, as a group, opiates (or opioid narcotics); we shall refer to them simply as narcotics. The compounds that have been studied most intensively are morphine, heroin (diacetylmorphine), and the synthetic congeners levorphanol, meperidine, and methadone. The structure-activity relationships among these drugs were discussed in chapter 1, where their chemical formulas and conformations are also given (p. 50 ff.).

The narcotics have complex pharmacologic effects.[78-80] They are exceedingly valuable clinically for allaying severe pain and alleviating anxiety. The aspect of their psychotropic action that accounts for their abuse by addicts is described as *euphoria*. This is a peculiar state of well-being, which seems to defy exact description.[81,50] After intravenous administration of morphine or heroin, the addict experiences an immediate sensation of physical pleasure akin to sexual orgasm.[82] A feeling of relaxation follows, which may be accompanied by increased loquaciousness, increased motor activity, or facilitation of social interaction. With higher doses, sedation is the prominent effect, with indulgence in daydreams and fantasies. Libido and aggressiveness are decreased as the subject becomes increasingly withdrawn and unresponsive to his surroundings, often drifting into sleep. It seems very likely that the analgesia produced by these drugs is intimately connected with the euphoriant effect as a whole, and that what is primarily altered is the emotional reaction and anxiety engendered by painful stimuli. Indeed, patients with intractable pain commonly report, after receiving a narcotic analgesic, that the pain is still perceived but "no longer bothers" them. Many years of research in the quest for a drug of this class that would be free of addiction liability has led to the view that analgesic potency and addiction liability may be inseparable. Recently,

[78] F. F. FOLDES, M. SWERDLOW, and E. S. SIKER: *Narcotics and Narcotic Antagonists*. Springfield, Ill., Charles C Thomas, 1964, pp. 88–112.

[79] N. B. EDDY, H. HALBACH, and O. J. BRAENDEN: Synthetic substances with morphine-like effect. Relationship between analgesic action and addiction liability, with a discussion of the chemical structure of addiction-producing substances. *Bull. World Health Organ.* 14:353 (1956).

[80] H. KRUEGER, N. B. EDDY, and M. SUMWALT: The pharmacology of the opium alkaloids. Part I. *Public Health Rep. 56:*Suppl. 165, 1941.

[81] H. ISBELL and W. M. WHITE: Clinical characteristics of addictions. *Amer. J. Med.* 14:558 (1953).

[82] R. D. CHESSICK: The "pharmacogenic orgasm" in the drug addict. *Arch. Gen. Psychiatr.* 3:545 (1960).

however, there has been some interest in the possibility that narcotic antagonists (e.g., nalorphine, pentazocine), which have analgesic effects, might have the desired properties.

Although, to some extent, the narcotics produce similar actions in all animal species, the euphoriant actions can be observed directly only in man. Moreover, man is much more sensitive to these drugs than are other species; the effective analgesic dose of morphine in man, for example, is about 0.2 mg/kg, whereas in the dog it is at least ten times higher. As in man, the predominant effects in monkeys, dogs, rabbits, and rats are sedative. In horses, cats, and mice, the predominant effects are excitatory. But these do not seem to be fundamental differences. In any species (including man), the narcotics produce a mixture of excitatory and depressant effects upon gross motor behavior, clearly excitatory effects like emesis, and specific actions such as analgesia and hypothermia that are not readily characterized as excitatory or depressant. Respiratory depression is produced in all animals. It is the cause of death from overdosage in man and most other species. Even in mice, where motor activity is greatly stimulated by the narcotics, death is caused by respiratory depression, which appears to be superimposed on the excitation caused at lower doses.

Most investigations of tolerance or physical dependence in animals have used analgesia as the criterion of drug effect. This has often been successful, but the results have to be interpreted with caution. In such investigations, animals are subjected to some standard procedure for inflicting a noxious stimulus, and their reaction is recorded. Often, the measure of analgesia is the latency of withdrawal from the stimulus. Analgesia is then defined as the drug-induced toleration of the noxious stimulus, and tolerance is defined as re-establishment of the reaction pattern despite the presence of the drug. Increasing the drug dosage should then once more produce analgesia, and the degree of tolerance can be defined in terms of the increase in drug dosage required to produce the same degree of analgesia as a standard dose did initially. However, the criteria of analgesia are somewhat uncertain, since the mere failure of an animal to lift its paw or flick its tail when heat or pressure is applied might signify interference with a simple spinal reflex rather than an analgesic action upon the brain. Moreover, in this type of experiment, whenever any influence causes the animal to become more responsive to noxious stimuli in the presence of drug, it will appear that pharmacologic tolerance has developed. At best, analgesia is an indirect measure of drug action in animals, and its interpretation remains somewhat uncertain. Experiments in which a narcotic drug directly produces a biologic response would seem better suited to the study of tolerance.

Tolerance to the Narcotics.   The duration of action of a single dose of a narcotic is determined by the route of administration and by the rate of elimination of the particular drug. If repeated doses are given, at appropriate intervals, the intensity of response diminishes; and then, in order to obtain the same response as formerly, the dose has to be increased. Thus, in the course of days or weeks, the tolerance, in human subjects or other species, may build up to a remarkable degree, until many times the lethal dose can eventually be tolerated. In man, for example, an initial dose of 100 to 200 mg of morphine would be sufficient to cause profound sedation, respiratory depression, anoxia, and death; but tolerant subjects have been known to take as much as 4 g without adverse effect.[83] Once tolerance has been established to one of the narcotics, the subject is found to be cross-tolerant to all narcotics, but not to drugs of a different series. Thus, morphine-tolerant individuals are also tolerant to heroin, methadone, meperidine, and so on, but not to alcohol or barbiturates. In other words, tolerance to narcotics is highly specific for the chemical structure of these compounds; it is not a physiologic adaptation to depressant agents in general.[84]

The usual course of addiction is for the addict to increase successive doses of narcotic just as much as is required to obtain the sought-for euphoric effect. The ability of addicts to "feel" this drug action and estimate its intensity has been used to establish the time course of the progression of tolerance in a remarkable experiment.[85] Postaddicts, who had not received any narcotic drugs for several months, were given heroin or morphine intravenously, four times daily. The dosage was started at 18 mg, in divided doses, on the first day, and was increased stepwise to 180 mg on the 19th day of the experiment. After each injection, the addicts were asked simply to judge the intensity of effect on an arbitrary scale. A dose-response curve for these estimates was established by administering various doses to other groups of postaddicts and considering only their responses to the first dose administered. A "tolerance index" could then be constructed as follows. Any given subjective judgment of intensity could be converted to a standard dose that would have been required to produce that same estimated intensity in nontolerant subjects. The tolerance index was defined as the ratio of this equieffective standard dose to the actual dose administered. Initially, at the first dose, the tolerance index would be 1.0, because the administered dose produces the same effect as the standard dose. As tolerance develops, the index becomes smaller, and it approaches zero as larger doses produce even smaller effects. The result of this experiment is shown in Fig. 9-16. It indicates that tolerance to mor-

[83] E. G. WILLIAMS and F. W. OBERST: A cycle of morphine addiction. Biological and psychological studies. I. Biological investigations. *Public Health Rep. 61:*1 (1946).

[84] N. B. EDDY: "The Phenomena of Tolerance," in *Origins of Resistance to Toxic Agents,* ed. by M. G. Sevag, R. D. Reid, and O. E. Reynolds. New York, Academic Press, 1955.

[85] W. R. MARTIN and H. F. FRASER: A comparative study of physiological and subjective effects of heroin and morphine administered intravenously in postaddicts. *J. Pharmacol. Exp. Therap. 133:*388 (1961).

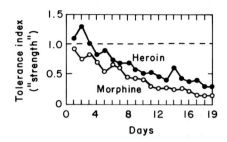

FIG. 9-16. COURSE OF DEVELOPMENT OF TOLERANCE TO HEROIN AND MOR-
PHINE. *Eight addicts were studied. Heroin or morphine was administered
intravenously four times daily. Morphine dose was increased gradually from
18 mg on the first day to 180 mg on the 19th day. Heroin dose was increased
from 7.2 mg to 76 mg. Subjects were asked to estimate the "strength" of the
drug, and these estimates were converted to a "tolerance index" as described
in the text. The tolerance index is the ratio of dose that would be required in a
nontolerant subject to dose actually administered to achieve the same estimated
effect in the tolerant subject. An index of zero would represent complete tolerance. (From Martin and Fraser, Fig. 6.*[85])

phine begins to develop without any lag, apparently at the very first dose
administered. After two to three weeks, a ten times higher dosage was
required to yield the same effects. Eventually (not shown), doses up to
about 20 times higher or more were tolerated, at which time the desired
effects were no longer obtained at all. The course of development of
tolerance to heroin is characterized by a lag of a few days, but then it
parallels the morphine course.

Similar experiments can be carried out with animals, using analgesia
or other objective response as criterion. Tolerance develops and is maintained most readily when the narcotic is given on a regular schedule, at
intervals short enough to keep the drug level elevated, and with dose
increments given as frequently as necessary to maintain whatever drug
effect is being followed. Drug-seeking behavior has been reported in
monkeys and other species leading to higher doses and tolerance.[86,87]
Operant conditioning techniques were applied to develop a self-administration procedure in rats.[88] These animals then maintained their state of tolerance by lever-pressing behavior, as summarized in Table 9-3. The rats were
given morphine intravenously, beginning at a low dose (2.5 mg/kg) and
followed by hourly injections on a geometrically increasing schedule. The

    [86] T. THOMPSON and C. R. SCHUSTER: Morphine self-administration, food-reinforced,
and avoidance behaviors in Rhesus monkeys. *Psychopharmacologia 5:*87 (1964).
    [87] M. H. SEEVERS and G. A. DENEAU: "Physiological Aspects of Tolerance and
Physical Dependence," in *Physiological Pharmacology: A Comprehensive Treatise,* ed. by
W. S. Root and F. G. Hofmann. New York, Academic Press, 1963, vol. 1, part A, p. 565.
    [88] J. R. WEEKS: Experimental morphine addiction: method for automatic intra-
venous injections in unrestrained rats. *Science 138:*143 (1962).

TABLE 9-3.   **Self-administration of morphine by "addict" rats**

Rats were given morphine intravenously in increasing dosage from 2.5 to 40 mg/kg hourly, and were then maintained at 40 mg/kg hourly for one to two days. Then they were placed in a fixed-ratio operant behavior situation; pressing a lever delivered the indicated dose intravenously. Reinforcement ratio represents number of lever pressings rats were required to perform in order to obtain the indicated dose. (From Weeks,[88] Tables 1 and 2. By permission of the American Association for the Advancement of Science.)

Reinforce- ment ratio	Single dose (mg/kg)	Responses of individual rats (A–I) (no. of lever pressings per hour)					Mean	Daily intake (mg/kg)
		A	B	C	D	E		
1:1	10	2.4	2.0	1.3	0.9	1.2	1.6	384
1:1	3.2	5.5	3.1	2.9	2.5	2.1	3.2	240
Withdrawal[a]		33	11	21	27	17	22	
		F	G	H	I			
1:1	3.2	1.8	1.1	1.9	3.5[b]		2.6	160
5:1	3.2	7.4	4.4	7.1	5.2		6.0	91
10:1	3.2	13	7.6	12	12		11	84
10:1	10	5.4	4.7	5.2	4.7		5.0	120

[a] Calculations on first 3 hours after withdrawal only.
[b] Based on last 7½ hours of 24-hour period only.

dosage was increased by 2.5 per cent each hour until a dose of 40 mg/kg was reached. This dose was then repeated hourly for a day or two. Finally, the rats were placed in a cage containing a lever, and they were connected to an infusion apparatus, so that pressing the lever would deliver a dose of 10 mg/kg intravenously. Under these conditions, the rats behaved as though they were addicted to the drug. They pressed the lever at a fairly constant rate, thus obtaining morphine injections on a continuing schedule. The animals stabilized their intake at a level somewhat less than one-half of what they had been getting, as shown by the first line of the table; 40 mg/kg would have required 4 lever pressings per hour, whereas the actual mean was only 1.6, delivering a daily dose of 384 mg/kg instead of the 960 mg/kg they had received previously. When the magnitude of the dose delivered by a single lever pressing was reduced to one-third (second line of table), the rate of lever pressing doubled; and thus, although the change in operant behavior was in the direction of maintaining the same drug input, the total actually fell somewhat, to 240 mg/kg per day. When the apparatus for drug injection was shut off (third line of table), the rate of lever pressing went up very sharply. The lower part of the table shows the effect, in a different group of rats, of changing the reinforcement ratio. When five or ten lever pressings were required to obtain a single drug injection, the rate of pressing increased, as might have been expected. Increasing the size of the single dose at the 10:1 reinforcement ratio caused a decrease in the rate of work.

These results demonstrate that in the rat made tolerant to large doses of morphine, the injection of morphine had a reinforcing effect upon the operant behavior. The rat evidently establishes a daily intake that is well below what could have been obtained with a higher rate of lever pressing; and, within limits, this daily intake is maintained even though the reinforcement ratio and the magnitude of the single dose are altered. The greatly increased rate of lever pressing when drug was withdrawn could be interpreted as drug-seeking behavior comparable with the intense craving during the early part of the withdrawal syndrome in humans. It is interesting that the rats failed to increase their drug intake to progressively higher levels when they had every opportunity to do so; perhaps a maximum degree of tolerance had been reached.

It has been suggested[87] that tolerance develops only to "depressant" but not to "excitatory" effects of the narcotics. It is well known in man, however, that tolerance develops to all the psychotropic actions, some of which (increased talkativeness, motor activity, emesis) would certainly have to be classified as excitatory. The mouse is a species in which the most prominent effect of the narcotics is to stimulate gross motor activity. These drugs cause a stereotyped kind of running back and forth that may well be described as a "running fit." That tolerance does indeed develop to such an excitatory action of levorphanol was demonstrated clearly a few years ago.[88a] An experiment with levorphanol is presented in Fig. 9-17. Three mice were maintained in a special cage traversed by a light beam falling on a photocell. Every interruption of the beam actuated a counter. Mice injected with saline remained quietly huddled together in the corner of the cage for most of the subsequent 8-hour period, the total number of counts not exceeding a few hundred. Levorphanol given subcutaneously at a dose of 20 mg/kg induced a great increase of running activity (curve 1) which continued for about 2 hours and then gradually ceased. The same dose was injected every 8 hours. The activity record after the second, fourth, and seventh injection (curves 2, 4, 7) showed a progressively diminishing effect. At the tenth injection (curve 10), the dose was increased to 60 mg/kg. The resulting increase in activity shows that, although the capacity to respond had not been lost, the sensitivity to levorphanol was changed. By comparing the magnitude of response with dose-response data obtained with native mice at their first injection, it could be estimated that the effect of the tenth injection was that to be expected from an initial dose of 4 mg/kg. In other words, in a period of three days, the effective potency of levorphanol had diminished by a factor of 15. Eventually, in these experiments, tolerance to doses of 400 mg/kg was obtained, which is well above

[88a] L. SHUSTER, R. V. HANNAM, and W. E. BOYLE, JR.: A simple method for producing tolerance to dihydromorphinone in mice. *J. Pharmacol. Exp. Therap. 140:*149 (1963).

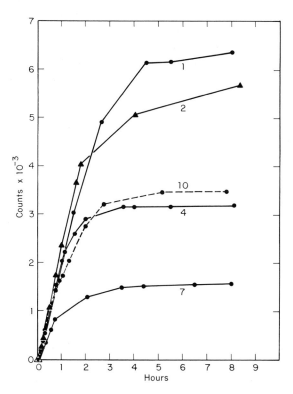

FIG. 9-17.   DEVELOPMENT OF TOLERANCE TO AN EXCITATORY EFFECT OF LEVOR-
PHANOL IN MICE.   *A group of three mice was placed in a special cage in which
interruption of a light beam activated a counter. Levorphanol was given subcutaneously every 8 hours in a dose of 20 mg/kg body weight. The "running
fits" induced by the drug are recorded above for the first, second, fourth, and
seventh injection at this dosage. Dosage was raised to 60 mg/kg at the tenth
injection, with result shown in* broken line. *(Unpublished data of Goldstein.)*

the lethal dosage in naive mice. Thus, tolerance developed to the respiratory
depressant effect as well as to the excitatory effect of levorphanol.

There is no doubt that after withdrawal of a narcotic from an addict
the tolerance largely disappears. Indeed, addicts often wish to undergo
withdrawal primarily to reduce the amount of drug needed daily, and
thereby temporarily alleviate the financial hardship imposed by the state
of tolerance. It is all the more remarkable, therefore, that an experiment
with rats, carried out with meticulous care, has shown long-persisting
tolerance to morphine analgesia as well as to an effect of the drug in a
test of swimming activity.[89] As the investigators point out, accurate

---

[89] J. COCHIN and C. KORNETSKY: Development and loss of tolerance to morphine
in the rat after single and multiple injections. *J. Pharmacol. Exp. Therap. 145:*1 (1964).

measurement of the rate of disappearance of tolerance is intrinsically difficult, "since the very procedures for testing for tolerance appeared to perpetuate the phenomenon whose decay was being measured." The experimental procedures adopted to circumvent this difficulty, although somewhat complex, merit detailed description. We shall confine the discussion to the effects on analgesia, measured by a hot-plate method. A rat is placed on a hot plate at 54.6°. After a latency period of 3 or 4 seconds, one hind limb is lifted in a characteristic manner. The test is repeated at 30-minute intervals for 210 minutes. If no drug has been given, the resulting curve of latency (seconds) against time (minutes) is flat, at 3 to 4 seconds, with a variation of approximately 1 second above or below the mean. When an analgesic drug is given, the latencies increase to as much as 30 seconds, the maximum permitted before the rat is removed from the hot plate. The total analgesic effect is expressed as the total area of the time-latency curve above the control baseline. The maximum possible analgesia score is: 210 min $\times$ (30 $-$ 3) sec, or 5,670 min   sec, where 30 seconds is the maximum permissible latency and 3 seconds, the normal latency.

In such an experiment, rats were pretested to determine the analgesic effect of 20 mg/kg of morphine and then distributed into groups. Three weeks later, the rats in group A were started on a schedule of morphine injections twice daily, building up to 100 mg/kg twice daily. These injections were continued for 70 days. Figure 9-18 shows that a high degree of tolerance was developed by this procedure. The first data point for the A_1 group represents the result of testing on the 68th day of chronic administration; the test dose of morphine (20 mg/kg) produced very little analgesia. During the withdrawal period, group A_1 was tested repeatedly; there was very little recovery of sensitivity to morphine. Groups A_2 to A_5 represent subgroups that were each tested only once during the withdrawal period; thus, A_2 was only tested at three months, A_3 only at five months, and so on. Here, the loss of tolerance was faster than when repeated test doses were given; but even group A_5, which received no morphine between cessation of the injection series and the test dose a whole year later, still showed a considerable degree of tolerance. Groups C_1 to C_6 demonstrate the same long persistence of tolerance even in animals that were never subjected to chronic morphine administration. These rats received 20 mg/kg once at the time of pretesting, and three months before the first data point, yet the analgesic effect of morphine was only 60 per cent as great as in naïve animals. Repeated testing (group C_1) produced increasing tolerance. When no further morphine was given (C_2 to C_6), there was little recovery of sensitivity to morphine even 11 months after the single dose of 20 mg/kg; but four months after that, there was full recovery. Groups N_1 and N_2 were litter mates of the rats used for the rest of the experiment, and were held until the times shown in the table without ever receiving morphine. Thus, for example, the only difference between N_1 and C_2 was

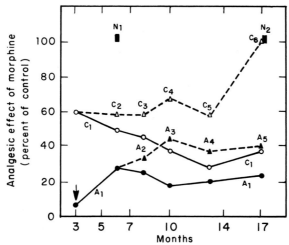

FIG. 9-18.   PERSISTENCE OF MORPHINE TOLERANCE IN RATS.   *Rats were tested for analgesia by the hot-plate method. The test dose of morphine was 20 mg/kg. All animals except groups N_1 and N_2 were tested once three months earlier than the first data points shown here. The animals in group A received twice daily injections of morphine (up to 100 mg/kg) beginning three weeks after the test dose, and continuing for ten weeks. Drug injections were terminated at* arrow. *Group A_1 was tested repeatedly as shown; groups A_2 to A_5 were each tested only once after withdrawal, as indicated. Groups C_1 to C_6 were treated identically after the pretesting, except that they received no course of chronic morphine administration. Groups N_1 and N_2 (controls) never received morphine, not even the initial test dose. Ordinates are per cent of the total analgesic effect of morphine on groups N_1 and N_2, expressed as area under the analgesia curve for 3½ hours after the test dose of morphine, as described in text. Abscissas are months after initial test dose of morphine. (From Cochin and Kornetsky, Fig. 3.*[89])

that the latter had received a single injection of morphine during pretesting nearly six months earlier.

The possibility that these results could have arisen from familiarity of the rats with the testing procedure rather than exposure to the drug was ruled out in additional control experiments. Interpretation of the finding that a single dose of morphine has such long-lasting effects (as in C_2) is difficult, and the abrupt disappearance of tolerance between 14 and 17 months is especially odd. The investigators found it difficult "to visualize a mechanism other than one involving an immune reaction of some kind" to explain their results.

Investigations of the mechanism of tolerance and of the mechanism of narcotic action have been hampered by the same difficulty—that the biochemical alterations produced by the drug in the whole brain are unlikely to have much to do with the specific biochemical changes that are responsible for the drug effects at the sites of drug action. For this reason, the study of tolerance might be furthered considerably if the several actions of the narcotics could be localized accurately in the brain. Recently, this goal has been attained for the hypothermic effect of morphine in the rat.[54,55] By means of a microinjection cannula it was shown that an area in the anterior hypothalamus is sensitive to minute amounts of morphine. It was also shown that when morphine was injected intravenously, the hypothermic effect could be blocked by microinjection of nalorphine, in minute amounts, into the very same hypothalamic region. Presumably, tolerant animals are tolerant to such microinjections of morphine. If so, it might be possible to compare drug effects at the cellular and subcellular levels in this localized region in tolerant and nontolerant animals.

Physical Dependence on the Narcotics.   Tolerance to the narcotics is invariably accompanied by physical dependence. The tolerant addict or experimental animal evidently functions well provided he continues to receive the drug. When a high degree of tolerance has been attained, even very large doses of narcotic may no longer produce any euphoriant effect; but drug intake has to be continued in order to avoid withdrawal symptoms. If drug administration is stopped, profound derangements ensue. At first, there is restlessness and intense craving for the drug. Yawning, running nose, lacrimation, and perspiration follow, with chills, fever, vomiting, panting respiration, loss of appetite, insomnia, hypertension, aches and pains, and loss of weight. The pupils become dilated and there are associated signs of hyperactivity of the sympathetic nervous system. Pilomotor stimulation (gooseflesh) accounts for the vernacular description of withdrawal as "cold turkey." In animals, severe disturbances of body function and behavior may also occur during the withdrawal period.[90,86,44] Human cells of non-neuronal origin have been made dependent upon morphine in cell culture, so that withdrawal of the drug resulted in cell degeneration or death;[91] but what relationship this bears to the withdrawal syndrome remains unknown.

The invention of a procedure for quantitating the intensity of the withdrawal syndrome in man[92] has contributed much to understanding its nature and to the study of addiction potential among new narcotics. Addicts or postaddicts are stabilized on a dosage of 240 to 340 mg of morphine daily. Careful measurements are then made, on a regular schedule, of respiratory rate, blood pressure, body temperature, hours of sleep, caloric intake, and body weight. At the same time, the presence or absence of

90 F. HUIDOBRO and C. MAGGIOLO: Studies on morphine. IX. On the intensity of the abstinence syndrome to morphine induced by daily injections of nalorphine in white mice. *Arch. Int. Pharmacodyn. 158:*97 (1965).

91 G. CORSSEN and I. A. SKORA: "Addiction" reactions in cultured human cells. *J. Amer. Med. Ass. 187:*328 (1964).

92 C. K. HIMMELSBACH: Studies of certain addiction characteristics of (a) dihydromorphine ("Paramorphan"), (b) dihydrodesoxymorphine-D ("Desomorphine"), (c) dihydrodesoxycodeine-D ("Desocodeine"), and (d) methyldihydromorphinone ("Metopon"). *J. Pharmacol. Exp. Therap. 67:*239 (1939).

certain signs (not subject to measurement) is noted, such as yawning, lacrimation, vomiting. For each manifestation, an arbitrary number of points is assigned, with a maximum limit set upon some, so that the total score will, to a degree, represent a balanced assessment of the intensity of the whole withdrawal syndrome. The evaluations and measurements are usually carried out once daily, but alternatively, they can be carried out on an hourly schedule. The actual point-scoring system is given in Table 9-4.

Figure 9-19 shows one of the earliest results of applying this technique. Sixty-five addicts were studied.[93] The various curves show the course of the physiologic variables that were measured quantitatively after withdrawal of morphine. The bottom curve is the total point score computed on a daily basis, including all the items listed in Table 9-4. The peak intensity at two days is evident, followed by a slow decline over a period of more than a week. The total intensity of the withdrawal syndrome is sometimes expressed as the area under such a curve.

TABLE 9-4. Point system for scoring intensity of withdrawal syndrome

Each day (left column) or each hour (right column) the subject is examined. The presence or absence of certain signs is noted, others are measured quantitatively. Points are assigned, up to the maximum values indicated. The total intensity is the sum of all the points scored each hour or each day. (From Himmelsbach,[92] Table 1.)

Signs	By day		By hour	
	Points	Limit	Points	Limit
Yawning	1	1	1	1
Lacrimation	1	1	1	1
Rhinorrhea	1	1	1	1
Perspiration	1	1	1	1
Mydriasis	3	3	3	3
Tremor	3	3	3	3
Gooseflesh	3	3	3	3
Anorexia (40 per cent decrease in caloric intake)	3	3		
Restlessness	5	5	5	5
Emesis (each spell)	5		5	5
Fever (for each 0.1° C rise over mean addiction level)	1		1	10
Hyperpnea (for each resp./min rise over mean addiction level)	1		1	10
Rise in A.M. systolic B.P. (for each 2 mm Hg over mean addiction level)	1	15	1	10
Weight loss (A.M.) (for each lb from last day of addiction)	1			

93 L. KOLB and C. K. HIMMELSBACH: Clinical studies of drug addiction. III. A critical review of the withdrawal treatments with method of evaluating abstinence syndromes. *Amer. J. Psychiatr. 94:*759 (1938).

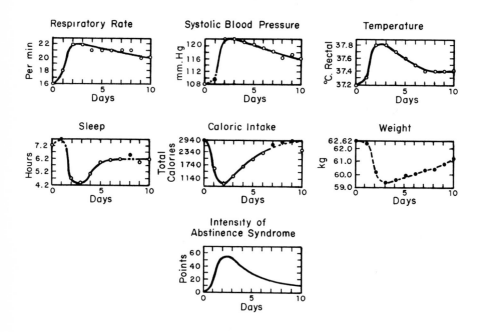

FIG. 9-19.   QUANTITATION OF THE WITHDRAWAL SYNDROME.   *Sixty-five addicts were stabilized on a dosage of 240 to 340 mg of morphine daily, then withdrawn abruptly at day zero. Careful observations and measurements were made for ten days. A representative sampling is shown in the* upper two rows. *The summation of scores (see text) for all the signs of withdrawal yielded the* curve at bottom. (*Adapted from Kolb and Himmelsbach, Fig. 1.*[93])

The method has proved extremely useful for comparing different drugs. The course of withdrawal is almost the same for morphine and heroin; but it is very different for methadone, and this has had some practical application in the clinical management of withdrawal. Figure 9-20 shows an experiment in which subjects were stabilized on methadone and then withdrawn.[94] Although methadone fully satisfied the addict's requirement while it was being administered, the subsequent withdrawal effects developed more slowly and did not reach as great an intensity as after morphine withdrawal. However, the total duration of the withdrawal period was longer with methadone. The intensity of withdrawal effects after

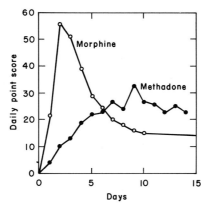

FIG. 9-20. COURSE OF WITHDRAWAL SYNDROME AFTER MORPHINE AND AFTER METHADONE. *Morphine and methadone were withdrawn (on day zero) after several months of administration. Intensity of the withdrawal syndrome was scored daily thereafter, as described in the text. Morphine data are average point scores of 65 subjects; methadone data are for five subjects. (From Isbell, Fig. 5.[94])*

morphine is nearly unbearable, and may even be life threatening, whereas the maximum intensity of the methadone withdrawal is tolerable. Therefore, the standard procedure adopted for withdrawal from morphine or heroin addiction is to substitute methadone for whatever drug was being taken, and then later to withdraw methadone.

The relationship between dosage administered during the period of addiction and the intensity of the subsequent withdrawal syndrome was studied in a large number of addicts who had been stabilized on various dosages of morphine from 40 to 400 mg daily.[95] For each group of subjects, the total score for intensity of the withdrawal syndrome was summed over seven days. Figure 9-21 gives the result. Clearly, the higher the dosage (i.e., the higher the degree of tolerance), the more intense was the subsequent withdrawal syndrome. The shape of the curve is interesting, because it suggests that a maximum degree of physical dependence is reached at dosages of about 400 mg/day. This flattening of the curve, however, may be artificially exaggerated by the fact that certain scores cannot exceed fixed maximum values (see Table 9-4).

Many attempts have been made to modify the withdrawal syndrome, especially by drug treatment of one sort or another. The only drugs that influence it are other narcotics.[96] A withdrawal syndrome can be terminated

95 H. L. ANDREWS and C. K. HIMMELSBACH: Relation of the intensity of the morphine abstinence syndrome to dosage. *J. Pharmacol. Exp. Therap. 81:*288 (1944).

96 C. K. HIMMELSBACH and H. L. ANDREWS: Studies on modification of the morphine abstinence syndrome by drugs. *J. Pharmacol. Exp. Therap. 77:*17 (1943).

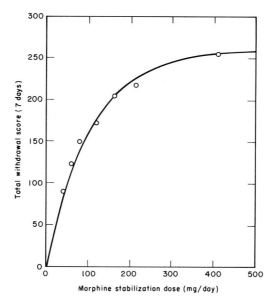

FIG. 9-21. RELATIONSHIP BETWEEN DOSAGE AND INTENSITY OF WITHDRAWAL SYNDROME. *Data for intensity of withdrawal syndrome in 127 addicts who had been stabilized on various dosages from 40 to 400 mg of morphine daily before abrupt withdrawal. Total scores for seven days of withdrawal are plotted against the stabilization dose prior to withdrawal. (Modified from Andrews and Himmelsbach, Fig. 2.[95])*

dramatically by administering the same drug that had been withdrawn, or another narcotic. Likewise, one narcotic can be substituted for another at any time during the period of physical dependence and tolerance, without precipitating signs of withdrawal. This cross-dependence is the basis not only of the methadone withdrawal procedure described earlier, but also of a newly introduced method of stabilizing addicts on an ambulatory basis while allowing them to engage in productive occupations.[97] The effectiveness of methadone by the oral route contributes to the practicality of this procedure.

Nalorphine, which blocks many primary effects of the narcotics[98] and prevents the development of tolerance[99] (cf. Fig. 5-24 for prevention of tolerance by levallorphan), is capable of evoking an immediate withdrawal syndrome if it is administered to a person (or experimental animal)

[97] V. P. DOLE and M. NYSWANDER: A medical treatment for diacetylmorphine (heroin) addiction. *J. Amer. Med. Ass. 193:*646 (1965).

[98] L. A. WOODS: The pharmacology of nalorphine (N-allylnormorphine). *Pharmacol. Rev. 8:*175 (1956).

[99] P. D. ORAHOVATS, C. A. WINTER, and E. G. LEHMAN: The effect of N-allylnormorphine upon the development of tolerance to morphine in the albino rat. *J. Pharmacol. Exp. Therap. 109:*413 (1953).

who is receiving a narcotic drug and has become physically dependent upon it. This action of nalorphine suggests very strongly that occupancy of receptors by the narcotic is associated with the state of physical dependence, and that displacement of the narcotic from the receptor sites precipitates the signs of withdrawal. Nalorphine has been used to estimate how rapidly physical dependence develops. It was found that in human subjects who had received morphine for only two to three days, and in whom no measurable withdrawal effects would have occurred on simple withdrawal of morphine, nalorphine produced a brief but authentic withdrawal syndrome.[100] This indicates, as did Fig. 9-16 for tolerance, that physical dependence is initiated very early, probably by the first dose of a narcotic drug.

The methods and findings described here have been applied to the practical problem of assessing the addiction liability of new narcotic drugs. Addicts and former addicts are used as subjects for these testing procedures, which are carried out under "blind" conditions. For example, a narcotic drug is given on a certain injection schedule, and then saline injections are substituted without the subject's knowledge. Under these conditions, the ability of a new drug to induce physical dependence can be tested by administering it for a long enough period of time and then observing the intensity of the withdrawal syndrome (if any) when the drug is stopped. An alternative test is to substitute the new drug for morphine to see if it will prevent the onset of a morphine withdrawal syndrome. Curiously, the most reliable way of finding out if a new drug is addictive is to give it to addicts under controlled "blind" conditions, and ask them if they like it! Addicts were able to identify morphine, heroin, and other narcotics, and to distinguish them from barbiturates, amphetamine, and placebos with remarkable accuracy. "If one were to select, on the basis of single doses, the most important single subjective response identifying a drug as being subject to morphine-like abuse, probably this measure would be whether the former opiate addict identifies the drug as an opiate ('dope')."[101] If a new drug met with the approval of addicts, it was concluded, that drug would probably have a very high addiction liability.

THEORIES OF TOLERANCE AND PHYSICAL DEPENDENCE

The mechanism of the development of tolerance and physical dependence is still unknown, but there has been no dearth of theoretical speculation. Inasmuch as tolerance develops to intravenous injections of

---

[100] A. WIKLER, H. F. FRASER, and H. ISBELL: N-allylnormorphine: effects of single doses and precipitation of acute "abstinence syndromes" during addiction to morphine, methadone or heroin in man (post-addicts). *J. Pharmacol. Exp. Therap. 109*:8 (1953).

[101] H. F. FRASER, G. D. VAN HORN, W. R. MARTIN, A. B. WOLBACH, and H. ISBELL: Methods for evaluating addiction liability. (A) "Attitude" of opiate addicts toward opiate-like drugs, (B) a short-term "direct" addiction test. *J. Pharmacol. Exp. Therap. 133*:371 (1961).

drugs, all explanations involving diminished absorption can be discounted. Moreover, in agreement with the earlier-cited results of experiments with alcohol and barbiturates, it has been shown by means of radioactive morphine in dogs that this drug is not excluded from the brain of the tolerant animal.[102] Dogs were made tolerant by injecting morphine at 8-hour intervals in increasing doses over a period of five weeks. The dose was stabilized at 2 mg/kg at each injection during the fifth week. Then, these dogs and others that had never received morphine were given a single subcutaneous dose of 2 mg/kg of radioactive morphine labeled in the N-methyl group. Periodically thereafter, dogs of both groups were sacrificed, and an exhaustive set of determinations was made on the tissues of various parts of the central nervous system. Plasma and cerebrospinal fluid levels were also determined. A method was used that determined only unconjugated morphine. The radioactive material after extraction was shown to be essentially all morphine (rather than any metabolite) by chromatography.

The radioactivity data obtained 35 minutes after the injection of radioactive morphine are given in Table 9-5. There were no remarkable differences in any part of the brain between nontolerant and tolerant dogs. Morphine concentrations were not actually determined; these may well have been higher in the tolerant than in the nontolerant animals because of residual morphine from previous injections, but the data refer only to the newly injected ^{14}C-morphine. It is quite clear that the administered drug was free to enter the various portions of the brain in both groups of dogs. In this same experiment, the plasma half-life of the injected morphine was the same in both groups of animals (about 1 hour). The radioactivity in cerebrospinal fluid of the tolerant dogs was somewhat higher than in the nontolerant dogs at comparable times. The plasma of tolerant animals contained less conjugated morphine than that of nontolerant animals, as would be expected from the demonstration (in rats) that liver glucuronide transferase activity decreases during the development of tolerance.[103] In summary, all the differences between tolerant and nontolerant animals seemed to be inconsequential and certainly not of sufficient magnitude to explain the tolerance. Similar results have been obtained in rats.[104] Thus, when tolerant animals are receiving large doses of a narcotic drug, the drug concentrations in their brains are very high. It follows that for narcotics, as for alcohol and barbiturates, the mechanism of tolerance has to be sought within the brain.

[102] S. J. MULÉ and L. A. WOODS: Distribution of N-C14-methyl labeled morphine. I. In central nervous system of nontolerant and tolerant dogs. *J. Pharmacol. Exp. Therap.* *136:*232 (1962).

[103] A. E. TAKEMORI: Enzymic studies on morphine glucuronide synthesis in acutely and chronically morphinized rats. *J. Pharmacol. Exp. Therap. 130:*370 (1960).

[104] T. JOHANNESSON and L. A. WOODS: Analgesic action and brain and plasma levels of morphine and codeine in morphine tolerant, codeine tolerant and non-tolerant rats. *Acta Pharmacol. Toxicol. 21:*381 (1964).

TABLE 9-5. **Distribution of radioactive morphine in the central nervous system of nontolerant and tolerant dogs**

Dogs were made tolerant to morphine by injections every 8 hours for five weeks, starting at 0.5 mg/kg and stabilizing at 2 mg/kg during the fifth week. N–^{14}C–Methyl-labeled morphine was given as a single subcutaneous injection (2 mg/kg) to these tolerant dogs and to non-tolerant controls. The distribution of radioactivity in brain 35 minutes later is shown here. Figures represent radioactive morphine, in μg/kg of tissue; nonradioactive morphine, present in the tissues prior to the injection, is not seen here. Figures are averages of two nontolerant and two tolerant animals. (From Mulé and Woods,[102] Tables 1 and 2.)

Region of brain		Radioactive morphine (μg/kg of tissue)	
		Nontolerant dogs	Tolerant dogs
Pyriform area (amygdala)		156	141
Olfactory tracts		122	113
Olfactory bulbs		184	204
Dorsal thalamus		147	137
Hypothalamus		138	123
Optic tr., N., chiasma		92	86
Pons		129	119
Midbrain		156	146
Cerebral peduncle		84	98
Fornix		149	146
Corpus callosum		99	109
Medulla		135	110
Trapezoid body		133	110
Caudate nucleus		169	162
Region of cerebrum or cerebellum			
Temporal	gray	209	177
	white	101	88
Prefrontal	gray	193	170
	white	110	92
Sensorimotor	gray	210	185
	white	110	71
Occipital	gray	247	200
	white	122	85
Parietal	gray	214	180
	white	102	91
Temporal conjugate	gray	—	0
	white	—	0
Cerebellar hemispheres	gray	194	181
	white	104	109
Vermis of cerebellum	gray	199	165
	white	124	114

TABLE 9-6.   **Tolerance and N-dealkylation in the rat**

Narcotic drugs or saline injections were administered intraperitoneally to rats for 14 days, in the following doses: morphine, 20 mg/kg twice daily initially and increased to 140 mg/kg twice daily; nalorphine alone, same schedule as morphine; nalorphine with morphine, dose ratio 1:2 (maximum morphine dose 280 mg/kg twice daily); normorphine, same as morphine, but maximum dose 75 mg/kg twice daily because of toxicity. Analgesia was determined by a hot-plate method; data show total area under the time-effect curve. For N-dealkylation by liver preparations, 10µmoles of substrate were used, and incubation time was 2 hours. All differences from the control were significant ($P<0.01$) unless otherwise indicated. (From Cochin and Axelrod,[105] Table 2.)

Group	Analgesic response to 20 mg/kg morphine sulfate (*min·sec*)	N-Demethylation of morphine sulfate (HCHO/g tissue) (*µmole*)	N-Deallylation of nalorphine HCl (normorphine/g tissue) (*µmole*)
Control	1,292.5	1.63	4.84
Morphine	99.3 (7.7%)	0.24 (14.7%)	2.15 (44.4%)
Morphine plus nalorphine	140.3 (10.9%)	0.43 (26.4%)	2.64 (54.5%)
Nalorphine	383.8 (29.7%)	0.68 (41.7%)	3.40 (70.3%)[b]
Normorphine	280.4 (21.7%)	0.70 (42.9%)[a]	3.73 (77.1%)[b]

[a] $P<0.05$.
[b] Not significant.

It has been demonstrated that the ability of rat liver microsomes to carry out N-dealkylation reactions with morphine and its congeners as substrates diminishes during morphine tolerance.[105] Typical data are shown in Table 9-6. Groups of rats were tested for their analgesic responses to a standard 20-mg/kg dose of morphine sulfate, using a hot-plate method. The whole time-action curve of the analgesic effect was integrated to obtain a measure of total analgesia produced by the drug, as described on p. 598. For the control group, after 14 days of saline injections this analgesic response was 1,292 min·sec. Rats that had received morphine on an increasing dosage schedule for the 14-day period were almost completely tolerant to the standard dose (7.7 per cent of control analgesia). In this experiment, nalorphine produced tolerance when administered alone and failed to prevent the development of tolerance when given with morphine.[106] Normorphine also induced tolerance to the test dose of morphine. The second

105 J. COCHIN and J. AXELROD: Biochemical and pharmacological changes in the rat following chronic administration of morphine, nalorphine and normorphine. *J. Pharmacol. Exp. Therap.* 125:105 (1959).
106 As noted earlier, nalorphine can block the development of tolerance to morphine. This blocking effect, however, like the antagonism of morphine analgesia, depends critically upon the nalorphine:morphine dose ratio, and probably differs for different species.

column of the table shows the loss of ability of rat liver from tolerant rats to catalyze removal of the N-methyl group from morphine. There was also a decrease, of smaller magnitude, in the N-deallylation of nalorphine. These findings suggested the possibility that the N-dealkylating system of liver might have its counterpart in brain. For example, the N-demethylation of morphine might be an essential step in its action; either the N-demethylating enzyme would itself be the morphine receptor, or the receptor would combine with the normorphine formed by the N-demethylation of morphine.[107] The latter hypothesis gains some support from the fact that normorphine is even more active than morphine when administered intracisternally, whereby it comes into direct contact with the brain tissue, whereas it may pass with more difficulty than morphine across the blood-brain barrier. However, no direct studies of the N-demethylation process in brain have been reported. According to this theory, tolerance would be accounted for by a decrease in N-demethylating capacity in brain tissue; but physical dependence would not be explained.

The phenomenon of tolerance has some features in common with immune processes. Successive challenges produce diminishing effects, as though something were synthesized in the body that antagonizes the drug action or combines directly with the drug and inactivates it. The time course of tolerance development (several days) could be consistent with the time required for synthesis of antibodies. Early claims that the serum of morphine-tolerant animals conferred protection against the lethal effects of morphine in normal animals[108] have been refuted.[109,110] However, recent studies have revived this theory, or proposed an alternative form that postulates the induction by narcotics of the synthesis of "silent receptors," i.e., macromolecules that interact with drug but do not produce any biologic effect.[111] It was noted earlier (p. 597) that some degree of tolerance, lasting as long as a year, resulted from a single injection of morphine in rats.[89] Although other explanations are not excluded, long-lasting tolerance could obviously be accounted for by some sort of immune process. A recent investigation produced evidence that a small peptide or protein, extracted from the brains of morphine-tolerant rats or dogs, could confer tolerance

107 A. H. BECKETT, A. F. CASY, and N. J. HARPER: Analgesics and their antagonists: some steric and chemical considerations. Part III. The influence of the basic group on the biological response. *J. Pharm. Pharmacol. 8:*874 (1956).

108 C. GIOFFREDI: L'immunizzazione per gli alcaloidi vegetali tentativi di sieroterapia negli avvelenamenti ricerche sperimentali. *Giorn. Int. Sci. Med. 19:*829 (1897).

109 E. J. PELLINI and A. D. GREENFIELD: Narcotic drug addiction. II. The presence of toxic substances in the blood serum in morphin habituation. *Arch. Int. Med. 33:*547 (1924).

110 A. G. DU MEZ and L. KOLB: Absence of transferable immunizing substances in the blood of morphine and heroin addicts. *Public Health Rep. 40:*548 (1925).

111 H. O. J. COLLIER: A general theory of the genesis of drug dependence by induction of receptors. *Nature 205:*181 (1965).

to the analgesic effect of morphine when it was injected into mice.[112] More conclusive evidence of tolerance conferred in this remarkable way would be protection against other effects of morphine, especially lethal effects; but such protection has not been reported. Finally, actinomycin D was found to block the development of tolerance to morphine in mice and rats, as measured by a standardized tail pressure test.[113] As has been noted, however, that the use of analgesia as a criterion for tolerance presents certain difficulties. The normal rat displays a spinal reflex or makes a coordinated withdrawal response from a noxious stimulus. Morphine abolishes this behavior; and as tolerance develops, the behavior returns. To say that a drug like actinomycin D blocks the tolerance means, in the framework of the experiment, that the animals did not display the behavior. Any agent that made them incapable of responding to the noxious stimulus in the presence of the drug, for whatever reason, would be interpreted as "blocking the development of tolerance." Caution is especially warranted in view of the generalized toxicity of actinomycin D in doses capable of blocking RNA synthesis in vivo.

It has been known for many years that morphine stimulates the adrenal medulla to secrete catecholamines. Interest in a possible role of catecholamines in morphine tolerance probably derives from the finding that tachyphylaxis to sympathomimetic amines is related to the tissue stores of releasable norepinephrine (p. 565). Clearly, morphine cannot simply be depleting the brain of catecholamines; reserpine does this, but it is not a narcotic analgesic. It is true, however, that catecholamines and their metabolites in urine are increased during morphine administration in both animals[114] and man.[115] The animal studies reported a further marked elevation during withdrawal, but in man there was a fall to control levels when morphine was withdrawn. It is certainly possible to imagine that analgesic and other effects of morphine are mediated by catecholamine release at specific loci in the brain. It has been reported that reserpine can abolish the analgesic effects of morphine under certain circumstances,[116,117] and that catecholamines can restore at least one morphine effect (lenticular

112 G. UNGAR and M. COHEN: Induction of morphine tolerance by material extracted from brain of tolerant animals. *Int. J. Neuropharmacol. 5:*183 (1966).

113 M. COHEN, A. S. KEATS, W. KRIVOY, and G. UNGAR: Effect of actinomycin D on morphine tolerance. *Proc. Soc. Exp. Biol. Med. 119:*381 (1965).

114 L.-M. GUNNE: Catecholamines and 5-hydroxytryptamine in morphine tolerance and withdrawal. *Acta Physiol. Scand. 58,* Suppl. 204:5 (1963).

115 H. WEIL-MALHERBE, E. R. B. SMITH, A. J. EISENMAN, and H. F. FRASER: Plasma catecholamine levels and urinary excretion of catecholamines and metabolites in two human subjects during a cycle of morphine addiction and withdrawal. *Biochem. Pharmacol. 14:*1621 (1965).

116 J. A. SCHNEIDER: Reserpine antagonism of morphine analgesia in mice. *Proc. Soc. Exp. Biol. Med. 87:*614 (1954).

117 M. MEDAKOVIĆ and B. BANIĆ: The action of reserpine and a-methyl-*m*-tyrosine on the analgesic effect of morphine in rats and mice. *J. Pharm. Pharmacol. 16:*198 (1964).

opacity in mice) after its abolition by reserpine.[118] On the other hand, it seems equally possible that sympathetic discharge accompanies the primary morphine actions as their consequence rather than their cause. Certainly no direct evidence has related the catecholamines in a causal chain to the biologic effects of the narcotics.

By analogy to the phenomenon of denervation hypersensitivity, a "disuse" hypothesis of narcotic tolerance has been advanced.[74] It is known that after denervation of sympathetically innervated effectors in the peripheral autonomic system, these effectors become hypersensitive to norepinephrine. The principal cause of this hypersensitivity is the loss of the uptake and storage capacity for norepinephrine that is ordinarily associated with adrenergic nerve endings, and which plays an important role in terminating the actions of norepinephrine. It is postulated that a long period of depression of the brain by narcotics, barbiturates, or alcohol causes a kind of functional denervation of central pathways, which sensitizes them so that they over-react when the drug is withdrawn. This theory, unsupported by any concrete evidence, is more descriptive than explanatory; moreover, it substitutes another unknown (the postulated central hypersensitivity) for the one it seeks to explain.

Assuming a centrally acting drug acted by increasing neurotransmitter levels at certain synapses, then tolerance to the drug would develop if the brain became tolerant to high levels of the neurotransmitter. It is interesting to note, therefore, that rats can become tolerant to abnormally high levels of acetylcholine in the brain caused by prolonged exposure to a cholinesterase inhibitor.[119] The inhibitor, an organic phosphate compound (Di-Syston), was injected at about one-half the LD50. It produced tremors, convulsions, and a variety of severe parasympathomimetic effects. When the same dose was repeated daily for 60 days, the effects diminished greatly; the animals, which had lost weight, began gaining again and the convulsions, tremors, and autonomic disturbances all but disappeared. Acetylcholinesterase and free acetylcholine levels in the rat brains were investigated, with the result shown in Fig. 9-22. The 24-hour course of enzyme inhibition and the consequent marked increase in acetylcholine following injection of the inhibitor were almost the same on the 60th day of Di-Syston injection as on the third day; if there was any real difference at all, the acetylcholine level was slightly higher on the 60th day, when the effects were minimal. Apparently, therefore, the brains of the tolerant animals had become refractory to high concentrations of acetylcholine. This was confirmed by measuring the LD50 of carbachol, an acetylcholine

118 A. A. SMITH, M. KARMIN, and J. A. GAVITT: Interaction of catecholamines with levorphanol and morphine in the mouse eye. *J. Pharmacol. Exp. Therap. 151:*103 (1966).

119 J. BRODEUR and K. P. DUBOIS: Studies on the mechanism of acquired tolerance by rats to O,O-diethyl S-2-(ethylthio)ethyl phosphorodithioate (Di-Syston). *Arch. Int. Pharmacodyn. 149:*560 (1964).

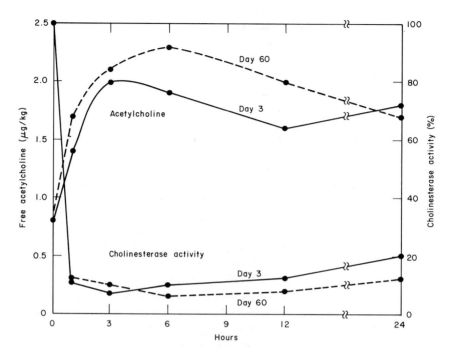

FIG. 9-22.   TOLERANCE OF RAT BRAIN TO A CHOLINESTERASE INHIBITOR.   *Female rats were given injections of the cholinesterase inhibitor Di-Syston (1.2 mg/kg) daily for 60 days. On the third and 60th days, mice were sacrificed periodically, and the brain cholinesterase activity (expressed here as per cent of normal) and free acetylcholine content were determined. (Data of Brodeur and Dubois, Table 1.[119])*

congener that is neither a substrate nor an inhibitor of acetylcholinesterase. The LD50 in the nontolerant rats was 2.0 mg/kg (95 per cent confidence limits 1.5 to 2.7); in the tolerant rats it had nearly doubled, to 3.9 mg/kg (2.9 to 5.2).

It is of interest, in view of speculations relating narcotic action to neurotransmitter release, that acute tolerance can be produced to some effects of morphine. Three decades ago[120,121] it was shown that dogs became tolerant to the peripheral vasodilation caused by morphine. Small doses repeated for many weeks led to but little tolerance, but large doses caused tolerance rapidly. The vascular bed of a denervated leg in the tolerant animal was shown to be tolerant to morphine infusions. It is now

120 C. F. SCHMIDT and A. E. LIVINGSTON: The action of morphine on the mammalian circulation. *J. Pharmacol. Exp. Therap. 47:*411 (1933).
121 C. F. SCHMIDT and A. E. LIVINGSTON: The relation of dosage to the development of tolerance to morphine in dogs. *J. Pharmacol. Exp. Therap. 47:*443 (1933).

known, however, that morphine is a histamine releaser, and that a large part of the acute vascular tolerance to morphine is really tolerance to histamine release or to histamine itself.[122] Very likely, therefore, the phenomenon is unrelated to narcotic tolerance in the brain.

Acute tolerance to morphine that may be more relevant is that of the isolated, electrically stimulated guinea pig ileum.[123] The tissue was suspended in an organ bath and stimulated coaxially (i.e., by electrodes placed inside and outside the lumen) with shocks of sufficient strength to elicit maximum contractions, which were recorded on a kymograph. These contractions could be blocked by atropine or potentiated by neostigmine; they were evidently due to electrical stimulation of postganglionic cholinergic nerves in the gut wall, causing release of acetylcholine. Morphine depressed the amplitude of the contractions. In the presence of morphine, the ileum retained its normal sensitivity to exogenously added acetylcholine. It appeared, therefore, that the primary effect of morphine was to diminish the output of acetylcholine caused by the electrical stimulation; and direct assay of released acetylcholine confirmed this. When the tissue was left in contact with morphine, or fresh morphine solutions were added, the effects of the drug soon wore off, and even high concentrations were then without effect. In this tolerant state, the contractions were normal in the presence of morphine; but when morphine was now washed out, the contraction amplitude decreased. The contractility in response to electrical stimulation could be restored by morphine, as though some sort of physical dependence had developed. Neither tolerance nor dependence could be produced with atropine, an unrelated drug that also depresses contraction amplitude; but all the morphine congeners tested had the same effects as morphine itself. Nalorphine, in this system, had morphine-like rather than antagonistic actions, but other investigators later showed that at appropriate dose ratios antagonism by nalorphine was demonstrable.[124]

Some evidence has been obtained that morphine may block acetylcholine release in brain as well as in ileum. An initial dose of morphine in naive mice caused an increase in the acetylcholine content of brain, but this increase did not occur in animals that had been made tolerant to morphine.[124a]

122 J. E. ECKENHOFF and S. R. OECH: The effects of narcotics and antagonists upon respiration and circulation in man. A review. *Clin. Pharmacol. Therap. 1:*483 (1960).

123 W. D. M. PATON: The action of morphine and related substances on contraction and on acetylcholine output of coaxially stimulated guinea-pig ileum. *Brit. J. Pharmacol. 12:*119 (1957).

124 B. M. COX and M. WEINSTOCK: The effect of analgesic drugs on the release of acetylcholine from electrically stimulated guinea-pig ileum. *Brit. J. Pharmacol. 27:*81 (1966).

124a K. HANO, H. KANETO, T. KAKUNAGA, and N. MORIBAYASHI: Pharmacological studies of analgesics. VI. The administration of morphine and changes in acetylcholine metabolism in mouse brain. *Biochem. Pharmacol. 13:*441 (1964).

The outstanding (but still rather mysterious) example of a biochemical effect in brain that is related both to morphine action and to
morphine tolerance is inhibition of potassium-stimulated oxygen uptake.[125-127] When slices of rat brain cortex are incubated in a manometric
apparatus for measuring oxygen uptake, the respiration is found to be
increased about 80 per cent in 5mM KCl, compared with the rate in a
low-potassium medium. Morphine at a concentration of 1mM was found
to inhibit this stimulated oxygen uptake almost completely. Rats were
given morphine daily to produce tolerance, and control animals were given
saline injections instead. Groups of animals were sacrificed daily, and in
vitro measurements of oxygen uptake were carried out in the presence and
absence of morphine. The results are shown in Fig. 9-23. As tolerance
developed, the inhibitory effect of morphine was lost. After the injections
were stopped, on the seventh day, the sensitivity to inhibition by morphine

FIG. 9-23.   COURSE OF CELLULAR ADAPTATION TO A MORPHINE EFFECT IN RAT
CORTEX SLICES.   *The rate of oxygen utilization of cortex slices (with glucose as
substrate) was measured in the presence of 5mM KCl. (In the absence of KCl,
the rate is about 54 per cent of the KCl-stimulated rate.) Rats were given
morphine (15 mg/kg) intraperitoneally twice daily; controls were given saline
injections on the same schedule. Groups of five to six rats were killed each day
and the effect of morphine in vitro (10⁻³M)* on the KCl-stimulated oxygen uptake was measured. On the seventh day* (arrow), *morphine injections were
stopped and the course of recovery followed thereafter. Mean values ± standard
errors are shown. (From Takemori, Fig. 1.[126])*

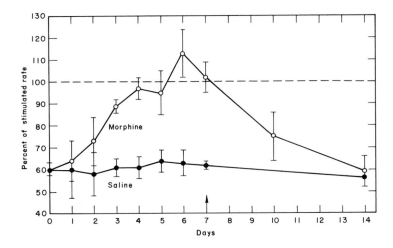

125 A. E. TAKEMORI: The influence of morphine on glucose utilization in cerebral
preparations of rats. *J. Pharmacol. Exp. Therap. 145*:20 (1964).
        126 A. E. TAKEMORI: Studies on cellular adaptation to morphine and its reversal by
nalorphine in cerebral cortical slices of rats. *J. Pharmacol. Exp. Therap. 135*:89 (1962).
        127 A. E. TAKEMORI: Cross-cellular adaptation to methadone and meperidine in
cerebral cortical slices from morphinized rats. *J. Pharmacol. Exp. Therap. 135*:252 (1962).

gradually returned. Moreover, when nalorphine was injected into the tolerant rats, and these animals were killed 30 minutes later, the tolerance to morphine inhibition in vitro had entirely disappeared. Within a certain range of molar ratios of nalorphine to morphine (1:4 to 1:10), the morphine inhibition of respiration in cortex slices from nontolerant rats could also be antagonized in vitro. Unfortunately, the basis of these effects and their exact relationship to the mechanisms of narcotic tolerance and physical dependence remain obscure.

Some theories invoke unspecified homeostatic adjustments to account for both tolerance and physical dependence. The primary drug effect allegedly is compensated for by the activation of pathways that produce opposite effects.[128,129] The abrupt withdrawal of the narcotic unmasks the full force of the compensatory mechanism, opposite in effect to that of the narcotic. The resulting withdrawal syndrome dies away as the compensatory mechanisms, no longer needed, wane.

Homeostasis at the biochemical level is invoked in a "derepression theory," which seeks to explain both tolerance and physical dependence in a unitary hypothesis based on well-known regulatory mechanisms.[130,131] The sole action of the narcotic is assumed to be the inhibition of an enzyme that catalyzes a reaction essential to neuronal function or synaptic transmission. Consider the following diagrammatic representation of a pathway leading to the biosynthesis of a substance C. Suppose that C, in a particular region of the brain, has an excitatory effect.

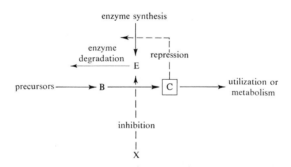

We have only to assume that the steady-state level of C is subject to autoregulation by the well-known mechanism of depressing the synthesis

[128] C. K. HIMMELSBACH: Symposium: can the euphoric, analgetic and physical dependence effects of drugs be separated? IV. With reference to physical dependence. *Fed. Proc. 2:*201 (1943).

[129] W. R. MARTIN and A. J. EISENMAN: Interactions between nalorphine and morphine in the decerebrate cat. *J. Pharmacol. Exp. Therap. 138:*113 (1962).

[130] L. SHUSTER: Repression and de-repression of enzyme synthesis as a possible explanation of some aspects of drug action. *Nature 189:*314 (1961).

[131] D. B. GOLDSTEIN and A. GOLDSTEIN: Possible role of enzyme inhibition and repression in drug tolerance and addiction. *Biochem. Pharmacol. 8:*48 (1961).

of the enzyme E which catalyzes its formation. The steady-state level of E is determined by its rates of synthesis and degradation, according to the plateau principle (chapter 4).

Now the model predicts two kinds of result, with different time courses. The inhibition of E by the drug X will cause an *immediate* decline in the concentration or availability of C; and if C was mediating an excitatory function, the effect will be depressant on that function. The decrease in C will increase the synthesis of E, and the enzyme level will rise. This will be a *delayed* effect, with time course of hours or days commensurate with the rate of protein turnover. The increased level of E will now produce C from B at the normal rate despite its partial inhibition by X, and the concentration of X will have to be raised in order to reduce the concentration of C again in the face of the higher enzyme level. Thus, tolerance will develop. When a high degree of tolerance has been produced, the following situation will obtain. The level of total enzyme and the drug concentration are both very high. Most of the enzyme is inhibited. The level of free enzyme is about what it was normally, and therefore the availability of C is normal, and neuronal function is normal in the presence of drug.

Withdrawal of drug will cause two effects. The *immediate* effect, as soon as the drug concentration declines sufficiently, is to disinhibit the large excess of enzyme that is present. A great overproduction of C results, with effects (in this instance excitatory) opposite to those of the primary drug effect. This is the withdrawal syndrome. The *delayed* effect, requiring days, will be a restoration of the original state of affairs. The excess of C depresses the new synthesis of E; and as the level of E declines, the concentration of C also falls. Thus, physical dependence and tolerance develop together and disappear together. The most attractive feature of this theory is its consonance with modern biochemical concepts and its ability to explain both tolerance and physical dependence in a unitary manner, without special ad hoc assumptions. A model system has been described, using a barbiturate in bacteria, which displays some features of the expected behavior.[132]

An even simpler form of this theory[133] requires no end-product repression of the enzyme. It is assumed that the enzyme is undergoing continual synthesis and degradation, and that the inhibitory interaction of drug with enzyme stabilizes the enzyme. As a consequence, the total amount of enzyme would increase, with half-time equal to the half-life of the enzyme (cf. chapter 4), and tolerance would develop as above. No change in the rate of enzyme synthesis would be required.

A rather similar theory advanced recently[111] also postulates that the drug inhibits synthesis or release of an essential endogenous substance, C,

132 D. B. GOLDSTEIN: Effects of barbital on amino acid metabolism in *Escherichia coli. Mol. Pharmacol. 1*:31 (1965).

133 A. GOLDSTEIN and D. B. GOLDSTEIN: Enzyme expansion theory of drug tolerance and physical dependence. *Res. Publ. Ass. Res. Nerv. Ment. Dis.,* in press, 1967.

in the brain. However, instead of attributing tolerance to an adaptive increase in the enzyme upon which the drug acts, the theory proposes that more receptors become available for combination with C. Because a greater total number of receptors are present, the number combined with C can be maintained at a normal level. Thus, despite continued depression of C levels by the drug, biologic function remains normal. When the drug is withdrawn, however, there will be a large increase in the amount of C, and because of the now excessive number of receptors, abnormal effects (i.e., withdrawal syndrome) will occur. Eventually the number of receptors will return to normal. Unfortunately, although both the derepression theory and this "receptor induction" theory have a certain plausibility, no experimental tests of their validity seem likely until some biochemical mechanism of tolerance and physical dependence can be clearly identified.

10

CHEMICAL MUTAGENESIS

If a drug produces permanent heritable change in a germ cell, the outcome will be an altered hereditary constitution (genotype) of the individual who will be the product of the union of that germ cell with another. A persisting change is thus introduced into the germ line of the species, unless the alteration is incompatible with survival. Permanent changes in the genotype (*mutations*) are produced by radiation and by chemical agents (*mutagens*). Mutations also occur spontaneously by unknown mechanisms. In the strict sense of the word, a mutation is a very sharply localized change in the genetic material (also called "point mutation"), as distinguished from deletions and other alterations of chromosome structure or number. In this discussion of chemical mutagenesis, we shall adopt the original broader meaning and consider all chemically induced modifications of the genotype.[1-7a]

INTRODUCTION

The sum total of the genetic information that specifies the structure, function, and development of each individual of a species is encoded in the DNA.[8] The zygote of sexually reproducing organisms contains two copies of this information, one derived from the sperm, the other from the ovum. All the information contained in all the genes is in the form of a

    1 A. M. SRB, R. D. OWEN, and R. S. EDGAR: *General Genetics,* 2nd ed. San Francisco, W. H. Freeman, 1965.
    2 C. STERN: *Principles of Human Genetics,* 2nd ed. San Francisco, W. H. Freeman, 1960.
    3 Symposium on molecular action of mutagenic and carcinogenic agents. *J. Cell. Comp. Physiol. 64:* suppl. 1, October 1964, pp. 1–186.
    4 J. H. TAYLOR, ed.: *Selected Papers on Molecular Genetics.* New York, Academic Press, 1965.
    5 J. H. TAYLOR, ed.: *Molecular Genetics, Part I.* New York, Academic Press, 1963.
    6 A. PULLMAN: "Molecular aspects of mutations," in *International Symposium on the Electronic Aspects of Biochemistry,* ed. by B. Pullman. New York, Academic Press, 1964, pp. 135–152.

linear code of three-letter words, the letters of which are the four nucleotide bases, adenine (A), guanine (G), cytosine (C), and thymine (T). Thus the "word" CGG specifies one piece of information, CAG another, and so forth. The mechanism whereby such information is translated into amino acid residues of proteins was discussed in chapter 8. Now we are concerned with the orderly replication of the genetic information and its passage from one generation to the next. The orderly replication of the genetic information is ensured by the mechanism of base-pairing by hydrogen bond formation in the double-stranded DNA helix. Since a given base on one strand uniquely specifies its partner on the complementary strand, the letters of the coding alphabet are really the four possible base pairs, A:T, T:A, G:C, and C:G. The obligatory pairing of purine against pyrimidine is ensured by the distance between the phosphate-deoxyribose backbones of the two helices; pyrimidine against pyrimidine would leave a gap between, and purine against purine would not fit the available space. The hydrogen bonding relationships are optimal for the matching of adenine to thymine and guanine to cytosine (Fig. 1-13). The process whereby the double helix unwinds during replication, each strand acting as template for the synthesis of a new complementary strand—the semiconservative replication mechanism—guarantees that all of the genetic information will be partitioned equally to daughter cells at every cell division and thus be transmitted accurately from generation to generation.

The following kinds of mutation are recognized:

1. *Base pair transformation.* A given base pair may be replaced in any of three ways. In one of these, the original purine is replaced by another purine, and the original pyrimidine by another pyrimidine; this kind of change is called a *transition*. In the other two possible changes, a purine is replaced by a pyrimidine or a pyrimidine by a purine; this is called a *transversion*.[9]

2. *Addition or deletion* of a base pair. This kind of change is known as a *frame shift mutation* because the ordered translation of the codons, triplet by triplet, will be profoundly disturbed. All the bases distal to the point of insertion or deletion will be out of register. As can be imagined, the consequences are usually much more drastic than those of a single base pair transformation.

3. *Large deletions and rearrangements.* Deletions of the genetic material occur in all sizes. The basic mutational process appears to be

[7] B. PULLMAN: "Aspects of the Electronic Structure of the Nucleic Acids in Relation to the Theories of Mutagenesis and Carcinogenesis," in *Biopolymers, Symposia No. 1,* 1964, pp. 141–159.

[7a] R. M. HERRIOTT: Mutagenesis. *Cancer Res. 26:*1971 (1966).

[8] J. D. WATSON: *Molecular Biology of the Gene.* New York, W. A. Benjamin, 1965.

[9] E. FREESE: The difference between spontaneous and base-analogue induced mutations of phage T4. *Proc. Nat. Acad. Sci. U.S.A. 45:*622 (1959).

breakage followed by *reconstitution* of fragments. This occurs in single DNA molecules and also at the gross level of the chromosomes. Segments may be inverted, exchanges may occur between chromatids (the paired subunits of the chromosome), and material may be translocated from one chromosome to another.

4. *Unequal partition of chromosomes* between daughter cells. This is known as *nondisjunction*. It may occur at meiosis or mitosis, and is frequently caused by chemical agents that disturb the orderly formation and function of the system of spindle fibers.

A fundamental distinction has to be made between two modes of action of mutagens. Agents of one class act directly upon the existing genetic material and therefore can be effective at any time in the cell cycle. Agents of the second class are only able to modify the course of a dynamic process such as DNA replication or chromosome movement; such mutagens may be effective only at a particular time in the cell cycle.

A type of chemical mutagenesis that does not fall readily into either of the above categories is that due to the incorporation of radioactivity into DNA. Here, the radioactive molecules must be present during DNA replication although the mutational events occur at some subsequent time, when radioactive disintegrations occur at sensitive sites. The mutations may occur in three ways. (*1*) The energy of a distintegration may rupture an internucleotide bond by a recoil effect. (*2*) Localized β or γ emission may be mutagenic by virtue of secondary bombardment of nearby purine or pyrimidine bases. (*3*) Transmutation of a radioactive atom may lead to altered chemical properties of a kind that can affect the fidelity of subsequent replications. It is well known that ^{32}P incorporated into DNA of bacteria and viruses causes both lethality and point mutations, probably by the first two mechanisms. The exact consequence of the transmutation itself ($^{32}P \rightarrow ^{32}S$) is not clearly understood. Both ^3H and ^{14}C are thought to be especially hazardous because they can be incorporated so readily into the nucleic acid bases and deoxyribose, and thus into DNA. The special hazard of ^3H is that it is so difficult to monitor routinely; its decay energy is so low and the mean path length of its β particles so short that Geiger counters are ineffective for detecting contamination. The special hazard of ^{14}C, which is present in fallout debris from nuclear bombs, is its exceedingly long radioactive half-life (more than 5,000 years); incorporation resulting in mutational effects in the human germ line could occur over a period of many millennia.[10]

The fidelity of the normal DNA replication process is remarkable. Spontaneous mutations, which are errors in this process, are rarely observed at a frequency greater than one per 10^5 replications. An interesting

[10] L. PAULING: Genetic and somatic effects of carbon-14. *Science 128:*1183 (1958).

experiment[11] demonstrated a similarly high degree of fidelity in vitro. The alternating copolymer of deoxyadenylic acid and thymidylic acid (dAT copolymer), in which each single strand has the base sequence . . . ATATAT . . . , was allowed to act as primer for the synthesis of new DNA catalyzed by DNA polymerase in the presence of all four deoxyribonucleoside triphosphates. Since every A specifies a complementary T, and vice versa, no G or C whatsoever should be incorporated; and the newly synthesized material should also have a strictly alternating . . . TATATA . . . sequence. Both of these expectations were confirmed. Less than one residue of G per 28,000 A and T residues was found.

The molecular basis of this fidelity of replication is far from clear. Certainly the simple difference in bond energies between "correct" (A:T, G:C) and "incorrect" (A:C, G:T) purine-pyrimidine pairs could not alone account for it. Presumably, some additional mechanisms stabilize the proper base pairs and somehow exclude or reject the wrong ones. An example of such a recognition mechanism is the recently discovered system for enzymic repair of DNA.[12, 12a] The repair enzymes excise segments containing erroneous bases (e.g., thymine dimers formed by ultraviolet irradiation) in one strand of the DNA, and permit their replacement by the alignment and linking of correct bases properly paired against those of the other (normal) strand. Thus defective regions of either strand are "patched." The existence of repair mechanisms greatly complicates the interpretation of data on mutagenesis, since the mutations we eventually see may be only a small fraction of those originally produced, the remainder having been repaired.

The sequence of base pairs in the DNA determines the corresponding sequence of bases in RNA. Only one strand of the DNA (the "sense" strand) is transcribed, serving as template for the synthesis of single-stranded RNA. The same base pairing mechanism operates as in replication, except that RNA contains uracil (U) instead of thymine, so that we have the base pair A:U instead of A:T. A small fraction of the total DNA specifies the structures of the two classes of ribosomal RNA and the modest number (64 or fewer) of transfer-RNA (tRNA) molecules. Most of the rest of the genome encodes the information for the sequence of amino acids in all the cell proteins. This information is first transcribed into messenger-RNA (mRNA), which serves as template for the assembly of proteins, as described in chapter 8 (p. 545 and Fig. 8-17).

[11] T. A. TRAUTNER, M. N. SWARTZ, and A. KORNBERG: Enzymatic synthesis of deoxyribonucleic acid, X. Influence of bromouracil substitutions on replication. *Proc. Nat. Acad. Sci. U.S.A. 48:*449 (1962).

[12] R. B. SETLOW: Physical changes and mutagenesis. *J. Cell. Comp. Physiol. 64:* suppl. 1, 51 (1964).

[12a] E. M. WITKIN: Radiation-induced mutations and their repair. *Science 152:*1345 (1966).

The fidelity of replication and transcription underlies the persistence of mutations, for any change that cannot be recognized as incorrect will remain encoded permanently in the genome. It is important to understand what is meant here by "incorrect." By the very nature of the genetic code, any one of the four normal base pairs is correct. Suppose, for example, that a particular sequence of 450 base pairs specifies a corresponding sequence of 150 amino acids in an enzyme. If one of these base pairs is changed to any of the three other normal pairs, the codon containing the new base pair may specify a different amino acid. Likewise, if one or more normal base pairs are added or deleted, or if a portion of the sequence is rearranged, the mutant DNA will be replicated in the usual way, and it will be perpetuated, as long as its protein (or RNA) products are compatible with survival. Indeed, this principle underlies all of evolution, for unless mutant DNA could function normally in replication and transcription, natural selection could not act upon the resulting phenotypes. It is only at a certain stage in the genesis of a mutation that an intrinsically abnormal base pair may be present. For instance, if an erroneous base pairing occurs during replication, so that A on an existing strand pairs with C (instead of T) on the new complementary strand, there will be a transient abnormal pair A:C. This may be recognized and repaired, by excision of a segment of the new strand that includes C and its restitution by a new segment. If there is no repair, normal base pairing will occur at the next replication, in both daughter duplexes, and one of these will become a permanent mutant. The reason is simply that by the usual rules of base pairing, A will pair with T, thus reconstituting the original base pair; but C will pair with G, yielding a G:C pair instead of the original A:T at this site.

Much of the fundamental work that led to our present understanding of the molecular basis of mutagenesis was done with mutants of bacteriophage T4 of *Escherichia coli,* known as rII mutants.[13,14] These are characterized by an abnormal plaque morphology (large plaques with very sharp edges, caused by unusually rapid lysis) and by their inability to grow on bacterial strain K, although they grow well on strain B. Thus, mutants are readily recognized by eye from among thousands of wild-type plaques; and wild-type revertants are efficiently selected by growth on bacteria of strain K. The rII mutants arise by a genetic change occurring anywhere within a particular region of the phage genome, designated the rII gene. But the gene product, a change in which accounts for the mutant morphology and functional abnormality on strain K, has not yet been identified.

The exact location of a given mutation within the gene can be established by the method of recombination. Phage recombination results

[13] S. BENZER: On the topography of the genetic fine structure. *Proc. Nat. Acad. Sci. U.S.A. 47:*403 (1961).

[14] S. BENZER: On the topology of the genetic fine structure. *Proc. Nat. Acad. Sci. U.S.A. 45:*1607 (1959).

from breakage and reunion of DNA in two different phage particles. Two mutant strains of the phage are inoculated together into a culture of *E. coli* B. The progeny, after lysis of the bacteria, are tested by spreading on strain K. Some wild-type plaques result, and their frequency is determined. If the experiment is done with two mutant strains thought to be different but in fact identical, then very few wild-type plaques are found, representing spontaneous back mutations.

As illustrated in Fig. 10-1, a wild-type recombinant can arise only if the damaged portions of the two genomes do not overlap. If the probability of breakage is constant throughout a gene, the frequency of recombination between two mutant sites will be a measure of the linear distance between them. Since the selection of wild-type recombinants on *E. coli* strain K is very efficient, extremely low frequencies of recombination can be detected. Two mutants are presumed to have been altered at the same site if wild-type recombinants cannot be obtained. The resolving power of the method is on the order of a single base pair, i.e., two mutants could probably be distinguished if they were mutated at adjacent base pairs. Deletions are recognized by their inability to yield recombinants with a series of mutants already mapped at different sites; deletions of a wide range of sizes have been thus identified.

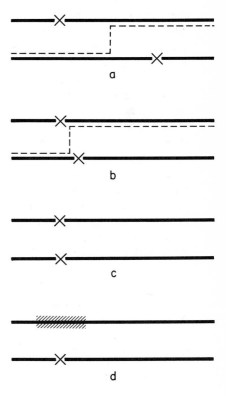

FIG. 10-1. RECOMBINATION OF MUTANTS DEFECTIVE AT DIFFERENT SITES. *Each diagram represents phage DNA from two strains. Mutant sites are indicated by X. Broken line represents replication or breakage and reunion. Hatched segment is a deletion.* a: *Wild-type recombinant is possible because mutations are at different sites.* b: *Wild-type recombinant is possible, but will occur less frequently than in* a. c *and* d: *Wild-type recombinants impossible because mutations or deletions are at identical sites.*

As detected by this technique, spontaneous mutations and those caused by chemical mutagens were plotted on a map of the rII gene. The sites of a large number of spontaneous mutations are shown in Fig. 10-2. They are scattered over the entire gene, but the distribution is far from random. At certain *hot spots* the mutability is many times greater than elsewhere. There are two very prominent hot spots for spontaneous mutation, one near the terminus of the A cistron, the other in the middle of the B cistron.[15] The spectrum of mutation sites in the terminal portion of the B cistron, after treatment by seven different chemical mutagens, is shown in Fig. 10-3. The spontaneous sites for this region are the same as already depicted in Fig. 10-2. These results indicate that the phenomenon of hot spots is not peculiar to spontaneous mutation but is seen with all the mutagens tested. It is also evident that hot spots are mutagen-specific. One of the spontaneous hot spots, for example, has no counterpart in any of the mutagen patterns. The largest hot spot in the 5-bromouracil pattern is not represented even once in the spontaneous pattern. The 2-aminopurine hot spot in segment 8 is represented by only an occasional mutant in any of the other patterns.

Hot spots were once taken at face value as representing sites of unusually high mutability. If this were true, then a hot spot would have to be imbedded in a special and rather rare sequence of base pairs. The reason for this deduction is simply that the four normal base pairs could account, at the most, for only four different degrees of mutability; and these would necessarily be associated with numerous sites throughout the gene. To account for exceptionally high mutability at one site we would have to invoke some influence of neighboring base pairs. Suppose there is one extraordinary hot spot out of 1,000 base pairs. Then a special sequence of at least five pairs will be required, since five is the smallest specified sequence that would occur randomly only once in 1,000 base pairs (actual probability $4^{-5} = 1/1024$). But advances in our understanding of the genetic code and the way it functions render such an explanation unlikely.

First, the very nature of the code makes certain sites more mutable than others. As Table 8-5 indicates, each of the 20 amino acids is coded in mRNA by more than a single codon, some by as many as six different codons. It is evident from the table that most of the degeneracy of the code is attributable to the base in the third (3′) position. Every codon has at least one degenerate partner that differs in the third position but represents the same amino acid. One-half of all the codons have three such degenerate

15 The rII gene clearly directs the synthesis of two proteins. The term *cistron,* now in general use to describe the portion of a gene that codes for a single protein, originated in these investigations with rII mutants. It was found that certain pairs of mutants would grow on *E. coli* K if inoculated together but not separately, whereas others would not. This phenomenon of complementation obviously depended upon each strain producing a normal gene product that could be used by the other. The test for this property was called a *cis-trans* test, whence the term *cistron.*

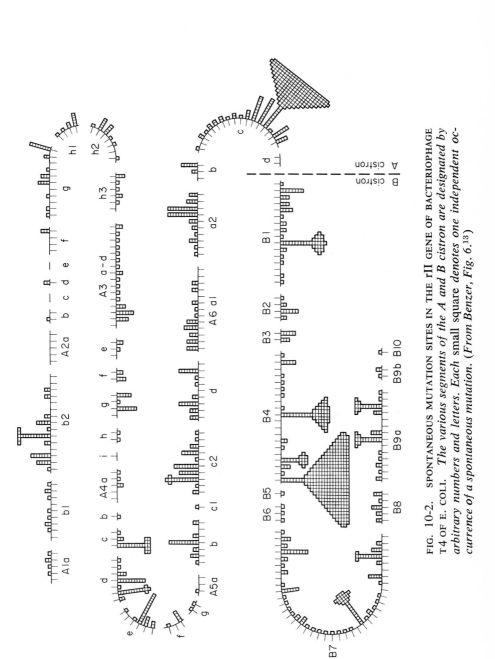

FIG. 10-2. SPONTANEOUS MUTATION SITES IN THE rII GENE OF BACTERIOPHAGE T4 OF E. COLI. *The various segments of the A and B cistron are designated by arbitrary numbers and letters. Each small square denotes one independent oc-currence of a spontaneous mutation. (From Benzer, Fig. 6.[13])*

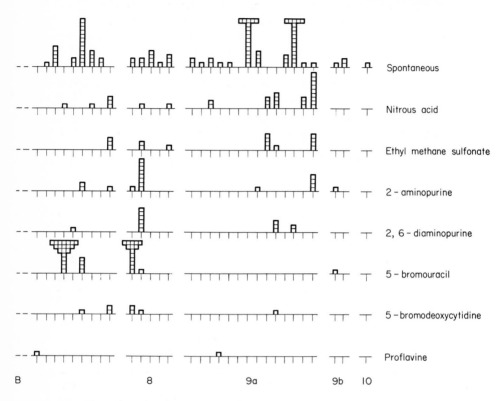

FIG. 10-3.   SPECTRUM OF MUTATION SITES FOR SPONTANEOUS MUTATIONS AND
FOR SEVEN DIFFERENT MUTAGENS.   *A small part of the rII gene is shown, the
terminal portion of the B cistron shown* at bottom *of Fig. 10-2. Each small
square denotes one independent occurrence of a mutation. The mutagens are
listed next to each row, at the right. Mutation sites are indicated by symbols at
bottom. (Modified from Benzer, Fig. 8.[13])*

partners. Obviously, a transition mutation in the DNA that results in a
corresponding change in the third position in the RNA codon (purine for
purine, or pyrimidine for pyrimidine) will have no effect whatsoever; the
"mutation" will be undetectable. And for one-half of the codons even a
transversion in the third position would be undetectable. Certain changes
in the first position will also have no effect (e.g., AGA→CGA = *Arg;*
CUG→UUG = *Leu*).

   Second, the apparent mutability of a given site will be determined
by the position and nature of the corresponding amino acid in the protein.
It is now clear that functional proteins tolerate amino acid replacement at
some positions but not at others. At certain critical locations any alteration
may produce a nonfunctional protein. But often the substitution of chemically similar amino acids (e.g., *Glu→Asp, Gln→Asn, Lys→Arg, Leu→Ile*)

has but little effect on the protein function. From this point of view, a hot spot could be a site at which the base pair alteration results in a codon specifying an amino acid that is incompatible with protein function when it occupies that particular position in the amino acid sequence. In general, mutations that have large effects upon a phenotypic function will be detected; but mutations at other sites, which lead to tolerated modifications of protein structure, will be overlooked.

Third, the identification of a special role in polypeptide chain termination for the codons UAA and UAG[16, 17] offers yet another explanation of hot spots. These two codons specify no amino acid (i.e., "nonsense"). Therefore, codons that can be transformed into these by alteration of a single base pair will seem to be more mutable than codons that cannot, because premature chain termination will nearly always produce a complete deficiency of the protein function. Thus, for example, a *Gln* position coded by CAA or CAG could readily be converted to "nonsense" by the single transition C→U, causing chain termination.

A surprising amount of information about the nature of the base pairs at the various mutant sites in the rII gene can be deduced from observations on induced reversions. A single example will illustrate the method and the argument.[9, 18-20] The base analogue 5-bromouracil (BU) is known to cause pyrimidine transitions. Most mutations induced by BU are also revertible by BU. This implies that BU can cause both transitions, C→T, and T→C, thereby transforming G:C (or C:G) to A:T (or T:A), and the reverse. Hydroxylamine acts preferentially upon C, causing the transition C:G (or G:C) to T:A (or A:T).[21-24] Most mutants caused by BU cannot be induced to revert by hydroxylamine. From this it is inferred that most BU mutants have an A:T (or T:A) pair at the mutant site, i.e., that BU itself preferentially induces the transition G:C→A:T (or C:G→T:A). This conclusion is further strengthened by the fact that, even under conditions that favored the selective modification of G residues, most BU mutants could not be made to revert by treatment with an alkylating agent.[25, 26]

Unfortunately, there is still no mutagen known that is absolutely specific for a single base. Consequently, the deductions about molecular

[16] A. O. W. STRETTON and S. BRENNER: Molecular consequences of the amber mutation and its suppression. *J. Mol. Biol. 12:*456 (1965).

[17] S. BRENNER and A. O. W. STRETTON: The *amber* mutation. *J. Cell. Comp. Physiol. 64:* suppl. 1, 43 (1964).

[18] S. BENZER and E. FREESE: Induction of Specific Mutations with 5-Bromouracil. *Proc. Nat. Acad. Sci. U.S.A. 44:*112 (1958).

[19] E. FREESE, E. BAUTZ-FREESE, and E. BAUTZ: Hydroxylamine as a mutagenic and inactivating agent. *J. Mol. Biol. 3:*133 (1961).

[20] D. R. KRIEG: Specificity of chemical mutagenesis. *Progr. Nucleic Acid Res. 2:*125 (1963).

[21] I. TESSMAN, R. K. PODDAR, and S. KUMAR: Identification of the altered bases in mutated single-stranded DNA. I. *In vitro* mutagenesis by hydroxylamine, ethyl methanesulfonate and nitrous acid. *J. Mol. Biol. 9:*352 (1964).

mechanisms are all indirect. This is especially so for rII mutants because the products of the rII gene have not been isolated. Explicit data about the changes induced by chemical mutagens have now been obtained in studies with tobacco mosaic virus (TMV),[27] and these confirm the earlier conclusions in most respects. Here, the virus RNA can be treated directly with a mutagenic agent, then inoculated into the plant host, and the virus protein obtained in large yield. Since the entire amino acid sequence of TMV protein has been determined, the observed changes can be correlated, through the genetic code, with the actions of the various mutagens. For example, treatment with the known deaminating agent nitrous acid resulted frequently in replacement of a threonine residue by isoleucine. Since the *Thr* codons are ACA, ACG, ACC, and ACU, whereas the *Ile* codons are AUC and AUU, it is obvious that nitrous acid deaminated C to U in the second position of an ACC or ACU codon. Similar detailed descriptions of mutagenesis are becoming available in other systems in which the gene product has been completely characterized.[28-30]

BASE PAIR TRANSFORMATIONS

The smallest unit of mutation is the single base pair. Base pair transformations can be brought about in two ways. A mutagen may react directly with a base of the DNA and modify it chemically. At the next replication the modified base may pair with a new partner. The subsequent replication will see the completion of the mutation process, for the new partner will pair correctly, and thus an entirely different base pair will be substituted for the original one. Figure 10-4 illustrates these steps for the hypothetical case of an adenine residue being deaminated to hypoxanthine. Hypoxanthine, from the standpoint of base pairing, is rather like guanine, for it has an oxygen atom at the 6-position. The first replication may then yield a normal duplex containing A:T and an abnormal one containing H:C. In the next replication, H:C will yield G:C as one of its products. Whether the other product is H:T or H:C is relatively unimportant; a mutant allele of the original A:T pair has already been formed and can now maintain itself permanently in subsequent replications.

22 I. TESSMAN, H. ISHIWA, and S. KUMAR: Mutagenic effects of hydroxylamine *in vivo. Science 148:*507 (1965).

23 D. M. BROWN and J. H. PHILLIPS: Mechanism of the mutagenic action of hydroxylamine. *J. Mol. Biol. 11:*663 (1965).

24 E. FREESE, E. BAUTZ, and E. BAUTZ-FREESE: The chemical and mutagenic specificity of hydroxylamine. *Proc. Nat. Acad. Sci. U.S.A. 47:*845 (1961).

25 E. BAUTZ and E. FREESE: On the mutagenic effect of alkylating agents. *Proc. Nat. Acad. Sci. U.S.A. 46:*1585 (1960).

26 D. R. KRIEG: Ethyl methanesulfonate-induced reversion of bacteriophage T4rII mutants. *Genetics 48:*561 (1963).

27 A. SIEGEL: Artificial production of mutants of tobacco mosaic virus. *Adv. Virus Res. 11:*25 (1965).

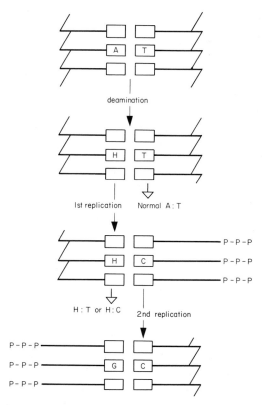

FIG. 10-4. MECHANISM OF A MUTAGENIC TRANSFORMATION BY DEAMINATION.
*Adenine is deaminated to hypoxanthine, which pairs like guanine. The result is
a mutagenic transition, A:T → G:C.*

Certain experimental findings have suggested a different scheme. It
is proposed[31] that when one base of a pair is altered by a mutagenic agent,
its partner is excised and replaced before replication occurs, so that all the
progeny are mutant. Alternatively, it is suggested[32] that at replication one
strand acts as master strand, the base on that strand determining both in-

[28] C. YANOFSKY, B. C. CARLTON, J. R. GUEST, D. R. HELINSKI, and U. HENNING: On
the colinearity of gene structure and protein structure. *Proc. Nat. Acad. Sci. U.S.A. 51:*266
(1964).

[29] C. YANOFSKY, E. C. COX, and V. HORN: The unusual mutagenic specificity of an
E. coli mutator gene. *Proc. Nat. Acad. Sci. U.S.A. 55:*274 (1966).

[30] G. STREISINGER, Y. OKADA, J. EMRICH, J. NEWTON, A. TSUGITA, E. TERZAGHI, and
M. INOUYE: Frameshift mutations and the genetic code. *Cold Spring Harbor Symp. Quant.
Biol. 31:*77 (1966).

[31] E. M. WITKIN and N. A. SICURELLA: Pure clones of lactose-negative mutants
obtained in *Escherichia coli* after treatment with 5-bromouracil. *J. Mol. Biol. 8:*610 (1964).

[32] H. E. KUBITSCHEK: Mutation without segregation. *Proc. Nat. Acad. Sci. U.S.A.
52:*1374 (1964).

coming bases; again, if the base on the master strand is altered, all the progeny will be mutant.

The second way a mutagen can cause a base pair alteration is by affecting the fidelity of replication. The mutagen itself may be incorporated into DNA and then pair incorrectly at a subsequent replication. Or the mutagen may cause erroneous base pairing in some less direct way, for example, by drastically altering the proportions of the four bases available for the replication process.

Mutagens of the first kind, which modify bases of an already-formed DNA duplex, are important experimental tools because they can be used in vitro. They have been employed to modify bacterial and plant viruses, transforming-DNA, and synthetic deoxyribonucleotide polymers.[20,33] After treatment, the DNA can be introduced into living cells to observe the results of the induced mutations; the treated synthetic polymer can be studied in the DNA polymerase reaction to see how the synthesis of a replica strand is modified.[34] Used experimentally, these direct-acting mutagens are very efficient, inasmuch as they are employed at extremely high concentrations and often under nonbiologic conditions of pH, temperature, ionic environment, and so on. In vivo their efficiency would be much lower, but they might nevertheless have a significant mutagenic action. Those mutagens that do act in vivo are likely to be effective at all stages of the cell cycle, whether or not the DNA is replicating. Mutagens of the second kind, which affect the fidelity of replication, will obviously be active only in proliferating cells at the time of DNA replication.

Once a base pair has been altered, several factors will determine the phenotypic delay, i.e., the time until the mutation is expressed. At first, the cell of mutant genotype has wild-type phenotype. This is because the gene products—messenger-RNA and protein—are still present and functional. Their disappearance and replacement by mutant messenger-RNA and protein (if any) will be determined by the messenger half-life and the rate of protein turnover. The rapidity of cell growth and division will influence the rate at which these gene products are diluted by simple partition into daughter cells. In multinucleate cells, only one nucleus will in general be mutant, so the phenotype will not become completely altered until cell divisions segregate the mutant nucleus into a cell of its own. In diploid organisms, the expression of the mutant trait will depend upon its dominance or recessivity, i.e., upon whether it is manifest in heterozygotes or only in homozygotes.

Among the mutagens that act directly upon DNA, one of the most specific is hydroxylamine, which appears to act selectively upon C residues

33 F. LINGENS: Wirkungsmechanismus einiger chemischer Mutagene. *Arch. exper. Pathol. Pharmakol. 253:*116 (1966).

34 T. KOTAKA and R. L. BALDWIN: Effects of nitrous acid on the dAT copolymer as a template for DNA polymerase. *J. Mol. Biol. 9:*323 (1964).

under weakly acidic conditions.[35] The resulting oxime has base pairing properties like those of T. In alkali, an entirely different reaction proceeds, whereby the pyrimidine or purine ring of T or G is split; but this evidently

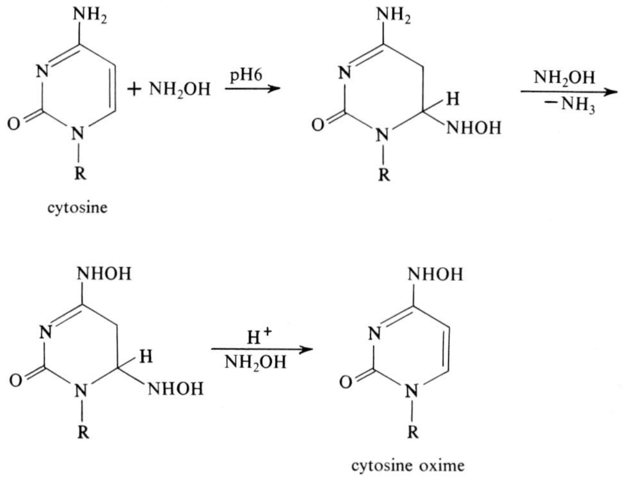

cytosine

cytosine oxime

leads to lethality rather than to a point mutation. The mutagenic effect of hydroxylamine, therefore, is almost exclusively to produce transitions in the direction G:C→A:T.[21, 22]

Nitrous acid is a nonspecific deaminating agent. It attacks all the bases except thymine, which has no amino group. As shown in Fig. 10-5, it transforms adenine to hypoxanthine, whose base pairing properties are like those of guanine; the end result is therefore a transition of the A:T→ G:C type. Nitrous acid deaminates cytosine to uracil, which behaves like thymine; so the result is a transition of the reverse kind, G:C→A:T. Finally, it deaminates guanine to xanthine. This transformation is probably lethal,[36] for xanthine has been found to be incapable of participating in the base pairing process. Replication may well be brought to a halt at the first xanthine residue encountered. Perhaps related to this is the fact that in phage a prominent effect of nitrous acid is to induce extensive deletions.[37]

That the mutagenic action of nitrous acid is really due almost entirely to the two postulated transitions, C→T and A→G, is indicated by

---

[35] It should be understood that the bacterial viruses that have been studied contain hydroxymethylcytosine rather than cytosine itself, but the base-pairing properties are identical to those of C, and no further distinction will be made here.

[36] W. VIELMETTER and H. SCHUSTER: The base specificity of mutation induced by nitrous acid in phage T2. *Biochem. Biophys. Res. Comm.* 2:324 (1960).

[37] I. TESSMAN: The induction of large deletions by nitrous acid. *J. Mol. Biol.* 5:442 (1962).

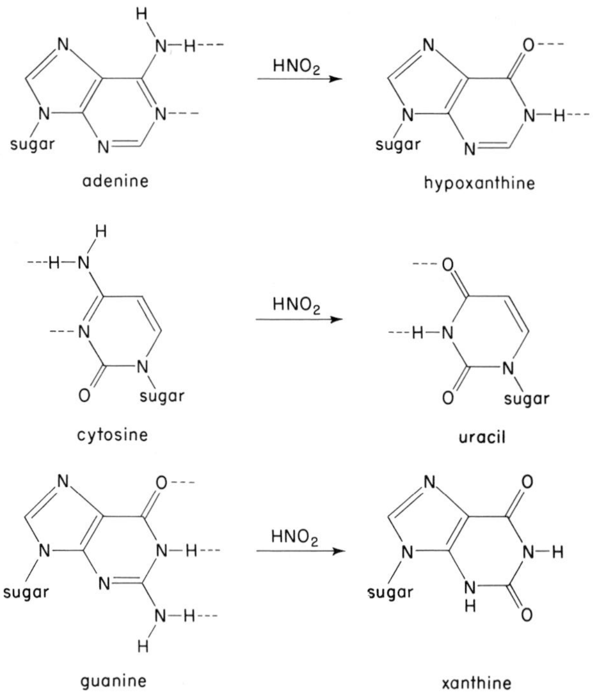

FIG. 10-5. DEAMINATION OF NUCLEIC ACID BASES BY NITROUS ACID. *Effect of nitrous acid upon the three bases subject to deamination. Dashed lines represent hydrogen bonds in the DNA helix. (From Kotaka and Baldwin, Fig. 1.[34])*

extensive studies with tobacco mosaic virus,[27] summarized in Table 10-1. Nineteen different amino acid replacements were observed in the TMV protein after mutagenic treatment with HNO_2. Many of these occurred repeatedly, so that altogether 63 occurrences were identified. The table shows that when the codons (from Table 8-5) for the original amino acid and the replacement amino acid are considered, all but a few of the observations are accounted for by C→U or A→G transition. In only three instances, representing only one or two occurrences each, was it impossible to account for the result by the postulated transitions; and those may well have been spontaneous rather than mutagen-induced events. Significantly, there was not a single instance suggesting the modification of a U residue, in agreement with the chemical impossibility of deaminating U.

The data for proline and phenylalanine, shown in Table 10-1, provide an interesting proof that the viral RNA strand itself, and not a complementary strand, acts as template for the synthesis of TMV protein. The codon for *Pro* (CC(x)) cannot be derived from a codon representing another amino acid by deamination, and the codon for *Phe* (UU(Py)) cannot be transformed to any other codon by deamination. If a complementary strand were the template for protein synthesis, then *Phe* should be re-

TABLE 10-1. **Mutagenic action of nitrous acid on tobacco mosaic virus RNA**

The observed amino acid replacements in TMV protein are interpreted in terms of the most probable single-base alterations, from the genetic code as given in Table 8-5. The triplet codons are read from 5′ at left to 3′ at right. Degeneracy in the 3′ position is indicated by (x) = any base, (Pu) = either purine, (Py) = either pyrimidine. (From Siegel, Table I,[27] modified and updated to correspond with more recent data on the code.)

Amino acid replacement	No. of occurrences	Probable codon alteration	Base alteration
Thr → *Ala*	2	AC(x) → GC(x)	A → G
Thr → *Ile*	10	AC(Py) → AU(Py)	C → U
Thr → *Met*	3	AC(Pu) → AU(Pu)	C → U
Ser → *Phe*	8	UC(x) → UU(Py)	C → U
Ser → *Leu*	2	UC(x) → UU(Pu)	C → U
Asn → *Ser*	6	AA(Py) → AG(Py)	A → G
Asp → *Gly*	2	GA(Py) → GG(x)	A → G
Asp → *Ala*	4	GA(Py) → GC(x)	A → C
Ile → *Val*	5	AU(Py) → GU(x)	A → G
Ile → *Met*	1	AU(Py) → AU(Pu)	Py → Pu
Pro → *Ser*	3	CC(x) → UC(x)	C → U
Pro → *Leu*	6	CC(x) → CU(x)	C → U
Leu → *Phe*	1	CU(Py) → UU(Py)	C → U
Gln → *Val*	2	CA(Pu) → GU(x)	?
Gln → *Arg*	1	CA(Pu) → CG(x)	A → G
Glu → *Gly*	2	GA(Pu) → GG(x)	A → G
Arg → *Gly*	3	AG(Pu) → GG(x)	A → G
Arg → *Lys*	1	AG(Pu) → AA(x) *or*	G → A *or*
		CG(x) → AA(x)	?
Val → *Met*	1	GU(x) → AU(Pu)	G → A

placed readily but should not be a replacement, whereas *Pro* should be a replacement but should never be replaced. The reason is that the *Phe* codon UU(Py) on the complementary strand would be represented by AA(Pu) on the viral RNA strand; and this should be subject to deamination, but could never arise by deamination. Similarly, the *Pro* codon CC(x) on the complementary strand would be represented by GG(x) on the viral RNA; and this should not be subject to mutagenic transformation by nitrous acid. In fact, as the table shows, the findings were exactly contrary; *Pro* was replaced nine times but was never a replacement, whereas *Phe* was a replacement nine times but was never replaced.

A recently discovered extremely potent mutagen, which somewhat resembles nitrous acid in its action on DNA, is N-methyl-N′-nitro-N-nitrosoguanidine.[38,39] The mechanism of its action is still unclear. At first, it

---

[38] J. D. MANDELL and J. GREENBERG: A new chemical mutagen for bacteria, 1-methyl-3-nitro-1-nitrosoguanidine. *Biochem. Biophys. Res. Comm. 3:*575 (1960).

[39] E. A. ADELBERG, M. MANDEL, and G. C. C. CHEN: Optimal conditions for mutagenesis by N-methyl-N′-nitro-N-nitrosoguanidine in *Escherichia coli* K12. *Biochem. Biophys. Res. Comm. 18:*788 (1965).

was thought that this agent might act indirectly by liberating nitrous acid or diazomethane, but now it is considered likely that it acts directly. Ade-

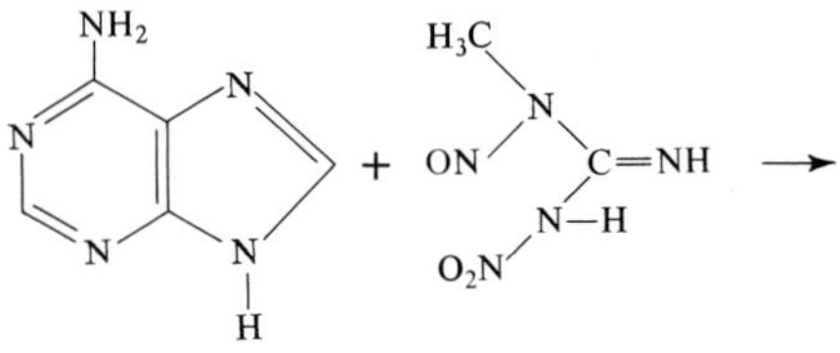

adenine   mutagen

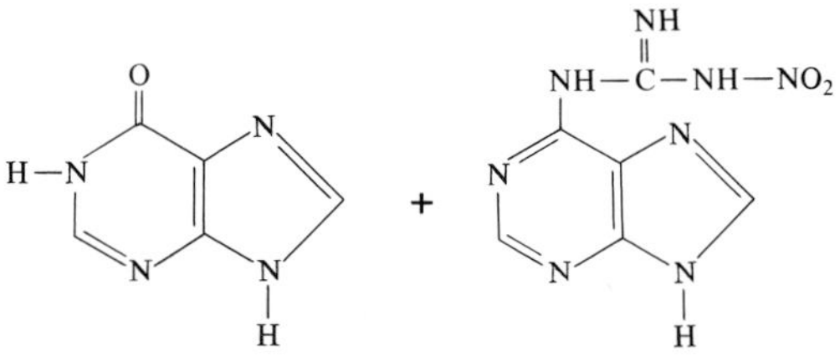

hypoxanthine   addition product

nine is deaminated to hypoxanthine, and a nitroguanidinium addition product may also be formed. The reaction with cytosine also appears to be an addition to the amino group. This mutagen is principally remarkable because it produces a variety of mutations within living cells at a concentration (about $100\mu g/ml$) that is not lethal. This behavior contrasts sharply with that of many mutagens, which act readily upon isolated DNA but are effective in vivo only at concentrations that cause much killing. Extensive lethality at mutagenic dosage is also the rule for irradiation mutagenesis.

Alkylating agents such as ethyl methanesulfonate (EMS), ethyl ethanesulfonate (EES), and the nitrogen mustards (p. 3 ff.) can carry out an electrophilic attack upon various functional groups (amino, carboxyl, sulfhydryl, phosphate) in proteins and nucleic acids. The mutagenicity of

ethyl methanesulfonate   ethyl ethanesulfonate
        (EMS)   (EES)

these compounds is largely attributable to alkylation of position 7 of guanine, as shown in Fig. 10-6. The effect of quaternizing the nitrogen atom

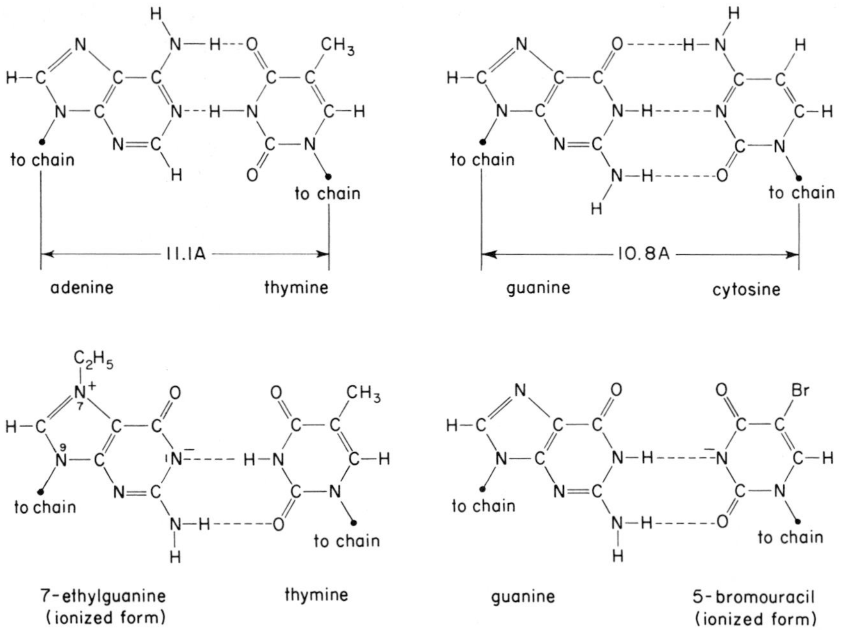

FIG. 10-6. NORMAL AND ABNORMAL BASE PAIRING. *The two normal base pairs are shown on* top line. *Alkylation of guanine at position 7 permits ionized form to pair with thymine (lower left). Ionization of 5-bromouracil permits pairing with guanine (lower right). All hydrogen bond distances are 2.8 to 3.0 A. (Modified from Strauss, Fig. 3.[40] By permission of Grune & Stratton.)*

is twofold: to weaken the bond between N-9 and the deoxyribose moiety, and to promote ionization at N-1 as shown.[41] It was first supposed that the bond-weakening effect at N-9 was the primary cause of the mutagenicity of alkylating agents. Depurination was postulated, followed, presumably, by the entry of any base opposite the resulting gap at the next replication. Thus, it was predicted that G→A transitions and both kinds of transversion (G→C, G→T) would be produced. However, careful study of the effects of EMS upon phage T4 indicated that by far the most common mutational events were transitions of the G:C→A:T type. Thus, anomalous pairing of 7-alkylguanine with thymine, secondary to the ionization at N-1 (as shown in Fig. 10-6), appears to account for most of the mutagenicity.[25,26,42] It is possible, of course, that depurination occurs and is lethal; if so, it could not be detected in a study of mutations.

[40] B. S. STRAUSS: Chemical mutagens and the genetic code. *Progr. Med. Genetics* 3:1 (1964).

[41] P. BROOKES and P. D. LAWLEY: Reaction of some mutagenic and carcinogenic compounds with nucleic acids. *J. Cell. Comp. Physiol. 64:* suppl. 1, 111 (1964).

[42] E. BAUTZ-FREESE: Transitions and transversions induced by depurinating agents. *Proc. Nat. Acad. Sci. U.S.A.* 47:540 (1961).

The mutagens that influence DNA through modifying the fidelity of replication are base analogues. The thymine analogue, 5-bromouracil (BU), is a typical example. After being first converted metabolically to the deoxyribose triphosphate, BU is incorporated extensively into DNA in place of T by entering the nascent DNA strand opposite A on the old strand. The extent of this replacement in some experiments has been quite remarkable, up to about one-half the total number of T residues. Obviously, the presence of BU instead of T does not seriously affect DNA function—either replication or transcription—since the organisms are viable and continue to grow and divide, either in normal medium or in the continued presence of BU. Thus, the A:BU pair functions like the A:T pair. At replication, BU specifies an incoming A on the nascent strand; and at transcription, BU specifies A on the nascent messenger-RNA.

Errors of incorporation or of replication are probably attributable to the ionized form of BU, which undergoes base pairing as though it were C (Fig. 10-6). This results from loss of a proton at N-1, so that a hydrogen bond can be formed with the H atom at N-1 of guanine. When it is being incorporated, BU may occasionally undergo this erroneous base pairing and thus enter opposite G, as illustrated in the first replication in Fig. 10-7. At subsequent replications, this BU might behave "normally," as though it were T, and thus the end result would be a G:C→A:T transition. Since it has been shown that BU is more likely to be ionized when it is free (as the deoxynucleoside triphosphate) than after its polymerization into DNA, errors of incorporation (rather than of replication) are probably the principal mechanism of BU mutagenesis.[20] Alternatively, as shown at the third replication in Fig. 10-7, a BU molecule, incorporated "correctly" in place of T, might behave as though it were C, pairing with an incoming G. Then the transition A:T→G:C will be the end result. As already noted, the patterns of mutation induction and reversion observed in phage conformed to these expectations; transitions of the G:C→A:T type were most frequent, but A:T→G:C transitions also occurred.[43] As long as the strand containing BU persists, occasional mutations would be expected to occur at any subsequent replication, i.e., whenever an incoming G is paired against BU. This phenomenon has been observed in phage as a peculiar "mottling" of the plaques, caused by new mutations arising after plaque formation has been initiated by phenotypically wild-type phage.[44]

The mechanisms are apparently similar for all the base analogues that can be incorporated. Purines replace purines, pyrimidines replace

43 B. D. HOWARD and I. TESSMAN: Identification of the altered bases in mutated single-stranded DNA. II. *In vivo* mutagenesis by 5-bromodeoxyuridine and 2-aminopurine. *J. Mol. Biol. 9:*364 (1964).

44 D. PRATT and G. S. STENT: Mutational heterozygotes in bacteriophages. *Proc. Nat. Acad. Sci. U.S.A. 45:*1507 (1959).

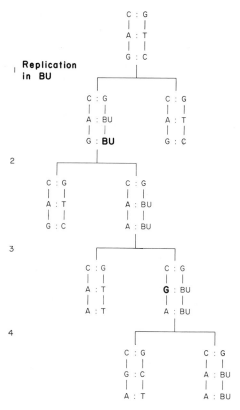

FIG. 10-7. MUTAGENESIS BY 5-BROMOURACIL (BU). *The commonest mecha-nism is shown at replication 1; BU enters opposite G, and the end result is a G:C → A:T transition. If BU that has already been incorporated pairs with an incoming G (as at replication 3), an A:T → G:C transition results.*

pyrimidines, so that transitions always result. The essential requirement is a certain ambiguity of structure with respect to those features that distinguish the normal purines or pyrimidines from each other. Thus, for example, 2-aminopurine resembles guanine at the 2-position but lacks the keto group at the 6-position. It seems to induce transitions in both directions.[9]

2-aminopurine   guanine

An interesting base-analogue mutagen that may be of some significance in man (p. 664 ff.) is caffeine. This is a fully methylated purine. Because it is substituted in the 7-position, it cannot form a stable bond to deoxyribose at the 9-position and is therefore not incorporated into DNA.

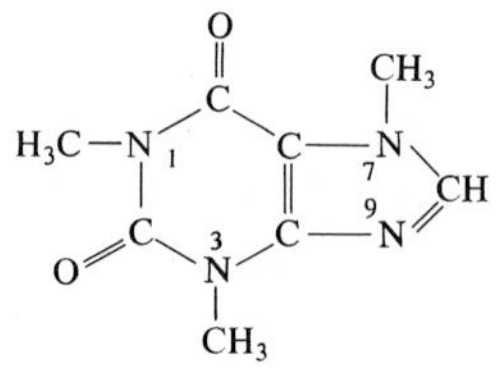

caffeine (1,3,7-trimethylxanthine)

Because it is known to inhibit some enzymes of purine metabolism,[45] it has been proposed that it alters the normal base ratios in the DNA precursor pool, thereby causing errors of base pairing. It is also possible that it may intercalate between base pairs[46] in the manner of the acridines (p. 640), and thus cause frame shift mutations. Finally, there is evidence that caffeine greatly enhances the rate of ultraviolet-induced mutation, apparently by impairing the operation of the normal repair mechanisms for excising and replacing radiation-damaged segments of DNA.[47]

Many drugs of the base analogue type have been employed in cancer chemotherapy. Some of these have been found to act as radiation sensitizers.[48] The mechanism remains obscure, but several interesting relationships have been discovered. Whereas the primary lesion in ultraviolet irradiation is the dimerization of adjacent thymine residues on the same DNA strand, this is clearly not the mechanism of damage by x-rays. Sensitivity to ultraviolet damage increases with the A:T content of bacterial cells, as would be expected; but sensitivity to the lethal effects of x-irradiation increases with G:C content. The alkylating agents (especially the nitrogen mustards) have long been recognized to have "radiomimetic" actions, and we have seen that their preferential effect is upon guanine residues. These facts suggest that x-rays may somehow damage G:C pairs. Bromouracil and other halogenated uracil compounds are good x-ray sensitizers, and their effectiveness is directly related to the extent of their

45 A. L. KOCH: "The mechanism of action of methyl xanthines in mutagenesis," in Symposium on *Information Theory in Biology,* ed. by H. P. Yockey, et al. New York, Pergamon Press, 1958, p. 136.

46 P. O. P. TS'O, G. K. HELMKAMP, and C. SANDER: Interaction of nucleosides and related compounds with nucleic acids as indicated by the change of helix-coil transition temperature. *Proc. Nat. Acad. Sci. U.S.A. 48:*686 (1962).

47 M. LIEB: Dark repair of UV induction in K12 (λ). *Virology 23:*381 (1964).

48 H. S. KAPLAN, J. D. EARLE, and F. L. HOWSDEN: The role of purine and pyrimidine bases and their analogues in radiation sensitivity. *J. Cell. Comp. Physiol. 64:* suppl. 1, 69 (1964).

incorporation into DNA. They also raise the melting temperature of DNA (i.e., the temperature at which hydrogen bonds between the two strands are broken), and this stabilizing effect is also related to the extent of incorporation. It is thought that these pyrimidine analogues may, at the points where they are incorporated, make the DNA backbone more vulnerable to breakage by radiation.

The sensitizing effects of purine analogues do not seem to be related to incorporation; indeed, some very good sensitizers are not incorporated into DNA at all. A good example is 6-mercaptopurine, a growth inhibitor used extensively in the palliative treatment of leukemias. Figure 10-8 shows an experimental determination of radiosensitization of *E. coli* by this agent. The sensitization was seen at all x-ray doses. A typical exponential killing curve (log linear as plotted) was seen in the presence and absence of the purine analogue, but the slope was increased about threefold by the sensitizing drug. Although 6-mercaptopurine happens to be a growth-inhibitory drug, growth inhibition is not requisite to the sensitizing action; thus, 6-chloropurine is a good sensitizer but has no inhibitory effect upon growth. It is likely that all drugs of the base analogue class have mutagenic actions under conditions of therapeutic use, but it is

FIG. 10-8. RADIOSENSITIZATION OF ESCHERICHIA COLI BY 6-MERCAPTOPURINE. *Cell populations were exposed to x-rays at the various dosages shown and survival was measured by colony counting after plating cells at appropriate dilution on agar plates. The exponential killing curves (note logarithmic scale of ordinates) are shown for cells exposed to 6-mercaptopurine (6-MP) and for controls. (From Kaplan et al., Fig. 7.[48])*

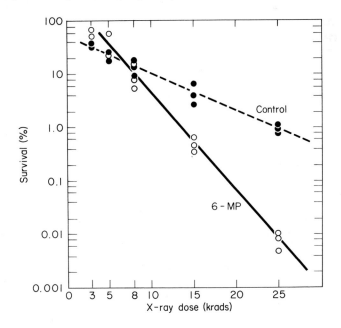

not known whether the induction of mutations plays any role in their pharmacologic actions as growth inhibitors or x-ray sensitizers.

FRAME SHIFT MUTATIONS

These changes are point mutations of an entirely different type from the alterations of single base pairs discussed above. They result from the addition or deletion of a base. This mechanism of mutagenesis was discovered during investigations with acridine dyes such as proflavine and acridine yellow. When bacteria infected with phage T4 were treated with

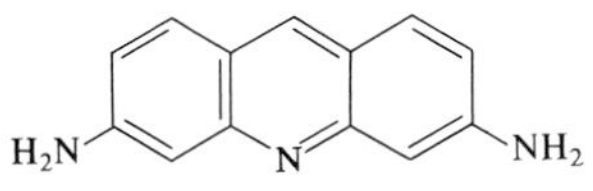

proflavin 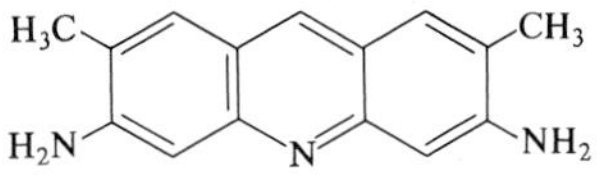   acridine yellow

an acridine, rII mutants were obtained that differed sharply from those already described, in that they could not be reverted by base analogues or by any of the other mutagens that cause transitions. Nor would acridines induce any reversion of transition mutants. On the other hand, many spontaneous mutants that were not revertible by the other mutagens could be reverted by treatment with acridines, and acridine mutants often reverted spontaneously. The elucidation of the mechanism of acridine mutagenesis was accomplished in a series of brilliant experiments that also established several fundamental principles of the coding and translation of genetic information.[49]

When the standard methods of recombination analysis were applied to acridine mutants, as described earlier, the mutations could all be mapped at single sites throughout the rII gene. These mutants were found to revert spontaneously (or by acridine treatment) in an interesting way. The revertants did not display truly wild-type behavior, but differed in some discernible way (e.g., plaque morphology, growth rate) from the wild type. The behavior was designated "pseudowild."

Figure 10-9 illustrates the procedures that were used to unravel the mechanism of acridine mutagenesis. A proflavin-induced rII mutant was chosen as starting material. It was arbitrarily designated (+), for reasons that will shortly become clear. This mutant strain (FCO, line 1 of Fig. 10-9) was grown on *E. coli* B and pseudowild revertants were isolated by plating on strain K. It will be recalled that the wild-type phage grows on

---

[49] F. H. C. CRICK, L. BARNETT, S. BRENNER, and R. J. WATTS-TOBIN: General nature of the genetic code for proteins. *Nature 192:*1227 (1961).

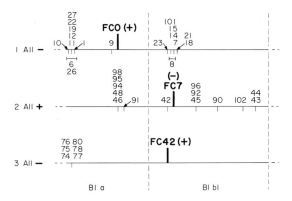

FIG. 10-9. READING-FRAME MUTATIONS IN T4 PHAGE. *This is a rough map, only approximately to scale, of the left end of the B cistron of the rII gene. The original mutant, FCO, was produced with an acridine dye. Line 1 shows the mapping of suppressors of FCO. Line 2 shows suppressors of FC7, one of the suppressors of FCO mapped on line 1. Line 3 shows, in turn, suppressors of FC42, seen on line 2 as a suppressor of FC7. For meanings of (+) and (−) see text. (Extracted from Crick et al., Fig. 2.[49] This map is now known to contain minor errors. An accurate map is given in Barnett et al.[49a])*

strain B or strain K, but that rII mutants fail to grow on strain K. Recombination analysis showed that the spontaneous pseudowild revertants were in reality double mutants. The new mutation, in every case but one, fell into a cluster on either side of the original FCO mutant site. Thus, the second mutation is an intragenic suppressor of the original mutation. The suppressors of FCO are identified by number and are given the arbitrary designation (−). When, by recombination with wild type, the (−) suppressors were obtained free of the FCO mutation, they all proved to be typical rII mutants. In other words, two rII mutations were somehow able to suppress each other when both were present in the same genome. One of these suppressors (FC7) was chosen for further study, as shown on line 2 of Fig. 10-9. Again spontaneous pseudowild revertants were selected, as indicated, and again each of these proved to be a typical rII mutant. Since they were capable of suppressing the FC7 (−) mutation, they were designated (+). The process was repeated again; line 3 shows the analysis of FC42 (+) and its suppressors, designated (−).

These results were interpreted by supposing that acridines caused the insertion or deletion of a base. As a consequence, the "reading frame" (i.e., the ordered sequence of triplets) would be shifted, so that all codons distal to the mutation site would be changed. Clearly, no functional gene product could be synthesized under these circumstances. However, a shift of the reading frame in the opposite direction would restore a correct

49a L. BARNETT, S. BRENNER, F. H. C. CRICK, R. G. SHULMAN, and R. J. WATTS-TOBIN: Phase-shift and other mutants in the first part of the rII B cistron of bacteriophage T4. *Phil. Trans. B Roy. Soc.* 252:487 (1967).

reading, except in the region between the two mutation sites. This is illustrated schematically in Fig. 10-10. Each normal codon is represented by a sequence of bases numbered 1-2-3 (top line). The insertion of an extra base (second line) throws all codons to the right out of register (3-1-2 instead of 1-2-3). Finally (3rd line), deletion of a base restores the reading frame to the right of the deletion, leaving only the region between the two sites out of register. Presumably, then, if the original mutation and its suppressor are not too far apart, and if they occur in a region of the gene corresponding to a portion of the protein product that will tolerate some amino acid replacements, a partially functional protein can result, and pseudowild behavior is seen. The lower part of Fig. 10-10 shows a similar result when the deletion is to the left of the insertion.

By recombination and appropriate selection procedures it was possible to construct artificial genomes containing any desired combination of (+) or (−) mutations. When two (+) or two (−) mutations were combined in the same genome, the result was a typical rII mutant; the gene was nonfunctional. Remarkably, however, when three (+) or three (−) mutations were combined, pseudowild behavior resulted. This constituted strong evidence that the genetic code was indeed a triplet code; for if each codon contained three bases, the addition or deletion of that number should restore the reading frame and produce a wild-type protein containing one extra (or one missing) amino acid.

FIG. 10-10. MECHANISM OF FRAME SHIFT MUTAGENESIS. *Each box represents a base pair. The base pairs in a codon are numbered 1, 2, and 3 in the reading direction from left to right (i.e., 5′ → 3′ on the messenger-RNA). Original configuration is shown in line a. Addition of a base produces configuration shown on line b, where all codons to right of addition are now missense. On line c, deletion of a base restores proper reading frame to right, leaves a few missense codons between the sites of addition and deletion. On line d, the deletion has been made to left of original addition, with a similar restorative result.*

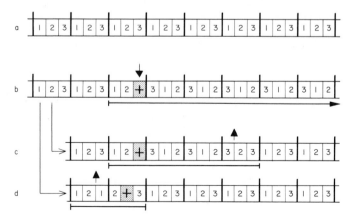

Direct confirmation of the insertion-deletion theory of acridine (and spontaneous) mutagenesis could not be obtained in the rII phage mutants because the gene product is still unknown. It was predicted, however, that if pseudowild double mutants of the (+) and (−) types could be studied in a system in which the protein product of the gene was available, "a string of amino-acids would be altered, covering the region of the polypeptide chain corresponding to the region on the gene between the two mutants."[49] This proof has now been accomplished with the enzyme lysozyme of phage T4, by amino acid sequence determinations.[30,50] The frame shift predicted by the theory really occurs. An illustration is presented in Fig. 10-11. The lysozyme from a pseudowild (+ and −) double mutant was found to differ from the wild-type enzyme with respect to five contiguous amino acids. The codons for all the amino acids in this region are shown. It is clear that the deletion of one base from the −*thr−lys− ser−* codons at the left and the insertion of a guanine or adenine residue in the −*asn−ala−* codons at the right would precisely account for the observed amino acid replacements. Because the polarity of each codon is known and it is also known that proteins are assembled (i.e., the message is read) from NH_2-terminus to COOH-terminus, this experiment shows conclusively that the genetic message is translated in the direction 5'→3' on the mRNA. The reason is that if the mRNA were translated in the

FIG. 10-11. FRAME SHIFT MUTATION IN PHAGE T4 LYSOZYME. *Portions of the amino acid sequences for the wild-type protein and for the lysozyme isolated from a pseudowild strain are presented. The pseudowild strain carries two frame shift mutations of opposite sign, i.e., an addition and a deletion. The codons corresponding to each amino acid are shown, as given in Table 8-5. The symbol* x *represents any one of the four bases. The polypeptide sequence is written with* NH_2-*terminus to left, polynucleotide sequence with 5'-terminus to left. (From Streisinger et al., Table 1.*[30]).

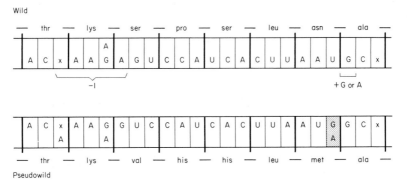

[50] E. TERZAGHI, Y. OKADA, G. STREISINGER, J. EMRICH, M. INOUYE, and A. TSUGITA: Change of a sequence of amino acids in phage T4 lysozyme by acridine-induced mutations. *Proc. Nat. Acad. Sci. U.S.A.* 56:500 (1966).

direction $3' \rightarrow 5'$, every codon shown in Fig. 10-11 would have to be reversed, left to right. If this were so, no set of codons corresponding to the wild-type sequence of amino acids could be converted to the pseudowild sequence by any simple transformation.

It has been proposed that acridine dyes cause the addition or deletion of bases at replication by becoming intercalated between the adjacent base pairs of the DNA.[51] These dyes (and similar compounds) are planar molecules of dimensions similar to those of normal base pairs (Fig. 10-12). Physical measurements of several kinds have given convincing evidence that they do indeed interact with DNA in a manner consistent with intercalation. They cause a local spreading of the distance between adjacent base pairs and a localized unwinding of the helix to accommodate this distortion. Acridines, like other organic cations that interact with DNA, raise the melting temperature. Figure 10-13 presents some possible modes of binding of acridines to DNA, including the generally favored intercalation model.

It was easy to imagine that the spreading of adjacent base pairs to twice their normal separation by acridine intercalation would permit the insertion of an extra base pair during replication. But rather strained explanations had to be advanced to account for base pair deletions on the same basis. It will be recalled that several observations pointed to the similarity of acridine-induced and spontaneous mutations. It was proposed[51] that reciprocal additions and deletions of bases could occur as a result of unequal crossover between homologous chromosomes. Recent findings on the nature of spontaneous mutation have confirmed this surmise.[52-54] A

FIG. 10-12. RELATIVE SIZES OF AN ACRIDINE (PROFLAVIN) AND A BASE PAIR. *The purine-pyrimidine base pair is shown* shaded, *its three hydrogen bonds are represented by* dotted lines. *The acridine is superimposed in* bold outline. (*From Lerman, Fig. 2.*[51])

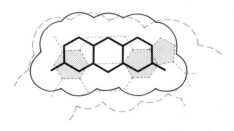

[51] L. S. LERMAN: Acridine mutagens and DNA structure. *J. Cell. Comp. Physiol. 64:* suppl. 1, 1 (1964).

[52] G. E. MAGNI: Origin and nature of spontaneous mutations in meiotic organisms. *J. Cell. Comp. Physiol. 64:* suppl. 1, 165 (1964).

[53] G. E. MAGNI, R. C. VON BORSTEL, and S. SORA: Mutagenic action during meiosis and antimutagenic action during mitosis by 5-aminoacridine in yeast. *Mutation Res. 1:*227 (1964).

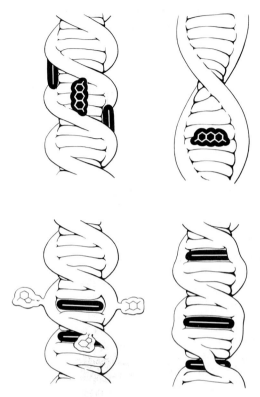

FIG. 10-13. POSSIBLE MODES OF BINDING OF ACRIDINES TO DNA. *The intercalation model at* lower right *is thought to be most probable. Local untwisting of the helix backbone permits the acridine molecule to be stacked between bases, without disturbing the hydrogen bonding of the bases themselves. In the model at* lower left, *the acridine occupies a space from which the base pairs have been rotated outward. (From Lerman, Fig. 1.[51])*

typical experiment employed a diploid strain of yeast with multiple genetic markers. Table 10-2 shows a portion of the genetic map for this organism. Genes for threonine, arginine, isoleucine, tryptophan, and methionine deficiency are present in the heterozygous state. The organism is homozygous for a histidine deficiency, and this gene is altered at the same site on both chromosomes. Yeast can be grown vegetatively as a diploid organism undergoing mitotic division; or, by providing an appropriate medium, it can be made to undergo meiotic division and form spores. It was found that the spontaneous reversion rate at various loci tested was 6 to 20 times higher at meiosis than in mitosis. This suggested the possibility that spontaneous mutation might be associated with recombinations that are known to arise frequently during meiotic crossover between homologous chromatids (Fig. 10-14).

[54] G. E. MAGNI: The origin of spontaneous mutations during meiosis. *Proc. Nat. Acad. Sci. U.S.A.* 50:975 (1963).

TABLE 10-2. **Spontaneous mutation and meiotic recombination in yeast**

A diploid strain was used that was heterozygous for various amino acid requirements and homozygous for a histidine requirement. Shown below is a segment of the fifth chromosome of this strain, with map distances in recombination units. Centromere is at left. Organisms were grown in a sporulation medium, spores were isolated and their phenotypes tested on various media. Numbers (N) of each parental and recombinant type are shown below for the markers on either side of the histidine marker. (After Magni,[54] p. 977 and Table 2.)

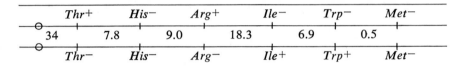

	Thr+		*His−*		*Arg+*		*Ile−*		*Trp−*		*Met−*
34		7.8		9.0		18.3		6.9		0.5	
	Thr−		*His−*		*Arg−*		*Ile+*		*Trp+*		*Met−*

Random spore analysis, phenotypes

		Nonrevertant spores				**Revertant spores**			
		Thr	His	Arg	N	Thr	His	Arg	N
Parental	{	+	−	+	92	+	+	+	26
	{	−	−	−	80	−	+	−	21
Recombinant	{	+	−	−	17	+	+	−	71
	{	−	−	+	13	−	+	+	45
Recombination frequency[a]			0.15				0.71		

[a] Fraction of recombinants among all spores tested.

The experiment summarized in Table 10-2 shows the clear association between reversion at the histidine locus and crossover in this same region. The effect of such a crossover would be to produce recombinants between the threonine and arginine loci. The data show that when non-revertant spores were examined (i.e., those in which the histidine deficiency was still present), the recombination frequency was found to be consistent with the map distance between the two loci. But the frequency of recombination between these same markers was very much higher in revertant spores (i.e., those that had regained the capacity to synthesize histidine). The interpretation was that the spontaneous mutations actually arose through crossover at meiosis, by a process of unequal crossover. Breakage of chromatids at nonidentical locations, followed by crossover and reunion, would yield two kinds of recombinant; one would gain one or more base pairs, the other would lose correspondingly. Thus, if the original deficiency mutation had been of the frame shift type, then unequal crossover could produce a reversion to wild or pseudowild by restoring the reading frame. It is possible, therefore, that the principal effect of intercalated acridines

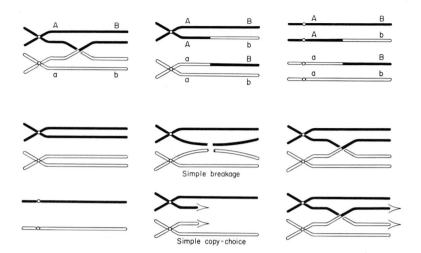

FIG. 10-14. CROSSOVER AT MEIOSIS. *In* upper line, *two homologous chromosomes are shown aligned, each comprised of two chromatids. Centromere is* small circle *at left.* A *and* B *are genes of one chromosome;* a *and* b *are the corresponding alleles on the other. Recombination yields two new genomes.* Middle *and* bottom *diagrams show alternative theories to account for crossover and recombination.* (*From Srb et al., Figs. 6-2 and 6-15.*[1])

is to induce or perpetuate unequal crossovers. There is, indeed, direct evidence in phage T4 that proflavin mutagenesis can occur in the absence of DNA replication, under conditions that favor recombinations due to DNA breakage and reunion.[55] Acridines have also been found to inhibit some of the mechanisms whereby defects in DNA are excised and repaired; possibly their apparent mutagenicity is attributable to blockade of the repair of spontaneous mutations.[56, 57]

CHROMOSOME BREAKAGE

The simplest mechanism of mutagenesis, the transition or transversion replacement of a single base pair, entails no break in the continuity of the DNA. The addition-deletion mechanism, which causes frame shift

[55] J. W. DRAKE: Studies on the induction of mutations in bacteriophage T4 by ultraviolet irradiation and by proflavin. *J. Cell. Comp. Physiol. 64:* suppl. 1, 19 (1964).

[56] R. DULBECCO: Summary of 1964 biology research conference. *J. Cell. Comp. Physiol. 64:* suppl. 1, 181 (1964).

[57] E. M. WITKIN: The effect of acriflavine on photoreversal of lethal and mutagenic damage produced in bacteria by ultraviolet light. *Proc. Nat. Acad. Sci. U.S.A. 50:*425 (1963).

mutations of the spontaneous and acridine type, may well arise, as indicated above, through an unequal crossover. Crossover, the exchange of homologous segments between chromatids, occurs normally in meiosis, where it serves to assort genetic characters into new genomes. It also occurs between homologous chromatids at mitosis. Crossing over requires either actual breakage and reunion of chromatids or a reciprocal switching of the replication mechanism from one chromatid to another ("copy choice").[58] These possibilities are diagrammed in Fig. 10-14. At the top of the figure are shown two homologous chromosomes in synaptic alignment at meiosis. The result, after centromere division, is the emergence of two new chromosomes, the reciprocal recombinants, in addition to the original pair. The lower part of the figure shows schemes for the two theories of crossover, neither of which in its simple form accounts for all the facts about crossover. Still unknown are the factors responsible for the frequency of crossover, the alignment of crossover points on the two chromatids, or the reunion and healing of breaks when they occur. Although there is still controversy about whether actual breakage and reunion are normal parts of meiosis, there is no doubt that ionizing radiation and a variety of chemical agents can cause chromatid breaks.

Broken ends of chromatids are known to be "sticky," in the sense that broken ends tend to heal together. An important consequence of this property is that once breakage is produced or repair of broken ends is inhibited, bizarre alterations of chromosome structure are possible. An illustration of how gene duplications, inversions, and deletions can occur through operation of a cycle of breakage, fusion, and bridge formation is shown in Fig. 10-15. At the top of the figure a chromosome from which a terminal segment has been broken is depicted. Such terminal fragments become lost because they are detached from the portion of the chromosome bearing the centromere, and therefore cannot move properly at mitosis or meiosis. If such a terminal deletion is compatible with continued life of the cell, the mutant will be defective in those characters controlled by the missing genes. After replication of the chromatid, the "sticky" broken ends join to form a dicentric chromatid. At the next anaphase, the centromeres will be pulled in opposite directions, forming an anaphase bridge, which eventually breaks. The new break heals after replication, and the cycle is repeated. The sequence of three genes, A, B, and C, is shown to undergo several possible changes in the course of these events. Sometimes broken ends reunite to form ring chromosomes. Sometimes a whole segment may be transposed elsewhere on the same chromosome, or even onto a different chromosome. A microphotograph showing anaphase bridges, detached terminal fragments, and extensive chromosome breakage is presented in

---

[58] J. H. TAYLOR: "The Replication and Organization of DNA in Chromosomes," in *Molecular Genetics,* ed. by J. H. Taylor. New York, Academic Press, 1963, chapter II.

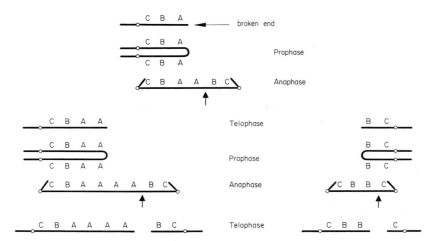

FIG. 10-15. THE CHROMOSOME BREAKAGE-FUSION-BRIDGE CYCLE. *A chromosome with a broken end is pictured at top.* Open circle *represents centromere.* A, B, C *are genes. Fusion of broken ends of the two chromatids is shown, yielding a dicentric chromosome. An anaphase bridge results in breakage (shown by* arrow), *followed by repetition of the cycle. Gene duplications and deletions result, as illustrated. (From McClintock, Fig. 1.[59])*

Fig. 10-16. Here, an alkylating agent was administered to mice bearing a transplantable carcinoma, and the tumor cells were examined 48 hours later.

The precise morphologic classification of the individual chromosomes of a diploid set (the *karyotype*), which has been applied increasingly to human and other cells in recent years, makes it easy to recognize the kinds of gross chromosome alterations described above. Agreement between deductions from genetic evidence and observed aberrant morphology has been remarkable. Especially in the giant salivary gland chromosomes of *Drosophila* have structural alterations been discernible that were predicted from genetic evidence. In all such cases the modified chromosomes replicate and undergo mitosis normally, provided the mutant phenotype is viable. In this way even major chromosome abnormalities can become established in the germ line of the species. And since hereditary defects have been associated with such visible abnormalities, it follows that agents capable of breaking chromosomes are also capable of causing genetic damage.

The mechanisms of chromosome breakage by x-rays or chemical mutagens are still poorly understood.[61] Because the effects of x-rays depend upon the presence of oxygen and can be modified by inhibitors of cell

59 B. MC CLINTOCK: The stability of broken ends of chromosomes in *Zea mays. Genetics 26:*234 (1941).

60 P. C. KOLLER: Comparative effects of alkylating agents on cellular morphology. *Ann. New York Acad. Sci. 68:*783 (1958).

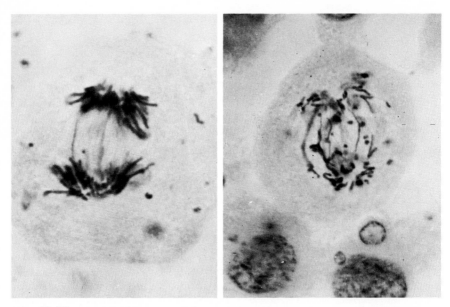

FIG. 10-16.   CHROMOSOME ABNORMALITIES INDUCED BY MECHLORETHAMINE. *Mice bearing Walker carcinoma 256 were given the nitrogen mustard mechlorethamine, a single dose of 1 mg/kg intraperitoneally. Microphotograph at* left *shows a cell at mitosis 48 hours later. Chromosome bridges (chiasmata) and fragments are evident. Photograph at* right *shows bridges and more severe fragmentation in a cell at mitosis 56 hours after drug treatment.* × *2500. (From Koller, Fig. 6,[60] by courtesy of the author.)*

respiration, it is assumed that the direct action of radiation upon a target molecule is only the first step in a complex biochemical process that leads eventually to a chromosome break. Alkylating agents are very effective chromosome breakers, mimicking radiation effects so closely that they have been called "radiomimetic."[62-64] An outstanding difference, however, is the absence of an oxygen requirement for their chromosome breaking action. Another difference is that long-delayed effects are much more commonly encountered after alkylating agents than after x-ray treatment. Bifunctional alkylating agents have been shown by physical methods of

[61] B. A. KIHLMAN: Biochemical aspects of chromosome breakage. *Adv. Genet. 10:*1 (1961).

[62] A. MICHAELIS, H. NICOLOFF, and R. RIEGER: Influences of EDTA on the induction of chromatid aberrations by triethylenemelamine and ethyl alcohol. *Biochem. Biophys. Res. Comm. 9:*280 (1962).

[63] J. J. BIESELE: Mitotic Poisons and the Cancer Problem. Amsterdam, Elsevier Publishing Co., 1958.

[64] A. T. NATARAJAN and M. D. UPADHYA: Localized chromosome breakage induced by ethyl-methane-sulfonate and hydroxylamine in *Vicia faba. Chromosoma 15:*156 (1964).

measurement to cross-link strands of DNA,[65] but this cross-linked material did not lose its biologic activity.[66] Moreover, the effectiveness of mono-functional alkylating agents as chromosome breakers[67] makes it very un-likely that cross-linking is an important mechanism of this mutagenic action. And a great many of the chemical mutagens that induce base pair trans-formations can break chromosomes.

It seems very likely, therefore, that chromosome breakage is related in some fundamental way to other mechanisms of mutagenesis. Bromouracil, for example, is a very good chromosome breaker in mam-malian cells in vitro,[68,69] suggesting that its incorporation instead of thymine may somehow lead to weak spots in the DNA. Hydroxylamine not only causes chromatid breaks but also inhibits the repair of breaks produced by x-rays.[70] It is difficult to extract a unifying theme from the tangled evidence about chromosome breakage. However, since breakage and reunion can be viewed as normal events in the cycle of replication of the genetic material, perhaps most chromosome breakers really act (as suggested by the hydroxylamine evidence) as repair inhibitors.

Caffeine derivatives and certain related purines also break chromo-somes, despite the fact that they are not incorporated into DNA.[71,61] One of the best chromosome breakers is 8-ethoxycaffeine, which causes

8-ethoxycaffeine   tetramethyluric acid

a variety of chromosome aberrations in bean root-tip cells during a stage in the mitotic cycle when DNA is not being synthesized.[72] Shortly after treatment, the chromosomes begin to appear "sticky"; after this stage there

[65] K. W. KOHN, C. L. SPEARS, and P. DOTY: Inter-strand crosslinking of DNA by nitrogen mustard. *J. Mol. Biol. 19:*266 (1966).

[66] K. W. KOHN and D. M. GREEN: Transforming activity of nitrogen mustard-cross-linked DNA. *J. Mol. Biol. 19:*289 (1966).

[67] C. AUERBACH: Mutagenic effects of alkylating agents. *Ann. New York Acad. Sci. 68:*731 (1958).

[68] T. C. HSU and C. E. SOMERS: Effect of 5-bromodeoxyuridine on mammalian chromosomes. *Proc. Nat. Acad. Sci. U.S.A. 47:*396 (1961).

[69] E. H. Y. CHU: Effects of ultraviolet radiation on mammalian cells. I. Induction of chromosome aberrations. *Mutation Res. 2:*75 (1965).

[70] N. S. COHN: The effect of hydroxylamine on the rejoining of x-ray-induced chromatid breaks in *Vicia faba. Mutation Res. 1:*409 (1964).

is the usual progression to abnormal mitoses and chromosome fragmentation. The closely related tetramethyluric acid behaves differently, in that it only affects cells that are in mitosis during treatment. Thus, after the initial "stickiness" and consequent breakage in some of the cells, no further aberrations are seen for about 24 hours. Then, a new wave of chromosome abnormalities appears as the cells damaged originally come once more into mitosis. It has been suggested that tetramethyluric acid, which is less lipid soluble than 8-ethoxycaffeine, cannot penetrate the nuclear membrane and thus acts only at mitosis, when that membrane has disintegrated.[61] With both these agents, as with most chromosome breakers, the frequencies of aberrations per cell and of cells containing aberrations are dose related.

Deletions are interesting because they occur in all sizes, both spontaneously and consequent to treatment with a mutagen. In bacteriophage T4, deletions were recognized by the fact that they could not be caused to revert to the wild type, and that they would not yield wild-type recombinants when crossed with certain point mutants.[14] The extent and position of each deletion was found by crossing it with point mutants whose positions had been mapped; every point mutant with which no wild-type recombinants were obtained must lie within the region of the deletion. The results of such studies led to a simple conclusion. Deletions can occur spontaneously anywhere along the rII gene. Their lengths range from a few base pairs to most of the gene. They can cross the boundary between two adjacent cistrons;[73] when this happens, the region of separation between the two protein products is deleted, and one continuous protein is probably synthesized, with a certain number of amino acids missing where one protein should end and the next should begin. Nitrous acid, it has already been pointed out, causes major deletions in phage DNA, perhaps by interrupting replication at points where guanine has been deaminated to xanthine (p. 632). Deletions are common results of chromosome breakage in higher organisms because of the loss of terminal segments after single breaks and loss of internal portions of chromatids after double breaks. It is not known if the mechanism of deletion is the same in all kinds of chromosomes.

Streptonigrin, an antibiotic from a streptomycete, has remarkable effects at extraordinarily low concentration upon chromosomes of cultured human leukocytes.[74] At $2 \times 10^{-9} M$, this compound produced an average of

[71] G. ODMARK and B. A. KIHLMAN: Effects of chromosome-breaking purine derivatives on nucleic acid synthesis and on the levels of adenosine 5'-triphosphate and deoxyadenosine 5'-triphosphate in bean root tips. *Mutation Res.* 2:274 (1965).

[72] D. SCOTT and H. J. EVANS: On the non-requirement for deoxyribonucleic acid synthesis in the production of chromosome aberrations by 8-ethoxycaffeine. *Mutation Res.* 1:146 (1964).

[73] S. BENZER and S. P. CHAMPE: A change from nonsense to sense in the genetic code. *Proc. Nat. Acad. Sci. U.S.A.* 48:1114 (1962).

[74] M. M. COHEN, M. W. SHAW, and A. P. CRAIG: The effects of streptonigrin on cultured human leukocytes. *Proc. Nat. Acad. Sci. U.S.A.* 50:16 (1963).

TABLE 10-3.   Some agents capable of breaking chromosomes

(Compiled from Biesele[63] and Kihlman.[61])

Urethane and other carbamates	4-Dimethylaminostilbene
Phenols	Naphthoquinone
Diamidines	Menadione
Ethyl alcohol and other alcohols	*p*-Phenylenediamine
Acridines	Various inorganic salts
Alkylating agents: triethylenemelamine, busulfan, mustards, diepoxybutane, and other diepoxides	Colchicine
	Acenaphthene
	Camphor and borneol
Caffeine and its congeners	Maleic hydrazide
Adenine and its analogues	N-Methylphenylnitrosamine
Coumarin	

nearly three breaks per cell in 12 hours; in contrast, bromouracil deoxyriboside at 40,000 times this concentration produced only two breaks per cell after 28 days. The streptonigrin effects comprised every kind of abnormality, including chromatid breaks (discontinuity of one chromatid in a pair), isochromatid breaks (discontinuity of both chromatids at the same position), acentric fragments, dicentric chromosomes, translocation cross-configurations, end-to-end association of chromosomes, anaphase bridges, uncoiling, and severe fragmentation.

Table 10-3 lists a wide variety of compounds that have been implicated as chromosome breakers. It is true that in most of the experiments plant materials like bean or onion root tips were used; but whenever human cells have been exposed in vitro to the same mutagens, similar effects were seen. In most investigations, fairly high concentrations of the agents were used in order to produce a large enough number of chromosome abnormalities for ready visualization. It is difficult to say what hazard may be presented by exposure of human cells in vivo to these same agents (some of which are drugs in common use) at ordinary doses. This problem is discussed in a wider context in a later section of this chapter.

METAPHASE POISONING (SPINDLE INACTIVATION)

The function of mitosis is to ensure the equipartition of the entire chromosome complement into two daughter cells at division. The function of meiosis is to partition the two representations of each chromosome into two germ cells. The processes that ensure the orderly preparation and execution of the anaphase movement—of sister chromosomes in mitosis, of homologous chromosomes in meiosis—are extremely complex.[75] The

[75] D. MAZIA: "Mitosis and the Physiology of Cell Division," in *The Cell, vol. III. Meiosis and Mitosis,* ed. by J. Brachet and A. E. Mirsky. New York, Academic Press, 1961, chapter 2.

essentials are: (*1*) proper duplication and polar positioning of the centrioles, to which the spindle apparatus will be attached; (*2*) correct alignment of the chromosome pairs on the equatorial plate at metaphase, each attached by its centromere to a spindle fiber; and (*3*) proper synthesis and functioning of the spindle fibers, mediating the poleward migration of the chromosomes at anaphase. Metaphase poisons disrupt this sequence of events and thereby produce arrested or grossly abnormal meiosis or mitosis.[76-80]

The mitotic apparatus consists largely of a special kind of protein saccharide. Most spindle poisons do not inhibit the synthesis of the mitotic apparatus but somehow alter or destroy its fibrillar character. that can assume a fibrillar configuration, and also of some RNA and poly-Disulfide bonds appear to play some essential role in the polymerization of proteins of the mitotic apparatus to form spindle fibers. Reagents that form mercaptides, such as phenylmercuric ion or arsenite, are spindle poisons in vivo and also dissolve the isolated mitotic apparatus. Furthermore, the mitotic apparatus can be protected from degradation during its isolation if a disulfide (e.g., dithiodiglycol) is present. At least some of the fibers, those that attach to the chromosome centromeres, appear to contain contractile elements, which probably depend upon energy from ATP. Thus, nonspecific uncoupling agents or respiratory poisons also inhibit mitosis.

The classic example of a specific spindle poison is colchicine.[63,78,81]

colchicine

This curious molecule, with two seven-membered rings, is derived from the plant *Colchicum autumnale,* the meadow saffron. At very low concentrations (about $10^{-8}M$) it disrupts spindle function by inhibiting the formation of fibrils; yet the specific protein of the mitotic apparatus can still be

[76] A. HUGHES: *The Mitotic Cycle.* New York, Academic Press, 1952.

[77] H. STERN: The physiology of cell division. *Ann. Rev. Plant Physiol.* 7:91 (1956).

[78] P. DUSTIN, JR.: New aspects of the pharmacology of antimitotic agents. *Pharmacol. Rev. 15*:449 (1963).

[79] A. BARTHELMESS: Chemisch induzierte multipolare Mitosen. *Protoplasma 48*:546 (1957).

[80] A. BARTHELMESS and J. EINLECHNER: Chemisch induzierte multipolare Mitosen. II. *Protoplasma 51*:325 (1959).

[81] A. LEVAN: The effect of colchicine on root mitoses in *Allium. Hereditas 24*:471 (1938).

demonstrated. Thus, colchicine seems to prevent formation of secondary bonds involved in a polymerization step; but its biochemical mechanism of action remains obscure. Its effects are strictly confined to metaphase, and at concentrations sufficient to block mitosis it does not inhibit DNA, RNA, or protein synthesis.[82] The cytologic picture of colchicine poisoning is so characteristic that it is called "colchicine mitosis" or simply "c-mitosis." At low concentrations unusual mitotic patterns develop, sometimes resulting in an incorrect distribution of chromosomes to the daughter cells. At higher concentrations the drug produces complete metaphase arrest; this accounts for its usefulness as a tool for obtaining a great many cells in mitosis. Polyploidy is frequently the outcome of colchicine treatment, because chromosomes in mitosis split but are unable to separate, and thus doubled in number enter a new cycle of replication.

Another plant product with similar action is podophyllotoxin, a polycyclic lactone related to the coumarins, which are also metaphase

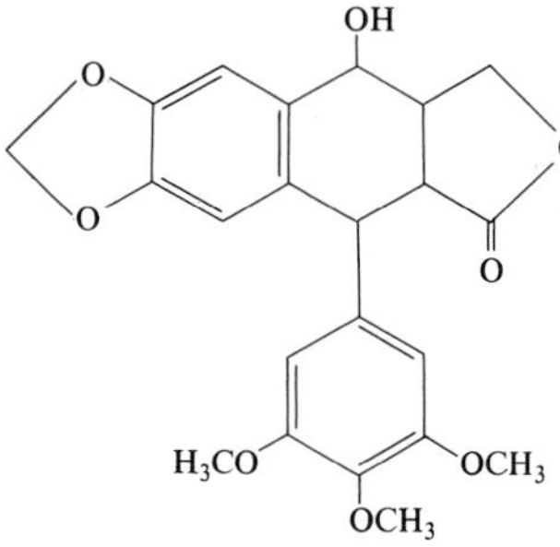

podophyllotoxin

poisons. Several medicinal plant alkaloids, some carcinogens (e.g., methylcholanthrene), androgenic and estrogenic hormones, chloral hydrate, and ether are among the commonly used drugs that can act as spindle poisons. Some agents used to treat cancer depend upon mitotic poisoning for their therapeutic effects; vinblastine[83] and griseofulvin are examples. Table 10-4 is a partial list of metaphase poisons, indicating how wide a variety of compounds have this action, at least under certain experimental conditions.

The complete arrest of mitosis is, of course, incompatible with viability. But partial metaphase inhibition can lead to a great variety of bizarre mitotic figures and unusual chromosome distributions in daughter

82 E. W. TAYLOR: The mechanism of colchicine inhibition of mitosis. I. Kinetics of inhibition and the binding of H3-colchicine. *J. Cell Biol. 25:* No. 1, Part 2, p. 145 (1965).

83 N. BRUCHOVSKY, A. A. OWEN, A. J. BECKER, and J. E. TILL: Effects of vinblastine on the proliferative capacity of L cells and their progress through the division cycle. *Cancer Res. 25:*1232 (1965).

TABLE 10-4.   Some metaphase poisons

(Compiled from Biesele[63] and Dustin.[78])

Colchicine	Apomorphine
Podophyllotoxin	Papaverine
Menadione	Hexachlorocyclohexane
Methylcholanthrene and other carcinogenic hydrocarbons	Coumarin and other lactones
Methyltestosterone, estradiol, and stilbestrol	Organic arsenicals, mercurials, and lead compounds
Naphthalene, acenaphthene, and congeners	Quinones and phenols
	Antifolic drugs
Chloral hydrate	Purine and pyrimidine base analogues
Penicillin	Amino acid analogues
Camphor and borneol	Heparin
Numerous benzene derivatives	Griseofulvin
Quinine	Vinblastine
Emetine	Phenylurethane

cells. As with gene mutations, here too the only effects that need concern us are those that allow cell survival. One of the most serious of these effects from the standpoint of genetic disease is the unequal partition of chromosomes to daughter cells, an event known as *nondisjunction*. This occurs when both chromosomes of a pair move into the same cell because of faulty attachment of a spindle fiber to a centromere or because of some defect in spindle function. Whether this occurs during mitosis in the gonadal germ cell line or during the meiotic divisions preceding the formation of spermatozoa and ova, abnormal gametes are produced. The gamete lacking a whole chromosome will usually not be capable of producing a viable zygote. But the gamete containing an extra chromosome can produce offspring. "Mongolism," characterized by mental deficiency as well as other abnormalities, is associated regularly with the presence of an additional copy of chromosome 21 ("21-trisomy").[84] People with this defect can be shown to have 47 chromosomes in all their body cells instead of the normal 46. Likewise, sexual abnormalities of several kinds have been traced to an unusual number of X or Y chromosomes.[85] The cause of "spontaneous" nondisjunction is unknown. The incidence of 21-trisomy increases significantly with increasing maternal age, but why older oocytes should be more prone to abnormal meiosis than younger ones remains obscure. The ability of exogenous compounds like colchicine to produce nondisjunction in some cells raises the possibility that drugs or other environmental agents may be contributing to the incidence of trisomy in man.

[84] J. LEJEUNE: The 21 trisomy—current stage of chromosomal research. *Progr. Med. Genetics 3*:144 (1964).

[85] W. M. DAVIDSON and D. R. SMITH, eds.: *Proceedings of the Conference on Human Chromosomal Abnormalities.* London, Staples Press, 1961.

CHEMICAL MUTAGENESIS IN ANIMALS AND MAN

The Human Germ Line

Inherited defects arise by mutation in the germ line. Each person may be regarded as a differentiated clone of cells derived from the fusion of a paternal and maternal gamete to form a zygote. Mutations can be introduced into the human germ line only during the reproductive life of the individual, a period of about 30 years on the average. Therefore the hazards of mutagenesis, chemical or otherwise, concern only the young population. These hazards are peculiar because genetic damage does not affect the exposed individual, but may remain concealed for generations until homozygosity makes it manifest.

Primordial germ cells are first distinguishable at about the sixth week of fetal life. Development proceeds differently in the two sexes. In the female, all the primary oocytes (about 400,000) are produced from undifferentiated oogonia during fetal life. No further cell divisions are believed to occur until puberty, when the monthly maturation of single ova begins. This maturation process entails two meiotic divisions, followed by the degeneration of three of the four meiotic products as polar bodies.

In the male, a population of primary spermatogonia persists in the germinal layer of the seminiferous tubules of the testis. These *stem cells* undergo mitosis about once every 12 days, giving rise to nonequivalent daughter cells. One daughter cell retains the characteristics of a primary spermatogonium, the other migrates toward the lumen of the tubule and becomes a primary spermatocyte, the progenitor of four mature spermatozoa. In this way stem cell renewal and sperm production continue throughout childhood and reproductive life; but before puberty the sperms degenerate.[86]

The continuity of the male germ line through one human generation is shown schematically in Fig. 10-17. Period 1 contains all the mitotic cycles (about 50 on the average)[87] between the zygote and the population of primordial germ cells; its duration is about six weeks. (In the female, another 17 mitotic cycles serve to produce all the primary oocytes in both ovaries.) Period 2 lasts until puberty, about 12 to 14 years; and period 3 encompasses the remainder of reproductive life. If the average generation time is taken to be 30 years, then these periods of stem cell renewal

---

[86] C. P. LEBLOND, E. STEINBERGER, and E. C. ROOSEN-RUNGE: "Spermatogenesis," in *Mechanisms Concerned with Conception,* ed. by C. G. Hartman. New York, Macmillan Co., 1963, chapter I.

[87] We are not speaking of the total number of cell divisions, which would be one less than the total cell population at the end of the period under consideration. We are concerned here with the number of times the chromosomes of any given cell in the final population have replicated.

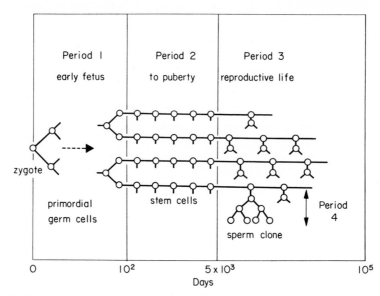

FIG. 10-17.   THE GERM LINE OF MAN.   *A schematic diagram showing the four periods of possible sensitivity to mutagens in the human male. (In the female, periods 2 and 3 are effectively absent, and period 4 represents the two meiotic divisions at the time of fertilization of the ovum.) (From Goldstein, Fig. 25.*[88]*)*

(average cycle 12 days) contain about 900 mitotic cycles in the male. (Periods 2 and 3 are absent in the female.) Finally, period 4 comprises the two meiotic divisions by which the male and female gametes are formed. Thus, on the average, a zygote is formed by the union of a sperm whose chromosomes have replicated approximately 950 times since the previous generation, and an ovum whose chromosomes have replicated only about 70 times in the same period.

It will be evident from this account that the occurrence of new mutations might follow a different course in the two sexes. *In the female,* mutagens that act only on replicating DNA or on the mitotic process should have effects primarily during fetal life. Mutagens that act on nonreplicating DNA might act throughout the female's life. Agents that disturb meiosis would act only at the time of conception, when the meiotic divisions occur. As discussed already (p. 645), this is probably the time when most spontaneous mutations occur. *In the male,* on the other hand, the risk of mutation by agents that act on replicating DNA or on the mitotic process should span the whole reproductive life cycle. The male stem cell line passes through so many more mitotic cycles than does the

[88] A. GOLDSTEIN: "Mutagens Currently of Potential Significance to Man and Other Species," in *Mutations. Second Macy Conference on Genetics,* ed. by W. J. Schull. Ann Arbor, University of Michigan Press, 1962, p. 167.

TABLE 10-5. **Partial sterility and translocations induced in mice by an alkylating agent**

Triethylenemelamine (0.2 mg/kg) was administered in a single intraperitoneal injection to male mice. These were mated daily to untreated females 1, 2, and 3 days after injection, and again after 10, 11, 12, and 13 days. F_1 males were tested for partial sterility and examined cytologically for translocations. (Data of Cattanach,[89] Tables 1 and 2. By permission of Springer.)

Litter size in matings with treated males	
Days after drug	**Average litter size**
1	6.3
2	5.3
3	7.3
10	1.7
11	2.0
12	1.6
13	3.6
Control	8.5

Sterility and translocations in F_i males			
Days after drug on which F_1 males were conceived	**Number tested**	**% sterile or semisterile**	**% showing translocations**
1–3	111	4.5	7.2
10–13	74	14.9	28.4

female that such mutagens should cause the accumulation of many more mutations in sperm than in ova, other factors being equal. Agents that only affect meiosis should act, in the male, during a period of a few weeks prior to the coitus that leads to conception.

It follows that mutations arising in relation to DNA replication and cell division, whatever their cause, should produce genetic defects whose incidence is correlated with paternal age but not with maternal age. Such a correlation is actually observed for two genetic diseases of man, hemophilia and chondrodystrophy. Mongolism, on the other hand, is correlated exclusively with maternal age, the implication of which has been discussed (p. 656). Since it remains somewhat uncertain which mutagenic agents act upon what stages of DNA replication or of the mitotic or meiotic cycle, only one practical conclusion can be derived, apart from the general injunction to minimize exposure to mutagens. Since by far the greatest number of mitotic cycles in the female germ line occurs during the first two months of fetal life, it seems wise to avoid unnecessary exposure of preg-

89 B. M. CATTANACH: The sensitivity of the mouse testis to the mutagenic action of triethylenemelamine. *Z. Vererbungs. 90:*1 (1959).

nant women to any potentially mutagenic agent from a time just prior to conception through the first trimester of pregnancy. This recommendation relates also to potentially teratogenic agents (cf. chapter 12).

Large differences in mutagenicity, depending upon the time of treatment, as demonstrated for mice in Table 10-5, are fairly typical. They reflect differences in sensitivity of the various stages of spermatogenesis. Since spermatogonia in the stem cell line, premeiotic (primary) spermatocytes, postmeiotic (secondary) spermatocytes, spermatids, and spermatozoa are all present simultaneously, they are all necessarily exposed to the mutagen. But if the treatment is brief and matings are conducted on successive days, one can distinguish which stages of germ cell maturation are most sensitive. If the litters conceived shortly after treatment are affected, then the agent must have caused mutations in the mature spermatozoa. The data of Table 10-5 show, on the contrary, that the most sensitive forms were those that required 10 to 13 days to mature after treatment; in mice, these would be the postmeiotic spermatids. In *Drosophila,* too, the spermatids are the germ cells most sensitive to alkylating agents and radiation. The quantitative differences between the stages, in oogenesis as well as in spermatogenesis, may be very great.[90,91]

Some Common Methods of Testing Mutagenicity in Animals

Since experiments on chemical mutagenesis are obviously out of the question in man, both on moral and technical grounds, our assessment of the mutagenic hazards associated with exposure to drugs and other agents necessarily rests upon genetic investigations in other animals. One naturally supposes that the sensitivity of the genetic apparatus to mutagens will be most nearly the same in closely related species. Although much of modern genetics rests upon experiments with *Drosophila,* mice have been used increasingly as a practical mammalian model.[92] Because large-scale breeding is often required, especially to detect low mutation rates, larger mammals are excluded on practical grounds. Induced dominant mutations are readily observed, but detection of induced recessive mutations requires the use of specially bred stocks of animals. Since recessive mutations are expressed in the homozygous state, a good test of mutagenesis is to mate an animal treated with a mutagen to an animal that is already heterozygous for certain traits. If the treatment induces a mutation at a corresponding locus, then some of the offspring will be homozygous for the mutant trait.

90 T. ALDERSON and M. PELECANOS: The mutagenic activity of diethyl sulphate in *Drosophila melanogaster.* II. The sensitivity of the immature (larval) and adult testis. *Mutation Res. 1:*182 (1964).

91 M. PELECANOS and T. ALDERSON: The mutagenic activity of diethyl sulphate in *Drosophila melanogaster.* III. The sensitivity of the immature (larval) and adult ovary. *Mutation Res. 1:*302 (1964).

92 D. GRAHN: "Mammalian Radiation Genetics," in *Methodology in Mammalian Genetics,* ed. by W. J. Burdette. San Francisco, Holden-Day, 1963, p. 127.

In devising such tests, advantage is often taken of the fact that the male is hemizygous for the X chromosome; thus, for example, one-half the male offspring of a treated female with an induced X-chromosome mutation will display the mutant trait.

A good example of the adroit use of sex linkage in a test for mutagenesis is the classical *ClB method* in *Drosophila*.[93] The procedure requires a stock of females heterozygous for two mutant traits carried on the same X chromosome—bar eye (a visible characteristic) and a recessive lethal trait. Males are treated with a mutagen and then mated to the special females. Female F_1 offspring with bar eye are selected for the next round of breeding. These animals will have the maternal X chromosome carrying the bar eye allele, and also the recessive lethal gene carried with it. Their other X chromosome is inherited from the treated males. The question is whether any recessive lethal mutations were induced in that X chromosome during the mutagen treatment.[94] The answer is obtained very simply by breeding these females with ordinary males and examining the sex of F_2 offspring. If a recessive lethal mutation is present in the X chromosome derived from the treated males, there will be no viable male F_2 offspring whatsoever, because both maternal X chromosomes would then carry recessive (but nonallelic) lethal mutations and all F_2 males would express one or the other lethal trait. Conversely, if any males are found, then no recessive lethals had been induced.

Dominant lethal mutations are detected by exposing males to a mutagenic treatment, mating them to normal females, and then simply observing the number of viable offspring. This test is frequently employed in mice. To ensure detection of nonviable embryos, the pregnant females are sacrificed just before term in order to count the number of live embryos, the number of dead embryos, and the number of corpora lutea (whence the number of preimplantation deaths can be estimated, since each corpus luteum represents one ovum).[95] Dominant lethals are often due to major chromosome abnormalities that are incompatible with development of the zygote.

Chromosome translocations have been observed microscopically in mice after the following selection procedure.[89] The F_1 male offspring of males originally treated with a mutagen were mated with normal females and their litter size was used as a preliminary screening criterion. Whenever

[93] H. J. MULLER: The measurement of gene mutation rate in Drosophila, its high variability, and its dependence upon temperature. *Genetics 13:*279 (1928).

[94] We are concerned here with mutations that are not allelic with the recessive lethal already carried by the female. In the occasional instance of induced mutation at the same gene locus, no F_1 offspring would be obtained, since the zygote would be homozygous for the lethal trait.

[95] M. PARTINGTON and A. J. BATEMAN: Dominant lethal mutations induced in male mice by methyl methanesulphonate. *Heredity 19:*191 (1964).

the average litter size derived from a given F_1 male was smaller than normal, a direct cytologic examination of that animal's testis was carried out. If 19 instead of the normal 20 chromosomes were seen consistently in metaphase configurations, a translocation was assumed to be present. Table 10-5 presents data of a typical experiment with an alkylating agent, in which dominant lethals as well as translocations were induced. The size of litters derived from treated males was greatly reduced 10 to 13 days after treatment. The translocation test showed that the male offspring of these same treated males carried translocations and were partially sterile, and again the peak effect was seen in offspring of males treated 10 to 13 days after drug treatment.

Another method, which has yielded important information about radiation mutagenesis in mice, is the *specific locus method*.[96] It, too, depends upon the expression of mutations when they are homozygous; the traits considered here are readily observable, visible abnormalities such as unusual coat color or peculiar shape of the ear. A special stock of mice was bred, heterozygous for seven such traits carried on seven different autosomal genes. Males or females are exposed to the mutagenic treatment and then mated to mice of the opposite sex belonging to the special stock. Then the F_1 offspring are examined. Whenever a mutation has been induced in one of the seven loci in a treated mouse, its offspring will be homozygous for that particular trait.

The method can be illustrated by an experiment on radiation mutagenesis. Males were given 600 roentgens of whole-body x-irradiation. They were then allowed to recover from the postirradiation sterility, so that the spermatozoa available for the matings developed from irradiated spermatogonia. These treated males were mated with females of the special stock, and unirradiated control males were also mated. In the control group, in which 37,868 offspring were examined, two mutant animals were found. In the irradiated group, in which 48,007 offspring were examined, 53 mutants were found. The mean mutation rate induced by x-irradiation was therefore computed to be $2.5 \pm 0.4 \times 10^{-7}$ per roentgen per locus. The disadvantage of this method is evident from the data; enormous numbers of animals have to be bred and examined. And although a good quantitative estimation can be made when mutagenesis is strong, the accuracy of estimate for a weak mutagen (e.g., one that only doubled the spontaneous mutation rate) would be very poor because of the extremely small number of mutations observed. Another problem is that the seven chosen genes differ considerably among themselves in their sensitivities to mutagenic treatments, so that "mean mutation rate" may have no relevance to actual rates at the most sensitive gene loci in man.

---

96 W. L. RUSSELL: X-ray-induced mutations in mice. *Cold Spring Harbor Symp. Quant. Biol. 16*:327 (1951).

Evaluation of the Hazards of Chemical Mutagens in Man

The difficulties of arriving at quantitative estimates of mutagenicity for chemical agents in human populations are very great. Indeed, it has yet to be shown that any chemical agent has produced genetic defects in man. Even in the case of radiation mutagenesis, which is generally accepted as a fact, most of the evidence comes from animal experimentation. The human exposed to radiation or to a chemical mutagen is not expected to be affected himself except at doses large enough to cause sterility. Even the offspring of the exposed person may seem unaffected if the induced mutation is recessive or incompletely expressed. Thus, many induced mutations will only be manifested in future generations through the eventual union of gametes both of which are heterozygous for the same recessive alleles. It follows that much of the data bearing directly upon the human species will have to be epidemiologic rather than experimental. It also follows that a conservative position with respect to mutagenic hazards in humans will be based frequently on common-sense judgments rather than on iron-clad proofs. By assuming a conservative position we mean that we wish to err, when in doubt, in the direction of overestimating the potential mutagenic hazard.[87]

A growing number of genetic diseases are being identified in man. Most estimates show[2] that every sperm or ovum carries several mutant genes, accumulated over the past history of the race, and that as many as one person in three carries a new mutation not present in either of his parents. These accumulated and newly altered mutant genes are attributed to past and present "spontaneous" mutation. And even if spontaneous mutation in humans arises principally from unequal crossovers during meiotic division, the question still remains whether or not the probability of such an event is influenced by exogenous factors. It is quite clear from what is known about radiation mutagenesis that lifelong exposure to background radiation could not account for more than a small fraction of the total spontaneous mutation rate. Occasionally, a "mutator gene" renders an organism and its progeny subject to very high spontaneous mutation rates, probably by production of an endogenous mutagen.[29,97-99] In addition, the human race is exposed to many exogenous compounds that are known to be mutagenic to lower forms of life. Since no estimates of the "spontaneous" mutation rate in man have been made in the absence of exposure to potentially mutagenic exogenous substances, the possibility must be enter-

97 B. L. S. PIERCE: The effect of a bacterial mutator gene upon mutation rates in bacteriophage T4. *Genetics 54:*657 (1966).

98 A. GOLDSTEIN and J. S. SMOOT: A strain of *Escherichia coli* with an unusually high rate of auxotrophic mutation. *J. Bacteriol. 70:*588 (1955).

99 H. P. TREFFERS, V. SPINELLI, and N. O. BELSER: A factor (or mutator gene) influencing mutation rates in *Escherichia coli. Proc. Nat. Acad. Sci. U.S.A. 40:*1064 (1954).

tained that some part of the apparent spontaneous rate may be due to exogenous chemical mutagens.

In organisms in which chemical mutagenesis has been demonstrated, the concentrations usually employed have been very high compared with those to which humans might be exposed. If extrapolation from such data to man is to have any validity, a knowledge of the dose-response relationship is essential. This relationship has been worked out for very few mutagens. Especially important is the question whether the probability of mutation is a simple product of dose (concentration) by duration of exposure. Is prolonged exposure of humans to very low doses equivalent in mutagenic efficiency to the short exposures at high doses in laboratory experiments? For radiation mutagenesis it is now known that chronic low-dosage exposure is several times less efficient than acute high-dosage exposure.

In the present state of our ignorance it would serve no purpose to list all drugs employed therapeutically and all environmental agents that might possibly be mutagenic to man. Such compilations are available,[100] but they may serve to distract attention from the few agents that deserve serious attention, either because of demonstrated strong mutagenicity in other species, or because of widespread human exposure coupled with evidence of weak mutagenicity in other species. Foremost among these are the alkylating agents and the analogues of nucleic acid bases, both used commonly in cancer chemotherapy. The inorganic nitrite ion, formerly used extensively as a food preservative, is certainly mutagenic (as nitrous acid) at the acid pH of the stomach, and perhaps at tissue pH. Organic nitrites are used medicinally, but their mutagenicity is unknown. Ethyl alcohol and nicotine are clearly mutagenic in various organisms, and a large part of the human race is exposed to them over long periods of time.

We shall take caffeine as prototype of a drug to which there is widespread exposure and for which there is evidence of mutagenicity in lower organisms. People who drink coffee several times daily establish and maintain a mean concentration equivalent to about $1 \mu g/ml$ throughout their body water.[87] This estimate is based on the total area under the time-concentration curve for subjects drinking three to four cups of coffee daily; naturally, the level fluctuates with each cup of coffee that is drunk. It is well established that caffeine permeates all cells and also crosses freely from the mother's blood into the fetus. Hence there is no doubt that the human germ line is exposed to this drug. Attempts to estimate what mutagenic effect, if any, will be produced by such exposure are beset by uncertainties. The evidence is summarized below.

Caffeine mutagenicity in *E. coli* is illustrated in Fig. 10-18. Here, the cells were grown at a constant exponential rate in a chemostat. The

100 A. BARTHELMESS: Mutagene Arzneimittel. *Arzneimittel-Forsch.* 6:157 (1956).

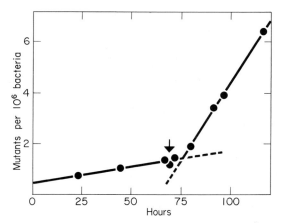

FIG. 10-18. MUTAGENIC EFFECTS OF CAFFINE ON ESCHĒRICHIA COLI. *The cells (strain B/1,t) were grown in a chemostat with limiting concentration of tryptophan in the input medium. Generation time = 5.5 hours. Samples were taken periodically and plated on phage T5. Ordinates are numbers of T5-resistant mutants per 10⁶ cells. Caffeine (150 μg/ml) was added at arrow. (Modified from Novick, Fig. 4.[101])*

steady-state population was maintained by continuous inflow of fresh medium containing a limiting concentration of tryptophan (required by this strain) and continuous outflow of the same volume of the culture. A small sample was removed periodically and plated on phage T5. Resistant mutants give rise to colonies, which can be counted. In this system the T5-resistant mutants grow at the same rate as the wild type. Therefore, if no new mutants arose, the proportion of mutants would remain constant. The observed linear increase in the proportion of mutants reflects a constant rate of appearance of new mutants; it is a direct measure of the mutation rate. It can be seen that when caffeine was added to the medium there was a short lag, and then the mutation rate increased ninefold. The concentration of caffeine was 150μg/ml, about 150 times the average concentration to which the germ cells of habitual coffee drinkers are exposed on a long-term basis.

If mutagenicity were a linear function of caffeine concentration without any threshold, and if all human genes were just as sensitive to caffeine as the gene controlling resistance to phage T5 in *E. coli,* then the following calculations might be in order: The concentration of caffeine that was employed produced an increment of the spontaneous mutation rate eight times the spontaneous rate itself. Therefore, the concentration required to double the spontaneous rate of mutation of the T5 gene would be 150/8, or 19μg/ml. The amount of radiation necessary to produce a

101 A. NOVICK: Mutagens and antimutagens. *Brookhaven Symp. Biol.* 8:201 (1956).

doubling of the spontaneous mutation rate in man is estimated to be about 200 roentgens, if administered over a long period of time. Then chronic exposure of habitual coffee drinkers to $1\mu g/ml$ of caffeine should be equivalent to approximately 200/19, or 10 roentgens of radiation.

It is interesting to make a similar computation in terms of the actual induced mutation rate per gene per cell cycle, to gain an idea of how many mutations per sperm (or ovum) might possibly be attributable to the drinking of caffeinated beverages. In the chemostat (Fig. 10-18), caffeine at $150\mu g/ml$ produced 17×10^{-8} mutations per hour in cells growing at a mean generation time of 5.5 hours. This amounts to 93.5×10^{-8} mutations of this gene per cell cycle, or 0.62×10^{-8} after reduction of the concentration by a factor of 150. The figure commonly used as a rough estimate of the number of mutable gene loci in man is 10^4. And we have seen that the male germ line undergoes about 950 cell division cycles between conception and age 30 (p. 658). Therefore the number of mutations per sperm caused by caffeine as a result of drinking coffee from age 15 to age 30 would be approximately $(0.62\times10^{-8}) \times 10^4 \times (950/2) = 2.9\times10^{-2}$. Thus, about 3 per cent of all sperm would carry a mutation caused by caffeine.

It may seem preposterous to estimate mutagenicity in the human from data on a single gene of *E. coli,* but there is no simple way to tell if this is as absurd as it seems. Mutagen specificity is so great, even between different genes of a single organism, that all extrapolations across species become suspect. Even in the same strain of *E. coli,* caffeine was much less mutagenic on the gene controlling resistance to phage T6. Another uncertainty concerns the question whether mutagenic action proceeds at a constant rate in real time, or at a constant rate per cell division cycle. There are conflicting data about this for caffeine, but in human cells caffeine seems to act primarily at the time of DNA replication,[102] suggesting that the rate per cell division cycle is the relevant factor. Surveying caffeine mutagenicity in a number of different species is one way to test the generality of the bacteriophage data. Certainly, if the mutagenic action turns out to be very weak in all species and on all genes tested, one gains confidence about the safety of such a drug in man. In *Drosophila,* studies were carried out by feeding larvae on caffeine-containing medium (2.5 mg/ml) and also by injecting males with single doses (about $400\mu g/g$).[103] The method of sex-linked lethals (p. 661) was used. The spontaneous mutation rate in these experiments, despite the very high caffeine dosage, was increased only fivefold, an effect equivalent to that obtained in *Drosophila* males with 150 roentgens of acute radiation. The radiation equivalent at $1\mu g/ml$ would be correspondingly lower.

102 W. OSTERTAG, E. DUISBERG, and M. STÜRMANN: The mutagenic activity of caffeine in man. *Mutation Res.* 2:293 (1965).

103 L. E. ANDREW: The mutagenic activity of caffein in *Drosophila. Amer. Naturalist* 93:135 (1959).

The specific locus method (p. 662) was used to assess caffeine mutagenicity in mice.[104] Ordinary mice were given caffeine (1 mg/ml) in their drinking water and then mated; their offspring were also given caffeine until ready to be mated. Thus, the treated mice had been exposed constantly from conception to mating. About 32,000 offspring of treated males mated to special stock females were examined, and about the same number of offspring of the reciprocal matings were also examined. Only one specific locus mutant was found, corresponding to a mutation rate per locus per gamete of 0.01×10^{-5} to 2.5×10^{-5} (the wide range represents the 95 per cent confidence limits). This mutation rate did not differ significantly from the spontaneous rate of 1.0×10^{-5}.

Another experiment assessed the frequency of dominant lethals and translocations induced by caffeine.[105] Male mice were given 3 mg/ml of caffeine in their drinking water. Male offspring of caffeine-treated males were studied at six weeks of age, first by determining litter sizes, then by examining testis preparations for translocations (p. 661). Of 201 F_1 males examined in this way, only 13 produced small litters; none of these semi-sterile animals showed typical translocations. Moreover, no dominant visible effects were seen in either the F_1 or the F_2 generation.

Recently, the chromosome-breaking action of caffeine has been studied in human (HeLa) cells in culture.[102] The cells were exposed to caffeine at various concentrations for 1 hour, then incubated for 24 hours, and chromosome analyses were carried out. As shown in Table 10-6, breaks and other abnormalities were produced, and the number of breaks was very nearly a linear function of caffeine concentration. The caffeine appeared to act only upon cells engaged in DNA replication. From the dose relationship it can be estimated that a concentration of $1\mu g/ml$ would produce a negligible increment in the spontaneous rate of chromosome breakage. In summary, the available data in bacteria, *Drosophila,* mice, and cells of human origin indicate that caffeine, at a concentration of $1\mu g/ml$, causes an increase of only a few per cent in the spontaneous mutation rate. It seems probable, therefore, that caffeine is not a significant mutagen in man.

A method that may prove useful for the study of mutagenic effects of drugs and environmental chemical agents in human populations makes use of the sex ratio as an indicator of sex-linked lethal mutations. The sex ratio is defined as the number of live-born boys per 100 live-born girls. If a man is exposed to a mutagen and a defect is induced on his X chromosome, then no male offspring will be affected (since sons inherit the paternal Y chromosome only), but female offspring may suffer partial or complete decrease of viability. Thus, the sex ratio at birth will increase

[104] M. F. LYON, R. J. S. PHILLIPS, and A. G. SEARLE: A test for mutagenicity of caffeine in mice. *Z. Vererbungs. 93*:7 (1962).

[105] B. M. CATTANACH: Genetical effects of caffeine in mice. *Z. Vererbungs. 93*:215 (1962).

TABLE 10-6.   Chromosome breaks induced by caffeine in cells of human origin

HeLa cells were cultured and treated for 1 hour with various concentrations of caffeine. Then the cells were washed with fresh growth medium and incubated another 24 hours. Chromosome analyses were performed, with the results tabulated below. Chromatid breaks (single chromatid) and isolocus breaks (both chromatids) were counted, and also translocations, dicentric chromosomes, and ring forms. (From Ostertag et al.,[102] Table 1.)

Caffeine (μg/ml)	Number of Chromosomes	Chromatid or isolocus breaks	Trans-locations	Dicentrics	Rings
0	4,187	4			
500	2,754	18		1	
1,000	3,693	47	*	2	
2,000	4,361	111	1		
3,000	2,663	106	1	2	
5,000	5,666	401	5	2	3
10,000	3,456	763	11	3	

* 2 cells with 10 translocations.

to the extent that nonviable female zygotes or fetuses are present. Conversely, if females are exposed to a mutagen, then one-half their male offspring will carry a mutant maternal X chromosome, and any recessive lethal alleles will be expressed. In this instance, the sex ratio will decrease. The method was used, with somewhat equivocal result, to ascertain whether or not genetic damage was produced among radiation-exposed survivors of the nuclear blast at Hiroshima.[106] There is also weak evidence suggesting that habitual smoking of cigarettes may be mutagenic; in several large statistical surveys it was found that in matings between smoker men and nonsmoker women, the sex ratio of their offspring significantly exceeded that found among nonsmokers.[107] However, the interpretation of this interesting finding is considerably beclouded by two facts: first, that the sex ratio in the entire white population of the United States is as high as 106 boys to 100 girls; and second, that even reciprocal matings (nonsmoker men with smoker women) yielded a high sex ratio, although mutation in the females should have lowered the sex ratio. Despite these difficulties, it may be that carefully constructed statistical studies in large populations containing both exposed and nonexposed people will be able to detect drug-induced mutations by their effects on the sex ratio.

[106] J. V. NEEL: *Changing Perspectives on the Genetic Effects of Radiation.* Springfield, Ill. Charles C Thomas, 1963.

[107] A. DAMON, R. L. NUTTALL, E. J. SALBER, C. C. SELTZER, and B. MAC MAHON: Tobacco smoke as a possible genetic mutagen: parental smoking and sex of children. *Amer. J. Epidemiol. 83:*530 (1966).

11

CHEMICAL

CARCINOGENESIS

Cancer is the malignant unrestrained proliferation of somatic cells. It occurs spontaneously and can also be induced by ionizing radiation, viruses, and chemicals known as *carcinogens*. Chemical carcinogenesis was discovered in man long before it could be demonstrated experimentally in animals. In 1775, cancer of the scrotum was recognized as an occupational disease of chimneysweeps, and prolonged exposure to soot was presumed to be the cause.[1] In the following century, other instances of coal tar carcinogenesis in industrial workers came to light. But it was not until 1915 that cancer was produced experimentally by applying coal tar to an animal's skin.[2] The subsequent identification and isolation of the responsible polycyclic hydrocarbons, the systematic exploration of structure-activity relationships, the discovery of carcinogenic properties among other groups of compounds, and the elaboration of theories of chemical carcinogenesis are among the most interesting developments in modern pharmacology.[3-8]

[1] G. WOLF: *Chemical Induction of Cancer*. London, Cassell and Co., Ltd., 1952.

[2] K. YAMAGIWA and K. ICHIKAWA: Experimental study of the pathogenesis of carcinoma. *J. Cancer Res. 3:*1 (1918).

[3] D. B. CLAYSON: *Chemical Carcinogenesis*. Boston, Little, Brown and Co., 1962.

[4] G. E. W. WOLSTENHOLME and M. O'CONNOR, eds.: *Ciba Foundation Symposium on Carcinogenesis*. Boston, Little, Brown and Co., 1958.

[5] E. BOYLAND, ed.: Causation of cancer. (Symposium). *Brit. Med. Bull. 14:*73 (1958).

[6] E. BOYLAND: Recent progress in carcinogenesis: biochemical aspects. *Progr. Exper. Tumor Res. 1:*162 (1960).

[7] E. BOYLAND, ed.: Mechanisms of carcinogenesis: chemical, physical and viral. (Symposium). *Brit. Med. Bull. 20:*87 (1964).

[8] E. C. MILLER and J. A. MILLER: Mechanisms of chemical carcinogenesis: nature of proximate carcinogens and interactions with macromolecules. *Pharmacol. Rev. 18:*805 (1966).

MECHANISM OF ACTION OF CHEMICAL CARCINOGENS

Methods of Experimentation

Only the most potent agents produce cancer in every exposed animal. With less potent agents, the incidence is low and has to be compared with the frequency of spontaneous cancer; therefore large numbers of animals may be required to demonstrate carcinogenicity. Exposure to a carcinogen usually has to be continued for a long time. But even when a brief exposure suffices, there is a long latent period before cancers start to appear. For these reasons the experimental animals have to be maintained for a long time. Mice and rats are used extensively for research on chemical carcinogenesis because they are mammals, cheap, easy to maintain in the laboratory, and their life spans are long enough for them to outlive the usual latent period.

Some carcinogens act primarily at the site of their application. If painted on the skin, they produce papillomatous epithelial growths that develop into squamous cell carcinomas. If injected subcutaneously, they produce sarcomas, i.e., malignant growths of the fibroblasts in connective tissues. If given by mouth, they may produce tumors of the gastrointestinal tract. Other carcinogens are principally effective when incorporated into the diet; they act on the liver to produce malignant hepatomas or tumors of the bile ducts. Some carcinogens act at widely dispersed sites throughout the body, regardless of the route by which they are taken in. Cutaneous application of such a compound might lead not only to skin cancer at the point of application but also perhaps to cancer of the intestine, lungs, or kidneys. Illustrative of carcinogenesis at a remote site is the effect of the hydrocarbon 3-methylcholanthrene (Fig. 11-5). When this substance was given to rats in the diet, it caused no hepatomas but produced cancer of the mammary glands in all the treated animals.[9] Similarly, administration of naphthylamine (p. 689) by any route leads to cancer of the bladder in susceptible species. The mammary cancers caused by 3-methylcholanthrene, the bladder tumors caused by naphthylamine, and indeed all cancers that develop in tissues remote from the site of carcinogen administration are not metastatic implants. They are primary tumors initiated by the carcinogen itself or by a product of carcinogen metabolism after absorption and distribution have taken place.

Species and strain differences bespeak the major role of genetic background in determining susceptibility to carcinogenesis. One source of variation is the known difference in activity of the drug-metabolizing enzymes among different species; this can account for greater differences

---

[9] G. PINCUS and E. P. VOLLMER, eds.: *Biological Activities of Steroids in Relation to Cancer.* New York, Academic Press, 1960.

of carcinogenic potency if the carcinogen has to be metabolized to an active product, or if an active carcinogen has to reach a remote site of action before being transformed to an inert metabolite. A good example of both processes is provided by 2-acetylaminofluorene (AAF), which is metabolized to an N-hydroxy derivative, now thought to be the active carcinogen (cf. p. 693). This conversion takes place in several species sensitive to the carcinogenic action of AAF, but not in the guinea pig, in which AAF is accordingly not a carcinogen. Moreover, the carcinogenic N-hydroxy metabolite is excreted in the urine as an inactive conjugate with glucuronic acid. Thus the liver glucuronyl transferase activity and the β-glucuronidase activity of the urine both profoundly influence the potency of AAF for the induction of bladder cancer. Besides differences in the metabolism of carcinogens there may be intrinsic differences in the sensitivities of various species to the carcinogenic process.

The influence of genetic constitution upon sensitivity to chemical carcinogens is revealed by strain differences within a single species.[10] Such differences are tissue specific, as is also true for differences with respect to spontaneous cancers. Mice have been bred selectively for a high incidence of spontaneous tumors at particular sites. For example, one strain may develop spontaneous mammary gland cancers at a rate of less than 1 per cent, whereas the incidence in a specially bred strain may be as high as 90 per cent. Sometimes a high susceptibility to spontaneous cancer of a particular tissue is associated with high sensitivity to induced chemical carcinogenesis at the same site, but this is not necessarily so. If a given carcinogen induces sarcomas at the site of subcutaneous injection and also lung carcinomas remote from the injection site, selective breeding may yield one strain in which the carcinogen produces only sarcomas, another in which only lung tumors develop. Azo dyes injected subcutaneously usually cause both sarcomas at the injection site and hepatomas; but some strains of mice develop few tumors of either kind in response to these agents. This pattern of genetic variation in susceptibility to cancer in general, susceptibility to cancer of particular tissues, and susceptibility to individual chemical carcinogens may also apply in the human. It is well known that certain kinds of cancer tend to run in families, and there is also a high concordance rate for the occurrence of specific types of cancer in monozygous twins.

Sex differences in cancer incidence and in responses to carcinogens may be related to hormonal influences.[9,11,12] A strain of mice that developed

10 O. V. ST. WHITELOCK, ed.: Genetic concept for the origin of cancer. *Ann. New York Acad. Sci. 71:*807 (1958).

11 F. BIELSCHOWSKY and E. S. HORNING: Aspects of endocrine carcinogenesis. *Brit. Med. Bull. 14:*106 (1958).

12 O. MÜHLBOCK and L. M. BOOT: "The Mechanism of Hormonal Carcinogenesis," in *Ciba Foundation Symposium on Carcinogenesis,* ed. by G. E. W. Wolstenholme and M. O'Connor. Boston, Little, Brown and Co., 1958, p. 83.

mammary cancer at a high rate after administration of a hydrocarbon carcinogen was found to produce unusually large amounts of estrogen. Estrogen administration to other strains was found to increase the yield of mammary tumors caused by the same carcinogen.

Malignant growths of hormone-sensitive organs often remain responsive to the hormones that ordinarily stimulate these organs. For example, prostate cancer can be treated by castration, to remove the major source of testosterone, and by administering estrogenic hormones. Thyroid tumors have been induced by pituitary thyroid-stimulating hormone or thiouracil (which causes increased output of the pituitary hormone). Pituitary hormones have also been used to produce tumors in the adrenal glands, ovaries, testes, and mammary glands. Insulin apparently plays some role in promoting tumor development, for the frequency of carcinogen-induced hepatomas and mammary carcinomas is much lower in alloxan-diabetic rats than in normal animals. It is not certain whether the hormones act as carcinogens in their own right or whether they alter the cellular environment in sensitive tissues in a way that makes them more susceptible to spontaneous carcinogenesis.[13]

Starvation antagonizes the initial effects of carcinogens. But after a malignant tumor has become established, it appears to have prior claim on whatever food reserves are available. Certain dietary factors may specifically affect carcinogenicity; riboflavin, for example, by a mechanism not yet understood, protects rats against the liver tumors induced by azo dyes.

If species, strain, sex, hormonal status, diet, and route of administration are carefully controlled, then reliable dose-response relationships can be found and the relative potencies of carcinogens can be described quantitatively. Figure 11-1 shows log dose-response curves for three hydrocarbon carcinogens administered to groups of 20 mice by single subcutaneous injections. The eventual incidence of sarcomas at the injection sites was recorded. The curves are approximately parallel, suggesting a similar mechanism of action of the three compounds. Under these conditions, 3,4-benzpyrene was about five times less potent than 1,2,5,6-dibenzanthracene or 3-methylcholanthrene. ED50 values and their confidence limits for carcinogenesis may be found in the same way as for any toxic drug action, as described in chapter 5. An interesting feature of the curves shown in Fig. 11-1 is their rather shallow slope. At least a tenfold increase of dose was required to span the range of response from an incidence of a few per cent to an incidence of nearly 100 per cent. This implies that laboratory experiments may tend to underestimate the likelihood that very small doses of a carcinogen will produce cancer in some animals. The

---

[13] "Spontaneous" carcinogenesis is used here as a convenient empirical term. It is recognized, of course, that the causes of spontaneously occurring cancer may be unrecognized carcinogens, viruses, or radiation.

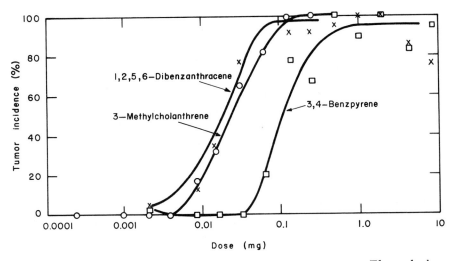

FIG. 11-1. DOSE-RESPONSE RELATIONSHIP FOR CARCINOGENS. *Three hydrocarbon carcinogens were administered subcutaneously, each to a group of 20 mice in a single dose. The incidence of sarcomas at the site of injection was noted. (From Bryan and Shimkin, Fig. 3.[14])*

reason is that with a small group of animals (e.g., less than 100) a dosage that causes no tumors at all will be judged ineffective, whereas the same dosage in a large population of the species would cause cancer in some animals. The same argument applies to estimating "safe" dosages of carcinogens in human populations on the basis of experimentation with a limited number of animals.

Initiation and Promotion

One of the most significant advances in understanding the mechanism of carcinogenesis was made about 20 years ago when it was discovered that the chemical induction of cancer involved two distinguishable processes, designated *initiation* and *promotion*.[15] Initiation is the production of an irreversible cellular change, which is a necessary but not sufficient condition for the development of cancer. Promotion is the process whereby a tumor is caused to develop in tissue in which initiation has already occurred; in such tissue, promotion is both necessary and sufficient for the development of cancer.

14 W. R. BRYAN and M. B. SHIMKIN: Quantitative analysis of dose-response data obtained with three carcinogenic hydrocarbons in strain C3H male mice. *J. Nat. Cancer Inst.* 3:503 (1943).

15 I. BERENBLUM and P. SHUBIK: A new, quantitative, approach to the study of the stages of chemical carcinogenesis in the mouse's skin. *Brit. J. Cancer* 1:383 (1948).

The discovery of these independent processes arose from observations on the latent period. It had been found that after injecting a coal tar hydrocarbon subcutaneously (as in the experiments shown in Fig. 11-1) there was a latent period of several wèeks during which no tumors were observed. Then tumors began to appear in some mice, and during the subsequent months, if the dose of carcinogen was large enough, all the animals would develop cancer. Two variables were discerned—the total frequency of tumors eventually attained (the variable plotted in Fig. 11-1) and the average latent period before the tumors appeared. As a rule, the more potent the carcinogen (as measured by the total tumor incidence), the shorter the average latent period was found to be; but sometimes these two variables seemed to be quite independent of each other. Such discrepancies led to the realization that the carcinogenic effect of the coal tar hydrocarbons was really a dual one. Other compounds were sought and found that had one or the other kind of action in pure form. Thus, two classes of substance could be identified—true initiators of the carcinogenic process and pure promoters of the development of cancer.

An initiator could be painted once on an area of mouse skin. When this painted area was left untreated, no cancers appeared. But when the same area was treated repeatedly with a promoter, cancers developed with predictable frequency. The total tumor incidence varied with the initiator and its dose, but the latent period was determined only by the promoter and by its mode of application. If, after the single application of the initiator to the skin, the treatment with promoter was delayed, the latent period was correspondingly delayed; but the eventual incidence of cancer remained constant. Reversing the order of administration of initiator and promoter abolished the carcinogenic effect.

The essential features of initiation and promotion are summarized schematically in Fig. 11-2. The diagram on the left depicts the tumor fre-

FIG. 11-2.   INITIATION AND PROMOTION IN CARCINOGENESIS.   (*From Berenblum and Shubik, Figs. 2 and 3.*[15])

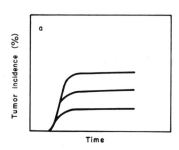

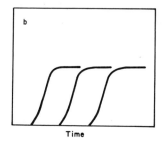

Different initiators painted once on mouse skin followed by constant schedule of treatment with promoter (croton oil).

Single painting with one initiator, followed by croton oil treatment after different periods of delay.

quency as a function of time when different carcinogens were used for the single initial painting and the course of treatment with the promoter was kept constant. The potencies of the several carcinogens are reflected in the different tumor frequencies attained, but the latent period was always the same. In the diagram on the right, a single carcinogen was used and the promoter treatment was delayed for different periods of time. Here, the tumor frequency remained the same, but the latent period varied. The most striking separation of initiating action from promoting action was achieved in experiments in which an initiator (urethane) was given by mouth. No tumors developed anywhere except on areas of skin that were painted repeatedly with the promoter, croton oil; and croton oil had no effect unless urethane had been administered previously. The conclusion drawn from all these experiments was that the initiator seems to cause an irreversible change in the cells of a certain number of mice after a single exposure, but that the altered cells are not able to develop into cancers except under the influence of a promoter.

Careful histopathologic studies of the early stages of carcinogenesis have revealed that promoting action is often associated with cell damage in the area where the malignancy will ultimately arise. Examples are the development of liver cancer following liver damage caused by carbon tetrachloride or other hepatotoxic agents, and of skin cancers during the regenerative healing process after severe burn damage. Stimulation of cell growth seems to be an important component of the action of hormones in promoting carcinogenesis in target organs. Subcutaneous injection of hydrocarbon carcinogens with mixed initiating and promoting actions results in considerable local cell death, followed eventually by the appearance of malignant cells among survivors at the periphery of the affected area. And croton oil, a typical promoter in experimental carcinogenesis, is a strongly irritant substance that causes extensive cell damage.

Some recent findings, however, cast doubt on the simple view that promotion requires cell damage.[16] A strain of rats was used in which spontaneous sarcomas have never been observed. Subcutaneous injections of sesame oil (a vehicle often chosen for subcutaneous administration of water-insoluble drugs because of its nonirritant qualities) produced no cancers. No cancers arose when the hydrocarbon 3-methylcholanthrene was fed in the diet of these rats. But when the carcinogen feeding was accompanied by sesame oil injections, all the rats developed sarcomas at the injection sites. More extraordinary, a small group of animals given injections of ordinary physiologic salt solution and fed the carcinogen also developed tumors at the injection sites.

More remarkable still has been the discovery that films of inert material, implanted subcutaneously in rats, cause a high incidence of

16 C. HUGGINS and L. C. GRAND: Sarcoma induced remotely in rats fed 3-methylcholanthrene. *Cancer Res. 23:*477 (1963).

TABLE 11-1.   **Carcinogenic effect of implantation of an inert surface**

Small glass coverslips were implanted subcutaneously in rats. After four months, the coverslips were removed from some rats (columns 1 and 2), and glass powder was introduced into the subcutaneous pocket where the coverslip had been (column 2). In other animals the coverslips were left in place (columns 3 and 4); some of these animals also received glass powder (column 4). The rats were kept for more than two years, and the number of sarcomas was noted. (Modified from Oppenheimer et al.,[17] Table 1.)

Group	1	2	3	4
Coverslip	Removed	Removed	*in situ*	*in situ*
Powder	None	Glass	None	Glass
No. of animals	25	27	24	27
Tumors	0	0	6	6
Percentage	0	0	25	22
Mean latent period (days)			503 ± 55	547 ± 103

sarcomas without administration of any accessory carcinogen.[17] Glass, plastic, and platinum foil were among the effective carcinogens. At first it was thought that a small extent of depolymerization of the plastics, or impurities in the other substances, might really be responsible. But then it was demonstrated that the same materials, in powdered form, or even as perforated films, were wholly ineffective. The reaction of subcutaneous tissues to an implanted impervious film of any kind is to form a pocket around the foreign body, lined with densely packed fibroblasts. The malignancy eventually arises at the periphery of this pocket lining not in direct contact with the film. That the pocket itself is not a sufficient stimulus for carcinogenesis is shown by the data of Table 11-1. Glass coverslips were introduced subcutaneously in groups of rats. After four months, if the coverslips were removed, the pockets became obliterated and no cancers developed. If a glass coverslip was replaced by an equal amount of glass powder, no cancers developed. If the coverslips were left in situ, then tumors developed in about one-fourth of the rats, whether or not glass powder was also introduced into the pocket. In these experiments, the usual foreign-body tissue reaction to the presence of glass powder was seen; this was clearly unrelated to the carcinogenic process.

The mechanism of carcinogenesis by implanted inert films has become a critical issue in controversies about the causes of cancer.[18] In these implants, cells apparently become malignant merely by the interposition of a barrier between them and other cells. Possibly some degree of local anoxia is involved. Perhaps the key to the action is the removal

---

[17] E. T. OPPENHEIMER, M. WILLHITE, I. DANISHEFSKY, and A. P. STOUT: Observations on the effects of powdered polymer in the carcinogenic process. *Cancer Res. 21*:132 (1961).

[18] F. BISCHOFF and G. BRYSON: Carcinogenesis through solid state surfaces. *Progr. Exper. Tumor Res. 5*:85 (1964).

from some cells of the growth-regulating influences of neighboring cells. The mechanism has not been clarified yet, but it could be imagined that the inert film, by modifying the cellular environment, acts like a promoter, favoring the development of sarcomas from spontaneously arising pre-cancerous cells. This view presupposes that such spontaneous transformation of normal cells to malignant ones is a continuous process analogous to spontaneous mutation, but that propagation of the transformed cells is restricted in the normal tissue environment.

There are significant analogies between chemical and radiation (x-ray) carcinogenesis.[19] It has been proposed that radiation carcinogenesis may be mediated indirectly by carcinogens produced in the tissues as a consequence of ionizing radiation. These carcinogens could be free radicals or other reactive molecules such as alkylating or arylating agents. That the tissue environment in the irradiated host plays an important role in radiation carcinogenesis was shown by means of transplantation experiments[20] in which thymus glands from nonirradiated mice, implanted into irradiated hosts, developed malignant tumors. Radiation seems to have both initiating and promoting actions.

The incidence of cancer in experimental animals is a function of the radiation dose, and the same relationship has been observed in human leukemia.[21] The dose relationship accords with the results obtained with chemical carcinogens that are pure initiators. On the other hand, exposure to x-rays results in tissue damage and tissue reaction as seen with croton oil and other promoters. Accordingly, regenerative hyperplasia of bone marrow regularly precedes the emergence of radiation-induced leukemia; and sensitivity to the induction of leukemia by x-rays is greatest at periods of rapid cell proliferation, as for example during fetal life.

Cancer as a Genetic Abnormality of Somatic Cells

Cancer cells, once established, differ from their tissue of origin in that they have become independent of the control mechanisms that ordinarily limit cell growth and division in differentiated tissues. This is not merely a question of growth rate but of a balanced relationship between growth rate and the necessary rate of cell renewal. The normal mitotic rate in intestinal epithelium or in bone marrow is higher than in many cancers; but even these rapidly growing tissues are under strict regulation, so that those cells that are shed into the intestinal lumen or destroyed in the circulation are exactly replaced. A vivid example of this kind of regulation is seen in the regeneration of excised tissue in a skin wound or after a partial hepatectomy. Cell proliferation is explosively rapid at first

19 Z. M. BACQ and P. ALEXANDER: *Fundamentals of Radiobiology,* 2nd ed. London, Pergamon Press, 1961.

20 H. S. KAPLAN: Some implications of indirect induction mechanisms in carcinogenesis: a review. *Cancer Res. 19:*791 (1959).

21 W. M. COURT-BROWN: Nuclear and allied radiations and the incidence of leukaemia in man. *Brit. Med. Bull. 14:*168 (1958).

but ceases when the normal architecture and tissue mass have been restored. Most impressive of all is the regulation displayed during embryonic development, when differentiation of structure and function bring rapid cell proliferation to an abrupt end. In contrast, even a slowly growing cancer continues its cycles of mitotic activity and cell growth inexorably, disrupting the normal relationships between adjacent cells, invading into capillaries and lymph channels, implanting metastatically in remote parts of the body, and eventually killing the host.

Associated with the property of undisciplined growth, and probably intimately related to it, is the tendency of cancer cells to become undifferentiated, to lose the distinguishing morphologic and biochemical features of their tissue of origin. This is not, however, an all-or-none property but varies in degree from tumor to tumor and often progresses during the evolution of a particular tumor. Some cancers of endocrine organs may even continue to produce their appropriate endocrine products, and they may respond to endogenous or exogenous hormones. Prostate and breast cancers, in particular, are often dependent on androgenic and estrogenic hormones, respectively.

That the loss of responsiveness to growth controls is an intrinsic property of the cancer cells is evidenced in a number of ways.[22] The very fact that cancer, whether spontaneous or carcinogen induced, can originate locally, in a particular tissue, rather than at multiple sites in the body, implicates a local cellular transformation as the essential prerequisite. When an area of mouse skin was painted once with an initiator and later transplanted to a different site, cancer developed only in the carcinogen-treated skin, regardless of how long transplantation was delayed. The same experiment was performed in a hybrid produced by mating a carcinogen-sensitive with a carcinogen-resistant strain of mice. This arrangement permitted transplantation of the carcinogen-treated skin of the hybrid to either of the parent strains. Cancer developed in the treated skin even after its transplantation to a resistant host in which the carcinogen would have been ineffective. Frequently, cancers that have achieved a sufficient degree of autonomy will grow malignantly after transplantation into hosts that would otherwise remain free of cancer.

A provocative recent development is the conversion of normal cells to cancer cells by carcinogens in vitro.[23,24,24a] In one such experiment,[24]

---

[22] M. H. SALAMAN: "The Use of Cocarcinogens in the Study of Carcinogenesis," in *Ciba Foundation Symposium on Carcinogenesis,* ed. by G. E. W. Wolstenholme and M. O'Connor. Boston, Little, Brown and Co., 1958, p. 70.

[23] Y. BERWALD and L. SACHS: *In vitro* transformation of normal cells to tumor cells by carcinogenic hydrocarbons. *J. Nat. Cancer Inst. 35:*641 (1965).

[24] E. BORENFREUND, M. KRIM, F. K. SANDERS, S. S. STERNBERG, and A. BENDICH: Malignant conversion of cells in vitro by carcinogens and viruses. *Proc. Nat. Acad. Sci. U.S.A. 56:*672 (1966).

[24a] C. HEIDELBERGER and P. T. IYPE: Malignant transformation in vitro by carcinogenic hydrocarbons. *Science 155:*214 (1967).

advantage was taken of a difference in chromosome number between two varieties of hamsters. Cells from lung tissue of the Chinese hamster (diploid number, $2n = 22$) were established in culture. They were grown for 12 days on agar containing a hydrocarbon carcinogen, while controls were grown on plain nutrient agar. All cells were then transferred to the ordinary agar. The carcinogen-treated cell cultures developed characteristic chromosome alterations, of the kind observed after chromosome breakage (e.g., terminal centromeres, cf. chapter 10); but the cells not exposed to carcinogens rarely showed such changes. The altered cells, implanted in the cheek pouch of the Syrian hamster ($2n = 44$), produced sarcomas, whereas untreated cells did not. The chromosome complement of the tumors showed that they originated from the cells that had been maintained in culture, not from cells of the host animal. The tumors consistently showed abnormal chromosomes of the same kinds identified in the carcinogen-treated cell cultures. The chromosome abnormalities noted here are consistent with many observations on unusual numbers of chromosomes (aneuploidy) or bizarre anomalies of certain chromosomes in animal and human cancers.[25] There is, for example, an exceptionally high frequency of chronic myelogenous leukemia in mongoloid individuals, who are trisomic for chromosome 21; and a peculiar chromosome has also been observed in leukemia not associated with mongolism. In many cancers, however, the chromosomes appear to be normal in number and gross appearance. And it could, of course, be argued that chromosome aberrations, when they occur, are the result rather than the cause of the cancer state.

It is abundantly clear that cancer cells differ genetically from their normal progenitors; and the phenotypic expression of this difference is the characteristic lack of response to growth-controlling mechanisms in the host. Since the initiation of the malignant change is abrupt, and since the change is apparently irreversible and heritable, it may be regarded as a somatic mutation. According to this view, initiation is tantamount to somatic mutagenesis. It is therefore supportive of this concept that ionizing radiation as well as alkylating agents and other mutagens also possess carcinogenic activity. Likewise, many substances originally discovered to be carcinogens have since proved to be mutagenic in microorganisms.[26] Spontaneous cancers might arise by spontaneous mutagenesis, perhaps initiated by unrecognized carcinogens.

The genotypic change alone may not suffice for the establishment of a cancer. The role of promoters could be to create a local environment favorable to the selection and propagation of the new mutants. One indispensable feature of this "favorable local environment" may simply be

[25] T. S. HAUSCHKA: The chromosomes in ontogeny and oncogeny. *Cancer Res.* *21*:957 (1961).

[26] R. W. BARRATT and E. L. TATUM: Carcinogenic mutagens. *Ann. New York Acad. Sci. 71*:1072 (1958).

the opportunity for sufficient cell division to permit phenotypic expression of an altered genotype. It will be recalled that even in actively multiplying bacteria there is a lag between the induction of a mutation and its expression, during which the wild-type gene product has to be "diluted" in the cytoplasm of progeny cells. In most tissues of higher organisms the rate of cell renewal is very slow. One can imagine that promoters act by inducing proliferative tissue reactions during which the precancerous mutant cells are stimulated to multiply. The carcinogen-induced mutation would only be expressed after the loss of those wild-type gene products that were concerned in the cell's response to growth-controlling substances in the tissue environment. Once a clone of mutant cells had become sufficiently large, it would fully express the phenotypic characteristics of cancer cells, thus becoming autonomous and independent of the promoter.

Molecular Interactions of Carcinogens with Cell Constituents

The considerable evidence suggesting a similarity between carcinogenesis and mutagenesis has led to the investigation of interactions between carcinogens and DNA. Evidence of such interactions is indisputable, but the relationship to carcinogenesis is not clear. For one thing, noncarcinogenic congeners often also interact with DNA. Polycyclic hydrocarbons raise the "melting temperature" at which the strands of the double helix separate, i.e., they stabilize the hydrogen-bonded structure. DNA also solubilizes the normally water-insoluble hydrocarbons, as would be expected in any hydrophobic bonding to a polyanionic macromolecule. An intercalation mechanism is suggested by the size and planarity of the carcinogens; dibenzpyrene, for example, can be superimposed almost perfectly upon the adenine-thymine pair, much as was shown for a mutagenic acridine in Fig. 10-12.[27,28] One proposal envisions a perturbation by carcinogens of the statistical distribution of electrons over the whole DNA helix.[29]

It was known for many years that most alkylating agents are also carcinogenic. Now it is becoming increasingly evident that carcinogens not previously thought capable of forming covalent bonds with cell constituents are transformed metabolically to alkylating or arylating agents. Two prominent actions of alkylating agents upon nucleic acids were noted in chapter 10—a reaction with the 7-position of guanine residues and (for the bifunctional agents) cross-linking of DNA strands. These reactions were also observed after carcinogenic alkylating agents had acted upon mouse tissues

---

[27] E. BOYLAND: Polycyclic hydrocarbons. *Brit. Med. Bull. 20:*121 (1964).

[28] P. O. P. TS'O and P. LU: Interaction of nucleic acids. I. Physical binding of thymine, adenine, steroids, and aromatic hydrocarbons to nucleic acids. *Proc. Nat. Acad. Sci. U.S.A. 51:*17 (1964).

[29] T. A. HOFFMANN and J. LADIK: A possible correlation between the effects of some carcinogenic agents and the electronic structure of DNA. *Cancer Res. 21:*474 (1961).

in vivo.[30] The extent of reaction with tissue DNA seemed very low, with less than one molecule bound per 10^8 molecular weight (150,000 base pairs) of DNA. At the same time, one in 50 molecules of RNA and about one in every 1,000 protein molecules were alkylated. Superficially it appears that the interaction with DNA was negligible compared with the interaction with protein. However, although it is difficult to suppose any serious consequence could ensue from the inactivation of so small a fraction of the total protein molecules in the cell, it is easy to imagine that a single "hit" on the cell's DNA could suffice to initiate the carcinogenic process.

Investigations on dimethylnitrosamine have yielded evidence of a relationship between carcinogenicity and alkylation in various tissues.[30] This compound is a very potent carcinogen, inducing various kinds of tumors in different tissues of experimental animals. It is converted to an active methylating agent in vivo (p. 697). When rats were treated with radioactive methyl-labeled dimethylnitrosamine, 7-methylguanine could be isolated from tissue nucleic acids, and N-methylhistidine from tissue proteins. In newborn rats, this carcinogen produced a high incidence of renal tumors and a low incidence of hepatic tumors; and there was a high degree of methylation in the kidney but little in the liver. In this instance, as with other carcinogens that have to be converted to active compounds, differences in the sensitivity of various tissues to the carcinogenic action may well arise from differences in distribution of the enzymes that mediate the essential conversion.

More decisive are data on the correlation between binding to DNA and carcinogenic potency in a group of related carcinogens. Figure 11-3 presents graphically the outcome of experiments in which seven different polycyclic hydrocarbons were painted on the skin of mice. In each case, the DNA was isolated and the bound hydrocarbon determined. It can be seen that although the total binding was small even for the compound bound in greatest amount, there was a good correlation between binding and carcinogenic potency. An important feature of this investigation was the fact that the binding was measured in the same tissue upon which the carcinogens acted directly. If an administered carcinogen had to be transformed metabolically to an active compound, which would then produce cancer at some tissue site, a correlation between DNA binding and potency would be expected only for the metabolic product, not for the administered substance itself.

The somatic mutation hypothesis has been criticized as too simplistic; and doubt has been expressed, in view of the seemingly small extent of interaction between carcinogens and DNA, that "cancer mutations" could be regularly produced. But no special ability of carcinogens to

---

[30] P. BROOKES: Quantitative aspects of the reaction of some carcinogens with nucleic acids and the possible significance of such reactions in the process of carcinogenesis. *Cancer Res.* 26:1994 (1966).

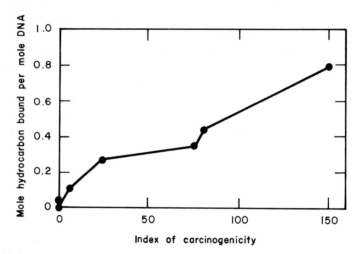

FIG. 11-3. RELATIONSHIP OF CARCINOGENIC POTENCY TO INTERACTION WITH DNA. *The extent of binding of certain carcinogenic hydrocarbons to mouse skin DNA is given on the y-axis, as moles of hydrocarbon bound per "mole" of DNA (estimated as containing 20,000 nucleotides, molecular weight 7×10^6). A measure of carcinogenic potency for application to mouse skin is given on the x-axis. Each solid circle represents a single hydrocarbon. The most potent carcinogen tested here was 7,12-dimethylbenzanthracene; the least potent were naphthalene and 1,2,5,6-dibenzanthracene. (From Brookes, Chart 5.*[30])

cause these particular mutations need be supposed. It should be borne in mind that the animal body is a medium in which there is strong positive selection in favor of "cancer mutants." If a mutagen in contact with tissues induces a lethal mutation in some of the millions of cells present, those cells will simply die and be replaced, undetected by the investigator. Also undetected would be deletions of enzymes and other proteins resulting from viable mutations. But a single mutation leading to loss of responsiveness to growth regulation could give rise to a clone of cancer cells.

An interesting alternative to the somatic mutation hypothesis has been proposed—that the primary carcinogenic interaction is with proteins rather than with nucleic acids. This viewpoint has been formulated in a so-called "deletion hypothesis."[31-33] When carcinogenic azo dyes were fed to rats and liver proteins were then fractionated, it was found that the carcinogen or a metabolite was bound to a lipoprotein globulin identifiable by its characteristic electrophoretic mobility. The same kind of experiment

31 J. A. MILLER and E. C. MILLER: The carcinogenic aminoazo dyes. *Adv. Cancer Res.* 1:339 (1953).

32 H. C. PITOT and C. HEIDELBERGER: Metabolic regulatory circuits and carcinogenesis. *Cancer Res.* 23:1694 (1963).

33 V. R. POTTER: Biochemical perspectives in cancer research. *Cancer Res.* 24:1085 (1964).

with polycyclic hydrocarbon carcinogens on mouse skin yielded a very similar protein fraction, to which a metabolite of the carcinogen was bound. Similar proteins, interacting strongly with carcinogens, were found in nuclear as well as cytoplasmic fractions. Most remarkable of all, when the induced malignant hepatomas from liver or the induced malignant carcinomas from skin were extracted, it was found that they no longer bound the carcinogen and that the characteristic lipoprotein had disappeared.[34,35]

Evidence of a protein deletion in cancer cells also comes from immunologic studies.[36,37] When a rabbit was immunized with extracts of normal rat liver, an antiserum was obtained that gave precipitin reactions rather indiscriminately with extracts of various rat tissues. However, if such an antiserum was first absorbed with rat kidney extract, an antibody activity remained that reacted selectively with liver extracts. If the reverse experiment was performed, using kidney extracts for immunization and absorbing it with liver extracts, a rather specific anti-kidney serum could be obtained. Using this method of identifying tissue-specific proteins, it was found that hepatomas induced by azo dyes lacked the liver antigen, and kidney tumors lacked the kidney antigen. Some experiments employing a fluorescent antibody technique permitting microscopic observation of the cells at different stages of carcinogenesis suggested that individual liver cells begin to lose their tissue-specific antigen at a very early stage in the process, even before rapid mitotic proliferation begins. This might indicate that the deletion of proteins designated "tissue-specific antigen" is part of the phenotypic change leading to cancer. However, the alternative interpretation is not ruled out—that the deletion is a secondary consequence rather than a cause of malignant growth and dedifferentiation. There is no reason to believe that the tissue-specific antigen deleted here is the same as the carcinogen-binding protein discussed earlier.

The findings about protein binding and protein deletion are by no means incompatible with somatic mutation. According to the somatic mutation hypothesis, mutation should result in deletion of a protein gene product that was essential for the cell's response to growth-controlling influences. Subsequently, during malignant growth, tissue-specific proteins

34 C. HEIDELBERGER: "The Relation of Protein Binding to Hydrocarbon Carcinogenesis," in *Ciba Foundation Symposium on Carcinogenesis*, ed. by G. E. W. Wolstenholme and M. O'Connor. Boston, Little, Brown and Co., 1958, p. 179.

35 G. R. DAVENPORT, C. W. ABELL, and C. HEIDELBERGER: The interaction of carcinogenic hydrocarbons with tissues. VII. Fractionation of mouse skin proteins. *Cancer Res.* 21:599 (1961).

36 H. N. GREEN: "Immunological Aspects of Cancer," in *Ciba Foundation Symposium on Carcinogenesis*, ed. by G. E. W. Wolstenholme and M. O'Connor. Boston, Little, Brown and Co., 1958, p. 131.

37 E. WEILER: "Loss of Specific Cell Antigen in Relation to Carcinogenesis," in *Ciba Foundation Symposium on Carcinogenesis*, ed. by G. E. W. Wolstenholme and M. O'Connor. Boston, Little, Brown and Co., 1958, p. 165.

could also be lost. The finding of protein deletions is therefore not surprising. What is curious is that one of the deleted proteins should be precisely the one with which the carcinogen has interacted. For if the primary action of the carcinogen were upon DNA, to produce a mutational alteration, then there is no reason why any direct relationship should exist between the carcinogen and the deleted protein or proteins. Rigorous proof is still lacking to show (*a*) that only a single protein is initially deleted, and (*b*) that the carcinogen interacts with that protein alone.

An interesting proposal has been advanced[32] to explain the protein deletion findings and at the same time to account for the permanent alteration in the properties of the cell. It would indeed be difficult to account for carcinogenesis on the basis of ordinary interactions between carcinogens and proteins. Certainly, cells could be killed by such interactions if enough of the functional proteins were inactivated. But if a cell survived, there would seem to be no obvious reason why its undamaged genetic apparatus could not direct the replacement of the inactivated proteins, once the carcinogen has been removed. There would be no basis, therefore, for a permanent change in cell heredity. The novelty of the proposal is that it invokes a carcinogenic interaction with a special class of proteins, the postulated repressors and derepressors of the transcription of genetic information.

Figure 11-4 presents the essential features of this hypothesis. The diagram presents the generally accepted features of the regulation of gene transcription.[38] The regulator gene directs the synthesis of a repressor protein R, which interacts with the operator gene O to shut off transcription

FIG. 11-4. POSSIBLE MECHANISM OF CARCINOGENESIS BY PHENOTYPIC MODIFICATION WITHOUT CHANGE IN GENOTYPE. *A possible self-perpetuating circuit. Regulator gene produces active repressor* R. *Product* P *inactivates repressor. As long as* S *is present, synthesis of enzyme* E *continues.* (*Modified from Pitot and Heidelberger, Chart 5.*[32])

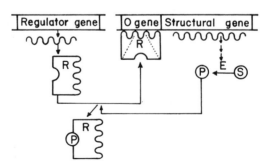

38 F. JACOB and J. MONOD: Genetic regulatory mechanisms in the synthesis of proteins. *J. Mol. Biol. 3:*318 (1961).

of the operon. Then the structural genes in that operon will not produce messenger-RNA for the synthesis of the proteins under control of that operon. In the diagram, enzyme E would not be formed under those conditions. Now suppose (as shown) that enzyme E catalyzed the synthesis of a product P from a precursor S. Product P is assumed to be in some way essential for the regulation of cell growth. P also combines with and inactivates the repressor protein R; in common parlance, P is an inducer of the enzyme. This is a self-perpetuating circuit because as long as S is present, P will be formed, R will be inactivated, and E will continue to be synthesized. If E is ever deleted, however, no more E can be made, for S cannot be transformed to P, and the operon remains shut. In such a situation, although no genotypic alteration has been induced, the cell will seem to have undergone a hereditary transformation. Obviously, if a carcinogen combined with E, inhibiting it, the end result would be permanent deletion of E and derangement of growth controls consequent to loss of P. Several more complicated schemes have been suggested, all capable of explaining the experimental observations on carcinogenesis and protein deletion.[32]

THE PRINCIPAL GROUPS OF CHEMICAL CARCINOGENS

Polycyclic Hydrocarbons

An intensive series of investigations during the period 1920–1940 sought to identify and isolate the active carcinogenic components of coal tar.[1] These studies led to the recognition of 3,4-benzpyrene[39] (Fig. 11-5) as the major coal tar carcinogen, and also to the synthesis and biologic testing of many related compounds. Consequently, a rather detailed and quite satisfactory picture of structure-activity relationships in this group has emerged. Figure 11-5 shows that all the carcinogenic hydrocarbons may be regarded as derivatives of phenanthrene. Phenanthrene itself, like the simpler anthracene, naphthalene, and benzene molecules, is completely devoid of carcinogenicity. Its tetramethyl derivative, 1,2,3,4-tetramethyl-phenanthrene (not shown) is weakly carcinogenic. Addition of a fourth benzene ring yields 1,2-benzanthracene or 3,4-benzphenanthrene, which are both carcinogenic. All other tetracyclic hydrocarbons are inert. Methyl substituents increase the carcinogenic potency of phenanthrene in a regular way; the 5,6-dimethyl derivative is nearly as potent as 1,2,5,6-dibenzanthracene. The related 3-methylcholanthrene is a very potent carcinogen, yet the homologous anthracene derivative (not shown), lacking the benzene

---

[39] The well-established common terminology is used throughout this chapter. In the newer official terminology, the benzene rings of a reference compound to which additional benzene rings are attached are designated by letters; thus, 3,4-benzpyrene is benzo(a)pyrene. *See:* International Union of Pure and Applied Chemistry. Definitive rules for nomenclature of organic chemistry. *J. Amer. Chem. Soc. 82*:5545 (1960).

Simple noncarcinogenic compounds

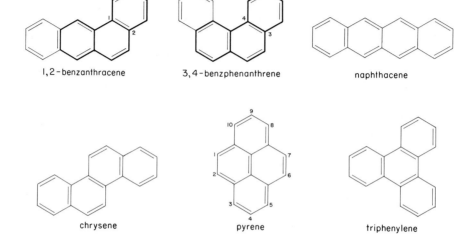

benzene   naphthalene   anthracene   phenanthrene

Tetracyclic compounds

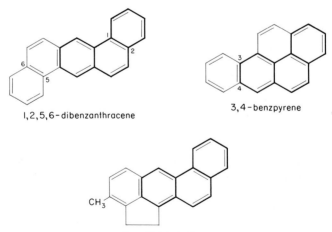

1,2-benzanthracene   3,4-benzphenanthrene   naphthacene

chrysene   pyrene   triphenylene

Pentacyclic compounds

1,2,5,6-dibenzanthracene

3,4-benzpyrene

3-methylcholanthrene

FIG. 11-5.   STRUCTURES OF SOME POLYCYCLIC HYDROCARBONS.   *The phenanthrene structure is emphasized in each of the carcinogenic compounds shown above. Phenanthrene itself is not carcinogenic, nor are pyrene, chrysene or triphenylene, despite their content of a phenanthrene moiety.*

ring at the 1,2-position (cf. 1,2-benzanthracene), is completely inactive. The potent carcinogen 3,4-benzpyrene is directly related to the 1,2-benzanthracene structure.

The principal necessary requirements for carcinogenicity may be summarized as follows: The entire polycyclic hydrocarbon must be coplanar. A phenanthrene nucleus must be present together with some substituents, preferably at least one additional benzene ring. The convex edge of the phenanthrene moiety must be free of substituents. In the series of tetracyclic hydrocarbons (Fig. 11-5), most of the noncarcinogenic compounds fail to conform to the necessary specification. Naphthacene lacks the phenanthrene nucleus, chrysene and triphenylene contain substituents in forbidden positions. The noncarcinogenicity of pyrene is considered below. Potency of the carcinogenic hydrocarbons is usually enhanced by methyl substitutions at appropriate positions, and the cyclization of adjacent methyl groups (as in 3-methylcholanthrene) further increases potency.

The relationships described above were worked out on an empirical basis. Our understanding of them has been deepened by the development of an electronic theory.[40,41] The polycyclic hydrocarbons are by no means chemically inert, but are characterized by a resonant system of π electrons, an orbital system extending over the entire molecule. Methods of quantum chemistry permit the calculation of electron densities associated with each part of the molecule. Such theoretical calculations led to the conclusion that a particular bond, represented by the 3,4-double bond of dibenzanthracene, was especially electron rich and therefore very reactive in the

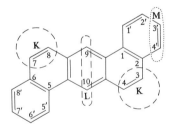

1,2,5,6-dibenzanthracene

carcinogenic compounds. This bond was designated the "K region." For carcinogenic activity, it appeared, the electron density of the K region had to exceed a certain value, and at the same time the competing reactivity toward para substitution at the 9,10-positions ("L region") had to be less

40 A. PULLMAN and B. PULLMAN: Electronic structure and carcinogenic activity of aromatic molecules. New development. *Adv. Cancer Res. 3:*117 (1955).

41 A. PULLMAN: "The Theory of Chemical Carcinogenesis and the Problem of Hydrocarbon-Protein Interactions," in *Biopolymers, Symposia No. 1,* 1964, pp. 47–65.

than a certain value. When these electronic indices were computed for a great many polycyclic hydrocarbons, the order with few exceptions corresponded to the order of carcinogenic potencies. The noncarcinogenic pyrene (Fig. 11-5), for example, even though it contains a phenanthrene nucleus, has an insufficient reactivity at its K region. Thus, reactivity of the K region appeared to be the key to carcinogenicity among the polycyclic hydrocarbons.

The concept of K region reactivity received strong experimental support when complexes of hydrocarbon carcinogens with mouse skin proteins were isolated,[42] as already described. It was found that the carcinogenic hydrocarbons attached to tissue proteins through their K regions, whereas noncarcinogenic congeners did not. For example, the dicarboxylic acid derivative shown below was identified after the application of

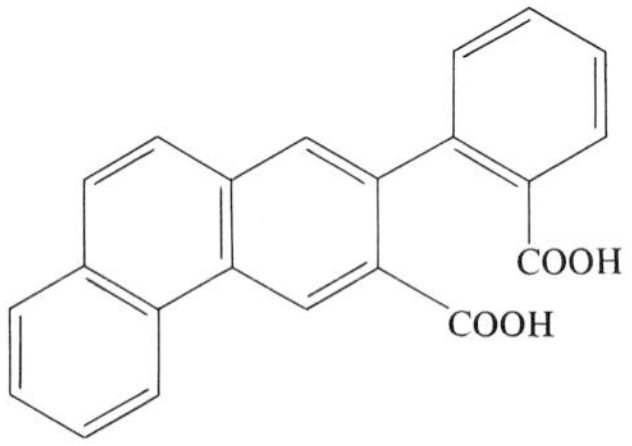

derivative of 1,2,5,6-dibenzanthracene

1,2,5,6-dibenzanthracene to mouse skin. On the other hand, the dicarboxylic acid derivative itself did not bind to mouse skin proteins at all.

Recent evidence has indicated[27] that formation of reactive epoxide intermediates at the K region may precede the binding to cell constituents. An example would be the metabolic conversion of 1,2-benzanthracene to the corresponding epoxide. Aliphatic epoxides are alkylating agents, aromatic epoxides are arylating agents. In some instances it has been

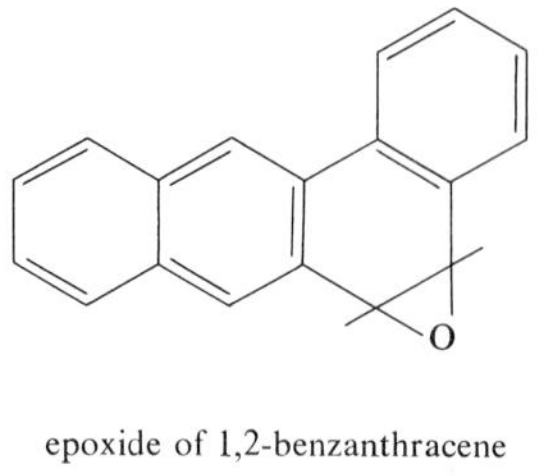

epoxide of 1,2-benzanthracene

[42] V. T. OLIVERIO and C. HEIDELBERGER: The interaction of carcinogenic hydrocarbons with tissues. V. Some structural requirements for binding of 1,2,5,6-dibenzanthracene. *Cancer Res. 18:*1094 (1958).

demonstrated that binding of the K region to cell components is followed by a metabolic hydroxylation of either carbon atom in the M region. Thus it is possible that the mechanism of action of polycyclic hydrocarbons is not unlike that of other carcinogens, whose chemical reactivities are more obvious.

The main significance of the electronic theory has been its ability to explain the empirical structure-activity findings in terms of a quantitative index of reactivity of a particular region of the carcinogen molecule. The theory directed attention toward chemical reactivity in a series of compounds that were generally regarded as inert, and thus set the stage for the discovery of covalent bonding between the polycyclic hydrocarbons and macromolecules in tissues.

Amines

AROMATIC AMINES

Certain aromatic amines were first discovered to be carcinogenic in man as a result of industrial exposure. Naphthylamine, long used in

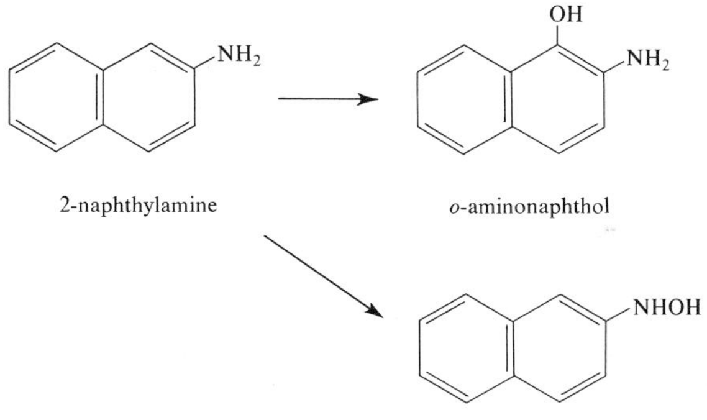

2-naphthylamine   *o*-aminonaphthol

2-naphthylhydroxylamine

the dye industry, was implicated in the causation of bladder cancer in exposed workers; the latent period was estimated to be about 15 to 20 years.[43] Studies on the induction of bladder cancers by aromatic amines in experimental animals have shed light on how differences in metabolic pathways may affect carcinogenicity.[44,45] It seems abundantly clear now that the aromatic amines themselves are not carcinogenic but give rise to

[43] A. L. WALPOLE and M. H. C. WILLIAMS: Aromatic amines as carcinogens in industry. *Brit. Med. Bull. 14:*141 (1958).

[44] D. B. CLAYSON: The aromatic amines. *Brit. Med. Bull. 20:*115 (1964).

[45] E. BOYLAND: The biochemistry of cancer of the bladder. *Brit. Med. Bull. 14:*153 (1958).

carcinogenic metabolites in vivo. Thus, 2-naphthylamine is transformed in the liver to two principal metabolites, the *o*-aminophenol and the hydroxylamine (N-hydroxy) derivative. When 2-naphthylamine itself was tested for carcinogenicity by direct implantation into the mouse bladder after incorporation into a wax pellet, no tumors were elicited. On the other hand, both the phenolic derivative and the hydroxylamine were potent carcinogens in this system.[44,46] The carcinogenic potency of the *o*-aminonaphthol remains somewhat uncertain because it can be converted to the hydroxylamine in vivo, and because a certain amount of absorption from bladder implants occurs, followed by re-excretion into urine.

The carcinogenic metabolites formed in the liver are rapidly conjugated there with glucuronic acid. In this manner the tissues are usually protected from exposure to the carcinogens, for the glucuronides are inert. The glucuronides are excreted into the urine. In man and the dog, the urine is known to contain a soluble β-glucuronidase which, under acid conditions, releases free carcinogen in the ureters and bladder. This mechanism has been established in several ways.[44,46] It was shown that the carcinogenic activity responsible for producing bladder cancer is present in the urine rather than in the bladder circulation. Dogs were subjected to a surgical procedure whereby blind pouches of bladder were constructed; these pouches received their normal blood supply but were no longer in contact with urine. Naphthylamine administration produced no cancers in the pouches. If the ureters were transplanted to the sigmoid colon, tumors developed in them but not in the bladder. Finally, an inhibitor of β-glucuronidase (glucosaccharo-1,4-lactone) greatly reduced the incidence of bladder tumors in dogs when it was fed simultaneously with 2-naphthylamine.

It must be evident from the foregoing account that both the potency of an administered carcinogenic amine and the sites at which it will produce cancer depend upon the activity of drug-metabolizing enzymes. Conversion to N-hydroxy or other active products, conjugation of these to glucuronides (or sulfate esters), and enzymic hydrolysis at sites of excretion all influence the end result. It is found, for example, that in contrast to man and the dog, mice and rats are refractory to bladder carcinogenesis by aromatic amines. Since N-hydroxynaphthylamine is carcinogenic by implantation in the mouse bladder, and since 2-naphthylamine itself produces cancers at other tissue sites after it is fed to rats, it is likely that some deficiency of β-glucuronidase action in rodent urine accounts for the absence of bladder tumors in these species.

Patients with bladder tumors induced by long exposure to naphthylamine have unusually high levels of β-glucuronidase in their urine.[45] It is not known whether these high enzyme levels predated the development of the

---

[46] G. M. BONSER, D. B. CLAYSON, and J. W. JULL: Some aspects of the experimental induction of tumours of the bladder. *Brit. Med. Bull.* 14:146 (1958).

bladder tumors; if so, this would be a good example of how genetically determined biochemical individuality might predispose to a particular kind of cancer. Administration of a β-glucuronidase inhibitor (glucosaccharo-1,4-lactone) has been proposed as a prophylactic measure for people accidentally exposed to carcinogens of the naphthylamine type.

The following schemes indicate possible chemical pathways whereby the metabolites of naphthylamine might form covalent bonds with cell constituents such as proteins or nucleic acids through quinone-imine intermediates.[44]

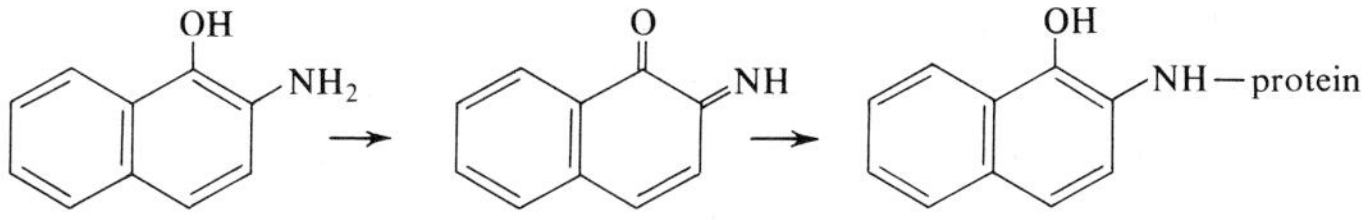

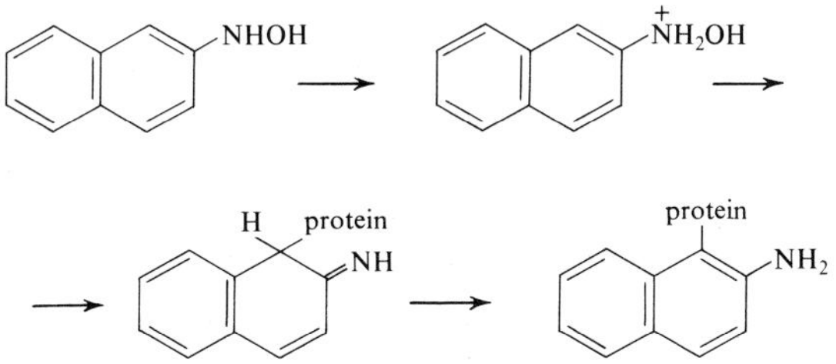

Since bladder tumors develop in people not known to have been exposed to aromatic amine carcinogens, attention was directed to the possibility that metabolites of endogenous amines might be carcinogenic. Tryptophan is metabolized in vivo to kynurenine, and then to *o*-aminophenol derivatives (Fig. 11-6) which are carcinogenic if implanted in the mouse bladder. One of these compounds, 3-hydroxyanthranilic acid, was found in the urine of patients with spontaneous bladder cancer at much higher concentration than in normal people or in patients with other kinds of cancer.[45]

Another aromatic amine carcinogen is 2-acetylaminofluorene (AAF):

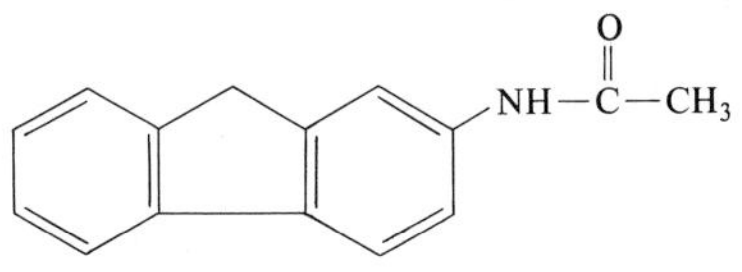

2-acetylaminofluorene (AAF)

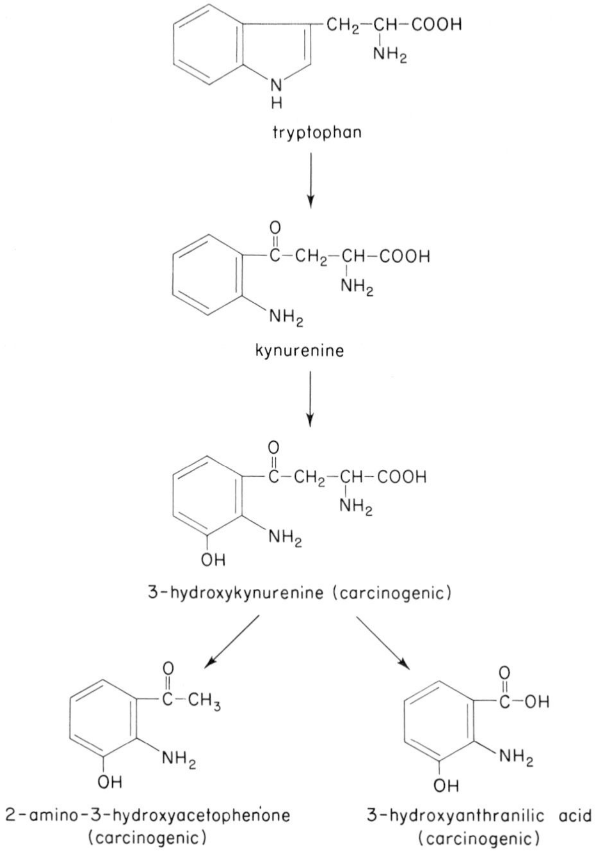

FIG. 11-6.   METABOLISM   OF   TRYPTOPHAN   TO   CARCINOGENIC   PRODUCTS.
(*Adapted from Boyland, Fig. 3.*[45])

This compound, when fed in small amounts in the diet of the rat, causes
cancers at many sites in the body. Most unusual has been a predilection
for inducing papillomas and squamous-cell carcinomas of the sebaceous
gland in the external ear duct. Originally it was supposed that deacetylation
occurred in the liver and that 2-aminofluorene was the active carcinogen.

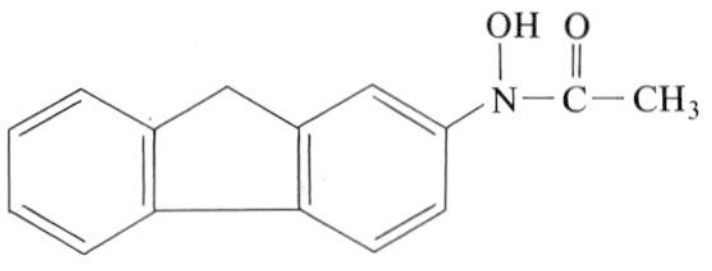

N-hydroxy derivative of AAF

It has become evident, however, that neither AAF nor 2-aminofluorene is directly carcinogenic. As already recounted for 2-naphthylamine, the analogous N-hydroxy derivative of AAF has been found to be a potent carcinogen.[48-50] AAF itself, for example, had no local carcinogenicity in rats after intraperitoneal injection, or in the intestinal tract after feeding. But the N-hydroxy derivative produced peritoneal sarcomas and gastric carcinomas upon direct contact.

The guinea pig provides a good further test of the hypothesis that N-hydroxy-AAF is the active carcinogen, for this species does not carry out the N-hydroxylation reaction. Accordingly, AAF is not a carcinogen in this species. The guinea pig is not, however, intrinsically refractory; when N-hydroxy-AAF was fed or injected, intestinal, peritoneal, and subcutaneous cancers were readily obtained.

The N-hydroxy derivatives in general are chemically reactive compounds, but the hydroxylamines (cf. naphthylhydroxylamine, p. 689) are especially reactive. It is therefore thought possible that N-hydroxy derivatives of acetylated amines may undergo deacetylation to hydroxylamines before reacting with tissue constituents to initiate the carcinogenic process. Failure to isolate such hydroxylamines may be attributed to their great instability. On the other hand, direct evidence has been obtained that N-acetoxy-AAF (i.e., an O-acetyl, N-acetyl compound) reacts in vitro

N-acetoxy-AAF

with guanine residues of salmon sperm DNA,[51] presumably without any preliminary modification of chemical structure.

Another group of aromatic amines, important because of their widespread use in industry, includes 4-aminodiphenyl and 4-aminostilbene

[47] J. H. WEISBURGER and E. K. WEISBURGER: Pharmacodynamics of carcinogenic azo dyes, aromatic amines, and nitrosamines. *Clin. Pharmacol. Therap. 4:*110 (1963).

[48] E. C. MILLER, J. A. MILLER, and H. A. HARTMANN: *N*-Hydroxy-2-acetylaminofluorene: a metabolite of 2-acetylaminofluorene with increased carcinogenic activity in the rat. *Cancer Res. 21:*815 (1961).

[49] J. A. MILLER and E. C. MILLER: Natural and synthetic chemical carcinogens in the etiology of cancer. *Cancer Res. 25:*1292 (1965).

[50] J. A. MILLER and E. C. MILLER: Metabolism of drugs in relation to carcinogenicity. *Ann. New York Acad. Sci. 123:*125 (1965).

[51] E. C. MILLER, U. JUHL, and J. A. MILLER: Nucleic acid guanine: reaction with the carcinogen N-acetoxy-2-acetylaminofluorene. *Science 153:*1125 (1966).

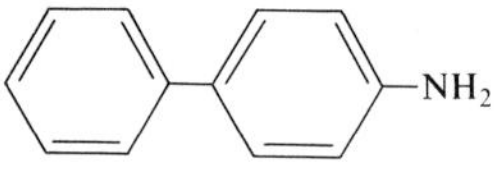

4-aminodiphenyl 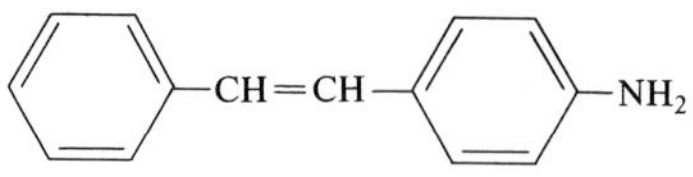   4-aminostilbene

and their N-methyl derivatives.[43] In their carcinogenicity and metabolic conversion to N-hydroxy derivatives in vivo, these compounds closely resemble AAF and naphthylamine. They cause tumors in various tissues in the rat after feeding, especially in the acoustic sebaceous gland, intestine, liver, and kidneys. They also induce sarcomas at the sites of subcutaneous injection. This fact could be taken to indicate that extensive metabolic conversion is not necessary, were it not for the finding, already cited (p. 676), that tumors can form at the site of injection of an inert substance after a carcinogen has been administered by mouth. It is quite possible, therefore, that when tumors develop at the site of injection of a presumed carcinogen, the injected compound was actually absorbed and subjected to metabolic transformation in the liver before it acted upon the tissues where the injections were made.

AZO DYES

The azo dyes first commanded attention as carcinogens when they were found to produce liver cancers after incorporation into the diet of rats. The best-known member of the group is dimethylaminoazobenzene, also

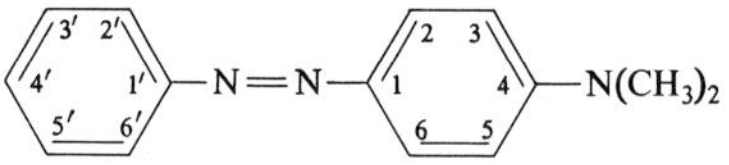

dimethylaminoazobenzene

called "Butter Yellow" because of its former use as a food coloring. Numerous studies of the structure-activity relationships in this group have provided a body of empirical data about the requirements for carcinogenicity. As with the polycyclic hydrocarbons, modifications that alter the coplanar configuration abolish carcinogenicity. Methylation of the nitrogen atom at position 4 is essential for activity, but the monomethyl and dimethyl derivatives are equally effective; in any case metabolic demethylation occurs in vivo. Substituents are tolerated (and sometimes increase potency) in position 3 (ortho to the amine nitrogen), as in the potent carcinogen *o*-aminoazotoluene. But substitution of any kind in position 2 (meta to the amino group) abolishes activity. Alkyl groups larger than methyl on the amine nitrogen decrease potency.

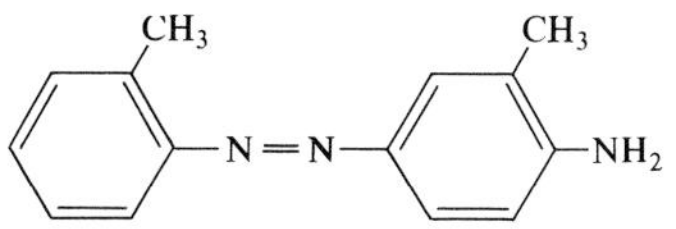

o-aminoazotoluene

Until recently the relationship of the azo dyes to other carcinogenic amines had been obscure. Although it seemed obvious that these compounds were transformed metabolically in the liver to active carcinogens, so many reactions occurred that it was uncertain which ones might be involved in carcinogenesis. Dimethylaminoazobenzene, for example, is demethylated to the monomethyl compound and to the primary amine, which is then acetylated. Ring hydroxylation at position 4' and also reductive cleavage of the azo linkage occur. Aromatic azo compounds are known to undergo benzidine rearrangements, so it was even possible to imagine a compound like 2,2'-azonaphthalene transformed by a series of steps to 3,4,5,6-dibenzcarbazole, a polycyclic hydrocarbon related to 1,2,5,6-dibenzanthracene. It now appears that the azo dyes, like other aromatic amines, are metabolized to N-hydroxy derivatives.[8] Small amounts of an N-hydroxy-N-acetyl metabolite were isolated from urine of rats and mice given dimethylaminoazobenzene by mouth. Such aromatic N-hydroxy compounds act as arylating agents (cf. N-hydroxynaphthylamine, p. 690). The isolation of a methylmercapto derivative from a protein-bound form of the azo dye in rat liver indicates that a methionine complex was formed in vivo. Figure 11-7 presents a postulated sequence of reactions that brings azo dye carcinogenesis into consonance with the probable mechanisms of carcinogenesis by other aromatic amines.

By feeding, intraperitoneal injections, and subcutaneous injections in rats it has recently been shown that N-hydroxy derivatives of non-methylated azo dyes are not carcinogenic.[52] This was true of N-hydroxy-4-aminoazobenzene and of N-hydroxy-N-acetyl-4-aminoazobenzene, just as 4-aminoazobenzene and N-acetyl-4-aminoazobenzene themselves are not carcinogenic. Presumably, the real carcinogen in this series is an N-hydroxy metabolite of N-methyl-4-aminoazobenzene, as indicated in Fig. 11-7. However, direct proof that this compound is carcinogenic has not yet been obtained.

[52] K. SATO, L. A. POIRIER, J. A. MILLER, and E. C. MILLER: Studies on the N-hydroxy-lation and carcinogenicity of 4-aminoazobenzene and related compounds. *Cancer Res.* 26:1678 (1966).

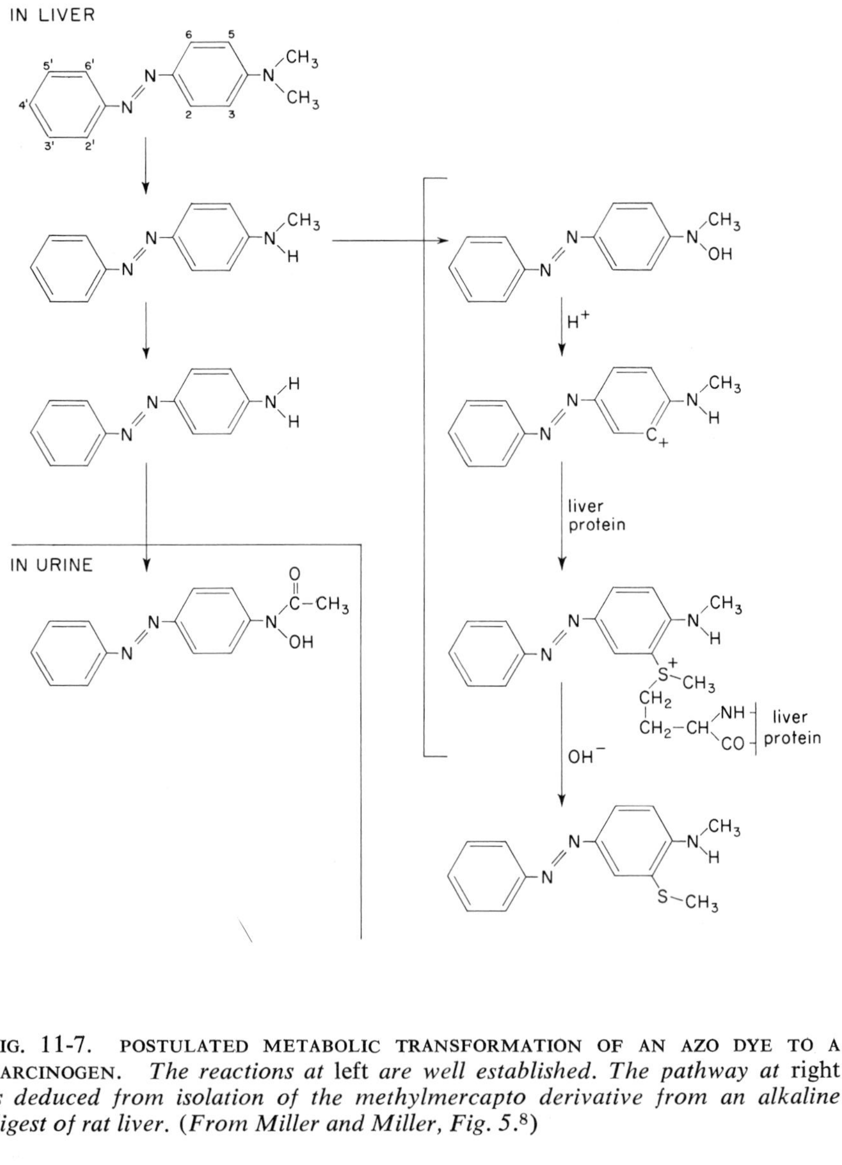

FIG. 11-7. POSTULATED METABOLIC TRANSFORMATION OF AN AZO DYE TO A CARCINOGEN. *The reactions at* left *are well established. The pathway at* right *is deduced from isolation of the methylmercapto derivative from an alkaline digest of rat liver. (From Miller and Miller, Fig. 5.*[8]*)*

NITROSAMINES

An interesting group of very potent carcinogens are the nitrosamines.[53] It will be recalled (p. 633) that one of the most potent mutagens is a nitrosamine. These agents are evidently converted through N-hydroxylation to alkylating agents. Figure 11-8 shows the probable scheme of metabolic transformation, but it is not certain if the actual alkylating intermediate is the diazoalkane (e.g., diazomethane from dimethylnitrosamine), or the diazonium salt, or carbonium ion. When dimethylnitrosamine was fed to rats, tumors of the liver, kidney, and lung were produced. The degree of methylation of tissue DNA and protein paralleled the carcinogenic potency for various tissues (p. 681). A naturally occurring carcinogen, cycasin, found in certain nuts (Cycad nuts) alkylates by a similar mecha-

FIG. 11-8. TRANSFORMATION OF NITROSAMINE TO AN ACTIVE CARCINOGEN. *A general scheme for the probable in vivo metabolic transformation is shown. The active alkylating agent may be the diazoalkane, the diazonium compound, or the carbonium ion. The R groups represent alkyl groups, usually methyl or ethyl. Dimethylnitrosamine is a potent carcinogen in vivo; the ultimate metabolic products would be methylating agents. (From Brookes, Chart 3.[30])*

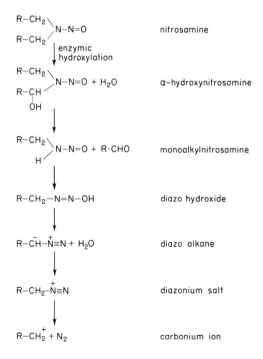

53 P. N. MAGEE and R. SCHOENTAL: Carcinogenesis by nitroso compounds. *Brit. Med. Bull. 20:*102 (1964).

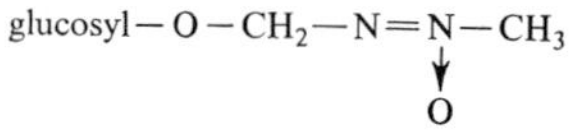

$$glucosyl - O - CH_2 - N = N - CH_3$$
$$\downarrow$$
$$O$$

cycasin

nism.[54] The compound is a glucoside of methylazoxymethanol. In vivo it breaks down to diazomethane, and its methyl group is transferred to the 7-position of nucleic acid guanine. It has also been shown to be mutagenic in bacteria.

URETHANE

Urethane is another chemically inert compound known to be carcinogenic. It is now known that urethane is converted to an alkylating agent by N-hydroxylation in vivo.[55] This conversion is known to occur in rats,

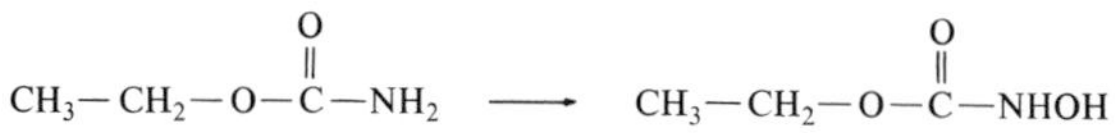

$$CH_3 - CH_2 - O - \overset{\overset{\displaystyle O}{\|}}{C} - NH_2 \longrightarrow CH_3 - CH_2 - O - \overset{\overset{\displaystyle O}{\|}}{C} - NHOH$$

urethane   N-hydroxyurethane

rabbits, and man. Alternative modes of alkylation are indicated by the isolation of two types of product from tissues. The urethane ethyl group may be transferred to form ethylmercapturic acid or S-ethylglutathione, both of which have been isolated after urethane administration. On the other hand, the entire N-hydroxyurethane moiety may be transferred; in this way, for example, N-acetyl-S-carbethoxycysteine is formed.

Alkylating Agents

The chemical reactivity of the alkylating agents was described in chapter 1, and their mode of action as mutagens was discussed in chapter 10. It was shown that the principal point of attack in the nucleic acids is the 7-position of guanine, and that numerous groups in proteins can be alkylated, such as the imidazole nitrogen atom of histidine, the sulfhydryl group of cysteine or methionine, the carboxyl groups of the dicarboxylic acids. The bifunctional alkylating agents can cross-link the strands of the DNA duplex (Fig. 1-2). That alkylating agents as a group are carcinogenic strengthens the analogy between carcinogenesis and mutagenesis. The most widely studied carcinogenic alkylating agents have been mechlorethamine

[54] D. W. E. SMITH: Mutagenicity of cycasin aglycone (methylazoxymethanol), a naturally occurring carcinogen. *Science 152:*1273 (1966).
[55] E. BOYLAND and R. NERY: The metabolism of urethane and related compounds. *Biochem. J. 94:*198 (1965).

(nitrogen mustard, Table 1-1), sulfonyl esters such as 1,4-dimethane-sulfonoxybutane (busulfan, Table 1-1), and epoxy compounds like the cyclohexane derivative shown below:

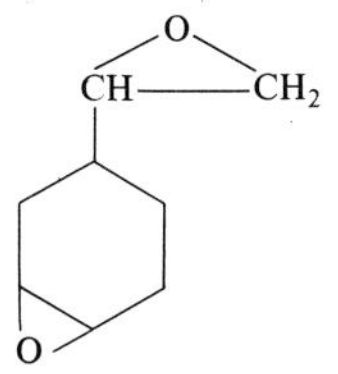

1-ethyleneoxy-3,4-epoxycyclohexane

Certain plant alkaloids (from *Senecio* species) are of great interest because they are alkylating agents with a pyrrolizidine structure.[49, 56] If added to the diet they produce liver cancer in rats. Since plants containing them are used in folk medicine or to prepare bush teas in Africa and India, they might contribute to the high incidence of hepatoma in certain geographic areas. The general structure is given below:

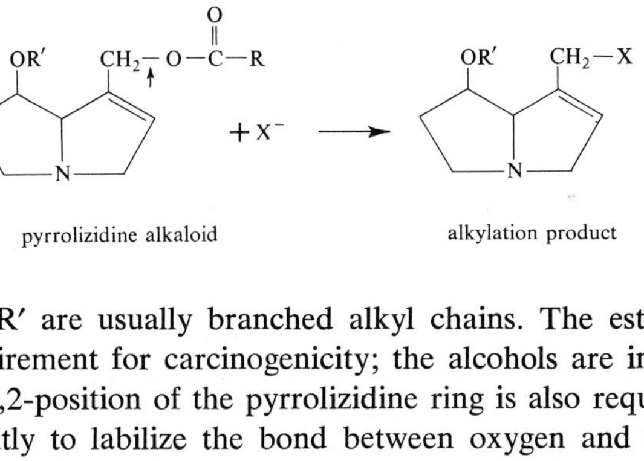

pyrrolizidine alkaloid   alkylation product

Both R and R′ are usually branched alkyl chains. The ester bond is an absolute requirement for carcinogenicity; the alcohols are inert. A double bond in the 1,2-position of the pyrrolizidine ring is also required; its function is evidently to labilize the bond between oxygen and the methylene group, indicated by the small arrow. The reaction shown represents the alkylation of any nucleophilic receptor anion, such as a sulfhydryl group.

Ethionine, the ethyl analogue of the amino acid methionine, is a liver carcinogen when it is fed to the rat.[57] The body's normal mechanism

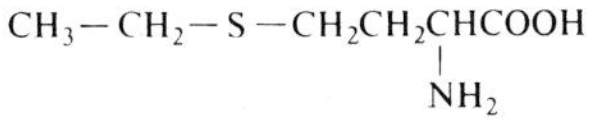

$$CH_3-CH_2-S-CH_2CH_2\underset{\underset{NH_2}{|}}{C}HCOOH$$

ethionine

56 C. C. J. CULVENOR, A. T. DANN, and A. T. DICK: Alkylation as the mechanism by which the hepatotoxic pyrrolizidine alkaloids act on cell nuclei. *Nature 195:*570 (1962).

57 E. FARBER: Ethionine carcinogenesis. *Adv. Cancer Res. 7:*383 (1963).

for methylation, in which methionine acts as a methyl donor, becomes a means of ethylation in the presence of ethionine. Normally, S-adenosylmethionine participates in the methylation of purines in molecules of transfer-RNA. When S-adenosylethionine is formed, the ethyl group (shown below in bold type) is transferred to purines and other acceptors:

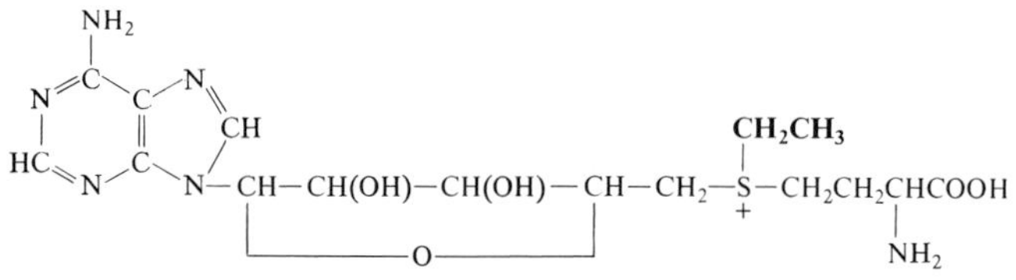

S-adenosylethionine

A number of lactones have been found to have carcinogenic activity, and some of these occur in fungi and higher plants.[58] Prototype of the group is β-propiolactone. The basis of the alkylating action of this

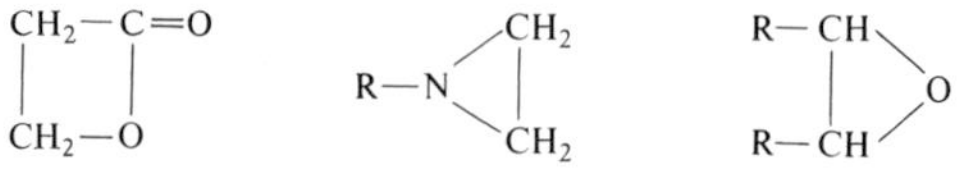

β-propiolactone   ethyleneimine   epoxide

compound is its strained ring structure, a feature common to such typical alkylating compounds as ethyleneimines and epoxides. β-Propiolactone is subject to two kinds of nucleophilic attack. Nonionized nucleophiles form addition products at the ester bond, ionized nucleophiles at the $-CH_2-O-$ bond, yielding carboxyethyl derivatives. For example, S-(2-carboxyethyl)-cysteine and 7-(2'-carboxyethyl)guanine have been isolated from organisms treated with β-propiolactone. In the same way, after exposure to the simple epoxide ethylene oxide, 7-(2'-hydroxyethyl)guanine could be isolated. That the intact lactone ring is essential to carcinogenesis was indicated by the finding that sarcomas were produced by subcutaneous injection of β-propiolactone in rats, whereas its hydrolysis product β-hydroxypropionic acid was inert.

Penicillin contains a β-lactam ring, which is essential to its antibacterial action, and which is opened in vivo when hapten-antigen complexes are formed (cf. chapter 7). This suggests the possibility that the drug might be carcinogenic; at very high doses it has indeed produced

---

[58] F. DICKENS: Carcinogenic lactones and related substances. *Brit. Med. Bull.* *20*:96 (1964).

sarcomas in rats, although there is no evidence of carcinogenicity under conditions of therapeutic use. Other naturally occurring lactone carcinogens include parasorbic acid, from the berries of the mountain ash, and a fungal product, aflatoxin, to be discussed later (p. 703):

parasorbic acid   aflatoxin B

Alkylation and Arylation in the Carcinogenic Process

Advances in our understanding of drug metabolism are leading to a unitary view of the biochemistry of carcinogenesis. Some years ago, when such compounds as the polycyclic hydrocarbons, the aromatic amines, and the azo dyes were thought of as rather nonreactive molecules, it was difficult to discern any common pathway that could account for the carcinogenic effects of such diverse chemical structures. The position has changed completely as a result of these recent developments, discussed earlier in detail: (*1*) The discovery of the carcinogenic properties of alkylating agents, and the relationship between their carcinogenic and mutagenic properties. (*2*) The elaboration of a theory that stressed the chemical reactivity of a particular region in the polycyclic hydrocarbon molecule, and the proof of that reactivity by isolation of complexes with tissue proteins and nucleic acids. (*3*) The demonstration that all the seemingly unreactive carcinogens undergo extensive metabolic transformation in vivo, that some of the metabolites are more carcinogenic than the parent compounds, and that metabolites are often active locally whereas the parent compounds are not.

One can now reasonably postulate that all carcinogens act by alkylation or arylation of cell constituents. Whether the target of such covalent attachment is a nucleic acid or a protein remains uncertain. As for the aromatic carcinogens, the requirement of a planar configuration and the demonstrated ability of several to intercalate between the base pairs of DNA suggest the speculation that a stereospecific interaction with DNA places the carcinogen in an optimum position to arylate guanine or other bases. According to this viewpoint, carcinogenesis would be the ultimate result of a somatic mutation caused in this way. Although this may be the most attractive explanation, it is certainly not the only one. It remains for future experimentation to identify the cellular target of carcinogen action.

CARCINOGENIC HAZARDS IN THE HUMAN ENVIRONMENT

Epidemic Outbreaks of Cancer

The preceding sections of this chapter have dealt with those groups of carcinogens about which most experimental evidence has been obtained. Some of these (e.g., the polycyclic hydrocarbons and the aromatic amines) first came to attention because they were associated with occupational cancer in man. Carcinogens of this kind are conspicuous because they affect a particular occupational group. When workers in a certain industry are found to have an inordinately high incidence of some kind of cancer, a carcinogen is suspected and soon identified, and means are found for eliminating it or protecting people against it. In this way measures have been developed to avoid contact with coal tars, special precautions are taken in the dye industry, and azo dyes have been eliminated from use as food colorings. In the same way exposure to ionizing radiation is carefully controlled, now that its carcinogenicity is appreciated.[59] The incident of the watch dial painters, who moistened their brushes alternately with a solution of radium salts and with saliva and died of osteogenic sarcoma, is not likely to be repeated. And the exposure of miners to radon-contaminated dust is now carefully regulated following the recognition of lung cancer as an occupational hazard. Nevertheless, we are still unexpectedly confronted from time to time by outbreaks of cancer on an epidemic scale—outbreaks that reflect the introduction of new carcinogens into our environment.[60, 61] Fortunately, these episodes often affect animals in the first instance, so that precautionary measures may be taken in time to protect the human population. Two epidemics of liver cancer in animals will illustrate the effects of a sudden increase in the intake of a carcinogen in the diet. The production of lung cancer by cigarette smoking in humans will illustrate the effects of a gradually increasing exposure of the population to a carcinogen.

Several years ago an epidemic of liver cancer afflicted the domestic trout population of the United States.[62] The suddenness with which the disease appeared and the very large numbers of fish involved were remarkable. It so happens that essentially all the trout living in rivers and lakes of this country are raised in hatcheries, and there they are fed on stock commercial diets. Since hepatoma is the characteristic form of cancer that

---

[59] J. B. LITTLE: Environmental hazards: ionizing radiation. *New England J. Med.* 275:929 (1966).

[60] Epidemiologic approaches to cancer etiology. Symposium sponsored by the American Cancer Society. *Cancer Res.* 25:1271 (1965).

[61] E. BOYLAND: The biological examination of carcinogenic substances. *Brit. Med. Bull.* 14:93 (1958).

[62] H. F. KRAYBILL and M. B. SHIMKIN: Carcinogenesis related to foods contaminated by processing and fungal metabolites. *Adv. Cancer Res.* 8:191 (1964).

develops when a carcinogen is eaten, it appeared likely that something was contaminating the fish diet. Experimental studies soon revealed that a control test diet could be devised that produced no tumors whatsoever. Extraction of the stock commercial diet with lipid solvents yielded an extract that was carcinogenic when added to the control diet. This finding led to a general survey of potential carcinogens administered to trout by addition to the diet. Table 11-2 presents results of feeding tests carried out for 20 months. Especially provocative was the finding that the insecticide DDT was carcinogenic, in view of the known widespread exposure of fish to insecticides used agriculturally on a wide scale. If there was any single cause of the trout hepatoma epidemic, however, it has not yet been identified.

Another extraordinary outbreak of cancer on an epidemic scale in animals was the turkey hepatoma that ravaged turkey flocks in England a few years ago.[62] In this instance the causative agent was tracked down and isolated. The turkeys had been fed on spoiled peanut meal contaminated with a fungus, *Aspergillus flavus,* that produced the carcinogen (named aflatoxin), a polycyclic lactone whose structure was shown on p. 701. Aflatoxin is an extraordinarily potent carcinogen. In the rat, for example, it produced hepatomas experimentally when fed at a daily dose of only 6μg, whereas dimethylaminoazobenzene had to be given at a dose 500 times larger to obtain the same high incidence of liver tumors.

The discovery of aflatoxin and the circumstances of the turkey hepatoma epidemic have raised the general question whether mycotoxicoses present any hazard of carcinogenesis for human populations. Espe-

TABLE 11-2.   **Production of trout hepatoma by substances fed in the diet**

Each substance was fed for 20 months at the concentration shown, and the number of hepatomas were then recorded. Of especial interest is the carcinogenic activity of the insecticide DDT. (From Kraybill and Shimkin,[62] Table VIII.)

Chemical	Dose in diet (mg/100 g)	Frequency No.	%
Control test diet	—	0/300	0
Dimethylnitrosamine	480	38/46	82
Aminoazotoluene	120	22/43	52
Aminoazotoluene	30	3/49	6
Dichlorodiphenyltrichloroethane (DDT)	8	4/11	36
2-Acetylaminofluorene	30	9/45	20
Thiourea	480	7/38	18
p-Dimethylaminoazobenzene	30	6/46	13
Tannic acid	120	6/48	13
Urethane	480	5/55	11
Carbon tetrachloride	120	4/44	10
Carbarsone	480	5/50	10

cially provocative are the statistics on the incidence of hepatic cancer in various populations. In Denmark, the incidence of this disease per 100,000 population is only 0.18; in the white population of the United States it is 1.7, nearly ten times higher. Among Bantus in South Africa, the incidence reaches 14, and this one disease comprises 68 per cent of all cancers in this ethnic group. The Bantus are known to eat moldy corn. The Japanese, who also have a high rate of hepatic cancer, may eat fungus-infected rice. It is possible that these characteristic dietary habits may account for the unusual prevalence of hepatoma among these groups. What dietary peculiarity accounts for the fact that the hepatoma rate is so much higher in the United States than in Denmark remains to be discovered.

Smoking and Lung Cancer

The connection between smoking and lung cancer was first observed in retrospective studies conducted over 25 years ago.[63] An increase in the frequency of primary carcinoma of the lung was noted in routine autopsies on males, and an inquiry was initiated into the smoking habits of patients with lung cancer and of an equal number of healthy subjects matched as to age. A significant difference was found between the two groups with respect to the frequency of heavy smoking. Since then, many more elaborate retrospective studies have been conducted, always with the same result. In addition, recent prospective studies have established beyond question that cancer of the lung is associated with cigarette smoking, and that the incidence of this cancer is directly related to the extent and duration of smoking. Most significant, the incidence of lung cancer decreased in a group of heavy smokers after they stopped smoking.[64]

The growing concern about the high and increasing incidence of lung cancer led to the appointment by the Surgeon General, in 1962, of an advisory group of scientists to review all the available evidence about the relationship between smoking and health. The extensively documented report of this committee was published in 1964.[65] The conclusions about lung cancer were summarized as follows:

"Cigarette smoking is causally related to lung cancer in men: the magnitude of the effect of cigarette smoking outweighs all other factors. The data for women, though less extensive, points in the same direction. The risk of developing lung cancer increases with duration of smoking and the number of cigarettes smoked per day, and is diminished by discontinued smoking. In comparison with non-smokers, average male

[63] F. H. MÜLLER: Tabakmissbrauch und Lungencarcinom. *Z. Krebsforsch.* 49:57 (1939).

[64] R. DOLL and A. B. HILL: Lung cancer and other causes of death in relation to smoking. *Brit. Med. J.* 2:1071 (1956).

[65] *Smoking and Health.* Report of the Advisory Committee to the Surgeon General of the Public Health Service, U.S. Public Health Service Publication No. 1103. Washington, D.C., U. S. Government Printing Office, 1964.

smokers of cigarettes have approximately a 9- to 10-fold risk of developing lung cancer and heavy smokers at least a 20-fold risk. The risk of developing cancer of the lung for the combined groups of pipe smokers, cigar smokers, and pipe and cigar smokers is greater than for non-smokers, but much less than for cigarette smokers."

With regard to cancer at other sites, the report states:

"Pipe smoking appears to be causally related to lip cancer. Cigarette smoking is a significant factor in the causation of cancer of the larynx."

The report goes on to indicate the presence of an association between tobacco use and cancer of the urinary tract or esophagus; but the data did not permit a decision as to whether these relationships are causal or not.

Table 11-3 presents some of the data of this report. These are pooled results of seven prospective studies initiated at various times between 1951 and 1960. The populations surveyed included British physicians, war veterans in Canada and the United States, and randomly chosen males in various parts of the United States. At the time a subject was enrolled in a study, his then-current smoking habits were recorded, as well as data about his age, occupation, and so on. More than one million usable questionnaire replies were obtained. Then, over a period ranging from about two to ten years, the cause of death was ascertained for every enrolled person who died. Since death rates are obviously related to age, it was necessary to adjust the mortality rates thus determined to take account of the age distributions in the smoker and nonsmoker groups. When this adjustment had been made, it was found that the overall mortality was considerably higher in the smoker group. On the average, it was about 70 per cent higher, and this difference was observed in all age groups. It was then asked whether the higher mortality for smokers applied uniformly to all causes of death, or whether certain specific causes of death were principally responsible.

The tabular data show that the mortality (expressed as the ratio of observed deaths in the smoker group to expected deaths if the death rate had been the same as in the nonsmoker group) was 11 times higher for cancer of the lung. It is especially noteworthy that whereas the mortality ratios were high for cancers of the lung, larynx, oral cavity, and esophagus, no such elevated ratios were observed for other kinds of cancer. Nor, in general, was there a comparably high mortality ratio for other causes of death. However, the mortality ratio for cardiovascular diseases, although only 1.7, accounts for such a large proportion of all deaths, that the role of smoking may be very important in terms of actual numbers of deaths, despite the relatively low ratio. It is also interesting that the mortality ratio is rather low for deaths due to accidents, suicide, and violence, suggesting that differences in temperament do not play a significant role in relation to the higher mortality of smokers than of nonsmokers.

TABLE 11-3.   **Mortality for specific causes of death among smokers and non-smokers in prospective studies**

The data are from prospective studies on more than one million men. Subjects were categorized as to their smoking habits at the time of enrollment in the study. In the entire group there were 37,391 deaths at the time the data were compiled (11,168 nonsmoker deaths and 26,223 smoker deaths). Column showing expected deaths was obtained by applying the death rate for nonsmokers to the number of smokers, making appropriate adjustment for the age distribution. If smokers and nonsmokers had the same death rate for a specific cause of death, the mortality ratio would be 1.0. (From *Smoking and Health,*[65] Table 19, p. 102.)

| Underlying cause of death | Deaths (smokers) | | Mortality ratio |
	Expected	Observed	
Cancer of lung	170.3	1,833	10.8
Bronchitis and emphysema	89.5	546	6.1
Cancer of larynx	14.0	75	5.4
Cancer of oral cavity	37.0	152	4.1
Cancer of esophagus	33.7	113	3.4
Stomach and duodenal ulcers	105.1	294	2.8
Other circulatory diseases	254.0	649	2.6
Cirrhosis of liver	169.2	379	2.2
Cancer of bladder	111.6	216	1.9
Coronary artery disease	6,430.7	11,177	1.7
Other heart diseases	526.0	868	1.7
Hypertensive heart disease	409.2	631	1.5
General arteriosclerosis	210.7	310	1.5
Cancer of kidney	79.0	120	1.5
All other cancer	1,061.4	1,524	1.4
Cancer of stomach	285.2	413	1.4
Influenza, pneumonia	303.2	415	1.4
All other causes	1,508.7	1,946	1.3
Cerebral vascular lesions	1,461.8	1,844	1.3
Cancer of prostate	253.0	318	1.3
Accidents, suicides, violence	1,063.2	1,310	1.2
Nephritis	156.4	173	1.1
Rheumatic heart disease	290.6	309	1.1
Cancer of rectum	207.8	213	1.0
Cancer of intestines	422.6	395	0.9
All causes	15,653.9	26,223	1.68

The quantitative relationship between the amount smoked and the death rate due to various diseases was ascertained in one of the most carefully conducted prospective studies.[64] In this investigation questionnaires were sent to all members of the medical profession in the United Kingdom (59,600 men and women). Complete replies were received from 34,494 men, who were thus enrolled in the study. Four years and five months later there had been 1,714 deaths from all causes among men over 35 years of age. Of these, 84 were due to lung cancer, 220 to other forms of cancer, 126 to other respiratory diseases, 508 to coronary thrombosis, and 779 to all other causes. Figure 11-9 shows the relationship between the death rates due to the various causes and the amount smoked. These data did not distinguish between cigarette, cigar, and pipe smokers; but further analyses showed a significantly higher death rate due to lung cancer among the cigarette smokers as compared with the other smokers. The figure as a whole shows that there was a striking positive correlation between the amount smoked and the death rate for lung cancer, and a weak positive correlation for other respiratory diseases and for coronary thrombosis, but not for other causes of death.

Most of the available data relate to males because the high incidence of lung cancer in men (but not in women) forced attention to males. It should not be concluded, however, that the sexes differ in sensitivity to tobacco carcinogenesis. Historically, women began smoking much later than men; and currently the incidence of smoking and the amount of tobacco consumed are much greater for men than for women. What investigations have been carried out indicate quite clearly that the incidence of

FIG. 11-9. RELATIONSHIP BETWEEN DEATH RATES FOR DIFFERENT DISEASES AND AMOUNT OF SMOKING. *Smokers are classified according to the grams of tobacco smoked each day (one cigarette contains about 1 g). The rates shown for each cause of death are the death rates as percentages of the death rate due to that cause for all men. For example, the death rate due to lung cancer among nonsmokers was only 9 per cent of the rate among all men (smokers and nonsmokers). If smokers and nonsmokers had the same death rate, the figure shown would be 100 for both. (From Doll and Hill, Table V.[64] By permission of the British Medical Association.)*

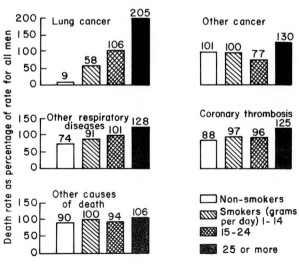

lung cancer among women is rising at a rate that reflects the increasing frequency of smoking among women.

Tobacco smoke contains various substances that could account for the carcinogenicity. The coal tar hydrocarbons are certainly present.[65, 66] 3,4-Benzpyrene is the most potent carcinogen, and it is found in the largest amount, about $16\mu g$ per 1,000 cigarettes smoked. Dibenzpyrene and 1,2,5,6-dibenzanthracene are present in smaller amounts but are also potent carcinogens. Tobacco smoke condensates are certainly carcinogenic when painted on mouse skin, but it has not been possible to produce lung cancers by smoke inhalation in experimental animals. In the light of our general knowledge about experimental carcinogenesis it may be that no suitable animal model exists, i.e., that species differences preclude the production of lung cancer by smoke inhalation in animals. It is also possible that conditions analogous to human smoking cannot be established in experimental animals, despite ingenious attempts to construct "smoking machines" that force the inhalation of cigarette smoke. Recently, pulmonary tumors have been induced in mice by subcutaneous injection of a nitrosamine that might well be formed in tobacco smoke.[67] Besides about 5 mg of nicotine, the smoke of one cigarette contains $100\mu g$ of secondary amine alkaloids, including nornicotine. This compound reacts with NO and NO_2 found in cigarette smoke to form nitrosonornicotine, the postulated carcinogen.

Another possible carcinogenic constituent of cigarette smoke is radioactive polonium-210.[68] This isotope is an α emitter with a half-life of 138 days. Its concentration in the urine of smokers was found to be about six times that in nonsmokers. The amount to which the lungs would be exposed in a person smoking 40 cigarettes daily was estimated to produce about seven times the background radiation. Computations based on several uncertain assumptions led to the conclusion that the deposition of the polonium isotope in the lungs could account quantitatively for the observed incidence of lung cancer in smokers, especially if cocarcinogens (promoters) in the smoke increased the tissue sensitivity to the local radiation.

The Problem of Eliminating and Excluding Carcinogens from the Environment

Guidelines for the protection of the population against the hazards of environmental carcinogenesis are very difficult to formulate. The course of the controversy over smoking is very revealing of the economic and

66 E. L. WYNDER and D. HOFFMANN: Experimental tobacco carcinogenesis. *Adv. Cancer Res. 8:*249 (1964).

67 E. BOYLAND, F. J. C. ROE, and J. W. GORROD: Induction of pulmonary tumours in mice by nitrosonornicotine, a possible constituent of tobacco smoke. *Nature 202:*1126 (1964).

68 E. P. RADFORD, JR., and V. R. HUNT: Polonium-210: a volatile radioelement in cigarettes. *Science 143:*247 (1964).

political barriers that impede action even after the scientific determination has been made. Certainly the evidence implicating cigarette smoking as a prime cause of cancer in humans is as thorough and convincing as one can expect to obtain. Nevertheless, cigarette consumption has continued to increase among young people, in whom the risk is greatest because their total exposure will be longest. And although in the United States some minor modifications of cigarette advertising techniques have been enforced, no major regulatory action by government has been forthcoming. Many argue, indeed, that the principle of personal liberty includes liberty to indulge in a pleasure like smoking at the expense of future illness and premature death.

What, then, of drugs, food additives, insecticides, industrial wastes, and air pollutants, about which there may be only indecisive evidence of carcinogenicity?[69] Suppose such a substance proved to be carcinogenic at some particular dosage and route of administration in laboratory animals. How is one to extrapolate the result to man? We do not even know if there is a threshold of dosage below which no cancers would occur, regardless of the size of the exposed population.[61, 70] And suppose a food additive or air pollutant were tested in 100 animals, or even 1,000, and yielded no cancers. It might then be asserted that the substance was not a strong carcinogen. But might it be capable, nevertheless, of causing an unacceptable cancer rate in a large exposed population? If only one person in 1,000 were affected, there would be 200,000 new cases of cancer in the United States. This result would be the more appalling because, unlike cigarette smokers, these victims would be exposed to the carcinogen through no choice of their own.

Unlike most drug toxicities, which are manifested fairly soon after exposure so that timely action is demanded by the public and can be taken by the authorities, the long-delayed effects of carcinogens rob the issue of urgency. Air pollution in our cities illustrates the contrast. Epidemics of smog-induced respiratory disease occur periodically, as recounted in chapter 5. These episodes may be characterized by a high mortality rate and therefore may have a high "visibility" in the arena of public affairs. As a rule, urgent measures are then called for to institute more rigid control measures. But considerable evidence indicates that the same air pollutants contain carcinogens, whose effects are potentiated by respiratory viruses.[71-73]

[69] W. C. HUEPER: Environmental carcinogenesis and cancers. *Cancer Res. 21:*842 (1961).

[70] N. MANTEL: The concept of threshold in carcinogenesis. *Clin. Pharmacol. Therap. 4:*104 (1963).

[71] P. KOTIN and D. V. WISELEY: Production of lung cancer in mice by inhalation exposure to influenza virus and aerosols of hydrocarbons. *Progr. Exper. Tumor Res. 3:*186 (1963).

[72] H. L. FALK and P. KOTIN: Chemistry, host entry, and metabolic fate of carcinogens. *Clin. Pharmacol. Therap. 4:*88 (1963).

[73] E. SAWICKI and K. CASSEL, JR., eds.: Symposium on Analysis of Carcinogenic Air Pollutants. *National Cancer Institute Monograph No. 9,* 1962.

Yet this ever-present hazard appears too remote to engender demands for immediate action, especially when drastic controls might be expensive or disrupt an accustomed way of life.

The position adopted by regulatory agencies is necessarily a compromise between the desire to eliminate all carcinogenic hazards and the necessity of weighing the magnitude of each hazard against the benefits derived from the hazardous substance or environment. It was easy to dispense with azo dyes as food colorings because adequate noncarcinogenic substitutes were readily available. The policy suggested for food additives by a special committee of the National Research Council[74] could probably be generalized to apply to all potentially carcinogenic substances:

> "Because of the vagueness of present knowledge concerning quantitative aspects of the carcinogenic process, use of any amount of a carcinogen as a food additive probably is justified only if (1) values to the public are such that banning the use would constitute an important loss or hardship, and (2) there is no reasonably good noncarcinogenic alternative."

[74] Subcommittee on Carcinogenesis, Food Protection Committee, Food and Nutrition Board, National Academy of Sciences-National Research Council: Problems in the Evaluation of Carcinogenic Hazard from Use of Food Additives. *Cancer Res. 21:*429 (1961).

12

CHEMICAL TERATOGENESIS

Certain chemical agents can affect the somatic cells of a developing embryo in such a way that defects of one or another organ system are produced. If the embryonic germ cells escape damage, only the individual himself will be affected; thus most congenital anomalies are not hereditary. Substances that cause abnormalities of fetal development are called *chemical teratogens.*[1-8]

A more remarkable process than embryogenesis is hard to imagine. The finely balanced interplay of cell proliferation, differentiation, migration, and finally organogenesis represents a precisely programmed sequence of events, repeating itself in each detail for every zygote of a species.[9, 10] Underlying the morphologic development of the embryo is a progressive unfolding of biochemical potentialities, a temporally regulated transcription and translation of genetic messages, the details of which we are only beginning to understand. Embryogenesis involves complex interactions in both time and space. In the earliest stages rapid cell multiplication is the rule. The numerous products of these early cell divisions have different potentialities, depending upon their relative positions in the embryonic mass. Differenti-

---

[1] T. M. RIVERS, ed.: National Foundation Conference on Congenital Malformations. *J. Chron. Dis. 10:*83 (1959).

[2] G. E. W. WOLSTENHOLME and C. M. O'CONNOR, eds.: *Congenital Malformations. Ciba Foundation Symposium.* Boston, Little, Brown and Co., 1960.

[3] M. FISHBEIN, ed.: *Birth Defects.* Philadelphia, J. B. Lippincott, 1963.

[4] J. WARKANY and H. KALTER: Congenital malformations. *New England J. Med. 265:*993, 1046 (1961).

[5] M. FISHBEIN, ed.: *Second International Conference on Congenital Malformations.* New York, The International Medical Congress, Ltd., 1964.

[6] J. G. WILSON: Experimental teratology. *Amer. J. Obstet. Gynecol. 90:*1181 (1964).

[7] D. A. KARNOFSKY: Drugs as teratogens in animals and man. *Ann. Rev. Pharmacol. 5:*447 (1965).

[8] J. M. SUTHERLAND and I. J. LIGHT: The effect of drugs upon the developing fetus. *Pediat. Clin. North Amer. 12:*781 (1965).

[9] W. J. HAMILTON, J. D. BOYD, and H. W. MOSSMAN: *Human Embryology,* 3rd ed. Baltimore, Williams and Wilkins, 1962.

[10] W. FUHRMANN: Genetics of growth and development of the fetus. *Pediat. Clin. North Amer. 12:*457 (1965).

ation begins very early, in some species as early as the two- or four-cell stage. Subsequent development of primordial tissue components and organ precursors depends strongly upon mutual interactions of adjacent cell groups, apparently through chemical mediators or modifiers.[11] Migration, infolding, interpenetration, and encompassing of one cell group by another characterize a later stage of organogenesis. These spatial rearrangements account for the ectodermal origin of many internal viscera, the encapsulation of the nervous elements of the adrenal medulla by the mesodermally-derived cortex, the segregation of germ cells in the gonads, and so on. Still later, midline closures of bilaterally symmetric tissues occur, such as the facial structures (lip and palate), the cranium, vertebrae, and anterior body wall. Final morphologic and functional development occurs at various times in different organs and is sometimes completed only after birth.

Two predictions could be made, a priori, on the basis of our knowledge of embryonic development: first, that so complicated a series of events could be interfered with in very specific ways; and second, that the result of such interference could depend strongly upon the timing. Because each step in embryogenesis may depend upon a previous one, and because numerous tissues and organs are developing in parallel, even a temporary delay in the development of one group of cells may throw it out of phase with the rest of the embryo and thus lead to an eventual malformation. This has been shown quite clearly to be the case for reno-ureteral defects induced by folic acid deficiency in rats. Here, the vitamin deficiency disturbed the migration of primordial cell groups so that later, after the brief vitamin deficiency was terminated, they could no longer attain their correct anatomic position.[12]

Research on teratogenesis was greatly stimulated on three occasions by the accidental discovery of an external agency capable of producing congenital malformation in man. With increasing awareness of the biologic effects of radiation came the finding, about 40 years ago, that pelvic x-irradiation during pregnancy can result in the birth of a malformed child. More surprising was the discovery in Australia[13] in 1940 that an unusually large number of blind or deaf children were born following an epidemic of the mild virus disease rubella. Even if the woman considered her illness trivial, seriously defective offspring were sometimes produced when the infection occurred during the first trimester of pregnancy. The experience served as an important stimulus to experimentation with chemi-

---

[11] Symposium on Specificity of Cell Differentiation and Interaction. *J. Cell. Comp. Physiol. 60:* suppl. 1, 1 (1962).

[12] M. M. NELSON: "Teratogenic Effects of Pteroylglutamic Acid Deficiency in the Rat," in *Congenital Malformations. Ciba Foundation Symposium,* ed. by G. E. W. Wolstenholme and C. M. O'Connor. Boston, Little, Brown and Co., 1960, p. 134.

[13] N. M. GREGG: Congenital cataract following German measles in the mother. *Trans. Ophthalmol. Soc. Australia 3:*35 (1941).

cal teratogens in animals. Finally, the thalidomide disaster of 1960–1962 (p. 727) showed that an ordinary drug can also produce fetal malformations on a large scale in human populations.

EXPERIMENTAL TERATOGENESIS

Methods

Animal experiments[14, 15] have chiefly employed rodents. Like humans, they are mammals and have a placenta, so that drugs are exposed to maternal tissues and subjected to maternal metabolism before entering the fetus. Sometimes, in experimental teratogenesis, it is desirable to circumvent these complications and study the effect of a teratogen applied directly to the fetus. In such studies the chick embryo proves very useful. Other advantages of rodents are their short gestation period (only three weeks in rat or mouse), the fact that they are multiparous (so that each treated female yields multiple experimental results), and their convenient size and inexpensiveness.

Experiments on teratogenesis begin with isolation of virgin females and determination of the estrous cycle by vaginal smears. Matings can then be arranged at the time of ovulation. Since the timing of teratogenic treatments is extremely critical (p. 717), it is essential to know precisely when conception occurs. After mating the females are isolated again, treated as desired with a teratogen, and sacrificed just before term. Since cannibalism is frequent among rodents, intervention before spontaneous delivery is really essential to obtaining reliable data. This procedure permits all implantation sites to be examined and every product of conception to be accounted for as a resorbed, dead, malformed live, or fully developed normal fetus. Gross examination will reveal the most obvious malformations, microscopic examination will reveal others. To be certain all anomalies are detected, an exhaustive gross and microscopic analysis of each fetus is required. Hitherto, in investigations of teratogenesis, the emphasis has been almost exclusively upon morphologic abnormalities; perhaps future studies will reveal whether teratogens induce biochemical deficits that are demonstrable in the full-term fetus.

Selectivity of Action in Teratogenesis

Of principal interest are teratogens that interfere directly with fetal development at doses that do not disturb placental function or cause serious maternal toxicity. A great many teratogenic agents meet this criterion

---

[14] H. KALTER and J. WARKANY: Experimental production of congenital malformations in mammals by metabolic procedure. *Physiol. Rev. 39:*69 (1959).

[15] J. B. E. BAKER: The effects of drugs on the foetus. *Pharmacol. Rev. 12:*37 (1960).

of selective toxicity for the fetus. There is often a considerable range between the dose that induces fetal malformation and the dose that causes maternal death. Indeed, the most dangerous teratogens may be just those that are well tolerated by the mother in a dose range that is selectively damaging to fetal organogenesis but is not seriously toxic to the fetus as a whole. An agent that is selectively toxic to the mother, or one that is so toxic to the fetus that fetal death and resorption (or abortion) occur, would not present much hazard as a teratogen.[16] It has been shown that even such maternal disorders as severe hemorrhagic anemia and liver damage do not have teratogenic consequences.[17] Most teratogens do not impair placental function, and the most convincing experiments on teratogenesis include a morphologic demonstration of placental integrity. That experimental fetal malformations are so easy to produce without significant harm to the mother is consistent with the effects of rubella and of thalidomide in humans, and points up the risk that drugs and other environmental agents, innocuous otherwise, might be responsible for unexplained human malformations.

All teratogens, when administered at high dosage or very early in embryonic development, can cause fetal death followed by abortion or resorption of the fetus. For example, actinomycin D (which inhibits DNA-dependent RNA synthesis) was administered once intraperitoneally to pregnant rats at various times in gestation.[18] On the 20th day of gestation the rats were sacrificed and all fetuses and implantation sites were examined. The peak effects occurred when the drug was given between the seventh and tenth day (cf. p. 718). Fetal death and the incidence of malformations among survivors ran a parallel course. Both effects were dose related, and the sensitivity to both was maximum at the same time in gestation.

Many substances can kill fetuses selectively but are not necessarily teratogenic for survivors. The mitotic poisons colchicine and podophyllotoxin are good examples. Lipopolysaccharides from *Brucella abortus* kill all rat fetuses when administered on the 11th day of gestation and display the same sharp dependence on time of administration as do compounds with teratogenic action. Lipopolysaccharides from several enteric bacteria are teratogenic in rats, and they are known to cause abortion in humans. Aminopterin, at a dose that kills most rat fetuses, is not teratogenic for survivors; yet aminopterin in the human, if it fails to produce abortion, results in fetal malformations. These observations, taken together with the significant statistical association between intra-uterine death, spontaneous abortion, stillbirth, and congenital malformation in the human, indicate a

[16] G. B. WEST: Teratogenic activity of drugs. *J. Pharm. Pharmacol. 16:*63 (1964).
[17] J. G. WILSON: Influence on the offspring of altered physiologic states during pregnancy in the rat. *Ann. N.Y. Acad. Sci. 57:*517 (1954).
[18] J. G. WILSON: Embryological considerations in teratology. *Ann. New York Acad. Sci. 123:*219 (1965).

close relationship between teratogenesis and the more general problem of reproductive wastage.

Genetic Influences

If embryogenesis is a programmed sequence, the essentials of the program must be recorded in the genes. Although we do not yet understand what controls the timing of gene expression or repression during embryogenesis, nor exactly how the enzymic products of gene expression intervene in embryonic differentiation, it is nevertheless obvious that genetic defects could derange the process in very selective ways. It is therefore not surprising to find many examples of a genetic role in congenital malformations. Mongolism and chondrodystrophy (a defect in the formation of bone from cartilage) are malformations whose causes appear to be primarily genetic, one associated with trisomy for chromosome 21, the other caused by a gene mutation. Such malformations do not fall under the heading of teratogenesis, since the basic defect was presumably present in the zygote and will affect the germ cells as well as all the somatic cells of the affected individual.

The distinction between genetic and purely phenotypic abnormalities is not completely sharp, however. If a mutagenic agent acted at an early enough stage in fetal development to affect germ cells and somatic cells alike, and if the alteration were compatible with survival, the phenotypic manifestations could occur in the affected individual. Experimentally it has been shown, for example, that when a vitamin antagonist, 6-aminonicotinamide, was injected into pregnant mice on the 13th day of gestation, cleft palate was produced in the offspring. Chromosome abnormalities were also produced (polyploidy and fragmentation) not only in the region of the deformed palates but also in other cells throughout the body of the fetus. Furthermore, similar chromosome changes were observed in the maternal bone marrow after treatment, but never in untreated controls.[19]

In the experiment with 6-aminonicotinamide, the teratogen was administered fairly late in fetal development, therefore the induced chromosome abnormalities must all have arisen during faulty mitoses. However, if such an agent were administered to a female at about the time of fertilization, the result could be a similar disturbance of meiosis in the ovum about to be fertilized. The consequent changes in chromosome number or morphology might be indistinguishable from those regarded as having been inherited from earlier generations.

A recent report suggests the possibility that this may really happen in human populations.[20] A "run" of sex chromosome aberrations was noted

---

[19] T. H. INGALLS, E. F. INGENITO, and F. J. CURLEY: Acquired chromosomal anomalies induced in mice by injection of a teratogen in pregnancy. *Science 141:*810 (1963).

[20] A. ROBINSON and T. T. PUCK: Sex chromatin in newborns: presumptive evidence for external factors in human nondisjunction. *Science 148:*83 (1965).

among infants born in one city during a particular five-month period. The study began as a routine systematic examination of the sex chromatin in human newborns. The sex chromatin is material with distinctive staining properties that is associated with one of the X chromosomes.[21] It is easy to establish, therefore, by staining and microscopic examination of cells from the amniotic membrane or the infant's buccal mucosa, whether the genetic constitution is normal XX or XY, or whether abnormalities such as XXY, XXX, or XO are present. During the first 18 months of the study there were no abnormalities out of 1,541 infants. In the next five months there were six out of 1,009. Finally, in the next four months there were none out of 817. Although the actual number of abnormalities was very small, the clustering of these few in a particular short period of time was most unlikely to have occurred by chance. Most interesting, during the same five-month period there was an increase in the number (also small) of cases of mongolism in this same community. The implication of the findings is that some exogenous mutagenic or teratogenic factor, perhaps a drug or virus, may have been at work in this community during the relevant period.

But most congenital malformations occur through faulty embryo-genesis, are not associated with any obvious abnormality of the chromosomes, and are not heritable. The nonheritable nature of the abnormalities has been demonstrated by brother-sister matings of malformed animals, and also on a large scale in human populations. Genetic factors, however, may play an important part in determining sensitivity to teratogens as well as the probability of spontaneous malformation.[22] One indication of the role of genetic factors is the considerable difference in sensitivity between species and between strains of the same species. In mice of a particular strain, for example, about 10 per cent of the young are born with cleft lip, which is ordinarily a very rare abnormality. Administration of thyroid hormone on the 11th and 12th days of pregnancy (but not at other times) sharply reduced the incidence of this malformation. Another strain of mice gave birth to young, 2 per cent of which had defects of the cranium or ribs; starvation during a particular 24-hour period of fetal life increased this incidence about tenfold. In three strains of rats, the azo dye trypan blue produced exencephalic offspring at wholly different frequencies, 17, 50, and 97 per cent, respectively. Cortisone produced cleft palate in all mouse fetuses of one strain, but in only 20 per cent of another; this difference was traced to earlier midline fusion of the palate in the more resistant strain. Cortisone also produced cleft palate in rabbits but no malformations whatsoever in rats. Yet cortisone strongly potentiated the actions of another teratogen, vitamin A, in rats.

21 M. A. FERGUSON-SMITH: The techniques of human cytogenetics. *Amer. J. Obstet. Gynecol. 90:*1035 (1964).

22 J. G. WILSON: Experimental studies on congenital malformations. *J. Chron. Dis. 10:*111 (1959).

Findings like those described above have led some investigators to the view that chemical teratogens act by bringing out "concealed weaknesses" of the developmental processes, which have a genetic basis. It has been suggested that many induced defects are really phenocopies, i.e., phenotypic changes of exactly the same kinds as are produced by faulty genes, brought about through the same biochemical disturbances. Supporting evidence was obtained in experiments with 6-aminonicotinamide in chicks.[23] This vitamin antagonist produces skeletal anomalies, principally micromelia (short upper appendages) and parrot beak, which also occur as mutations. Specially bred stocks heterozygous for these defects had increased sensitivity to the teratogen. Conversely, in a stock possessing modifying alleles that reduce the frequency of mutant defects of the skeleton (chondrodystrophy), the teratogen had reduced efficacy.

An intriguing finding in experimental teratogenesis with multiparous animals is the regularity with which some fetuses escape unscathed while others in the same litter suffer severe and even multiple malformations. A particularly striking example is afforded by trypan blue.[30a] Administered uniformly to more than 200 pregnant rats on the seventh, eighth, and ninth days of gestation, it caused death and resorption of nearly one-half the fetuses, numerous malformations in one-half the survivors, but apparently no effects at all in the remaining one-quarter of the original group. The response differences could not be ascribed to differences between mothers, inasmuch as dead, malformed, and normal fetuses appeared to be randomly admixed in the individual rats and even in the same uterine horn. Such findings, which are quite common with all sorts of teratogens, suggest that the genotype of the fetus may play an important role in determining its susceptibility to a teratogen. Whether the surviving normal offspring in such an experiment could be interbred to produce a teratogen-resistant line is not known.

Sensitive Periods

Perhaps the most interesting finding in experimental teratogenesis has been the discovery of special times during fetal development when malformations of any kind can be induced, and of sharply limited critical periods for the various specific malformations. During the early phase of cell proliferation no malformations can be induced. At this time all teratogens have nonspecific all-or-none effects; the embryo may be killed, but if it survives it becomes a normal individual. All cells at this stage may be so much alike that no selectively toxic action is possible upon those that will eventually form particular organ systems. Alternatively, damaged cells that have undergone partial differentiation may still be replaceable by

---

23 W. LANDAUER: Gene and phenocopy: selection experiments and tests with 6-aminonicotinamide. *J. Exper. Zool. 160:*345 (1965).

others that escaped injury. Very late in fetal development it is also difficult to produce abnormalities, since the processes of organogenesis have been largely completed. In each species there is, therefore, a relatively short period of sensitivity to teratogens, when early organogenesis is in progress. In the rat and mouse this sensitive period extends from about the fifth to the 14th day of the 23-day gestation period. In the human there is only meager experimental evidence, but the timetable of embryologic development[9] suggests a period extending roughly from the third week through the third month of pregnancy. At the 20th day after fertilization the cephalo-caudal segmentation of the embryo into somites is just beginning. These segments are the precursors of the axial skeleton and musculature. At about 30 days the limb buds make their appearance, and by 60 days organ differentiation in the fetus (now 30 mm long) is well under way. Accordingly, rubella-induced malformations of the eye, ear, and heart occur principally between the fourth and eighth weeks. Thalidomide interference with limb formation is chiefly a hazard of the same period, the second month of pregnancy.

Figure 12-1 illustrates these timing effects quite dramatically in the rat treated with actinomycin D, which presumably disrupts organo-

FIG. 12-1.   CRITICAL TIMING OF TERATOGENIC EFFECTS OF ACTINOMYCIN D IN THE PREGNANT RAT.   *Actinomycin D was given intraperitoneally in a dose of 75μg/kg once during pregnancy, at various times after copulation in different animals. The per cent of gross malformations among fetuses that survived to term is shown. Not shown are fetal resorption, high when the drug was given early in pregnancy, low in late pregnancy. (From Tuchmann-Duplessis and Mercier-Parot, Fig. 2.[24] By permission of Little, Brown.)*

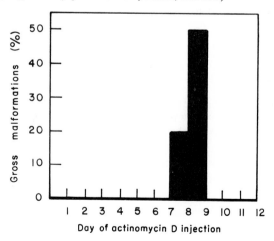

[24] H. TUCHMANN-DUPLESSIS and L. MERCIER-PAROT: "The Teratogenic Action of the Antibiotic Actinomycin D," in *Congenital Malformations. Ciba Foundation Symposium,* ed. by G. E. W. Wolstenholme and C. M. O'Connor. Boston, Little, Brown and Co., 1960, p. 115.

genesis by blocking the synthesis of RNA. A fixed dose of this antibiotic caused resorption of nearly all fetuses when administered during the first few days of pregnancy. The frequency of resorptions (not shown) fell to about 10 per cent when the drug was given as late as the 13th day. The incidence of malformations among surviving fetuses showed an extremely sharp peak when the drug was given between the seventh and ninth days.

Specific critical periods for various malformations in the rat, caused by a single teratogen, vitamin A in excessive dosage, are shown in Table 12-1. The sensitive periods correlate well with the known sequence of organogenesis in this species. In general, if it is known with certainty at what time in gestation a particular organ completes its differentiation, then a congenital malformation of that organ could only have been caused by a teratogen that acted prior to that time. This rule often enables one to eliminate a suspected teratogen or unusual occurrence as a cause of human malformation, because the timing is not compatible with the observed effect.

The need for exact timing of teratogenic treatments imposes two technical requirements upon all experimentation. First, the time of conception must be known accurately. This is not difficult in rodents, for even when matings are not arranged according to the estrous cycle, the presence of a seminal plug in the vagina effectively dates the event. In humans, on the other hand, numerous factors, including irregularities of ovulation and menstruation, conspire to make accurate timing very difficult. Second, the onset and offset of teratogen action must be well defined and abrupt. With physical treatments such as x-ray or anoxia, the situation is ideal because the exposure can be limited to a period of seconds or minutes. When chemical teratogens are used, the situation is complicated by the time courses of absorption, metabolism, and excretion. Moreover, the actual

TABLE 12-1. **Critical timing of teratogenic effects of excessive vitamin A administration in the rat**

60,000 International units of vitamin A were given by mouth for three days, beginning at different times in pregnancy. Figures are percentages of all surviving fetuses displaying the particular malformation. Plus sign indicates some defects (not more exactly enumerated) of the specified kind. (Data of Giroud and Martinet, cited by Kalter and Warkany.[14])

	Day of pregnancy				
	5–7	8–10	11–13	14–16	18–20
Anencephaly	9	53	0	0	0
Eye defects	4	73	0	0	0
Cleft palate	4	22	92	49	0
Spina bifida	0	3	0	0	0
Limb defects	0	0	+	0	0
Cataract	0	0	0	+	+

teratogen may be a metabolite rather than the administered compound. The most successful experiments have employed a systemic route of administration for rapid onset and an antagonist for rapid termination. In an investigation of the teratogenicity of 6-aminonicotinamide, for example, rats were given the compound on the 11th day of pregnancy, followed 2 hours later by the vitamin nicotinamide at a dose known to overcome acute deficiencies caused by the antagonist. This extremely brief teratogenic treatment sufficed to produce cleft palate in the offspring.[25]

Specificity and Variety of Teratogens

It might be imagined that all deleterious influences operating at a particular critical time in organogenesis would produce the same pattern of malformations, i.e., that there would be timing specificity but no teratogen specificity. This is not true. Table 12-2 shows that when rats were subjected to four different vitamin deficiencies at the same time in pregnancy, the resulting malformations were very different. Teratogen-specific effects were also obtained in the chick, where maternal and placental factors are excluded. Presumably, the active forms of all the vitamins are required by all growing cells. It must be assumed, therefore, that quantitative differences in these requirements at critical stages of development of

TABLE 12-2.   Teratogen specificity in the rat

(From Wilson,[22] Table VIII.)

Agent	Most frequent defects	Other defects
Vitamin A deficiency	Coloboma of retina, ectopic ureters, diaphragmatic hernia	Hermaphroditic tendency, fused kidneys, postlental fibroplasia, various cardiovascular defects
Riboflavin deficiency	Shortened long-bones and mandible, fused ribs and toes, cleft palate	Open interventricular septum, hydronephrosis, hydrocephalus, microphthalmia, hernias
Folic acid deficiency	"Universal teratogen"	Affected virtually every organ and system in body, varying considerably with time of treatment
Irradiation	Anophthalmia, encephalocele, etc., renal agenesis	Microphthalmia, various spinal cord and cardiovascular defects, facial clefts, micromelia

25 F. C. FRASER: "General Discussion," in *Congenital Malformations. Ciba Foundation Symposium,* ed. by G. E. W. Wolstenholme and C. M. O'Connor. Boston, Little, Brown and Co., 1960, p. 282.

TABLE 12-3. **Some chemical teratogens in rats, mice, rabbits, or chicks**

(Data compiled from Kalter and Warkany,[14] Cahen,[26] and Woollam.[27])

VITAMIN DEFICIENCY: vitamins A, D, and E, ascorbic acid, riboflavin, thiamin, nicotinamide, folic acid, panthothenic acid.

VITAMIN ANTAGONISTS: antifolic drugs, 6-aminonicotinamide, 3-acetylpyridine.

VITAMIN EXCESS: vitamin A, nicotinic acid.

HORMONE DEFICIENCY: pituitary, thyroid, insulin (alloxan diabetes).

HORMONE ANTAGONISTS: thiouracil derivatives.

HORMONE EXCESS: thyroxine, cortisone, hydrocortisone, insulin, vasopressin, androgens, estrogens, epinephrine.

ALKYLATING AGENTS: nitrogen mustard, chlorambucil, and others.

PURINE AND PYRIMIDINE ANALOGUES: azaguanine, 6-mercaptopurine, fluoro-deoxyuridine, and others.

AMINO ACID ANALOGUES: azaserine, diazo-oxo-norleucine (DON).

CARBOHYDRATES: 2-deoxyglucose, galactose, bacterial lipopolysaccharides.

ANTIBIOTICS: tetracyclines, penicillin, streptomycin, actinomycin D.

SULFONAMIDES: sulfanilamide, certain antidiabetic sulfonamides.

AGENTS CAUSING ANOXIA: carbon monoxide, carbon dioxide, etc.

AZO DYES: trypan blue, Evans blue, Niagara Sky Blue 6B.

HEAVY METALS: phenylmercuric acetate, inorganic mercury salts, strontium, lead, thallium, selenium; also chelating agents (EDTA).

MISCELLANEOUS: trypaflavin (acriflavin), urethane, colchicine, nicotine, eserine, quinine, pilocarpine, saponin, ricin, chlorpromazine and derivatives, thiadiazole, triazene, boric acid (chick only), salicylate.

---

each organ must underlie the differential effects of the teratogenic treatments, so that at a given moment one organ is more sensitive to riboflavin deficiency, another to vitamin A deficiency, and so on.

A considerable number and variety of chemical teratogens have been investigated, many of which are listed in Table 12-3. The frequent production of fetal malformations by nutritional deficiency is of interest because of its possible relationship to human congenital malformations. The earliest published data on chemical teratogenesis of any kind dealt with vitamin A deficiency in pigs;[28] when the diet was deficient in this vitamin throughout pregnancy, all the young were abnormal and a variety of malformations occurred. Subsequent matings of the same sows yielded normal offspring, as did brother-sister matings between the malformed animals. In the 35 years since that investigation, the teratogenic effects of other vitamin deficiencies have been established, as shown in the table. Contrary to the long-held view that the fetus has first claim on available

[26] R. L. CAHEN: Evaluation of the teratogenicity of drugs. *Clin. Pharmacol. Therap. 5:*480 (1964).

[27] D. H. M. WOOLLAM: Principles of teratogenesis: mode of action of thalidomide. *Proc. Roy. Soc. Med. 58:*497 (1965).

[28] F. HALE: Relation of vitamin A to anophthalmos in pigs. *Amer. J. Ophthalmol. 18:*1087 (1935).

nutrients, vitamin deficiencies are selectively damaging to the fetus; teratogenic effects are manifested at degrees of vitamin deficiency too slight to injure the mother. This may well reflect the high requirement of the growing fetus and its lack of stored reserves such as are contained in maternal tissues. On the other hand, general malnutrition, in contrast to specific vitamin deficiency, has only rarely been found to be teratogenic. It is also of interest that vitamin excess, at least of vitamin A, can produce fetal malformations, especially exencephaly and cleft palate.

The list (Table 12-3) indicates that hormone deficiencies and excesses can prove teratogenic of themselves. Hormones can also potentiate or antagonize the effects of other teratogens. Thus, cortisone increases the incidence of malformations caused by vitamin A, whereas insulin has the opposite effect. Thyroxine antagonizes the teratogenic action of vitamin A, and the antithyroid compound methylthiouracil increases that teratogenic effect. Moreover, thyroxine can reduce the incidence of at least one spontaneous genetically-determined anomaly (p. 716). Such findings suggest that disturbances of hormonal balance might play a role in the etiology of malformations in the human. There is a persistent belief among some clinicians that "concealed endocrinopathies" such as prediabetic states or incipient hypothyroidism may account for reproductive wastage and infertility in some women, and it is claimed that hormone treatment improves matters; but there is no convincing evidence to support these opinions.

That growth inhibitors should be teratogenic is not surprising. Actinomycin D is a potent teratogen. In the rat it causes disorganization of development of the optic nerve, anencephaly, spina bifida, cleft palate and lip, extrusions of the viscera, ectocardia, and dextrocardia.

A few of the antidiabetic sulfonamides have proved to be teratogenic. But the effect is probably unrelated to the lowering of the blood glucose level, inasmuch as some drugs of this class have no teratogenic action at doses that lower blood sugar to the same degree. Likewise, some antibacterial sulfonamides (e.g., sulfanilamide) are teratogenic, but not others. Structure-activity relationships have not been worked out systematically for teratogenesis induced by this group of drugs.

Phenylmercuric acetate administered intravaginally at a dose of 1.1 mg to pregnant mice on the seventh day of gestation caused major abnormalities of the brain, eye, and tail in 15 per cent of the offspring.[14] The possible significance of this finding is that the compound is included in many contraceptive jellies and creams to which women may be exposed periodically.

Boric acid is teratogenic in chicks, causing a pattern of deformities that appears to be identical with that produced by riboflavin deficiency.[29, 30]

---

[29] W. LANDAUER: On the chemical production of developmental abnormalities and of phenocopies in chicken embryos. *J. Cell. Comp. Physiol. 43:* suppl. 1, 261 (1954).

[30] W. LANDAUER and E. M. CLARK: On the role of riboflavin in the teratogenic activity of boric acid. *J. Exper. Zool. 156:*307 (1964).

Riboflavin prevented these teratogenic effects. The implication is that boric acid produces riboflavin deficiency, but how it does this remains obscure.

One of the most interesting of all teratogens is the azo dye trypan blue.[30a,31] Administered subcutaneously to rats in a dose of 10 mg between

trypan blue

the seventh and tenth days of gestation, it regularly causes malformations of the brain (hydrocephalus secondary to maldevelopment of the aqueduct) and also of the eyes, vertebral column, and cardiovascular system. Similar malformations are caused in rabbits and in chicks. One of the puzzling aspects of trypan blue teratogenesis has been the apparent absence of dye granules from the rat embryo, although they are plentiful in the maternal reticuloendothelial system and also in the placenta. Apparently the dye is excluded by the yolk sac membrane that envelops the rat embryo at about the ninth day of gestation. When the dye was injected directly into the yolk sac in embryo explants, teratogenic effects were obtained even on the 11th day.[32] In the rabbit, on the other hand, trypan blue gains access to the embryonic blastocyst throughout the gestation period.

The structural requirements for teratogenic activity among the azo dyes are extraordinarily exacting. In the closely related dye Evans Blue, all four sulfonate groups are shifted to new positions, marked by asterisks in the formula given above. This small change suffices to reduce the teratogenic potency considerably although the pattern of malformations remains the same. If the only change introduced into the trypan blue structure is the substitution of methoxy groups for methyl in the central part of the molecule (Niagara Blue 4B, Niagara Sky Blue 6B), teratogenic activity drops to an even lower level but is still demonstrable. No other azo dye tested was teratogenic, but many possible small changes were not explored. The dye closest in structure to the active ones, yet in itself wholly inactive, was azo blue, which differs from trypan blue only in the removal of two sulfonate and two amino groups and a shift of the remaining sulfonate groups to a new position.

30a J. G. WILSON: Teratogenic activity of several azo dyes chemically related to trypan blue. *Anat. Record 123:*313 (1955).

31 C. GILBERT and J. GILLMAN: The morphogenesis of trypan blue induced defects of the eye. *S. African J. Med. Sci. 19:*147 (1954).

32 M. M. TURBOW: Teratogenic effect of trypan blue on rat embryos cultivated *in vitro. Nature 206:*637 (1965).

azo blue

TERATOGENESIS IN MAN

Congenital Malformations in Human Populations

Infertility, spontaneous abortions, stillbirths, and neonatal deaths are major tragedies of human life, but more tragic by far is the birth of a seriously malformed infant. Congenital malformations have been recognized since prehistoric times, and were once attributed to divine or satanic intervention, to hybridization with other species, or to frightening experiences of the pregnant woman. The birth of a malformed child was early regarded as a portent of future events, whence the term "monster," from the Latin root meaning "to show, to indicate." The long history of irrational attitudes toward congenital deformity still conditions much present-day thinking among uninformed people.[33]

The tendency of a mother to attribute the birth of a deformed child to some unusual event during her pregnancy greatly complicates objective investigation. All retrospective studies are suspect on this account. A retrospective study begins with the birth of the malformed child and seeks clues to causative factors that may have operated during the preceding nine months. Controls are normal infants born at about the same time and place. The basic difficulty is that the mother of a malformed child is more likely to remember, exaggerate, or even imagine extraordinary events during pregnancy than is the mother of a normal child. It is possible to compensate for some of these inevitable biases and thus to extract useful information, but the retrospective study is unsatisfactory at best.

In the prospective study all pertinent information about a pregnancy is recorded before delivery, before it is known whether or not the child is normal. Whereas retrospective investigations can deal intensively with small numbers of individuals, the prospective investigation, by its very nature, must deal with extremely large groups in order to include a significant number of congenital malformations. Consequently, data are collected by many physicians, nurses, midwives, and other health personnel, and reliability tends to decrease as the numbers become larger. Only a few prospective studies have ever been carried out, and it is from these

---

[33] J. WARKANY: Congenital malformations in the past. *J. Chron. Dis. 10*:84 (1959).

that we have most of the meaningful statistics about congenital malformations in humans.

A five-year investigation dealt with about 6,000 pregnancies that were followed in the clinics of teaching hospitals in New York City.[34] Of these pregnancies, 5 per cent terminated in fetal death after the third month. No information was obtained about earlier terminations. Another 2 per cent ended in stillbirths, and a further 2 per cent in live-born infants who died within the first month of life. Thus, the total reproductive loss amounted to no less than 9 per cent. Of all infants alive at one month of age, 7 per cent bore some congenital malformation. Of those who had died earlier, 14 to 30 per cent were malformed. And out of all who died during the first year of life, 71 per cent were malformed. These findings show that congenital malformations are associated with a high infant mortality rate. It is also known that fetal malformation is common in cases of intra-uterine death or stillbirth. It is really not surprising that major malformations of the vital organs should be incompatible with life. But it is also evident that relatively minor malformations (e.g., of the musculoskeletal system) may reduce life expectancy, especially when survival rates are examined for the first five years of life.[35] It may be that the obvious malformations apparent to the examiner are accompanied by related but occult functional derangements elsewhere.

Deleterious genes, throughout the biologic world, are eliminated by the poorer survival of carriers to the reproductive age; but no such eugenic purpose is served by the premature death of congenitally malformed individuals. In most cases such people are not suffering from a genetic defect, and if they live to reproduce, their children are likely to be quite normal. Moreover, history affords many examples of congenitally malformed people who have made notable contributions to society.

In the New York study cited above, great care was exercised to record every manifest malformation, no matter how trivial. Accordingly, such conditions as supernumerary breast and pilonidal sinus accounted for a considerable part of the total. A prospective study conducted in Birmingham, England,[35] covered a population ten times larger and excluded malformations considered unimportant. The incidence of stillbirths was the same as in the New York study, but the total frequency of individuals classed as malformed was only about 2 per cent. This figure is also in good agreement with that observed in a Japanese population of about the same size.[35] In all these large-scale investigations, the principal serious deformities affected the nervous system, but malformations were found in

34 R. MC INTOSH, K. K. MERRITT, M. R. RICHARDS, M. H. SAMUELS, and M. T. BELLOWS: The incidence of congenital malformations: a study of 5,964 pregnancies. *Pediatrics 14:*505 (1954).

35 T. MC KEOWN and R. G. RECORD: "Malformations in a Population Observed for Five Years After Birth," in *Congenital Malformations. Ciba Foundation Symposium,* ed. by G. E. W. Wolstenholme and C. M. O'Connor. Boston, Little, Brown and Co., 1960, p. 2.

all organ systems. The principal ones (in order of decreasing frequency) were: talipes (clubfoot), cardiac anomalies, spina bifida and associated vertebral defects, hydrocephalus, anencephalus, and cranioschisis (failure of midline closure of the skull), cleft lip or palate, mongolism, hip dislocation, pyloric stenosis, and polydactylism. It should be noted that in surveys like this one some of the malformations observed are known to be genetically determined and thus not relevant to the problem of teratogenesis.

There were significant differences in the frequencies of some conditions between the Japanese and the English populations, between the English and the New York groups, and even between the New York sample and an earlier population surveyed (retrospectively) in Philadelphia.[36] A number of these differences cannot be rationalized on the basis of inconsistent diagnostic criteria or different likelihoods of missing a malformation entirely. Clubfoot, for example, which could hardly be overlooked, occurred with frequencies (per 1,000 total births) of 1.4, 4.4, 5.3, and 0.3 in the Japanese, English, New York, and Philadelphia groups, respectively. For hydrocephalus, the corresponding figures were 0.5, 2.6, 0.9, and 1.4; and for spina bifida, 0.3, 3.0, 1.6, and 0.9. In the Japanese group, hip dislocations occurred at an incidence of 7.1 per 1,000, in the English group at 0.7 per 1,000. Such large differences may, of course, be related to genetic differences among the several populations, but they also suggest the possibility that environmental influences may have played a considerable role in causing the malformations.

Curious seasonal variations in the incidence of the more common congenital malformations have been noted.[37] A survey of all births in Birmingham, England, during 1950 revealed that anencephaly tended to occur in infants born in December and January, hare lip in March, patent ductus arteriosus in August. These clustered to a degree that differed significantly from the variations to be expected by chance. It was postulated that a chemical teratogen in food or environment, or virus infections might have been responsible.

Accidental Human Exposure to Teratogens

Only rarely has it been possible to observe directly the result of an experiment on teratogenesis in the human. A few cases have been reported in which acute anoxia caused by carbon monoxide or morphine, taken with suicidal intent early in pregnancy, was followed by the birth of a malformed child; but cause-and-effect relationships in such episodes are uncertain. After the discovery that the antifolic drug aminopterin could cause

---

[36] D. P. MURPHY: *Congenital Malformations,* 2nd ed. Philadelphia, J. B. Lippincott, 1947.

[37] J. H. EDWARDS: "The Epidemiology of Congenital Malformations," in *Second International Conference on Congenital Malformations,* ed. by M. Fishbein. New York, The International Medical Congress, Ltd., 1964, p. 297.

abortion, it was occasionally taken for this purpose. Some fetuses that survived such attempts were grossly malformed.[4] Progestational steroids, used in the treatment of habitual abortion, have produced abnormalities of the genitalia (masculinization) in the female fetus.[38] For this reason the oral contraceptives that contain progesterone-like steroids are contra-indicated in pregnancy or suspected pregnancy. Toxoplasmosis and syphilis during pregnancy may also cause fetal malformations by direct invasion and destruction of fetal tissue.[4]

Until recently the most dramatic instance of an outbreak of con-genital malformations was the Australian experience associated with a rubella epidemic (p. 712).[13] A variety of effects not previously attributed to any exogenous agent were clearly associated with this virus infection. These included cataract and other abnormalities of the eyes, deafness, cardiac defects, and mental retardation. When rubella occurred during the first or second month of pregnancy, the heart and eye defects predominated, but hearing defects were most common when the disease occurred in the third month. Rubella contracted after the third month of gestation was without effect. Early estimates based upon the retrospective method of data collection led to the impression that three-quarters or more of pregnant women who contracted rubella during the first four months of pregnancy would give birth to a defective child. More careful prospective studies have yielded a much lower figure, about 17 per cent.

The experience with rubella, the experimental evidence for tera-togenesis by various chemical agents, and the isolated instances of con-genital abnormality in humans caused by antifolic drugs should have alerted the medical community to the likelihood that increasing drug use would sooner or later result in unexpected teratogenic actions. But it required a major catastrophe to demonstrate that what happens in experimental ani-mals can also happen in the human being.[39] Thalidomide was introduced in the late 1950's in West Germany, England, and other countries, as a tranquilizing agent and hypnotic. It was effective and seemed remarkably nontoxic. Although a typical therapeutic dose was about 100 mg, patients

thalidomide

[38] H. JACKSON: Antifertility substances. *Pharmacol. Rev.* *11*:135 (1959).

[39] G. W. MELLIN and M. KATZENSTEIN: The saga of thalidomide. *New England J. Med.* *267*:1184, 1238 (1962).

recovered from ingestion of as much as 14 g taken with suicidal intent. About 1960, some scattered reports indicated that patients receiving this drug for a long time sometimes developed neurologic disturbances.

Shortly after the introduction of thalidomide into therapy, there was an increase in the number of infants born with phocomelia, a shortening or complete absence of the limbs.[40] The data are interesting. At the University Pediatric Clinic in Hamburg, for example, not a single case of phocomelia was seen in the decade 1949–1959. In 1959, there was a single case; in 1960, 30 cases; and in 1961, 154 cases. Comparable increases in the frequency of this anomaly, previously almost unknown, occurred simultaneously in many parts of the world where thalidomide was in use. Finally, in November 1961, an astute pediatrician[41] suspected an association between phocomelia and the ingestion of thalidomide by the pregnant mother. Subsequent investigations in several countries[42,43] indicated that in practically every case of phocomelia the mother had taken thalidomide between the third and eighth weeks of pregnancy. Sometimes only a few doses during the critical period sufficed.

The critical period for each kind of malformation produced in the human fetus has been established by careful retrospective analysis.[44] When thalidomide was taken 35 to 36 days after the last menstrual period (approximately 21 to 22 days of gestation), absence of the external ears and paralysis of the cranial nerves resulted. Three to five days later (about 24 to 27 days of gestation), the phocomelia effect was at its maximum. A day or two later, similar defects of the legs occurred. The sensitive period terminated 48 to 50 days after the last period (34 to 36 days of gestation) with the production of hypoplastic thumbs and anorectal stenosis.

That thalidomide was responsible for the outbreak of phocomelia is beyond reasonable doubt. But it is still uncertain what exact degree of risk is attached to the ingestion of this drug by a pregnant woman. If a large number of pregnant women were given thalidomide during the critical period, what fraction of the infants would be malformed? Some investigators believe that practically all would be affected, since it was difficult to find well-authenticated instances of thalidomide ingestion followed by the birth of normal infants. Others place the risk very much lower, believing that the retrospective method of investigation exaggerates such an association to an extreme degree.[27] Thus, a woman who has given birth to a malformed child will readily recall (or even imagine) taking

[40] H. B. TAUSSIG: A study of the German outbreak of phocomelia. The thalidomide syndrome. *J. Amer. Med. Ass. 180:*1106 (1962).

[41] W. LENZ: Kindliche Missbildungen nach Medikament-Einnahme während der Gravidität? *Deutsche med. Wochenschr. 86:*2555 (1961).

[42] R. T. WILLIAMS: Teratogenic effects of thalidomide and related substances. *Lancet 1:*723 (1963).

[43] W. G. MC BRIDE: The teratogenic action of drugs. *Med. J. Australia 2:*689 (1963).

[44] W. LENZ: Epidemiology of congenital malformations. *Ann. New York Acad. Sci. 123:*228 (1965).

thalidomide, especially when the effects of the drug have been publicized; but a woman with a normal child, who may also have taken thalidomide during pregnancy, has no particular interest in recalling that fact.

Thalidomide was withdrawn from the market at the end of 1961, and the outbreak of phocomelia subsided promptly. In the United States, the drug had not been approved by the Food and Drug Administration and was therefore never in general use. The total number of infants throughout the world that were deformed by thalidomide must be around 10,000. Although phocomelia is the most obvious and directly disabling abnormality, congenital malformations of the internal organs are also common in the affected children.

Lessons of the Thalidomide Catastrophe

A major consequence of the thalidomide experience was the institution of improved procedures for screening new drugs. Teratogenic effects had not been examined routinely in the past, partly because the potential seriousness of the problem had been underestimated, but also because effective methods had not been developed. As had been shown for numerous other teratogenic agents, thalidomide displays a strong species specificity. In rats, for example, congenital abnormalities could not at first be produced by this drug. In certain strains of white rabbits, it was found that carefully timed administration of thalidomide between the eighth and 16th days of pregnancy led to typical limb malformations.[45] Subsequent work with rats showed that this species was sensitive after all, but only on the 12th day of gestation.[46] More recently, a syndrome of thalidomide-induced malformations has been produced in monkeys that is very much like that seen in human beings.[47]

A possible cause of species differences in the teratogenicity of thalidomide, and of differences in sensitivity among humans, may be variations in metabolic pathways. Thalidomide is extensively metabolized, and it is now considered probable that one of the metabolites, rather than thalidomide itself, is the actual teratogenic agent.[48] Hydrolysis of amide bonds and ring hydroxylation alone could account for more than 100 metabolites, of which a dozen or so have been identified in vivo.[42] When the piperidine ring is opened, a glutamine or glutamic acid derivative is formed, as shown below:

[45] V. LARSEN: The teratogenic effects of thalidomide, imipramine HCl and imipramine-N-oxide HCl on white Danish rabbits. *Acta Pharmacol. Toxicol. 20:*186 (1963).

[46] G. BIGNAMI, D. BOVET, F. BOVET-NITTI, and V. ROSNATI: Drugs and congenital abnormalities. *Lancet 2:*1333 (1962).

[47] C. S. DELAHUNT and L. J. LASSEN: Thalidomide syndrome in monkeys. *Science 146:*1300 (1964).

[48] H. KEBERLE, P. LOUSTALOT, R. K. MALLER, J. W. FAIGLE, and K. SCHMID: Biochemical effects of drugs on the mammalian conceptus. *Ann. New York Acad. Sci. 123:*252 (1965).

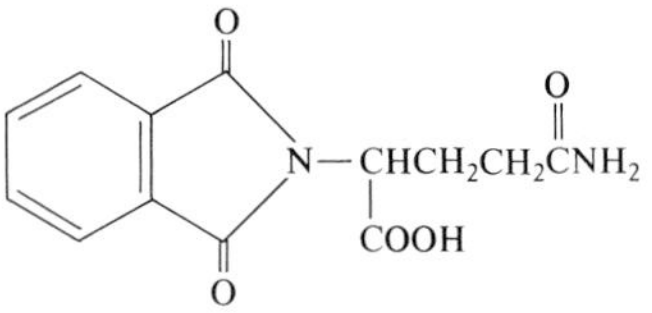

glutamine derivative
of thalidomide

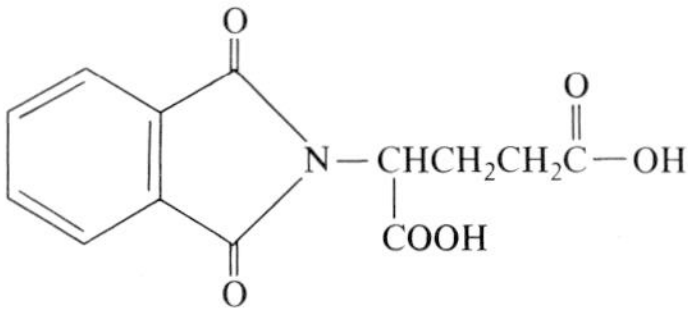

deaminated derivative
(phthalylglutamic acid)

Decarboxylation of phthalylglutamic acid yields a monocarboxylic acid, which is the most abundant metabolite.

Early studies showed that none of the metabolites were teratogenic when injected into pregnant rabbits under the same conditions in which thalidomide showed its characteristic actions. It was discovered, however, that this was due to the inability of the metabolites to pass from maternal plasma into the fetus in appreciable quantity. Figure 12-2 shows that when thalidomide was administered, it was all converted to the monocarboxylic acid in the fetus.[48] Radioactive thalidomide was used, and samples of the plasma and of allantoic fluid were subjected to paper electrophoresis. Localization of the radioactivity peaks shows that after 4 hours thalidomide itself, the monocarboxylic acid, and a dicarboxylic acid were all present in plasma; but only the monocarboxylic acid could be found in the allantoic fluid.

In the aftermath of the thalidomide episode there has been intensified investigation of various drugs, both established ones and new ones, with respect to teratogenicity. An antihistaminic, meclizine hydrochloride, and a related compound, cyclizine, were found to cause skeletal abnormalities in rats.[49] This finding was alarming because drugs of this kind were widely available without prescription, and since they relieve nausea, they were likely to be used precisely at the critical period of pregnancy for relief of "morning sickness." This, indeed, was a major reason why thalidomide had such devastating effects.[27] However, extensive prospective studies in populations of pregnant women have not revealed any abnormal frequency

---

[49] C. T. G. KING: Teratogenic effects of meclizine hydrochloride on the rat. *Science* *141*:353 (1963).

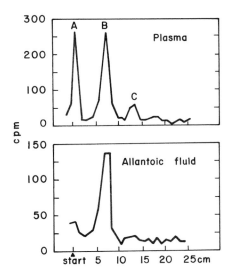

FIG. 12-2. CONVERSION OF THALIDOMIDE TO A MONOCARBOXYLIC ACID DERIVA-
TIVE IN THE RABBIT FETUS. *Samples of plasma* (above) *and allantoic fluid*
(below) *were subjected to paper electrophoresis 4 hours after administration of
radioactive thalidomide to a pregnant rabbit. Anodal migration is toward the
right; distance is shown on x-axis. Radioactivity in the paper is shown on y-axis.*
Peak A, *thalidomide;* peak B, *monocarboxylic acid derivative;* peak C, *dicarboxylic acid derivative. Neither carboxylic acid passed from plasma into allantoic fluid if injected into the rabbit. (From Keberle et al., Fig. 10.[48])*

of malformations or abortions in women taking these drugs.[50,51] Although
warnings were issued about possible teratogenicity,[52] it does not seem
that they are especially hazardous. Anti-inflammatory steroids have recently
been shown to cause cleft palate in the mouse,[53,54] but their possible
teratogenicity in humans remains an open question. Even caffeine, probably
the most widely used of all drugs, has been reported to produce fetal
abnormalities in mice,[55] although at doses (per kg) at least 50 times higher
than those taken by people.

Drugs with known teratogenic effects should obviously not be used
by pregnant women, but these same drugs might well be effective and

50 J. YERUSHALMY and L. MILKOVICH: Evaluation of the teratogenic effect of
meclizine in man. *Amer. J. Obstet. Gynecol. 93:*553 (1965).

51 G. W. MELLIN: Drugs in the first trimester of pregnancy and the fetal life of
*Homo sapiens. Amer. J. Obstet. Gynecol. 90:*1169 (1964).

52 Title 21, Code of Federal Regulations, Chapter I, Parts 3, 130, and 131, Food
and Drug Administration, 1966.

53 B. E. WALKER: Cleft palate produced in mice by human-equivalent dosage with
triamcinolone. *Science 149:*862 (1965).

54 L. PINSKY and A. M. DI GEORGE: Cleft palate in the mouse: a teratogenic index of
glucocorticoid potency. *Science 147:*402 (1965).

55 H. NISHIMURA and K. NAKAI: Congenital malformations in offspring of mice
treated with caffeine. *Proc. Soc. Exper. Biol. Med. 104:*140 (1960).

harmless in men, in women beyond the menopause, and in children. A practical question is whether pregnancy can be recognized soon enough to avoid inadvertent administration of teratogens during the time of fetal sensitivity. The problem is presented schematically in Fig. 12-3. We know that the sensitive period for teratogenesis coincides with the phase of organ differentiation. In the human embryo the period of organogenesis begins at about the 20th day of gestation (the first somite stage) and continues most vigorously through the third month.[9] A continuing process of finer morphologic and biochemical differentiation goes on throughout the second trimester; and even premature infants born in the seventh or eighth month are incompletely developed in some respects. In the woman with regular menses, ovulation occurs approximately 14 days (12 to 16 days) prior to the onset of the next menstrual period, and fertilization takes place within a day or two after ovulation.[56,57] Thus, at fetal age 20 days, the missed period is more than a week overdue, and most pregnancy tests are already positive.[58] This hypothetical woman with perfectly regular menstrual cycles will know she is pregnant just in time to discontinue potentially

FIG. 12-3.   RELATIONSHIP OF TERATOGENIC SUSCEPTIBILITY TO DIAGNOSIS OF PREGNANCY.   *The diagram applies to a hypothetical, perfectly regular 28-day menstrual cycle. Pregnancy will be recognized before the earliest time the fetus is susceptible to teratogenic action; before fetal age 20 days, abortion will be the likely result of damage to the fetus. Variability in the time of ovulation will delay recognition of pregnancy until beyond fetal age 20 days.*

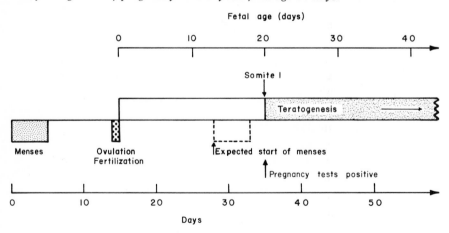

56 C. F. FLUHMANN: *The Management of Menstrual Disorders.* Philadelphia, W. B. Saunders, 1956.

57 D. L. GUNN, P. M. JENKIN, and A. L. GUNN: Menstrual periodicity; statistical observations on a large sample of normal cases. *J. Obstet. Gynecol.* 44:839 (1937).

58 K. E. PASCHKIS, A. E. RAKOFF, and A. CANTAROW: *Clinical Endocrinology,* 2nd ed. New York, Hoeber-Harper, 1958.

teratogenic medications. Unfortunately, however, the length of the menstrual period varies widely, not only between women, but also in the individual woman.[59] Fully one-third of all women have a range of 13 days or more between their shortest and longest cycles, whereas only one woman in ten varies less than five days.[57] The greater the irregularity of past periods, the longer will be the time needed for the missed period to be noted and for the woman to consider herself pregnant. It follows that for the population as a whole, if women of child-bearing age are permitted access to medications that are potentially teratogenic, an unacceptably large proportion of them will have exposed their embryos to the risk of malformation before pregnancy is recognized. Clearly, then, the only safe course is to set up special safeguards for the administration of drugs to all women in the child-bearing age.

It is clear that the risks of chemical teratogenesis, like those of chemical mutagenesis (cf. chapter 10), are accentuated during the first trimester of pregnancy. Until much more information becomes available, the very diversity of known teratogens and mutagens should dictate caution.[60] Whenever a drug is being administered to a woman of child-bearing age, the possibility of pregnancy should be kept in mind. A woman who is known to be pregnant should not be exposed to drugs at all during the first trimester, unless the need is pressing. At least until experimental or statistical investigations show them to be harmless, caffeine, nicotine, and alcohol, to which people are so frequently exposed, should be regarded as possibly hazardous to the fetus during the first three months of pregnancy.

The thalidomide experience served to bring drug-induced teratogenesis out of the realm of laboratory curiosities and into the social arena. It focused attention throughout the world upon the need for more thorough testing of all possible adverse drug effects in many animal species before drugs are approved for human use. Because exhaustive animal testing is time consuming and expensive, and because new techniques often have to be devised, one consequence is a slowing of the rate at which new drugs are introduced into therapeutics.[61] Another lesson of the thalidomide tragedy has not yet been learned well. An effective system for the gathering of data on adverse drug reactions and a method for data analysis on a national or international scale are urgently needed.[62-65] When the unex-

59 L. B. AREY: The degree of normal menstrual irregularity. *Amer. J. Obstet. Gynecol. 37:*12 (1939).

60 V. APGAR: Drugs in pregnancy. *J. Am. Med. Ass. 190:*840 (1964).

61 F. C. FRASER: "Experimental Teratogenesis in Relation to Congenital Malformations in Man," in *Second International Conference on Congenital Malformations,* ed. by M. Fishbein. New York, The International Medical Congress, Ltd., 1964, p. 277.

62 A. G. MAC GREGOR and W. L. M. PERRY: Detection of drug toxicity. *Lancet 1:*1233 (1962).

63 C. R. GREEN: The frequency of maldevelopment in man. *Amer. J. Obstet. Gynecol. 90:*994 (1964).

pected happens, as when a very promising and apparently safe drug begins to produce rare congenital anomalies, it is imperative that the association of drug with adverse effect be established with all haste so that preventive measures can be taken. A centralized system of data collection and analysis would have signaled the association of thalidomide with phocomelia much sooner than the means by which it was finally recognized, and the epidemic could have been aborted sooner.[66] The important general problem of protecting society from adverse drug effects is discussed in chapter 14.

The problem of congenital malformation in the human is similar in some respects to the problem of mutation. Both occur spontaneously, and both can also be produced by external physical or chemical treatments. In neither one have the causes of the spontaneous events been ascertained. In both, deliberate experiments are for the most part confined to laboratory animals, while human data must be largely of a statistical nature. More prospective statistical investigations in humans might bring to light associations, as yet unsuspected, between environmental influences during pregnancy (including exposure to drugs) and the subsequent birth of a malformed child.

Chemical teratogenesis, like chemical mutagenesis, is a challenging new area of pharmacologic investigation. Our present understanding of mechanisms of action in this field is pitifully primitive. We do not know how any teratogen really acts, nor whether chemical teratogens play any significant part in spontaneous human malformations. With increasing knowledge about the biochemical events in normal embryogenesis should come better understanding of teratogenesis. Eventually, therefore, as with other diseases of man, practical means may be developed for the prevention of congenital malformations.

[64] T. H. INGALL and M. A. KLINGBERG: Implications of epidemic embryopathy for public health. *Amer. J. Public Health 55:*200 (1965).

[65] I. LECK: Examination of the incidence of malformations for evidence of drug teratogenesis. *Brit. J. Prevent. Social Med. 18:*196 (1964).

[66] F. O. KELSEY: Problems raised for the FDA by the occurrence of thalidomide embryopathy in Germany, 1960–61. *Amer. J. Public Health 55:*703 (1965).

13

DRUG DEVELOPMENT

INTRODUCTION

In primitive societies medicine men performed the functions of physician and priest, gathering herbs or animal organs, processing and mixing them according to sacred rituals, and employing them in ceremonial rites. Ancient and medieval prescriptions blended an irrational multiplicity of natural products with religious and astrologic lore. A tenth-century prescription reads: "Against dysentery, a bramble of which both ends are in the earth, take the nether root, delve it up, cut nine chips with the left hand and sing three times the Miserere Mei Deus and nine times the Pater Noster; then take mugwort. . . ."[1] The traditional symbol ℞, still employed in some modern prescriptions, may stand for the Latin *recipe* ("take"), but there are scholars who believe it to be derived from the symbol of the planet Jupiter, ♃, under whose auspices the healing arts were conducted. Even today there persists among many people a belief in the magical powers of medications, in the potency of herbal mixtures, and in other practices of folk medicine.[2,3]

Until fairly recent times few questioned the efficacy of the traditional remedies. One who did was Paracelsus (1493–1541), professor at the University of Basel, who regarded much of the contemporary practice of medicine as fraud. Rejecting the authority of Galen (ca. 130–ca. 200) he spoke out in condemnation of the herbal mixtures, contending that useful drugs were diluted to impotent concentrations by the abundance of inert ingredients. He recognized the dose relationship between the desirable action of a drug and its toxic effects. Attacked for using "poisons" when he tried to administer potent single substances, he replied that any active drug could be toxic if given at excessively high dosage. He introduced heavy metals into therapy and used volatile agents to anesthetize animals.

---

[1] C. H. LA WALL: *Four Thousand Years of Pharmacy*. Philadelphia, J. B. Lippincott, 1927.

[2] W. G. BLACK: *Folk-Medicine; A Chapter in the History of Culture*. London, Elliot Stock, 1883.

[3] D. C. JARVIS: *Folk Medicine*. New York, Holt, 1958.

But he made acceptance of his views virtually impossible by his open disdain for the leading physicians of his time. The era of scientific medicine was not yet at hand, and Paracelsus had little lasting impact upon the established traditions.[4]

The 18th century saw major advances in therapeutics. The cinchona alkaloids were imported from South America to Europe, where it became obvious that they were highly effective in the treatment of malaria. Withering (1741–1799) identified the leaf of the purple foxglove (*Digitalis purpurea*) as the active principle in a folk remedy for "dropsy" (i.e., edema caused by congestive heart failure), and thereby introduced into therapeutics one of the most important of all pharmacologic agents. Jenner (1748–1823) expounded the principle of vaccination, foreshadowing the prevention of virus infections by specific immunization.

But it was the scientific revolution in medicine during the 19th century, led by men like Claude Bernard (1813–1878), that laid the basis for a rational therapy. With the development of experimental methods for testing actions of drugs in animals and man came the possibility of separating the useless from the efficacious remedies. At about the same time there began the explosive development of organic chemistry. The first isolation and crystallization of an active drug from a natural source was the accomplishment of a pharmacist's assistant, Sertüner (1783–1841), who obtained pure morphine from natural opium in 1803. Pure quinine was isolated from cinchona bark in 1820. In the latter part of the century the German dye industry led the way toward the deliberate synthesis of new drugs and the molecular modification of existing ones.

At the beginning of the 20th century there remained voluminous pharmacopeias containing many drugs of unproved worth. This gave rise to a school of nihilism in therapeutics, exemplified by Osler (1849–1919), who adopted an attitude of skepticism toward all drugs and stressed the overriding importance of diagnosis. "Patients are more often damaged than helped," he wrote, "by the promiscuous drugging which is still only too prevalent." A less rational reaction produced the doctrines of *homeopathy,* which held that drugs become more effective as the dose is reduced.

But nihilism was already doomed by the ever-growing number of dramatic successes achieved by new pharmacologic agents. Morton (1819–1868) had changed the character of all surgery and childbirth by the introduction of ether as an anesthetic. Lister (1827–1912) and Semmelweis (1818–1865) had made surgery and obstetrics tolerably safe by using antiseptics to prevent infection. Ehrlich's (1854–1915) victory over syphilis by the use of an entirely new synthetic compound

4 J. M. STILLMAN: *Paracelsus: His Personality and Influence as Physician, Chemist and Reformer.* Chicago, The Open Court Publishing Co., 1920.

ushered in the era of modern chemotherapy; and Behring's (1854–1917) successful preparation of antitoxins opened the way to specific immunologic attack on infectious diseases. Still later, the isolation of insulin and the dramatic demonstration of its efficacy in diabetes[5] showed incontrovertibly how specific pharmacologic therapy could transform a uniformly fatal disease into a mere inconvenience of life. By this time the synthesis of barbiturates, salicylates, and procaine by the German chemical industry made it apparent to physicians and to the public that manufacturers could readily keep pace with demand, once the value of a drug had been demonstrated.

Since World War II there has been an unprecedented expansion of basic research in the biomedical sciences, accompanied by a vast program of research and development in the pharmaceutical industry. The tangible effects have been a remarkable increase in the kinds and number of new drugs available for clinical use and a continuous expansion in the list of disease conditions that can be cured, ameliorated, or prevented by drugs. In the years from 1939 to 1957, for example, total drug sales in the United States increased ten times, from 149 million to 1,677 million dollars.[6]

The beneficial changes have brought new problems. Not so very long ago the physician compounded for his own patients whatever few medicinal agents he required. Thus, courses in botany, pharmacognosy (the study of crude drugs), and the preparation of medicines were a regular part of the medical curriculum. Today, the physician prescribes drugs but rarely dispenses them, and he must choose among a myriad of commercially available preparations. The pharmacist's role has also changed. He is rarely called upon to compound a medication; usually he dispenses drugs already made up in the appropriate dosage forms.

Drugs are produced today almost exclusively by large industrial firms. Some drugs are for sale directly to the public ("over the counter"), while others are available only on prescription. Conflicts have sometimes arisen between economic interests of the manufacturer and the interest of the medical profession and the public concerning the safety, efficacy, and cost of new drugs. It has been a matter of some controversy whether the production, promotion, pricing, and sales procedures that are appropriate to other commodities in the consumer market are necessarily also suitable for products that are essential to the practice of medicine and that directly affect public health. The rapid growth of this relatively young industry has provoked legislative inquiry and periodic revision of the legal basis of

5 F. G. BANTING and C. H. BEST: The internal secretion of the pancreas. *J. Lab. Clin. Med.* 7:251 (1922).

6 L. LASAGNA: "The Drug Industry and Medicine Avenue," in *The Doctor's Dilemmas.* New York, Harper & Row, 1962, p. 131.

governmental control over the introduction, promotion, and distribution of new drugs.[7,8]

From the business point of view, the uncertain outcome of research and development creates an urgent necessity for the industry to capitalize upon promising pharmacologic agents, often before their full effects and scope of usefulness have been worked out thoroughly, and before their adverse effects in man have been adequately evaluated. It has been typical to first overestimate the merit of a new drug and underestimate its toxicity before initial overenthusiasm gradually gives way to a balanced perspective on the drug's proper place in therapy. This pattern has been exemplified in recent years by the antihistamines, chloramphenicol, the tetracycline antibiotics, the phenothiazine and meprobamate types of tranquilizers, and the "psychic energizers."

The modern pattern and pace of drug development create a serious problem for physicians and others who wish to keep informed about the efficacy and safety of new drugs. Especially difficult is the task of choosing from among a variety of agents, each one claimed by its manufacturer to be superior to the others. Textbooks cannot keep abreast of current progress, and there is not sufficient time for one person to read and appraise all the medical literature. In this chapter we shall explain, with detailed illustration, how new drugs are developed, tested, and made ready for clinical trial prior to their introduction into medical use. In the following chapter we shall describe the procedures that are used to evaluate drugs in man and the guidelines for the selection and prescription of drugs.

QUALITATIVE AND QUANTITATIVE ESTIMATION OF DRUG ACTION

The ideal drug has a perfectly selective biologic action. It has no side effects and no toxicity. There is no such drug, but the aims of drug development are to approach this ideal. The desired effect must be well defined, and a procedure is needed that can determine whether or not a particular drug has the specified effect. If it has, a quantitative method is needed to estimate its potency and its selectivity of action. Related drugs can then be compared to see which is most selective for the desired pharmacologic effect. The initial steps in drug development for determining whether or not a compound possesses the desired actions are sometimes referred to as *screening,* and the procedures themselves as *screens.* Quanti-

---

[7] Hearings before the Subcommittee on Antitrust and Monopoly of the Committee on the Judiciary, United States Senate, 86th Congress, First Session, Pursuant to Senate Resolution 57: Part 14. *Administered Prices in the Drug Industry (Corticosteroids).* Publication No. 35621, Washington, D.C., U.S. Government Printing Office, 1960.

[8] Federal Food, Drug, and Cosmetic Act. As amended: *Code of Federal Regulations,* Title 21. Washington, D.C., U. S. Government Printing Office, 1963.

tative determinations of potency and toxicity by means of dose-response relationships are known as *bioassays*.

Screening

A pharmacologic screen consists of a specified set of procedures to which a series of compounds can be subjected.[9] The screen may employ animals or it may consist of procedures carried out in vitro. In general, since the dosage is completely unknown at the outset, one administers various doses up to the "maximum tolerated dose," i.e., the range in which toxicity occurs. The question, then, is whether or not the desired therapeutic effect is obtained at nontoxic doses. The earliest example of a large-scale screening program was that carried out in the original search for a chemotherapeutic agent to cure syphilis.[10] The spirochete *Treponema pallidum* is pathogenic for rabbits, so potentially useful drugs could be screened in this species. Only the 606th compound tested, arsphenamine ("salvarsan") showed a decisive enough margin between curative and toxic doses; and this drug was eventually introduced into clinical use.

A prototype that illustrates the general organization of a mass screening program is the Malaria Survey conducted during World War II in the United States.[11] Seventeen university and commercial laboratories participated and over 15,000 compounds were screened. The problem was to find an antimalarial agent to replace quinine, the sources of which had fallen into enemy hands. The human malaria parasite of main interest, *Plasmodium vivax,* does not infect other species. Canaries, chicks, and ducks have specific forms of malaria, and these were chosen as convenient screens. This illustrates a general difficulty about animal screens—even with infectious diseases the conditions are not exactly the same in animals and in man; and with noninfectious human diseases it may be extremely difficult to find any suitable animal model. Here, the behavior of certain known antimalarial drugs gave some assurance that the avian malarias could be expected to respond to at least some agents that were also effective in man. The birds were infected under specified conditions, parasite counts were performed at regular intervals, and the reduction of parasitemia was specified as the criterion of response. A concrete example of one of the testing procedures exemplifies the general scheme.

Chicks seven to eight days old and about 50 g in weight were inoculated via the jugular vein with heparinized chick blood infected with *Plasmodium gallinaceum,* 16 million parasitized red blood cells being administered. The parasitemia in untreated birds reaches its peak on

[9] A. BURGER: Approaches to drug discovery. *New Engl. J. Med. 270:*1098 (1964).

[10] P. EHRLICH and S. HATA: *Die experimentelle Chemotherapie der Spirillosen.* Berlin, Springer, 1910.

[11] F. Y. WISELOGLE, ed.: *A Survey of Antimalarial Drugs. 1941–1945.* Ann Arbor, J. W. Edwards, 1946.

the fourth to seventh day, when 60 to 90 per cent of the red cells are parasitized; and over 99 per cent of the birds die. Treatment with a test drug was given twice daily by mouth, beginning just before the birds were infected, and continuing for four days. Five birds were used for each test group, and a series of 50 to 120 birds were used for appraisal of a single drug. An untreated control group was included in each series. The maximum tolerated dose of the drug was first determined by administering it on the same schedule to uninfected birds in a preliminary trial. The test doses then began with the maximum tolerated dose and decreased geometrically by a divisor of 2. Each series also included groups of birds on standard doses of quinine, the drug of reference. The count of parasitized red cells was determined on the day after the last drug dose. Quinine, at a dose of 32 mg/kg daily, given as described, reduced the parasitemia to below 25 per cent of the control. This extent of reduction was chosen as criterion of drug effect, and if it was not achieved at the maximum tolerated dose, then the drug under test was considered to be unpromising. The lowest dose that achieved the criterion was expressed as a "quinine equivalent," the ratio of the dose of quinine to the dose of the test drug for this specified effect. Thus, if the test drug were effective at a dose of 3.2 mg/kg daily, the quinine equivalent would be 32/3.2, or 10. Toxicity tests were also carried out routinely in mice, rats, dogs, and monkeys. All groups of animals in which parasite counts gave evidence of drug activity, according to the criteria described here, were followed to see if the drug had any curative activity.

Table 13-1 is a typical extract from the final voluminous report of the Malaria Survey.[11] It deals with Survey Number 7,618, the 4-amino-quinoline derivative chloroquine, which became the drug of choice for the suppression of vivax malaria as a result of these screening studies. The coded information is interpreted as follows: A-1, A-2, and A-2a are screening procedures conducted at the National Institutes of Health. A-1 is the procedure described above, using chicks. The other two procedures employed sporozoites from mosquitoes, rather than infected red cells, in a test for prophylactic action that would prevent the establishment of infection. The quinine equivalent for the suppressive test was 15, as indicated by the symbol Q 15. In the prophylactic tests, since quinine has no such activity, the reference drug was sulfadiazine (D), and the data show that even at the maximum tolerated dose (mtd) the sulfadiazine equivalent was rather low. The remaining entries refer to tests conducted at other laboratories. They show that high quinine equivalents were the rule whenever suppressive activity was tested. The only other inactive outcome was in S-2, a prophylactic test on canaries. The information grouped at the bottom refers to toxicity tests. Here, the quinine equivalents were lower, on the whole, than for the antimalarial effects, signifying the possibility that chloroquine might have a wider margin of safety than quinine. Consider,

TABLE 13-1. **Sample data from the Survey of Antimalarial Drugs**

The extract shown for Survey Number 7,618, chloroquine, the suppressive antimalarial that became the drug of choice as a result of the mass screening conducted'in the years 1941–1945. Meaning of symbols is explained in text. (From Wiselogle,[11] vol. II, p. 1145.)

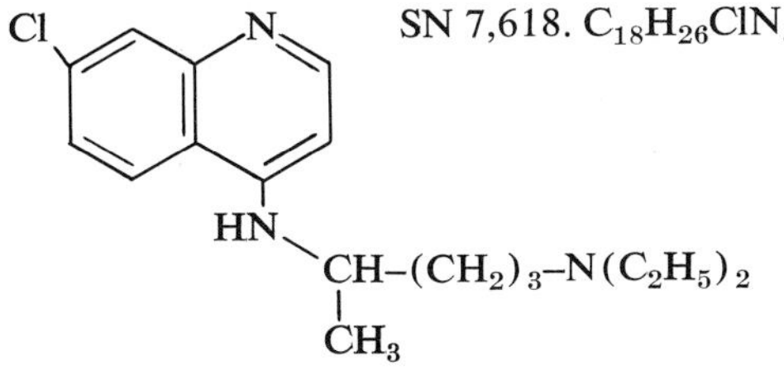

Drug tested		Screening procedures and results		
SN 7,618. $C_{18}H_{26}ClN_3$. *chloroquine.*		A-1	Q	15	
		A-2	D	< 6	at mtd
		A-2a	D	< 0.8	at mtd
		B-4	Q	15	
		B-9	active		
		D-1	Q	10	
		D-1	Q	15	
		D-2	Q	60	
		Q-4	Q	15	
		Q-8	Q	30	
		S-1	Q	15	
		S-2	inactive		
		1-A	Q	10	
		1-B	Q	5	
		1-D	Q	5	
		1-U	Q	5	
		1-U	Q	10	

for example, the outcome in the chick, of studies A-1 and 1-A, conducted in the same laboratory. In A-1, as we have seen, the desired reduction of parasitemia was accomplished with $\frac{1}{15}$ the dose of quinine. In 1-A, the maximum dose that did not cause suppression of growth over a four-day period was taken as criterion, and here chloroquine was toxic at $\frac{1}{10}$ the dose of quinine. If the toxicity equivalent is significantly lower than the suppressive equivalent, the therapeutic ratio (cf. chapter 5) of chloroquine is greater than that of quinine.

Out of more than 15,000 compounds tested in the antimalarial survey, two were clearly superior to other drugs then available. One of these, chloroquine, was superior to quinine as a suppressive antimalarial. As it turned out, chloroquine had been synthesized previously and tested in 1934 by the German pharmaceutical industry under the name "resochin." However, information about it did not become available in other countries until after World War II. The other outstanding product of the Malaria Survey was primaquine (SN 13,272), superior to any drug then known in its ability to eradicate the tissue forms of the malaria parasite and thus bring about radical cure of the disease.

It seems curious that the two major drugs to emerge from the Malaria Survey were quinolines, and that both are so closely related to the

4-amino- and 8-aminoquinolines that had been in clinical use as anti-malarials for many years. Perhaps something about the design of the antimalarial survey led to this outcome. It is known now that not all anti-malarials are quinoline derivatives. A program conducted in Great Britain at the same time as the Malaria Survey in the United States yielded a completely new class of antimalarials, namely, antifolic compounds with anti-malarial activity. Here, the follow-up of initial observations on sulfadiazine led to deliberate molecular modifications such as described later in this chapter.

Screening has been very useful, in general, for finding anti-infective agents. Of the antibiotics, penicillin was discovered by complete accident, but all the others have been obtained through exhaustive screening of soil samples from various parts of the world. For these agents the "screen" consists of determination, in vitro, of antibacterial and antifungal activity. The common antibiotics, such as streptomycin, are rediscovered again and again, at great expense. The probability of discovering a new antibiotic of value through repetitive application of the same screening procedure obviously diminishes year by year.

Apart from infectious diseases the analogy between human illness and animal models may be tenuous, and drug screening in animals may fail to reveal a useful action or may falsely suggest great utility. Some human illnesses have no discernible animal counterpart; examples are mental depression, idiopathic epilepsy, and essential hypertension. There is great incentive to find effective anticancer drugs, and large-scale screening has been conducted for many years, using transplantable rodent tumors. But it is not at all certain that these are biologically equivalent to spontaneous cancer in man. Often, although an exact counterpart of a human disease is not known in animals, enough is known of the mechanisms of the human disease so that an artificial equivalent can be produced in animals, or a meaningful screen can be devised for some specific drug effect. Even though a disease analogous to essential hypertension may not exist among ordinary laboratory animals, reduction of blood pressure can nevertheless be sought in an animal screen. In the same way, empirical "analgesia" tests can be conducted in animals, even though it is not certain that they feel pain in the same way we do. A screen based on abolishing the "tail flick" of a rat subjected to a thermal stimulus (cf. p. 592) does serve to identify the known analgesic drugs; and similar screens have been employed successfully to find new analgesics.

Although spontaneous diabetes mellitus is very rare in laboratory animals, the ability of a drug to lower blood sugar can be used as an empirical screen for possible antidiabetic action. In a typical example, adult male guinea pigs were used. The animals were fasted overnight (to reduce the variation of blood sugar level from recent feeding), then divided into groups of three animals each. Since effectiveness by the oral route was sought, the test drug was given by mouth, at three dose levels, beginning with a fairly high dose and decreasing by a divisor of 2, as in the antimalarial screen. Blood samples were taken periodically over an 8-hour period. If the blood sugar level after 8 hours was lower than 80 per cent of the control level, the test outcome was considered positive. The dose decrementation procedure was repeated with fresh animals, until no response was obtained. These data then permitted a log dose-response curve to be constructed for each drug that gave a positive test, so that quantitative comparisons of potency could be carried out. Table 13-2 presents a typical result of such screening. The ED50 dose of this particular compound is seen to be about 62 mg/kg. An important aim in the design of a screen is to minimize the waste of animals that yield no information, i.e., animals tested at doses higher or lower than the effective dose range.

TABLE 13-2. **Hypoglycemia induced in guinea pigs by various doses of a new drug**

Animals were fasted overnight, then divided into groups of three animals each. The test drug was given by mouth. Blood sugar levels were determined for 8 hours and the maximum reduction was recorded as per cent of the initial level. (From Stewart and Young,[12] Table 5.1. By permission of Butterworth.)

Oral dose (g/kg)	Maximum response in each guinea pig (% of initial blood sugar)	Mean response (%)
First test		
2.0	23,44,32	33
1.0	29,32,29	30
0.5	33,39,29	34
Second test		
0.5	34,37,36	36
0.25	22,29,16	22
0.125	30,30,45	35
Third test		
0.125	40,41,37	39
0.0625	37,45,60	47
0.0313	80,56,67	68
Fourth test		
0.0313	64,71,65	67
0.0156	84,80,72	79
0.0078	84,80,76	80

12 G. A. STEWART and P. A. YOUNG: Statistics as applied to pharmacological and toxicological screening. *Progr. Med. Chem. 3:*187 (1963).

Here, this was accomplished by beginning with a dose expected to produce a large effect, restricting the testing to three doses on a given day, and repeating the lowest dose on the next day to ensure detection of variation between days.

Occasionally drugs are subjected to "blind screening,"[13] in which specific criteria for particular desired actions have not been established in advance. The aim is to see if a new compound or group of compounds has useful pharmacologic activity of any sort. Such screens can be standardized so that they are neither too cumbersome nor too expensive. For example, in searching for effects of neuropharmacologic interest, very detailed observations of animal behavior, motor activity, coordination, state of the righting reflex, and so on, may be made according to carefully compiled checklists. The simple procedures for observing and handling mice are standardized, so that all technical personnel are able to produce reliable data. An arbitrary scoring system is used for each type of behavior observed. Table 13-3 presents a score card used in this type of screening. The scale of scores runs from zero to 8. For normal signs, the reference score is 4; subnormal responses are scored less than 4; supernormal, more than 4. The reference score for abnormal responses is zero. Since a normal mouse grooms itself, the normal score under "grooming" is set at 4; at a dose of 1 mg/kg, the mice are seen to have engaged in excessive grooming activity, for a score of 5 was assigned. Vocalization does not normally occur, so the normal score is zero; at a dose of 3 and 10 mg/kg, the mice evidently vocalized slightly, for scores of 1 were assigned. The general pattern of dose-related effects is often quite characteristic of a given drug, and the method can serve to detect potentially useful kinds of neuropharmacologic action. The drug portrayed in the table, for example, at doses that produced certain autonomic effects but that were not lethal, had generally sedative actions. The mice became less alert, more incoordinated, and passive (tranquilized). Muscle tone was greatly relaxed, and at the higher doses the animals were in the prone position, with decreased respiratory rate.

Thus far we have talked about techniques of screening. As for the extent of screening, it is difficult to formulate criteria for terminating a screening program. If a potentially useful compound turns up early in a series, is it worth trying to improve on it by extensive molecular modifications? If no promising compound turns up, how long should the search continue? There is some evidence that marketable drugs tend to be found fairly early in a series. For example, 16 pharmaceutical manufacturing firms responded to a questionnaire sent out to a total of 70 firms in Switzerland, the United Kingdom, and the United States.[14] With respect to 79

[13] R. A. TURNER: "The Organization of Screening," in *Screening Methods in Pharmacology,* New York, Academic Press, 1965, pp. 22–41.

[14] J. R. VANE: "A Plan for Evaluating Potential Drugs," in *Evaluation of Drug Activities: Pharmacometrics,* vol. 1, ed. by D. R. Laurence and A. L. Bacharach. New York, Academic Press, 1964, pp. 23–45.

TABLE 13-3. Profile checklist for "blind" neuropharmacologic screening

Arbitrary scores are assigned to the various categories of behavior, as described in text. The tests are conducted with groups of three mice, at various doses increasing by a factor of 3. Normal score for each category is shown at top; higher score is increase, lower score is decrease in the particular behavior. (From Irwin, reproduced in Turner,[13] Fig. 5.)

TEST | TEST NO. P-3 | CHEMIST

SPECIES: MOUSE SEX: MALE ROUTE: oral WEIGHT (GM): 18–24 B.F. = 1.18

PERPHENAZINE — VEHICLE H_2O — pH = 5, pH = 3

CNS ACTIVITY AND ACUTE TOXICITY SCREEN — 0.2% SOL. / INSOL. — 2.0% SOL. / INSOL.

mg/kg Dose (3 anim./dose)	Alertness	Visual Placing	Passivity	Stereotypy	Grooming	Vocalization	Restlessness	Irritability (Aggression)	Fearfulness	Reactivity (Envir.)	Spontaneous Activity	Touch Response	Pain Response	Startle Response	Straub Tail	Tremors	Twitches	Convulsions	Body Posture	Limb Position	Staggering Gait	Abnormal Gait	Righting Reflex	Limb Tone	Grip Strength	Body Sag	Body Tone	Abdominal Tone	Pinna	Corneal	IFR	Writhing	Pupil Size	Palpebral Opening	Exophthalmos	Urination	Salivation	Piloerection	Hypothermia	Skin Color	Heart Rate	Respir. Rate	Lacrimation	Misc.	No. Acute	No. Delayed
Normal Score	4	4	0	0	4	0	0	0	0	4	4	4	4	0	0	0	0	0	4	4	0	0	0	4	4	0	4	4	4	4	4	0	4	4	0	0	0	0	0	4	4	4	0		0	0
.01																																														
.03																																														
.10		3			5					3	3									3			2	3	3		3	3	2	3	2			3												
.30		2				1				2	2					1				3	1		3	3	2	2	2	2	2	2	1			2												
1						1				1	1	1	1							2	1		3	1	1	3	1	1	1	1	1			2												
3	1	1								1	1	1	1							1			4	1	1	8	0	0	0	1	1			1		1										
10	0	1	5							0	0	1	1			2			Pr	0			7	0	1	8	0	0	1	0	0			1		1						3T	1			
30	0	0	8							0	0	0	1						Pr	0			8	0	1	8	0	0	0	0	0					1						3T	1			
100	0	0	8							0	0	0	0						Pr	0			8	0	0	8	0	0	0	0	0			1		2			1	3		2T				
300	0	0	8							0	0	0	0						Pr	0			8	0	0	8	0	0	0	0	0			1		2						1T	1			
1000																	1																			2										

useful drugs that had been developed in their laboratories, they indicated that if every series had been terminated at the 40th compound synthesized, only 18 per cent of the useful drugs would have been missed. Yet the average series length was 147 compounds. It seems, therefore, that nearly three-fourths of the synthesis and testing was useless. One reason for increased yield early in a series is probably that the best efforts and rationale go into the first few compounds and the congeners related to them. Some of the "excess" synthesis and screening may be related to a desire to secure patents on related compounds in order to reduce competition. Some also may be attributable to unavoidable time lag between synthesis and screening. On the other hand, examples are plentiful of important drugs that are perfected only after hundreds of others have been synthesized, tested, and discarded.

Bioassay

A bioassay is a procedure for determining the quantitative relationship between the dose (or concentration) of a drug and the magnitude of biologic response it evokes. One purpose of bioassay is to ascertain the potency of a drug, or more usually, the comparative potencies of two or more drugs. In this use the bioassay serves as the quantitative part of any screening procedure. An example already presented is the determination of quinine equivalents of potential antimalarials.

Another purpose of bioassay is to standardize preparations of impure drugs, so that each contains the same specified pharmacologic activity. In this use bioassay serves as a guide in the commercial production of drugs when chemical analyses will not suffice. This is especially important before the exact chemical structure of a drug is known, as with most antibiotics shortly after their discovery. Penicillin exemplifies the usual course of events. This antibiotic was used very widely in the form of impure extracts of the culture media in which the *Penicillium* mold was grown, and the pharmacologic activity was expressed in arbitrary *units*. A unit is always defined at first in terms of biologic activity. The unit of penicillin was the amount required to inhibit completely the growth of a test organism, *Staphylococcus aureus,* Oxford strain, in 50 ml of a defined culture medium. Eventually, when penicillin was crystallized and its chemical structure worked out, it turned out that one unit was equivalent to $0.6\mu g$ of pure penicillin G. When that stage has been reached, the unit serves no further purpose and should be dropped.

Standardization of impure drugs is essential if dosage is to have any meaning. The physician has to be able to prescribe a dose that will always, as nearly as possible, represent the same pharmacologic activity. And the bioassay procedures are rigorously defined by appropriate public agencies. In the United States the standards for "biologics" (vaccines, serums, and toxins) are set by the Division of Biologics Standards of the National

Institutes of Health. Standards for antibiotics are set by the Food and Drug Administration. Standards for other classes of drugs are set by the United States Pharmacopeia.[15] International standards are also available.[16] Other drugs still standardized by bioassay include hormones such as corticotropin, glucagon, insulin, oxytocin, and vasopressin, and natural products such as digitalis, heparin, and tubocurarine. Bioassays of hormones are required even though the chemical structures of the active principles may be known. Because it may not yet be practical to package and sell the chemically pure substance, preparations pure enough for clinical use are made instead from the endocrine glands of animals. The hormone content of such preparations may vary from batch to batch.

Three different approaches may be employed in bioassays:[17]

1. The threshold dose is measured for obtaining a specified biologic end point. For example, an extract of digitalis is infused into a pigeon's vein at a prescribed rate. The threshold dose is the amount that has been infused at the moment of cardiac standstill. This is the standard procedure for the assay of powdered digitalis.

2. A graded biologic response is measured at several doses, and the potency of the unknown is compared with that of a standard preparation of the same drug. In the testing of new antihistamine drugs, each unknown might be compared with a standard antihistaminic agent, such as diphenhydramine, with respect to its relative potency in antagonizing the effect of histamine on the guinea pig ileum in a tissue bath (cf. Figs. 1-57 and 1-66). Another example is the official procedure for standardizing insulin, described below.

3. A quantal response is measured, the percentage of positive effects at each dose being recorded. The unknown is then compared with a standard with respect to potency in causing the quantal effects. The commonest application of this approach is the testing of toxicity (e.g., LD50 determinations), as described in chapter 5.

The United States Pharmacopeia contains an excellent working summary of the procedures of bioassay, and of the statistical analysis of bioassay data (U.S.P. XVII, pp. 843–861).[15] The reader is referred elsewhere for fuller treatment of the principles and mathematics of bioassay.[18-20] We choose here, for illustration, the standardization of insulin by bioassay (U.S.P. XVII, p. 306). *Insulin Injection* is defined as "a sterile,

[15] *The Pharmacopeia of the United States of America,* 17th Revision. Easton, Mack Publishing Co., 1965.

[16] *Pharmacopoea Internationalis* (International Pharmacopoeia), 1st ed. vol. I, 1951; vol. II, 1955; Supplement, 1959; Geneva, World Health Organization.

[17] J. H. GADDUM: *Pharmacology,* 5th ed., New York, Oxford University Press, 1959, pp. 497–543.

[18] J. H. GADDUM: Simplified mathematics for bioassays. *J. Pharm. Pharmacol.* 5:345 (1953).

[19] D. J. FINNEY: *Statistical Method in Biological Assay.* New York, Hafner, 1952.

[20] A. GOLDSTEIN: *Biostatistics: An Introductory Text.* New York, Macmillan, 1964.

acidified solution of the active principle of the pancreas which affects the metabolism of glucose." It "possesses a potency of not less than 95 per cent and not more than 105 per cent of the potency stated on the label, expressed in U.S.P. Insulin Units." Long before the chemical structure of insulin was known, the unit of insulin activity was defined as the amount of insulin that reduces the blood sugar level of a 2-kg rabbit to 45 mg per 100 ml in 5 hours. Today, the unit is expressed in terms of a U.S.P. Zinc-Insulin Crystals Reference Standard, containing about 22 units per mg. Two solutions are prepared from the standard: standard dilution 1, containing 1.0 unit per ml, and standard dilution 2, containing 2.0 units per ml. Two solutions of the unknown are also prepared, to contain, as nearly as can be estimated, the same activities as the two standard dilutions.

Rabbits of a specified weight are maintained on a prescribed feeding schedule. They are divided into four equal groups of at least six animals each, and the same volume (usually 0.30 to 0.50 ml) of each of the four solutions is injected subcutaneously into the rabbits according to the following design:

GROUP	1ST INJECTION	2ND INJECTION
1	Standard dilution 2	Sample dilution 1
2	Standard dilution 1	Sample dilution 2
3	Sample dilution 2	Standard dilution 1
4	Sample dilution 1	Standard dilution 2

The second injection is made at least 24 hours after the first. At 1 hour and 2.5 hours after each injection, blood is drawn from the marginal ear vein and the blood sugar levels are determined. For purposes of computation, the blood sugar levels at both times are given equal weight. This bioassay exemplifies the simplest design capable of yielding reliable confidence limits for the estimated relative potencies of the standard and the unknown. It is known as a *2 × 2 assay* because two dose levels of unknown are compared with two dose levels of standard (cf. Fig. 5-10). The design incorporates several important features whose purpose is to reduce variability and therefore to improve the reliability of the result. The use of six or more rabbits in each group ensures that an aberrant response of one animal will not unduly influence the outcome. The *crossover,* in which each rabbit is used twice, once for a standard injection and once for an unknown injection, ensures that differences between rabbits will not be falsely ascribed to a difference between standard and unknown, as might happen if the standard were tested on one group of animals and the unknown on another. The plan of the crossover also ensures that differences between responses on different days will not be ascribed to potency differences between the solutions, for all four solutions are tested on each day. Finally, the measurement of blood sugar level at two times after an injection ensures that minor differences in the rate of onset or offset of the insulin action will not unduly influence the assay.

An illustration of this assay is presented in Fig. 13-1. In this demonstration experiment, the "unknown" was actually another solution of the standard; the two dilutions of "unknown," U_1 and U_2, each contained 1.41 times as much insulin as the respective dilutions of standard, S_1 and S_2. The mean responses are plotted as per cent fall in blood sugar against log dose. The best parallel lines are drawn through the points. The potency difference is given by the horizontal distance M between the two lines. Since the x-axis is logarithmic, M is a difference in logarithms, corresponding to a *potency ratio*. Here, M was found to be 0.179, and antilog 0.179 is 1.51. Naturally, the experimentally determined value of M is not likely to correspond precisely with the true value. But the confidence limits of M should include the true value; and in this example the true value, 1.41, was well within the computed 95 per cent confidence interval. The computations for obtaining the confidence interval may be found elsewhere.[19,20] In the usual bioassay, of course, there will be a solution containing an unknown amount of insulin. In such an assay, M will represent the potency ratio for the dilutions employed in the assay (i.e., U_1/S_1 or

FIG. 13-1. BIOASSAY OF INSULIN. *2 x 2 assay as described in text. Each point is the mean response of a group of rabbits given one dose of standard (S_1, S_2) or unknown (U_1, U_2). Dose is expressed in units per rabbit. The "unknown" potency was known to be 1.41 times that of the standard. (From Bliss and Marks, Fig. 1.[21])*

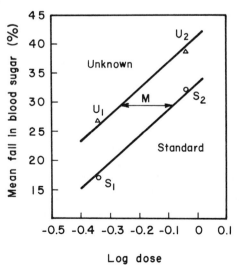

[21] C. I. BLISS and H. P. MARKS: The biological assay of insulin. II. The estimation of drug potency from a graded response. *Quart. J. Pharm. Pharmacol.* 12:182 (1939).

U_2/S_2), whence the potency of the unknown stock solution will have to be determined. In the best conducted assay, the two lines would be superimposed and the value of M would be zero. This would simply mean that the unknown had been diluted successfully to match the standard. The potency ratio of the dilutions would be 1.0. The dilutions of the unknown would contain 1.0 and 2.0 units/ml, exactly as the dilutions of the standard. The insulin content of the original unknown solution could then be obtained by correcting for whatever dilution had been made.

A bioassay does not necessarily employ as criterion of biologic response the same effect that is made use of in the clinical application of a drug. A corollary effect may be employed, as when insulin is sometimes assayed by its convulsant effect in laboratory animals. Inasmuch as the convulsions are a direct consequence of the blood sugar lowering action, results may be obtained without the necessity of determining blood sugar levels. Side effects may usually be employed for a bioassay, provided they are inseparable from the main drug effect and caused by the same compound rather than by a contaminating impurity. Table 13-4 gives data for the potencies of the two posterior pituitary hormones oxytocin and vasopressin, assayed by five different procedures.[22,23] The reference standard was an extract of pituitary glands containing both kinds of activity. The table shows that three methods yielded the same result for pure oxytocin, even though only the rat uterus assay is directly related to the therapeutic

TABLE 13-4.   Bioassay methods for posterior pituitary hormones

Shown are the relative potencies of pure oxytocin and pure vasopressin, in terms of the U.S.P. Posterior Pituitary Standard. Figures are potencies in U.S.P. units per mg of substance. Oxytocic activity was measured by the contractile response of the isolated rat uterine horn; avian depressor activity, by blood pressure lowering in the fowl; milk-ejecting activity, in the female rabbit; pressor activity, by rise of blood pressure in the rat; and antidiuretic activity, by reduction of urine volume in the dog. (From Van Dyke et al.,[22] Table I. By permission of Rockefeller University Press.)

	Potency by assay method (units/mg)				
Hormone	Oxytocic (rat uterus)	Avian depressor (fowl)	Milk-ejecting (rabbit)	Pressor (rat)	Antidiuretic (dog)
Oxytocin	500	500	500	7	3
Vasopressin	30	85	100	600	600

[22] H. B. VAN DYKE, K. ADAMSONS, JR., and S. L. ENGEL: Aspects of the biochemistry and physiology of the neurohypophyseal hormones. *Rec. Progr. Hormone Res. 11*:1 (1955).

[23] M. SCHACHTER and J. MORLEY: "Biologically Active Polypeptides," in *Evaluation of Drug Activities: Pharmacometrics,* vol. 2, ed. by D. R. Laurence and A. L. Bacharach. New York, Academic Press, 1964, pp. 627–648.

action of this drug in the human. Similarly, two methods yielded the same result for pure vasopressin, although only the antidiuretic action in the dog is directly related to the therapeutic action in man. These findings justify the prescribed U.S.P. assays for these hormones,[15] both of which employ side effects rather than a main therapeutic effect. Oxytocin is assayed by the avian depressor procedure; its potency is compared with the standard in causing fall of blood pressure when injected intravenously in the chicken. Vasopressin is assayed by the rat pressor procedure rather than by antidiuresis, the effect of interest in man; yet this hormone does not have significant pressor effect in man. The table shows, incidentally, that each hormone has a small amount of activity ordinarily associated with the other, as noted in the discussion of structure-activity relationships in this group of compounds (cf. chapter 1).

Sometimes it is even possible to use a lethal effect as an appropriate assay. A good example is the standardization of digitalis. Digitalis is the dried leaf of the foxglove plant. The reference standard is a mixture of many preparations of powdered dried leaves, representing an average composition of the several glycosides contained in the plant. The U.S.P. Digitalis Unit is the activity contained in 100 mg of this standard powder. The assay of unknown preparations of powdered leaf is conducted as follows: An alcoholic extract (a *tincture*) is prepared and diluted with physiologic saline solution. A fixed volume of this solution is administered repeatedly to an anesthetized pigeon, by the intravenous route, at 5-minute intervals, until the animal dies of cardiac arrest. At least six pigeons are used for the standard and six for the unknown. The reason cardiac arrest can be used as an end-point for digitalis assay is that, as with all the cardiac glycosides, the therapeutically effective dosage is a constant fraction of the lethal dosage. Another effect invariably associated with cardioactive glycosides is emesis; formerly, emesis in the pigeon was the basis of standardization of digitalis preparations.

METHODS OF DEVELOPING NEW DRUGS

Purification of Drugs from Natural Sources

Natural products were once the source of all drugs, and the purification of medicinal substances from plants became a major concern of medicinal chemistry during the 19th century. In recent years, progress in analytic and preparative methods stimulated a resurgence of interest in this field.[24] Natural products and their derivatives still represent an important fraction of all drugs in clinical use. An analysis of over 300 million

---

24 N. BOHONOS and H. D. PIERSMA: Natural products in the pharmaceutical industry. *BioScience 16*:706 (1966).

prescriptions for the year 1960 revealed that 47 per cent were for drugs of natural origin, mostly antibiotics.[25]

Occasionally, native lore provides clues to plants with pharmacologic activity.[26] Digitalis, opiates, and the *Cinchona* alkaloids (quinine and quinidine) came into modern medicine by this route. Curare was obtained from a South American plant long used by natives to prepare arrow poisons. Cardiac glycosides from *Strophanthus* seeds and physostigmine from Calabar beans exemplify useful drugs employed as poisons in the native habitat. *Rauwolfia serpentina* was used for centuries in India as a native remedy for a variety of illnesses; only in recent years were its tranquilizing properties recognized in Western medicine and its active principle, reserpine, isolated. Atropine, pilocarpine, nicotine, ephedrine, cocaine, theophylline, and numerous other drugs were obtained first by purifying extracts of plants alleged to have medicinal qualities. But despite these useful contributions to the modern pharmacopeia, folk medicine is a notoriously unreliable guide in the search for active products. There has been intensive interest, for example, in discovering antifertility agents. According to the natives of certain Pacific islands, about 200 different local plants are efficacious in reducing male or female fertility. Extracts made from 80 of these were fed at high dosage levels to rats for periods up to four weeks without any effect upon pregnancies or litter sizes.[27]

ANTIBIOTICS

The purification of antibiotics offers a good illustration of the essential procedures. The work begins with the discovery of antibacterial or antifungal activity in the culture medium in which the organisms under investigation have grown. The earliest deliberate search for antibiotics was initiated on the rational basis that soil organisms might have evolved that are capable of attacking and destroying competing microorganisms in the soil.[28] Soil samples were incubated in the presence of pathogens in the hope of producing an enrichment with respect to any antibiotic-producing organism that might be present. From such a culture was obtained a gram-positive spore-forming bacterium, *Bacillus brevis,* which produced antibacterial substances. The crude material, called *tyrothricin,* could be dissolved in alcohol and then separated into two crystalline fractions by adding ether. The material that precipitated under these conditions was called *gramicidin;* the soluble material, crystallizable from acetone, was

25 R. A. GOSSELIN: The status of natural products in the American pharmaceutical market. *Lloydia 25:*241 (1962).

26 M. B. KREIG: *Green Medicine.* Chicago, Rand McNally, 1964.

27 J. R. PRICE: "Antifertility Agents of Plant Origin," in *A Symposium on Agents Affecting Fertility,* ed. by C. R. Austin and J. S. Perry. Boston, Little, Brown and Co., 1965, pp. 3–17.

28 R. J. DUBOS: Studies on a bactericidal agent extracted from a soil bacillus. I. Preparation of the agent. Its activity in vitro. *J. Exper. Med. 70:*1 (1939).

called *tyrocidine*. Table 13-5 shows the differences in antibacterial and hemolytic activities of these two antibiotics. Gramicidin is seen to be highly selective against the test organisms, preventing growth of the gram-positive staphylococci but not the gram-negative *Escherichia coli*. This agent was found to be effective also against pneumococci, streptococci, diphtheria bacilli, and the aerobic sporulating bacilli. Tyrocidine, on the other hand, was equally active against gram-negative and gram-positive organisms. Gramicidin produced no hemolysis, whereas tyrocidine was hemolytic within the concentration range of its antibacterial activity. Because of its toxicity, the crude mixture, tyrothricin (about one part gramicidin to four parts tyrocidine), is employed only for topical application as a solution or ointment.

TABLE 13-5. **Antibacterial and hemolytic activity of crude gramicidin and tyrocidine**

Bacteria were grown on meat infusion peptone agar in the presence of the amount of each antibiotic shown in 3 ml of bacterial suspension. Hemolysis was determined by incubating the amount shown with 1 ml of a 10 per cent suspension of washed erythrocytes; results were the same for all incubation times from 15 minutes to 24 hours. Symbols: — = no bacterial growth or no hemolysis; ++++ = abundant bacterial growth or complete hemolysis. (From Dubos and Hotchkiss,[29] Tables I and III.)

	Amt. of antibiotic (mg)	Bacterial growth		Hemolysis
		E. coli	*Staphylococcus*	
Gramicidin	0.500	++++	—	
	0.400			—
	0.200			—
	0.100	++++	—	—
	0.050			—
	0.020			—
	0.010	++++	—	
	0.005	++++	—	
	0.002	++++	+	
Tyrocidine	0.500	—	—	
	0.400			++++
	0.200			++++
	0.100	—	—	+++
	0.050	—	—	+
	0.025	+++	—	
	0.020			—
	0.010	++++	++++	

29 R. J. DUBOS and R. D. HOTCHKISS: The production of bactericidal substances by aerobic sporulating bacilli. *J. Exper. Med.* 73:629 (1941).

More powerful methods of separation soon showed that neither gramicidin nor tyrocidine is a single compound; both are mixtures of closely related cyclic polypeptides. By the procedure of countercurrent distribution (cf. p. 212) tyrocidine, for example, was resolved into three pure substances. That complex polypeptides as nearly identical as tyrocidines A and B should be completely separable well illustrates the

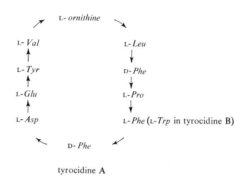

tyrocidine A

resolving power of this technique.[29a] Once pure compounds were obtained, the usual methods of protein chemistry for determining amino acid composition and sequence could be applied.[30] In this instance it was important to establish the steric configuration of each amino acid, for two phenylalanine residues turned out to be of the unusual D type.

The successful isolation of these antibiotics from soil microbes was followed by an extensive search for others. Indeed, the "rediscovery" and practical development of penicillin were apparently stimulated in part by these "interesting studies on the acquired bacterial antagonism of a soil bacterium which have led to the isolation from its culture medium of bactericidal substances active against a number of gram-positive microorganisms."[31] Other antibiotics discovered by screening procedures, isolated, crystallized, identified chemically, and introduced into clinical use include bacitracin (1943), streptomycin (1944), polymyxin B and chloramphenicol (1947), chlortetracycline (1948), neomycin (1949), oxytetracycline (1950), erythromycin (1952), vancomycin and novobiocin (1956), paromomycin (1959), and gentamicin (1963). Besides these and others with antibacterial action, several antifungal agents and a number with some anticancer activity have also been isolated and purified. The rate

---

29a In the representation of a cyclic peptide arrows indicate the polarity of the peptide bonds, —CO → NH—.

30 T. P. KING and L. C. CRAIG: The chemistry of tyrocidine. V. The amino acid sequence of tyrocidine B. *J. Amer. Chem. Soc.* 77:6627 (1955).

31 E. CHAIN, H. W. FLOREY, A. D. GARDNER, N. G. HEATLEY, M. A. JENNINGS, J. ORR-EWING, and A. G. SANDERS: Penicillin as a chemotherapeutic agent. *Lancet* 2:226 (1940).

of introduction of new antibiotics into clinical use has been approximately one per year, and it is not yet evident if this rate is slowing down.

VINCA ALKALOIDS

The isolation and identification of the active alkaloids in the leaves of the periwinkle plant (*Vinca rosea*) afford an example of the application of modern analytical chemistry to the problem of separation and complete chemical identification of very complex compounds. Crude preparations of plants of this species enjoyed a reputation in some parts of the world for being useful in diabetes. Extracts of the plant were therefore assayed for hypoglycemic activity. No such hypoglycemic activity was ever observed in tests with plant extracts, but in the course of the work it was noticed that treated rats frequently suffered a fatal fulminating infection. Investigation showed that the fatal septicemia was secondary to a massive leukopenia. Depression of the white cell count was then adopted as bioassay criterion, permitting the isolation of one of the responsible alkaloids, vinblastine, in 1958.[32] At the same time, in another laboratory, routine screening of the crude plant materials in an anticancer program revealed activity against a transplantable lymphocytic leukemia of mice.[33] This antileukemic action proved to be a convenient screening tool, and by 1963 over 30 different alkaloids had been purified, four of which (vinblastine, vinleurosine, vincristine, and vinrosidine) were found to have antileukemic activity.[34]

We can distinguish three characteristic phases of these investigations. First, biologic activity is detected in crude material, and a bioassay system is set up to permit the identification of active fractions and the rapid discarding of inactive ones. Second, the crude material is fractionated by the most appropriate chemical procedures, all fractions are tested, active fractions are further fractionated, and so on, until pure crystalline compounds are obtained. Third, the chemical structures of the pure compounds are determined. Nowadays, the second and third phases may be carried out with astonishing speed by large teams of chemists. Only about three years were required to isolate the more than 30 *Vinca* alkaloids, although they are very much alike in chemical structure. The techniques employed were generally similar to those described for the isolation of drug metabolites (cf. chapter 3). Differential extraction into organic solvents was the first step; with proper pH control, this permitted separation of the alkaloids according to their degree of basicity. The second procedure used was

32 R. L. NOBLE, C. T. BEER, and J. H. CUTTS: Role of chance observations in chemotherapy: *Vinca rosea*. *Ann. N. Y. Acad. Sci.* 76:882 (1958).

33 I. S. JOHNSON, H. F. WRIGHT, G. H. SVOBODA, and J. VLANTIS: Antitumor principles derived from *Vinca rosea* Linn. I. Vincaleukoblastine and leurosine. *Cancer Res.* 20:1016 (1960).

34 I. S. JOHNSON, J. G. ARMSTRONG, M. GORMAN, and J. P. BURNETT, JR.: The vinca alkaloids: a new class of oncolytic agents. *Cancer Res.* 23:1390 (1963).

chromatography on columns of alumina gel. Chemical identification was carried out more or less concurrently with isolation.[35] Here, the powerful newer techniques of infrared spectroscopy, nuclear magnetic resonance, and mass spectroscopy were combined with the older methods of degradation and elemental analysis. By 1965, the complete molecular structures, stereochemistry, and absolute configuration of two of these molecules were reported, based upon x-ray diffraction analysis of the crystalline material (Fig. 13-2).

Other *Vinca* alkaloids are quite closely related to the compound shown in Fig. 13-2; they are monomers or dimers containing indole or

FIG. 13-2.   CONFORMATIONAL STRUCTURE OF VINBLASTINE AND VINCRISTINE. (*From Moncrief and Lipscomb, Fig. 3.*[36] *By permission of Munksgaard.*)

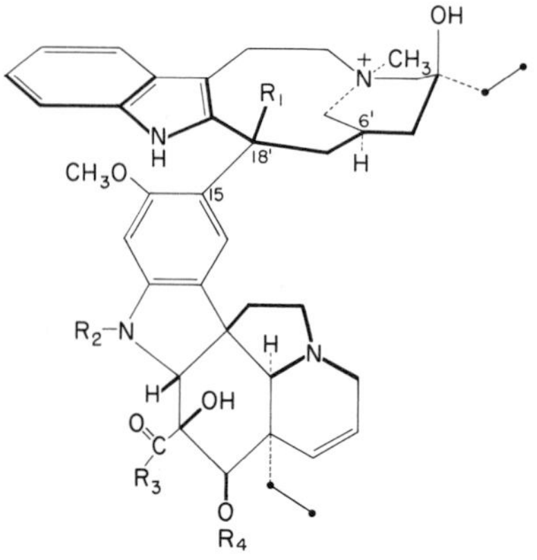

a

b

Two-dimensional representation of vincristine methiodide as determined by x-ray crystallographic methods. Vinblastine and vincristine have no methyl group on the 6'-position; they are tertiary amines. Carbon atoms are shown as dots *joined by bonds.* Heavy lines *are meant to indicate bonds projecting toward the reader,* broken lines *indicate bonds projecting away from the reader. The bond between the 15- and 18'-positions can rotate freely in solution.* R$_1$, COOCH$_3$; R$_3$, OCH$_3$; R$_4$, COCH$_3$. *In vinblastine,* R$_2$, CH$_3$; *in vincristine,* R$_2$, CHO.

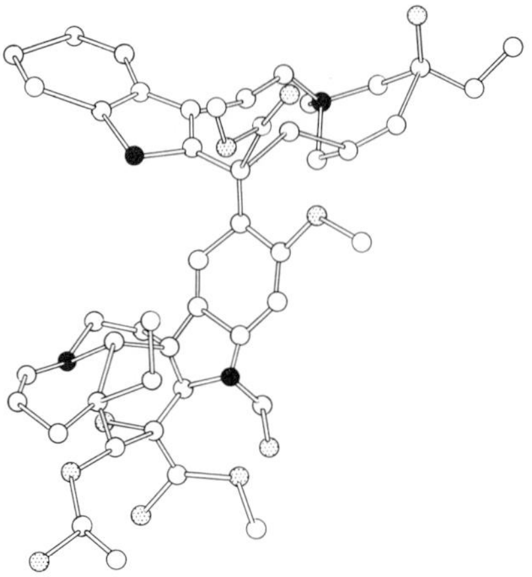

The vincristine methiodide molecule as it actually appears in the crystal. Carbon atoms are open circles, nitrogen atoms are solid black circles, oxygen atoms are stippled circles. Hydrogen atoms are not shown. (Drawing by courtesy of W. N. Lipscomb.)

35 N. NEUSS, M. GORMAN, W. HARGROVE, N. J. CONE, K. BIEMANN, G. BÜCHI, and R. E. MANNING: Vinca alkaloids. XXI. The structures of the oncolytic alkaloids vinblastine (VLB) and vincristine (VCR). *J. Amer. Chem. Soc.* 86:1440 (1964).

36 J. W. MONCRIEF and W. N. LIPSCOMB: Structure of leucrocristine methiodide dihydrate by anomalous scattering methods; relation to leurocristine (vincristine) and vincaleukoblastine (vinblastine). *Acta Crystallographica* 21:322 (1966).

dihydroindole residues. The conclusive determination of so many complex structures within only a few years after the compounds were first isolated is a truly extraordinary achievement. In contrast to this rapid progress, it may be noted that the structure of the far simpler morphine alkaloid, which had been isolated from crude opium in 1803, was only tentatively established in 1925 and not confirmed until many years later; and its spatial configuration was only worked out about ten years ago.

Curiously, it now seems that the original notion about hypoglycemic activity in *Vinca* extracts may not have been entirely without merit. Several of the highly purified alkaloids (not the cytotoxic ones described above) can indeed lower the blood sugar of fasting rats.[37] This activity was not readily discernible in crude extracts, probably because of the severe reactions caused by the cytotoxic alkaloids also present.

STEROIDS

Steroid hormones can be isolated from animal sources, but not in sufficient amounts or at low enough cost to supply a mass market. The practical advances of recent years in the therapeutic use of anti-inflammatory glucocorticoids and the introduction of oral contraceptives rest entirely upon the systematic purification of steroids from various natural sources and their use as starting materials for new organic syntheses.

The first practical impetus to research in this area came during World War II when a false rumor circulated that Germany had perfected an adrenal cortical hormone capable of protecting airmen from the effects of high altitude. As a result, American pharmaceutical firms were requested by the government to investigate the possibility of large-scale production of steroid hormones. Eventually, a complicated 31-step process was developed for producing the adrenal hormone cortisone from deoxycholic acid (Fig. 13-3). Following the discovery in 1949 of a dramatic therapeutic effect of cortisone in patients with rheumatoid arthritis,[38] there began an intensive competitive search on the part of drug manufacturers for an inexpensive way of producing synthetic steroid hormones.[39] At that time, the possible starting materials consisted of cholesterol, the bile acid deoxycholic acid, the plant sterols like stigmasterol (from soy beans), the sapogenins like diosgenin or hecogenin, or the closely related aglycone sarmentogenin.[40]

---

[37] G. H. SVOBODA, M. GORDON, and M. A. ROOT: Alkaloids of *Vinca rosea* (Catharanthus roseus). XVIII. A preliminary report on hypoglycemic activity. *Lloydia* 27:361 (1964).

[38] P. S. HENCH, E. C. KENDALL, C. H. SLOCUMB, and H. F. POLLEY: The effect of a hormone of the adrenal cortex (17-hydroxy-11-dehydrocorticosterone: compound E) and of pituitary adrenocorticotropic hormone on rheumatoid arthritis. *Proc. Staff Meetings Mayo Clin.* 24:181 (1949).

[39] N. APPLEZWEIG: *Steroid Drugs.* New York, McGraw-Hill, 1962.

[40] When the sugar residues are removed from a glycoside, what remains is known as an *aglycone,* also called *genin.*

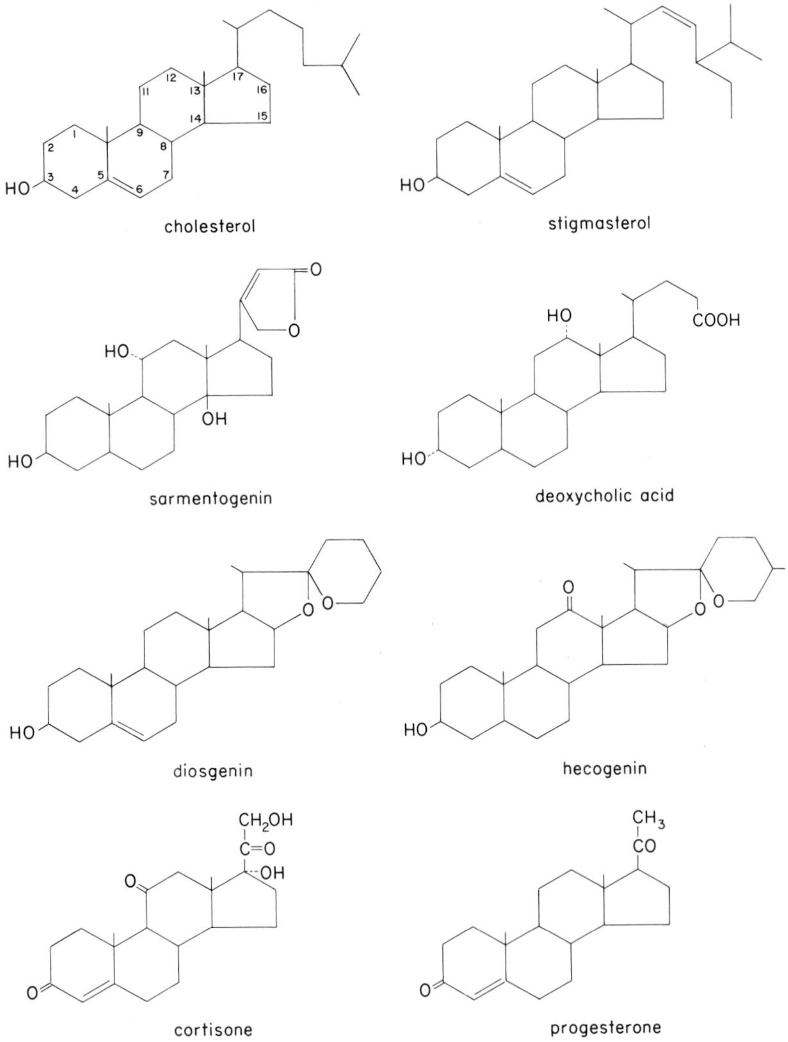

FIG. 13-3.   STRUCTURES OF SOME NATURALLY OCCURRING STEROIDS.

The structures of all these compounds are given in Fig. 13-3. Cortisone and progesterone are typical of the adrenal cortical hormones and sex hormones, respectively, which were to be end-products of the desired synthesis.

Of the naturally occurring steroids, cholesterol is plentiful and inexpensive; but, unfortunately, the cleavage of its side chain is difficult, so that an efficient economic synthesis was not possible. Deoxycholic acid was far easier to handle; furthermore, it already has an oxygen atom in position 12, which could be shifted (although with some difficulty) to position 11. But deoxycholic acid, derived from ox bile, was itself expensive and limited in amount. In the early days, when supplies of cortisone were derived from deoxycholic acid, a one-week supply of cortisone for one arthritic patient would have cost about $6,000.

Stigmasterol also seemed to be a promising starting material, especially because of the double bond in its side chain, which made it easier to modify than cholesterol. But stigmasterol too was in relatively short supply and expensive. The situation precipitated an almost frantic search for plant sterols that would be cheap, plentiful, and readily modified in the chemical laboratory. The years 1949 and 1950, for example, were marked by a "great *Strophanthus* search,"[26] an effort to find a reputed source of sarmentogenin in a variety of *Strophanthus* in Africa. Sarmentogenin was especially sought after because it already contained an oxygen atom at position 11, as in cortisone and hydrocortisone. This sterol was known to exist, for it had been isolated from a batch of *Strophanthus* seeds in 1915, but no one knew where they had come from or exactly what variety of the plant produced them. Sarmentogenin might well have provided a satisfactory starting material, but an adequate source was never discovered.

At last, Mexican yams (*Dioscorea*) were found to contain the sterol diosgenin (Fig. 13-3), which could be converted by an economic process to progesterone.[41] Within less than ten years of the discovery of this source, the price of progesterone, which had been selling at about $80 per gram, fell to $1.75 per gram. The final breakthrough was the discovery in 1952 of a way to use progesterone in the synthesis of adrenal cortical hormones. This required introduction of an oxygen atom in position 11. A strain of *Rhizopus* was isolated that could carry out an enzymic hydroxylation of progesterone to 11α-hydroxyprogesterone.[42] The price of progesterone now fell to 48 cents per gram, and the production of low-cost adrenal cortical hormones became a reality. Nowadays, progesterone sells for less than 15 cents per gram.

[41] R. E. MARKER and N. APPLEZWEIG: Steroidal sapogenins as a source for cortical steroids. *Chem. Eng. News* 27:3348 (1949).

[42] D. H. PETERSON, H. C. MURRAY, S. H. EPPSTEIN, L. M. REINEKE, A. WEINTRAUB, P. D. MEISTER, and H. M. LEIGH: Microbiological transformations of steroids. I. Introduction of oxygen at carbon-11 of progesterone. *J. Amer. Chem. Soc.* 74:5933 (1952).

A curious by-product of the developments recounted above was the accidental discovery that halogenated steroids were highly potent with respect to glucocorticoid activity, with relatively little mineralocorticoid (sodium-retaining) action. In the conversion of 11α-hydroxy steroids produced by the microbial reaction to biologically active 11β-hydroxy compounds, halogen was introduced in the 9-position. Partly because biologic testing was a routine procedure, and partly to help determine that the substitution had the correct configuration, the halogenated intermediates were tested; they proved to be surprisingly potent.[43] It was found, for example, that 9α-fluorohydrocortisone was more than ten times as potent as cortisol with respect to anti-inflammatory effects.[43a] It thus became evident that steroids with greater selectivity of action than the natural hormones could be synthesized. The end result was the introduction into clinical use of such fluorinated anti-inflammatory steroids as dexamethasone, triamcinolone, and fluocinolone acetonide.

CARDIAC GLYCOSIDES

In this important group of drugs, synthetic alternatives to the naturally occurring agents have not yet been found. Plants of the genera *Digitalis* (foxglove), *Strophanthus* (dogbane, related to oleander and periwinkle), and *Urginea* (squill) contain pharmacologically active sugar derivatives of sterols, which are known collectively as cardiac glycosides. Their most important actions are to improve the contractility of the failing heart and to produce partial heart block in atrial fibrillation. These effects were originally obtained by the oral administration of dried powdered digitalis leaves.[44] Standardization by means of bioassay made it possible for the physician to rely upon the potency of such crude material; indeed, powdered digitalis is still widely used as an inexpensive and effective agent for routine maintenance in congestive heart failure.

The impetus for purification came principally from a hope that compounds with lower toxicity relative to their cardiac activities might be discovered. This hope has not materialized. Although differences in potency have been found, it has also become apparent that the major toxic effects (cardiac arrhythmias, emesis, visual disturbances) are inseparable from the therapeutically useful actions on the heart. But the extensive programs of purification, identification of chemical structures, and biologic testing have yielded important practical dividends of another kind. By careful selection of the right plants as starting materials in order to exploit the

[43] L. H. SARETT, A. A. PATCHETT, and S. L. STEELMAN: The effects of structural alteration on the anti-inflammatory properties of hydrocortisone. *Fortschr. Arzneimittelforsch.* 5:11 (1963).

[43a] J. FRIED and E. F. SABO: 9α-Fluoro derivatives of cortisone and hydrocortisone. *J. Amer. Chem. Soc.* 76:1455 (1954).

[44] W. WITHERING: *An Account of the Foxglove, and Some of its Medical Uses; with Practical Remarks on Dropsy, and Other Diseases. Medical Classics.* 2:305 (1937).

differences in types of glycoside between one plant and another, and by fractional crystallization and other methods of chemical separation, it has been possible to obtain in pure form several new drugs with useful therapeutic properties.

The unique cardiac activity depends upon the presence of a five- or six-membered unsaturated lactone ring at position 17 in the β configuration, a hydroxyl group at position 14, and a *cis* conformation of rings C and D. These requirements are exemplified in the structure of digitoxigenin, the agylcone of digitoxin, which is the principal glycoside in

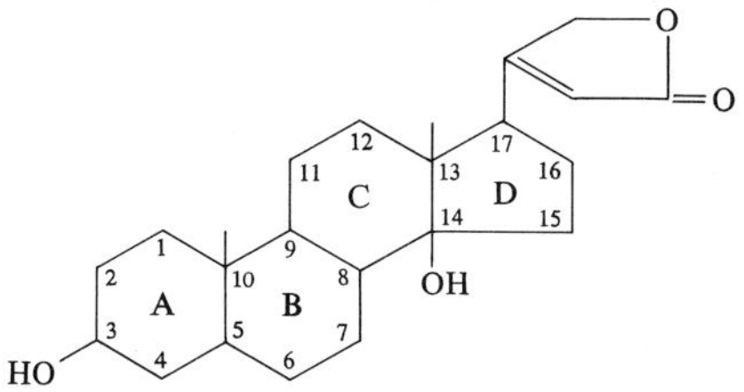

digitoxigenin

digitalis leaves. Although these compounds are found in nature as glycosides, with various sugars attached at position 3, the sugar residues are not essential to the pharmacologic activity. Each kind of plant produces its own characteristic mixture of glycosides. The aglycones (genins) differ from one another in the lactone moiety or in the number and position of substituents on the sterol nucleus. The glycosides differ with respect to the number and kinds of sugar residues and their state of acetylation.

Table 13-6 illustrates with selected data from a large-scale investigation that both the aglycone and the sugar residues influence potency. Potency was determined by intravenous infusion in cats, using cardiac standstill as end-point. Strophanthidin, purified from seeds of *Strophanthus Kombé,* differs from digitoxigenin in having a hydroxyl group at position 5, and also $-CHO$ instead of $-CH_3$ at position 10.

Purified glycosides have been useful for two reasons. First, it is often desirable to digitalize a patient by a parenteral route. For this purpose purified glycosides are obviously better than extracts of dried leaf, and several preparations are now available for this use. Second, the various glycosides have been found to differ with respect to rate of onset and duration of action. These important differences are exemplified by a comparison of digitoxin with digoxin, the active component of lanatoside C, which is the main glycoside of *Digitalis lanata* leaf. Both compounds are triglycosides with identical sugar residues, and the genins differ only by the presence of a hydroxyl group in position 12 of digoxin. The fate of the

TABLE 13-6. Relative potencies of various aglycones and glycosides

The pure substances were tested by slow intravenous infusion in cats, to determine the amount required to produce cardiac stand-still. Ten cats were used for each compound. (Recalculated from Chen et al.,[45] Figs. 1 and 2.)

	Aglycone						
	Digitoxigenin				**Strophanthidin**		
Sugars	Compound	M.W.	Lethal dose (μmoles)		Compound	M.W.	Lethal dose (μmoles)
None	digitoxigenin	374	1.25		strophanthidin	404	0.83
Cymarose	somalin	519	0.59		cymarin	549	0.20
Glucose	digitoxigenin glucoside	555	0.23		strophanthidin glucoside	576	0.15
(Digitoxose)$_3$	digitoxin	765	0.43				

[45] K. K. CHEN, F. G. HENDERSON, and R. C. ANDERSON: Comparison of forty-two car-diac glycosides and aglycones. *J. Pharmacol. Exp. Therap. 103:*420 (1951).

two glycosides has been studied by means of radioactive labelling.[46,47] Digitoxin is excreted very slowly by the kidneys and is further conserved by the mechanism of an enterohepatic cycle. It is largely metabolized in the body, with a biologic half-life of nine to ten days. Digoxin is much more readily excreted than digitoxin; its biologic half-life is only about 9 hours. Moreover, the onset of action of digoxin after intravenous administration is much more rapid than that of digitoxin. Rapid onset and short duration of action appear to be related, in general, to the presence of polar substituents on the sterol nucleus. The glycoside with the most rapid onset of action (a few minutes) is ouabain, from *Strophanthus gratus* seeds.[48] Its aglycone, ouabagenin, has hydroxyl groups at positions 1, 5, and 11 and a primary alcohol group at position 10, in addition to the usual hydroxyl groups at positions 3 and 14.

Modification of Chemical Structure

There are various reasons for modifying the chemical structure of existing drugs to obtain new ones. Usually the aim is to improve the selectivity of action, by finding molecular changes that will increase a desired biologic action relative to a side effect. Sometimes the aim is to modify absorption, distribution, or elimination in order to obtain more useful properties. Sometimes the aim is to achieve a substantial reduction in the cost of production. Sometimes the aim is simply to find a marketable alternative drug that will compete with an existing one. A large investment of effort and funds may sometimes yield only a trivial modification, producing a drug that offers no real advantage over others already available.

MODIFICATION TO IMPROVE SELECTIVITY OF ACTION

The result most frequently sought in molecular modification of drug structures is to eliminate or reduce the intensity of an unwanted side effect and thereby improve the therapeutic ratio for the desired action. A straightforward example is given in Table 13-7, showing a comparison of antihistaminic drugs. The antihistaminic potencies were measured by subcutaneous injection of various doses into groups of ten guinea pigs, and then 30 minutes later giving a uniformly lethal dose (0.5 mg/kg) of histamine intravenously. The ED50 was the dose estimated to protect one-half of all animals from the histamine lethality. The LD50 was determined by intraperitoneal injection in mice, as described in chapter 5. The thera-

[46] G. T. OKITA, P. J. TALSO, J. H. CURRY, JR., F. D. SMITH, JR., and E. M. K. GEILING: Metabolic fate of radioactive digitoxin in human subjects. *J. Pharmacol. Exp. Therap.* *115:*371 (1955).

[47] J. E. DOHERTY and W. H. PERKINS: Studies with tritiated digoxin in human subjects after intravenous administration. *Amer. Heart J. 63:*528 (1962).

[48] H. GOLD: The choice of a digitalis preparation. *Connecticut Med. J. 9:*193 (1945).

TABLE 13-7. **Therapeutic ratios of four antihistaminic drugs**

Molecular modifications were made in the series with the general structure $R-CH_2-CH_2-N(CH_3)_2$. ED50 was determined in groups of ten guinea pigs given a lethal dose of histamine (0.5 mg/kg) intravenously 30 minutes after subcutaneous injection of the test drug. LD50 was determined by the intraperitoneal route in mice, except as noted. (Data of Winter[49] and Roth and Govier.[50] By permission of Williams and Wilkins.)

Compound	R	ED50 (μmole/kg)	LD50 (μmole/kg)	LD50/ED50
Diphenhydramine	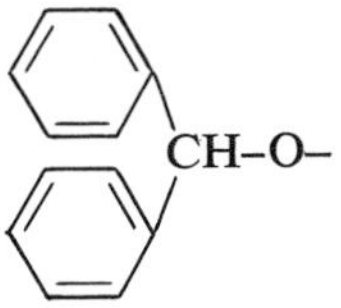 (two phenyl rings) CH–O–	0.21	480	2,300
Hetramine	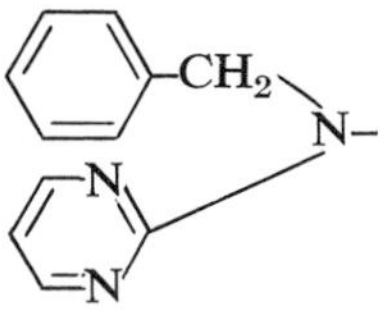 (phenyl)–CH₂ N– (pyrimidine ring)	0.51	260	500
Tripelennamine	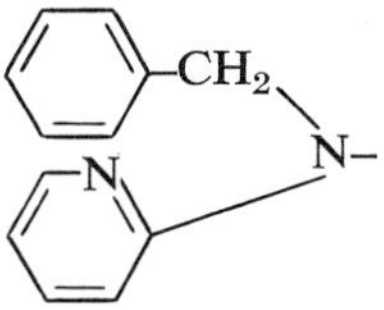 (phenyl)–CH₂ N– (pyridine ring)	0.012	230	19,000
Pyrilamine	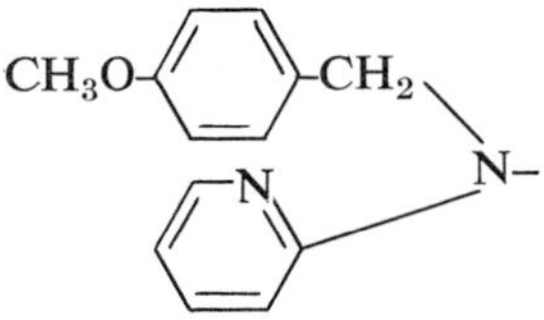 CH_3O–(phenyl)–CH₂ N– (pyridine ring)	0.0037	250	68,000
Chlorpheniramine racemic	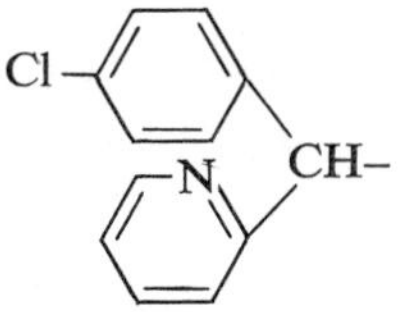 Cl–(phenyl) CH– N– (pyridine ring)	0.47	680*	1,400
(+)		0.20	620*	3,100
(–)		19.	450*	24

* By mouth in guinea pigs.

peutic ratio is given in the last column of the table; the larger this ratio, the safer is the compound estimated to be. The data show that the toxicities of the first four compounds (tested in mice) were approximately the same, whereas their potencies varied over a range of more than 100-fold. In this series, therefore, it was possible to separate toxicity from antihistaminic potency by molecular modifications. The poor potency and low therapeutic ratio of hetramine are presumably responsible for its not being employed in man, although its *p*-methoxy derivative, thonzylamine, is a useful and effective antihistaminic drug. The other compounds are all so safe that the large differences between their therapeutic ratios, as revealed by the animal tests, have turned out to be unimportant clinically. All members of the group are useful.

Chlorpheniramine is particularly interesting because it was resolved into (−) and (+) stereoisomers, which were tested separately.[50] The toxicities, determined in guinea pigs, were about the same. The antihistaminic action, on the other hand, was highly stereospecific; nearly all the potency was accounted for by the (+) isomer. Thus, from the standpoint of safety, a twofold improvement was accomplished by resolving the racemic mixture; and the more active isomer had a therapeutic ratio more than 100 times greater than the less active one.

The local anesthetics have been explored very thoroughly to see what advantages can be gained by molecular modification. Cocaine (Table 13-8), a complex ester alkaloid obtained from coca leaves, was introduced into ophthalmology as a topical anesthetic in 1884. Its central stimulant and addictive properties were soon recognized, and in 1905 several synthetic dialkylaminoalkyl aminobenzoates were discovered to have local anesthetic properties. One of these, procaine, displaced cocaine (except for topical ophthalmologic use) and became the standard local anesthetic.[51] Of the hundreds of other compounds with similar activity that have been synthesized and tested in the past 60 years, a few have been preferred to procaine because of greater stability or longer duration of local anesthesia. But it is not really clear that they are superior to procaine from the standpoint of central nervous system toxicity or local tissue irritancy.

Some comparative structure-activity data are summarized in Table 13-8 for a series of oxygen and sulfur analogues, and also for cocaine and three of the newer and widely used synthetic agents.[52] Local anesthesia was determined in guinea pigs by injecting a fixed volume containing different

49 C. A. WINTER: A study of comparative antihistaminic activity of six compounds. *J. Pharmacol. Exp. Therap. 90:*224 (1947).

50 F. E. ROTH and W. M. GOVIER: Comparative pharmacology of chlorpheniramine (chlor-trimeton) and its optical isomers. *J. Pharmacol. Exp. Therap. 124:*347 (1958).

51 S. WIEDLING and C. TEGNER: Local anesthetics. *Progr. Med. Chem. 3:*332 (1963).

52 F. P. LUDUENA and J. O. HOPPE: 2-Alkoxy benzoate and thiolbenzoate derivatives as local anesthetics. *J. Pharmacol. Exp. Therap. 117:*89 (1956).

TABLE 13-8.   Potency, irritancy, and lethal toxicity in a series of local anesthetics

The upper part of the table compares oxygen and sulfur analogues in a series of the general formula:

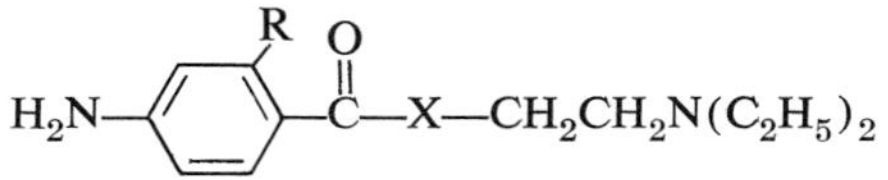

$$H_2N-\underset{R}{\overset{O}{\underset{\|}{C}}}-X-CH_2CH_2N(C_2H_5)_2$$

The threshold concentration for local anesthesia was determined by the intracutaneous wheal method in the guinea pig, irritancy by the trypan blue method in rabbits, and lethal toxicity as LD50 values after intravenous injection in mice. Therapeutic ratios for irritancy/local anesthesia and lethal toxicity/local anesthesia were computed, and each of these ratios was expressed relative to procaine. Thus, the higher the relative therapeutic ratio, the greater the spread between toxic and local anesthetic dose, relative to that for procaine. The lower part of the table gives the same data for four local anesthetics belonging to other series. (From Luduena and Hoppe,[52] Tables 1 and 2.)

Compound	R	X	Local anesthesia (mM)	Tissue irritancy (mM)	Relative therapeutic ratio	Lethal toxicity (mM)	Relative therapeutic ratio
Procaine	H	O	8.8	176	1.0	220	1.0
Thiocaine		S	1.26	23	0.9	31	1.0
(V) (#3260)	OCH$_3$	O	4.66	156	1.7	250	2.1
		S	0.85	73	4.3	20	0.9
Propoxycaine (#3766)	O(CH$_2$)$_2$CH$_3$	O	0.81	75	4.6	22	1.1
		S	0.09	15	8.4	1.7	0.8
Sympocaine (#3800)	O(CH$_2$)$_3$CH$_3$	O	0.312	39	6.2	11.5	1.5
		S	0.087	4.7	2.7	1.7	0.8
(IX) (#4510)	O(CH$_2$)$_5$CH$_3$	O	0.116	5.4	2.3	5.5	1.9
		S	0.051	1.5	1.5	0.9	0.7

Compound	Structure					
Lidocaine	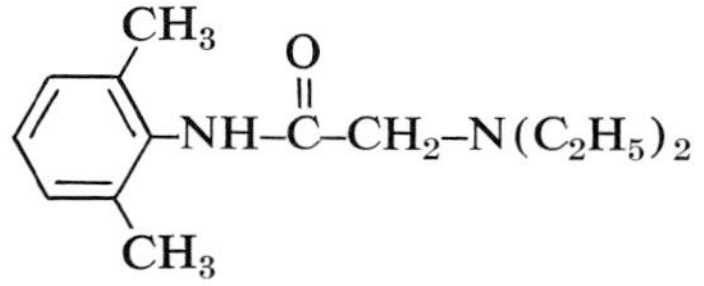 (structure)	2.69	62	1.2	85	1.3
Cocaine	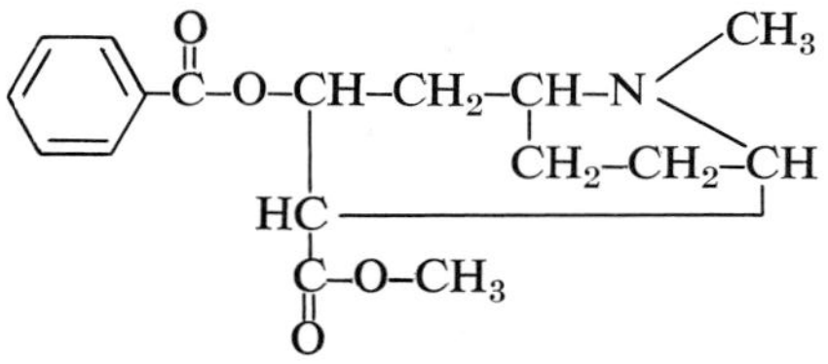 (structure)	1.16	79	3.4	62	2.1
Tetracaine	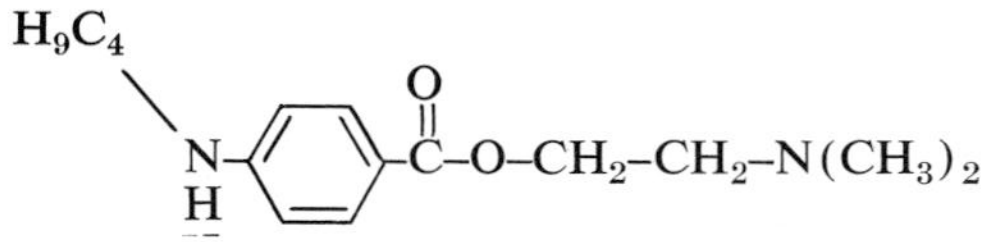 (structure)	0.69	12	0.9	27	1.6
Dibucaine	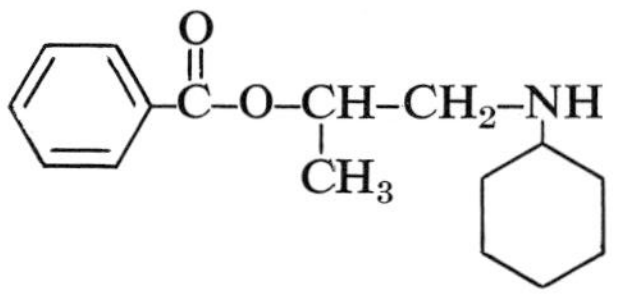 (structure)	0.45	5.6	0.6	14	1.2

concentrations of a drug and then testing the response to pinpricks in the area of the wheal formed by the drug solution; an arbitrarily defined threshold anesthetic concentration was thus determined.[53] Irritancy was estimated in the rabbit by injecting the drug at various concentrations subcutaneously and giving trypan blue intravenously; capillary damage in the vicinity of the injected drug causes visible dye leakage into the tissues, and a threshold irritant concentration can thus be estimated. Finally, lethal toxicity was determined by measuring LD50 in the mouse by intravenous injection. Therapeutic ratios were computed as irritancy dose/anesthetic dose and LD50/anesthetic dose. Then, for ease of comparison, these therapeutic ratios were expressed relative to those for procaine, set equal to unity. Compounds with relative therapeutic ratio greater than 1 are therefore safer than procaine with respect to irritancy or lethal toxicity in this assessment.

The data illustrate several interesting points. For the series in the upper part of the table, as the alkyl portion of the R group becomes longer, the absolute potency shows a regular increase, both in the oxygen series and in the sulfur series. This is true, with few exceptions, for all three pharmacologic actions. Moreover, every sulfur compound is more potent than its oxygen analogue. These findings are consistent with the general relationship between lipid/water partition coefficient and potency among drugs that act upon the nervous system, for the lipid solubilities of these compounds undoubtedly follow the same trend (cf. chapter 2). Despite the wide range of potencies, the relative therapeutic ratio with respect to lethal toxicity remains within very narrow limits. Some compounds, on the other hand, do show an unusually favorable relative therapeutic ratio with respect to tissue irritancy, up to eight times better than procaine in the most favorable case.

The four compounds at the bottom of the table are used widely for local anesthesia in man. From the standpoint of these animal testing procedures, cocaine would seem to have the most favorable properties of the four, with a therapeutic ratio two or three times that of procaine. Lidocaine, tetracaine, and dibucaine, by the same criterion, seem no better than procaine. These data illustrate a practical point of some importance in drug development. It is impossible to predict a priori whether molecular modifications will be capable of producing substantial improvement in the therapeutic ratio. Sometimes, as in the antihistamine series, the most troublesome side effect proves to be unrelated to the therapeutic action; then molecular modification can be fruitful. But in the local anesthetic series, as Table 13-8 shows, no important improvement in therapeutic ratio could be achieved. Nevertheless, in the course of structure-activity studies advantages of other kinds may be found. Thus, procaine was adopted initially

---

[53] E. BÜLBRING and I. WAJDA: Biological comparison of local anesthetics. *J. Pharmacol. Exp. Therap. 85:*78 (1945).

for infiltration anesthesia, not because it was less toxic than cocaine but primarily to avoid the addiction liability of cocaine. Tetracaine, dibucaine, and to some extent lidocaine are preferred for topical anesthesia of mucous membranes because they have a much longer duration of action than procaine.[54] Lidocaine is more stable than procaine and therefore has a longer duration of action after subcutaneous injection. None of these important favorable properties would have been evident from the potency and toxicity tests alone.

MODIFICATION TO ALTER ABSORPTION, DISTRIBUTION, OR ELIMINATION

The oral route of administration is really the only convenient one for drugs that have to be given on a continuing basis. Much effort has been devoted, therefore, to the modification of drug structure to improve absorption from the gastrointestinal tract. In the most elementary case the water solubility has to be improved; salts of some drugs are so insoluble that they pass through the intestinal tract essentially unchanged. This happened with calcium salts of the tetracyclines.[55] Calcium was present in the calcium diphosphate used as filler in the antibiotic tablets. It complexed tightly with the tetracycline, so that slow and irregular absorption resulted. When the problem was recognized, it was readily solved by modifying the composition of the filler.

A more relevant example of water solubility as a limitation to oral absorption is seen with the phenylbutazone analogues shown in Table 13-9. Of the numerous compounds studied, only the first three were soluble enough at pH 7.0 to permit effective absorption by the oral route; yet all the compounds listed were effective anti-inflammatory agents when tested intravenously in experimental animals.

One of the most successful molecular modifications leading to orally active preparations concerns the estrogenic and progestational steroids. The natural hormones estradiol and progesterone are quite ineffective by mouth. In a standard assay procedure, for example, using the rabbit, progesterone is wholly inactive by the oral route at 40 times the dose that elicits a moderate effect when given intramuscularly. It is not completely clear why these steroids should be inactive by mouth. Nothing about their structures suggests that absorption would be poor. It is known from studies with radioactive estradiol and progesterone that after intravenous administration their biotransformation to metabolites occurs within a few min-

---

[54] J. ADRIANI, R. ZEPERNICK, J. ARENS, and E. AUTHEMENT: The comparative potency and effectiveness of topical anesthetics in man. *Clin. Pharmacol. Therap. 5:*49 (1964).

[55] W. P. BOGER and J. J. GAVIN: An evaluation of tetracycline preparations. *New England J. Med. 261:*827 (1959).

TABLE 13-9. Water solubilities and oral absorption of phenylbutazone analogues

Solubilities were determined at pH7.0. (From Brodie and Hogben,[56] Table VII.)

Structure:

$$C_6H_5-N-C(=O)-CH(R)-C(=O)-N-C_6H_5$$

Compound	Structure	Solubility (mg/ml at pH 7·0)	Absorption after oral administration to man
Phenylbutazone	R = $CH_2CH_2CH_2CH_3$	2.2	rapid and complete
p-hydroxyphenylbutazone	R = $CH_2CH_2CH_2CH_3$	10.	rapid and complete
G-1	R = $CH_2CH_2SC_6H_5$	1.6	rapid and complete
G-3	R = $CH_2CH_2CH_2C_6H_5$	0.14	slow and incomplete
G-8	R = $CH_2CH_2SC_6H_3op(CH_3)_2$	0.13	slow and incomplete
pp-dichlorophenylbutazone	R = $CH_2CH_2CH_2CH_3$	0.09	slow and incomplete
pp-dimethylphenylbutazone	R = $CH_2CH_2CH_2CH_3$	0.12	slow and incomplete
G-23	R = $C(=O)-CH_2CH_2CH_3$	0.12	slow and incomplete

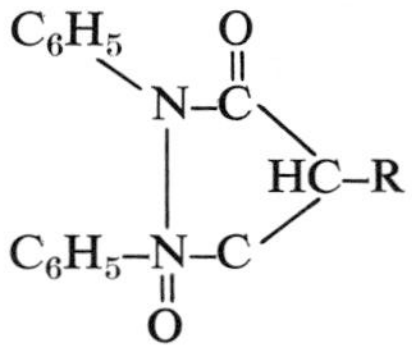

utes.[57, 58] It is likely, therefore, that rapid metabolism as they pass from the portal circulation through the liver, and possibly also degradation within the intestinal tract, reduce the amounts that reach the systemic circulation to less than effective levels. Several modified steroids, chiefly 19-nor derivatives, on the other hand, are highly effective by mouth;[59] norethindrone (19-nor-17α-ethynyltestosterone), for example, was found to be equally active by the oral and intramuscular routes of administration.[60] These modifications, leading to orally effective progestational hormones, have produced the oral contraceptive agents.[61-63] It is noteworthy that the entire impact of this new field of drug action depended here for obvious reasons upon the development of compounds that would be effective when taken by mouth.

Molecular modifications that alter the distribution of a drug within the body can have profound effects upon its pharmacologic properties. Often such modifications involve changes in the lipid/water partition coefficient (cf. chapter 2). Thiopental was developed from pentobarbital by replacement of an oxygen atom by a sulfur atom. This simple replacement was found, on a purely empirical basis, to convert an anesthetic with moderate duration of action to an ultrashort-acting one. As already explained (p. 177), the rapid entry of thiopental into the brain after intravenous injection, and its equally rapid efflux from the brain, account for its very fast onset and offset of action; and this rapidity of passage across the blood-brain barrier is due to the drug's very high lipid/water partition coefficient. The same property accounts for the eventual sequestration of thiopental in fat depots, prolonging the persistence of drug in the body. Certain N-alkyl thiobarbiturates are even more fat soluble.[64] N-Methylthiopental, for example, has so high a lipid/water partition coefficient that fat depots continue to act as a sink for it even after repeated anesthetic doses have been given. In principle, this is a useful improvement. With thiopental, recovery from anesthesia after repeated doses becomes slower as the fat depots become equilibrated. With N-alkyl barbiturates, it may be possible to maintain fast recovery after injections of a larger total amount of anesthetic because of the greater capacity of the body fat to sequester these drugs. The clinical value, however, has not yet been established.

56 B. B. BRODIE and C. A. M. HOGBEN: Some physico-chemical factors in drug action. *J. Pharm. Pharmacol.* 9:345 (1957).

57 J. ZANDER: "The Chemical Estimation of Progesterone and its Metabolites in Body Fluids and Target Organs," in *Progesterone. Brook Lodge Symposium,* ed. by A. C. Barnes. Augusta, Mich., Brook Lodge Press, 1961, pp. 77–89.

58 W. H. PEARLMAN: "Circulating Steroid Hormone Levels in Relation to Steroid Hormone Production," in *Hormones in Blood. Ciba Foundation Colloquia on Endocrinology,* vol 11, ed. by G. E. W. Wolstenholme and E. C. P. Millar. Boston, Little, Brown and Co., 1957, pp. 233–251.

59 R. HERTZ, W. TULLNER, and E. RAFFELT: Progestational activity of orally administered 17α-ethynyl-19-nortestosterone. *Endocrinol.* 54:228 (1954).

60 D. A. MC GINTY and C. DJERASSI: Some chemical and biological properties of 19-nor-17α-ethynyltestosterone. *Ann. N. Y. Acad. Sci.* 71:500 (1958).

Lipid solubility and storage in body fat also play a role in the duration of action of steroid sex hormones. Women being treated for menopausal symptoms with the orally effective estrogen ethinyl estradiol 3-cyclopentyl ether showed a much more persistent drug effect after discontinuance of therapy than did women receiving the parent compound, ethinyl estradiol.[65] Direct determination of drug levels in body fat after oral administration of these drugs to experimental animals showed that the cyclopentyl ether accumulated in fat, forming a depot from which slow release continued, but the nonetherified hormone did not. A similar phenomenon has been observed with methyltestosterone and its 3-cyclopentyl enol ether.[66] Here again, although both compounds were absorbed well from the intestine, only the ether accumulated significantly in fat, thus providing low but effective hormone levels for a long time. Administered by the oral route, therefore, the ether appeared to be more effective than methyltestosterone itself.

The recognition that ionized compounds are more or less excluded from the brain (cf. chapter 2) has led to deliberate molecular modifications for the purpose of promoting or hindering the ability of a drug to pass the blood-brain barrier. An example is the cholinesterase reactivator pralidoxime (p. 397), a quaternary compound. Since inhibition of acetylcholinesterase within the central nervous system is important in the toxicity of organophosphate insecticides and nerve gases, attempts have been made to develop nonionic reactivators of the pralidoxime type. Such agents include diacetylmonoxime (DAM) and monoisonitrosoacetone (MINA) (Fig. 5-19). On the other hand, tertiary amines like atropine and physostigmine, which enter the brain readily, have been modified by producing quaternary derivatives in order to secure peripheral autonomic effects without the complication of central actions. Examples are atropine methyl nitrate and neostigmine.

Finally, structural modification can alter the metabolic fate of a drug to shorten or prolong its duration of action. A good example is the development of procainamide from procaine. Procaine was known to have useful properties as an agent that could abolish certain cardiac arrhythmias; but it is an ester and rapidly hydrolyzed by plasma and liver esterases. Simple substitution of the amide linkage for the ester group produced procainamide. The useful cardiac actions were not lost but the hydrolysis rate in vivo was greatly reduced.[67] Another example, discussed in chapter 3, is

61 V. A. DRILL: *Oral Contraceptives.* New York, McGraw-Hill, 1966.

62 G. PINCUS: The Control of Fertility. New York, Academic Press, 1965.

63 C. DJERASSI: Steroid oral contraceptives. *Science 151:*1055 (1966).

64 E. M. PAPPER, R. C. PETERSON, J. J. BURNS, E. BERNSTEIN, P. LIEF, and B. B. BRODIE: Physiological disposition of certain N-alkyl thiobarbiturates. *Anesthesiology 16:*544 (1955).

65 A. MELI, A. WOLFF, and W. L. HONRATH: The mechanism by which 3-etherification with cyclopentyl alcohol enhances the oral activity of ethynylestradiol. *Steroids 2:*417 (1963).

66 A. MELI, W. L. HONRATH, and A. WOLFF: Mechanism by which 3-enol etherification enhances the oral activity of methyltestosterone in rats. *Endocrinology 74:*79 (1964).

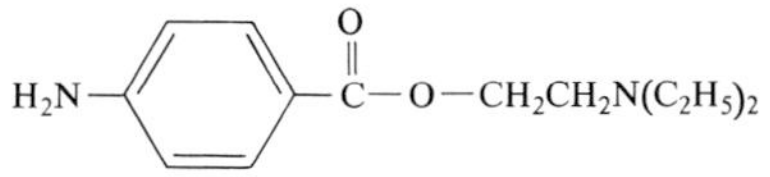

$$H_2N-\langle\ \rangle-\overset{\overset{\displaystyle O}{\|}}{C}-O-CH_2CH_2N(C_2H_5)_2$$

procaine

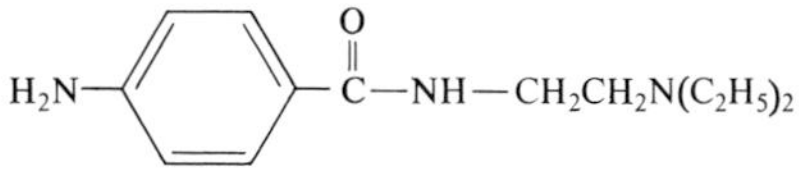

$$H_2N-\langle\ \rangle-\overset{\overset{\displaystyle O}{\|}}{C}-NH-CH_2CH_2N(C_2H_5)_2$$

procainamide

the mild antipyretic analgesic acetanilid. The production of aniline in vivo by deacetylation leads to methemoglobinemia. Modification of the acetanilid structure by hydroxylation in the para position yielded a compound that was not subject to significant deacetylation, and therefore was less toxic. In the barbiturate series, the principal effect of substituent modification is to alter rates of metabolism and thus duration of action. Barbital is essentially not oxidized at all, phenobarbital very slowly, pentobarbital and secobarbital more rapidly; and the durations of hypnotic action throughout the series closely parallel the rates of drug metabolism.

The structure of penicillin can be modified to prevent its degradation by pathogenic bacteria, as discussed already in chapter 8. The usefulness of the penicillins in staphylococcal infections was compromised by the fact that strains of this pathogen produce and secrete a β-lactamase (penicillinase), and thus resist the bactericidal action of the antibiotic by destroying it. The enzyme attacks the internal peptide bond, which forms the essential β-lactam ring; thus, penicillins are converted to inactive penicilloic acids:

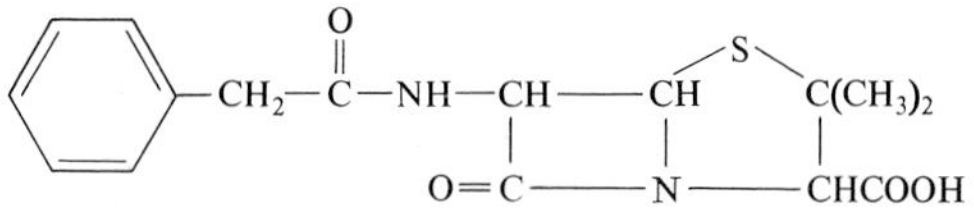

penicillin G

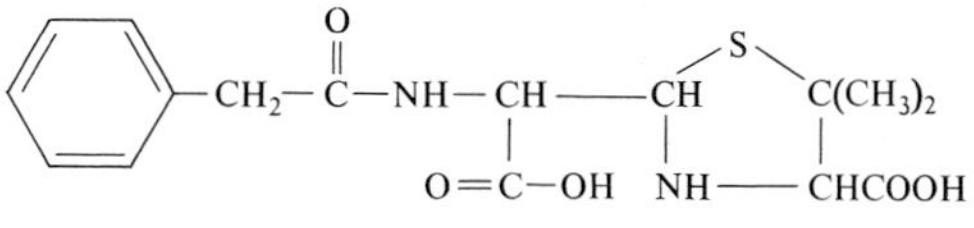

penicilloic acid

[67] L. C. MARK, H. J. KAYDEN, J. M. STEELE, J. R. COOPER, I. BERLIN, E. A. ROVENSTINE, and B. B. BRODIE: The physiological disposition and cardiac effects of procaine amide. *J. Pharmacol. Exp. Therap.* 102:5 (1951).

In an effort to combat this problem, semisynthetic penicillins were sought which might be resistant to cleavage by penicillinase. It was known that antibacterial activity is found in numerous penicillins with different acidic substituents. The first step was to·use an amidase to remove the phenylacetate residue from penicillin G. The resulting 6-aminopenicillanic acid could then be used as a starting material to be coupled with various organic acids.

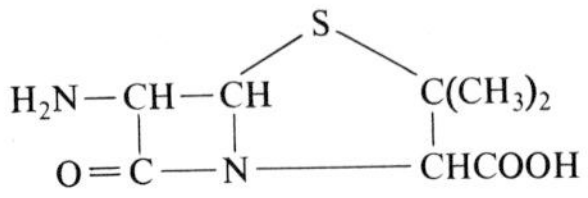

6-aminopenicillanic acid

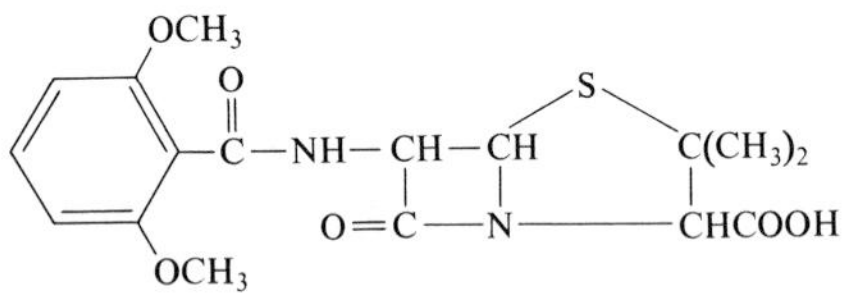

methicillin

When the compounds thus formed were assayed for resistance to penicillinase, several suitable drugs were obtained.[68] One of these was methicillin, the structure of which is shown above.

The resistance of methicillin to hydrolysis by the penicillinase of *Staphylococcus pyogenes* and of *Bacillus cereus* is shown in Table 13-10, compared with penicillin G. The staphylococcal enzyme did not degrade methicillin at all in the 60-minute incubation period, and the *B. cereus* enzyme degraded it much more slowly than penicillin G. Table 13-11 shows the comparison of antibacterial activity against a number of strains of *S. pyogenes,* some sensitive and others highly resistant to penicillin G. Although methicillin was much less potent against the Oxford strain of *S. aureus* than was penicillin G, the important finding was that all the penicillinase-producing penicillin-resistant strains were moderately sensitive to methicillin. Subsequent research has led to the production of several other penicillinase-resistant semisynthetic penicillins.

MODIFICATION TO REDUCE COST

Because drugs are only useful if they are widely available to meet the need, cost is an important factor in drug development. Some molecular

---

[68] A. V. S. DE REUCK and M. P. CAMERON, ed.: *Resistance of Bacteria to the Penicillins. Ciba Foundation Study Group No. 13.* Boston, Little, Brown and Co., 1962.

TABLE 13-10. **Resistance of methicillin to penicillinase**

Penicillinase from *S. pyogenes* and from *B. cereus* was incubated in buffer at 37° with added penicillin G or methicillin. The course of the hydrolytic degradation of the penicillin was followed. (From Rolinson et al.,[69] Tables VII and VIII.)

| Time (min) | S. pyogenes penicillinase | |
	Penicillin G (μg/ml)	Methicillin (μg/ml)
0	1,000	1,000
5	330	1,000
10	0	1,000
60	0	1,000
	B. cereus penicillinase	
0	2,000	2,000
1	0	1,740
2	0	1,610
3	0	1,500
4	0	1,400
5	0	1,330

TABLE 13-11. **Antibacterial activity of methicillin and penicillin G**

Methicillin and penicillin G were assayed for growth inhibition against several strains of *Staphylococcus,* by a tube dilution method. The minimum inhibitory concentrations are given. Strains of bacteria are identified by code number. The sensitive Oxford strain of *S. aureus* was the one originally used to assay penicillin. (Selected data from Rolinson et al.,[69] Table II.)

| Bacterial strain | Minimum inhibitory concentration (μg/ml) | |
	Penicillin G	Methicillin
Oxford	0.02	1.25
No. 1083	125.	2.5
1089	125.	2.5
1112	125.	1.25
1091	62.5	2.5
1111	50.0	2.5
1095	25.0	2.5
1104	12.5	2.5
1098	5.0	2.5
1096	5.0	1.25
1108	2.5	1.25
1084	1.25	1.25

[69] G. N. ROLINSON, F. R. BATCHELOR, S. STEVENS, J. C. WOOD, and E. B. CHAIN: Bacteriological studies on a new penicillin—BRL 1241. *Lancet* 2:564 (1960).

modifications have yielded drugs that are better than the parent primarily because they are cheaper. Diethylstilbestrol is a good example. It was introduced in 1938 at a time when the natural estrogenic hormones were both scarce and extremely expensive.[70] It is a synthetic, orally active compound with estrogenic activity, apparently as useful as the natural estrogens, and widely used today. Curiously, it is not even a steroid; but its three-dimensional structure does have certain features in common with the steroid hormones:

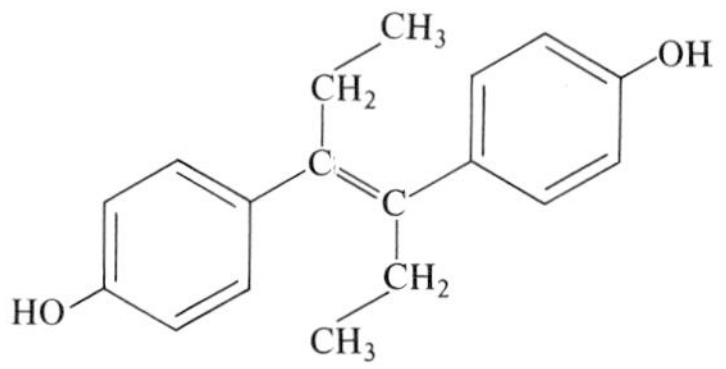

diethylstilbestrol

A similar case involves the narcotic analgesics. Methadone is an uncomplicated synthetic compound seemingly unrelated to the structure of the opiate narcotics, but its actions are almost indistinguishable from theirs. It was developed during World War II in Germany, when shortage of supplies of morphine made it imperative to develop new and inexpensive substitutes. Now it is clear that the conformational structure of methadone is closer to that of the opiates than had been realized by the chemists who made it (cf. p. 52).

Chloramphenicol was first isolated from cultures of *Streptomyces venezuelae* in 1948.[71] For a few years the antibiotic was in short supply and very expensive. When the structural formula was elucidated, it turned out to be a relatively easy compound to synthesize, so it was no longer necessary to depend upon cumbersome fermentation and isolation procedures. Although no change in molecular structure is involved here, this is an example of reduction in cost of a natural product through chemical synthesis.

The insect sex attractant produced by female gypsy moths is extremely potent; $10^{-7}\mu g$ is effective in attracting males in field trials. The substance has been useful in insect control and eradication programs carried out by the United States Department of Agriculture. The structure of the

[70] E. C. DODDS, L. GOLBERG, W. LAWSON, and R. ROBINSON: Oestrogenic activity of alkylated stilbœstrols. *Nature 142:*34 (1938).

[71] Q. R. BARTZ: Isolation and characterization of chloromycetin. *J. Biol. Chem. 172:*445 (1948).

active agent was determined on 20 mg of material isolated from a half-million female moths.[72] Unfortunately, synthesis of the natural attractant proved very difficult. However, a closely related compound, two carbon atoms longer, could be derived readily from ricinoleic acid, abundant in castor oil. The artificial attractant, named *gyplure,* is as potent as the natural substance.[73]

```
                              OH
                              |
              CH₃             CH₂     CH₃
              |               |       |
     OH       CH₂             CH₂     CH₂
     |        |               |       |
     CH₂      CH₂             CH₂     CH₂
     |        |               |       |
     CH₂      CH₂             CH₂     CH₂
     |        |               |       |
     CH₂      CH₂             CH₂     CH₂
     |        |               |       |
     CH₂      CH₂      O      CH₂     CH₂      O
     |        |        ||     |       |        ||
     CH₂      CH—O—C          CH₂     CH—O—C
     |        |        |      |       |        |
     CH₂      CH₂      CH₃     CH₂     CH₂      CH₃
     |        |               |       |
     CH══CH                   CH══CH
```

          natural attractant   gyplure

  (+)-10-acetoxy-*cis*-7-hexadecen-1-ol

Synthesis of New Drugs

INVENTION OF DRUGS DE NOVO

The inventive pharmacologist or medicinal chemist is sometimes pictured as devising unprecedented drug actions de novo, predicting the requisite chemical structures on rational grounds, and then actually synthesizing effective drugs to fit the specifications. This has certainly happened, but rarely. The history of the development of dimercaprol as an antidote to the arsenical war gas lewisite (cf. p. 386) approaches this ideal. So does the development of the cholinesterase-reactivating agent pralidoxime (PAM), tailored on rational grounds to the inferred structure of the acetylcholinesterase active center (p. 397). Perhaps the synthesis and trial of some antimetabolites used in cancer chemotherapy could be attributed to rational design, but serendipity also played a part. For example, the intro-

---

[72] M. JACOBSON: Insect sex attractants. III. The optical resolution of *dl*-10-acetoxy-*cis*-7-hexadecen-1-ol. *J. Organ. Chem.* 27:2670 (1962).

[73] M. BEROZA: "Agents Affecting Insect Fertility," in *Agents Affecting Fertility,* ed. by C. R. Austin and J. S. Perry. Boston, Little, Brown and Co., 1965, pp. 136–158.

duction of folic acid antagonists for the treatment of childhood leukemia was based on the chance observation that folic acid seemed to exacerbate the disease process.[74] Folic acid analogues, including aminopterin, were being developed concurrently as an outgrowth of nutrition studies with microorganisms. The partial success achieved in inducing remissions of leukemia with aminopterin led to the synthesis of numerous structurally related compounds, of which methotrexate (p. 426) has been the most useful. The principle having been established, a great variety of anti-metabolites were synthesized—analogues of the amino acids (e.g., ethionine, *p*-fluorophenylalanine), purines (e.g., 6-mercaptopurine), pyrimidines (e.g., 5-fluorouracil), and so on, as detailed in chapter 1.

The diuretic agent ethacrynic acid was developed as part of a deliberate attempt to synthesize inhibitors of sulfhydryl enzymes that would not contain heavy metals.[75] The rationale for this approach was the belief that the highly effective organic mercurial diuretics owed their effects to inactivation of sulfhydryl groups in essential $-SH$ enzymes of the renal tubule cells. Mercurials were toxic, so there was sound motivation for developing a new class of drugs. An aryl oxyacetic acid derivative containing an α,β-unsaturated ketone was found to react with $-SH$ groups in vitro and to be a potent diuretic. The structure of this compound, ethacrynic acid, and its mode of combination with thiols are shown below:

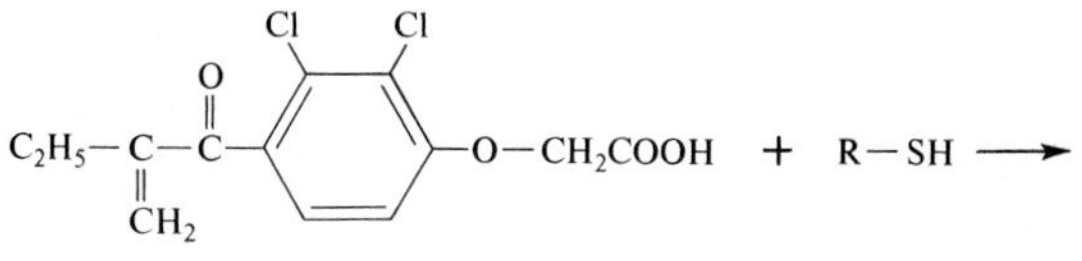

$$C_2H_5-\overset{\overset{\displaystyle O}{\|}}{\underset{\underset{\displaystyle CH_2}{\|}}{C}}-C\!\!\!\left\langle\!\!\!\begin{array}{c}Cl \quad Cl\\ \\ \end{array}\!\!\!\right\rangle\!\!\!-O-CH_2COOH \quad + \quad R-SH \longrightarrow$$

ethacrynic acid

$$C_2H_5-\underset{\underset{\displaystyle R-S}{\underset{\displaystyle |}{CH_2}}}{\underset{\displaystyle |}{CH}}-\overset{\overset{\displaystyle O}{\|}}{C}\!\!\!\left\langle\!\!\!\begin{array}{c}Cl \quad Cl\\ \\ \end{array}\!\!\!\right\rangle\!\!\!-O-CH_2COOH$$

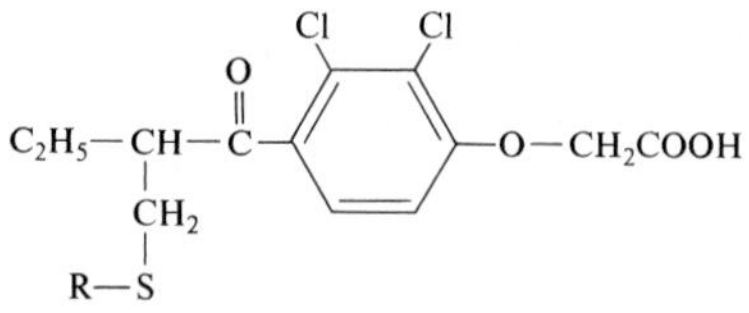

postulated sulfhydryl addition product

[74] S. FARBER, L. K. DIAMOND, R. D. MERCER, R. F. SYLVESTER, JR., and J. A. WOLFF: Temporary remissions in acute leukemia in children produced by folic acid antagonist, 4-aminopteroyl-glutamic acid (aminopterin). *New Engl. J. Med.* 238:787 (1948).

[75] K. H. BEYER, J. E. BAER, J. K. MICHAELSON, and H. F. RUSSO: Renotropic characteristics of ethacrynic acid: a phenoxyacetic saluretic-diuretic agent. *J. Pharmacol. Exp. Therap.* 147:1 (1965).

Curiously, ethacrynic acid is less active as an inhibitor of sulfhydryl enzymes in vitro than are the organic mercurials. Moreover, its diuretic action, unlike that of the mercurials, is not antagonized readily by dimercaprol. Its mechanism of action is still unknown; it would not be surprising if it turned out to have nothing to do with sulfhydryl groups. It is also uncertain whether ethacrynic acid itself will be useful clinically, for it can interfere with the concentrating ability of the kidney, possibly by an effect on the loop of Henle, and it can also cause excessive potassium loss.[76]

Some drugs are developed primarily to influence the pharmacologic behavior or disposition of other drugs. Examples are SKF 525A (p. 249), which inhibits the metabolism of many drugs, and disulfiram (p. 253), which inhibits a step in the oxidation of ethyl alcohol. The monoamine oxidase inhibitors also fall into this category. Another such drug is probenicid. This compound was originally developed for the purpose of conserving

$$HOOC - \langle \rangle - SO_2N(CH_2CH_2CH_3)_2$$

probenecid

penicillin by blocking its renal tubular secretion. For some time after penicillin was introduced into therapy it was very scarce, and its rapid clearance by the kidneys was a real handicap. It was found that the same active transport system was responsible for penicillin excretion as for the tubular secretion of numerous other anions like phenolsulfonphthalein, p-aminohippurate, and p-aminosalicylate. Probenecid, which could be administered by mouth, competed with penicillin for this secretory mechanism and thereby effectively prolonged the duration of penicillin action.[77] During its use for this purpose it was observed to increase the excretion of uric acid,[78] although at low doses it decreased urate excretion, probably by inhibiting the same transport system in the renal tubules. Large doses evidently inhibit the reabsorption of urate from the glomerular filtrate. Perhaps a specific transport system for reabsorption of this anion is blocked by probenecid, but the mechanism is not yet understood. Thus, although conservation of penicillin is no longer important and other means are available for prolonging its duration of action, probenecid has found an important

[76] M. D. MILNE: Renal pharmacology. *Annu. Rev. Pharmacol. 5:*119 (1965).

[77] K. H. BEYER, H. F. RUSSO, E. K. TILLSON, A. K. MILLER, W. F. VERWEY, and S. R. GASS: "Benemid" p-(di-*n*-propylsulfamyl)-benzoic acid: its renal affinity and its elimination. *Amer. J. Physiol. 166:*625 (1951).

[78] J. H. SIROTA, T. F. YÜ, and A. B. GUTMAN: Effect of benemid (p-(di-n-propyl sulfamyl)-benzoic acid) on urate clearance and other discrete renal functions in gouty subjects. *J. Clin. Invest. 31:*692 (1952).

new use as a uricosuric agent in the treatment of gout, a disease characterized by high uric acid levels in the body.

The history of the development of the antifolic-type antimalarial
drugs illustrates the roundabout path that is often followed before a new
kind of drug is perfected. When the screening of possible antimalarials began during World War II (cf. p. 739), it was known that the sulfonamides
suppressed the erythrocytic phase of avian malaria, although they were not
effective in the human disease. Since sulfadiazine was one of the most effec-

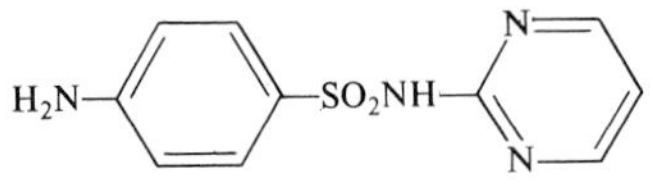

sulfadiazine

tive compounds in the series, attention was focused on the pyrimidine ring.
Simple pyrimidine derivatives, such as shown below, were ineffective. But
since a diethylamino alkylamino side chain was an important component
of the then-known antimalarials (e.g., quinacrine, pamaquin), an attempt
was made to link such a moiety to an aromatic pyrimidine compound.[79]
This eventually yielded an active drug, code number 2666, shown below:

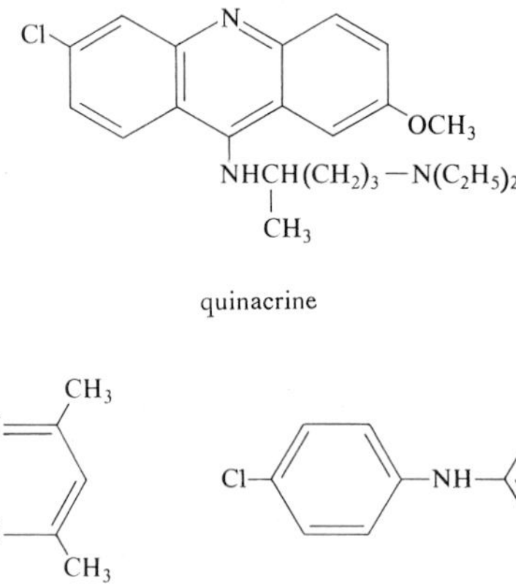

quinacrine

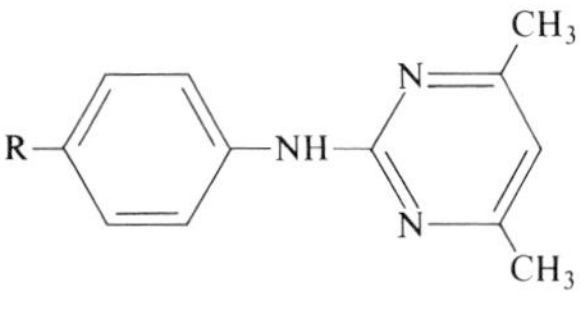

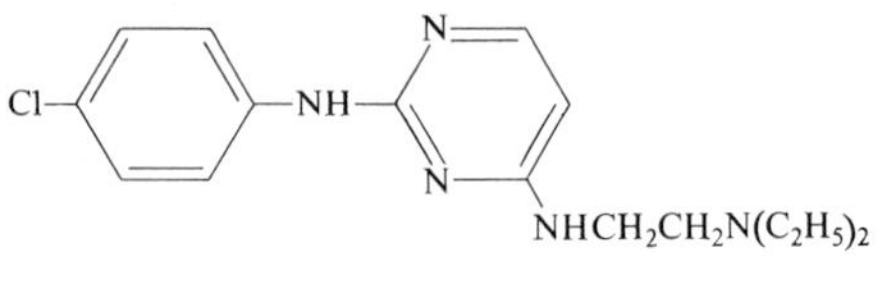

compound 2666

inactive   *active*

Further modification of the structure of compound 2666, guided by a
bioassay of activity against avian malaria, led to the finding that introduc-

[79] F. H. S. CURD, D. G. DAVEY, and F. L. ROSE: Studies on synthetic antimalarial
drugs. II. General chemical considerations. *Ann. Trop. Med. 39*:157 (1945).

tion of a guanidinium group between the benzene ring and the pyrimidine ring increased the potency greatly. Compound 3349 was thus obtained:

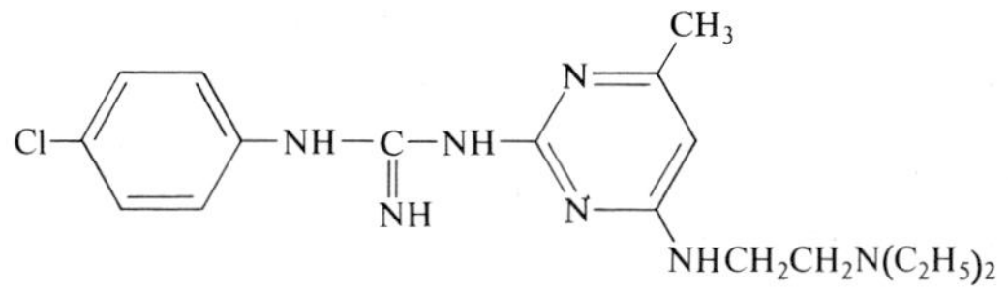

compound 3349
very active

It now appeared that the biologic activity might well arise in a system of conjugated alternating carbon and nitrogen atoms, of which the pyrimidine ring was a part. This proved to be a fruitful lead, for when the pyrimidine ring was opened, high activity was retained, even when the typical antimalarial side chain had been discarded:

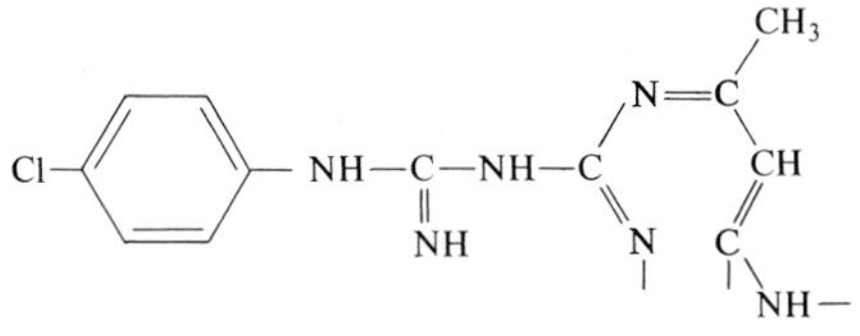

skeleton of compound 3349
(pyrimidine ring opened)

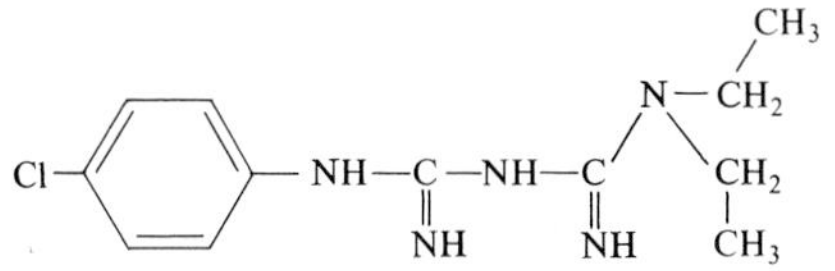

compound 3936

very active

Finally, manipulation of the substituents on the terminal nitrogen atom revealed that the isopropyl group was most active, yielding the highly effective antimalarial chloroguanide.[80] Remarkably, no part of the rationale that guided these syntheses survived intact; chloroguanide is not a sulfonamide, does not contain a pyrimidine ring, and lacks the quinacrine side chain.

[80] F. H. S. CURD, D. G. DAVEY, and F. L. ROSE: Studies on synthetic antimalarial drugs. X.—Some biguanide derivatives as new types of antimalarial substances with both therapeutic and causal prophylactic activity. *Ann. Trop. Med. 39:*208 (1945).

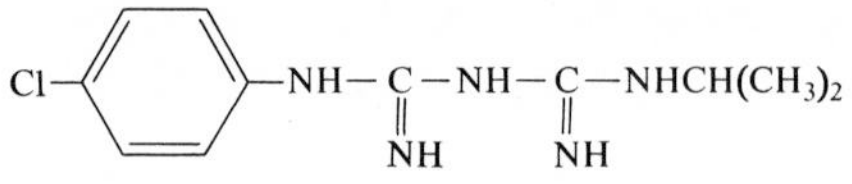

chloroguanide

The subsequent development of the antifolic antimalarial pyrimethamine makes an even more extraordinary story. It was observed in the course of investigations on antagonists of folic acid in *Lactobacillus casei* that 2,4-diaminopyrimidines were highly effective, and it was noted that one of the most potent could be considered, in a formal sense, to be a structural analogue of chloroguanide:[81]

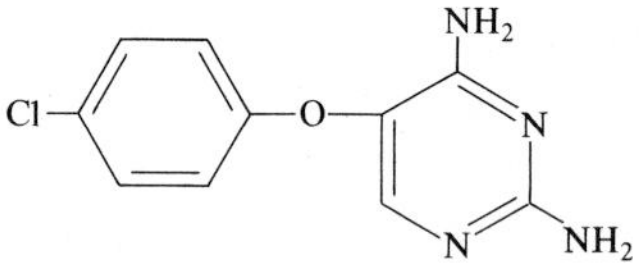

2,4-diamino-5-*p*-chlorophenoxypyrimidine 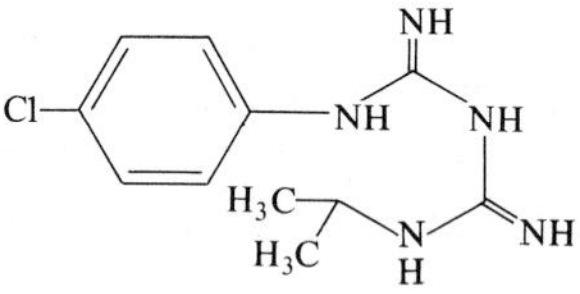   chloroguanide

This relationship led to the testing of the 2,4-diaminopyrimidines for antimalarial activity and of chloroguanide for antifolic activity, both with a positive outcome. Further, it was found that chloroguanide was completely inactive when added to serum in an in vitro test using exoerythrocytic forms of *Plasmodium gallinaceum,* whereas serum taken from an animal that had been treated with the drug was active.[82] Thus, the antimalarial action of chloroguanide must be due to a metabolic product of the drug. The active metabolite was subsequently isolated and identified.[83] It turned out to be a triazine, the very one that had been proposed as a formal analogue of the 2,4-diaminopyrimidines. This active metabolite, interestingly,

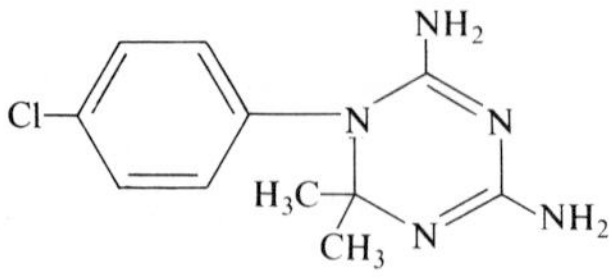

active metabolite of chloroguanide

    [81] E. A. FALCO, G. H. HITCHINGS, P. B. RUSSELL, and H. VANDER WERFF: Antimalarials as antagonists of purines and pteroylglutamic acid. *Nature 164:*107 (1949).

    [82] F. HAWKING and W. L. M. PERRY: Activation of paludrine. *Brit. J. Pharmacol.* 3:320 (1948).

    [83] A. F. CROWTHER and A. A. LEVI: Proguanil—the isolation of a metabolite with high antimalarial activity. *Brit. J. Pharmacol.* 8:93 (1953).

is less useful as an antimalarial than is chloroguanide itself, because it is excreted too rapidly.

Finally, a large number of diaminopyrimidines were tested in avian, mouse, and monkey malaria, and the best of these compounds, pyrimethamine, was introduced into clinical use.[84]

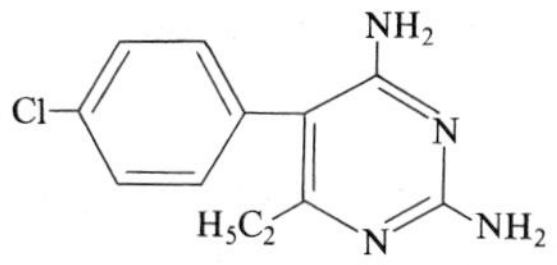

pyrimethamine

It is clear, therefore, that the essential structure for antimalarial activity of the antifolic type is, after all, a pyrimidine ring (or the closely related triazine ring), with amino, alkyl, and aryl substituents. This structure may be regarded as an analogue of the pteridine portion of the folic acid molecule.

EXPLOITATION OF SIDE EFFECTS OF EXISTING DRUGS

The commonest pattern in the development of new drugs is not invention de novo but rather the exploitation of side effects of existing drugs. An action seen as undesirable in one therapeutic context may become the primary drug action in another. Phenylbutazone, for example, was developed as an antirheumatic drug, but it had considerable uricosuric action too. Studies on its metabolism in vivo (p. 228) provided leads for the development of two wholly new drugs, in which these two actions were largely separated. Oxyphenbutazone retains antirheumatic activity with greatly reduced uricosuric effect; sulfinpyrazone is more potent than phenylbutazone in uricosuric action but has no antirheumatic activity.

What is required in this kind of development is awareness of the potential usefulness of a side effect, a bioassay for following potency as chemical structure is modified, and an imaginative and flexible approach to the possibilities of chemical synthesis. This pattern of perfecting new families of drugs is nowhere better illustrated than in the sulfonamide series. These drugs were introduced into medicine as antibacterial agents in 1935. The astute exploitation of their side effects has led to wholly new and useful drugs of three kinds—diuretic, antidiabetic, and antithyroid.

Diuretic Sulfonamides. Carbonic anhydrase inhibitors and thiazide diuretics have their origin in the early days of sulfonamide chemotherapy.

[84] E. A. FALCO, L. G. GOODWIN, G. H. HITCHINGS, I. M. ROLLO, and P. B. RUSSELL: 2:4-Diaminopyrimidines—a new series of antimalarials. *Brit. J. Pharmacol.* 6:185 (1951).

Patients receiving sulfanilamide tended to develop metabolic acidosis with an alkaline urine. Investigation revealed that this side effect was due to inhibition of renal carbonic anhydrase. This enzyme catalyzes the hydration of dissolved carbon dioxide in the kidney cells:

$$CO_2 + H_2O \underset{\text{anhydrase}}{\overset{\text{carbonic}}{\rightleftharpoons}} H_2CO_3 \rightleftharpoons H^+ + HCO_3^-$$

The carbonic acid thus formed dissociates very rapidly to yield hydrogen ions and bicarbonate. The rate at which hydrogen ions are made available for secretion into the lumen of the renal tubules is limited by the rate of hydration of CO_2, a relatively slow process in the absence of the enzyme. Thus, inhibitors of carbonic anhydrase cause a decrease in the rate of acidification of the urine, and this accounts for the alkaline urine and metabolic acidosis. Since K^+ as well as H^+ normally exchanges for Na^+ across the tubular epithelium, potassium excretion tends to increase as proton excretion decreases. Therefore the urine, in the presence of a carbonic anhydrase inhibitor, contains more sodium and potassium ions than usual, together with bicarbonate and chloride anions. The additional salt excretion is accompanied by an osmotic equivalent of water; hence the increased urine volume.

Sulfanilamide itself was too toxic for use as a diuretic, and it was soon displaced from use as an antibacterial agent by safer sulfonamides. These newer derivatives of sulfanilamide all had substituents on the sulfonamide nitrogen atom, as shown below:

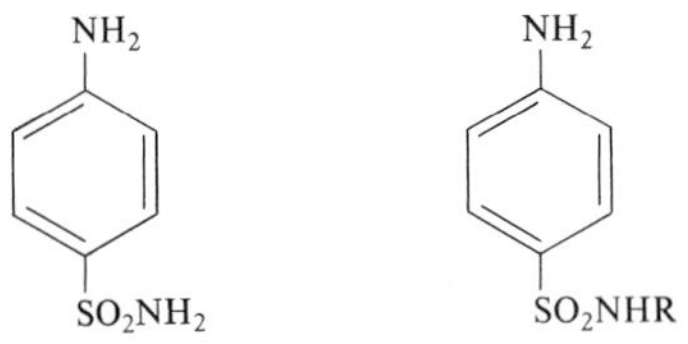

sulfanilamide   substituted sulfonamide

Of all the sulfonamides, only unsubstituted sulfanilamide itself was a carbonic anhydrase inhibitor and diuretic. Thus, a requirement for this action was evidently a free primary amine group in the sulfonamide moiety. Contrasting requirements are found with respect to the amino group *para* to the sulfonamide moiety. Here, free $-NH_2$ is essential for the antibacterial action, but not for the diuretic effect.

Deliberate modification of structure to improve potency with respect to carbonic anhydrase inhibition led to heterocyclic sulfonamides like benzothiazole-2-sulfonamide, hundreds of times more potent than

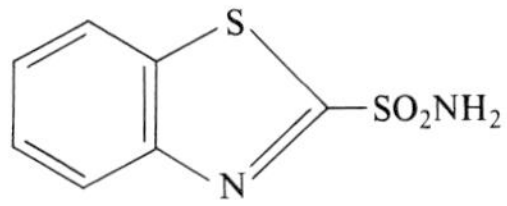

benzothiazole-2-sulfonamide

sulfanilamide when tested against the enzyme in vitro. But this compound had no diuretic action when administered orally to dogs. The inactivity in vivo was probably related to rapid metabolism. An ethoxy derivative proved

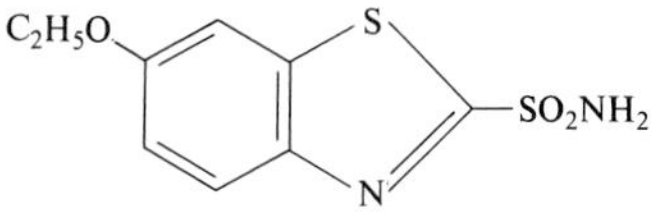

6-ethoxybenzothiazole-2-sulfonamide

effective as a diuretic in animals and man.[85-88] Further study showed that acetylation of the free amino substituent of a thiadiazole compound further enhanced enzyme inhibition. Thus, acetazolamide was selected as the best

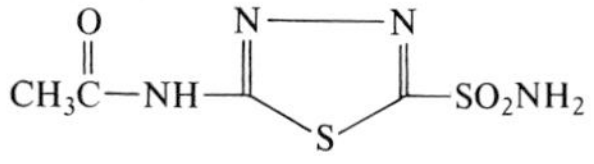

acetazolamide

of the heterocyclic sulfonamides. This drug, 300 times more potent than sulfanilamide as a carbonic anhydrase inhibitor, soon became established as a clinically useful oral diuretic agent.

Acetazolamide, however, was not an ideal diuretic. For one thing, the maximum diuresis possible was limited by the amount of hydrogen ion that would normally be excreted, since only as much sodium could be lost as would ordinarily have exchanged for protons in the tubules—only

[85] J. M. SPRAGUE: "Some results of molecular modifications of diuretics," in *Molecular Modification in Drug Design. Advances in Chemistry,* Series No. 45. Washington, D.C., American Chemical Society, 1964, pp. 87–101.

[86] R. O. ROBLIN, JR., and J. W. CLAPP: The preparation of heterocyclic sulfonamides. *J. Amer. Chem. Soc. 72:*4890 (1950).

[87] W. H. MILLER, A. M. DESSERT, and R. O. ROBLIN, JR.: Heterocyclic sulfonamides as carbonic anhydrase inhibitors. *J. Amer. Chem. Soc. 72:*4893 (1950).

[88] R. V. FORD, C. L. SPURR, and J. H. MOYER: The problem of bioassay and comparative potency of diuretics. II. Carbonic anhydrase inhibitors as oral diuretics. *Circulation 16:*394 (1957).

about 10 to 15 per cent of the total filtered electrolyte. Moreover, the metabolic acidosis can be troublesome, and excessive potassium loss can be dangerous. Thus, the search for better diuretics continued. The next step was to alter the assay procedure, paying less attention to carbonic anhydrase inhibition and more to actual in vivo diuretic activity. Data obtained in dogs with seven compounds related to acetazolamide are shown in Table 13-12, in comparison with acetazolamide itself and with sulfanilamide. The first column shows the chemical structure, the second column gives the concentration required for 50 per cent inhibition of carbonic anhydrase in vitro. The next column gives the intravenous dose administered, and the subsequent columns show the excretion of the principal cations (Na^+ and K^+) and of Cl^-. The bicarbonate ion excretion can be approximated by the difference between total cations and chloride ion and by the pH, according to the Henderson-Hasselbalch equation.

During the course of the studies that led to the development of acetazolamide, the chlorobenzene derivative shown just below it in Table 13-12 was tested. Although it was only half as potent as acetazolamide in inhibiting carbonic anhydrase, it proved to be highly effective in enhancing the excretion of sodium and chloride, and to a lesser extent potassium and bicarbonate. This suggested that compounds of the acetazolamide type might have diuretic properties not attributable to carbonic anhydrase inhibition, and a concerted attempt was made to find such compounds which would selectively promote sodium and chloride excretion. Chemical manipulation of one of the two sulfonamide groups of the chlorobenzene compound led to chlorothiazide. This agent was less than $\frac{1}{20}$ as potent an inhibitor of carbonic anhydrase as acetazolamide (although still ten times more potent than sulfanilamide), but was five to ten times more potent than acetazolamide in promoting the loss of sodium and chloride; yet it was less potent in promoting potassium and bicarbonate loss. Nevertheless, some effect on potassium excretion remained, so efforts were made to develop still better agents.

Omission of the chloride group from chlorothiazide abolished the enhancement of chloride ion excretion. On the other hand, introduction of a trifluoromethane group in place of chlorine at the same position led to a compound, flumethiazide, with full diuretic potency but a pronounced further reduction in carbonic anhydrase inhibition. The reduced analogues hydrochlorothiazide and hydroflumethiazide were more potent than their parent molecules, with even less enzyme inhibitory activity. Finally, benzhydroflumethiazide, an extremely potent diuretic, was essentially devoid of activity as a carbonic anhydrase inhibitor.

The diuretic potency of various thiazides varies over a range of 10,000-fold. But there is a biologic limit to the amount of diuresis that can be achieved. If log dose-response curves are plotted for various thiazide diuretics, it is found that they are essentially parallel, as expected

TABLE 13-12. Development of diuretic agents from sulfanilamide by molecular modifications

Studies were carried out under standard conditions in dogs. Carbonic anhydrase inhibition was determined in vitro with enzyme derived from beef erythrocytes. Doses were given intravenously by infusion at the rates shown; a dose very nearly equivalent to the amount infused per hour was given initially as a priming dose. (From Beyer and Baer,[89] Table 3.)

Compound	50% Inhibition of carbonic anhydrase ($\times 10^6 M$)	Intravenous dose (mg/kg·hr)	\(\mu\)Eq/min excreted Na	K	Cl	pH
Sulfanilamide H_2NSO_2–⬡–NH_2	13	control	14	14	3	6.8
		30	51	25	13	6.9
Acetazolamide H_2NSO_2–C(N–N / S)–C–NH–CCH_3 (O)	0.07	control	43	22	21	6.3
		3.0	186	128	53	8.0
1,3-disulfonamido-6-chlorobenzene H_2NSO_2–⬡(SO_2NH_2)(Cl)	0.14	control	42	24	15	5.9
		3.0	468	101	303	7.4
Chlorothiazide H_2NSO_2–⬡(SO_2–NH–CH=N)(Cl)	1.7	control	11	11	7	6.1
		0.05	20	24	7	6.6
		0.25	115	34	80	6.7
		1.25	308	65	236	6.9
Dechloro-chlorothiazide H_2NSO_2–⬡(SO_2–NH–CH=N)	9.9	control	26	40	3	6.4
		7.5	150	43	18	7.6
Flumethiazide H_2NSO_2–⬡(SO_2–NH–CH=N)(CF_3)	42	control	55	19	6	6.4
		0.05	143	20	62	6.9
		0.25	262	40	197	6.9
		1.25	321	57	241	7.0
Hydrochlorothiazide H_2NSO_2–⬡(SO_2–NH–CH_2–N–H)(Cl)	23	control	62	34	43	6.5
		0.01	126	32	122	5.9
		0.05	265	33	291	5.5
		0.25	414	39	427	5.9
Hydroflumethiazide H_2NSO_2–⬡(SO_2–NH–CH_2–N–H)(CF_3)	170	control	5	8	2	5.6
		0.05	74	43	43	7.1
		0.25	363	66	309	7.0
		1.25	459	77	453	6.7
Benzhydroflumethiazide H_2NSO_2–⬡(SO_2–NH–CH–CH_2–⬡ / N–H)(CF_3)	310	control	25	22	18	5.9
		0.002	94	36	124	5.5
		0.01	321	53	318	5.9
		0.05	493	61	455	6.4

when the mechanism of action of different drugs is the same (cf. p. 79). The maximum diuresis produced by large doses of the weakest member of the group cannot be exceeded at any dose of the most potent member. The important feature of the molecular modifications, therefore, is not the increase in absolute potency achieved. The unimportance of absolute potency is indicated clearly by a comparison of chlorothiazide and hydrochlorothiazide, both of which are promoted for clinical use. Advertisements for the two drugs, made by the same firm, as well as descriptions prepared by experts for the guidance of physicians[90] are identical except with regard to the recommended dosage—250 mg for chlorothiazide, 25 mg for hydrochlorothiazide.

The sole value of molecular modifications in this series has been the significant increase in therapeutic ratio that results from the complete separation of carbonic anhydrase inhibition from the promotion of electrolyte excretion. It is thought that the thiazides somehow specifically interfere with sodium chloride reabsorption in the renal tubules, but their exact mechanism of action is not yet known.

In retrospect, the important turning points in the development of the thiazide diuretics can be recognized. First came the decision to exploit a toxic side action of sulfanilamide. This could not really be done effectively until progress in renal physiology led to better understanding of the mechanism of hydrogen ion excretion. Indeed, the recognition of the diuretic effects of carbonic anhydrase inhibitors helped to disclose the role of this enzyme in normal proton secretion by the renal tubules. Then, dissatisfaction with the limited diuretic capability of carbonic anhydrase inhibitors and the astute observation that, in sulfonamides of the thiazide type, diuretic action seemed not to correlate well with enzyme inhibitory potency led to further fruitful developments.

Antidiabetic Sulfonamides. The antidiabetic sulfonylureas also had their origin in a chance observation. Patients with typhoid fever under treatment with an isopropylthiadiazole derivative of sulfanilamide became weak and dizzy. Investigation revealed varying degrees of hypoglycemia in those who received the drug. Further study showed that the effect could be produced in animals (although larger dosage was required) and that it

$$H_2N-\!\!\left\langle\!\!\!\bigcirc\!\!\!\right\rangle\!\!-SO_2NH-\underset{\|}{C}\underset{S}{\overset{N-\!\!-N}{\diagdown}}\underset{\|}{C}-CH(CH_3)_2$$

sulfanilamidoisopropylthiadiazole

[89] K. H. BEYER and J. E. BAER: Physiological basis for the action of newer diuretic agents. *Pharmacol. Rev. 13:*517 (1961).

[90] Council on Drugs, American Medical Association: "Diuretics," in *New Drugs.* Chicago, American Medical Association, 1965, chapter 31, pp. 279–302.

was mediated by the release of insulin from the pancreatic islets.[91] In other words, this orally effective drug stimulated insulin release. In the absence of functional islets it was ineffective.

The deliberate search for orally effective antidiabetic agents was not undertaken for several years, even though it was recognized that the ineffectiveness of insulin by mouth makes the maintenance therapy of diabetes troublesome. Perhaps it was felt that a drug requiring functional islet tissue for its action would be useless in diabetes. As it has turned out, however, there are mild cases of the disease that are benefitted by drugs of this kind. Systematic screening was eventually conducted,[92] using as assay the reduction in blood sugar level of normal animals, as described earlier (p. 742). These studies led to the conclusion that the hypoglycemic action depended primarily upon the urea-like structure formed by a nitrogen and carbon atom of the thiadiazole ring and the nitrogen atom of the sulfonamide grouping (shown in boldface in the structural formula). Thus, it became clearly evident that the basic structure for this activity was $Ar-SO_2NHCONH-R$, where Ar is aryl and R is an alkyl group. Changes within the urea moiety did not prove advantageous, but modification of the aryl and alkyl groups yielded compounds of greater potency and also greater duration of action. In carbutamide the aryl group is unchanged *p*-aminobenzene, but the R substituent is *n*-butyl instead of isopropyl. Tolbutamide has the same R group as carbutamide but the aryl moiety is *p*-toluene. This compound is oxidized in the body, the methyl group being converted to $-COOH$, and the duration of action is accordingly rather brief. Replacement of methyl by chlorine and *n*-butyl by *n*-propyl yielded

$$Cl-\!\!\!\left\langle\!\!\bigcirc\!\!\right\rangle\!\!\!-SO_2NH\overset{O}{\overset{\|}{C}}NHCH_2CH_2CH_3$$

chlorpropamide

chlorpropamide, most potent of the series, with a long duration of action.[93, 94]

Antithyroid Sulfonamides. The antithyroid drugs of the thiouracil type had their origin in the accidental observation, in 1941, that rats re-

---

[91] A. LOUBATIÈRES: The hypoglycemic sulfonamides: history and development of the problem from 1942 to 1955. *Ann. N. Y. Acad. Sci. 71:*4 (1957).

[92] H. FRANKE and J. FUCHS: Ein neues antidiabetisches Prinzip; Ergebnisse klinischer Untersuchungen. *Deut. Med. Wochensch. 80:*1449 (1955).

[93] W. M. MC LAMORE, G. M. FANELLI, S. Y. P'AN, and G. D. LAUBACH: Hypoglycemic sulfonylureas: effect of structure on activity. *Ann. New York Acad. Sci. 74:*443 (1959).

[94] J. A. SCHNEIDER, E. D. SALGADO, D. JAEGER, and C. DELAHUNT: The pharmacology of chlorpropamide. *Ann. N.Y. Acad. Sci. 74:*427 (1959).

ceiving sulfaguanidine developed goiters.[95] The original purpose of the investigation had been to study the role of intestinal bacteria in the biosynthesis of essential nutrients, and sulfaguanidine was being used to

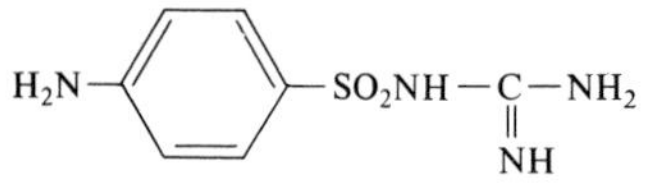

$$H_2N-\!\!\!\!\bigcirc\!\!\!\!-SO_2NH-\underset{\underset{NH}{\|}}{C}-NH_2$$

sulfaguanidine

sterilize the gut. Other investigators observed similar goitrogenic effects in rats given phenylthiocarbamide (PTC) for an entirely different purpose.[96]

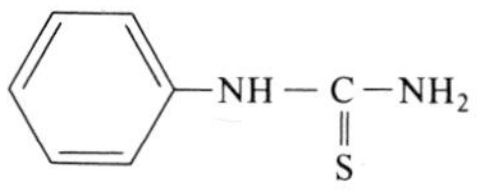

$$\bigcirc\!\!\!\!-NH-\underset{\underset{S}{\|}}{C}-NH_2$$

phenylthiocarbamide (PTC)

The bitter taste of this substance (cf. p. 461) was being exploited in experiments on free-choice diets; hypertrophy and hyperemia of the thyroid gland developed when the drinking water contained quite low concentrations of PTC.

In the systematic screening investigations that followed, it was found that thiourea itself was a potent goitrogen, and that among the sulfonamides sulfadiazine was most active.[97,98] Since sulfadiazine contains

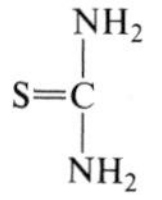

$$S\!=\!\underset{\underset{NH_2}{|}}{\overset{\overset{NH_2}{|}}{C}}$$

$$H_2N-\!\!\!\!\bigcirc\!\!\!\!-SO_2NH-\!\!\!\!\bigcirc\!\!\!\!$$

thiourea 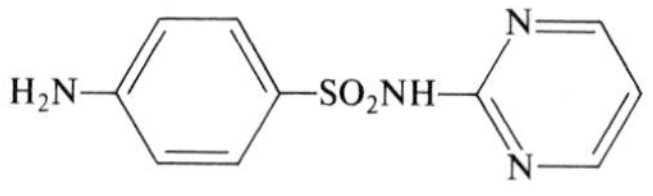   sulfadiazine

a pyrimidine ring, it was logical to incorporate the thiourea moiety in a pyrimidine, and thus thiouracil was obtained. This drug proved satisfactory

[95] J. B. MAC KENZIE, C. G. MAC KENZIE, and E. V. MC COLLUM: The effect of sulfanilylguanidine on the thyroid of the rat. *Science 94:*518 (1941).

[96] C. P. RICHTER and K. H. CLISBY: Toxic effects of the bitter-tasting phenylthiocarbamide. *Arch. Pathol. 33:*46 (1942).

[97] C. G. MAC KENZIE and J. B. MAC KENZIE: Effect of sulfonamides and thioureas on the thyroid gland and basal metabolism. *Endocrinology 32:*185 (1943).

[98] E. B. ASTWOOD, J. SULLIVAN, A. BISSELL, and R. TYSLOWITZ: Action of certain sulfonamides and of thiourea upon the function of the thyroid gland of the rat. *Endocrinology 32:*210 (1943).

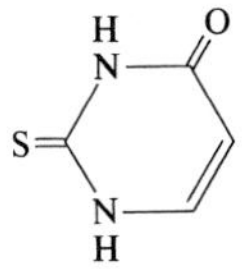

thiouracil

for clinical use in the treatment of hyperthyroidism.[99] The mechanism of action of this family of drugs is to produce a blockade of thyroid hormone synthesis. The resulting goiter was due to overstimulation of the gland by pituitary thyroid-stimulating hormone in response to low circulating levels of thyroid hormone.

Thiouracil produced toxic reactions, particularly agranulocytosis, at a rather high frequency; in one study, the incidence was 13 per cent in a population of 2,490 treated patients. Modifications of the thiouracil structure were studied in an attempt to find a safer compound with the same antithyroid action.[100] Two superior drugs emerged. Propylthiouracil

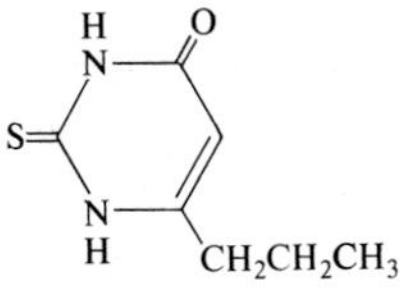

propylthiouracil 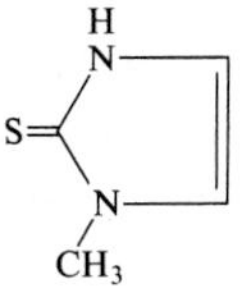   methimazole

in effective clinical dosage caused toxic reactions in only 3 per cent of a large group of patients. Methimazole, in which the pyrimidine ring has been modified more drastically, also has a very low toxicity.

99 E. B. ASTWOOD: Treatment of hyperthyroidism with thiourea and thiouracil. *J. Amer. Med. Ass. 122:*78 (1943).

100 W. P. VANDERLAAN and V. M. STORRIE: A survey of the factors controlling thyroid function, with especial reference to newer views on antithyroid substances. *Pharmacol. Rev. 7:*301 (1955).

14

THE SELECTION OF DRUGS

FOR CLINICAL USE

STEPS LEADING TO THE CLINICAL TRIAL

After a new drug has been developed, the next step is its subjection to a battery of tests in laboratory animals. Current requirements in most countries place upon the manufacturer the responsibility of submitting proof of efficacy and safety in exhaustive animal tests in order to obtain permission to conduct clinical trials with the drug. The procedure in the United States is illustrative of the kinds of controls that are essential if the public health and welfare is to be protected. The governmental regulatory agency concerned is the Food and Drug Administration (FDA) (cf. p. 820). An application to conduct clinical trials must include the chemical formula of the drug, the steps followed in its synthesis or purification, and the methods employed for quality control during production and for bio-assay and standardization of potency. The form of administration (tablet, capsule, solution, etc.) and the route of administration must be specified, as well as the proposed dosage. Information has to be furnished about the general pharmacology of the drug, its absorption, distribution, metabolism, and excretion. Dose-effect relationships must have been explored. Toxi-cologic investigations in a variety of species must have been carried out, both by acute and chronic administration; and details have to be furnished about the numbers of animals used for the various tests. Certain tests have to be carried out to rule out the possibility of teratogenic actions if the drug is to be used in women of child-bearing age. Finally, the rationale of the proposed clinical use has to be explained, supported by animal experiments giving evidence of efficacy in relation to that use.[1]

The obvious purpose of the foregoing requirements is to ensure that it is reasonably safe to start investigations in human subjects. The

---

[1] C. G. ZUBROD: General problems in the selection of drugs for clinical trial. (Part I, Symposium on Clinical Drug Evaluation and Human Pharmacology). *Clin. Pharmacol. Therap. 3:*239 (1962).

actual kinds of pharmacologic and toxicologic studies in animals will be determined in large measure by the properties of the particular drug. Typical procedures have been described throughout the earlier chapters of this book, especially in chapters 3 and 5 with respect to drug metabolism and toxicity, respectively. As pointed out several times previously, animal studies, no matter how exhaustive, do not necessarily predict the outcome of administering a new drug to humans.[2,3] Qualitative and quantitative species differences in absorption, distribution, and metabolism, as well as in intrinsic responsiveness to certain drug actions create an element of uncertainty that could only be circumvented if man himself were the test animal. It has been proposed, for this reason, that after the basic animal studies are completed, it might be efficient to carry out an exploratory trial in a single patient prior to embarking on a large-scale clinical trial.[4] The proper dose for this patient could be found by gradual incrementation, and elementary information could be obtained about blood levels and about the dose-response relationship. The risk would be limited to one patient, and it would be economical to provide 24-hour observation of this single individual in order to reduce the risk still further.

Finally, the proposed protocols for clinical trial of the new drug must be submitted for approval. There has been a growing awareness on the part of medical scientists that definitive appraisal of the efficacy and safety of drugs requires an expertise and clinical facilities that most physicians do not have at their disposal. Modern biostatistical procedures for clinical trials are not, as a rule, feasible in the ordinary practice of medicine. Furthermore, clinical trials often require a larger number of patients with a particular disease than would be encountered by a practitioner in a reasonable period of time. For these reasons clinical trials of new drugs are required to be conducted by specially qualified investigators, whose training and experience must be documented. Assurance must also be provided that informed consent will be obtained from every subject who is to participate in the trial (cf. p. 815).

When FDA approval has been obtained, the manufacturer may ship the new drug, "for investigational use only," to the investigators who are to conduct the trials. At periodic intervals, a progress report has to be furnished to the FDA, including notification of any adverse effects that have occurred. If any doubt develops during the trials about the safety of the new drug, the manufacturer is obliged to notify the FDA and to discontinue the clinical evaluation. The FDA itself may order the investigation stopped at any time if evidence develops that the drug is unsafe.

2 S. IRWIN: Drug screening and evaluative procedures. *Science 136:*123 (1962).

3 G. ZBINDEN: The problem of the toxicologic examination of drugs in animals and their safety in man. *Clin. Pharmacol. Therap. 5:*537 (1964).

4 C. C. PFEIFFER: Exploratory trials of new drugs in man. (Part XI, Symposium on Clinical Drug Evaluation and Human Pharmacology). *Clin. Pharmacol. Therap. 3:*397 (1962).

DRUG EVALUATION IN MAN: THE CLINICAL TRIAL

The systematic procedure for the evaluation of drugs in groups of people is known as the *clinical trial*.[5-8a] One might wonder why special techniques should be required at all. Certainly many drugs (e.g., opium for pain, quinine for malaria) earned an established place in therapy long before the days of modern experimental science. But experience has shown that "clinical impressions" can be misleading. Many a therapeutic regimen has ultimately been proved useless despite traditional and unquestioning employment. Especially when a drug's alleged effect is less than dramatic one cannot accept without decisive proof that there has been any therapeutic effect at all. Ascorbic acid, flavinoids, other vitamins, antihistamines, and antibiotics, for example, have at one time or another enjoyed wide popularity for preventing or aborting the common cold, but no properly designed experiments have ever borne out their reputation.

Rigorous methods of drug evaluation in man were slow to be accepted, even after controlled animal experimentation had been on a firm basis for many decades. In part this reluctance reflected a feeling of helplessness in the face of the vast number of variables encountered in studies with human beings. Each person, it was argued, is unique; the expression of disease processes is so individualized that no valid comparisons are possible, objective criteria fail, and only "clinical judgment" will suffice. But, on the contrary, it is precisely because of the variability between people that sound experimental design, unbiased observation, and valid statistical analysis of data are indispensable.[9]

Placebo Controls and Concurrent Comparisons

Except in an unconscious patient, every drug administration consists of more than the mere introduction of a particular chemical substance into the body. The act of prescribing or actually administering a drug is an integral part of the total relationship between physician and patient. The physician wishes the drug to produce a certain effect and expects it to do so, or he would not have given it. The patient wishes desperately for the drug to be effective, and if he has confidence in the physician he shares

[5] L. J. WITTS, ed.: *Medical Surveys and Clinical Trials*, 2nd ed. London, Oxford University Press, 1964.

[6] M. C. SHEPS: The clinical value of drugs: Sources of evidence. *Amer. J. Public Health 51*:647 (1961).

[7] Seminar on the clinical evaluation of drugs, in *Clin. Pharmacol. Therap. 4*:255–260, 371–392, 531–547 (1963).

[8] A. B. HILL: *Statistical Methods in Clinical and Preventive Medicine*. New York, Oxford University Press, 1962.

[8a] A. GOLDSTEIN: *Biostatistics: An Introductory Text*. New York, Macmillan, 1964.

[9] J. WORCESTER: The statistical method. *New Engl. J. Med. 274*:27 (1966).

the latter's expectations. Thus, drug administration often occurs in a situation characterized by biased expectations and enhanced suggestibility on both sides.

Health and disease are greatly influenced by psychic and emotional factors. Symptoms and disease complexes of psychosomatic origin are just as "real" as those arising from simple organic causes. In the same way, psychic responses to drugs and psychic modifications of drug actions are real phenomena to be reckoned with. All those reactions to drug administration that arise from the very act of taking the drug and that are unrelated to the pharmacologic actions of the drug are known as *placebo effects*. An inert substance masquerading as a drug is called a *placebo*. The Latin word means "I shall please"; it referred originally to medications given merely to placate the patient when no specific remedy was available. All drugs may produce placebo effects. This complicates the interpretation of drug responses in man and necessitates special controls to enable one to distinguish between pharmacologic and placebo effects of drugs.[10]

If the physician is aware, for example, that certain toxic manifestations may occur and warns the patient, or if the patient himself has heard (rightly or wrongly) about untoward reactions, the patient may then anticipate effects other than the desired beneficial ones. This is illustrated in a study of the side effects produced by the oral contraceptive agents.[11] During the early field trials among Puerto Rican women, many annoying symptoms were reported, such as headache, nausea, dizziness, and abdominal pain. The investigators thought it possible that some of these might be due to fear of the novel and untried contraceptive pill. A group of women using conventional methods of birth control was selected from the same native population, and divided into two subgroups. One received placebo pills, the other received contraceptive pills. All the women were advised to continue the same contraceptive practices they had been using hitherto, and they were admonished to note any adverse effects. It was put to them that the pills had to be tried out to see if they were suitable for continued use. Another group of women, in a different town, were simply given the contraceptive pills without any admonition. Table 14-1 gives the results. Clearly, most of the side effects noted were due to the admonition and not to the drug. Consistent with this result, other studies showed that the incidence of side effects declined to a very low level with continued use of the drug in large groups of women.

Placebos are still occasionally prescribed as medication, quite apart from their use as controls in human experimentation. A physician may employ a placebo diagnostically, to assess the psychic component of a patient's symptom complex, which may be amenable to relief by suggestion. When a placebo is used therapeutically, the physician has usually decided

---

10 S. WOLF: The pharmacology of placebos. *Pharmacol. Rev. 11:*689 (1959).
11 G. PINCUS: Control of conception by hormonal steroids. *Science 153:*493 (1966).

TABLE 14-1.   Placebo side effects in the trial of an oral contraceptive

Reactions included complaints of physical ill-being such as nausea, vomiting, headache, vertigo, gastrointestinal distress, and malaise. Data are per cent of cycles in which reactions were reported. Meaning of "admonition" is described in text. (From Pincus,[11] Table 20. By permission of the American Association for the Advancement of Science.)

Group	No. of patients	No. of cycles	Reactions (%)
No admonition, drug	15	48	6.3
Admonition, drug	13	30	23.3
Admonition, placebo	15	41	17.1

to his own satisfaction that no better course of treatment is indicated and that some benefit may result from the placebo effect. With improvements in diagnosis and with greater understanding of the need for psychiatric treatment of anxiety and other emotional states, this frank use of placebos in medicine is rightly falling into disfavor. Placebo medication carries with it the danger that thorough diagnosis and more appropriate treatment may be neglected. And sometimes placating the patient with lactose capsules may be too easy a way to temporize in a difficult situation.

Some investigations have suggested that approximately 30 per cent of all people are suggestible and tend to give positive responses of various sorts to placebos. These so-called placebo reactors, if they could be identified in advance of an experiment, could be excluded from it. Other studies have shown, however, that the frequency of placebo responses differs widely from experiment to experiment, that the same individuals may react more or less readily to a placebo at different times, and that circumstances can be found in which nearly all people respond to placebos. It is impractical, therefore, to identify and exclude placebo reactors.[12] The only alternative, if we are to gain meaningful information about drug actions, is to take account of placebo responses within each experiment, to whatever extent possible. The problem is really one of establishing a control group that is identical to the experimental group in all respects except for the one variable (i.e., the drug) that is under study. Even in animal experimentation we follow the same principle. Animals subjected to a surgical procedure are compared with sham-operated controls. Animals injected with a drug are compared with others injected with the drug-free vehicle (e.g., saline solution). Thus, if we wish to test a drug in humans in the simplest kind of

---

[12] G. HONIGFELD: Non-specific factors in treatment. I. Review of placebo reactions and placebo reactors. *Dis. Nerv. System* 25:145 (1964).

design, we would compare drug administration with placebo administration, all other conditions being identical in the two groups.

Placebo controls are not always necessary or desirable. If a useful drug is already available and the question is whether or not a new drug is superior, a placebo control would be inappropriate. Moreover, there would be no justification for withholding an effective drug from some patients merely for the sake of scientific curiosity. The appropriate clinical trial in such a case would be a comparison between the old drug and the new.

A large part of the variability in biologic experimentation arises from individual differences between subjects. This part of the total variability can be minimized by arranging matters so that each subject acts as his own control. A comparison between drug and placebo (or between two drugs) might be carried out as follows: All subjects receive placebo, and on a different occasion they all receive the drug. Then instead of comparing all drug responses with all placebo responses, each subject's response to the two treatments is noted on an individual basis. A group of differences is thus generated between drug and placebo responses for individual subjects, and such data can be tested for significance by standard statistical methods.[8,8a] This crude design has a serious flaw, however. There is no way to tell how much of the observed difference between drug and placebo might have been due to differences in conditions on the occasions of the respective drug and placebo administrations. Moreover, it is possible that the prior administration of a placebo might in itself modify the subsequent response to a drug.

The design usually adopted to circumvent this difficulty is called a *crossover*. The subjects are divided randomly into two groups, one to receive the placebo first, and drug later, the other to receive placebo and drug in reversed order. Crossover is an elementary example of the more general principle of balancing experimental designs so that all variables (drugs, order of administration, dosage, route of administration, etc.) appear systematically in all possible configurations. This is often accomplished by means of a Latin square, as shown in Table 14-2.[13] Here, a drug is being tested at three dose levels, designated *a, b,* and *c;* and a placebo is also being employed. Four days are allotted for the experiment, and the subjects are assigned randomly to four groups, as shown. The Latin square provides a framework for ensuring a proper balance. Each dose and the placebo are tested on every day; each group receives every treatment; *a* precedes *b* half the time and follows *b* half the time; and so on. The data obtained in a balanced design of this kind are readily subjected to an analysis of variance, to determine which effects differ significantly from one another.

13 R. A. FISHER and F. YATES: *Statistical Tables for Biological, Agricultural and Medical Research.* 6th ed. London, Oliver and Boyd, 1963.

TABLE 14-2.   A Latin-square design

The conduct of the experiment is prescribed by the Latin square. This is one of many possible 4×4 Latin squares. Here, *a, b,* and *c* represent different dosages of a drug under test. Subjects are assigned randomly to the four groups.

	Day 1	Day 2	Day 3	Day 4
Group 1	a	b	c	placebo
Group 2	b	a	placebo	c
Group 3	c	placebo	b	a
Group 4	placebo	c	a	b

Implicit in the concept of balanced experimental design is the principle that the various treatments must be compared at the same time. It is only rarely possible to evaluate a new drug or other treatment properly in comparison with previous experience. The severity of the illness being treated may have been different in the past, as with virus infections due to different strains. The populations compared may be quite different in ways not apparent to the investigator; without purposeful matching and randomization there can never be assurance of equivalence. Ancillary treatments change with time, hospital and nursing care improve, medical and surgical techniques are perfected, accessory new drugs come into use, general progress occurs in sanitation and in living standards.

It is true, of course, that if a previously fatal disease is cured by a new drug, the event is so markedly different from all past experience that it may usually be accepted without elaborate controls. This was the case when subacute bacterial endocarditis was first cured by massive penicillin infusions. Table 14-3 presents a summary of results in a large number of patients with miliary tuberculosis or tuberculous meningitis, conditions that were uniformly fatal prior to the introduction of streptomycin into therapy in 1946. There is no question about the efficacy of chemotherapy in these conditions. The data also show better results when streptomycin was supplemented with *p*-aminosalicylate than when it was used alone, and still better results when isoniazid was added.

Usually, treatment effects are less dramatic than the reduction of mortality from 100 per cent to 5 per cent shown in Table 14-3. The question then arises whether the improved outcome would have occurred even without the drug. The introduction of penicillin for the treatment of syphilis, for example, appeared to change the incidence of that disease considerably; but the use of the drug was accompanied by mass education and public health measures that would have contributed to the control of venereal diseases even if penicillin had not been introduced. As a rule, clinical trials are meaningless unless they embody concurrent comparisons.

TABLE 14-3. Effect of chemotherapy on mortality from miliary and miliary-meningeal tuberculosis

Patients were male adults treated in Veterans Administration hospitals between 1946 and 1959, and followed for five to ten years. (From Falk,[14] Tables 3 and 8.)

Drug treatment	Type of tuberculosis	No. of patients	Mortality (%)
None (retrospective; patients before 1946)	miliary	—	100
	miliary-meningeal	—	100
Streptomycin only	miliary	63	47
	miliary-meningeal	114	94
Streptomycin + PAS*	miliary	102	18
	miliary-meningeal	51	78
Streptomycin, PAS, and isoniazid	miliary	188	5
	miliary-meningeal	52	23

* *p*-aminosalicylate

Randomization

A very important aspect of the design of a clinical trial is the method used to assign subjects to experimental groups. It is essential that at the outset of the experiment the various groups be as nearly equivalent as possible in every way. It might be supposed that any essentially haphazard procedure would work, provided subjects were not selected deliberately for one group or another on the basis of their disease state or likely response to drug treatment. But experience has shown that haphazard methods are very unreliable. The investigator may unconsciously allocate the more seriously ill patients to the treatment he believes will be most beneficial. It is well known in animal experimentation that inadvertent selection can bias the experimental outcomes. If a large group of mice, for example, is to be divided into two groups, one to receive a drug, the other to serve as control, then merely removing one-half the mice to another cage will not suffice. Heavier, more sluggish, and more docile mice are easier to catch, and therefore the two groups will not be equivalent. Since we cannot really know what complex physiologic differences may be associated with ease of capture in this situation, it must be concluded that no valid experiments whatsoever could be performed with groups of mice selected in this way.

The literature on human experimentation offers numerous examples of inadvertent selection. All patients on one hospital ward, for

---

[14] A. FALK: U.S. Veterans Administration–Armed Forces Cooperative Study on the chemotherapy of tuberculosis. XII. Results of treatment in miliary tuberculosis: a follow-up study of 570 adult patients. *Amer. Rev. Resp. Dis. 91*:6 (1965).

example, may be given one drug, all patients on a different ward receive another drug or a placebo. But what were the circumstances that led to a particular patient being placed on one ward or the other, and might these circumstances have selected inadvertently for qualities that will affect the response to the drugs? In an investigation of the efficacy of drugs that prevent blood clotting in the treatment of coronary thrombosis, drugs or placebos were assigned according to the day of admission to hospital. After the experiment was well under way, it was discovered that the purpose of the investigation and the method of assigning medications had become known to the physicians in the community. If a physician believed that treatment with the untried drug would be beneficial, he would arrange, if possible, to have his patients admitted on the appropriate day for admission to the drug group; in this way the equivalence of the groups was destroyed and conclusions about the merit of the drug were invalidated.[5] Even assigning patients to groups on an alphabetic basis according to surnames may be hazardous, since names often connote ethnic, national, religious and other characteristics possibly related to the variables under study.

For all these reasons it is the invariable rule to assign medications *randomly.* A random design is not the same as a haphazard one; randomness must often be planned very carefully. The criterion of random assignment to groups is that no characteristic of a subject whatsoever shall play any part in determining to what group he is assigned. The simplest way of accomplishing this is by the use of chance devices: coin tossing for two groups, die throwing for up to six groups, drawing lots, and so on. The most versatile chance device is the table of random numbers,[13] illustrated in Table 14-4. Such a table consists of a sequence of digits generated by

TABLE 14-4.   Random digits

A selection of 400 random digits from a very large sequence. (Extracted from the table published by The Rand Corporation,[15] p. 89.)

95523	16893	48247	03407	31665	66917	98339	69569
62477	35693	90285	00994	74594	90414	80392	86873
57327	96854	12771	31236	89768	32495	67307	16957
41636	48701	55198	93603	58155	89862	55728	80036
69743	71852	38521	70835	21981	20370	40829	38049
27583	54945	40301	09374	64651	87504	46483	54700
43193	77444	60036	96246	56872	23543	71399	46681
74121	08564	82161	68832	23596	93906	44956	42941
32155	01757	32402	01704	13312	93761	79236	70219
24415	95858	89258	11388	42821	07595	90003	02631

[15] THE RAND CORPORATION: *A Million Random Digits with 100,000 Normal Deviates.* Glencoe, Ill., The Free Press, 1955.

some procedure that ensures equal probability for any digit to appear at any point in the sequence. The sequence is tested exhaustively by statistical procedures, to make sure there was no malfunction of the device (e.g., a computer) that generated the sequence. The table is used as follows: If there is a known number of subjects to be assigned to a certain number of experimental groups, every subject is given a serial number. Then the table is entered at an arbitrary point and the first group is filled by taking numbers in sequence. Let us assume there are 60 subjects to be allocated equally to four groups. The subjects will be numbered serially from 01 to 60. Now, to fill the first group we enter Table 14-4 at upper left and read out two-digit numbers. Numbers greater than 60 are ignored, as are numbers already assigned. The first number, 95, we ignore. Subject 52 is the first subject assigned to the first group. Following the same procedure, the first group also receives subjects 31, 48, 24, and so on, until 15 assignments have been made. Then the second and third groups are filled in the same way. The remaining 15 subjects are placed in the fourth group. No characteristic of any subject will have played any part in his assignment to a group.

Often, in a clinical trial, the patients cannot be identified at the outset. A drug is going to be tested, perhaps, on patients who will be reporting to a clinic over a period of months. The procedure for making group assignments is exactly as described, by table of random numbers, except that the serial numbers picked from the table refer to the sequence in which patients will present themselves at the clinic. Using the same example as above, the assignment of 60 patients to four treatment groups, the procedure would be as follows. First, the sequence numbers 1 to 60 are listed; these represent patients, in the order in which they will be admitted to the study. These patients are assigned to the four treatment groups, a priori, by drawing numbers from the table of random numbers. Thus the 52nd, 31st, 48th, 24th patient, and so on, would be assigned to the first treatment group. After 15 such assignments had been made, filling that group, the second and third treatment groups would be filled in the same way. The remaining 15 unassigned sequence numbers would form the fourth treatment group. In this way all members of the sequence would be preassigned, before they present themselves, in a randomized manner and by a procedure that establishes groups of equal size. Then when each patient actually enters the clinic, assigning him to a treatment group simply means referring to the prepared list of assignments.

Blind Designs

If at all possible, the subjects should be unaware of what medication they are receiving. The importance of this requirement depends somewhat upon the magnitude of the drug effect. If a drug were developed that cured leukemia, a disease now uniformly fatal, it would probably not influence the outcome of the test if treated patients knew they were receiving that drug. But usually, because of the influence of expectations upon an experimental outcome, such knowledge by the subjects would throw most of the conclusions into doubt. Especially if one wishes to assess the frequency or severity of side effects is it important that the nature of the treatment be concealed from the patients. Obviously, all medications (including placebo) must be identical in appearance and should, if possible, be administered on the same schedule. Such a design, in which the subjects are unaware of the nature of the medications, is called *blind*.

It may not be easy or practical to maintain blind conditions. The drug may produce unmistakable side effects that are not produced by a placebo. Antihistaminics, for example, produce drowsiness, whereas placebos presumably do not. Any subject receiving an antihistaminic and becoming drowsy may conclude that he has been given a potent drug, and this knowledge may well influence his expectations about whatever other pharmacologic action is under test. If the medication is being administered by mouth, the drug may have a characteristic taste; in this case one may try to match the taste by adding appropriate inert materials to the placebo. Even when the material is contained in a capsule there may be an aftertaste that identifies the drug to the subject.

It is equally important, but not so obvious, that the investigators who deal with the subjects in the course of the experiment, and who evaluate the results, must be unaware of which medications have been assigned to which subjects. The personnel who actually administer the medications often cannot deceive the subjects; if they know what drug is being administered or that a placebo is being given, their behavior will betray their knowledge in numerous ways. And when the results of an experiment are being evaluated, subjective bias comes strongly into play if the assignment of medications is known. This is true not only for evaluations in which the criteria are subjective (e.g., assessment of improvement in schizophrenic patients),[16] but even for objective criteria such as size of lesions on an x-ray plate or the sedimentation rate of erythrocytes. No procedure is immune to distortion by an observer's bias. Blood cells can be counted inaccurately, spectrophotometers can be misread, pathologic changes in a tissue specimen can be detected or overlooked, roentgenographic anomalies can be exaggerated or discounted, psychotic patients can be adjudged more tractable or more hostile. The only sure way to eliminate bias of this kind is to arrange matters so that not only the subjects but also the investigators directly involved in the experimental procedures and evaluations remain unaware of the allocation of drugs or placebos from the beginning to the end of the experiment. Such a design is called *double blind*.

---

[16] L. E. HOLLISTER and J. E. OVERALL: Methodology for the clinical investigation of psychotherapeutic drugs. *J. New Drugs* 5:286 (1965).

In practice, the conduct of a double-blind clinical trial is not as difficult as might be imagined. Once the decision has been made how the random assignments of subjects to groups is to be carried out, the medications are coded by serial number (see below), and the code is locked away securely. Safeguards are provided so that in case of adverse reaction, or for any reason involving the welfare of a patient, the code can be broken for that patient, who is then removed from the study. In the pioneering clinical trials organized by the British Medical Research Council, for example, the coding of the medications for assignment to patients all over the United Kingdom was done by a person who was to have no personal contact with the subjects. The code was retained in a safe in London, and only after all the final evaluations had been completed was the code consulted to identify each subject's medication.[17]

The labeling of medications must convey no information about their nature. Some early trials were conducted in the following simple way: On a hospital ward, capsules of drug were kept in a jar labeled *A* and capsules of placebo, identical in appearance to the drug capsules, were kept in a jar labeled *B*. No one could decide from these letters which was the drug, but enough information was conveyed, nevertheless, to invalidate the results. Because of the two jars, both the medical personnel and the patients deduced that two different medications were being compared. More serious, the conditions were present for a spread of subjective bias across the whole experiment. A few subjects, experiencing real or fancied effects of either medication, would spread the word to other patients; whereupon biased expectations concerning *A* or *B* would soon develop throughout the subject groups. The medical personnel, likewise, observing some apparent effect of one or the other drug, would soon generalize this effect unconsciously to all *A* or to all *B* patients. Therefore, the only admissible procedure is to label every subject's medications individually by a serial number or by subject's name. If serial numbers are used, care must be taken to avoid assigning any distinctive pattern of numbers to particular medications, such as odd numbers for drug and even numbers for placebo.

Two Trials with Antihistamines: An Illustrative Contrast

Two studies on the effects of antihistamine drugs on the course of the common cold, conducted within two years of each other, present an interesting contrast between a poorly designed and a well-designed clinical trial. In the first investigation,[18] a total of 572 patients were treated between October 1, 1947 and May 1, 1948 in dispensaries at military bases.

---

17 MEDICAL RESEARCH COUNCIL: The prevention of whooping-cough by vaccination. *Brit. Med. J. 1*:1463 (1951).

18 J. M. BREWSTER: Antihistaminic drugs in the therapy of the common cold. *Ind. Med. 18*:217 (1949).

The subjects were those who reported that they had colds, provided that the examining physicians found "no evidence to disprove it." The group included military personnel, their dependents, and civilian employees. Therapy was started at any stage of the illness. Five different antihistamines and a placebo were used. "An effort was made to give various drugs to patients in succession and without selection," but apparently no rigorous randomization procedures were followed. Thus there was no assurance that the treatment groups would be matched with respect to age, sex, time of onset of illness, or severity of symptoms. Amphetamine was "frequently given" with the first dose of an antihistamine to counteract the sedative effects. Double-blind procedures do not appear to have been followed. "Cure" was defined as eradication of symptoms within 24 hours and absence of symptoms during the subsequent 48 hours. Of 319 patients with no history of allergy, 262 were treated with antihistamines, and 105 of these were cured. Of 57 such patients given placebo medication, only five were cured. From a statistical standpoint this difference is highly significant. Remarkably, 19 of 21 patients treated with an antihistamine drug within 1 hour of onset of their colds were cured. Unfortunately, only two patients in the placebo group were treated as early as this, as a result of the failure to randomize or to match groups with respect to duration of symptoms. If one wonders about the criteria for diagnosis that permit treatment to be instituted "within 1 hour of onset," the principal investigator comments: "When one has been unusually susceptible to colds all his life as the writer has been, and then lives an entire year without a cold as he has done by the simple expedient of taking one or two doses of an antihistaminic drug at the first hint of a cold, the problem of diagnosis becomes academic."

Poorly designed studies of this kind, conducted by investigators who were strongly biased toward a certain outcome and took no precautions to eliminate that bias, led to the widespread promotion and sale of antihistamine drugs for the treatment of the common cold. Despite recognition by experts that the evidence was unsatisfactory,[19] it was only with the carrying out of proper trials that justifiable action could be taken to protect the public against false claims of efficacy of these drugs.

A large-scale, well-designed trial of the usefulness of one antihistamine drug, thonzylamine, was carried out in Great Britain and Northern Ireland in the winter and spring of 1950, under the direction of the Medical Research Council.[20] Subjects over 15 years of age who met the following criteria were admitted to the trial: "A catarrhal inflammation of the upper respiratory passages usually without pyrexia but with watery or mucous

[19] COUNCIL ON PHARMACY AND CHEMISTRY: Status report on antihistaminic agents in the prophylaxis and treatment of the common "cold." *J. Amer. Med. Ass.* 142:566 (1950).
[20] MEDICAL RESEARCH COUNCIL: Clinical trials of antihistaminic drugs in the prevention and treatment of the common cold. *Brit. Med. J.* 2:425 (1950).

discharge from the nose and associated with sneezing, fullness in the head and nose, and sometimes with cough, headache, sore throat, hoarseness and running eyes." People who had recently taken antihistamines or who had evidence of other infectious disease were excluded.

Subjects were assigned randomly to drug or placebo groups. The nature of the tablets given to each patient was not known to the patient or to the dispensing physician. Each box of tablets for each subject was marked with a serial number. Subjects in the drug group received three tablets daily of the antihistamine, 50 mg each, for three days. Subjects in the placebo group received three similar tablets daily of an inert substance containing an insignificant amount (5 mg) of quinine sulfate. Immediate swallowing of the medication was encouraged so that taste would not help identify the drug. A standard form was provided upon which the medical officer was to record pertinent data upon admission of each subject to the trial and during the progress of the trial.

A total of 775 subjects received the antihistamine and an equal number received the placebo medication. The final analysis omitted 394 records (196 from the drug group, 198 from the placebo group) because they were incomplete. The results therefore concern 579 subjects who had received the drug and 577 who had received the placebo. The effectiveness of the randomization procedure may be judged by the data of Table 14-5, which shows the frequency of presenting symptoms at the

TABLE 14-5.   **Frequency of presenting symptoms at first visit**

These symptoms were recorded by the medical examiners at subject's entry into the study, *before* he was assigned randomly to drug or placebo group. (From Medical Research Council,[20] Table IV. By permission of the British Medical Journal.)

Symptoms	Persons given anti-histaminic treatment		Persons given placebo treatment	
	No.	%	No.	%
Watery nasal discharge	359	62.0	337	58.4
Mucoid nasal discharge	114	19.7	118	20.5
Purulent nasal discharge	49	8.5	42	7.3
Blocked nose	321	55.4	307	53.2
Fullness in the head	385	66.5	390	67.6
Sneezing	413	71.3	408	70.7
Sore throat	217	37.5	231	40.0
Hoarseness	183	31.6	177	30.7
Cough	242	41.8	226	39.2
Headache	196	33.9	207	35.9
Feeling ill	44	7.6	46	8.0

TABLE 14-6. Percentages of subjects cured or improved by treatment

"Cured" and "improved" are defined in text. Numbers of patients are given in parentheses under each category. Figures are percentages. Differences are given with standard errors. D = Antihistaminic drug; P = placebo. (From Medical Research Council,[20] Table V. By permission of the British Medical Journal.)

		Duration of cold before treatment										
		Under 1 day			1 Day			2 Days			3 Days or more		
Day of observation		D (201)	P (173)	Difference	D (180)	P (213)	Difference	D (96)	P (84)	Difference	D (102)	P (107)	Difference
First day	improved*	47.8	45.1	2.7±5.2	47.2	38.5	8.7±5.0	50.0	40.5	9.5±7.4	48.0	45.8	2.2±6.9
Second day	cured	13.4	13.9	−0.5±3.6	7.8	6.6	1.2±2.6	3.1	4.8	−1.7±2.9	6.9	6.5	+0.4±3.5
	cured or improved	68.2	64.7	3.5±4.9	58.3	55.4	2.9±5.0	59.4	57.1	2.3±7.4	57.8	62.6	−4.8±6.8
One week	cured	48.8	46.8	2.0±5.2	42.2	37.1	5.1±5.0	31.3	33.3	−2.0±7.0	29.4	36.4	−7.0±6.5
	cured or improved	80.6	74.6	6.0±4.3	77.8	77.5	0.3±4.5	70.8	79.8	−9.0±6.5	70.6	78.5	−7.9±6.0

* Includes the few patients (nine on drug and five on placebo) who said they were cured on the first day.

TABLE 14-7. **Side effects attributed to treatment**

Figures are numbers of subjects in each group reporting the various side effects at some time during the trial. (From Medical Research Council,[20] Table VIII. By permission of the British Medical Journal.)

Main symptoms	Persons given antihistaminic treatment	Persons given placebo treatment
Drowsiness, lassitude, listlessness	26	35
Dizziness, giddiness, vertigo	21	13
Headache	21	16
Headache combined with other nervous symptoms	11	6
Depression with or without other nervous symptoms	2	5
Insomnia	3	1
Gastrointestinal	13	12
Combined gastrointestinal and nervous symptoms	8	7
Miscellaneous	16	16
Total	121	111

first visit, as recorded by the medical officer. The nearly identical figures in the two groups are noteworthy. The duration of symptoms before treatment (not shown here) also showed a nearly identical distribution in the two groups.

For the evaluation of drug effect two criteria were established. The term "cured" referred to those persons who were completely free of symptoms and who were found to be without objective signs on examination. The term "improved" referred to those persons who on questioning and examination were found to be improved but not cured since the previous examination. Table 14-6 gives the percentages of subjects cured or improved after one day, two days, or a week, categorized according to the duration of their colds before treatment. The data as a whole give little indication of any drug effect as compared with placebo. When all the results were combined, regardless of duration of cold before treatment, 48.0 per cent of the drug group and 42.1 per cent of the placebo group were cured or improved at the end of the first day's treatment. The small difference in favor of the drug was just significant in a technical, statistical sense, according to the investigators, "but even if it be real it is so small that it clearly has no practical importance." Even this small difference vanished on the second day, when the combined data showed cumulative percentages of 8.8 and 53.0 in the drug group and 8.5 and 51.3 in the placebo group, for "cured" and "improved," respectively. It was concluded that thonzylamine had little or no value in the treatment of the common cold. It was felt that the minor difference in favor of the drug on the first day might have been attributable to a slight sedative effect, or possibly to the unwitting inclusion of some subjects suffering from hay fever or allergic rhinitis. Table 14-7 gives the frequencies of side effects attributed to treatment. Here there were no significant differences between drug and placebo. The large number of side effects reported in both groups may have been symptoms due to the infection but erroneously attributed to the medication.

Sequential Trials

The conventional type of controlled clinical trial described above, in which subjects are assigned randomly to treatment groups of predetermined size, can be inefficient. If one treatment were very much superior to another, this might be revealed decisively before all the members of all the groups have been treated. Especially when not all the subjects are at hand initially but will be placed in groups and treated as they present themselves over a period of time, it is not reasonable to go on with the trial after the results become clear. Moreover, in addition to the economic disadvantage of continuing an unnecessary trial, there is the ethical objection that after a certain point in the trial, some subjects will necessarily be treated with a medication or regimen already shown to be inferior. The same general argument applies when there is no important difference between treatments under test. It should be possible to decide this as soon as possible, and discontinue the trial without necessarily completing the treatments and observations on all the members of all the groups. The designs developed to permit such efficient and timely termination of drug evaluations are known as *sequential trials*.[21]

In sequential trials observations are paired so that the alternative treatments (e.g., drug and placebo) are represented in each pair. A pair might consist of two observations on the same patient, one after each treatment, or actually of a pair of patients, each receiving a different treatment. By some criterion adopted in advance, one treatment will be rated as better than the other in a given pair. This outcome is called a *preference*. Let the alternative treatments be designated A and B, and suppose that relief of symptoms in a chronic disease is the criterion of evaluation. Then if a patient receives A for one week and B for another, and A is judged superior, a preference is recorded for A. If prolongation of life is the criterion, patients having been matched and paired at the outset with respect to age, sex, and severity of disease, then whenever a patient dies a preference is recorded for the treatment being received by the surviving member of his pair. Pairs within which no preference can be assigned do not enter the analysis at all.

---

[21] P. ARMITAGE: *Sequential Medical Trials.* Springfield, Charles C Thomas, 1960.

The design is shown schematically in Fig. 14-1. The total number of preferences is indicated on the x-axis. Every preference for *A* is plotted by moving a path one unit diagonally up and to the right; every preference for *B,* by moving diagonally down and to the right. In the example illustrated, there were three preferences for *A,* then one for *B,* then three more for *A,* and so on. Obviously, if *A* is really better than *B,* the line will continue indefinitely upward; and if *B* is better than *A,* it will move indefinitely downward. The aim is to terminate the trial as soon as one of the following conclusions can be drawn: (*a*) that one treatment is superior to the other; or (*b*) that there is no important difference between the treatments. These terms require a priori definition. In deciding that one treatment is superior to the other, we declare the null hypothesis false; as in any statistical procedure, we do this at a certain level of significance. If the level of significance (here designated 2*α*) is 0.05, then we will accept a chance of 1 in 20 of being wrong when we declare a superiority of one treatment over the other, i.e., we shall say there is a difference 5 per cent of the time when none really exists. In the diagram, the choice of a level of significance determines the positions of the upper and lower boundaries, for when either of these boundaries is reached, we shall declare one treatment superior and terminate the trial. It might be supposed that these boundaries would be given directly by the binomial probabilities, but the sequential nature of the decision-making process complicates the compu-

FIG. 14-1. BOUNDARY DIAGRAM FOR A SEQUENTIAL TRIAL. *Here, 2α = 0.05, 1 − β = 0.95, and the specified value of θ₁ is 0.75. The values of α and β at the boundaries are approximate. See text for explanation. (Plotted from specifications of Armitage.*[21]*)*

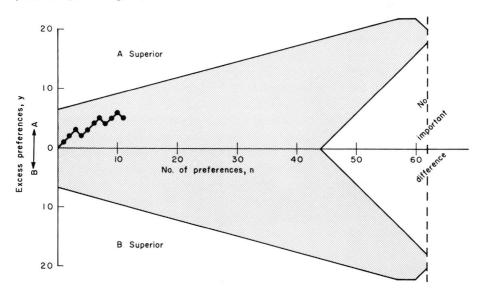

tation of probabilities.[22] From a practical point of view the boundary specifications for $2\alpha = 0.05$ and $2\alpha = 0.01$ may be obtained from appropriate tables.[21] Figure 14-1 depicts upper and lower boundaries for the significance level most often adopted, $2\alpha = 0.05$.

The next thing that has to be specified is the power of the procedure, i.e., the probability with which a specified difference between the treatments will be detected if it exists. Usually one wishes to be fairly sure of finding a real difference, so the power (designated $1-\beta$) is usually chosen to be a large fraction, commonly 0.95. This means that a real difference of a specified magnitude will be found 95 times out of 100 trials, on the average.

Finally, the *specified difference* referred to above has to be decided upon. This will be the degree of superiority of one treatment over another considered important enough to be worth discovering. The point here is that small differences between treatments will require very large numbers of subjects to prove. In any trial, sequential or otherwise, the importance of the objective has to justify the magnitude of the trial. Suppose, for example, that treatment A were so nearly equivalent to treatment B that it would be judged superior in only 51 per cent of all cases. To distinguish between this slight superiority and complete equivalence would require a vast number of subjects; it would obviously not be worth the effort. A useful feature of the sequential trial is that it forces an explicit decision about these criteria before the trial is begun, so that the investigator is forced to recognize both the minimum and maximum number of subjects that may be required. The term used to express the specified difference is θ_1, defined as the true frequency of preference for the superior treatment, $\theta_0 = 1 - \theta_1$ being the true frequency of preference for the inferior treatment. For equivalent treatments, $\theta_1 = \theta_0 = 0.50$. In the diagram of Fig. 14-1, the value specified for θ_1 is 0.75; that is to say, we will not consider a difference important unless one treatment is preferred to the other 75 per cent of the time, in the long run. Now the laws of probability determine that if there really is a difference of that magnitude, there will be a sufficient number of excess preferences for the superior treatment so that the path traced as described earlier will be expected to intersect an upper or lower boundary before the total number of preferences exceeds a certain limit. That limit, for the parameters chosen here, is 62. In other words, if a superiority of A (or B) is not demonstrable with a sample size of 62 preferences, we can declare (with 95 per cent probability of being correct) that it does not exist. Or, in terms of the boundary diagram, if the path crosses the vertical broken line at $n = 62$ before it crosses an upper or lower boundary, there is no important difference between the treatments, and the trial can be terminated.

[22] A. WALD: *Sequential Analysis.* New York, John Wiley and Sons, 1947.

The wedge-shaped indentation of the right boundary has a simple explanation. Because the path traced by the sequential preferences cannot rise or fall at more than a 45-degree angle, it follows that there are certain positions at the right of the diagram from which the path could no longer intersect an upper or lower boundary within the total permissible number of preferences. Thus, if the path were at $y = 0$ by the 44th preference, the trial would be over, because even if every subsequent preference were in favor of one treatment, an upper or lower boundary could not be reached.

Figure 14-2 presents a boundary diagram for a higher value of the specified difference ($\theta_1 = 0.85$) and for the 0.01 level of significance as well as the 0.05 level. It is of interest to note the effect of these changes on the shape of the diagram. The main result of insisting that a treatment difference be greater in order to be defined as "important" is that the right boundary moves to the left. Thus, the maximum number of preferences necessary to conclude that there is no important difference has diminished here from 62 to 33. The result of using a more rigorous level of significance for the decision that there is a difference i.e., for the path to intersect an upper or lower boundary, is a need for a greater excess of preferences in favor of one treatment.

The specifications for drawing boundary diagrams for different chosen values of θ_1, at $2\alpha = 0.05$ or $2\alpha = 0.01$, and $1-\beta = 0.95$ are given elsewhere.[21]

FIG. 14-2. BOUNDARY DIAGRAM FOR A SEQUENTIAL TRIAL. *Here, $1 - \beta = 0.95$, as in Fig. 14-1; but $\theta_1 = 0.85$. Two boundary diagrams are shown, one for $2\alpha = 0.05$, the other for $2\alpha = 0.01$. Values of α and β at the boundaries are approximate. See text for explanation. (Plotted from specifications of Armitage.[21])*

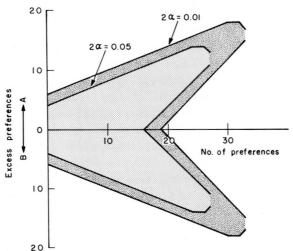

TABLE 14-8. **Rate of myocardial infarction in two treatment groups**

> Patients with angina pectoris or a previous myocardial infarction were maintained on the anticoagulant phenindione at two dosage levels. The higher dosage reduced the prothrombin levels to 20% of normal, on the average; on the lower dosage, prothrombin levels were 50% of normal. The infarction rate in the 20% group was significantly lower than in the 50% group ($P < 0.01$). (From Borchgrevink,[23] Table 17.)

	No. of patients	Observation period in patient years	Infarctions No.	Infarctions %	Infarction rate (% per year)
20% Group					
Women	21	32	0	0.0	0.0
Men	82	110	2	2.4	1.8
Total	103	142	2	1.9	1.4
50% Group					
Women	18	25	1	5.6	4.0
Men	82	98	12	14.6	12.2
Total	100	123	13	13.0	10.6

A trial of anticoagulant therapy was conducted to see if it would reduce the risk of myocardial infarction in patients with angina pectoris or previous infarction. The trial was started in 1957 as a conventional design with two groups to be filled randomly as patients presented themselves. One group was to receive an anticoagulant, phenindione, at sufficiently high dosage to reduce the plasma prothrombin level to 20 per cent of normal. The other group was to receive the same drug, but at lower dosage, sufficient to reduce the plasma prothrombin level to 50 per cent of normal. These were called the "20% group" and "50% group," respectively. A control group was considered unjustified, since there was already evidence of a beneficial effect of anticoagulant therapy in preventing recurrences of myocardial infarction. But since no information was available about optimum dosage, and since overdosage carries a risk of hemorrhage, it was considered proper to conduct a trial of high versus low dosage. The published description of this study[23] exemplifies the adoption, in advance, of rigorous criteria for admission of patients to the study, establishment of subgroups according to sex, history, and plasma cholesterol level, and random assignment of patients within each subgroup to one or the other treatment. Of 394 patients with a history of angina pectoris or previous myocardial infarction, 191 did not meet the initial criteria; most of these

23 C. F. BORCHGREVINK: Long-term anticoagulant therapy in angina pectoris and myocardial infarction. A clinical trial of intensive versus moderate treatment. *Acta Med. Scand. 168*, Suppl. 359:1 (1960).

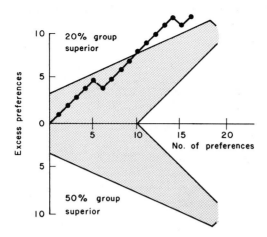

FIG. 14-3.   RESULT OF SEQUENTIAL TRIAL: MYOCARDIAL INFARCTION OR DEATH IN TWO TREATMENT GROUPS.   *This graph is for the same experiment summarized in Table 14-8. Patients were paired, one from the 20% group (high dosage of phenindione) and one from the 50% group (low dosage). If a patient developed a myocardial infarction or if he had a cardiovascular death, a preference was given to the group to which the other patient in the pair belonged. Here, $2\alpha = 0.05$, $1 - \beta = 0.95$, $\theta_1 = 0.90$. (From Borchgrevink, Fig. 11.[23])*

had angina pectoris for longer than the two years established as maximum. There remained 203 patients, 103 assigned to the high dosage group, 100 to the low dosage group. The patients were followed closely throughout the study, their plasma prothrombin levels were determined periodically, and twice a year all were examined by physicians unaware of the treatment group to which they belonged. Episodes of myocardial infarction and all deaths occurring during the study were subjected to careful scrutiny in order to obtain as exact a diagnosis as possible. The study was terminated in 1960. Table 14-8 shows the data on myocardial infarctions in the two groups. The difference in favor of the high dosage ("20%") group was highly significant.

In 1959, the newly introduced sequential method came to the attention of the investigators. Accordingly, the subjects were followed by this procedure too. The result is shown in Fig. 14-3. Each time there was a death or myocardial infarction, a preference was given to the treatment group to which the other patient of the pair belonged. The upper boundary was crossed by the tenth event. The study could have been closed at this time, seven months before the prearranged termination. During those final seven months, six more patients had attacks of myocardial infarction and two of these died, both of them in the low dosage ("50%") group. It is not known, of course, whether raising the dosage for all patients, as soon as the superiority of the high dosage had been demonstrated, would have been timely enough to alter the outcome for those six patients,[24] but these results certainly demonstrate vividly a principal advantage of the sequential method.

Critical Appraisal of Reports on Clinical Trials

Physicians and others concerned with drug actions in man are increasingly called upon to examine critically the experimental evidence on which claims of drug efficacy are based. Three fundamental questions should be asked about any published report describing the outcome of a clinical trial.

1. *Was the experimental design adequate?* Was the drug compared with a placebo or with an established standard drug in a double-blind design? Were the patients assigned randomly to the various treatment groups? Is it stated explicitly what precautions were taken to exclude subjective bias at every stage of the experiment, especially during the evaluative procedures? Were the patients included in the trial typical of those for whom the drug is now recommended, or did the conditions of selection for the trial or of nonspecific treatment during the trial favor the new drug? Were the trials conducted by reputable independent investigators, qualified by experience in the design and conduct of such trials? Were the trials carried out, for example, under the aegis of an independent academic or research institution? If there is any serious doubt that these questions can all be answered affirmatively, there is usually no point in proceeding further, for the most elegant statistical analysis cannot salvage meaningful data from a poor experiment.

2. *Are the results claimed for the new drug statistically significant?* If the experimental design was adequate, then the next question to be settled is whether observed differences between the treatment groups are likely to have been due to the treatments or to chance fluctuations unrelated to the treatments employed. The published results should contain enough of the raw data to permit the reader to make his own statistical analysis, should he wish to do so.[8a, 9] And the investigators, when making statements about statistical significance, should always indicate what procedures were used. If the groups do not differ significantly (at the chosen level of significance), then the drug's proponent has failed to prove his point, for the results might well have come about by chance. This does not mean, of course, that the drug is worthless. A better experimental design, which reduces the variation between subjects, a larger number of subjects, or a different schedule of drug administration are some of the changes that might, in a new trial, reveal a positive drug effect.

3. *Are the benefits claimed for the drug in comparison with an established treatment or placebo of practical significance in the context of*

---

[24] MEDICAL RESEARCH COUNCIL: An assessment of long-term anticoagulant administration after cardiac infarction. *Brit. Med. J.* 2:837 (1964).

the proposed use of the drug? If the superiority of the drug over alternative treatment is real, then the next question is whether the drug offers any important advantage. A small advantage in favor of the drug under test may be real (i.e., not due to chance) yet not important enough to matter. "A difference, in order to *be* a difference, has to *make* a difference." And especially if the new drug is only slightly better than the established treatment, has it been tried in enough patients to reveal uncommon side effects? Has its toxicity been studied thoroughly enough under the conditions in which it will actually be used? It must be assumed that new risks, as yet unrecognized, may emerge, and this likelihood has to be weighed against the better-known efficacy and toxicity of the established drug. Will the new drug be substantially more expensive for the patient than equivalent medications that have been in use for a long time? Finally, has the drug's relative value been assessed by competent independent professional groups charged with the function of evaluating new drugs (cf. p. 835)?

Ethics of Human Experimentation

Well-designed and properly executed clinical trials are essential for gaining valid information about drugs. But all experimentation with human beings is subject to ethical restraints. A fundamental distinction is recognized between research in which the aim is therapeutic for the individual patient and research in which the aim is purely scientific and may be without therapeutic value to the person who is the subject.[25] As for the first kind of research, the doctor must be free to use a new drug or other therapeutic measure "if in his judgment it offers hope of saving life, reestablishing health, or alleviating suffering."[26] If it is possible and consistent with the patient's welfare, a full explanation should be given and his consent should be obtained.

If a wholly new drug of unknown value is being tested in a clinical trial with patients whose condition, there is reason to hope, may be benefitted by it, is it ethically justifiable to assign some of these patients to a placebo group? The answer seems reasonably clear. To conduct such a trial in an uncontrolled fashion would really be unethical; for, since no valid information would then be obtained, risks would be assumed without any possible benefit.

An investigator, however, has no inherent right to conduct experiments on other human beings at all, regardless of the potential benefits to humanity. In every experiment the *informed consent* of the subjects (or their guardians) must be secured.[27] In the postulated situation, the patients

[25] MEDICAL RESEARCH COUNCIL: Responsibility in investigations on human subjects. *Brit. Med. J. 2:*178 (1964).

[26] DECLARATION OF HELSINKI: Recommendations guiding doctors in clinical research. *World Med. J. 11:*281 (1964).

[27] H. K. BEECHER: Consent in clinical experimentation: myth and reality. *J. Amer. Med. Ass. 195:*34 (1966).

would be told (*1*) that a new drug has been developed that might be beneficial to them; (*2*) that it can only be tested properly in a controlled way, so that some patients will receive the drug whereas others will receive different treatments; (*3*) that these assignments will be made by chance; (*4*) that certain risks are likely; and (*5*) that other unanticipated risks may materialize. Consent should then be obtained in writing. This is in essence the procedure that was followed in setting up large-scale trials of the killed-virus poliomyelitis vaccine before its effectiveness was known, except that parents had to give consent for their children.[28] It is obvious that certain children contracted the disease and died or were paralyzed because they were in the placebo group instead of the vaccine group. But the risk to the control group was not greater than before the trial of the vaccine, which had potential hazards of its own; and the controlled trial was the only way to determine whether or not the vaccine was effective.

No patient may justifiably be denied the benefits of the best treatment available. Certainly, therefore, placebo controls are not permissible if an effective drug is already known. Therefore any new drug must be evaluated in a comparative trial against the best existing one. This was how isoniazid and *p*-aminosalicylate were tested for the treatment of pulmonary tuberculosis in extensive clinical trials after streptomycin was in wide and effective use.[29] The anticoagulant studies described earlier (p. 812) were based on the same principle of comparative evaluation without a placebo control. In order to deny no one the benefits of an improved therapy, investigators have the obligation to conduct every trial efficiently, not to accept any unnecessary risk, and to arrive at a conclusion and terminate a trial as soon as possible, so that the benefits, if any, can be extended promptly to all who are in need.

More difficult questions arise with research of the second kind, when those who are to be subjects of a clinical trial, whether patients or normal volunteers, are unlikely to benefit in any direct way from the experiment—at least no more than humanity as a whole. The history of medicine affords fine examples of contributions made by heroic volunteers toward the eventual understanding and control of disease. One such was the deliberate infection of human volunteers with yellow fever for the purpose of establishing the mode of transmission of this illness by mosquitoes.[30] Another was the infection of prisoner volunteers during World War II with malaria parasites in order to test the efficacy of new and much-

[28] POLIOMYELITIS VACCINE EVALUATION CENTER: Evaluation of 1954 field trial of poliomyelitis vaccine. *Amer. J. Public Health 45:* Number 5, Part 2 (1955).

[29] S. PHILLIPS: VII. Comparison of isoniazid alone with isoniazid-PAS in the original chemotherapy of noncavitary pulmonary tuberculosis. *Amer. Rev. Resp. Dis. 80:*641 (1959).

[30] H. A. KELLY: *Walter Reed and Yellow Fever*, 3rd ed. Baltimore, The Norman, Remington Co., 1923.

needed antimalarial drugs.[31] Trials of this sort are exceedingly important, and they need to be carried out. But they can only be conducted with subjects who freely give their informed consent in the fullest sense of the term. A responsible adult, in full command of his reason, may wish to serve as an experimental subject and to suffer a certain degree of discomfort or minor risk for remuneration, or in the hope of helping others. Altruistic motivation may be especially strong in patients who know they are victims of an incurable disease. Prisoners may feel sincerely that they can atone for past antisocial behavior by making a contribution to the progress of medical research, and there may also be the more selfish hope of more favorable consideration by a parole board. In all cases, the investigator is obliged not only to explain fully what is proposed, including the possible hazards, but also to avoid exerting undue pressure or exploiting a relationship of dependency or trust between the subject and himself. The subject, in short, must choose freely and without coercion.

Many potentially informative experiments simply cannot be carried out. Sometimes the optimal design would be transparently unethical because it would cause harm needlessly. It has been asserted, for example, that women who contract mumps at a critical stage of pregnancy may give birth to congenitally malformed infants. Obviously, the most decisive proof of whether or not this is true would be obtained by infecting large numbers of women with mumps during pregnancy. Just as obviously, such an experiment would be unthinkable, so that less direct means of attacking this problem are called for. Often the prospective epidemiologic approach is appropriate. By this means, i.e., by recording the occurrences of infectious disease in pregnant women and then observing the outcome of the pregnancy, the question of teratogenesis by mumps was fairly well settled. In a prospective study in which the well-known anomalies after rubella were observed there was no evidence of any fetal malformations caused by mumps, nor by measles or chickenpox.[32] On occasion, a proposed experiment may seem important and justifiable to the investigator, yet he cannot obtain the consent of truly informed subjects. Then such experiment is also unthinkable. The needs of scientific research do not supersede the rights of individuals.

The ghastly "experiments" carried out by doctors on unwilling prisoners under the Nazi regime in Germany led to the formulation of standards for human experimentation, first in the so-called Nuremberg Code,[33] and more recently in the *Declaration of Helsinki* of the World

[31] A. S. ALVING, B. CRAIGE, JR., T. N. PULLMAN, C. M. WHORTON, R. JONES, JR., and L. EICHELBERGER: Procedures used at Stateville Penitentiary for the testing of potential antimalarial agents. Symposium on Malaria. *J. Clin. Invest. 27:*2 (1948).

[32] A. B. HILL, R. DOLL, T. MC L. GALLOWAY, and J. P. W. HUGHES: Virus diseases in pregnancy and congenital defects. *Brit. J. Prevent. Soc. Med. 12:*1 (1958).

[33] Trials of War Criminals before the Nurenberg Military Tribunals under Control Council Law No. 10; Vol. II, p. 181. Washington, D.C., U.S. Government Printing Office, 1950.

Medical Association.[26] This document codifies the ethical principles that should guide investigators working with patients or other human subjects. Since the obligations and ethical responsibilities of clinical investigators have not been universally understood and accepted,[34] it seems appropriate to reproduce this statement verbatim, except for the omission of three introductory paragraphs of a rather general nature:

DECLARATION OF HELSINKI

In the field of clinical research a fundamental distinction must be recognized between clinical research in which the aim is essentially therapeutic for a patient, and clinical research the essential object of which is purely scientific and without therapeutic value to the person subjected to the research.

I. BASIC PRINCIPLES

1. Clinical research must conform to the moral and scientific principles that justify medical research, and should be based on laboratory and animal experiments or other scientifically established facts.
2. Clinical research should be conducted only by scientifically qualified persons and under the supervision of a qualified medical man.
3. Clinical research cannot legitimately be carried out unless the importance of the objective is in proportion to the inherent risk to the subject.
4. Every clinical research project should be preceded by careful assessment of inherent risks in comparison to foreseeable benefits to the subject or to others.
5. Special caution should be exercised by the doctor in performing clinical research in which the personality of the subject is liable to be altered by drugs or experimental procedure.

II. CLINICAL RESEARCH COMBINED WITH PROFESSIONAL CARE

1. In the treatment of the sick person the doctor must be free to use a new therapeutic measure if in his judgment it offers hope of saving life, re-establishing health, or alleviating suffering.

   If at all possible, consistent with patient psychology, the doctor should obtain the patient's freely given consent after the patient has been given a full explanation. In case of legal incapacity consent should also be procured from the legal guardian; in case of physical incapacity the permission of the legal guardian replaces that of the patient.
2. The doctor can combine clinical research with professional care, the objective being the acquisition of new medical knowledge, only to the extent that clinical research is justified by its therapeutic value for the patient.

III. NON-THERAPEUTIC CLINICAL RESEARCH

1. In the purely scientific application of clinical research carried out on a human being it is the duty of the doctor to remain the

---

34 H. K. BEECHER: Ethics and clinical research. *New Engl. J. Med. 274:*1354 (1966).

protector of the life and health of that person on whom clinical research is being carried out.

2. The nature, the purpose, and the risk of clinical research must be explained to the subject by the doctor.

3a. Clinical research on a human being cannot be undertaken without his free consent, after he has been fully informed; if he is legally incompetent the consent of the legal guardian should be procured.

3b. The subject of clinical research should be in such a mental, physical, and legal state as to be able to exercise fully his power of choice.

3c. Consent should as a rule be obtained in writing. However, the responsibility for clinical research always remains with the research worker; it never falls on the subject, even after consent is obtained.

4a. The investigator must respect the right of each individual to safeguard his personal integrity, especially if the subject is in a dependent relationship to the investigator.

4b. At any time during the course of clinical research the subject or his guardian should be free to withdraw permission for research to be continued. The investigator or the investigating team should discontinue the research if in his or their judgment it may, if continued, be harmful to the individual.

USE AND MISUSE OF DRUGS

The existence of potent drugs in great variety poses new dangers to the public health. Ill-advised self-medication can be more harmful than in former times. Drug ingestion has become a major method of suicide, and drugs are a principal cause of accidental poisoning among children (cf. chapter 5). Even when prescribed by a physician, medication is more dangerous nowadays than formerly. The irrational mixtures of old were ineffective, on the whole, but they were also usually innocuous. Today, even when they are administered correctly, drugs carry a certain risk of untoward adverse effects and even of fatal reactions, as described in earlier chapters.

Legal Controls over Drug Availability

There are obvious differences between drugs and ordinary commodities. The consumer has no way to judge the efficacy of a drug or its hazards, and therefore these judgments have to be made for him by others. Prescription drugs are unique in that the consumer exercises no choice whatsoever but depends entirely upon the physician's judgment. Drugs that are to be sold directly to the public ("across the counter") have to be considered first by qualified experts with respect to their efficacy and safety. For both types of drug, procedures have to be specified in law whereby information upon which valid decisions can be based will be made available to the physician or to others. Throughout most of the world, these procedures are embodied in legislation and regulated by governmental agencies entrusted with control over the manufacture, export, import, sale, advertising, and prescription of drugs. Some of the regulatory mechanisms are international in scope, as for addicting drugs. A brief description of the regulatory mechanisms in the United States will be given; the procedures in other countries usually differ only in detail.

The first national legislation establishing controls over drugs in the United States was the pure food and drug law of 1906. The present legislative basis of such controls is the Federal Food, Drug, and Cosmetic Act of 1938, as amended. This act, including amendments adopted in 1962 and 1965, establishes the authority of the government to safeguard the public health against certain potential hazards, and to protect the consumer's interest.[35-37] The *Food and Drug Administration* (FDA) is the regulatory agency charged with enforcing these laws. The main provisions of the legislation require:

1. that foods, drugs, and cosmetics be labeled accurately to show all ingredients and their amounts;
2. that drugs deemed unsafe for unsupervised use not be sold except on prescription;
3. that wholly unsafe drugs not be marketed at all, even for prescription use;
4. that physicians be informed fully by the manufacturer about toxic potentialities and side effects of prescription drugs;
5. that false and misleading claims not be made either in advertising or in the labeling of drugs;
6. that advertisements and promotional brochures describe all adverse effects and contraindications; and
7. that drugs acting on the central nervous system and liable to abuse be subject to especially rigorous controls.

Technically, in the United States, the authority of the federal agencies extends only to drugs shipped in interstate commerce. From a practical standpoint this covers nearly all manufacturers and nearly all drugs. But there are, in addition, state laws that extend similar controls to drugs manufactured and sold entirely within a state. Moreover, through the licensing of pharmacists, physicians, dentists, and veterinarians, states can exercise special authority over the prescribing and sale of drugs.

[35] Federal Food, Drug, and Cosmetic Act. As amended. Code of Federal Regulations, Title 21. Publication No. 667340. Washington, D.C., U.S. Government Printing Office, 1963.

[36] New Drug Regulations under the Federal Food, Drug, and Cosmetic Act. U.S. Department of Health, Education, and Welfare; Food and Drug Administration. Publication No. 691934. Washington, D.C., U.S. Government Printing Office, 1963.

[37] Fact Sheet. Drug Abuse Control Amendments of 1965. Public Law 89-74, 89th Congress. U.S. Department of Health, Education, and Welfare, Food and Drug Administration. Washington, D.C., U.S. Government Printing Office, 1965.

When clinical trials of a new drug have been completed, the manufacturer, if he believes the drug to be safe and efficacious, submits a *New Drug Application,* containing all the documented claims for the drug. Upon approval by the FDA (in Great Britain by the *Safety of Drugs Committee*[38]) the drug may be marketed as a prescription item or, if specific approval has been obtained, for sale directly to the public. Surveillance by the regulatory agency continues, with collection of data designed to uncover any long-term adverse effects. At any time after a drug is in use, the FDA may require a change in the labeling, in advertising claims, or in the information furnished to physicians; or it may even order the drug withdrawn. The Kefauver-Harris amendments of 1962 required, for the first time, that the efficacy of drugs be established as well as their safety.[36] As a result, the FDA is now engaged in an evaluation of the efficacy of the many drugs already in use prior to 1962, and the procedures for approval of the introduction of new drugs have been modified accordingly.

Continuing surveillance of drugs after their introduction into clinical use is important for several reasons, some of which were already pointed out in chapter 5:

1. Clinical trials necessarily involve a much smaller number of subjects than will eventually be exposed to a new drug. Consequently, after a drug comes into general use, adverse reactions may occur which, because of their relatively low frequency, were not observed previously. The hematologic toxicity of chloramphenicol, for example, was not discovered for several years. Another example is meprobamate, originally claimed to be a safe and nonaddicting tranquilizer. An intensive promotional campaign led to extremely widespread use, the sales of this drug exceeding 50 million dollars per year in 1956–58.[39] As it turned out, meprobamate had a serious addicting potential and produced dangerous withdrawal effects; it also caused suicidal depression in some psychiatric patients.[40] In 1965 it was dropped from the U.S. Pharmacopeia. Another sedative and hypnotic agent, glutethimide, had a rather similar history.[41]

2. A different population than was tested in the clinical trials may be placed at risk. Thalidomide exemplifies this problem (p. 727). The special effects of drugs upon the fetus during early pregnancy were not even considered when this drug was introduced into use after clinical trials had indicated a high degree of safety in adults of all ages. Another interesting example concerns an orally active agent capable of interfering with spermatogenesis.[42] Clinical trials were conducted with a group of prisoner

[38] D. DUNLOP: Use and abuse of drugs. *Brit. Med. J.* 2:437 (1965).

[39] Administered Prices. Hearings before the Subcommittee on Antitrust and Monopoly of the Committee on the Judiciary, U.S. Senate, 86th Congress, First Session, p. 8910. Publication No. 35621. Washington, D.C., U.S. Government Printing Office, 1961.

[40] Meprobamate. *Medical Letter* 2:87 (1960).

[41] Doriden. *Medical Letter* 4:61 (1962).

[42] J. MAC LEOD: "Human seminal cytology following the administration of certain antispermatogenic compounds," in *A Symposium on Agents Affecting Fertility,* ed. by C. R. Austin and J. S. Perry. Boston, Little, Brown and Co., 1965, pp. 93–123.

volunteers. The drug appeared to be effective and reversible, and there was no indication of adverse side effects. When it was used by nonprisoners, however, it was discovered to act like disulfiram (p. 253). When alcohol was ingested after the drug had been taken, alarming symptoms developed. The enforced abstinence of the prisoner subjects made them a completely nonrepresentative sample, in which the peculiar toxicity of this drug could not have been discovered.

3. Technologic advances may alter the criteria for evaluation after a drug is in general use. This applies to a great many drugs that were introduced into medicine before the modern clinical trial was perfected; consequently, satisfactory evaluations of such drugs were never really carried out. Moreover, if a newer, more effective, and safer drug is developed for some particular medical use, then older and more hazardous drugs should obviously be withdrawn after convincing evidence of their inferiority has been obtained in comparative clinical trials.

4. Chronic toxicity in man may develop only after exposure for a much longer time than could be studied in the clinical trials. Possible carcinogenic actions of drugs fall into this category. The carcinogenic effects of tobacco smoke could not have been discovered except after smoking had been prevalent for many years. Especially with drugs that are to be used on a very large scale, continuing surveillance will be important for detecting possible long-term hazards. There has been concern, for example, about possible carcinogenesis by the oral contraceptives, since some cancers of the female reproductive organs and breasts are hormone dependent. Continuous observation of women receiving these drugs has revealed, thus far, no increase in the incidence of cancer.[43]

If continuous surveillance of drug use is to have any validity, two requirements have to be met. *First,* physicians and hospitals must report all adverse reactions that might possibly be due to drug administration. *Second,* data must be available on the total usage of each drug, so that the number of adverse reactions can be assessed in relation to the total number of people exposed to the drug. An effective national or world-wide system for accomplishing both requirements is within the capacity of present-day computer technology, but no such system yet exists.[44]

Other governmental agencies are concerned in the control of drugs. A special agency of the National Institutes of Health, the *Division of Biologics Standards,* is responsible for licensing serums, vaccines, and other biologic products, including human blood and its derivatives. Standards are established for safety and potency, and each batch manufactured must be standardized by bioassay (p. 746). Periodic inspection of manufacturing

---

[43] V. A. DRILL: *Oral Contraceptives.* New York, McGraw-Hill, 1966.

[44] The Bureau of Medicine of the FDA and the Council on Drugs of the American Medical Association both solicit reports of adverse reactions from physicians, but this falls far short of an adequate data gathering system.

facilities is carried out by agents of the Division. The *Federal Trade Commission* has general authority to prevent dissemination of false claims with respect to drugs (as to any other commodity) in interstate commerce. Advertising of proprietary "over the counter" drugs comes under its special purview. Remedies are sold for widespread ills like arthritis, the common cold, headaches, "nervous tension"; and vitamins and food supplements are recommended widely for conditions not likely to be improved by them. It was reported that in a single year (1963), 396 million dollars were spent for products claimed to be beneficial for the common cold or cough.[55] The *Federal Communications Commission* has authority to act against false advertising on radio and television. The *Postmaster General* can deny the use of the mails for fraudulent claims or illegal shipments of useless medicines and therapeutic devices.

Every government exercises special control over drugs that are subject to abuse, especially the addicting drugs upon which dependence may develop (cf. chapter 9). In the United States, legal controls over narcotics were established by the *Harrison Narcotic Act* of 1914.[45] This law, ostensibly a revenue measure, vests control in a *Bureau of Narcotics* in the Treasury Department. It regulates the importation, marketing, and prescribing of specified drugs, principally opium and its derivatives (including synthetic opioids), coca leaf and its derivatives, and marihuana.[46] To keep the law abreast of new developments, the Secretary of the Treasury is empowered to place new drugs under the Act. The importer, manufacturer, distributor, pharmacist, and practitioner are all required to keep exact records accounting for all narcotic drugs. The pharmacist must account for his stock of narcotics, keep his records open for inspection, and retain narcotic prescriptions on file for two years. He is forbidden to supply narcotics except on a valid prescription for legitimate medical use. When he dispenses a narcotic, he is required to label the container with his name and registry number, the serial number of the prescription, the name and address of the patient, and the name, address, and registry number of the prescribing practitioner. The physician, dentist, or veterinary surgeon must register with the Bureau of Narcotics, pay a yearly fee, and obtain a registry number to be shown on all his narcotic prescriptions. He is then permitted to prescribe narcotics for legitimate medical use.

The Bureau of Narcotics has adopted the position that prescribing for an addict in order to satisfy his needs is not legitimate medical use

---

[45] U.S. Treasury Department, Bureau of Narcotics. Regulations No. 5, Part 151 of Title 26 (1954), Code of Federal Regulations. Regulatory Taxes on Narcotic Drugs. Opium, Coca Leaves, Isonipecaine or Opiates. Revised October 1964. Washington, D.C., U.S. Government Printing Office, 1964.

[46] Certain preparations (e.g., cough mixtures) containing narcotics in small amounts are excluded from the provisions of the Act; these are called *exempt preparations*. A record must be kept by the pharmacist who dispenses them showing the name and address of each purchaser, the date, and the name and quantity of the exempt preparation. In some states the dispensing of exempt preparations is no longer permitted.

within the meaning of the Act. It has also considered that the treatment of addiction by gradual withdrawal or by methadone substitution cannot be carried out effectively except in a closed institution.[47] These doctrines and the punitive approach of the Bureau of Narcotics toward the addiction problem, coupled with the severe penalties provided for violations of the Act, have led the medical profession as a whole to disengage itself from the medical aspects of drug addiction. Addicts have been sentenced to confinement in the Federal hospitals established for this purpose, and there they have been withdrawn from narcotics. The high rate of relapse of addicts after return to their home environments,[48] however, and the modern tendency to view some aspects of criminality more objectively and less emotionally than in former times have reopened the question of what our approach to addiction should be. Opiate addiction is clearly a social problem; the total number of addicts is estimated at about 50,000, largely concentrated in the slum ghettos of a few large cities. The White House Conference of 1962 proposed a greater role for the medical profession in investigating and treating this disease. New approaches to possible ambulatory treatment of addicts in their own communities and to social rehabilitation are being explored.[49-53]

It has been recognized in recent years that the problem of drug abuse is much larger than that of addiction to opiates, cocaine, and marihuana. Although attended by much publicity, the numerical significance of opiate addiction is trivial. The most important drug of abuse, both from the standpoint of numbers and of personal and social consequences, is certainly alcohol. In 1962 it was estimated that there were five million alcoholics in the United States, "a number far exceeding all other types of drug abuse combined."[53] Yet alcohol enjoys a peculiar social approbation that grants it immunity from the intensified concern over drug abuse in general. Central stimulants and depressants such as amphetamine, barbiturates, meprobamate, mescaline, and lysergic acid diethylamide (LSD) are also abused by many more people than are heroin or morphine. It has been estimated that one-half of the total output of these agents is sold illegally. The widespread distribution of these drugs rests upon their indiscriminate marketing by unethical manufacturers. The Drug Abuse Control Amendments of

[47] AMERICAN MEDICAL ASSOCIATION COUNCIL ON MENTAL HEALTH AND NATIONAL ACADEMY OF SCIENCES–NATIONAL RESEARCH COUNCIL COMMITTEE ON DRUG ADDICTION AND NARCOTICS: Narcotics and medical practice. The use of narcotic drugs in medical practice and the medical management of narcotic addicts. *J. Amer. Med. Ass. 185:*976 (1963).

[48] H. J. DUVALL, B. Z. LOCKE, and L. BRILL: Followup study of narcotic drug addicts five years after hospitalization. *Public Health Rep. 78:*185 (1963).

[49] E. M. SCHUR: *Narcotic Addiction in Britain and America: The Impact of Public Policy.* Bloomington, Ind., Indiana University Press, 1962.

[50] R. BRAIN: The report of the interdepartmental committee on drug addiction. *Brit. J. Addict. 57:*81 (1961).

[51] New York Academy of Medicine, Committee on Public Health Report on drug addiction. II. *N.Y. Med. J. 63:*1977 (1963).

1965 to the Federal Food, Drug, and Cosmetic Acts gives the FDA special powers to control the distribution of any drugs deemed to have "a potential for abuse because of their depressant or stimulant effect on the central nervous system or because of their hallucinogenic effect."[37] Agents of the FDA are given authority to make arrests or to seize shipments if there is evidence of illegal traffic. An elaborate set of requirements for record keeping is supposed to make it possible to determine the point in the chain of distribution at which diversions into illegal channels occur. These amendments are unusual in that they permit the FDA to take appropriate action without having to prove in each instance that the offender is engaged in interstate commerce. Refilling of prescriptions for drugs of this class is also subject to limitations: no more than five times, nor more than six months after the initial date of prescription.

Self-Medication and Iatrogenic Disease

Excessive self-medication is responsible for many ills. The toxic effects of drug misuse have been documented elsewhere (cf. chapter 5). Proprietary drugs sold across the counter include cough remedies, analgesics, skin lotions, food supplements, vitamins, laxatives, "tonics," antacids, and many others.[54] Table 14-9 shows expenditures on such home remedies in 1963, amounting to nearly two billion dollars in the United States. It is questionable whether the benefits to be derived from most of these preparations outweigh the potential harm they do. They account for poisonings when taken in excess, by accident or with suicidal intent, they cause allergic and other adverse reactions, and their use often delays proper medical attention to serious illnesses.

The physician is often consulted about the remedies purchased by patients for self-medication. The mild analgesics are a good example. Ordinary aspirin is as effective, and safer, for most patients than any of the related drugs (phenacetin, aminopyrine, dipyrone, acetaminophen) marketed as substitutes or in combinations with aspirin. Well-controlled trials have also failed to confirm any advantage of "buffered" aspirin preparations over ordinary aspirin[56, 57]; indeed the insignificant quantity of antacid incorporated in the tablet could hardly exert any important effect. Yet physicians have apparently accepted the manufacturers' claims about these

52 V. P. DOLE and M. NYSWANDER: A medical treatment for diacetylmorphine (heroin) addiction. *J. Amer. Med. Ass. 193:*646 (1965).

53 White House Conference on Narcotic and Drug Abuse Proceedings, Washington, D.C. (1962). Publication No. 0-672872. Washington, D.C., U.S. Government Printing Office, 1963.

54 C. S. KEEFER, ed.: A symposium on home medication and the public welfare. *Ann. N.Y. Acad. Sci. 120:*807 (1965).

55 H. G. MANDEL: Therapeutic range and extent of use of home remedies. *Ann. N.Y. Acad. Sci. 120:*902 (1965).

56 R. C. BATTERMAN: Comparison of buffered and unbuffered acetylsalicylic acid. *New Engl. J. Med. 258:*213 (1958).

TABLE 14-9.   Consumer expenditures for home remedies

Data are for proprietary drugs purchased without prescription in the U.S. during the year 1963. (From Mandel,[55] Table 2, originally from *Drug Topics,* July 27, 1964.)

Type of medication	Expenditure (in millions of dollars)
Total packaged medications	1,900
Analgesics, internal	414
Cough and cold items	396
Vitamin concentrates, nonprescription	200
Laxatives	170
Analgesics, external	104
Tonics	93
Antacids	76
External antiseptics	51
Diarrhea remedies	41
Suntan lotions and oils	31
Acne aid products	29
Sleeping aids, nonprescription	18
Hemorrhoidal suppositories and ointments	16
Poison ivy remedies	15
Motion sickness preparations	15
Burn remedies	12

analgesics and have recommended them, despite their considerably greater cost.[58, 59]

The misuse of prescription drugs is also a real problem. A drug prescribed for one illness may be saved and used on another occasion, or a drug prescribed for one patient may be used by another member of the family. The physician can exert a measure of control over this abuse by prescribing just enough of a drug to suffice for the current illness, and by educating his patients to discard left-over medications.

Iatrogenic diseases (Greek *iatros* = physician) are those caused by the physician, by prescribing a drug when none is needed or by poor selection of drugs or drug dosage. Several examples have been given elsewhere in this book of severe or even fatal reactions to drugs that were administered needlessly. The history of the use of chloramphenicol illustrates how easily lessons are forgotten. Sales of this antibiotic dropped sharply after the first reports of aplastic anemia in the period 1950 to 1952, and reached a minimum in 1954. By 1958, however, sales had climbed to five times the

[57] G. A. CRONK: Laboratory and clinical studies with buffered and nonbuffered acetylsalicylic acid. *New Engl. J. Med. 258:*219 (1958).

[58] Aspirin, Bufferin and Ecotrin. *Medical Letter 1:*7 (1959).

[59] Gastrointestinal disturbances with aspirin. *Medical Letter 7:*75 (1965).

1954 level, and by 1960 enough of this drug was being sold in the United States to supply more than three million people with a 10-g course of treatment. In a series of 30 cases of aplastic anemia seen in a three-year period, eight patients had received chloramphenicol. Most of these patients died; yet they had received the drug for minor infections or other conditions in which this antibiotic is not indicated.[60] And chloramphenicol is still used widely for infections that would respond to safer medications. Antibiotics, in general, seem to be used with less caution than other drugs. In a survey of prescribing practices in hospitals it was found that they were often used incorrectly. Sometimes no antibiotic whatever should have been used; in other cases the selection of antibiotic was incorrect.[61]

The irrational use of drug combinations exposes patients to several compounds needlessly, each of which can cause toxic or allergic effects. Few drug combinations have any legitimate place in modern medicine, for reasons already explained (p. 265). Yet such mixtures abound and presumably are being prescribed. One such remedy contains codeine (antitussive), pseudoephedrine (sympathomimetic), chlorcyclizine (antihistaminic), aspirin and phenacetin (analgesic), and caffeine (stimulant). It is a prescription drug recommended for the symptomatic relief of upper respiratory infections.[62] The probability that a patient would have symptoms for which all these drugs are indicated, and for which the doses of all are appropriate, is surely vanishingly small.

A special hazard today is the effect of drugs upon skill in driving a motor vehicle; and since driving is so nearly universal, the physician must keep this in mind when prescribing any drug. A patient's need to drive is an important factor to be considered in deciding if a drug should be given at all. The main effects of tranquilizer and sedative agents and the side effects of numerous drugs of other kinds may all impair driving ability.[63] "Polypharmacy is especially dangerous for motorists because potentiating, additive, and antagonistic drug actions increase the difficulty of predicting effects. This problem is compounded by the use of preparations containing multiple drugs; prescribing each drug separately is less hazardous, an advantage that may outweigh the inconvenience of taking two or more tablets."[64]

Drug Nomenclature and Drug Prices

Every drug has a nonproprietary name. Before a manufacturer receives approval to market a drug, this name must be agreed upon. *The United States Adopted Names Council* is a collaborative enterprise of the

---

60 W. DAMESHEK: Chloramphenicol—a new warning. *J. Amer. Med. Ass. 174:*1853 (1960).

61 C. MULLER: Medical review of prescribing. *J. Chron. Dis. 18:*689 (1965).

62 "Emprazil-C" tablets and shotgun therapy. *Medical Letter 6:*24 (1964).

63 Drugs and auto accidents. *Medical Letter 8:*53 (1966).

64 C. J. G. PERRY and A. L. MORGENSTERN: Drugs and driving. *J. Amer. Med. Ass. 195:*376 (1966).

United States Pharmacopeia (*U.S.P.*), National Formulary (*N.F.*), and Council on Drugs of the American Medical Association.[64a] This organization receives information about the proposed new drug from the manufacturer, who also suggests a nonproprietary name. That name, or an alternative, is agreed upon with the manufacturer, and is then published as the U.S. Adopted Name (*USAN*) of the drug. It will become the official designation if the drug is admitted to *U.S.P.* or *N.F.*, and international agreement to the same nomenclature will be sought through the mechanisms of the World Health Organization. The FDA has legal authority to designate an official name, but in most cases this will probably be the one recommended by the USAN Council.

Pharmaceutical manufacturers prefer to have their products known and prescribed by trade name. It usually turns out that the trade name is shorter, simpler, more euphonious, and easier to remember than the nonproprietary name.[65] Table 14-10 illustrates this phenomenon by a parallel list of nonproprietary names and trade names of drugs selected randomly from *New Drugs,* 1965 edition.[66] The method of selection, decided upon before consulting the volume, was to begin at page 20, selecting the first drug description encountered thereafter, and then to move forward 40 pages at a time, following the same procedure. Thus the list of 12 drugs was generated. Even when salt designations (e.g., hydrochloride) were omitted from consideration, the mean and median syllable contents of the nonproprietary names were significantly longer than those of the trade names. The comparison of euphonic quality of names in the two lists is also revealing, although not subject to quantitative analysis.

It is certainly desirable for the physician to be able to identify the manufacturer of every drug. FDA regulations ensure this by requiring that the manufacturer's identity be indicated on the package, the package inserts, and all drug advertising. There may be good reason why a physician should wish to prescribe (or avoid prescribing) the product of a particular manufacturer; but these considerations do not justify the existence of trade names. For most commodities other than drugs, the brand name indicates the manufacturer, and the names of the products are common nouns, e.g., beans, peaches, beef stew, etc. When a single drug like digitoxin is called Crystodigin, Purodigin, Digitaline Nativelle, etc., these are really not brand names in the commonly accepted sense but a new category of substitute nomenclature.[67]

[64a] The functions of *U.S.P., N.F.,* and the Council on Drugs are discussed in the next section of this chapter.

[65] C. MULLER: Institutional drug purchasing. Factors influencing choices by pharmacists and physicians. *Hospitals 39* (June 16): 97 (1965).

[66] A.M.A. COUNCIL ON DRUGS: *New Drugs, 1965 Edition.* Chicago, American Medical Association, annual.

[67] S. GARB: Teaching medical students to evaluate drug advertising. *J. Med. Educ. 35:*729 (1960).

TABLE 14-10.   Nonproprietary and trade names of a random selection of new drugs

> In *New Drugs,* 1965 edition,[66] the first drug encountered after opening to page 20 was recorded; the same procedure was followed for pages 60, 100, 140, etc. The number of syllables in each drug name is indicated in parentheses following the name; in this computation salt names (also in parentheses) were omitted.

Nonproprietary names		Trade names	
Demethylchlortetracycline (Hydrochloride, *N.F.*)	(8)	Declomycin	(4)
Hexetidine	(4)	Sterisil	(3)
Amitriptyline (Hydrochloride)	(5)	Elavil (Hydrochloride)	(3)
Benactyzine (Hydrochloride)	(4)	Suavitil	(3)
Acetylcysteine	(6)	Mucomyst	(3)
Glycopyrrolate	(5)	Robinul	(3)
Cyclandelate	(4)	Cyclospasmol	(4)
Triamterene	(4)	Dyrenium	(4)
Dydrogesterone	(5)	Duphaston	(3)
Tolbutamide (U.S.P.)	(4)	Orinase	(3)
Cyclophosphamide	(5)	Cytoxan	(3)
(Calcium) Ipodate	(3)	Oragrafin	(4)
Median syllable content	(4.5)		(3.0)
Mean syllable content	(4.8)		(3.3)

There are good reasons why the physician should think about drugs, refer to them, and prescribe them by their nonproprietary names.[68, 68a] The practice encourages accurate recognition of each drug. The textbooks and current medical literature generally avoid trade names, especially because there are so often multiple trade names for the same drug manufactured by different companies. The burden of name memorizing is greatly reduced if only a single name is remembered for each drug. Sometimes, the same drug is given different trade names when promoted for different uses; the antihistaminic agent diphenhydramine is called Benadryl when it is used to relieve allergies and Dramamine when it is used to prevent motion sickness. Alternatively, a mixture of two or more drugs is usually given a single trade name, making it easier to overlook the fact that more than a single active ingredient is present. Finally, a single drug used for one purpose may masquerade under two trade names because one manufacturer has licensed another manufacturer to produce the drug; the tranquilizer meprobamate is known as Miltown and also as Equanil.

International communication and understanding in the fields of pharmacology and therapeutics also requires uniformity of nomenclature,

---

[68] D. G. FRIEND: One drug—one name. *Clin. Pharmacol. Therap.* 6:689 (1965).
[68a] R. BURACK: *The Handbook of Prescription Drugs.* New York, Random House, 1967.

especially when patients and their medications can move so rapidly from country to country. A dramatic illustration of the chaos that can result unless an international nonproprietary nomenclature is followed is illustrated in Table 14-11. Here, 21 names are listed by which a single common analgesic drug, 1-methyl-4-phenylpiperidine-4-carbonic acid ethyl ester, is known in different parts of the world.

Finally, the question of nomenclature has a direct bearing upon the price of drugs. Consistent use of nonproprietary names in prescribing will, it is agreed, in the long run lower the cost of medications for the patient. Organizations responsible for welfare and medical care on a large scale recognize this and insist on nonproprietary nomenclature because of the substantial savings that result.[69] The conscientious physician will also take an interest in what his patient has to pay for the drugs he prescribes. He will be aware of variations in cost and, whenever possible, will prescribe the cheaper drug if it meets the requirements. Numerous examples can be cited in which expensive preparations offer no advantage over cheaper ones. Thyroid, *U.S.P.*, for instance, is the dried powder of the thyroid gland of cattle. For the ordinary maintenance therapy of hypothyroidism it is entirely suitable, and there is no evidence that a purified form of this hormone offers any advantage.[70] Yet Sodium Liothyronine, *U.S.P.* (triiodothyronine) is marketed and widely prescribed as a trade name preparation at more than three times the cost. Another typical example concerns the antihistamine drug chlorpheniramine maleate. After exclusive patent rights

TABLE 14-11.   Synonyms of a single drug in various parts of the world

The list contains trade names and nonproprietary names of one analgesic drug, 1-methyl-4-phenylpiperidine-4-carbonic acid ethyl ester. The official name of this drug in the United States is meperidine.

Alodan	Eudolat
Amphosedal	Isonipecaine
Antiduol	Mefedina
Centralgin	Meperidine
Demerol	Meperine
Dispadol	Pantalgine
Dolantin	Pethidine
Dolantol	Piridosal
Dolopethin	Sauteralgyl
Dolosal	Suppolosal
Dolvanol	

69 C. MULLER and R. WESTHEIMER: Formularies and drug standards in metropolitan hospitals. *Hospitals 40* (Jan. 16): 97 (1966).

70 P. H. LAVIETES and F. H. EPSTEIN: Thyroid therapy of myxedema. A comparison of various agents with a note on the composition of thyroid secretion in man. *Ann. Intern. Med. 60:*79 (1964).

had expired, several firms began to market this compound. Samples of the drug from 20 different companies were subjected to laboratory analysis of their content and of tablet disintegration time; all were found to conform to *U.S.P.* specifications. The price paid by the pharmacist ranged from $1.40 to $17.50 per thousand tablets; the highest price was being charged for the brand previously patented and identified by the trade name by which this drug is most widely known.[71]

Whether or not prescribing by nonproprietary name actually results in lower costs depends, of course, upon the pharmacist; he may supply the least expensive brand, but he is also free to supply a more expensive one. When a brand name is specified in the prescription, he has no choice. A recent survey by a nonprofit organization in New York City revealed some remarkable differences in cost for the same drug. At one pharmacy a prescription for reserpine cost $2.95, whereas the same amount and dosage form of the same drug at the same pharmacy cost $8.95 when prescribed under a trade name. In a different neighborhood, the identical supply of reserpine prescribed under its nonproprietary name cost $1.25. The greatest price difference was found for prednisone, which ranged from $1.25 when sold under its nonproprietary name at one pharmacy to $11.50 when sold under a trade name at another.[72] Sometimes, on the other hand, manufacturers' prices appear to have been set at identical levels regardless of brand name. Senate committee hearings, for example, elicited the information that three companies, during each of four years ending in 1960, sold cortisone acetate, each under its own trade name, at $5.48 per gram, hydrocortisone under three trade names at $7.99 per gram, and prednisone or prednisolone under three trade names at $35.80 per gram.[73] Another problem is that it may be nearly impossible to find simple, inexpensive drugs on the market, even when these are listed in an official or unofficial compendium. Decavitamin Capsules, *U.S.P.,* for example, are ideal for those conditions in which a vitamin supplement is indicated; their composition meets the known daily requirements for ten vitamins in correct proportions. Yet most manufacturers find it more profitable to market costly, complicated, highly advertised mixtures; consequently, the ordinary *U.S.P.* vitamins are hard to find.

SOURCES OF INFORMATION ABOUT DRUGS

Although regulation of the availability of drugs by governmental agencies can serve as a safeguard, the chief responsibility in the administration of drugs rests upon the physician. He is obliged to choose for his

[71] Chlorpheniramine maleate tablets. *Medical Letter* 7:18 (1965).

[72] E. C. BURKE: "Drug Prices Here Held Inequitable," in *The New York Times,* Oct. 20, 1965, p. 39.

[73] Administered Prices. Hearings before the Subcommittee on Antitrust and Monopoly of the Committee on the Judiciary, U.S. Senate, 86th Congress, First Session. Publication No. 35621, p. 7884. Washington, D.C., U.S. Government Printing Office, 1961.

patients the most effective and least dangerous medications available. The choice of drugs is constantly changing as new ones are introduced and old ones are superseded, and as new information about old and new drugs is reported in the medical literature. The physician's unique position as prescriber of drugs makes him the target of intense pressures—from patients to "do something" and from pharmaceutical firms to use their particular products. His ability to choose wisely among drugs and to avoid drugs when that is the best course depends upon his making good use of all sources of information.[74, 75] The primary sources are the journals of pharmacology, therapeutics, and medicine, which publish the results of experiments and clinical observations upon which all drug evaluation has to rest. These raw findings, in turn, are collated, summarized, and interpreted in review articles published as occasional features in the regular journals or in special review journals. Textbooks are useful in clarifying fundamentals, or for detailed information about those aspects of pharmacology in which progress has been slow. But since textbooks are at least a few years out of date, they are not likely to be very helpful if one wishes to assess the merit of a newly introduced medication. In practice, there are four major sources of current information about drugs. First, there are the official compendiums—the *United States Pharmacopeia* and the *National Formulary*. Second, there are unofficial compendiums—lists and indexes of available drugs. Third, there are critical evaluations written by disinterested experts. Fourth, there are package inserts, advertisements, and promotional brochures about drugs, and personal visits by representatives of pharmaceutical manufacturers. In this section we shall discuss and explain these four sources of information.

Official Compendiums

THE UNITED STATES PHARMACOPEIA AND OTHER PHARMACOPEIAS

The United States Pharmacopeia (U.S.P.)[76] is a descriptive catalogue of official drugs. It is published at intervals of five years by a committee of the Pharmacopeial Convention. This Convention is comprised of representatives of the medical and pharmaceutical professions appointed by the appropriate departments of the Federal Government, by medical, pharmaceutical, and chemical organizations, and by colleges of medicine and pharmacy. The *Pharmacopeia* was given official status by the Federal Food, Drug, and Cosmetic Act of 1906. The purpose of the *Pharmacopeia*

---

[74] C. D. MAY: Aids to wise choice among new drug products marketed in the United States. *Clin. Pharmacol. Therap. 5:*7 (1964).

[75] P. TALALAY, ed.: *Drugs in Our Society.* Baltimore, The Johns Hopkins Press, 1964.

[76] THE UNITED STATES PHARMACOPEIAL CONVENTION, INC.: *The Pharmacopeia of the United States of America (The United States Pharmacopeia)*, 17th revision. Easton, Pa., Mack Publishing Co., 1965.

is "to provide authoritative standards for substances and their preparations that are used in the practice of the healing arts; it establishes titles, definitions, descriptions, and standards for identity, quality, strength, and purity, and also, where practicable, methods for their examination and formulas for manufacturing." (p. xxviii)[76] The current edition is *U.S.P. XVII,* published in 1965.

Prescribing a *U.S.P.* drug by its official name ensures that the pharmacist will supply to the patient an exactly defined substance, since the manufacturer, in order to comply with FDA regulations, must conform to the *U.S.P.* standards. Let us examine two typical entries in *U.S.P. XVII,* one a drug that is a pure chemical substance (Sodium Warfarin), the other a crude material of biologic origin (Vasopressin Injection).

Sodium Warfarin is listed with its structural formula, chemical name, and molecular weight. "Sodium Warfarin is an amorphous solid or a crystalline clathrate consisting of isopropyl alcohol and sodium warfarin. It contains not less than 97 per cent and not more than 102 per cent of $C_{19}H_{15}NaO_4$, calculated on the solvent-free basis." There follow paragraphs with the following headings: *Description, Solubility, Identification, pH, Loss on drying, Heavy metals, Absorbance in alkaline solution, Assay, Packaging and storage.* Finally the *Category* ("Anticoagulant"), *Usual dose,* and *Usual dose range* are given. Separate entries for Sodium Warfarin for Injection, and Sodium Warfarin Tablets specify the additional requirements to be met by those particular dosage forms.

Vasopressin Injection "is a sterile solution in water for injection of the water-soluble, pressor principle prepared by synthesis or obtained from the posterior lobe of the pituitary of healthy domestic animals used for food by man. Each ml. of Vasopressin Injection possesses a pressor activity equivalent to 20 *U.S.P.* Posterior Pituitary Units." The Posterior Pituitary Unit is defined with reference to a *U.S.P.* Posterior Pituitary Reference Standard; such standards are made available by the *U.S.P.* Close collaboration is maintained with the World Health Organization, which provides International Standards for certain substances. The bioassay procedure for comparing Vasopressin Injection with the reference standard is specified and the calculations of potency are described. "The calculated vasopressin activity of the Injection is not less than 17 and not more than 24 *U.S.P.* Posterior Pituitary Units in each ml."

The *U.S.P.* does not give information about the pharmacologic actions or therapeutic properties of drugs. It gives the average dose or dose range primarily to alert the pharmacist to possible gross errors in prescriptions.

Other countries have their own pharmacopeias, serving the same purpose and organized according to much the same pattern, as for example

the *British Pharmacopoeia* (*B.P.*).[77] Under the auspices of the World
Health Organization an *International Pharmacopoeia*[78] has been published,
which "constitutes a collection of recommended specifications, which are
not intended to have legal status as such in any country, but are offered to
serve as references so that national specifications can be established on a
similar basis in any country." This undertaking may serve as a step toward
the adoption of uniform drug standards and nomenclature by all govern-
ments.

THE NATIONAL FORMULARY

The National Formulary (*N.F.*)[79] is another compendium of official
drugs. It is published by a committee of the American Pharmaceutical
Association at intervals of five years, coinciding with revisions of the *U.S.P.*
The current edition is *N.F. XII,* published in 1965. It lists drugs that are
not included in *U.S.P.* but are nevertheless widely used. *N.F.* is very similar
to *U.S.P.* in purpose, format, and usefulness, and it has the same official
standing in Federal drug legislation. A few examples of drugs included in
N.F. but not in *U.S.P.* will illustrate the major differences between these
two compendiums.

1. Aprobarbital, *N.F. XII,* is in clinical use but is not included in
U.S.P., probably because its properties were not considered sufficiently
different from other barbiturates already in *U.S.P.*

2. Codeine Sulfate, *N.F. XII,* is not included in *U.S.P.* because it
is not substantially different from Codeine Phosphate, which is included.

3. Brown Mixture, *N.F. XII,* is an aqueous solution of five ingredients. It is a palatable cough syrup containing paregoric (tincture of opium).
No such ready-made mixtures are found in *U.S.P.*

4. *N.F.* retains a considerable variety of materials of plant origin,
compounded according to exact directions but of unknown chemical composition. These have long since been dropped from *U.S.P.* Examples are
Almond Oil, Caraway Oil, Plantago Seed, Juniper Tar, and Camphor Lini-
ment. They may be used as vehicles or additives in the preparation of
medicinal mixtures, but not usually for any pharmacologic value of their
own.

Unofficial Compendiums

The *Merck Index,*[80] new editions of which are published periodically, lists structural formulas and physical properties of an enormous
number of chemical compounds, including many drugs.

[77] GENERAL MEDICAL COUNCIL: *British Pharmacopoeia.* London, The Pharmaceutical Press, 1963.

[78] WORLD HEALTH ORGANIZATION: *Pharmacopoea Internationalis* (*International
Pharmacopoeia*), 1st ed. Geneva, vol. I, 1951; vol. II, 1955; Supplement, 1959.

[79] AMERICAN PHARMACEUTICAL ASSOCIATION: *The National Formulary,* 12th revision. Washington, D.C., 1965.

[80] *The Merck Index of Chemicals and Drugs,* 7th ed. Rahway, N.J., Merck and
Co., 1960.

The *American Drug Index,*[81] published annually, is essentially a dictionary in which drugs can be looked up. Listings are by nonproprietary names and also by trade names; the manufacturers of each drug are listed, as well as the dosage forms in which the drug is supplied.

The *Modern Drug Encyclopedia and Therapeutic Index*[82] is a similar listing of drugs by trade names as well as by nonproprietary names. It includes a detailed description of the composition of each preparation, the name of the manufacturer, the form in which it is supplied, the medicinal uses, and the principal cautions to be observed. It also contains a useful list of U.S. Adopted Names (cf. p. 827), and corresponding trade names.

Physicians' Desk Reference[83] is published annually and distributed without charge to over 200,000 physicians and others in the health professions. It lists the products of all the major drug manufacturers in various arrangements—by brand name, manufacturer, major ingredient, and therapeutic indication. It gives the compositions, indications, contraindications, and dosage forms of nearly all medications available on the market. A useful feature in identifying medications in cases of poisoning is a series of full-sized natural color pictures of tablets, pills, and capsules containing a listed medication. The expenses of producing this catalogue are borne by the manufacturers whose products are described in it, and they prepare these descriptions themselves.[84] New products are often presented in much more detail than older and well-established drugs. The volume is helpful in determining what products are available, and in exactly what form, but it cannot be considered a guide to therapy.

Critical Evaluations

NEW DRUGS

New Drugs[66] is an annual review volume prepared by the Council on Drugs of the American Medical Association. The Council is a group of pharmacologists and clinicians associated with academic institutions. It draws upon a wide panel of consultants in its work of drug evaluation. *New Drugs* attempts to provide the physician with up-to-date information on drugs introduced during the previous ten years. The Council considers clinical and laboratory evidence submitted by manufacturers and obtained from other sources, and prepares monographs dealing with the "actions, uses, dosage, contraindications, hazards, limitations, and other pertinent properties" of drugs. These monographs appear from time to time in the

81 C. O. WILSON and T. E. JONES: *American Drug Index.* Philadelphia, J. P. Lippincott, annual.

82 R. S. GOODHART and L. A. ZEICHNER, eds.: *Modern Drug Encyclopedia and Therapeutic Index.* New York, The Reuben H. Donnelley Corp., annual.

83 *Physicians' Desk Reference.* Oradell, N.J., Medical Economics, annual.

84 J. R. DI PALMA: "Prescription Writing and Useful Tables," in *Drill's Pharmacology in Medicine,* ed. by J. R. DiPalma, 3rd ed. New York, McGraw-Hill, 1965, pp. 1443–1459.

regular column of the Council on Drugs in the *Journal of the American Medical Association,* and are subsequently included in the annual volume. "Since a monograph on a drug is included whether or not the Council's opinion is favorable, *New Drugs* is in no sense a list of 'approved or accepted' drugs." The book is organized on the basis of therapeutic classifications such as antibacterial agents, anticonvulsants, vasopressor agents, adrenal corticosteroids, etc. Every chapter begins with a general discussion of the family of drugs to be considered; then the individual drugs are presented. For each drug is given the official name (if *U.S.P.* or *N.F.*), adopted name (cf. p. 827) or other nonproprietary name, the structural formula and description, actions and uses, adverse reactions and precautions, dosage and preparations, manufacturer and trade name, year of introduction, and year of evaluation by the Council. Because of the unavoidable delay between the introduction of new drugs and their appearance in textbooks or admission to the official compendiums, *New Drugs* could fill an important need by providing critical evaluations of recently introduced drugs. Evaluation, as a practical guide to therapy, however, would mean comparing new drugs with each other and new drugs with old. Instead, this volume serves primarily as a descriptive catalogue of agents introduced during the past decade.

THE MEDICAL LETTER

The Medical Letter on Drugs and Therapeutics[85] publishes biweekly critical appraisals of drugs in the form of brochures that fit into a looseleaf binder. The articles are written and edited by a group of distinguished physicians affiliated with teaching hospitals and medical schools. It is concise, informative, and highly regarded in academic circles. It began publication in 1959; its present circulation is about 30,000. This publication is particularly useful for the evaluation of very new drugs because such information is often printed at the time when they are being promoted most vigorously by their manufacturers. The busy practitioner, even if he had the time, might not have access to the pertinent data during this early period.

The Medical Letter is characterized by a cautious and conservative approach toward all drug therapy, and by a healthy skepticism toward exaggerated promotional claims for new drugs. It devotes a large fraction of its pages to alerting the physician to up-to-date reports of adverse drug reactions. It compares new drugs with existing ones. It analyzes the evidence upon which claims for the superiority of new drugs are based. It offers general instruction about matters of therapeutic importance, such as dosage schedules in infants and old people, immunization of infants and

[85] H. AARON, ed.: *The Medical Letter on Drugs and Therapeutics.* New York, Drug and Therapeutic Information, Inc., biweekly. 305 East 45th Street, New York 10017.

children, and the usefulness of over-the-counter remedies. It concerns itself with quality standards and with the comparative prices of equivalent medications.

In several instances its adverse judgment upon a newly promoted drug has been borne out by subsequent events. For example, in its very first issue *The Medical Letter* questioned the belief that meprobamate had unique virtues in relieving anxiety or tension; six years later meprobamate was dropped from *U.S.P.* In January 1966 it sharply attacked the validity of claims for a life-sustaining effect of pentaerythritol tetranitrate in patients with myocardial infarction. In an intensive advertising campaign in the medical journals, the manufacturer had advanced these claims on the basis of one unpublished, poorly designed study. A few months later the FDA ordered that all claims of efficacy of nitrites other than for relief of angina pectoris be withdrawn.

DRUGS OF CHOICE

Drugs of Choice[86] is a large and valuable multiauthor textbook designed to aid the physician in choosing from among the many drugs available for the treatment of any condition. The emphasis is upon drugs that have been in use long enough for clinical experience to have accumulated. The organization is by chapters devoted to therapeutic indications. A valuable section lists unusual toxic reactions to drugs. An extensive index, including trade names, is provided. *Drugs of Choice* is published every two years.

UNITED STATES DISPENSATORY

The *United States Dispensatory*[87] is, in essence, an encyclopedia of drugs and their actions. It includes all drugs that are official in *U.S.P., N.F.,* the *British Pharmacopoeia,* or the *International Pharmacopoeia.* It also includes (in a separate section) a very large number of drugs not included in the pharmacopeias. Each entry contains, in addition to the descriptive information that would be found in the pharmacopeia, a monograph about the pharmacologic actions of the drug. The article under Vasopressin Injection (*U.S.P., B.P., I.P.*), for example, compares the descriptions in the three pharmacopeias. It describes the history of the determination of structure of the hormone, and its chemical properties, with references to the original literature. Then, under "Uses," follows a five-page article tantamount to a concise textbook description of the pharmacologic actions, with further references. The 25th edition (1960) contained more than 2,000 pages.

---

[86] W. MODELL, ed.: *Drugs of Choice.* St. Louis, C. V. Mosby, biennial.
[87] A. OSOL and G. E. FARRAR, JR.: *The Dispensatory of the United States of America,* 25th ed. Philadelphia, J. B. Lippincott, 1960.

PERIODICAL REVIEW JOURNALS

No attempt is made here to list all periodicals in which reviews of selected fields of pharmacology or therapeutics may appear. Many are cited in the footnote references throughout this book. A few, however, merit special mention. *Pharmacological Reviews*[88] is a quarterly containing comprehensive reviews of selected fields. The emphasis is usually upon fundamental mechanisms of drug action rather than upon therapeutic applications. *Annual Reviews of Pharmacology*[89] and *Advances in Pharmacology*[90] are annuals containing reviews of selected subjects. Each year most of the major topics in pharmacology are covered. *Pharmacology for Physicians*[91] is a monthly periodical, in the form of a brochure, serving the needs of the practitioner. In each issue an expert discusses the basic pharmacology that provides the rationale for proper therapeutic use of a particular group of drugs. *Clinical Pharmacology and Therapeutics*,[92] a monthly journal containing original articles dealing with the effects of drugs in man, also publishes frequent reviews of value to the physician who wishes to keep abreast of modern developments in drug therapy.

Advertising and Promotion

Advertising of prescription drugs is directed at physicians. It takes the form of package inserts, advertisements in medical journals, mailings directly to physicians, and personal visits by agents of the manufacturers (detail men). Package inserts are the small leaflets that are required by law to accompany each package of a drug. They are exceedingly useful sources of information, for they describe the chemical structure of the drug, its pharmacology, clinical use, toxicities, contraindications, and recommended doses. The contents of these inserts are reviewed by the FDA, to ensure that they represent a full and accurate disclosure about the drug. Pharmaceutical manufacturers are required to send copies of these inserts to physicians upon request. The wise physician will insist upon studying the package insert for every drug he intends to prescribe.

[88] G. H. ACHESON, ed.: *Pharmacological Reviews*. A publication of the American Society for Pharmacology and Experimental Therapeutics. Baltimore, Williams and Wilkins, quarterly.

[89] H. W. ELLIOTT, W. C. CUTTING, and R. H. DREISBACH, eds.: *Annual Review of Pharmacology*. Palo Alto, Calif., Annual Reviews, Inc., annual.

[90] S. GARATTINI and P. A. SHORE, eds.: *Advances in Pharmacology*. New York, Academic Press, annual.

[91] W. MODELL, ed.: *Pharmacology for Physicians*. A publication of the American Society for Pharmacology and Experimental Therapeutics. Philadelphia, W. B. Saunders, monthly.

[92] W. MODELL, ed.: *Clinical Pharmacology and Therapeutics*. St. Louis, C. V. Mosby, monthly.

The quality of advertisements for drugs spans a wide range. The best is informative and educational[93]; the worst is insulting to the practitioner's intelligence. In the most restrained type of advertising a pharmaceutical firm merely brings its name to the attention of physicians, or points out some well-established drugs manufactured by it. In the most insidious kind of advertising the claims for a new drug preparation are exaggerated or misleading. References to the literature often convey the impression that the claims are substantiated by reputable published research, whereas the articles cited may deal only indirectly with the supposed virtues of the new drug, or may consist of poorly designed and uncontrolled clinical trials.[94] Flagrant disregard of the truth may be prevented by alert governmental regulatory agencies. But there is a wide area of advertising claims which, although not actually false, nevertheless fall short of what ought to be required to convince a properly conservative physician. Drug combinations, which should almost never be used (cf. p. 265), are especially prone to be overvigorously promoted. The reason is that although the separate components may be available in competing brands at reasonably low prices, the combination, given a unique name and a higher price, becomes a precious commodity of one manufacturer.

In testimony before a U.S. Senate investigating committee,[95, p. 7901] one large drug company reported that it had 430 detail men, and a subsidiary company was reported to have over 100 detail men. The president of the company estimated that the average salary of a detail man was $7900. At that time the firm was paying over four million dollars per annum for this type of promotion of its products. The president of the Pharmaceutical Manufacturers Association stated: "A key factor in getting medicines off the shelf and into use is the professional service representative, often referred to as a detail man. . . . In a survey by the American Medical Association, approximately two-thirds of the physicians in America rated the detail man as their top source of new product information."[95, p. 10729]

The natural desire of the physician to have all new remedies at his command makes him vulnerable to claims for new wonder drugs. But he should realize that the natural desire of the pharmaceutical manufacturer to sell his products will not always coincide with the best practice of medicine and the best interest of the patient. The physician need not be and should not be dependent upon industry for information about drugs. Numerous sources of informed and disinterested expert opinion are available to

[93] J. G. SEARLE, L. D. BARNEY, F. BOYER, G. R. CAIN, L. C. DUNCAN, R. A. HARDT, D. M. JOHNSON, and E. G. UPJOHN: The pharmaceutical industry. *J. Med. Educ.* 36:24 (1961).

[94] C. D. MAY: Selling drugs by "educating" physicians. *J. Med. Educ. 36:*1 (1961).

[95] Administered Prices. Hearings before the Subcommittee on Antitrust and Monopoly of the Committee on the Judiciary, U.S. Senate, 86th Congress, First Session. Publication No. 35621. Washington, D.C., U.S. Government Printing Office, 1961.

him. The situation, as summarized by a British professor of therapeutics, probably is about the same in most parts of the world:

> ". . . there is the formidable and skilled promotion of drugs by the pharmaceutical houses, some of which is subject to justifiable criticism in violating truth and good taste. Nevertheless, the cure for this is in the hands of the medical profession, for no ethical drug (that is, no drug which has to be prescribed and cannot be bought over the counter) can reach the public save through its intermediary. . . . Thus the advertising of ethical drugs, on which vast sums of money are expended, is not directed, like the advertising of most commodities, at the population of the country as a whole but at the relatively small number of its duly qualified medical men who are sought after, chased, wooed, and importuned to a fantastic extent. . . . We should stop bemoaning this attack on our professional maturity and begin to realize how justified it must be, for no advertising which does not work will continue to run. In our society the market-place may not be responsive to idealism but it is always sensitive to sales curves. . . . Let us as doctors but withhold our approval of new drugs and preparations until conclusive evidence has been presented in support of the claims made for them and it will cease to be economically feasible to market new drugs without such evidence."[38]

PRINCIPLES OF

PRESCRIBING

A prescription is a letter to the pharmacist telling him what to do. Any unambiguous letter would suffice, but certain conventions simplify matters. Clarity and complete lack of ambiguity are the only real essentials. Because the life and health of a patient may be at stake, special safeguards against human error have to be employed. These are:

1. *Ordinary language.* Writing prescriptions in Latin is an obsolete affectation, conducive to misunderstanding and error. The patient's respect should be based upon the physician's medical knowledge, skill, and compassion, not upon a false show of erudition.

2. *Legibility.* It is not desirable, through illegibility any more than through the use of Latin phrases and abbreviations, to obscure the nature of the remedy from the patient. Except in extraordinary circumstances, the patient should be told exactly what drug is being prescribed, what it is expected to accomplish, and what adverse effects should be watched for. It is often necessary for a patient or his family to be able to tell a new physician what medication has been taken. The potentially life-saving value of a proper description on the label of a medication in cases of poisoning has already been pointed out. One rare circumstance calling for concealment of the nature of a drug is the deliberate administration of a placebo. Another that may possibly call for cryptic labeling would be the administration of agents with addiction liability, which might be subject to abuse by unauthorized persons.

3. *Metric system.* The obsolete apothecary system of grains, ounces, and drachms is dangerous and unnecessary. The ancient symbols ℥ for *ounce* (30 ml) and ℨ for *drachm* (4 ml) are nearly alike, and fatal overdoses have resulted from this resemblance. The abbreviation *gr.* (meaning *grain,* 60 mg) is easily mistaken for *gram* (1,000 mg), also with catastrophic consequences. The only units needed are grams (for solids) and milliliters (for liquids), but symbols are not even required for these, as

will be shown below. The metric system is now used exclusively in *U.S.P.,* and it is gradually becoming official in the English-speaking countries; elsewhere it has been in effect for many years.

4. *Decimal line.* This is simply a vertical line that serves as a decimal point throughout the prescription. It is usually printed on the prescription blank. Numbers written to the left of the line are whole grams (of a solid) or milliliters (of a liquid). Numbers written to the right of the line are decimal fractions of a gram or milliliter. The decimal line is an absolute safeguard against a misplaced or misread decimal point, a spot of ink seeming to be a decimal point, or an omitted decimal point. A few illustrations will suffice:

		3	means	3 grams, or 3 ml
		05	means	50 mg, or 0.05 ml
Water	120		means	120 ml of water
Codeine Phosphate		042	means	42 mg of Codeine Phosphate
Sodium Fluoride		1		"Weigh 100 mg of Sodium
Wild Cherry Syrup,			means	Fluoride and add Wild Cherry
to make	60			Syrup to a final volume of
				60 ml."

A prescription contains four parts: the preliminary section, the prescription proper, the label, and the physician's signature. The *preliminary section* includes various kinds of identifying data. The following items should be on all prescriptions, and they will also satisfy the more rigorous legal requirements for narcotic prescriptions. The practitioner's name, address, and narcotic registry number should be given; these are usually printed at the top of the prescription blank, and his telephone number and office hours, although not required, are often included too (Fig. I–1). The prescription must bear the date of writing; predating is not only poor practice in general, but is illegal for narcotic prescriptions. The patient's name and address must be included for reference purposes, for identification of the medicine after it has been prepared, and to reduce the danger of unauthorized persons obtaining drugs. If a child's name and an adult's name might be confused, the patient's age should be stated (Fig. I–2). The pharmacist will copy the identifying data about the patient onto the label of the container in which the drug is dispensed.

The *prescription proper* tells the pharmacist what drugs to use and what to do with them (Fig. I–2). This part of the prescription used to be prefixed by the symbol ℞, but there is no legal requirement for retaining this vestige of a colorful past. The prescription should almost always specify a single drug, identified by its nonproprietary name. A good rule is to look up the dose unless one is absolutely certain about it. The pharmacist is alerted to gross errors by the statement of "average dose" in the various

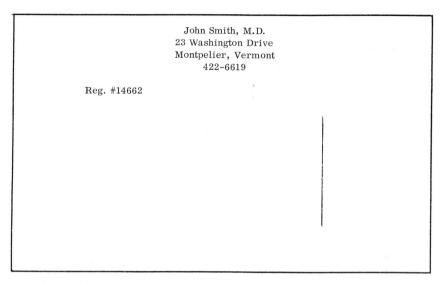

John Smith, M.D.
23 Washington Drive
Montpelier, Vermont
422–6619

Reg. #14662

FIG. I-1. A SUITABLE PRESCRIPTION BLANK. *The narcotic registry number is shown at left. The decimal line is printed at right.*

reference sources at his disposal, and the wise pharmacist will question the physician about an unusual dosage; but his obligation is to dispense exactly what the physician prescribes.

The *label* is the physician's instruction to the patient. The pharmacist copies verbatim onto the label of the container whatever the physician writes in this section. It should contain, first of all, the name and unit dosage (or concentration) of the drug, e.g., *Chlorpheniramine Maleate, 4 mg,* or *Dyclonine Hydrochloride, 0.5%*. The instructions for taking the medication should be written in simple language that the patient will understand, and should not contain technical abbreviations or shorthand the pharmacist will have to translate. Amounts should be specified in terms of common household measures like teaspoonful (about 5 ml) or tablespoonful (about 15 ml); if exact quantities of liquids are required, a calibrated dropper should be furnished. Associating the taking of medicine with mealtimes, bedtime, or other regular daily activities helps to ensure regularity of administration. The vague label *"Take as directed"* should be avoided, for oral directions are too prone to be misunderstood.

The *physician's signature* establishes the prescription as an authoritative document for which the physician assumes full responsibility. The signature should be written in ink or indelible pencil exactly as a bank check would be signed. An academic degree (M.D., D.D.S., D.V.M.) is not a necessary part of the signature.

The calculations upon which the prescription proper and the label will be based require four decisions:

1. What will be the size of the single dose?

2. In what form will the single dose be taken (tablet, capsule, teaspoonful of solution, approximate amount of an ointment, etc.)?

3. How often is the single dose to be repeated?

4. How many single doses are to be supplied?

FIG. I-2. TWO COMPLETE PRESCRIPTIONS. *Upper prescription is refillable, lower one (a narcotic prescription) could not be refilled under any circumstances.*

John Smith, M.D.
23 Washington Drive
Montpelier, Vermont
422–6619

Reg. #14662   May 12, 1967

Mrs. Wilma Jones
110 N. 6th Street

Neostigmine Bromide Tablets | 015
Dispense 75

Label: Neostigmine. One tablet after breakfast
and supper.

Refillable monthly.   John Smith (signed)

John Smith, M.D.
23 Washington Drive
Montpelier, Vermont
422–6619

Reg. #14662   May 12, 1967

Charles Jones, Jr., Age 2
110 N. 6th Street

Meperidine Hydrochloride   0 | 2
Wild Cherry Syrup, to make   60 |

Label: Meperidine. One teaspoonful with water, every
four hours, if needed for pain.
KEEP OUT OF REACH OF CHILDREN

John Smith (signed)

If the drug is to be taken as a solid (as tablets, pills, capsules, etc.), the prescription should be written for the single dose, and the number of such doses to be dispensed should be indicated. It is wise to ascertain what ready-made forms of the desired drug are already available, to avoid making the pharmacist compound medications needlessly.

Examples:

Griseofulvin | 125
Dispense 100 such capsules.

Glyceryl Trinitrate Tablets | 004
25 such.

The pharmacist (or manufacturer) is always free to add inert bulk ingredients, if necessary. For example, a tablet weighing only 4 mg, as prescribed above, would be very inconvenient, and therefore other substances like starch or lactose will be added.

If the drug is to be dissolved in a liquid or semisolid vehicle, two alternative procedures may be followed. If the medication is available as a suitable ready-made preparation, this can be specified by stating the drug concentration and the total amount required. Concentrations are often stated by manufacturers as amount *per 5 ml* (i.e., per single dose), thus simplifying calculations.

Example:

Acetyl Sulfamethoxypyridazine
Oral suspension 250 mg/5ml
Dispense   120

If the pharmacist is to prepare the medication, it will be necessary to decide on the single dose and the volume of vehicle in which it is to be contained. Then these numbers are both multiplied by the number of single doses to be furnished. Finally, a recheck of the completed prescription determines if the correct single dose will actually be obtained when the instructions on the label are followed.

Example:

Suppose the single dose of Codeine Phosphate is to be 30 mg, contained in a teaspoonful of syrup, and that 12 doses are to be prescribed.

$$30 \text{ mg} \quad \text{in} \quad 5 \text{ ml}$$
$$\times \ 12 \ = \ 360 \text{ mg} \quad \text{in} \quad 60 \text{ ml}$$

Codeine Phosphate | 36
Aromatic Elixir to make   60
Label: Codeine, one teaspoonful every 4 hours, if needed, for pain.

The choice of a liquid vehicle depends primarily upon palatability and upon efficiency in masking the odors and tastes of drugs. If water suffices, there is no need for another vehicle. Drugs to which children may have access are better not made too palatable; but drugs intended for very young children have to be made tasteful, for they are given more easily in liquid than in solid form.

The same procedure applies to ointments.

Example:

Suppose Dyclonine Hydrochloride, a local anesthetic, is to be used for relief of pain and itching due to an anal fissure. An effective concentration is 1 per cent, the patient is likely to use about 1 gram of ointment at each application, he is likely to use the medication four or five times daily, and the supply is to last a week. Then:

0.01 gram   in   1 gram   of ointment
$\times 4 \times 7 = 28$ doses $=$ approximately 30 doses
0.3 gram   in   30 grams of ointment

Dyclonine Hydrochloride | 3
Petrolatum, to make   30 |
Label: Dyclonine Ointment. Apply externally as needed.

Figure I–2 presents two examples of complete prescriptions, one for medication to be taken indefinitely for a chronic disease, the other for a narcotic to be used for a few days only. Unless expressly indicated, prescriptions are not refillable. However, permission to refill may be given by the physician over the telephone, except for specially restricted drugs. Prescriptions for certain central stimulants, depressants and hallucinogens may be refilled only five times and not after six months. Narcotic prescriptions may never be refilled.

LIST OF ABBREVIATIONS AND SYMBOLS

A   adenine; also Ångstrom
AAF   2-acetylaminofluorene
AcCh   acetylcholine
ALA   δ-aminolevulinic acid
Ala   alanine
AMP   adenosine monophosphate
APS   adenosine 5′-phosphosulfate
Arg   arginine
Asn   asparagine
Asp   aspartic acid
ATCase   aspartyl transcarbamylase
ATP   adenosine triphosphate
ATPase   adenosine triphosphatase
BAL   dimercaprol, British anti-lewisite
BP   *British Pharmacopoeia*
BSP   Bromsulphalein, sulfobromoph-thalein
BU   5-bromouracil
C   cytosine
C5   pentamethonium
C6   hexamethonium
C10   decamethonium
C.A.   carbonic anhydrase
CNS   central nervous system
CoA   coenzyme A
COHb   carboxyhemoglobin, carbon monoxide-hemoglobin
COMT   catechol-O-methyl transferase
CSF   cerebrospinal fluid
CTP   cytidine triphosphate
Cys   cysteine
DAM   diacetylmonoxime
DAO   diamine oxidase
DAP   2,6-diaminopurine

DDE   dichlorodiphenyldichloroethy-lene
DDT   chlorophenothane, dichlorodi-phenyltrichloroethane
DEAE   diethylaminoethyl
DFP   diisopropylfluorophosphate
DMSO   dimethyl sulfoxide
DNA   deoxyribonucleic acid
DON   diazo-oxo-norleucine
DTPA   diethylenetriaminepentaacetic acid
ED50, ED_{50} median effective dose
EDC   effective drug concentration
EDTA   edatate, edathamil, ethylene-diamine tetraacetate
EES   ethyl ethanesulfonate
EMS   ethyl methanesulfonate
EPI   epinephrine
FA   folic acid
FAH_2 dihydrofolic acid
FAH_4 tetrahydrofolic acid
FDA   Food and Drug Administration
FU   5-fluorouracil
FUdRP   5-fluorodeoxyuridylic acid
G   guanine
G6PD   glucose 6-phosphate dehydro-genase
Gln   glutamine
Glu   glutamic acid
Gly   glycine
GSH   reduced glutathione
GSSG   oxidized glutathione
Hb   hemoglobin
His   histidine

I   inosine
Ile   isoleucine
i.m.   intramuscular
IMP   inosine monophosphate, inosinic acid
i.v.   intravenous
K_i enzyme (or drug)-inhibitor dissociation constant
K_m enzyme (or drug)-substrate dissociation constant, Michaelis constant
LD50, LD_{50} median lethal dose
LDR   log dose-response
Leu   leucine
LSD   lysergic acid diethylamide
Lys   lysine
MAO·   monoamine oxidase
Met   methionine
MINA   monoisonitrosoacetone
MMAP   monomethyl-4-aminoantipyrine
6-MP   6-mercaptopurine
mRNA   messenger-RNA
NAD   nicotinamide adenine dinucleotide (formerly DPN)
NAD+   oxidized form of NAD
NADH   reduced form of NAD (formerly DPNH)
NADP   nicotinamide adenine dinucleotide phosphate (formerly TPN)
NADP+   oxidized form of NADP
NADPH   reduced form of NADP (formerly TPNH)
NE   norepinephrine
N.E.D.   normal equivalent deviation
NEPI   norepinephrine
NF National Formulary
P-450, P_{450} CO-binding pigment, reticulochrome, a "mixed function" oxidase
PAB, PABA   *p*-aminobenzoic acid
PAH   *p*-aminohippuric acid
PAM, 2-PAM   pralidoxime, pyridine aldoxime methiodide
PAPS   3′-phosphoadenosine 5′-phosphosulfate
PAS   *p*-aminosalicylic acid
PBI   protein-bound iodine

PCMB   *p*-chloromercuribenzoate
Phe   phenylalanine
pK_a negative logarithm of acid dissociation constant
p.o.   by mouth, *per os.*
POB   *p*-hydroxybenzoic acid
polyC   polycytidylic acid
polyU   polyuridylic acid
Pro   proline
PRPP   5-phosphoribosyl-1-pyrophosphate
PSP   phenolsulfonphthalein
PTC   phenylthiocarbamide, phenylthiourea
RBC   red blood cell, erythrocyte
RNA   ribonucleic acid
S   solubility of a gas (Ostwald coefficient); *also* sedimentation constant (Svedberg)
SAR   structure-activity relationship
s.c.   subcutaneous
Ser   serine
T   thymine
$t_{\frac{1}{2}}$ half-time, half-life
TBG   thyroxine-binding α-globulin
TD50, TD_{50} median toxic dose
TEPP   tetraethylpyrophosphate
THAM   tris(hydroxymethylamino) methane, Tris
Thr   threonine
T_m maximum transport capacity
TMV   tobacco mosaic virus
tRNA   transfer-RNA
Trp   tryptophan
Tyr   tyrosine
U   uracil
UDP   uridine diphosphate
UDPG   uridine diphosphate-glucose
UDPGA   uridine diphosphate-glucuronic acid
USAN   United States Adopted Name
USP United States Pharmacopeia
Val   valine
V_d apparent volume of distribution
VMA   vanillylmandelic acid
V_{max} maximum reaction velocity
μ population mean
σ population standard deviation